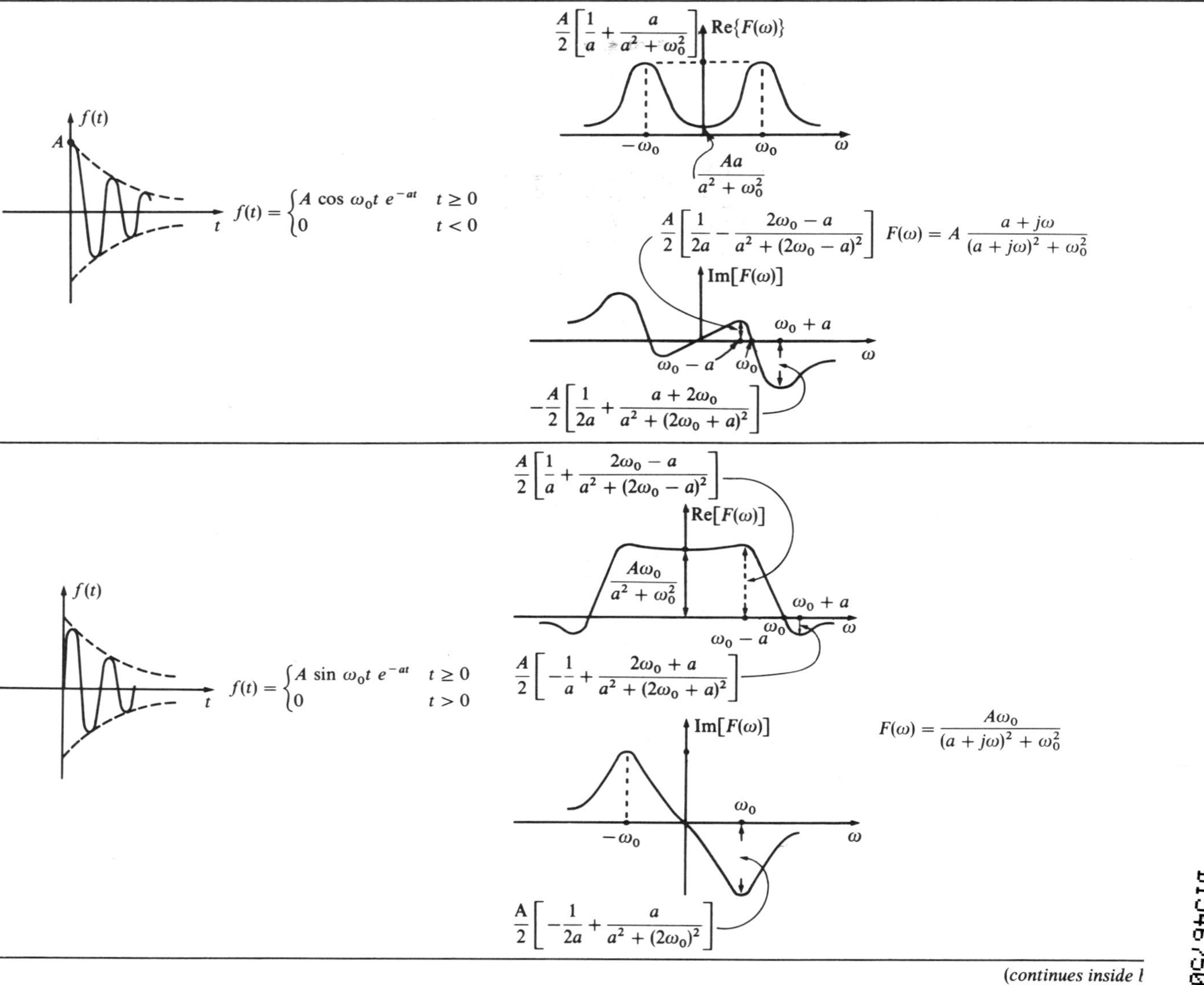

(continues inside l

Elements of Signals and Systems

Alexander D. Poularikas
University of Alabama at Huntsville

Samuel Seely
Formerly of University of Rhode Island

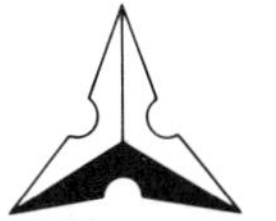

PWS-KENT Publishing Company
Boston

PWS-KENT
Publishing Company

20 Park Plaza
Boston, Massachusetts 02116

THE PWS-KENT SERIES IN ELECTRICAL ENGINEERING

Introductory Network Theory, Blackwell and Grigsby

Biomedical Engineering and Instrumentation: Basic Concepts and Applications, Bronzino

Microprocessor System Design: 68000 Hardware, Software, and Interfacing, Clements

Power System Analysis and Design with Personal Computer Applications, Glover and Sarma

Digital Design: A Pragmatic Approach, Johnson and Karim

Assembly Language for the PDP-11: RT-RSX-UNIX, Second Edition, Kapps and Stafford

VAX Assembly Language and Architecture, Kapps and Stafford

Signals and Systems, Poularikas and Seely

Applied Electromagnetism, Second Edition, Shen and Kong

PWS-KENT Publishing Company is a division of Wadsworth, Inc.

Library of Congress Cataloging-in-Publication Data

Poularikas, Alexander D., 1933–
Elements of signals and systems.

Bibliography: p.
Includes index.
1. Signal processing. I. Seely, Samuel, 1909–
II. Title.
TK5102.5.P657 1987 621.38′043 87-8989
ISBN 0-534-91440-3

Printed in the United States of America

88 89 90 91 92 — 10 9 8 7 6 5 4 3 2 1

Sponsoring Editor: Robert Prior; Production Coordinator: Robine Storm van Leeuwen; Production: Technical Texts, Inc./Sylvia Dovner; Interior Design: Ellie Connolly; Cover Design: Robine Storm van Leeuwen; Typesetting: Santype International Limited; Printing and Binding: R. R. Donnelley & Sons Company

To my wife, Barbara, and my children, Natasha and Demitri ADP

To my wife, Helen SS

Preface

Elements of Signals and Systems is designed for use in a one-semester, first course in signals and systems. This book is distinctive in that the discussion of continuous time (analog) and discrete time (digital) systems is presented in parallel form in each chapter. We have tried to adhere to this plan throughout but did find it necessary, because of their content and importance, to include the Laplace transform and the Z-transform in separate, sequential chapters. The only prerequisites are a first course in ac circuits and mathematics through differential equations.

We have included many, carefully chosen examples to show the wide applicability of the material and methods presented in this text. An understanding of the concepts of signals and systems is also important in fields outside of electrical engineering. To illustrate this diversity, we include a large number of examples drawn from chemistry, biomedical engineering, process control, economics, heat transfer, nuclear physics, and other areas. These examples show that systems in general possess two features: the input signals to the system are functions of one or more independent variables and the systems produce output signals when excited by input signals.

The modeling of signals and systems is inherently mathematical and involves mathematical forms not ordinarily studied by undergraduate engineering majors. We have included enough mathematical material to serve in understanding the classical solution of differential and difference equations, convolution (continuous and discrete time), Fourier series, discrete Fourier series, Fourier integral transforms, discrete Fourier transforms, fast Fourier transforms, Laplace transforms, and Z-transforms. These discussions are always accompanied by a large number of examples to illustrate their use and applicability. An appendix on matrix theory is included as support material to state equation development. Where a given development might involve extensive mathematical demands, we indicate this by a dagger (†) at the section title.

The text consists of eight chapters. Chapter 1 presents the mathematical description of continuous time and discrete time signals and discusses their representation in periodic, nonperiodic, and truncated formats. Linear systems are introduced in Chapter 2. Topics include modeling of system elements, block diagram representation, and an introduction to the application of convolution methods. Chapter 3, entitled "Periodic Signals and Their Spectrums," develops the classical topic of the

Fourier series and includes a discussion of the Gibbs phenomenon and the use of windowing functions. A similar discussion follows on discrete Fourier series that apply to periodic discrete sequences. Chapter 4 presents the Fourier integral transform, its properties, and its applications. Also discussed are the discrete Fourier transform, its application to discrete signals, and coefficient determination employing fast Fourier transform techniques.

Chapter 5 is devoted to the formulation of systems of linear equations in state variable form. Alternate forms for writing state equations for both analog and discrete systems are studied as well as the techniques for solving these equations in matrix form. Appendix A supplements this study. Presented in Chapter 6 is a study of the Laplace transform, its properties, and the tabular method for deducing the inverse Laplace transform. The application of Laplace methods to the solution of continuous time system problems when expressed in differential equation or in state equation form is included. Chapter 7 gives a parallel development of discrete system equation solutions and the use of the Z-transform in their solution in both difference equation and state equation form. The final chapter, Chapter 8, covers digital filter design and shows how to develop digital filters to approximate prescribed analog filter behavior. Digital filters of the FIR and IIR types are studied in some detail, along with discussion of their special properties.

This book is an outgrowth of our recent book, *Signals and Systems* (PWS-KENT Publishing Company, Boston, 1985), which employs a series approach to discrete and continuous time systems and which is appropriate for a two-semester sequence or accelerated one-semester course. Professors who prefer the series approach should investigate that text.

We are grateful to our reviewers for their hard work and valuable comments: K. S. Arun, University of Illinois at Urbana-Champaign; Michael P. Smyth, Widener University; Gerald T. Volpe, University of Bridgeport; and John J. Westerkamp, University of Dayton. We would also like to thank our editor at PWS-KENT, Bob Prior, and Sylvia Dovner of Technical Texts for their invaluable assistance.

Contents

1

Signals and Their Functional Representations 1

1.1 Some Applications Involving Signals 2
1.2 Information of a Signal 5
1.3 Functional Representation of Signals 8
1.4 Signal Conditioning 19
1.5 Representation of Signals 22
Problems 28

2

Linear Systems 32

Continuous and Discrete Modeling 33
2.1 Properties of Systems 33
2.2 Modeling Simple Systems 36
2.3 Solution of First-Order Systems 45
2.4 Evaluation of Integration Constants: Initial Conditions 55
2.5 Block Diagram Representation 62
2.6 Discrete Systems and Equations 68
2.7 Digital Simulation of Analog Systems 73
2.8 Digital Simulation of Higher-Order Differential Equations 83
Convolution and Correlation 87
2.9 Convolution of Continuous Time Signals 87
2.10 Impulse Response 97
2.11 Convolution of Discrete Time Signals 108
2.12 Correlation 113
Problems 115

3

Periodic Signals and Their Spectrums 133

3.1 Complex Functions 134
3.2 Fourier Series of Continuous Functions 139
3.3 Features of Periodic Continuous Functions 150
3.4 Linear Systems with Periodic Inputs 158
3.5 Discrete Time Fourier Series 163
3.6 Convolution of Periodic Discrete Sequences 172
Problems 174

4

Nonperiodic Signals and Fourier Transforms 183

Continuous Time Functions 184
4.1 Direct and Inverse Fourier Transforms 184
4.2 Properties of Fourier Transforms 189
4.3 Some Special Fourier Transform Pairs 218
Sampling of Signals and the Fourier Transform 226
4.4 Fundamentals of Sampling 226
4.5 Sampling Theorem 230
4.6 Reconstruction of Sampled Signals 238
Discrete Time Transform 240
4.7 Discrete Fourier Transforms 240
4.8 Properties of the DFT 243
4.9 Fast Fourier Transform 262
Problems 269

5

State Variables and State Equations 277

State Representation of Continuous Time Systems 278
5.1 State Equation Formulation 278
5.2 State Equations in First Canonical Form 283
5.3 State Equations in Phase Variable Form 290
5.4 Solution of Continuous Time State Equations: Force-Free Conditions 295
5.5 Complete Solution of Continuous Time State Equations 302
5.6 State Response to Periodic Inputs 307
5.7 Initial State Vectors and Initial Conditions 308
State Space Representation of Discrete Systems 309
5.8 State Representation of Discrete Time Systems 309

5.9 Solution to Discrete Time State Equations 320
5.10 Continuous Time Systems with Sampled Inputs 324
Problems 325

6

Laplace Transform 331

6.1 Preliminary Comments 332
6.2 Bilateral Laplace Transform 333
6.3 One-Sided Laplace Transform 334
6.4 Properties of the Laplace Transform 336
6.5 Systems Analysis: Transfer Functions of LTI Systems 347
6.6 Inverse Laplace Transform 355
6.7 Problem Solving by Laplace Transforms 362
6.8 Frequency Response of LTI Systems 372
6.9 Laplace Transforms and the State Equations 380
6.10 Stability of LTI Systems 387
Problems 391

7

Z-Transform 403

7.1 *Z*-Transform 403
7.2 Convergence of the *Z*-Transform 407
7.3 Properties of the *Z*-Transform 414
7.4 *Z*-Transform Pairs 428
7.5 Inverse *Z*-Transform 430
7.6 Transfer Function 435
7.7 Frequency Response of Discrete Systems 443
7.8 *Z*-Transform Solution to Difference Equations 449
7.9 *Z*-Transform Solution to Discrete Time State Equations 457
7.10 More on Higher-Order Difference Equations 461
Problems 474

8

Elements of Digital Filter Design 484

8.1 General Aspects of Filters 485
8.2 Butterworth Filter 487
8.3 Chebyshev Low-Pass Filter 495
8.4 Elliptic Filters 503
8.5 Phase Characteristics 504
8.6 Frequency Transformations 504

8.7 Digital Filters 510
8.8 Finite Impulse Response (FIR) Filters 510
8.9 Impulse-Invariant Response Method in IIR Filters 519
8.10 Bilinear Transformation 527
8.11 Frequency Transformations for Digital Filters 532
8.12 Recursive versus Nonrecursive Designs 537
Problems 538

Appendix A

Matrix Mathematics 542

A.1 Introduction 542
A.2 Definitions 543
A.3 Matrix Algebra 544
A.4 Functions of a Matrix 548
A.5 Cayley-Hamilton Theorem 550
Problems 556

Appendix B

Mathematical Formulas 558

B.1 Trigonometric Identities 558
B.2 Orthogonality 559
B.3 Summation of Trigonometric Forms 560
B.4 Summation Formulas 560
B.5 Series Expansions 561
B.6 Logarithms 562
B.7 Some Definite Integrals 562

Bibliography 563
Answers to Selected Problems 564
Index 576

1

Signals and Their Functional Representations

A knowledge of a broad range of signals is of practical importance in describing human experiences. Signals, which are transmitted from one point to another, provide the basis for us to see, hear, feel, and act. In engineering systems, signals carry information or carry energy. For example, signals may be the high-energy microwave pulses in radar or the high energy necessary for performing controlled machine tool operations. They may be telephone or radio signals or the pulses that dictate the operation of a digital computer. The signals with which we are concerned may be the cause of an event or the consequence of an action.

The characteristics of a signal may be one of a broad range of shapes, amplitudes, time durations, and perhaps other physical properties. In many cases, the signal will be expressed in analytic form; in other cases, the signal may be given only in graphical form. The signals may be indications on instruments that are read periodically or they may be data provided in chart or tabular form.

It is the purpose of this chapter to introduce the mathematical representations of signals, their properties, and their applications, as essential preliminaries to our subsequent studies. These representations are in different formats depending on whether the signals are periodic, nonperiodic, or truncated; whether they represent experimental data; or whether they are deduced from graphical presentations.

1.1 Some Applications Involving Signals

The electrical engineer who is concerned with the design, analysis, synthesis, detection, and processing of signals will have to consider signals of many different amplitudes and shapes and time durations that can vary significantly. When concerned with a computer, the engineer must deal with millions of pulses per second; when concerned with radar signals, which are originally transmitted in megawatt-strength pulses at recurrence rates of a few thousand per second, the engineer must deal with the reflected signal pulse trains that are often hidden in noise and are often very weak. Cardiologists, on the other hand, are interested in the signal waveshape and its recurrence rate since they base their judgment of a patient's heart on the cardiogram (the heart signal).

Signals in electrical engineering are often encountered as variations of current and voltage versus time. Often, however, many time-varying voltage or current signals have been transformed from other types of signals, such as pressure versus time, electrical conductivity versus depth in a well, light intensity versus the sun's position above the horizon, and acceleration of machine parts. Appropriate forms of transducers play important roles in such transformations. Additionally, some signals are continuous functions of time, while others are discrete functions of time. Continuous time signals are a familiar form to the electrical engineer; discrete time signals are somewhat less common. Discrete time signals are found in many fields of endeavor. For example, the daily chart that gives the temperature, blood pressure, and pulse rate of a patient in a hospital provides discrete time data. Likewise, the geographic distribution of towns, the crime distribution in a city, and the population distribution of animal species in a geographic area are discrete variable entities.

The most common discrete time signals with which the electrical engineer comes in contact are the result of sampling continuous signals. This procedure, called **discretization**, produces a sequence of discrete values. Discretization is often accomplished with an electronic instrument known as an **analog to digital** (A/D) converter. When continuous time mathematical functions are to be manipulated in a digital computer, we must discretize the functions, which requires that the words or data to be entered into the computer be written in discrete form deduced from the continuous function. Chapter 4 presents a theorem that provides a guide to finding the appropriate number of discrete samples needed to represent uniquely a continuous function in its discretized form.

Mathematically, signals are presented as functions of one or more independent variables. For example, heat loss from a surface can be modeled by relating mathematically the temperature of the surface versus time, and a barometric chart can be presented as a function of two spatial variables: height and location. For convenience in our present studies, we will consider functions of one independent variable, usually time.

It is important that we understand the different classes of signals and the various mathematical means for their description. Only with a good understanding of the mathematical models of the signals can we proceed intelligently. Also, it must be understood that more than one way exists for describing a given signal waveform. The choice depends upon the signal and the required form in which an analysis is to be undertaken. Suppose, for example, that a recurring square wave is the signal under consideration. An immediate mathematical circumstance is that no exact continuous function representation exists for this signal over the entire period. Such signals are described over a period by piecewise continuous functions. To obtain an approximate functional representation of this signal, we can proceed in several different ways. One procedure is to replace this piecewise continuous function by a sequence of step functions, the amplitudes and displacements of which are chosen appropriate to the function being represented. A step function is nonanalytic owing to the discontinuity that exists in its description, although it is a waveform that can be conveniently handled.* A second method is to express the function over a designated range by a polynomial approximation that can be obtained using interpolation formulas. A third method is to express the square wave by a series representation in terms of orthogonal functions. The most common series representation is in terms of trigonometric sine and cosine functions—that is, a **Fourier series** expansion. Other orthogonal sets of more complicated functions can also be used.

Most signals that are subsequently processed in a system are contaminated by noise, either during or after they have been generated. *Noise* is viewed in its generalized sense to mean any additional peculiarity that appears superimposed on the original signal and so basically distorts or degrades it. Often noise is an undesirable effect, and engineers have spent and continue to expend considerable effort in their work to diminish or eliminate such noise. There are occasions when an interfering signal, which might be considered to be a form of noise, is deliberately introduced in a particular application. Examples of deliberately introduced interfering signals are to be found in electronic countermeasures in radar, in the scrambling of satellite TV programs to service only paying viewers, and in efforts to encrypt telephone messages to insure security. Encryption is a means for secure communication employing special codes. During World War II, a special transoceanic telephone system was established between the United Kingdom and the United States. This source was depended on by Prime Minister Churchill and Presidents Roosevelt and Truman and by many high-ranking officials and generals for their radio-telephone conferences. In this communication system, the signal (voice) at one terminal was mixed with randomized "one-time" keys (the introduced scrambling scheme) with appropriate decoding circuitry at the second terminal to recover the signal. The system, invented and developed by a team at the Bell Telephone Laboratories and code-named SIGSALY, was unbreakable (as proved mathematically)—a truly secure system.

Also used for radio-telephone communication by President Roosevelt to talk with several of his ambassadors in Europe was an A-3 scrambler. By the fall of 1941, the Deutsche Reichspost had broken the A-3 code, and, thereafter, Adolf Hitler was privy to all such messages.

* A function is analytic, or regular, in a region if it and all its derivatives exist in the region.

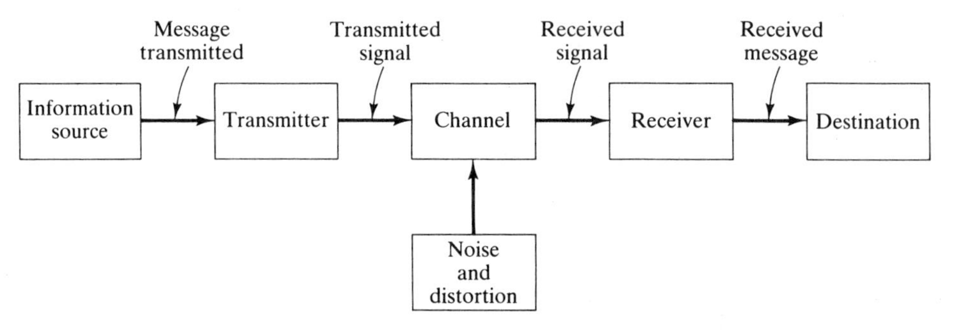

Figure 1.1 Generalized Communication System

Scientists from the Soviet Union and Eastern European countries assembled at a research center on the outskirts of Moscow, code-named MARVINO, to develop a secure system. Like the creators of SIGSALY, they based their work on the vocoder, a Bell Telephone Laboratories invention. Among those who worked on the scrambler program at MARVINO was Aleksandr Solzhenitsyn, a physicist and mathematician later jailed for anti-Soviet agitation. He immortalized the project in his novel *The First Circle.*

Ordinarily, signals cannot be transmitted over long distances directly as produced. They must be modified or conditioned, usually "riding" on another signal for their transmission. A typical example is the transmission of voice or music over radio waves. At other times, we may translate a particular signal into a completely different form. The use of smoke signals by Indian tribes is an example of **coding** signals for transmission through space. Most of us are generally familiar with the Morse code as a means of translating letters and numbers into dots and dashes.

Present-day engineers have gone further in studying signals and have been able to establish a *quantitative* description and measure of the information contained in a signal. To develop their theory, they created a conceptual model communication system, as shown in Figure 1.1. To simplify the discussion, let us consider a person who is transmitting a message as the **information source**. The output of the information source is called a **message**—it is what the person is saying. The **transmitter** is an apparatus that transforms the message into a form that allows it to be transmitted. A telephone handset that converts the acoustic message into a varying electrical current in the telephone line is such a transmitter. The communication **channel** is the medium over which the message is transmitted. The wires between two telephone receivers constitute a channel. The air space between a transmitting antenna and the receiving antennas in radio transmission is also a channel.

Because of the properties of the elements making up the communication system, distortion often occurs. **Distortion** is an operational effect of the system on the signal, whereas noise involves unpredictable perturbations (variations) of the signal. Clearly, to be useful, the output of the channel, which is the **received signal**, must resemble to some extent the original signal. For example, the received message is what we hear in the telephone receiver. The **destination** is the final element of a communication system. It can be a person or an apparatus depending upon the original intent of the system.

1.2 Information of a Signal

As noted above, the information content of a signal can be quantified in mathematical terms. We wish to examine the essential ideas involved in this study. Note that when we talk about the information content of a message, it must be done in terms of the properties of the total experimental configuration that produces the message rather than any individual message. To be able to give a quantitative definition of information, we must consider not only the individual message that is transmitted, but also the **set of all messages** of which the one chosen is a member.

Shannon, in 1948, made the first integrated mathematical attempt to deal with the amount of information in a message and its consequences. This work and his subsequent papers laid the foundation for the new science now known as **information theory**. In this theory, two *equally possible* outcomes of an experiment were used to define the **unit of information**, which is called **one bit** (b).* The words "equally possible" involve a probabilistic notion. For discrete events, and the discussion is limited to these, the probability that a particular event will happen is equal to the number of times that the event appears to the number of times that we repeat the experiment. It seems reasonable that the ratio will approach some limit as the number of trials becomes very large. If, for example, we flip an unbiased coin one hundred times, we will find that the total number each of heads and tails will be close to fifty. We can conclude that the probability of flipping a head or a tail is 0.5. For experiments involving more than two possible states, we would find that the probability of each event would be p_i.

As a second example, suppose that in a certain community, 25 percent of all girls are blondes and 75 percent of all blondes have blue eyes. If we denote the probability of a girl being a blonde as $p_1 = 0.25$ and the probability of a blonde having blue eyes as $p_2 = 0.75$, then the probability that a girl will be a blonde with blue eyes is $p_1 p_2 = 0.25 \times 0.75 = 0.1875$.

The mathematical relation defining the amount of information or the information content, assuming that the different events are not influenced by each other, is given by the relation

$$\begin{aligned} H &= -p_1 \log_2 p_1 - p_2 \log_2 p_2 - \cdots - p_n \log_2 p_n \\ &= -\sum_{i=1}^{n} p_i \log_2 p_i \qquad \text{bits/symbol (or message)} \end{aligned} \tag{1.1}$$

* The term *bit* has two meanings—that given here as a unit of information and also to denote a binary digit in digital systems.

where $\log_2$ denotes the logarithm with base 2. Also,

$$p_1 + p_2 + \cdots + p_n = 1 \tag{1.2}$$

The term $-\log_2 p_i$ can be considered as the weight or quantity of information per event. As an example, suppose that a baby has just been born at a neighbor's house and the question is asked, What is the baby? The answer—It's a boy—then gives a specific amount of information—that is, $-\log(\frac{1}{2}) = \log 2 = 1$ bit if it is supposed that a boy or girl was equally likely, so that the a priori probability is $\frac{1}{2}$.

Example 1.1

A coin-flipping experiment is undertaken. Find the information content.

Solution For an unbiased coin, we can write

p_1 = probability that a head appears = 0.5

p_2 = probability that a tail appears = 0.5

By (1.1),

$$H = -0.5 \log_2 0.5 - 0.5 \log_2 0.5 = -\log_2 0.5 = \log_2 2 = 1 \text{ bit} \tag{1.3}$$

If the coin was a biased one with probabilities $p_1 = 0.8$ and $p_2 = 0.2$, then in this case, $H = 0.721$ b. ■

Example 1.2

Refer again to the community where 25% of all girls are blondes and 75% of all blondes have blue eyes. Suppose further that 50% of all girls in the community have blue eyes. If you know that a girl has blue eyes, how much additional information do you get by being informed that she is a blonde?

Solution Denote the following probabilities:

$p_1 = 0.25$	probability of blonde hair for community
$p_2 = 0.75$	probability of blue eyes for blonde girls of the community
$p_3 = 0.5$	probability that the particular girl has blue eyes
p_x	probability that the particular girl is blonde

Clearly, since the particular girl is one of the community, then

$$p_3 p_x = p_1 p_2 \qquad \text{or} \qquad p_x = \frac{p_1 p_2}{p_3} = \frac{0.25 \times 0.75}{0.5} = 0.375$$

Thus, the additional information that the girl is blonde is

$$-\log_2 0.375 = 1.42 \text{ b}$$ ■

Another meaning of (1.1) relates to messages as events. If p_i denotes the probability of occurrence of the ith elementary message, then $-\sum_i p_i \log p_i$ stands for the summation over all values of i of $p_i \log p_i$, where n is the total number of elementary messages. Let us suppose that we investigate an event that is *sure* to occur any time that we perform an experiment; for example, suppose that we hear "Good morning" every time we lift the telephone receiver. For the sure event $p = 1$, then $H = -\log_2 1 = 0$. Thus, the outcome of the experiment is a foregone conclusion, and the information carried by the conclusion is zero. As another example, consider the birth of a seventh child to a family of six boys. It would be expected, therefore, that the next child would also be a boy. The report by the doctor that the newborn is a girl carries with it more information than if the newborn had been a boy. Thus, the smaller the probability of an event, the greater the information content of the message.

In information theory, H represents entropy. In information theory, as in thermodynamics, **entropy** is a measure of randomness or unpredictability. If a stream of 1s and 0s goes humming by, the entropy of a given bit is 1 if, given all past history of the stream, the next bit has an equal probability of being a 1 or a 0.

For a stream of data symbols, H is usually calculated as **entropy per character**—that is, the average minimum number of bits needed to transmit a symbol given that a certain number of past symbols are known. Comparison of the entropy rate with the bit rate is straightforward. Consider a 9600 bits per second (b/s) data transmission that takes place by 2400 discrete signal events per second, each conveying 4 b (coded as one of 16 different amplitude–phase combinations). A discrete signal event per second is called a **baud**. Thus, for the present situation, there are 2400 baud. Consider alphanumeric encoded data, say of 10 b, where the first bit is a space, the next 7 b are information, the next bit is a parity indicator, and the last bit is a mark. At the information source, 3 of each 10 b has an entropy of 0. If all characters are equiprobable, then for a channel that passes 1000 b/s,

$$\text{entropy rate} = \frac{7}{10} \text{ kilobaud}$$

If the source is English text, the letters have different probabilities and the channel baud figure is less than half this bit rate (see Problem 2).

The quantification of information is very helpful. An interesting and important example is the transmission of information through optical fibers. It has been estimated that under ideal conditions, we can transmit a data rate of 100 Gb/s = 10^{11} b/s through a single-mode optical fiber. What does this figure mean? An idea of its magnitude is possible by considering the information content of the symbols of a book. Let us assume that each letter of the alphabet or a space is equally likely to appear in a given transmission (we know that this assumption is not true—see Problem 2). In this case, each letter or a space needs $-\log_2(1/27) = 4.76$ b. Since each line of a book has about 60 letters including spaces and each page has about 40 lines, then a 500-page book contains $60 \times 40 \times 500 = 1.2 \times 10^6$ letters and spaces. To transmit this book through the optical fiber would require $1.2 \times 10^6 \times 4.76 = 5.71 \times 10^6$ b; hence, the tiny ideal fiber could transmit $10^{11}/(5.71 \times 10^6) = 1.75 \times 10^4$ books/s. In practice, for a number of reasons, the actual data rate would be considerably less.

More specifically, when optical fiber communication technology was first demonstrated in 1977, a 1.5 Mb/s system carrying telephone traffic using a multimode fiber and an AlGaAs/GaAs laser light source emitting at 0.85 μm required repeater spacing of under 10 km. The AT&T TAT-8 transatlantic optical cable will use 1.3 μm single-frequency laser diodes and single-mode optical fibers at 296 Mb/s and will carry 32,000 simultaneous two-way digitized telephone circuits (or the equivalent in combinations of data, voice, and video) for distances of more than 35 km between electro-optic repeaters. More recently, dramatic improvements in optical fiber characteristics using single-mode fibers with an InGaAsP/InP laser light source at 1.55 μm have demonstrated repeater spacings exceeding 120 km at 1 Gb/s data rates. In 1984, several long-distance carriers deployed single-mode transmission systems that operated at speeds higher than 400 Mb/s (600 simultaneous 64-kb/s voice circuits) with repeater spacings in excess of 25 km.

The present practical data rate for optical fiber communication is limited by a number of factors, including attenuation characteristics of the fiber (a lower-bound set by Rayleigh scattering) and pulse distortion arising from the chromatic distortion of the fiber. The problem here arises because the index of refraction of the laser changes when the pulse is injected into the laser diode, thereby changing the laser's wavelength. Thus, because of dispersion of the optical fibers—that is, light at different wavelengths travels through the fiber with different speeds—a localized pulse, which is made up of all wavelengths, will experience smearing. At very high bit rates (greater than 1 Gb/s) this pulse-smearing severely limits the bit rate–distance product that can be attained.

1.3 Functional Representation of Signals

Periodic Continuous Time Signals

The most fundamental periodic continuous time signal that we will encounter in our studies is the trigonometric sine function shown in Figure 1.2. The reason for the importance of this waveform is that any periodic signal can be approximated by the sum of carefully chosen sine and cosine functions. The idea of adding sine and cosine functions in describing general periodic functions dates back to the time of the Babylonians, who used ideas of this type in their prediction of astronomical events. In the 18th century, Euler's observations that vibrating strings produce sinusoidal motion was followed half a century later by the work of Jean Baptiste Joseph Fourier. Fourier claimed that any periodic signal could be represented by an infinite sum of sine and cosine functions, each function having a different, though integrally related, frequency. This representation feature is also true for nonperiodic functions, but, in this case, a continuum of frequencies is involved. This matter will be studied in considerable detail in later chapters.

Sometimes, eliminating some of the frequencies that make up a complicated signal causes practical undesired effects. An example familiar to us occurs in our

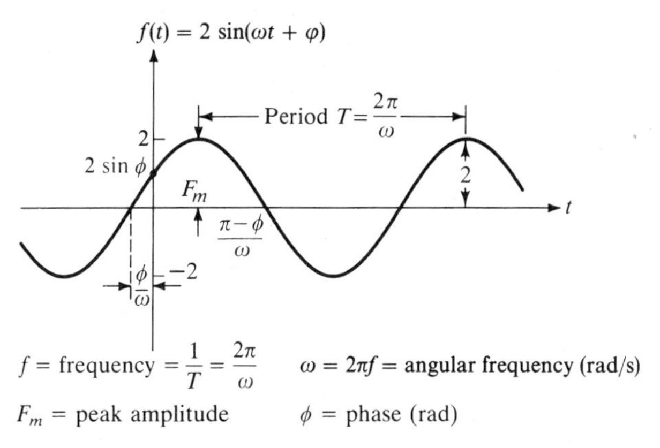

Figure 1.2 The Sine Function

telephone conversations. Telephone companies transmit many voice channels over the same lines in the interest of making optimum use of the transmission capacity of the lines. To optimize this number for the cable wire being used, they are forced to limit the maximum frequency or bandwidth of each voice channel to 4000 Hz (cycles/s). Because of this frequency bandwidth limitation, there are times when we cannot recognize the voice of a familiar person talking at the other end of the line.

The question of frequency bandwidth is also important when we want to purchase an amplifier for our hi-fi system. The salesperson will defend the price of the amplifier by telling us that the particular model under consideration has a flat frequency response extending from 100 Hz to 14,000 Hz. What the person really is telling us is that this amplifier will reproduce the signal of almost any instrument in an orchestra from percussion to piccolo without loss in the quality of its output. Essentially, the amplifier will reproduce all frequencies over the stated range without attenuation. Distortion due to phase changes with frequency can occur over the frequency range.

The sine wave is a **periodic continuous function**. Any function $f(t)$ is periodic with period T if

$$f(t \pm T) = f(t) \tag{1.4}$$

A periodic nonsinusoidal function (square wave) is shown in Figure 1.3a; a number of periodic waveforms produced by different musical instruments are shown in Figure 1.3b.

In general, signals are real functions of time since they denote the results of physical phenomena. However, for mathematical convenience, it is very useful to present sinusoidal functions as components of complex-valued functions of time, called *complex signals*. An important complex signal is the exponential function $e^{j\omega t}$. We expand this exponential function into a Maclaurin power series for

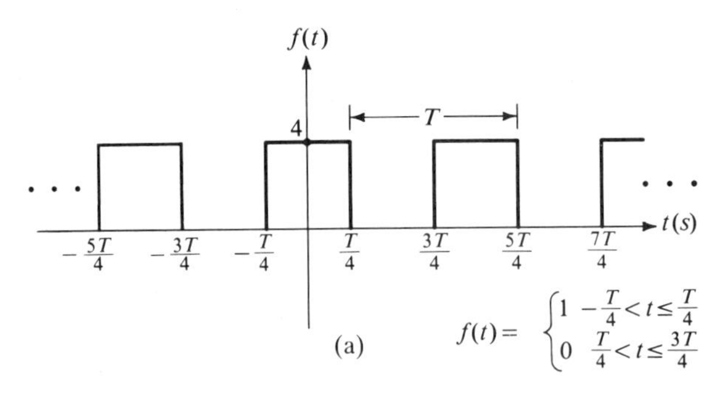

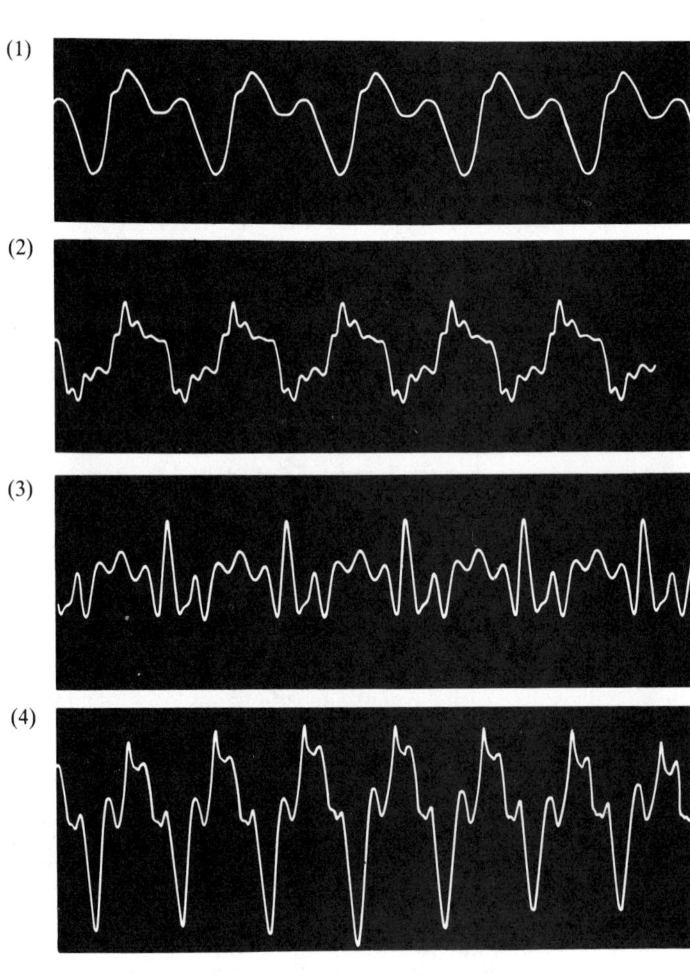

Figure 1.3 Continuous Periodic Waves. (a) Square wave. (b) Waveforms of (1) flute, (2) clarinet, (3) oboe, (4) saxophone. (From D.C. Miller, *Sound Waves and Their Uses*, Macmillan: New York, 1938. Reprinted by permission.)

e^x, where $e^x = 1 + x + x^2/2! + x^3/3! + \cdots$, writing $j\omega t$ for x. Thus,

$$e^{j\omega t} = 1 + j\omega t + \frac{(j\omega t)^2}{2!} + \cdots + \frac{(j\omega t)^n}{n!} + \cdots$$

$$= \left[1 - \frac{(\omega t)^2}{2!} + \frac{(\omega t)^4}{4!} - \cdots\right] + j\left[\omega t - \frac{(\omega t)^3}{3!} + \frac{(\omega t)^5}{5!} - \cdots\right] \quad \textbf{(1.5)}$$

We note that the real and imaginary parts of this expansion are equal, respectively, to $\cos \omega t$ and $\sin \omega t$, and we have

$$\boxed{e^{j\omega t} = \cos \omega t + j \sin \omega t} \quad \textbf{(1.6)}$$

If we set $-j$ for j in (1.5), we obtain the relation

$$e^{-j\omega t} = \cos \omega t - j \sin \omega t \quad \textbf{(1.7)}$$

By combining (1.6) and (1.7), we obtain the Euler formulas

$$\boxed{\cos \omega t = \frac{e^{j\omega t} + e^{-j\omega t}}{2} \qquad \sin \omega t = \frac{e^{j\omega t} - e^{-j\omega t}}{2j}} \quad \textbf{(1.8)}$$

Observe from (1.6) that we can also write

$$\cos \omega t = \mathrm{Re}(e^{j\omega t}) \qquad \text{and} \qquad \sin \omega t = \mathrm{Im}(e^{j\omega t})$$

where Re and Im denote the words *real part of* and *imaginary part of*, respectively. Note that the imaginary part is also real.

Periodic Discrete Time Signals

Our ability to convert continuous signals into equivalent discrete form is extremely important and will be studied in considerable detail later. Here, we examine certain features of typical discrete signals. Refer to Figure 1.4, which shows several discrete signals. In these figures, t_k specifies discrete times and $f(t_k)$ specifies the value of the function $f(t)$ at the particular time t_k. Observe that the function $f(t)$ as shown is defined only at the discrete times t_k. For convenience, we will write $f(k)$ instead of $f(t_k)$ as the value of the function at time t_k.

The definition of a periodic discrete time signal is

$$f(k) = f(k + nT) \qquad n = 1, 2, 3, \ldots \quad \textbf{(1.9)}$$

where T is the period of the function. A cosinusoidal discrete function is written

$$f(k) = \cos k(2\pi/N)n = \cos k\omega_s \quad \textbf{(1.10a)}$$

where $\omega_s = 2\pi n/N$. It can also be written in the form

$$f(k) = \mathrm{Re}\{e^{jk\omega_s}\} \quad \textbf{(1.10b)}$$

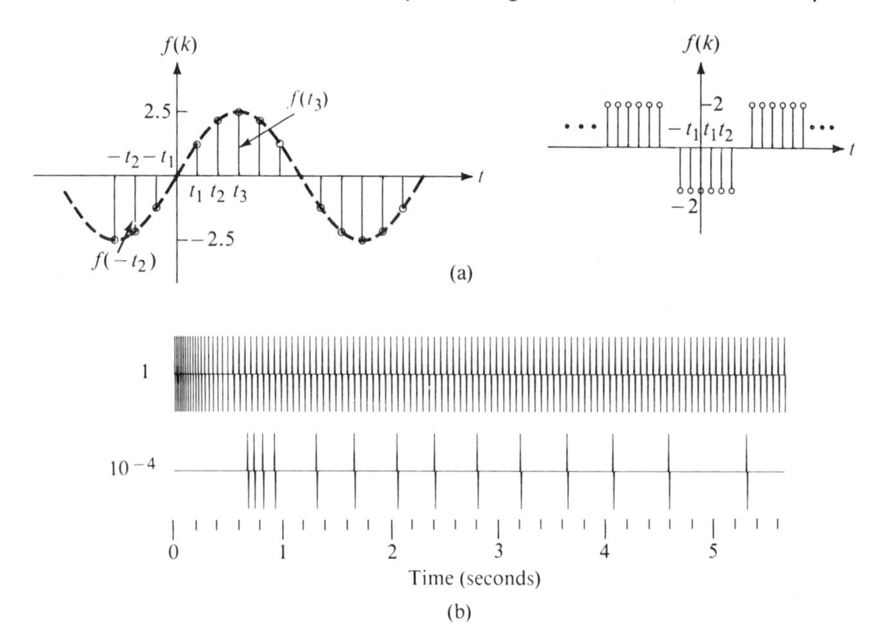

Figure 1.4 (a) Typical discrete periodic signals. (b) Discrete firings of Limulus optical nerve at two different light intensity levels. (From W. H. Miller, F. Ratliff, and H. K. Hartline, "How Cells Receive Stimuli," in *Perception: Mechanisms and Models, Scientific American*, September 1961, p. 127. Reprinted by permission of The Rockefeller Institute, New York.)

where k, n, and N are integers. Since the function $f(k)$ is periodic, then for each n and N, we must have

$$\exp\left(jk\frac{2\pi}{N}n\right) = \exp\left[j(k + N_0)\frac{2\pi}{N}n\right] = [\exp(jk\omega_s)]$$
$$\exp\left[j\frac{2\pi}{N}n\frac{N}{\gcd(n, N)}\right] = \exp[jk\omega_s] \tag{1.11}$$

where N_0 is the fundamental period and it is equal to N divided by the **greatest common divisor** (gcd) of n and N—that is,

$$N_0 = \text{fundamental period} = \frac{N}{\gcd(n, N)} \tag{1.12}$$

We conclude from this development that the function $\exp(jk\omega_s)$ is the same at frequencies ω_s, which are multiples of 2π. Thus, for the complete description of the wave, we need consider only the intervals $0 \le \omega_s \le 2\pi$ or $-\pi \le \omega_s \le \pi$ in which to choose ω_s. Furthermore, if no gcd exists, the discrete exponential is not periodic.

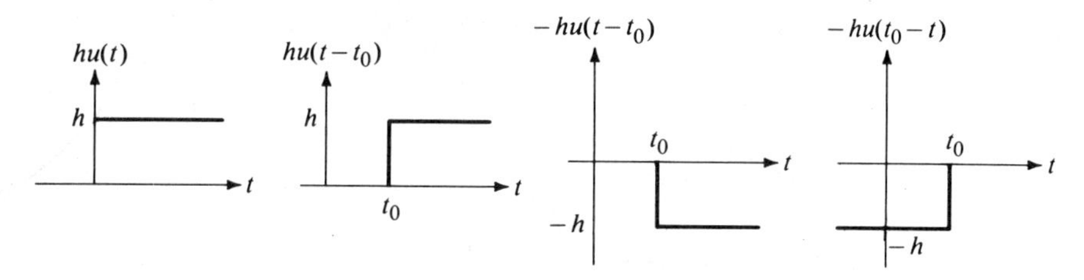

Figure 1.5 The Step Function and Some of Its Shifted and Reflected Forms

Nonperiodic Continuous Signals

This section introduces a number of special functions for describing particular classes of signals. Many of these functions have features that make them particularly useful directly or indirectly in describing other functions in the solution of engineering problems. At this point, little more than a catalog of these signals and their mathematical description is presented.

Unit Step Function. The **unit step function** $u(t)$ is an important signal for analytic studies; moreover, it has many practical applications. Note that the step function shown in Figure 1.5 is continuous after its application, but there is a discontinuity at the instant of application. Mathematically, therefore, the step function is not a regular function. As a well-known example of a step function, when we turn the key in the ignition of our car, we actually introduce a step voltage function (the battery voltage) to the starting motor. Likewise, any constant force when applied to a body at a particular time t is also described by a step function.

The unit step function is defined by the relation

$$u(t) = \begin{cases} 1 & t > 0 \\ 0 & t < 0 \end{cases} \quad \text{or} \quad u(t - t_0) = \begin{cases} 1 & t - t_0 > 0 \\ 0 & t - t_0 < 0 \end{cases} \tag{1.13}$$

It is clear from this definition that the value of the function is unity for positive arguments and zero for negative arguments. The function is not defined at $t = 0$, but we will see that this is no problem. The step function of height h and some of its shifted forms are shown in Figure 1.5.

Rectangular Pulse Function. The **pulse function** is the result of an on-off switching operation of a constant voltage source to an electric circuit. This waveform has considerable practical utility. For example, its narrow pulses are used to modulate the transmitters in radar equipments, and it is the waveshape of the recurring timing signals (clock pulses) that control the total operation of any digital computer.

A rectangular pulse function of height h and its shifted form are shown in Figure 1.6. The mathematical representation is developed from the appropriate

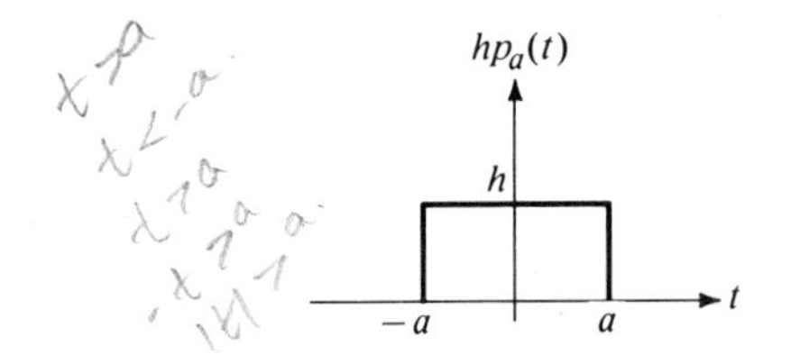

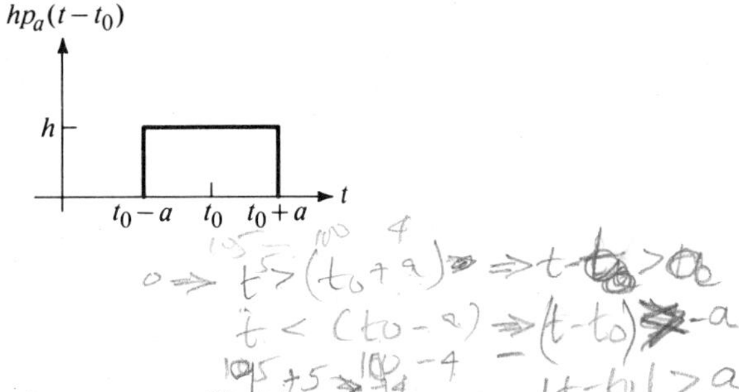

Figure 1.6 Rectangular Pulse Function

choice of step functions. Pulse functions are specified by

$$p_a(t) = [u(t+a) - u(t-a)] = \begin{cases} 0 & |t| > a \\ 1 & |t| < a \end{cases}$$
$$p_a(t-t_0) = [u(t-t_0+a) - u(t-t_0-a)] = \begin{cases} 0 & |t-t_0| > a \\ 1 & |t-t_0| < a \end{cases} \quad \textbf{(1.14)}$$

Sinc Function. This function plays an important role in the reconstruction of special signals. As a function of ω, it also represents the frequency content of the pulse function, as will be learned in a later chapter. The **sinc function** is defined by the expression

$$\operatorname{sinc}_a(t) = \frac{\sin at}{t} \qquad -\infty < t < \infty \quad \textbf{(1.15)}$$

It is shown in Figure 1.7 for three different values of a.

Nonperiodic Discrete Signals

Delta Function. The delta function $\delta(t)$, often called the *impulse* or *Dirac delta* function, occupies a central place in signal analysis. Many physical entities, such as point sources, point charges, concentrated loads on structures, and voltage or current sources acting for very short times can be modeled as delta functions. The **delta function** $\delta(t)$ has very peculiar properties; it exists only at time t_0 and is characterized as follows:

$$\delta(t-t_0) = 0 \qquad t \neq t_0 \quad \textbf{(1.16a)}$$
$$\int_{t_1}^{t_2} f(t)\delta(t-t_0)\,dt = f(t_0) \qquad t_1 < t_0 < t_2 \quad \textbf{(1.16b)}$$

By (1.16), the delta function exists only at the point $t = t_0$ (the argument is zero).

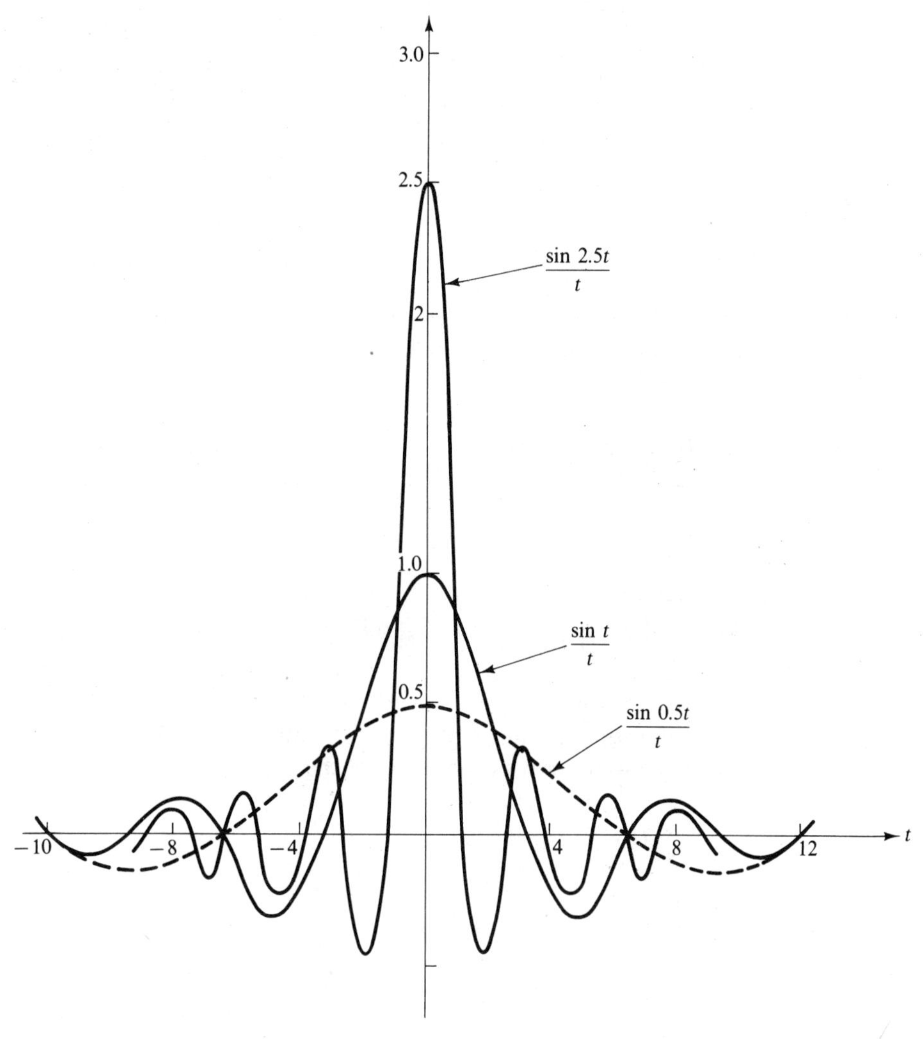

Figure 1.7 Sinc Function for Three Different Values of a

Further, these equations show that the impulse function can be used to extract from a function $f(t)$ the specific value that exists at the time t_0, where $f(t)$ is a continuous function at t_0. Several delta functions are shown in Figure 1.8; Figure 1.8b illustrates graphically (1.16b). Observe that the definition of the delta function is not presented in functional form, but is presented by its behavior under the integral sign. Despite the fact that the delta function is not an analytic function, a rigorous mathematical definition for this type of function was given by Laurent Schwartz in his work on the **theory of generalized functions**.

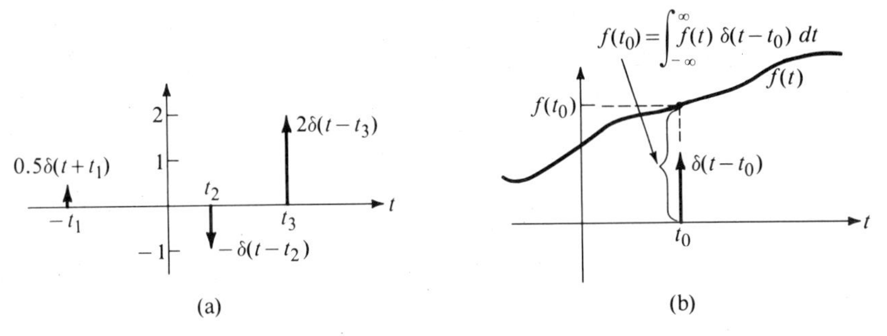

Figure 1.8 (a) Representation of several delta functions. (b) Illustrating the effect of multiplying a well-behaved function and a delta function.

If the function $f(t)$ contained in (1.16) is a constant equal to unity, then

$$\int_{t_1}^{t_2} \delta(t - t_0)\,dt = 1 \qquad t_1 < t_0 < t_2 \tag{1.17}$$

This integral shows that the area under the delta function is unity. The height of the spikes shown in Figure 1.8 denotes the areas of the delta functions.

To see how the delta function can be created, consider that a current of very short duration ε and amplitude $1/\varepsilon$ is applied to the circuit shown in Figure 1.9. From the well-known expression for the capacitor,

$$v(t) = \frac{1}{C}\int_0^t i(t)\,dt$$

we obtain for $C = 1F$,

$$v(t) = \int_0^{\varepsilon} \frac{1}{\varepsilon}\,dt = \int_0^{\varepsilon/2} \frac{2}{\varepsilon}\,dt = \int_0^{\varepsilon/4} \frac{4}{\varepsilon}\,dt = 1$$

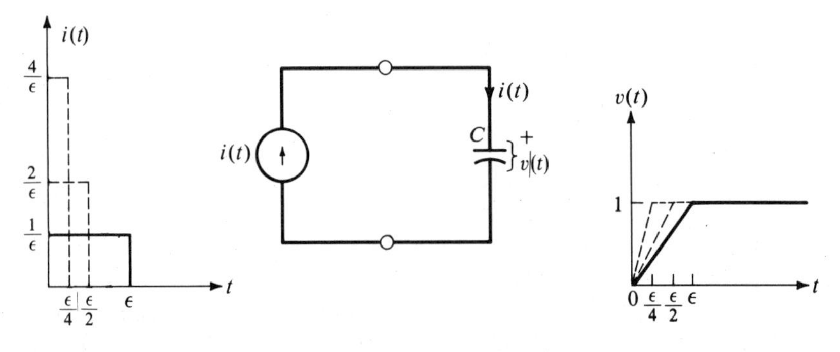

Figure 1.9 Voltage on a Capacitor due to an Impulse Current Source

In this example, the area under the function will always be equal to unity for any $\varepsilon \to 0$, and it will be zero everywhere else except at $t = 0$, where it is undefined.

Observe further in this particular example, which involves the integral of the delta function, that in the limit, as $\varepsilon \to 0$, the current function will produce a step voltage of 1 V in the circuit. It is a general result for a delta function that the integral of the delta function produces a step function.

Despite its special properties, the importance of the delta function will become apparent when we study the response of linear systems (those with linear elements) to an arbitrary input. We will learn that if we know the output of a linear and time-invariant system (a system composed of elements that do not vary with time and are linear) to a delta function input, we can use this knowledge to find the output of the system to an input that is any well-behaved function. A well-behaved function is one that may have a finite number of discontinuities of finite amplitude on a finite time interval and has finite derivatives at both sides of each discontinuity.

The definition given in (1.16) is less than satisfying, but it does indicate the unusual behavior of this particular function, and it will suffice for our subsequent work. A more satisfying definition is possible by considering a function that behaves like a delta function upon taking some appropriate limit (see Problem 17).

Example 1.3

Find the velocity of a free body with mass m on a frictionless surface when a unit impulse function force is applied at $t = 0$.

Solution Using the Newton force law $f(t) = ma(t) = m\,dv(t)/dt$, we find

$$v(t) = \frac{1}{m}\int_{0-}^{t} f(t)\,dt = \frac{1}{m}\int_{0-}^{t} \delta(t)\,dt = \frac{1}{m} \qquad t > 0$$

This result indicates that the velocity is a step function: It is zero until $t = 0$ and then assumes the value $1/m$ (m/s) for times $t > 0$. We conclude also that the derivative of the step function $u(t)$ is equal to the delta function $\delta(t)$. This conclusion is the converse of the property made above. We may write, in general,

$$\frac{du(t - t_0)}{dt} = \delta(t - t_0) \tag{1.18}$$

■

Comb Function. The comb function is an array of delta functions that are spaced T units apart and that extend from $-\infty$ to $+\infty$. The function is illustrated in Figure 1.10; its mathematical description is

$$\text{comb}_T(t) = \sum_{k=-\infty}^{\infty} \delta(t - kT) \qquad k = 0, \pm 1, \pm 2, \ldots \tag{1.19}$$

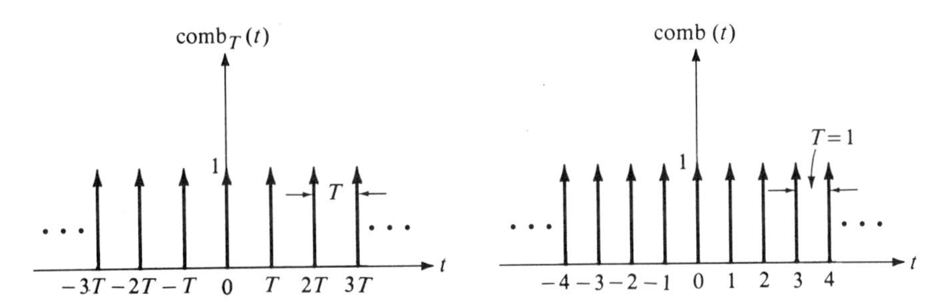

Figure 1.10 Comb Function

Discrete Step Function. The discrete step function, the discrete version of $u(t)$, is an array of delta functions that extends from 0 to ∞ and that is spaced T units apart, as shown in Figure 1.11. But the discrete-type delta function $\delta(k - k_0)$ is equal to unity at $k = k_0$ and is zero for $k \neq k_0$. Clearly, the **discrete step function** bears a close resemblance to the comb function, except that it extends only in the positive direction. Its mathematical description is

$$u(k) = \begin{cases} 1 & \text{for } k = 0, 1, 2, \ldots \\ 0 & \text{for } k = \text{negative} \end{cases} \tag{1.20}$$

Arbitrary Sampled Function. The comb function can be used in the representation of any continuous function in its sampled or discrete form. The property of the delta function permits us to write

$$f(t)\delta(t) = f(0)\delta(t)$$
$$f(t)\delta(t - t_0) = f(t_0)\delta(t - t_0)$$

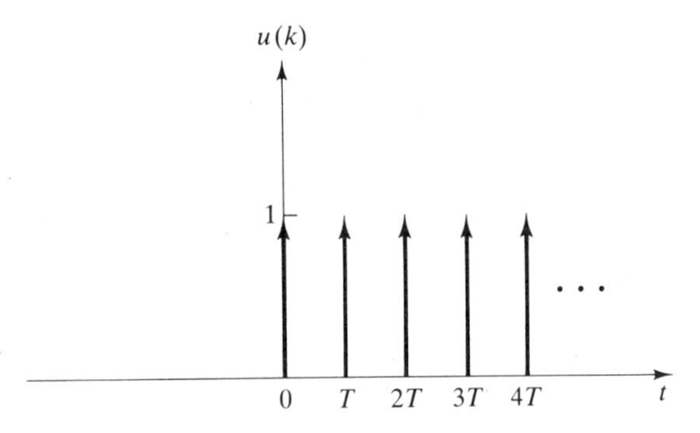

Figure 1.11 Discrete Step Function

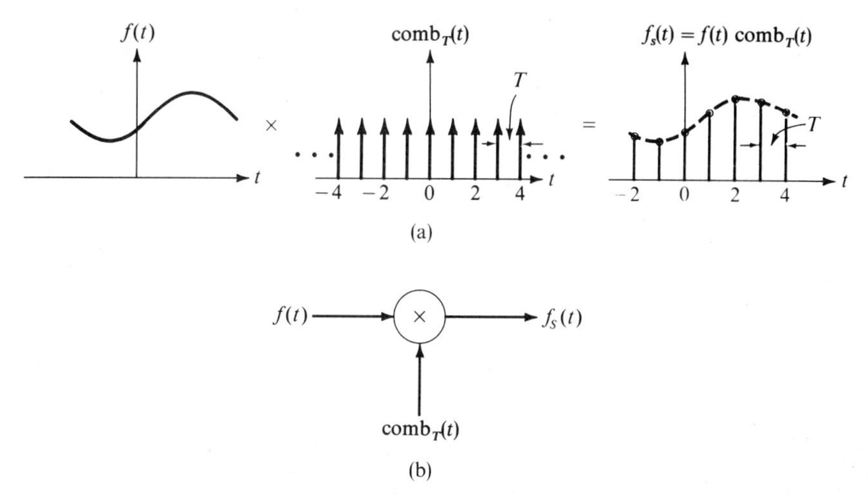

Figure 1.12 (a) Representation of the discrete form of an arbitrary function. (b) Representation of the operational form.

Therefore,

$$f_s(t) = f(t)\,\mathrm{comb}_T(t) = \sum_{k=-\infty}^{\infty} f(kT)\delta(t - kT) \tag{1.21}$$

where $f_s(t)$ denotes the sampled version of the function $f(t)$. Figure 1.12a shows graphically the functions $f(t)$, $\mathrm{comb}_T(t)$, and $f_s(t)$. Figure 1.12b displays operationally the process of combining $f(t)$ and $\mathrm{comb}_T(t)$.

1.4 Signal Conditioning

As discussed earlier in Section 1.2 in connection with signal communications, it is often desired to transmit slowly varying signals over long distances without wires—for example, voice or low-frequency audio information. To accomplish this, a radio transmission channel is required. Otherwise, if we were to transmit these frequencies directly, and they would be in the range from about 50 Hz to 10 kHz, the required antenna system would have to be appropriate to the signal, wavelengths that are in excess of 3×10^4 m, since $\ell \doteq \lambda/2$, where λ is the wavelength and $\lambda = c/f = 3 \times 10^8/f$ m. It is not practical to build an efficient antenna system of approximately 10 km in length. To circumvent this problem, one often resorts to the radio scheme known as **amplitude modulation** (AM), the elements of which are shown in Figure 1.13. This approach requires that the signal $f(t)$ must be multiplied with the signal produced by a high-frequency oscillator (a continuous wave oscillator). What is achieved in this method is that the signal $f(t)$ has been shifted on the frequency scale from its

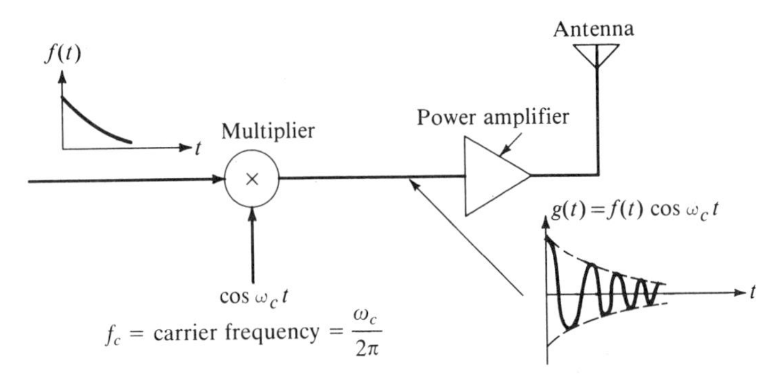

Figure 1.13 Illustrating the Usefulness of Modulation (Multiplication) of Signals

original zero-frequency reference to that of the frequency of the high-frequency oscillator. The result at the antenna is a high-frequency signal and, for the signal shown in Figure 1.13, is the decaying exponential variation of the original signal that controls the amplitude of the high-frequency component. If the AM radio station is in the 500 kHz to 1100 kHz frequency range (the standard broadcast band), the antenna length would be roughly 75 m long for a radiated frequency of 1000 kHz. At the receiving point, a circuit would be needed to extract the original signal. This circuit, called a **demodulator**, shifts the frequency of the modulated signal from the high-frequency carrier level back to its original frequency level. The most simple form is an *RC* circuit that acts as an envelope detector. Actually, the circuits are more complicated than those discussed here for both the modulation and demodulation, but the essential requirements are those that have been discussed.

Most of the signals that we encounter in nature are **analog**, or continuous time, signals. A basic reason is that physical systems cannot respond instantaneously to rapidly changing inputs. Moreover, in many cases, the available signal is not in electrical form, thus requiring the use of a transducer (mechanical, electrical, thermal, and so forth) to provide an electrical signal that is representative of the system signal. Generally, these transducers cannot respond instantaneously to changes and tend to smooth the signals. What we actually observe are close replicas of the desired signals, not signals identical with the original one. The closeness depends, of course, on the sensitivity of the transducer.

Depending on the signal processing requirements, detected signals become useful if we are able to analyze them and if we are able to perform mathematical operations on them. The digital computer is of tremendous value in such signal processing operations, but digital computers are discrete systems that accept only discrete information, thus requiring that analog signals be converted into equivalent digital signals. This topic was discussed in general terms in Section 1.3, but the practical realization of very rapid analog to digital conversion is accomplished with an analog to digital (A/D) converter. Often, the processed digital signals are converted back to analog form because humans are better able to observe analog

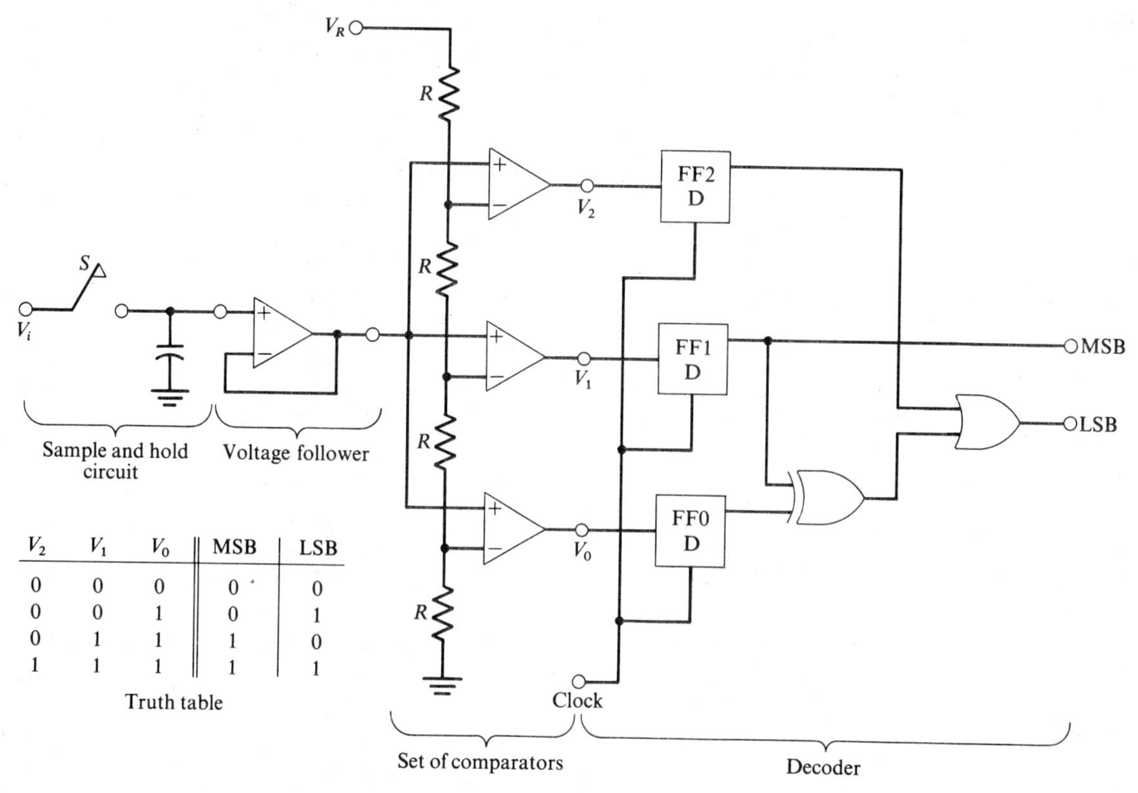

V_2	V_1	V_0	MSB	LSB
0	0	0	0	0
0	0	1	0	1
0	1	1	1	0
1	1	1	1	1

Figure 1.14 Simple Two-Bit Analog to Digital (A/D) Converter

signals. This transformation is accomplished using a digital to analog (D/A) converter. The A/D converter shown in Figure 1.14 is one of many schemes that are used in practice.

If a voltage V_i is available, the conversion starts by closing and opening the electronic switch S at a rate that is long enough for capacitor C to charge to V_i. The "sampled" input voltage will be "held" after the electronic switch is opened by the voltage follower because the input resistance of the operational amplifier configuration is extremely high and does not load the circuit. If the sampled voltage V_i is just a bit larger than $V_R/4$, the first comparator saturates, thereby providing an output V_o, which is taken as logic 1. The other output voltages will be zero: $V_1 = V_2 = 0$. Therefore, at the clock pulse, the output of D-type flip-flop FFO is 1 and the outputs of FF1 and FF2 are 0. The output from the XOR gate (exclusive OR) is $0 + 1 = 1$, and the output of the OR gate is $0 + 1 = 1$. As a consequence, the least significant bit (LSB) is 1 and the most significant bit (MSB) is 0. If the sampled voltage is larger than $V_R/2$, the first and second comparators saturate, resulting in outputs V_o and V_1, with $V_2 = 0$. By following the same reasoning as before, with due account of the XOR and OR gates, the output is that given in the truth table. When the sampled signal is greater than $V_R/3$, all comparators saturate. The result is the output shown in the truth table of Figure 1.14.

1.5 Representation of Signals

In the previous sections, it was noted that a given signal waveform must often be represented in mathematical form, regardless of whether the function is non-analytical, whether it is given graphically by an experimentally determined output from some transducer, or whether it is given in chart form or tabular form. One approach is to represent a specified function by a combination of elementary functions called **basis functions**. The exponential function $\exp(j\omega t)$ is a basis function. The principal motivation in employing basis functions is that straightforward mathematical operations are possible from such a representation; also, a better understanding of the system behavior is possible using such representations.

When we consider the effects of a physical system on an arbitrary signal $f(t)$, we are actually studying the output of the system when the input is $f(t)$. Because a system is usually described by a mathematical operator, it is evident that the output of the system is equivalent to the effect that the operator has on the signal. However, mathematical operations—for example, integration—are difficult to perform unless $f(t)$ possesses certain special properties. Therefore, if we can find a set of simple basis functions $\{\varphi_i\}$ with such special properties that the function $f(t)$ can be represented by a linear combination of these basis functions, we will have achieved our objective. For linear systems, it will be relatively easy to determine the effect of the operator on $f(t)$ by finding the effect of the operator on each basis function and then adding these effects, an application of the principle of superposition.

To establish certain ideas that will be helpful in understanding the procedure, consider a vector in space. Let $\mathbf{a}_i (i = 1, 2, 3)$, known as a **basis set**, denote the three orthogonal unit vectors along the Cartesian coordinate axes. An arbitrary vector $\mathbf{F}$ can be expanded in the form

$$\mathbf{F} = F_1\mathbf{a}_1 + F_2\mathbf{a}_2 + F_3\mathbf{a}_3 = \sum_{i=1}^{3} F_i\mathbf{a}_i \tag{1.22}$$

where the F_i's are the projections of $\mathbf{F}$ on each coordinate axis. By taking into consideration the orthogonality of the vector set $\mathbf{a}_i$, given by

$$\mathbf{a}_i \cdot \mathbf{a}_j = \begin{cases} 1 & i = j \\ 0 & i \neq j \end{cases} \tag{1.23}$$

the components of $\mathbf{F}$ are specified by

$$F_i = \frac{\mathbf{F} \cdot \mathbf{a}_i}{\mathbf{a}_i \cdot \mathbf{a}_i} \tag{1.24}$$

where $\mathbf{F} \cdot \mathbf{a}_i = F_i$ is the (inner) product, and F_i is the projection of the vector $\mathbf{F}$ on the a_i axis. Note that since *any* three-dimensional vector $\mathbf{F}$ can be represented as a linear combination of the three orthogonal vectors $\mathbf{a}_1$, $\mathbf{a}_2$, and $\mathbf{a}_3$, the system is called *complete*—that is, $\mathbf{F}$ is contained in the space *spanned* by the basis set $\{\mathbf{a}_i\}$. On the other hand, a three-dimensional vector $\mathbf{F}$ cannot be represented as a linear combination of only two orthogonal vectors, say $\mathbf{a}_1$ and $\mathbf{a}_2$. Therefore, the two-dimensional orthogonal set is *incomplete* to represent three-dimensional vectors, and the basis set does not span the space containing $\mathbf{F}$.

Now, let us apply these same ideas to functions. It may be possible to express an arbitrary function $f(t)$ as the sum of its components along a set of mutually orthogonal functions that form a complete set over the interval $t = a$ to $t = b$. Thus, if we write $\varphi_i(t) \triangleq \mathbf{a}_i$ and $c_i \triangleq F_i$ (the symbol $\triangleq$ indicates equivalence, by definition), then (1.22) assumes the equivalent form

$$f(t) = \sum_{i=1}^{\infty} c_i \varphi_i(t) \tag{1.25}$$

Multiply (1.25) by $\varphi_j(t)\,dt$ or by $\varphi_j^*(t)\,dt$ if the φ_i's are complex functions (the asterisk means complex conjugate functions—the function φ_j with all complex components replaced by their negative values) and integrate over the range of definition $[a, b]$ of $f(t)$. The result is

$$\int_a^b f(t)\varphi_i(t)\,dt = \sum_{i=1}^{\infty} c_i \int_a^b \varphi_i(t)\varphi_j(t)\,dt$$

or

$$\int_a^b f(t)\varphi_i(t)\,dt = c_i \int_a^b \varphi_i^2(t)\,dt = c_i \|\varphi_i\|^2 \tag{1.26a}$$

from which it follows that

$$c_i = \frac{\int_a^b f(t)\varphi_i(t)\,dt}{\int_a^b \varphi_i^2(t)\,dt} = \frac{\int_a^b f(t)\varphi_i(t)\,dt}{\|\varphi_i\|^2} \qquad i = 0, 1, 2, \ldots \tag{1.26b}$$

where

$$\left[\int_a^b \varphi_i^2(t)\,dt\right]^{1/2} = \|\varphi_i\| \tag{1.26c}$$

is called the *norm* of the function φ_i and is a real number. Equation (1.26) is the result of the assumed orthogonality property over the interval $t = a$ to $t = b$:

$$\int_a^b \varphi_i(t)\varphi_j(t)\,dt = \begin{cases} \|\varphi_i\|^2 & i = j \\ 0 & i \neq j \end{cases} \tag{1.27}$$

If the value of $\|\varphi_i\|^2 = 1$, the basis functions φ_i are called **orthonormal**. The functions under consideration and the functions that constitute an orthogonal set must be **square integrable**—that is, they must obey the relations

$$\int_a^b |f(t)|\, dt < \infty \qquad \text{and} \qquad \int_a^b f^2(t)\, dt < \infty \tag{1.28}$$

including the case when the interval $[a, b] = (-\infty, \infty)$.

■ Example 1.4

Show that the set of functions

$$f(t) = \{1, \cos t, \cos 2t, \ldots \cos nt, \ldots\}$$

constitutes orthogonal basis functions over the interval $[0, \pi]$.

Solution Form the relations

$$\int_0^\pi 1 \cos nt\, dt = 0$$

$$\int_0^n \cos nt \cos mt\, dt = 0 \qquad m \neq n$$

$$\int_0^\pi \cos^2 nt\, dt = \frac{\pi}{2}$$

Observe that this set constitutes basis functions on the interval $0 < t \leq \pi$. The function will become orthonormal if each is multiplied by $\sqrt{2/\pi}$. ■

The trigonometric function $\cos \omega_0 nt$ (similarly, $\sin \omega_0 nt$) is one of the most important basis functions and one that we will use frequently in our study of linear systems. The complex representation of these functions is

$$\varphi_n(t) = \exp(j\omega_0 nt) \qquad n = 0, \pm 1, \pm 2, \ldots$$

since $\text{Re}\{\exp(jn\omega_0 t)\} = \text{Re}\{\cos n\omega_0 t + j \sin n\omega_0 t\} = \cos n\omega_0 t$; $\text{Im}\{\exp(jn\omega_0 t)\} = \sin n\omega_0 t$. These expressions form the basis for the Fourier series expansion of periodic functions. We will study this matter in some detail in Chapter 3. The main reason for learning about basis functions is that they are the **eigenfunctions** of linear time-invariant systems.

A **linear time-invariant** (LTI) **system** is one in which any time shift at the input results in the same time shift at the output. Further, **superposition** applies to LTI systems, which means that the output of a system to multiple inputs is the sum of the outputs due to each component of the input. That is, no interaction occurs in the system among input components. Therefore, an eigenfunction input to an LTI system results in an output that is equal to the input multiplied by a complex constant. For sinusoidal function inputs, the output has the same form as the input, with the possible difference that its magnitude, as well as its phase, may be changed. This matter will receive more attention in Chapter 2.

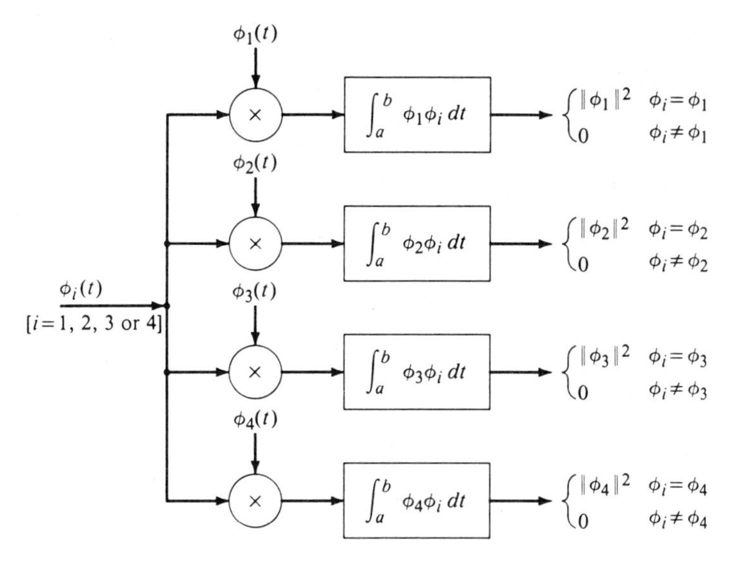

Figure 1.15 Detection Scheme Using Orthogonal Functions

Orthogonal functions are also important in detection theory. Suppose, for example, that we send four messages corresponding to four orthogonal functions φ_1, φ_2, φ_3, and φ_4, respectively. If we construct a receiver having the properties shown in Figure 1.15, we observe that each channel will respond only when the incoming signal is equal to the input signal of that channel. Because of the orthogonality of the functions, the remaining channels will produce no output.

■ Example 1.5

Given below are several of the complete set of orthonormal functions in the range $-1 \leq t \leq 1$ known as **Legendre polynomial functions**:

$$\varphi_0(t) = \frac{1}{\sqrt{2}} \qquad \varphi_1(t) = \sqrt{\frac{3}{2}}\, t$$

$$\varphi_2(t) = \frac{1}{2}\sqrt{\frac{5}{2}}\,(3t^2 - 1) \qquad \varphi_3(t) = \frac{1}{2}\sqrt{\frac{7}{2}}\,(5t^3 - 3t)$$

Find the value of the integral

$$I = \text{mean square error} = \int_{-1}^{1} [t^2 - f_a(t)]^2\, dt$$

using two different approximating functions

a. $f_a(t) = c_0\, \varphi_0(t) + c_1 \varphi_1(t)$

b. $f_a(t) = c_0\, \varphi_0(t) + c_1 \varphi_1(t) + c_2\, \varphi_2(t)$

Solution First we must find the appropriate c_i's so that the function $f_a(t)$ approximates $f(t) = t^2$ in the range $-1 \le t \le 1$. Using (1.26), we find

$$c_0 = \frac{\int_{-1}^{1} t^2(1/\sqrt{2})\,dt}{\int_{-1}^{1} (1/\sqrt{2})^2\,dt} = \frac{\sqrt{2}}{3}$$

$$c_1 = \frac{\int_{-1}^{1} t^2\sqrt{(3/2)}t\,dt}{\int_{-1}^{1} [\sqrt{(3/2)}t]^2\,dt} = 0$$

Therefore, the first-order approximation of $f(t) = t^2$ with Legendre polynomials is $f_a(t) = \sqrt{2}/3$, so

$$I = \int_{-1}^{1}\left(t^2 - \frac{\sqrt{2}}{3}\right)^2 dt = 0.216$$

For case b, following the same procedure as above, we find that $c_2 = 2\sqrt{10}/15$, and so

$$f_a(t) = \frac{\sqrt{2}}{3} + \frac{1}{3}(3t^2 - 1)$$

In this case, the integral for I is

$$I = \int_{-1}^{1}\left(t^2 - \frac{\sqrt{2}}{3} - t^2 + \frac{1}{3}\right)^2 dt = 0.038$$

From these results, we observe that the **mean square error** (MSE), which is an indicator of how close the approximating function is to the given function, decreases as we add more and more terms from the basis set. It can be shown that if we use a complete set of orthonormal functions, the MSE will approach zero as the number of terms approaches infinity. ∎

A second approach to a representation of signals makes use of a known development from the calculus, namely, that a function that is continuous and possesses continuous derivatives can be written in the form of a Taylor expansion:

$$f(t) = f(t_0) + (t - t_0)\left.\frac{df}{dt}\right|_{t=t_0} + \frac{(t-t_0)^2}{2!}\left.\frac{d^2 f}{dt^2}\right|_{t=t_0} + \cdots + \frac{(t-t_0)^{n-1}}{(n-1)!}\left.\frac{d^{n-1}f}{dt^{n-1}}\right|_{t=t_0} + R_n \qquad \textbf{(1.29)}$$

where R_n is the *remainder* that vanishes as $n \to \infty$. This expression shows that a function $f(t)$ at any time t can be written in terms of its value at a different instant of time t_0, provided that the value of the function and all of its derivatives are known at the same instant t_0. In many cases, these quantities are not known and we must then resort to other methods.

A third approach, and one that is related to the other approaches, is to approximate the function by polynomials. The characteristic feature of most numerical methods is that values of the function $f(t)$ are given for a set of distinct values of t, but not for intermediate values. These intermediate values can be estimated on the hypothesis that $f(t)$ can be replaced by a polynomial that agrees with $f(t)$ at the points where its values are known. The simplest case is that of linear interpolation, which involves taking only two adjacent values of $f(t)$ from a table and calculating intermediate values on the supposition that the first derivative $f^{(1)}(t)$ is constant in the interval specified by the two values. This approach is accurate provided that $f^{(1)}(t)$ changes little in the interval. Often, however, allowance must be made for higher derivatives. The use of a polynomial for curve fitting can never be mathematically exact unless $f(t)$ is itself a polynomial. It can, in suitable circumstances, be as accurate as the tabulated values that are available.

Suppose that a function $f(t)$ is approximated by a polynomial

$$f_a(t) = \sum_{n=0}^{N} \alpha_n t^n \tag{1.30}$$

It is assumed that the function $f(t)$ is known (collocates) at $N + 1$ points with values $f(t_0), f(t_1), \ldots f(t_N)$, where $t_0 < t_1 < t_2 \cdots < t_N$. Equation (1.30) leads to the set of equations

$$\begin{aligned}
\alpha_0 + \alpha_1 t_0 + \alpha_2 t_0^2 + \cdots + \alpha_N t_0^N &= f(t_0) \\
\alpha_0 + \alpha_1 t_1 + \alpha_2 t_1^2 + \cdots + \alpha_N t_1^N &= f(t_1) \\
\vdots \qquad \vdots \qquad \vdots \qquad\qquad \vdots \quad &\quad \vdots \\
\alpha_0 + \alpha_1 t_N + \alpha_2 t_N^2 + \cdots + \alpha_N t_N^N &= f(t_N)
\end{aligned} \tag{1.31}$$

This set of equations can be solved for the coefficients α_i. This is conveniently done by writing this set of equations in matrix form:

$$\begin{bmatrix} 1 & t_0 & t_0^2 \cdots & t_0^N \\ 1 & t_1 & t_1^2 \cdots & t_1^N \\ \vdots & \vdots & \vdots & \vdots \\ 1 & t_N & t_N^2 \cdots & t_N^N \end{bmatrix} \begin{bmatrix} \alpha_0 \\ \alpha_1 \\ \vdots \\ \alpha_N \end{bmatrix} = \begin{bmatrix} f(t_0) \\ f(t_1) \\ \vdots \\ f(t_N) \end{bmatrix} \tag{1.32}$$

or, more compactly,

$$\mathbf{TA} = \mathbf{F} \tag{1.33}$$

where $\mathbf{T}$, $\mathbf{A}$, and $\mathbf{F}$ denote the matrixes in (1.32). Using matrix methods, we find for $\mathbf{A}$, the expression

$$\mathbf{A} = \mathbf{T}^{-1}\mathbf{F} \tag{1.34}$$

where $\mathbf{T}^{-1}$ is the matrix inverse of $\mathbf{T}$, which involves a procedure to be discussed later.

■ **Example 1.6**
Find a three-term polynomial approximation for the function $f(t) = \cos(\pi/2)t$ over the interval $-1 \leq t \leq 1$.

Solution If we arbitrarily select the three points at $t_0 = -1$, $t_1 = 0$, and $t_2 = 1$ in a three-term expansion, as given by (1.30), the resulting set of equations is

$$f_a(-1) = \alpha_0(-1)^0 + \alpha_1(-1)^1 + \alpha_2(-1)^2 = \alpha_0 - \alpha_1 + \alpha_2 = 0$$
$$f_a(0) = \alpha_0 (0)^0 + \alpha_1 (0)^1 + \alpha_2 (0)^2 = \alpha_0 + 0\alpha_1 + 0\alpha_2 = 1$$
$$f_a(1) = \alpha_0 (1)^0 + \alpha_1 (1)^1 + \alpha_2 (1)^2 = \alpha_0 + \alpha_1 + \alpha_2 = 0$$

Solving this set of equations, we obtain for the coefficients $\alpha_0 = 1$, $\alpha_1 = 0$, and $\alpha_2 = -1$. The approximating function is

$$f_a(t) = 1 - t^2$$

which is the equation of a circle. A better approximation is possible by using more terms in the polynomial expansion. ■

Problems

Section 1.2

1. Plot $H = -p_1 \log_2 p_1 - p_2 \log_2 p_2$ versus p_1 for the value $0 < p_1 < 1$ and show that the information is a maximum at $p_1 = 0.5$. Remember that $p_1 + p_2 = 1$ is always true.
2. The probability of occurrence of letters in the English language is given in the following tabulation:

Symbol	Probability p	Symbol	Probability p
Word space, or blank	0.2	L	0.029
E	0.105	C	0.023
T	0.072	FU	0.0225
O	0.0654	M	0.021
A	0.063	P	0.0175
N	0.059	YW	0.012
I	0.055	G	0.011
R	0.054	B	0.0105
S	0.052	V	0.008
H	0.047	K	0.003
D	0.035	X	0.002
		JQZ	0.001

Find the information per symbol.

3. When a pair of dice is rolled, a certain person is informed that the result is a seven. How much information is there in this message?
4. Consider a transmission channel having only three symbols: A, B, and C. Suppose that the duration of A is 1 unit, B is 2 units, and C is 3 units.
   a. Find the transmission capacity if $p_A = \frac{1}{6}$, $p_B = \frac{2}{6}$, and $p_C = \frac{3}{6}$.
   b. Repeat (a) if $p_A = \frac{3}{6}$, $p_B = \frac{2}{6}$, and $p_C = \frac{1}{6}$.

Section 1.3

5. Plot the given functions and, from these, conclude what type of signal you will eventually find if you add more terms conforming to the pattern given.
   a. $f(t) = (4/\pi)(\sin 2\pi t + \frac{1}{3} \sin 6\pi t)$
   b. $f(t) = (4/\pi)(\sin 2\pi t + \frac{1}{3} \sin 6\pi t + \frac{1}{5} \sin 10\pi t + \frac{1}{7} \sin 14\pi t)$
6. Find the amplitude r and phase φ of the sine function $f(t) = r \cos(\omega t + \varphi)$ if $f(t)$ is given by the expression $f(t) = a \cos \omega t + b \sin \omega t$.
7. Show that $(d/dt)e^{j\omega t} = j\omega e^{j\omega t}$.
8. Draw the following functions:
   a. $f(t) = 2u(t) + u(t-2) - 2u(t-3)$
   b. $f(t) = -2u(-t) + u(2-t) - 2u(3-t)$
9. The sketch shown in Figure 1.16 represents a system integrator—that is, the output is the integral of the input. Show that when the input is a unit step function of amplitude a, the output is a linearly increasing function called a *ramp* function.

Figure 1.16

10. Determine which of the following signals are periodic. For those signals that are periodic, determine their fundamental frequencies.
    a. $f(t) = -4 \sin(-3.4 \times 10^{-6} t + \pi/6)$
    b. $f(t) = 2.5 \cos(2\pi \times 10^2 t + 30°)u(-t)$
    c. $f(t) = 2.5 \cos^2(2\pi \times 10^{-3} t) - 2.5 \sin^2(2\pi \times 10^{-3} t)$
    d. $f(t) = \sum_{k=0}^{\infty} e^{-jk3t}$
    e. $f(k) = 2 \cos(2\pi k/8 + 30°)$
    f. $f(k) = \sin^2(k/12)$
    g. $f(k) = 2 \sin(2k/4)\sin(k/4)$
11. Plot the following signals:
    a. $f(t) = \sin(3t - 20°)u(t-2)$
    b. $f(t) = \mathrm{Re}(e^{-j2t}e^{j30°})u(t+1)$
    c. $f(t) = \sin(0t)$ $f(t) = \sin[(\pi/8)t]$ $f(t) = \sin[(\pi/4)t]$ $f(t) = \sin[(\pi/2)t]$
    $f(t) = \sin(\pi t)$ $f(t) = \sin[(3\pi/2)t]$ $f(t) = \sin[(7\pi/4)t]$ $f(t) = \sin[(15\pi/8)t]$
    $f(t) = \sin(2\pi t)$
    d. The following values of $f(k)$: $\sin(0k)$, $\sin[(\pi/8)k]$, $\sin[(\pi/4)k]$, $\sin[(\pi/2)k]$, $\sin(\pi k)$, $\sin[(3\pi/2)k]$, $\sin[(7\pi/4)k]$, $\sin[(15\pi/8)k]$ and $\sin(2\pi k)$.

    Draw an important conclusion about the difference between continuous and discrete sinusoidal functions from Problems 11c and 11d.

12. If $f(t) = u(t) - u(1 - t)$, sketch the following functions:
a. $f(-t)$ **b.** $f(2 - t)$ **c.** $f(t - 1)$

13. If $f(t) = p(t - 2) + p(t + 2)$, sketch the following functions:
a. $f(t - 2)$ **b.** $f(t + 1) - f(t - 1)$

14. Two discrete time signals are shown in Figure 1.17. Find the following signals:
a. $f(k)g(k)$ **b.** $f(-k)g(k)$ **c.** $f(k - 2)g(1 - k)$
d. $f(k + 1)g(k + 2)$ **e.** $(-1)^k f(k) + 0.8^k g(k)$

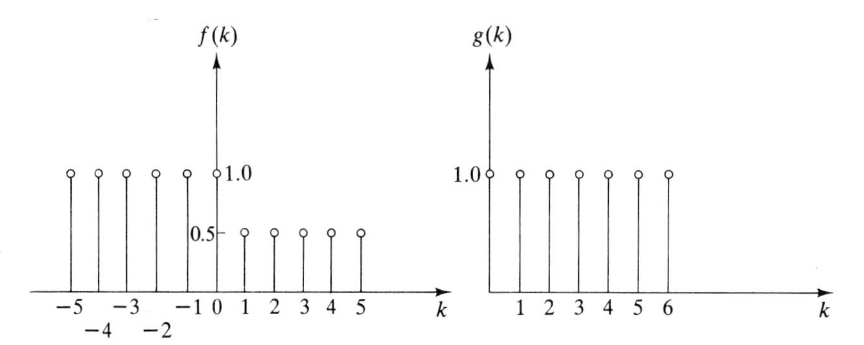

Figure 1.17

15. Sketch the following discrete signals:
a. $f(k) = u(k) + \cos(k + 30°)$ **b.** $f(k) = 2(0.8)^k$
c. $f(k) = \delta(k + 2) - 2\delta(k - 2)$ **d.** $f(k) = u(k) - u(k - 4)$ **e.** $f(k) = -u(3 - k)$

16. Sketch the following discrete signals:
a. $f(k) = (-1)^k 2(0.9)^k \quad k \geq 0$ **b.** $f(k) = 0.5(1.1)^k \quad k \geq 0$
c. $f(k) = (0.9)^k \sin(\pi/8)k \quad k \geq 0$ **d.** $f(k) = (1.1)^k \sin(\pi/8)k \quad k \geq 0$

17. Show that the following sequences lead to delta functions:
a. $(1/a)u(t) - (1/a)u(t - a) \quad a \to 0,\ a \geq 0$
b. $ae^{-at}u(t) \quad a \to \infty,\ a > 0$
c. $(1/2\sqrt{\pi a})e^{-t^2/4a} \quad a \to 0,\ a \geq 0$
Hint: Show that the peak increases and the duration decreases as a varies; also, show that the area under each curve is 1.

18. Express the functions shown in Figure 1.18 in terms of unit step functions.

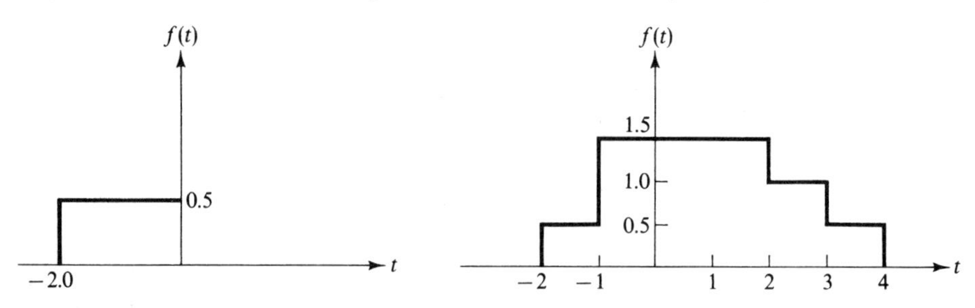

Figure 1.18

19. Express the values of the following functions in algebraic form:
a. $e^{j\pi/2}$ **b.** $e^{-j\pi/2}$ **c.** $e^{j\pi}$ **d.** $e^{-j\pi}$ **e.** $e^{jk2\pi}$ (k = integer)

20. If a function $f(t)$ is continuous at the origin, what is the value of $\int_{-a}^{a} f(t)\delta(-t)\,dt$? What can you infer from your answer?

21. Evaluate the integrals.
   a. $\int_{-2}^{2} e^{-t^2}\dot{\delta}(t)\,dt$ **b.** $\int_{-2}^{2} e^{-t^2}\dot{\delta}(t-1)\,dt$
   Because e^{-t^2} is a symmetric function, and in the light of the value of the integrals, what can we tell about the type function $\dot{\delta}(t)$, the time derivative of $\delta(t)$.
   Hint: In the evaluation, integrate by parts.

22. Evaluate the integrals.
   a. $\int_{-2}^{2}(3t^2+1)[\delta(t)+2\delta(t+1)]\,dt$ **b.** $\int_{-2}^{2} e^{-t}[\delta(t+1)+2\delta(t-1)]\,dt$
   c. $\int_{-2}^{2} t[\delta(t+1)+\delta(t)+\delta(t-1)]\,dt$

Section 1.4

23. If the carrier signal is $v_c = \cos\omega_c t$ and the modulating frequency is $f(t) = \cos\omega_m t$ with $\omega_c \gg \omega_m$, sketch the form of the amplitude-modulated function $g(t)$ (refer to Figure 1.13).

24. Determine the frequency spectrum (frequencies present) in the modulated signal $g(t) = \cos\omega_m t\cos\omega_c t$, where the modulating frequency is $\omega_m = 10^3$ rad/s and the carrier frequency is $\omega_c = 1.2\times 10^6$ rad/s.

25. Determine the frequency spectrum of the modulated signal $g(t) = (1 + 0.1\cos\omega_m t)\cos\omega_c t$, where the modulating frequency is $\omega_m = 10^3$ rad/s and the carrier frequency is $\omega_c = 1.2\times 10^6$ rad/s. What observations are evident when comparing these results with those of Problem 24?

26. A modulated signal is applied to the input of the circuit shown in Figure 1.19. Sketch the form of the output signal if the RC constant is large compared with the reciprocal of the carrier frequency.

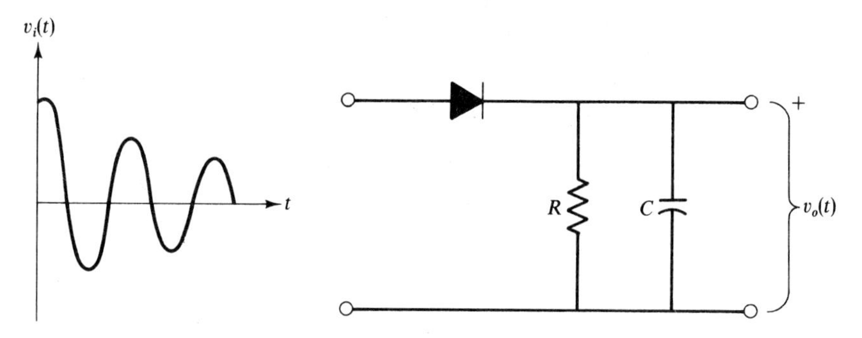

Figure 1.19

Section 1.5

27. Find the MSE if we approximate the function $f(t) = t^4$ with orthogonal Legendre functions up to the second order.

28. Find a three-term parabolic approximation to the function $f(t) = \sin(\pi/2)t$ over the interval $[-1, 1]$.

29. If we consider any signal $f(t)$ as denoting a voltage that exists across a 1-ohm resistor, then the integral $E = \int_a^b [f^2(t)/1]\,dt$ joule represents the energy dissipated in the resistor during the time interval $[a, b]$. A signal is called an *energy signal* if $\int_{-\infty}^{\infty} f^2(t)\,dt < \infty$. Determine which of the following functions is an energy function:
   a. $f(t) = u(t)$ **b.** $f(t) = e^{-t}u(t)$ **c.** $f(t) = e^{-t^2}$

Linear Systems

Every **physical system** is broadly characterized by its ability to accept an **input**—voltage, pressure, displacement, and the like—and to produce an output response to this input. To study the behavior of a system, the procedure is to model mathematically each element that the system comprises and then consider the interconnected array of elements. The analysis of most systems can be reduced to the study of the relationships among certain input excitations and the resulting outputs. The interconnected system is described mathematically, the form of the description being dictated by the domain of description—that is, whether it is a time domain or frequency domain description.

Critical to this process are:

1. A mathematical modeling of the elements that the system comprises, and these elements might be complicated structures.
2. A mathematical description of their interconnection.
3. Solutions to the mathematical equations for the specified input and prescribed initial state of the system.
4. Desirably, as a criterion of reasonableness, a careful examination of the final response equations.

This chapter addresses these aspects of system description and system analysis. System description is discussed both mathematically and graphically. Three different methods for carrying out the solution process for continuous time systems are studied initially. A somewhat parallel approach is considered for discrete time systems, although the details differ from those for continuous time systems. An interesting feature of our study is the applicability of these methods to examples from a variety of disciplines outside of the engineering domain: economics, biomedicine, chemistry, physics, and others.

Continuous and Discrete Modeling

2.1 Properties of Systems

As already noted, every physical system is able to accept an input and to produce an output response to this input. For example, a modern video-disc player is an optoelectronic system whose input is the reflection (or transmission) of laser light from the grooves of the record and whose output is a video signal that is viewed on a television screen. Figure 2.1a shows a diode laser optical recording system with readout path and readout elements of the optical disc system (tracking mirror, quarter-wave plate, polarizing beam splitter, and photodetector). Figures 2.1b, 2.1c, and 2.1d show additional information about the optical system. A telescope is an optical system that accepts the irradiance of the stars as its input and produces their images on a film as its output. A seismograph is an apparatus that registers the shocks and motions of the earth due to earthquakes. An elementary seismograph consists of a delicately mounted spring: Its input is the force caused by an earthquake and its output is the subsequent oscillations of the earth.

When the input–output properties of a system's elements can be described as proportional, time derivative, or integral functions, the resulting description is given by an integrodifferential equation. This form of description is evident when we apply the Kirchhoff voltage law to a series *RLC* circuit that has a voltage source as its input and the circuit current as its output. Such systems can be shown in circuit diagram or in block diagram form. We will restrict our attention to systems made up of **lumped parameters**—that is, a system with a finite number of discrete elements, each of which is able to store or dissipate energy or, if it is a source, to deliver energy. Such systems are described by ordinary differential equations. Figure 2.2a shows such a simple system. We can also represent the same system in a **block diagram** that describes the **terminal properties** of the network—that is, the relationship between its input $i(t)$ and its output $v(t)$, as shown in Figure 2.2b. We observe from this example that such a block diagram gives no information about the structure of the system that it represents.

Figure 2.3a shows the circuit representation of a noninverting operational amplifier. Its block diagram representation is given in Figure 2.3b. For the connections shown, this system is a **scalar multiplier**. In this figure, the symbol ⊳ represents an ideal amplifier of infinite gain with both inverting (−) (output signal out of phase with respect to input) and noninverting (+) (output signal in phase with input signal) input terminals and with infinite input impedances. While these conditions are idealized, they are closely approximated in practice.

We can also have systems with **distributed parameters** instead of distinct discrete elements, although each infinitesimal part of these systems can be modeled in lumped parameter form. Their description is accomplished using partial differential equations. One such system is the telephone line. Such systems are not dealt with in this book.

Systems with random parameters are called **stochastic systems**, and those

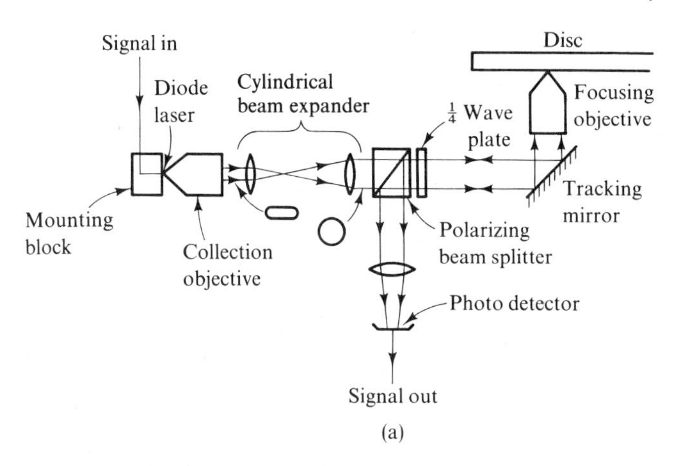

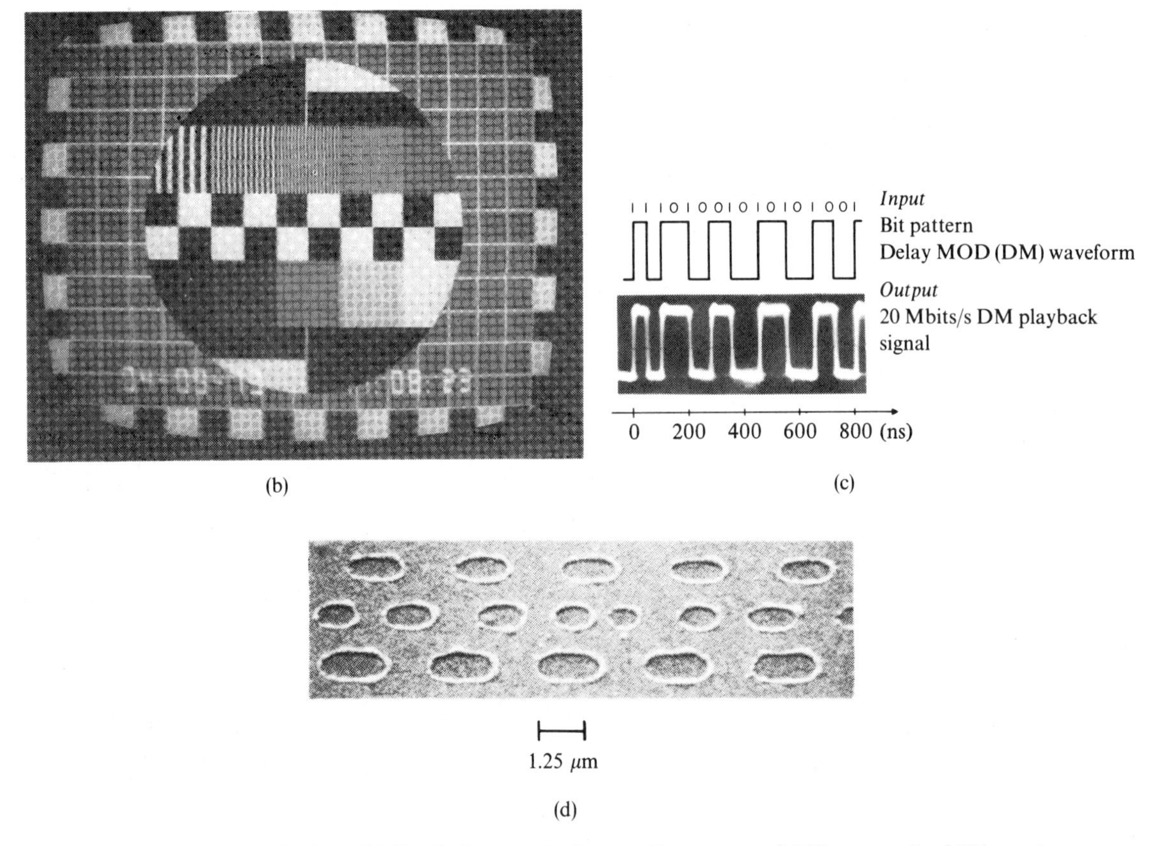

Figure 2.1 Optical Recording. (a) Diode laser optical recording system. (b) Photograph of TV monitor playback of video signal recorded and read out with a diode laser. (c) Diode laser recording and playback of 20 Mb/s delay mode (DM) digital signal. (d) Three-channel (125 Mb/s) optical disc recordings. [From R. A. Bartolini, "Optical Recording: High-Density Information Storage and Retrieval," *IEEE Proceedings*, vol. 70 (1982), p. 589. © 1982 IEEE.]

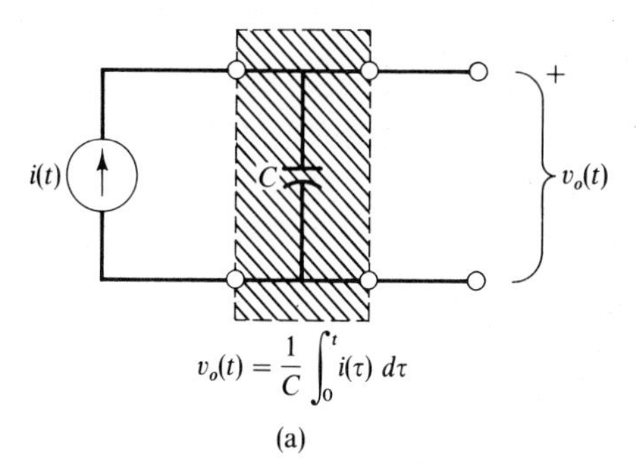

Integrator

$i(t)$ Input → $\frac{1}{C}\int_0^t d\tau$ → $v_o(t) = \frac{1}{C}\int_0^t i(\tau)\, d\tau$ Output

(b)

Figure 2.2 Simple Integrating System. (a) Circuit diagram. (b) Block diagram.

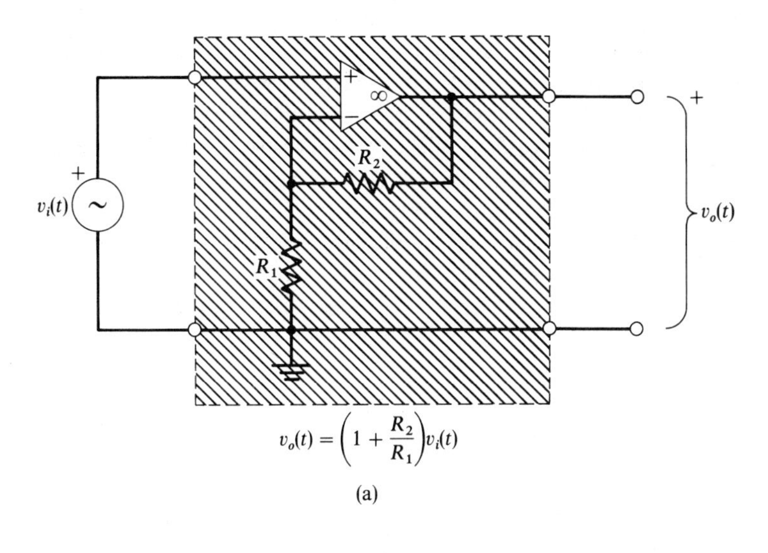

Scalar

$v_i(t)$ Input → $1 + \frac{R_2}{R_1}$ → $v_o(t)$ Output

(b)

Figure 2.3 Simple Scale Multiplying System. (a) Circuit diagram. (b) Block diagram.

systems with parameters that are not random are called **deterministic systems**. Both system categories may use time in a continuous form and may be described by differential equations; in such cases, both are continuous time systems. If excitations are introduced to systems at distinct instants of time and the systems are described by difference equations, these systems are termed **discrete time systems**.

Systems can be linear or nonlinear. A **linear system** is one for which a linear relation exists between cause and effect, or between excitation and response. If the relation between cause and effect is nonlinear, the system is termed **nonlinear**. A casual inspection will not show linearity because both lumped and distributed elements can be linear. We will find that systems analysis can often be carried out in closed mathematical form for systems composed of linear elements. This analysis is rarely possible for nonlinear systems, but we can often closely approximate nonlinear systems by linear systems and thereby effect a closed-form solution. Extreme care is necessary in such cases since the assumption of linearity may completely negate important features of the nonlinear system. This book is confined to linear systems, but we must be aware that physical systems, when analyzed in detail, might actually be nonlinear. In the analysis of nonlinear systems, we can approximate them as linear systems for small variations around their operating points, a common approach in electronics and in control theory.

Systems for which an output at any time t_0 is a function only of those input values that have occurred for $t \leq t_0$—that is, the system response never precedes the system excitation—are nonanticipatory, or *causal*, systems. Ordinary physical systems are causal. While noncausal systems are possible and are used in many applications, our study is restricted to causal systems.

Systems whose parameters vary with time are called **time-varying systems** and are not considered in this book. The focus here is on systems with constant parameters, called **linear time-invariant** (LTI) **systems**. It is important to note that within these limitations, the number of specific systems is almost limitless. Thus, while the book's emphasis is on the study of some relatively simple electrical and mechanical systems, some examples describing other types of systems are presented to show that the methods learned here have much wider applications.

2.2 Modeling Simple Systems

As already noted, an essential requirement in continuous time, or analog, systems analysis is a mathematical input–output description of the elements that make up the interconnected system. The requirement exists because we wish to perform mathematical studies on systems comprising hardware components or carry out designs mathematically that will ultimately be realized by hardware. It must be stressed that the analysis or design can be no better than the quality of the models used. The essential ideas in the modeling process are reviewed here.

Electrical Elements

Capacitor. The linear capacitor is an idealized circuit element in which energy can be stored in electric form. In its most elementary form, the *capacitor* consists of two closely spaced metallic plates that are separated by a single or multiple layers of nonconducting (insulating) dielectric material, such as air, glass, or paper. The schematic representation of the capacitor is shown in Figure 2.4a. Terminal properties of a linear time-invariant capacitor are described graphically by a charge–voltage relationship of the form shown in Figure 2.4b. The capacitors used in most electronic circuits are essentially time invariant, although the capacitor microphone used in radio studios is an example of a linear time-varying capacitor.

By definition, the capacitance C is

$$C = \frac{q}{v} \qquad \frac{\text{coulomb}}{\text{volt}} = \text{farad (F)} \tag{2.1}$$

Since the current is given by

$$i = \frac{dq}{dt} \qquad \frac{\text{coulomb}}{\text{second}} = \text{ampere (A)} \tag{2.2}$$

we obtain the relations

$$v(t) = \frac{1}{C}\int_{-\infty}^{t} i(\tau)\, d\tau \tag{2.3a}$$

$$i(t) = C\,\frac{dv(t)}{dt} \tag{2.3b}$$

As descriptive of their inherent properties, the current $i(t)$ is termed a **through variable**, and the voltage $v(t)$ is called an **across variable.**

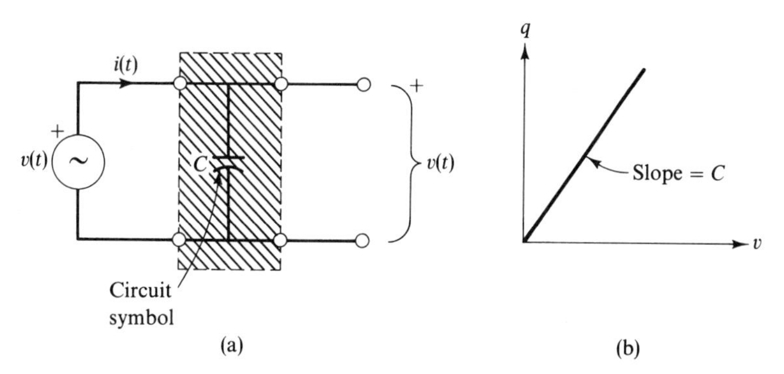

Figure 2.4 Capacitor. (a) Capacitor element and its circuit representation. (b) Charge–voltage characteristics of a linear capacitor element.

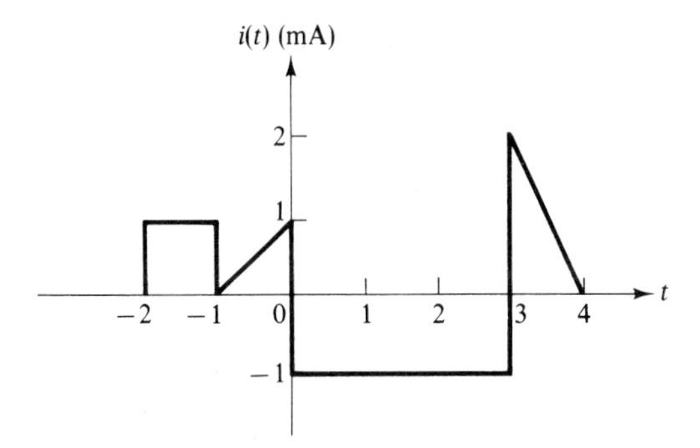

Figure 2.5 Current Delivered to 1 μF Capacitor

■ Example 2.1

Find the voltage across a 1 μF capacitor at $t = 2$ s if the current through it has the waveshape shown in Figure 2.5.

Solution Apply (2.3a); we obtain

$$v(2) = \frac{1}{1 \times 10^{-6}} \int_{-\infty}^{2} i(\tau)\, d\tau = 10^6 \left[\int_{-2}^{-1} 10^{-3}\, d\tau + \int_{-1}^{0} 10^{-3}(\tau + 1)\, d\tau + \int_{0}^{2} (-10^{-3})\, d\tau \right] = -0.5 \times 10^{-3} \text{ V}$$

The negative sign indicates that the voltage polarity at $t = 2$ s is opposite to the polarity initially assumed as the reference condition shown in Figure 2.4a. ■

Inductor. Another important electrical element that stores energy, but in the magnetic field, is the **inductor**, sometimes called a coil or solenoid. The terminal properties of linear inductors are described graphically by the flux linkage–current relationship ψ, i shown in Figure 2.6b. Figure 2.6a shows the circuit representation of the inductor, and Figure 2.6c gives a rough illustration of the flux linkages. The simple telephone receiver is an example of a time-varying inductor.

By definition, the inductance of an inductor is written

$$L = \frac{\psi}{i} \qquad \frac{\text{weber}}{\text{ampere}} = \text{henry (H)} \tag{2.4}$$

Combine this with Faraday's law

$$v(t) = \frac{d\psi}{dt} \qquad \text{volt (V)} \tag{2.5}$$

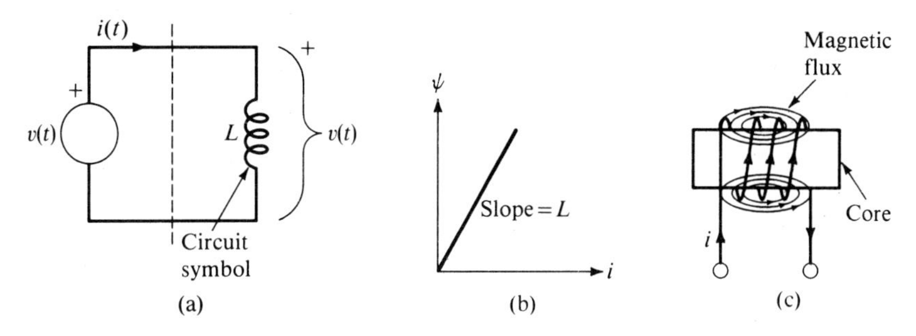

Figure 2.6 Inductor. (a) Inductor element and its circuit representation. (b) Linear flux–current relationship. (c) Illustration of flux linkages.

to obtain the relations

$$i(t) = \frac{1}{L}\int_{-\infty}^{t} v(\tau)\, d\tau \tag{2.6a}$$

$$v(t) = L\,\frac{di(t)}{dt} \tag{2.6b}$$

■ **Example 2.2**

Find the voltage across a 3 H inductor at $t = 2$ ms if the current through it is that shown in Figure 2.7.

Solution From (2.4) and (2.5), we obtain

$$v(2) = 3\,\frac{di(t)}{dt}\bigg|_{t=2\times10^{-3}} = 3\,\frac{d[4\times10^{-6} - (t - 2\times10^{-3})^2]^{1/2}}{dt}\bigg|_{t=2\times10^{-3}} = 0$$

■

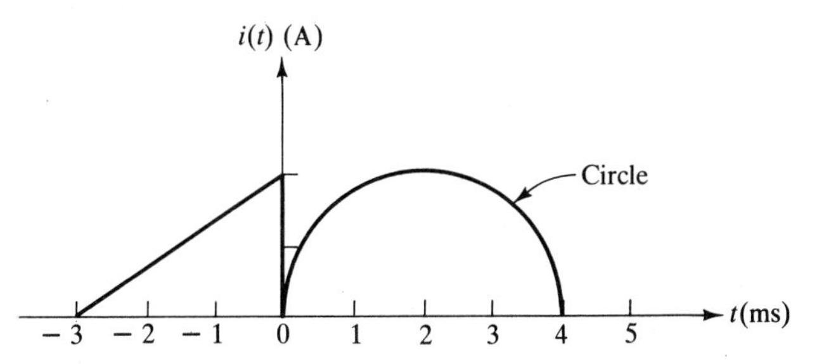

Figure 2.7 Current Delivered to 3 H Inductor

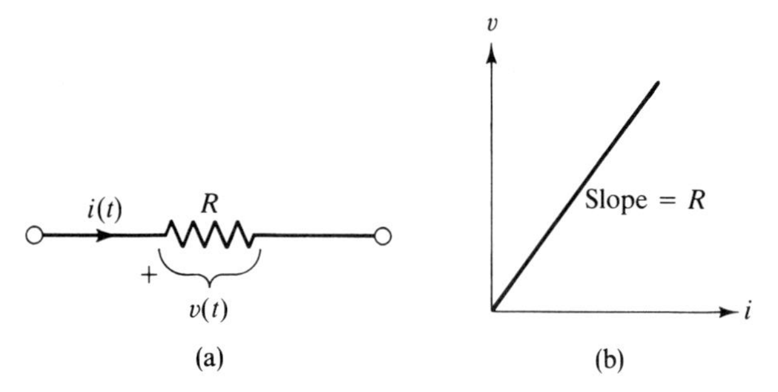

Figure 2.8 Resistor. (a) Network representation of the resistor. (b) Linear voltage–current relationship.

Resistor. Unlike the capacitor and inductor, each of which stores energy, the *resistor* shown in Figure 2.8a dissipates energy. The v, i characteristic for a linear resistor, as shown in Figure 2.8b, is a straight line with proportionality factor

$$R = \frac{v(t)}{i(t)} \qquad \frac{\text{volt}}{\text{ampere}} = \text{ohm } (\Omega) \tag{2.7a}$$

$$G = \frac{i(t)}{v(t)} \qquad \text{mho } (\mho) \tag{2.7b}$$

where R = resistance (ohm) and $G = 1/R$ = conductance (mho). The network representation is shown in Figure 2.8. Ordinary resistors are usually assumed to be time invariant, but the carbon microphone in the ordinary telephone set is a time-varying resistor.

Mechanical-Translational Elements

Ideal Mass Element. Bulk matter as a single unit is defined as a **mass element**. The dynamics of a mass element are described by Newton's second law of motion

$$f(t) = M\frac{dv(t)}{dt} = M\frac{d^2x(t)}{dt^2} \qquad \text{newton} = \text{kg}\cdot\text{m}\cdot\text{s}^{-2}\ (\text{N}) \tag{2.8}$$

which relates the force $f(t)$ to the acceleration $dv/dt = d^2x/dt^2$. The motion variable v enters in a relative form: It is the velocity of the mass relative to the velocity of the ground, which is zero; hence, v is an **across** variable. The force $f(t)$ is transmitted

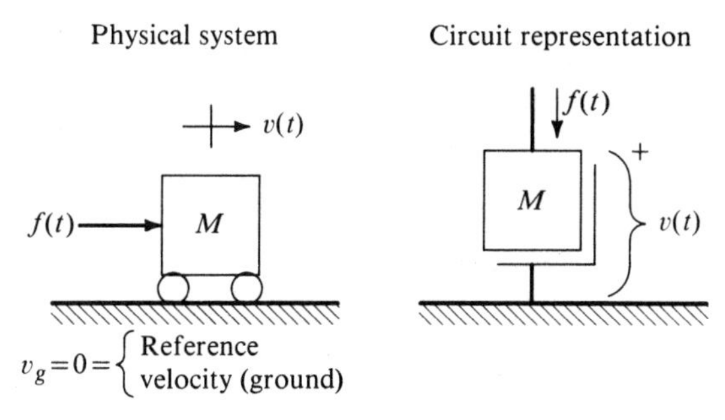

Figure 2.9 Schematic Representation of the Mass Element

through an element; hence, it is a **through** variable. The integral form of (2.8) is given by

$$v(t) = \frac{1}{M} \int_{-\infty}^{t} f(\tau)\, d\tau \tag{2.9}$$

It is interesting to compare (2.9) and (2.3). This comparison shows that an analogy exists between the mass in a mechanical system and the capacitor in an electrical system. A schematic representation of the mass element is shown in Figure 2.9.

Spring. A **spring element** is one that stores energy due to the elastic deformation that results from the application of a force. Over its linear region, the spring satisfies Hooke's law that relates the force to the displacement by the expression

$$f(t) = Kx(t) \qquad \text{newton (N)} \tag{2.10}$$

where K is the spring constant, with units newton/m.

By differentiating (2.10) with respect to time, we obtain the relation

$$v(t) = \frac{1}{K} \frac{df(t)}{dt} \tag{2.11}$$

Refer to the schematic representation of the spring in Figure 2.10 and use (2.10) and (2.11). We have

$$f(t) = K[x_1(t) - x_2(t)] = K \int_{-\infty}^{t} [v_1(\tau) - v_2(\tau)]\, d\tau = K \int_{-\infty}^{t} v(\tau)\, d\tau \tag{2.12}$$

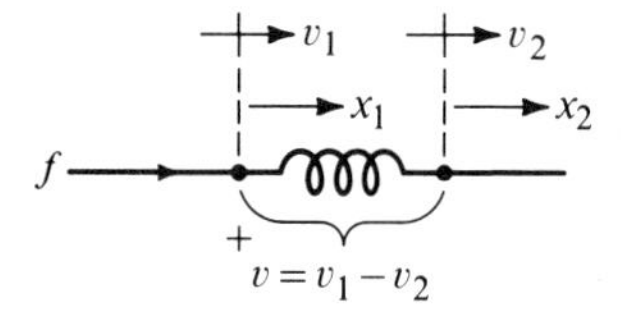

Figure 2.10 Schematic Representation of the Spring

If $x_1 > x_2$, there is a compressive force and $f > 0$. If $x_1 < x_2$, there is a negative, or extensive, force. Attention is called to the analogy between the spring and the inductor.

Damper. Consideration of this element is limited here to viscous friction, which, for a linear dependence between force and velocity, is given by

$$f(t) = Dv(t) \tag{2.13a}$$

from which

$$v(t) = \frac{1}{D} f(t) \tag{2.13b}$$

where D is the damping constant (newton-second/m). A mechanical damper and its schematic representation are shown in Figure 2.11. Observe the analogy between the damper and the resistor.

By maintaining the parallelism between through and across variables, which also leads to a parallelism in the resulting network topology, we found that mass and capacitor, spring and inductor, and damper and resistor were analogous quantities. From a purely mathematical point of view, a parallelism between velocity and current and force and voltage could be chosen, in which case, we would obtain an

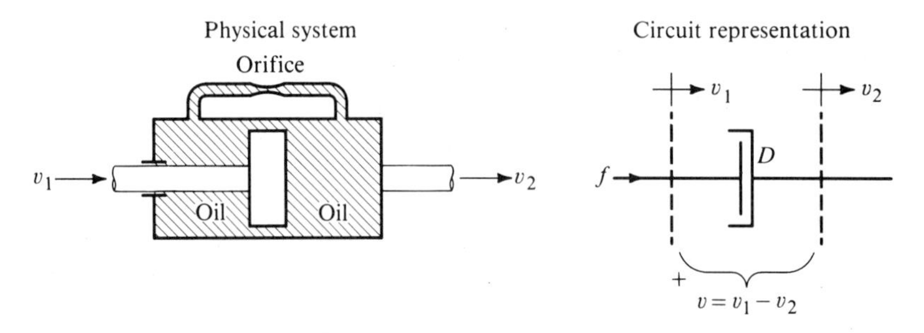

Figure 2.11 Physical and Diagrammatic Representations of a Dash Pot (Damper)

analogy between mass and inductor, spring and capacitor, and damper and resistor. In this case, the topology would be dually related—that is, a parallel connection of mechanical elements would lead to an analogous series connection of electrical elements. Some of the older writings, particularly in acoustics, employed this dual relationship; this text is confined only to the through and across variable parallelism, thereby also maintaining the parallel topological structure.

Mechanical-Rotational Elements

Inertial Element. A set of rotational mechanical elements and rotational variables exists that bears a one-to-one correspondence to the translational mechanical elements and the translational variables that have been discussed above. In the rotational system, *torque* ($\mathcal{T}$) is the through variable and **angular velocity** ($\omega = d\theta/dt$) is the motional or across variable. The corresponding fundamental quantities are

J = polar moment of inertia	corresponds to M in translation
K = rotational spring constant	corresponds to K in translation
D = rotational damping constant	corresponds to D in translation
$\mathcal{T}$ = torque	corresponds to f in translation
$\omega = d\theta/dt$, angular velocity	corresponds to $v = dx/dt$ in translation

In this rotational set, J is the rotational parameter and the proportionality factor between torque and angular acceleration. When the motion is considered on one axis only,

$$\mathcal{T} = \frac{d(J\omega)}{dt} \tag{2.14a}$$

and, for systems with constant J,

$$\boxed{\mathcal{T} = J\frac{d\omega(t)}{dt} = J\frac{d^2\theta(t)}{dt^2}} \qquad \text{newton-meter} \tag{2.14b}$$

J, the moment of inertia of a rotational body, depends on the mass and the square of a characteristic distance of the body, called the **radius of gyration** k. This is given by

$$J = Mk^2 \qquad \text{kg} \cdot \text{m}^2 \tag{2.15}$$

For a simple point mass rotating about an axis at a distance r from the center of mass, $k = r$ and

$$J = Mr^2 \tag{2.16}$$

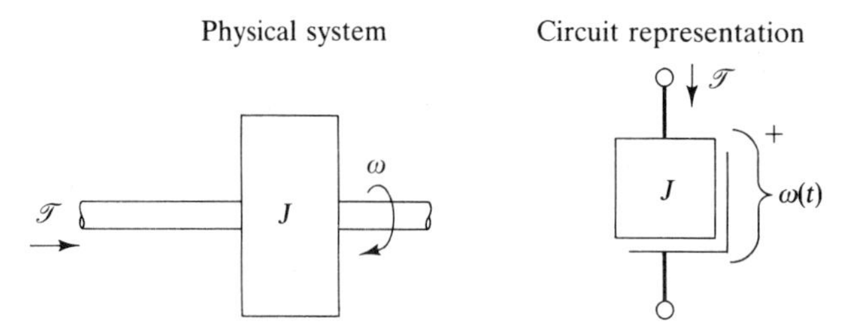

Figure 2.12 Schematic Representation of Rotational Inertia

For a simple disc of radius r rotating about its center, $k = r/\sqrt{2}$, with

$$J = \frac{1}{2} Mr^2 \tag{2.17}$$

Figure 2.12 shows the linear inertial elements.

Spring. A rotational spring is one that will twist under the action of a torque. A linear spring element is described by the pair of equations

$$\mathscr{T}(t) = K\theta(t) = K \int_{-\infty}^{t} \omega(\tau)\, d\tau \tag{2.18a}$$

$$\omega(t) = \frac{1}{K} \frac{d\mathscr{T}(t)}{dt} \tag{2.18b}$$

A schematic representation of the rotational spring is shown in Figure 2.13.

Damper. The rotational damper differs from the translational damper principally in the character of the motion. A schematic representation is given in Figure 2.14, and the equations that describe a rotational damper are

$$\mathscr{T}(t) = D\omega(t) \tag{2.19a}$$

$$\omega(t) = \frac{1}{D} \mathscr{T}(t) \tag{2.19b}$$

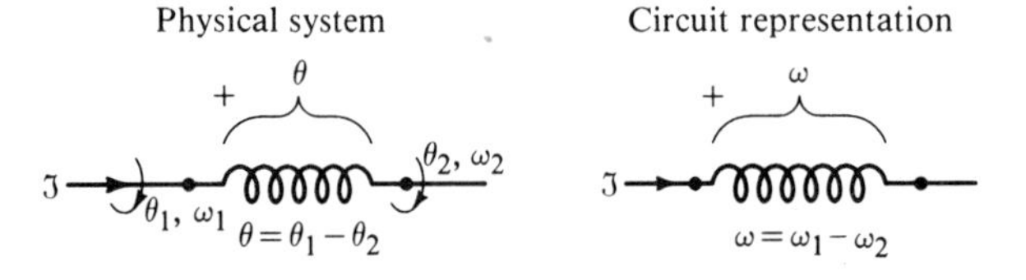

Figure 2.13 Schematic Representation of a Rotational Spring

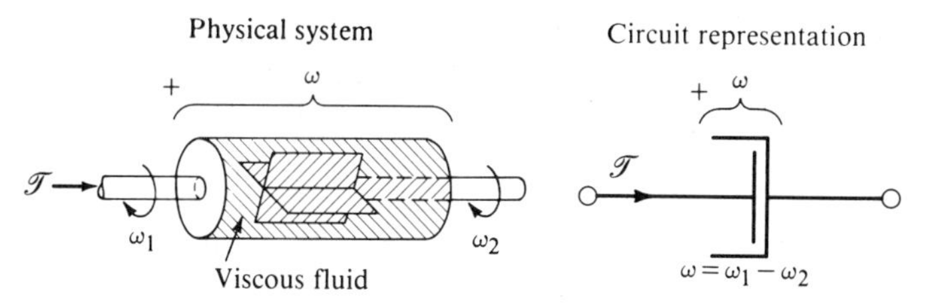

Figure 2.14 Schematic Representation of a Rotational Viscous Damper

2.3 Solution of First-Order Systems

We wish to study the characteristics and behavior of systems of interconnected elements through their mathematical formulations. We develop this mathematical description by the use of Kirchhoff's current and voltage laws for electrical systems and by the use of D'Alembert's principle for mechanical systems. The resulting system equations that are given as one or more differential equations require, as the next step, the solution of the mathematical problem in a form that will yield the trajectory (output value) that satisfies the initial conditions that apply to the system at some specified time, known as the **initial time**. This chapter examines **first-order systems**—that is, those systems described by first-order differential equations.

Consider the simple electrical system shown in Figure 2.15a. An application of the Kirchhoff voltage law yields

$$L \frac{di(t)}{dt} + Ri(t) = v(t)$$

or

$$\frac{L}{R} \frac{dv_o(t)}{dt} + v_o(t) = v(t) \tag{2.20}$$

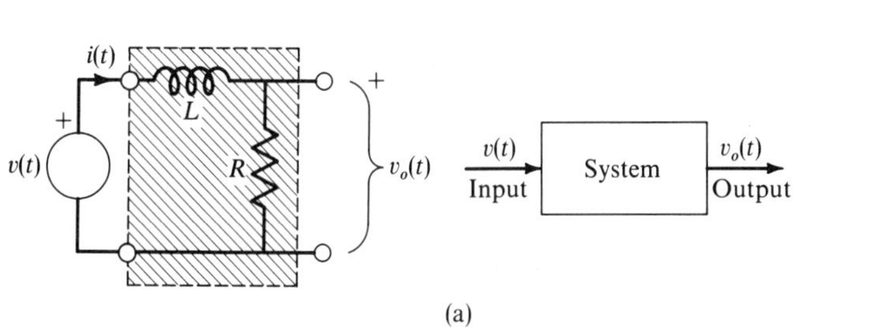

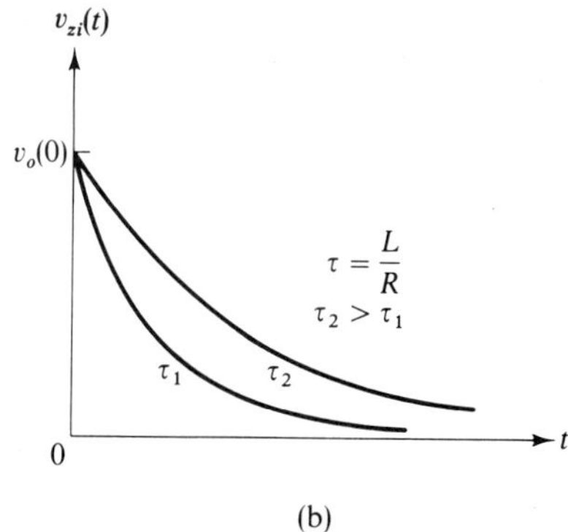

Figure 2.15 Simple *RL* Electrical System and Zero-Input Response

where we set $v_o(t) = Ri(t)$. Observe that (2.20) is a first-order, ordinary, differential equation since it involves only the first derivative of the dependent variable $v_o(t)$. In the present system, we have only one **energy-storing** element (the inductor) and only one **forcing function** (source) $v(t)$.

To find the unknown function $v_o(t)$ requires that we find the solution to (2.20). A fundamental requirement in the solution of differential equations is that the complete solution must contain as many arbitrary constants as the order of the differential equation being solved. Hence, we must have additional information if we are to obtain a solution that meets all conditions of the problem. This added information is specified by a knowledge of the *state*—that is, condition—of the system at a particular time, usually taken as initial time $t = 0$, without loss of generality.

A number of different techniques exist for solving differential equations. Initially, two methods are considered: the method of variation of parameters and the standard method of differential equations. Other techniques, such as convolution and transform methods are considered later.

To apply the **method of variation of parameters**, the procedure is to solve the differential equation as a two-step process. First, we write the differential equation in its **homogeneous** form, which means that we neglect the effect of the forcing function. We thus consider

$$\frac{L}{R}\frac{dv_o(t)}{dt} + v_o(t) = 0 \tag{2.21}$$

The solution of this homogeneous equation is known as the **zero-input response**. This response is due entirely to energy stored in the system; in this case, in the magnetic field of the inductor. Electrical energy may be stored in the electric fields of capacitors. In the case of mechanical systems, kinetic energy is stored in the masses and potential energy in the deformation of springs.

To solve (2.21), we try a solution of the form

$$v_o(t) = Ae^{st} \tag{2.22}$$

where A is an unknown constant and s is a constant having the units of frequency s^{-1}. The basis for the suggested form of the solution is found in (2.21), which requires that the sum of the solution and its derivative shall be zero. Substituting this trial solution in (2.21), we obtain

$$\frac{L}{R}Ase^{st} + Ae^{st} = 0$$

or

$$\left(\frac{L}{R}s + 1\right)Ae^{st} = 0 \qquad \text{or} \qquad \left(s + \frac{R}{L}\right)Ae^{st} = 0 \tag{2.23}$$

If we were to set $A = 0$, we would obtain the trivial case. Therefore, we impose the requirement that $(s + R/L) = 0$, which thus requires that

$$s = -\frac{R}{L}$$

This result, combined with (2.22), yields the zero-input solution

$$v_o(t) = Ae^{-t/(L/R)} \tag{2.24}$$

If we choose $v_o(t)|_{t=0} = v_o(0)$, then, for this *initial state*,

$$v_o(0) = Ae^{-0/(L/R)}$$

from which we see that $A = v_o(0)$ and, finally,

$$v_{ozi}(t) = v_o(0)e^{-t/(L/R)} \tag{2.25}$$

Observe that it was necessary to evaluate only a single arbitrary constant for this first-order differential equation. This solution is shown in Figure 2.15b for two values of $L/R = \tau$.

Our next step is to solve (2.20) with the forcing function present. Thus, we are to find a solution to the *nonhomogeneous* differential equation

$$\frac{dv_o(t)}{dt} + \frac{R}{L}\,v_o(t) = \frac{R}{L}\,v(t) \tag{2.26}$$

To proceed, we multiply both sides of this equation by $e^{+t/(L/R)}$, a form suggested by (2.25). We recognize that we can write the result

$$\frac{d}{dt}\,[e^{t/(L/R)}v_o(t)] = \frac{R}{L}\,e^{t/(L/R)}v(t) \tag{2.27}$$

Integrate both sides of this equation from 0 to t to obtain

$$e^{t/(L/R)}v_o(t)\Big|_0^t = \frac{R}{L}\int_0^t e^{\tau/(L/R)}v(\tau)\,d\tau$$

or

$$e^{t/(L/R)}v_o(t) - v_o(0) = \frac{R}{L}\int_0^t e^{\tau/(L/R)}v(\tau)\,d\tau$$

This result is written in the form

$$v_o(t) = \underbrace{v_o(0)e^{-t/(L/R)}}_{\substack{\text{zero-input}\\ \text{response } v_{ozi}(t)}} + \underbrace{\frac{R}{L}\,e^{-t/(L/R)}\int_0^t e^{\tau/(L/R)}v(\tau)\,d\tau}_{\text{zero-state response } v_{ozs}(t)} \tag{2.28}$$

Let us assume that at $t = 0$, the initial voltage $v_o(0) = 2$ V and that the ratio $L/R = 1$. Under these conditions, the output voltage for an assumed input unit step voltage $v(t) = u(t)$ is

$$v_o(t) = 2e^{-t} + e^{-t}\int_0^t e^{\tau}\,d\tau = \underbrace{2e^{-t}}_{v_{ozi}} + \underbrace{(1 - e^{-t})}_{v_{ozs}} = \underbrace{e^{-t}}_{v_{ot}} + \underbrace{1}_{v_{os}} \qquad t > 0 \tag{2.29}$$

Here, v_{ot} identifies the **transient** component of the solution and v_{os} identifies the **steady state** component. These latter forms are deduced directly when we use the standard method in solving differential equations.

Observe that we have used the results of the zero input to obtain the zero-state response, the sum being the total solution. While this method does not provide a practical procedure for solving higher-order differential equations, the conclusion that a knowledge of the solution of the system equations to one set of conditions—here, to zero excitation—allows us to find the complete solution to any excitation function is a most important concept. This same general concept will appear again in our studies, specifically when we consider the convolution integral and transform methods.

We now carry out the solution to (2.20) using the *standard solution techniques of differential equations.* This approach provides the transient and steady state solutions directly. The first step in this procedure is to find the solution to the homogeneous equation (2.21). The result is given by (2.24). This solution is known as the **homogeneous** solution. Next, we solve the nonhomogeneous equation (2.26) for unit step function excitation. The equation under survey is

$$\frac{dv_o(t)}{dt} + \frac{R}{L} v_o(t) = \frac{R}{L} \qquad t > 0 \tag{2.30}$$

We assume a trial solution of the form $v_o(t) = B$, where B is a unknown constant. A constant was selected because the input to the system is a constant. We substitute the trial solution into this equation. From this, we find $B = 1$. Therefore, the complete solution is

$$v_o(t) = \underbrace{Ae^{-t/(L/R)}}_{v_{ot}(t)} + \underbrace{1}_{v_{os}(t)} \qquad t > 0 \tag{2.31}$$

where $v_{os}(t)$ is the *particular*, or *steady state*, solution. For the initial condition $t = 0$, $v_o(0) = 2$, and $L/R = 1$, (2.31) becomes

$$2 = A + 1 \qquad \text{or} \qquad A = 1$$

and the solution is

$$v_o(t) = e^{-t} + 1 \qquad t > 0$$

which is identical with (2.29), as it should be.

■ Example 2.3 *Computer System*

Find the zero-input, zero-state, transient, and steady state responses of the magnetic head of the computer disk drive modeled in Figure 2.16a. Consider only the mass of the head structure and the friction due to air and arm of the assembly. The mass is equal to 10^{-3} kg, and the air friction constant $D = 10^{-4}$ N · s/m.

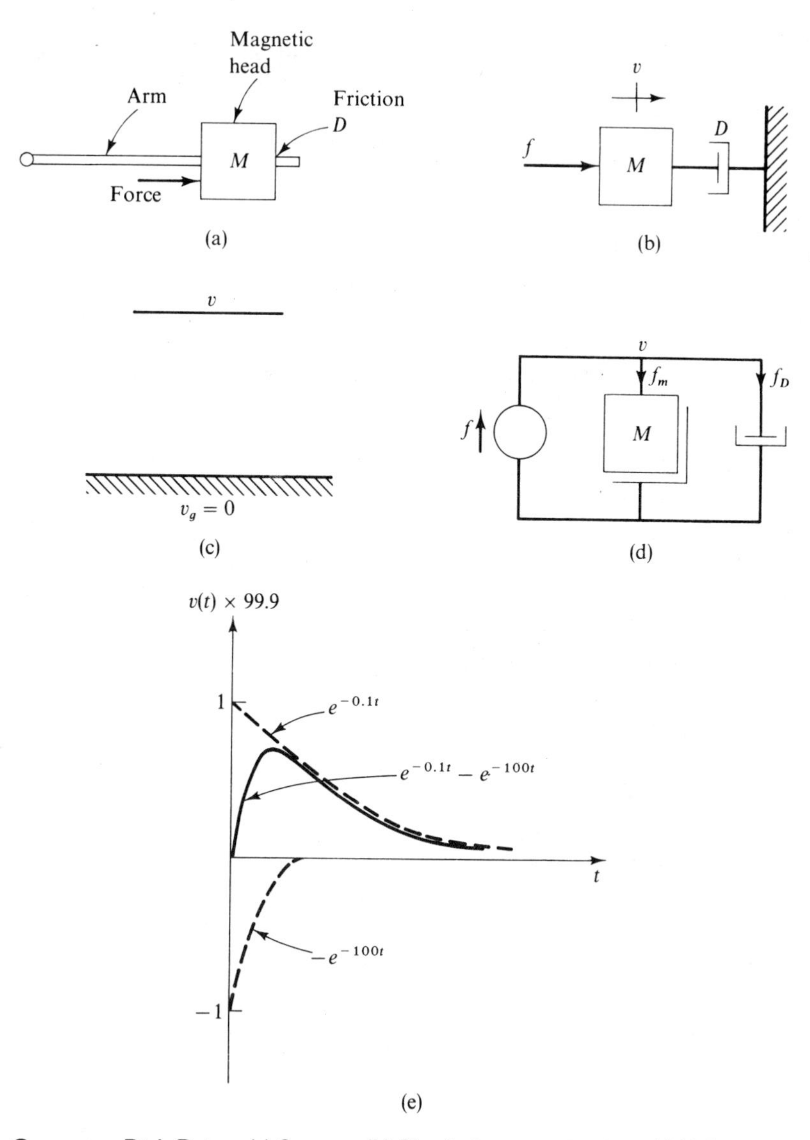

Figure 2.16 Computer Disk Drive. (a) System. (b) Physical representation. (c) Velocity diagram. (d) Circuit diagram. (e) Velocity response.

Solution First, we represent the system in its physical representation, as shown in Figure 2.16b. Next, we create a diagram that indicates the two velocities: the ground velocity equal to zero and the velocity of the mass, as shown in Figure 2.16c. From the ground node to velocity, we connect the force source, the mass, and the damping effect, as shown in Figure 2.16d. This figure is the equivalent circuit representation of the system.

At the node, D'Alembert's principle requires that the algebraic sum of the forces must be equal to zero. Hence, we write

$$f_M + f_D = f \tag{2.32}$$

or

$$M\frac{dv}{dt} + Dv = f \tag{2.33}$$

It has been assumed that the friction force is proportional to velocity v, with a friction coefficient D.

We assume that the force f is an exponential function $f(t) = 10^{-3} \times e^{-100t}u(t)$. The differential equation under consideration is then

$$\frac{dv}{dt} + 0.1v = e^{-100t} \qquad t > 0 \tag{2.34}$$

We first employ the method of variation of parameters. The solution to the homogeneous equation is easily found to be

$$v_{zi}(t) = v(0)e^{-0.1t} \tag{2.35}$$

where $v(0)$ is the initial velocity (state) of the system. To find the solution of the nonhomogeneous equation, multiply both sides of (2.34) by $e^{0.1t}$ and rearrange the result to the form

$$\frac{d}{dt}[e^{0.1t}v(t)] = e^{0.1t}f(t)$$

Integrate both sides of this equation from 0 to t, combine the result with $v_{zi}(t)$, and rearrange the resulting equation to

$$\begin{aligned} v(t) &= \underbrace{v(0)e^{-0.1t}}_{v_{zi}} + \underbrace{e^{-0.1t}\int_0^t e^{0.1\tau}e^{-100\tau}\,d\tau}_{v_{zs}} \\ &= v(0)e^{-0.1t} + \frac{1}{99.9}(e^{-0.1t} - e^{-100t}) \end{aligned} \tag{2.36}$$

To proceed employing the standard methods of differential equations, first refer back to (2.34). The particular solution of (2.36) is obtained if we assume a trial solution of the form $v(t) = Be^{-100t}$. Again, the trial solution was selected to be proportional to the input to the system. Combine this assumed solution with (2.34). We obtain

$$B(-100)e^{-100t} + 0.1Be^{-100t} = e^{-100t}$$

From this, we find that

$$B = \frac{1}{99.9}$$

The complete general solution is given by

$$v(t) = Ae^{-0.1t} + \frac{1}{99.9} e^{-100t} \tag{2.37}$$

where A, the unknown arbitrary constant, can be deduced from the specified initial conditions. At $t = 0$, the initial velocity is $v(0)$, so that

$$v(0) = A + \frac{1}{99.9} \qquad \text{or} \qquad A = v(0) - \frac{1}{99.9}$$

Combine this value of A with (2.37) to find

$$v(t) = v(0)e^{-0.1t} + \frac{1}{99.9}(e^{-0.1t} - e^{-100t}) \tag{2.38}$$

which is the same result given by (2.36). If we further assume that the initial velocity $v(0)$ is zero, the velocity of the head becomes

$$v(t) = \frac{1}{99.9}(e^{-0.1t} - e^{-100t}) \tag{2.39}$$

This response is a pulse-type function and does not show the discontinuity at $t = 0$ of the input function e^{-100t}. Figure 2.16e graphically shows (2.39). ■

■ **Example 2.4** ***Electro-optics***

In many applications, such as reading product codes in supermarkets, printing, and so forth, an optical scanner, as shown in Figure 2.17a, is used. If the applied torque is given by $\mathscr{T}(t) = 10(1 + \cos \omega_0 t)u(t)$, find the zero-input and zero-state responses of the angular velocity of the mirror. As the mirror rotates, a friction force is developed that is proportional to its angular speed. The friction constant D is equal to 0.05 N · m · s/rad, and the polar moment of inertia J is equal to 0.1 kg-m^2. Also, determine the transient and steady state terms using standard differential equation techniques.

Solution The physical system is modeled as shown in Figure 2.17b; the circuit diagram is developed in Figures 2.17c and 2.17d. Apply D'Alembert's principle for rotational systems, which requires that the algebraic sum of the torques be zero. We thus have

$$\mathscr{T}(t) = \mathscr{T}_J(t) + \mathscr{T}_D(t) = \text{inertial torque} + \text{frictional torque}$$

Using the known form for each term, we write

$$0.1\frac{d\omega}{dt} + 0.05\omega = 10(1 + \cos \omega_0 t)u(t)$$

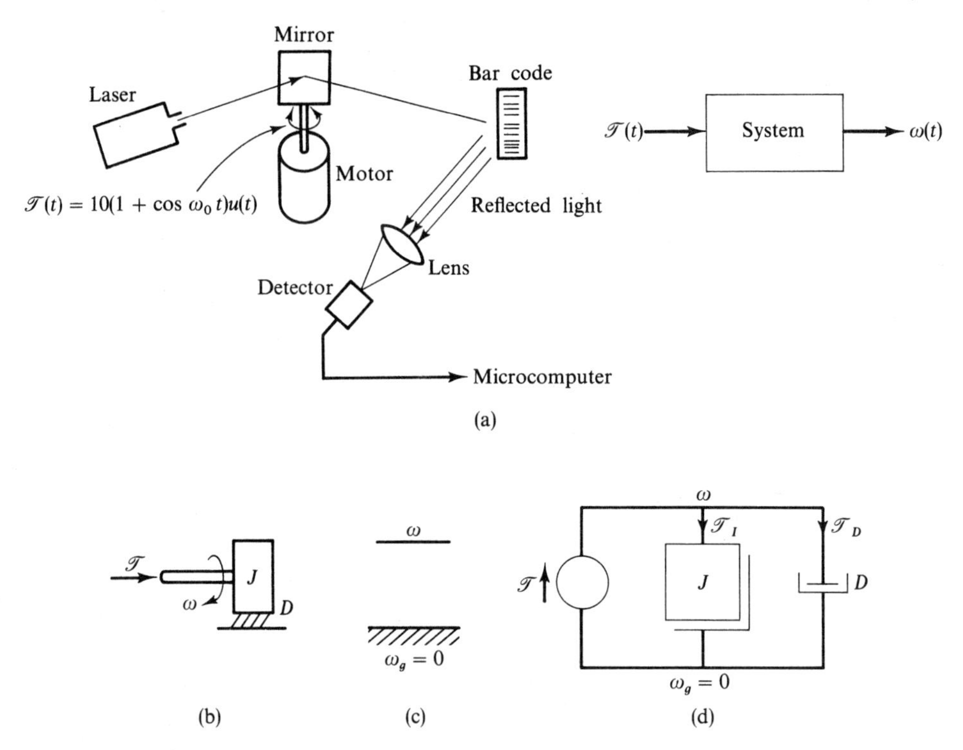

Figure 2.17 Electro-optical Scanner. (a) Physical system. (b) Physical representation. (c) Velocity diagram. (d) Circuit representation.

or, equivalently,

$$\frac{d\omega}{dt} + 0.5\omega = 100(1 + \cos \omega_0 t)u(t) \tag{2.40}$$

The zero-input solution is readily found from the homogeneous equation, and the result is

$$\omega_{zi} = \omega(0)e^{-0.5t} \tag{2.41}$$

Also, following the same procedure as in the previous example, we obtain

$$\begin{aligned}\omega(t) &= \underbrace{\omega(0)e^{-0.5t}}_{\text{zero input}} + \underbrace{100e^{-0.5t}\int_0^t (1 + \cos \omega_0 \tau)e^{0.5\tau}\, d\tau}_{\text{zero state}} \\ &= \omega(0)e^{-0.5t} + 200(1 - e^{-0.5t}) \\ &\quad + \frac{200(\cos \omega_0 t - e^{-0.5t}) + 400\omega_0 \sin \omega_0 t}{1 + 4\omega_0^2}\end{aligned}$$

For $\omega(0) = 1$,

$$\omega(t) = 200 - 199e^{-0.5t} + \frac{200}{1 + 4\omega_0^2}(\cos \omega_0 t - e^{-0.5t} + 2\omega_0 \sin \omega_0 t) \quad \textbf{(2.42)}$$

Now, let us use standard techniques of differential equations to find the transient and particular solutions, assuming that $\omega(0) = 1$. The transient solution is

$$\omega_t(t) = Ae^{-0.5t} \quad \textbf{(2.43)}$$

To find the particular solution, we split the input function into two parts: a constant equal to 1 and $\cos \omega_0 t$. The complete particular solution is the sum of the particular solutions due to each part. Specifically, for the forcing function 100,

$$\frac{d\omega_{p1}}{dt} + 0.5\omega_{p1} = 100$$

We use the trial solution $\omega_{p1} = A$, from which we find that $A = 200$, so that

$$\omega_{p1} = 200 \quad \textbf{(2.44)}$$

To obtain ω_{p2} from the differential equation

$$\frac{d\omega_{p2}}{dt} + 0.5\omega_{p2} = 100 \cos \omega_0 t \quad \textbf{(2.45)}$$

We assume the trial solution $\omega_{p2} = B \cos \omega_0 t + C \sin \omega_0 t$. Note that even though the input is only a cosine function, we must use both sine and cosine terms in the trial solutions. Combine this solution with (2.45):

$$(0.5B + \omega_0 C) \cos \omega_0 t + (-\omega_0 B + 0.5C) \sin \omega_0 t = 100 \cos \omega_0 t$$

Equating the coefficients of like terms, we find that

$$0.5B + \omega_0 C = 100$$
$$-\omega_0 A + 0.5C = 0$$

From these, we find

$$B = \frac{200}{1 + 4\omega_0^2} \qquad \text{and} \qquad C = \frac{400\omega_0}{1 + 4\omega_0^2}$$

The complete solution is

$$\omega(t) = Ae^{-0.5t} + 200 + \frac{200 \cos \omega_0 t + 400\omega_0 \sin \omega_0 t}{1 + 4\omega_0^2}$$

For $\omega(0) = 1$, this equation becomes

$$1 = A + 200 + \frac{200}{1 + 4\omega_0^2} \qquad \text{or} \qquad A = -199 - \frac{200}{1 + 4\omega_0^2}$$

Finally, therefore,

$$\omega(t) = -199e^{-0.5t} - \frac{200}{1 + 4\omega_0^2} e^{-0.5t} + 200 + \frac{200 \cos \omega_0 t + 400\omega_0 \sin \omega_0 t}{1 + 4\omega_0^2}$$

which is identical with (2.42). ■

To illustrate the applicability of the general methods just considered to problems outside of the normal engineering discipline, let us consider an example from economics.

■ Example 2.5 *Economics**

Suppose that the rate of change in the price $P(t)$ of a commodity is proportional to the difference between the demand $D(t)$ and the supply $S(t)$ in the market at any time t. Determine and study the equation that describes the economical system for the case where D and S are linear functions of price: $D(t) = a - bP(t)$ and $S(t) = -c + dP(t)$ with a, b, c, and d positive constants.

Solution The controlling equation dictated by the statement of the problem is

$$\frac{dP(t)}{dt} = \alpha[D(t) - S(t)] \tag{2.46}$$

where α is a proportionality constant known as the *adjustment* constant. For the case where D and S are linear functions of price, this equation becomes

$$\frac{dP(t)}{dt} + \alpha(b + d)P(t) = \alpha(a + c) \tag{2.47}$$

The solution of this differential equation is found to be

$$P(t) = \left[P(0) - \frac{a + c}{b + d}\right]e^{-\alpha(b+d)t} + \frac{a + c}{b + d} \tag{2.48}$$

Let us denote the **equilibrium price**—that is, the price for which supply equals demand—by $\bar{P}$. Then

$$D = S = a - b\bar{P} = -c + d\bar{P}$$

From this,

$$\bar{P} = \frac{a + c}{b + d}$$

* From N. Finizio and G. Ladas, *An Introduction to Differential Equations* (Belmont, CA: Wadsworth Publishing Co., 1982), p. 36.

Table 2.1 Particular Solution

	Excitation Function (Input)	Trial Solution
1.	Polynomial $f(t) = a_0 + a_1 + a_2 t^2 + \cdots + a_n t^n$ (Some a_i's may be zero.)	Polynomial $f(t) = c_0 + c_1 t + c_2 t^2 + \cdots + c_n t^n$ (No c_i's are set to zero.)
2.	Exponential function $f(t) = Ae^{\alpha t}$	Exponential function $f(t) = Be^{\alpha t}$
3.	Sine or cosine function $f(t) = A \cos t + B \sin t$ (A or B may be zero.)	Sine and cosine function $f(t) = C_1 \cos t + C_2 \sin t$ (Both C's are different from zero.)
4.	Combination of above cases	Split excitation into its separate parts, solve the individual equations, then add the results.

and (2.48) becomes

$$P(t) = (P(0) - \bar{P})e^{-\alpha(b+d)t} + \bar{P} \tag{2.49}$$

From this we see that as $t \to \infty$, the price of the commodity $P(t) \to \bar{P}$. ■

Table 2.1 is an aid in finding the particular solution of differential equations for different types of excitation functions. It shows the forms of the trial solutions that must be introduced to find the particular solution for the specified form of excitation function.

2.4 Evaluation of Integration Constants: Initial Conditions

Once the complementary solution and the particular solution have been deduced for a given differential equation, the next step is to determine the constants of integration that arise in the complementary solution, if the general solution is to be converted to a solution that satisfies all conditions of a particular problem. The data necessary for this determination are provided by initial conditions that exist in the system. For electrical systems, these conditions are the known charges on all capacitors (usually given as initial voltages across the capacitors) and known currents through all inductors at some specified initial time, usually taken as $t = 0$. In the more general case, the initial conditions would be specified by initial through and across variables pertinent to the system elements. If these initial voltages and currents are zero, the system is said to be **initially relaxed**. In all cases, the specified initial conditions must be applied to the complete solution to determine the constants of integration. In this way, the character of the system disturbance is taken into account. If the system disturbance involves more than the switching of excitation functions—for example, the switching of system elements—such changes must be taken into account. A number of different switching operations are possible.

Switching of Sources. The most common switching operation is that of introducing an excitation source into the circuit. The most common input waveforms are the step function, sinusoids, pulses, and the decaying exponential. As shown in Table 2.1, the excitation function establishes the form of the particular solution. The specification that the circuit is initially relaxed provides sufficient relations to evaluate the constants of integration.

Conservation of Charge. If the initial voltages across capacitors are not zero and if, during the switching operation, the total system capacitance remains unchanged, then the voltage across each capacitor will be the same before and after the switching instant. This result assumes the absence of switching impulses to one or more of the capacitors. It follows from the fact that the terminal relation for the capacitor is $i = C\,dv/dt$, and in the switching operation during the interval from $t = 0-$ to $t = 0+$, when C is a constant,

$$\int_{v(0-)}^{v(0+)} C\,dv = \int_{0-}^{0+} i\,dt \tag{2.50}$$

The value of the integral on the right is zero unless i is an impulse function. Equation (2.51) is a statement of conservation of charge (conservation of momentum in mechanics). If no current impulse is applied during the switching interval, then

$$Cv(0+) - Cv(0-) = 0 \tag{2.51}$$

and the voltage across the capacitor remains constant during the switching operation.

Conservation of Flux Linkages. If initial currents exist in inductors and if, during the switching operation, the total inductance of the system remains unchanged, then the current through each inductor will remain unchanged over the switching instant. This result follows directly from the fact that the terminal relation for the inductor is $v = L\,di/dt$ and, with L constant over the switching interval,

$$\int_{i(0-)}^{i(0+)} L\,di = \int_{0-}^{0+} v\,dt \tag{2.52}$$

The right-hand side will be zero in the absence of voltage impulses. In the absence of voltage impulses during the switching interval,

$$Li(0+) - Li(0-) = 0 \tag{2.53}$$

and the current through the inductor remains constant during the switching operation. This is a statement of conservation of flux linkages. This condition is the dual of that for the voltage across the capacitor.

Circuit Behavior of L and C. In the light of the foregoing discussion, for circuits with **constant excitation**:

1. Capacitors behave as open circuits in the steady state.
2. Inductors behave as short circuits in the steady state.

General Switching. In those cases where L or C or both are changed instantaneously during a switching operation, and in the absence of switching impulses, (2.51) and (2.53) must be modified to the following forms:

For capacitors: conservation of charge

$$\begin{gathered} q(0+) = q(0-) \\ C(0+)v(0+) = C(0-)v(0-) \end{gathered} \tag{2.54a}$$

For inductors: conservation of flux linkages

$$\begin{gathered} \psi(0+) = \psi(0-) \\ L(0+)i(0+) = L(0-)i(0-) \end{gathered} \tag{2.54b}$$

As a practical matter, circuits with switched L or C are easily accomplished by placing switches across all or part of the L or C of a circuit.

■ Example 2.6

Consider the circuit shown in Figure 2.18a, which shows the switching of the circuit resistance. Observe that the total circuit resistance is R_1 before opening the switch and $R_1 + R_2$ after the switching operation at $t = 0$. Find $i(t)$ for $t > 0$.

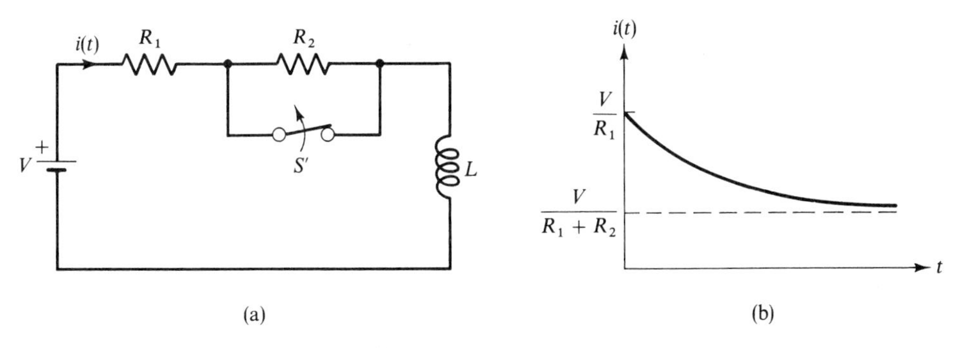

Figure 2.18 Resistor Switching. (a) Switching of R in a circuit with an initial current. (b) Transient response following switching.

Solution The initial current prior to the switching instant is assumed to be constant since the source is assumed to be on for a long time and any transient effect has disappeared. The initial current has the value

$$i_0 = i(0-) = \frac{V}{R_1} \tag{2.55}$$

After opening the switch at $t(0+)$, the controlling differential equation is

$$L\frac{di(t)}{dt} + (R_1 + R_2)i(t) = V \tag{2.56}$$

This differential equation has a transient solution, $i_t(t) = Ae^{-(R_1+R_2)t/L}$, and a particular solution, $i_p(t) = V/(R_1 + R_2)$. The total solution is

$$i(t) = i_t(t) + i_p(t) = \frac{V}{R_1 + R_2} + Ae^{-(R_1+R_2)t/L} \tag{2.57}$$

To evaluate the constant A, we impose the initial condition, which is $i(0-) = i(0+)$, since no energy storing elements were altered. Then, by (2.53), no instantaneous change in current will occur, and $i(0-) = i(0+)$. Thus,

$$\frac{V}{R_1} = \frac{V}{R_1 + R_2} + A$$

from which we find that

$$A = V\left(\frac{1}{R_1} - \frac{1}{R_1 + R_2}\right) = \frac{VR_2}{R_1(R_1 + R_2)}$$

The final solution is

$$i(t) = \frac{V}{(R_1 + R_2)}\left(1 + \frac{R_2}{R_1}e^{-(R_1+R_2)t/L}\right) \tag{2.58}$$

This is sketched in Figure 2.18b. ■

■ Example 2.7

Refer to Figure 2.19a, which shows the switching of L in a circuit with an initial current. Prior to switching, the inductance is L_1, and after switching, the total circuit inductance is $L_1 + L_2$. Switching occurs at $t = 0$. Find an expression for the current in the circuit after switching.

Solution The current in the circuit prior to switching for assumed steady state conditions is

$$i(0-) = \frac{V}{R_1} \tag{2.59}$$

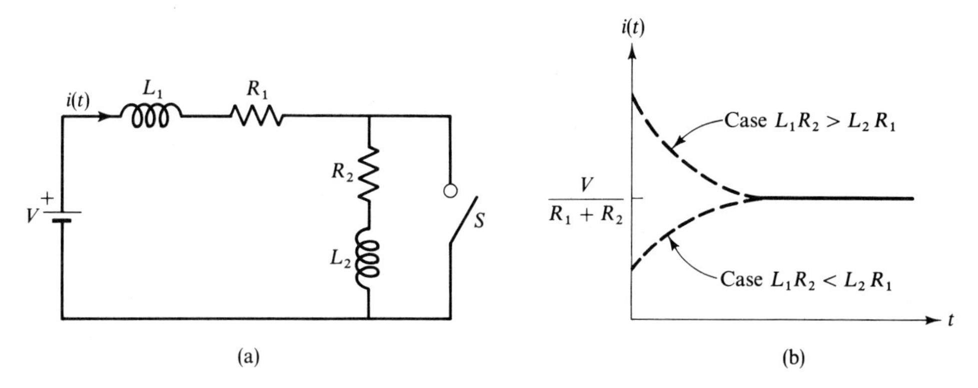

Figure 2.19 Inductor Switching. (a) Switching of *L* in a circuit with initial current. (b) Response of the *RL* circuit when *L* is switched.

To find the current after switching, we employ the law of conservation of flux linkages given by (2.54b). Thus, over the switching period

$$L_1 i(0-) = (L_1 + L_2) i(0+) \tag{2.60}$$

from which

$$i(0+) = \frac{L_1}{L_1 + L_2} i(0-) = \frac{L_1}{L_1 + L_2} \frac{V}{R_1} \tag{2.61}$$

Now, because there has been a change in circuit parameters, a transient current will result. The circuit dynamics is found from the controlling differential equation, following the pattern of the previous problem, with the general solution

$$i(t) = \frac{V}{R_1 + R_2} + A e^{-(R_1 + R_2)t/(L_1 + L_2)} \tag{2.62}$$

At the switching instant $t = 0+$,

$$i(0+) = \frac{V}{R_1 + R_2} + A = \frac{L_1}{L_1 + L_2} \frac{V}{R_1}$$

from which

$$A = V\left[\frac{L_1}{R_1(L_1 + L_2)} - \frac{1}{R_1 + R_2}\right] = \frac{(L_1 R_2 - L_2 R_1)V}{R_1(R_1 + R_2)(L_1 + L_2)} \tag{2.63}$$

The final solution is given by the expression

$$i(t) = \frac{V}{R_1 + R_2}\left[1 + \frac{L_1 R_2 - L_2 R_1}{R_1(L_1 + L_2)} e^{-(R_1 + R_2)t/(L_1 + L_2)}\right] \tag{2.64}$$

The nature of this function is illustrated in Figure 2.19b. This figure shows that the current may rise or fall at the switching instant, depending on the relative

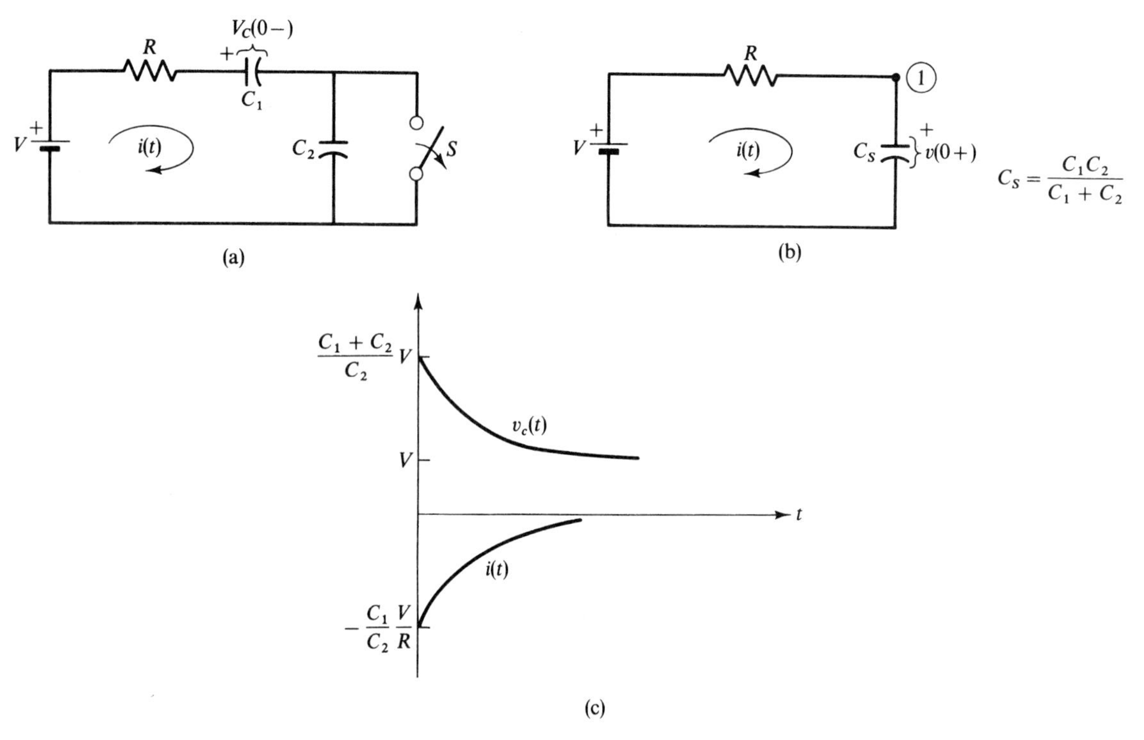

Figure 2.20 Capacitor Switching. (a) Switching of capacitors. (b) Equivalent circuit after switching has taken place. (c) Voltage and current in the circuit.

values L_1R_2 and L_2R_1, with or without a time delay until the circuit current assumes its final altered value. Observe that if $R_2 = 0$, the current will recover to its original value. ■

■ Example 2.8

Consider the circuit shown in Figure 2.20a. The switch S that has been closed for a long time is opened at time $t = 0$. Find $i(t)$, assuming that C_1 was fully charged when the switched was opened.

Solution At steady state, $i(0-) = 0$ and $v_c(0-) = V$. Upon opening the switch, conservation of charge requires that [see (2.54a)]

$$C_1 v(0-) = C_s v(0+)$$

where C_s denotes the total capacitance of the two capacitors C_1 and C_2 in series $[C_s = C_1C_2/(C_1 + C_2)]$. Hence, we write

$$C_1 v(0-) = \frac{C_1C_2}{C_1 + C_2} v(0+)$$

from which

$$v(0+) = \frac{C_1 + C_2}{C_2} v(0-) = \frac{C_1 + C_2}{C_2} V \tag{2.65}$$

Observe that the switching operation reduces the total capacitance of the circuit with a resulting increase in the instantaneous voltage.

We proceed with the solution of the problem by writing the differential equation with respect to the voltage across the capacitor C_s, as shown in Figure 2.20b. Use ① as a node about which to write the node equation:

$$RC_s \frac{dv_c}{dt} + v_c = V \tag{2.66}$$

This equation defines the system conditions in terms of v_c as the dependent variable.

By proceeding as in the previous two examples, we find that the transient solution is given by

$$v_{ct}(t) = Ae^{-t/RC_s} \tag{2.67}$$

Since V is constant for $t > 0$, the steady state solution is equal to $v_{cs}(t) = V$. The total solution is

$$v_c(t) = V + Ae^{-t/RC_s} \tag{2.68}$$

At the switching instant $t = 0+$,

$$v_c(0+) = V + A = \frac{C_1 + C_2}{C_2} V$$

hence,

$$A = \frac{C_1 + C_2}{C_2} V - V = \frac{C_1}{C_2} V$$

Thus,

$$v_c(t) = V\left(1 + \frac{C_1}{C_2} e^{-t/RC_s}\right) \tag{2.69}$$

To find the current in the capacitor, and hence in the circuit, we use the fact that $i = C(dv/dt)$ and obtain

$$i(t) = C_s \frac{dv_c(t)}{dt} = -\frac{C_1 V}{C_2 R} e^{-t/RC_s} \tag{2.70}$$

Figure 2.20c sketches the voltage across the equivalent capacitor C_s and the current in the circuit. ■

2.5 Block Diagram Representation

The description of system interconnections to this point has been a mathematical one that employed the fundamental laws of Kirchhoff, D'Alembert, and others to specify the interconnection of the components of a system by means of differential equations. A second procedure is one that graphically displays the interconnected models and then employs techniques of graphical reductions to write the circuit equations. Two important graphical methods exist: the block diagram and the signal flow graph (SFG). These representations are closely related, and consideration here is limited to block diagrams.

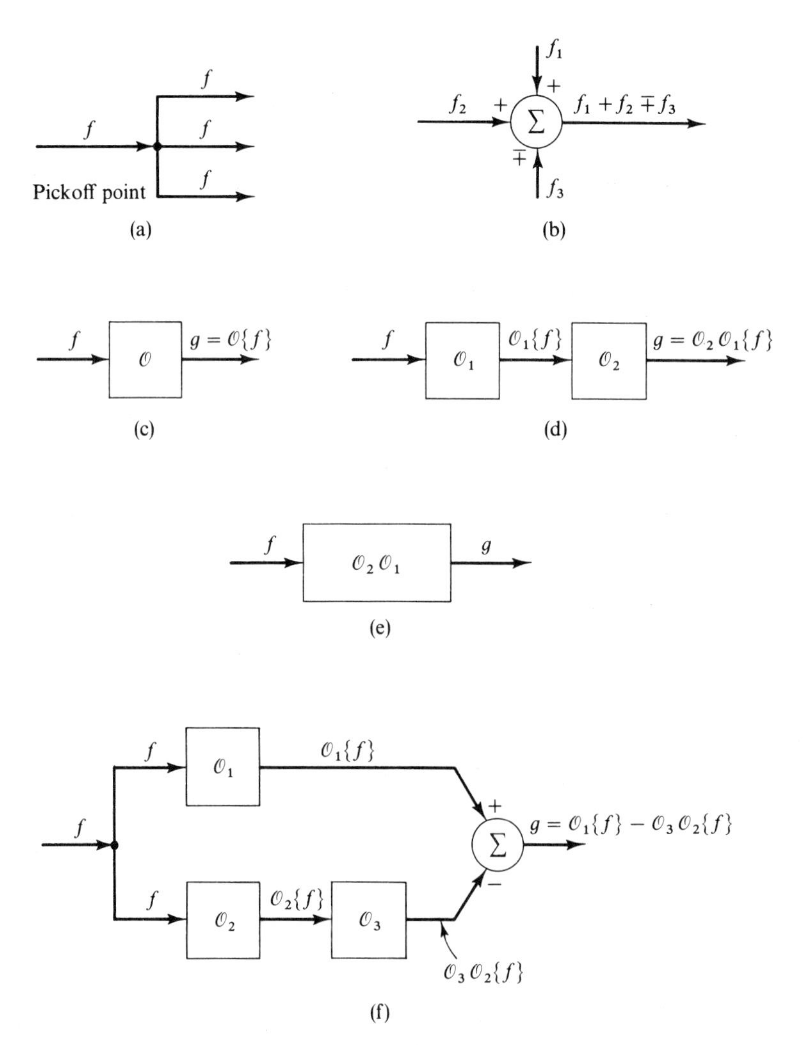

Figure 2.21 Elementary Rules of Block Diagram Operations

Block diagram portrayals possess the important feature that the signal paths from input to output are placed in sharp focus without displaying the hardware of the system. Furthermore, it provides tools of analysis that often possess advantages over other methods. We will usually proceed in block diagram developments through a series of mathematical equations that are given graphical portrayal.

It is also possible to proceed by means of an interconnection pattern of the system elements and then to deduce the equations for the connected system. This method is often advantageous because it makes unnecessary some of the steps in the indirect development. Further, through this graphical presentation, system changes are often more readily accommodated in the analysis than through equations.

Refer to Figure 2.21. Figure 2.21a shows a **pickoff point** that transmits the variable to different branches. Observe that the magnitude of the variable is not divided, but is transmitted to all branches at its original strength. Figure 2.21b shows a **summation point** and the resulting output, Figure 2.21c shows a system that is characterized by an operator—for example, an integrator, differentiator, constant, and the like.

To facilitate our understanding of the block diagram representation of systems, it is convenient to think of the block as a multiplier. Thus, if $\mathcal{O} = a$ in Figure 2.21c, then the output is $g = af$. Figure 2.21d shows two blocks in cascade. Clearly, the output is just the successive operation of the operators on the input. If $\mathcal{O}_1 = a$ and $\mathcal{O}_2 = b$, the output is baf. Figure 2.21e shows a combined configuration of the individual configurations discussed above. Figure 2.21f shows the details of a more complicated circuit.

Figure 2.22 shows a typical block diagram representation of a feedback system.

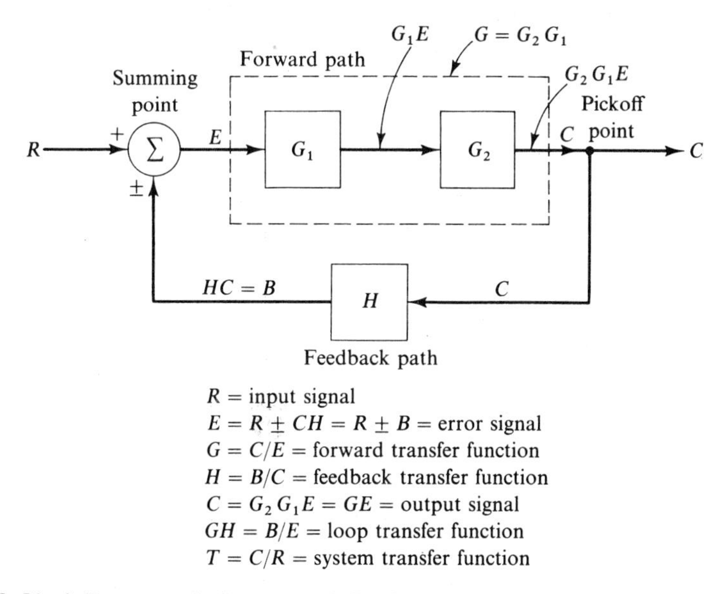

Figure 2.22 Block Diagram of a System with Feedback. All operators are assumed constant multipliers.

The terminology is that used extensively in control system engineering. It is a fundamental configuration of physical and man-made systems.

To understand the block diagram representation, consider the RL circuit shown in Figure 2.15. The differential equation that represents the system is

$$\frac{L}{R}\frac{dv_o(t)}{dt} + v_o(t) = v(t) \tag{2.71}$$

The presence of the summation will require a summation point in the block diagram. Write this equation in the form

$$v_o(t) = v(t) - \frac{L}{R}\frac{dv_o(t)}{dt} \tag{2.72}$$

This expression shows that the output is equal to the input minus (L/R) times the derivative of the output. A block diagram representation of this equation is shown in Figure 2.23a.

Suppose that we write (2.71) in the form

$$\frac{L}{R}\frac{dv_o(t)}{dt} = v(t) - v_o(t) \tag{2.73}$$

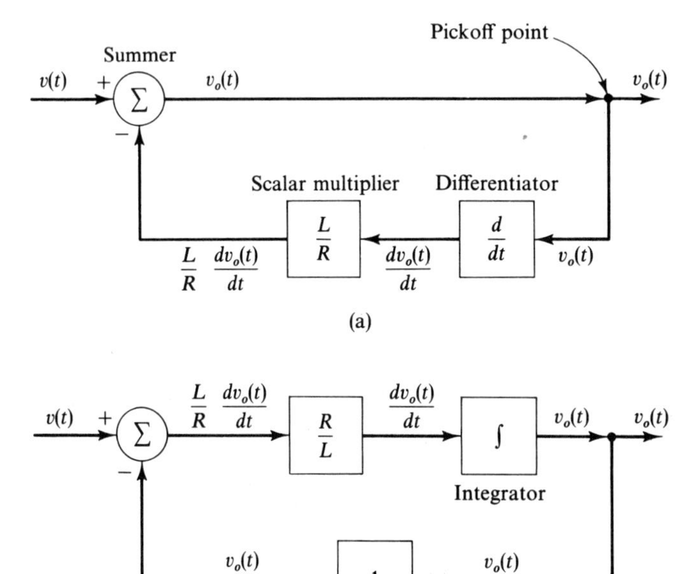

Figure 2.23 Block Diagram Representation of the System Shown in Figure 2.15

This expression shows that the output of the summation point $(L/R)\, dv_o(t)/dt$ is the difference between the input $v(t)$ and the output $v_o(t)$. The block diagram representation is shown in Figure 2.23b.

A similar procedure applied to the economic system described by (2.46) and (2.47) results in the block diagrams shown in Figures 2.24a and 2.24b, respectively.

A block diagram representation of a given system can often be reduced by block diagram reduction techniques to achieve a block diagram with fewer blocks than the original diagram. The representative block diagram symbols and a number of the basic reduction rules are contained in Figure 2.25.

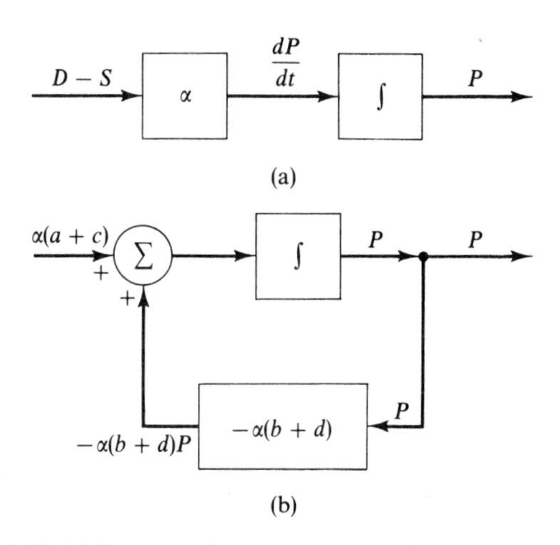

Figure 2.24 Block Diagram Representation of an Economic System

System Diagram	*Equivalent Diagram*	*Observations*
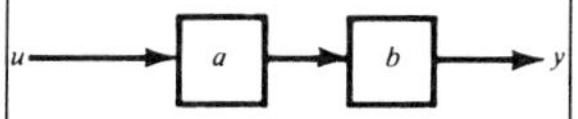 u → [a] → [b] → y	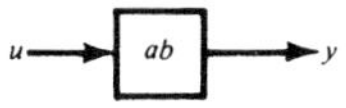 u → [ab] → y	Two blocks in cascade
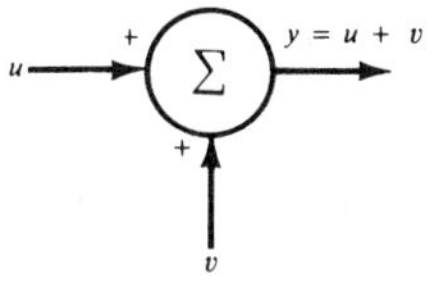 u (+), v (+) → Σ → $y = u + v$		Summation point

Figure 2.25 Properties of Block Diagrams *(continues)*

■ Example 2.9

Use Figure 2.25 to reduce the complex systems shown in Figures 2.26a and 2.26b to single-block form. The operators are constant multipliers.

System Diagram	*Equivalent Diagram*	*Observations*
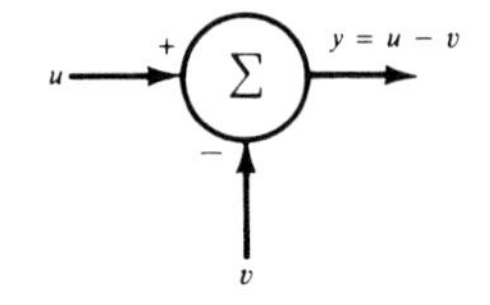 u, $+$, Σ, $-$, v, $y = u - v$		Subtraction point
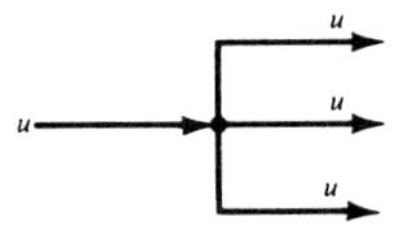 u, u, u, u		Pickoff point
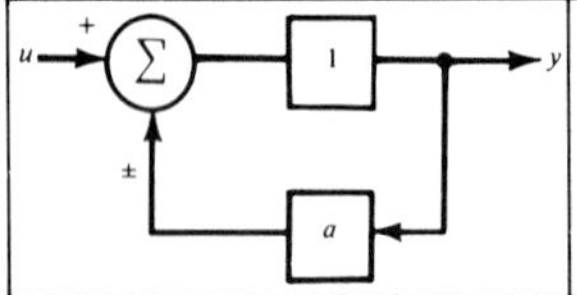 u, $+$, Σ, $\pm$, 1, a, y	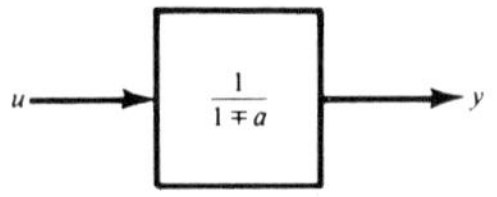 u, $\frac{1}{1 \mp a}$, y	Feedback loop
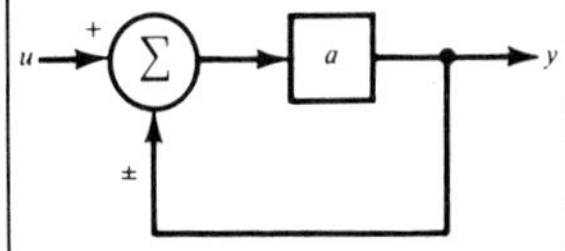 u, $+$, Σ, $\pm$, a, y	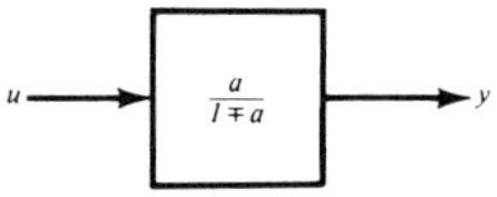 u, $\frac{a}{1 \mp a}$, y	Special case of unit feedback loop
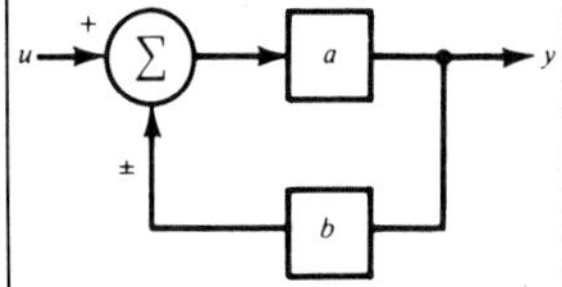 u, $+$, Σ, $\pm$, a, b, y	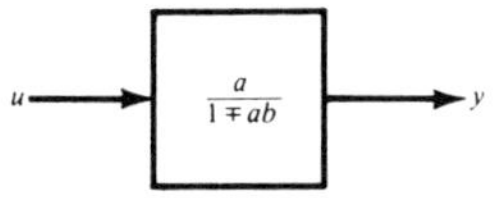 u, $\frac{a}{1 \mp ab}$, y	Complete feedback loop
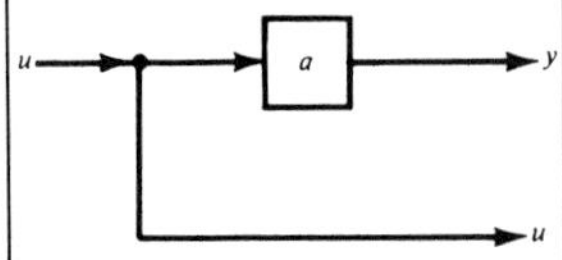 u, a, y, u	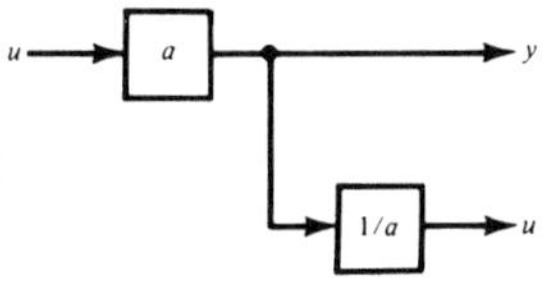 u, a, y, $1/a$, u	Moving a pickoff point ahead

Figure 2.25 (*continued*)

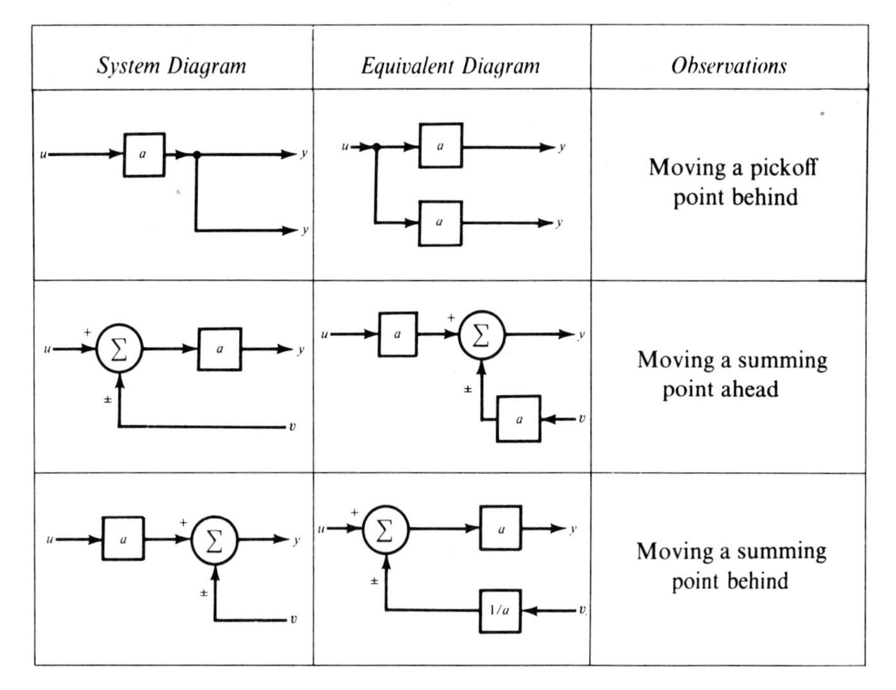

Figure 2.25 *(continued)*

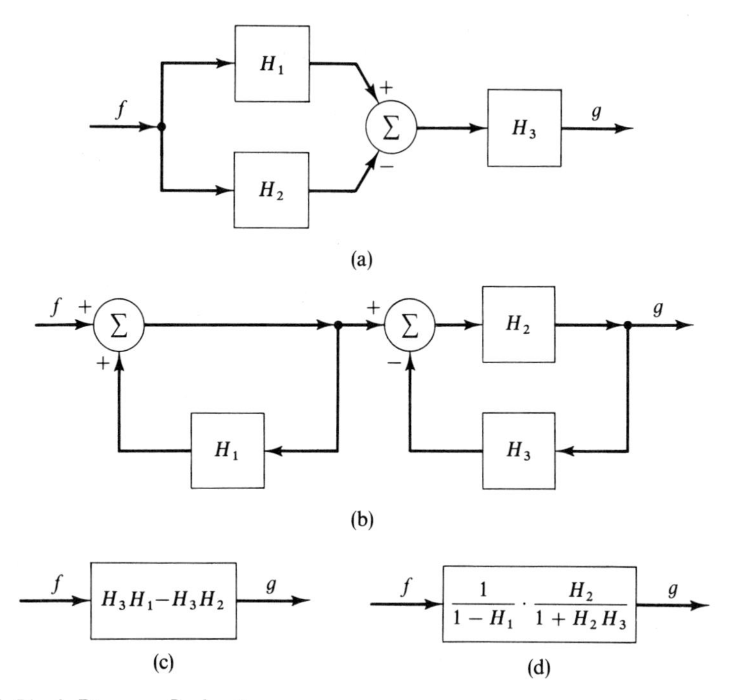

Figure 2.26 Block Diagram Reduction

Solution We observe from Figure 2.26a that the output of the summer is $H_1 f - H_2 f$. This summer output is the input to the next block, the output of which is $g = H_3(H_1 f - H_2 f) = H_3 H_1 f - H_3 H_2 f$. This result is shown in Figure 2.26c.

Refer now to Figure 2.26b. By entry 5 of Figure 2.25, the equivalent representation of the first feedback loop operator is equal to $1/(1 - H_1)$. By entry 7 of Figure 2.25, the equivalent representation of the second feedback loop operator is $H_2/(1 + H_2 H_3)$. These two equivalent blocks are in cascade, and the final operator is the product of these equivalent blocks. The final reduction is shown in Figure 2.26d. ■

2.6 Discrete Systems and Equations

When we dealt with continuous, or analog, systems, our interest was in the relationship between an input signal $v(t)$ and an output $g(t)$. Hence, we were interested in finding the appropriate system operator $\mathcal{O}$ that when multiplied by the input, would yield the relation between the output and the input. Similarly, a **discrete**, or **digital, system** establishes a relationship between two discrete signals: an input $v(k)$ and an output $g(k)$. An actual discrete system is a combination of many electronic circuits, such as amplifiers, shift registers, and gates. However, it is represented here in simple block diagram form.

In a discrete time system, a **discrete source** produces discrete time signals that are pulses of assumed zero width and finite height. A discrete signal sequence may arise by pulse sampling a continuous time excitation function, usually at uniform time intervals. It might represent a sequence of narrow pulses generated in a pulse-generating source. It might also represent actual discrete signals produced in physical processes.

Another element of the discrete system is the **scalar multiplier**, a component that produces pulses at its output that are proportional to discrete pulses at its input. There is also a **delay element** that produces an output identical with that at its input, but delayed by a predetermined number of time units. The symbol z^{-1} is used to denote a delay of one time unit; two delay units are denoted z^{-2}; hence, z^{-n} denotes a delay of n time units. These three discrete system elements are illustrated graphically in Figure 2.27.

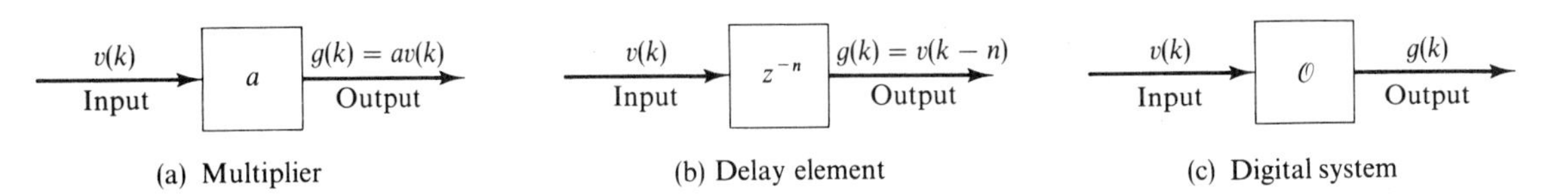

Figure 2.27 Digital System Entities. (a) Multiplier. (b) Delay element. (c) Digital system.

A group of such connected discrete elements and adders (summing points or summers) with appropriate pickoff points constitute a discrete system. Discrete sources are its inputs, and the resulting signals in its various parts are the outputs, or response, of the system. The analysis of the behavior of such systems will parallel, to some extent, the systems analysis procedures in continuous time systems.

■ **Example 2.10**

A discrete system and its input are shown in Figure 2.28. Find its output.

Solution By inspection, it is seen that the output from the summer is a signal consisting of two pulses: a pulse of height 1 at $k = 0$ and a pulse of height 2 at $k = 2$. These pulses are each delayed by 2 time units, giving the output shown. ■

■ **Example 2.11**

Find the output of the discrete system shown in Figure 2.29 for the input shown.

Solution Clearly, the output signal is the sum of the input signal plus a replica of this signal, but delayed by 2 time units. The result is shown in the figure. ■

A system consisting of discrete time elements with a discrete time input signal sequence is described by a **difference equation**. This description is to be contrasted with the description of linear, lumped, time-invariant systems that are described by ordinary differential equations. Depending on the number and character of the ele-

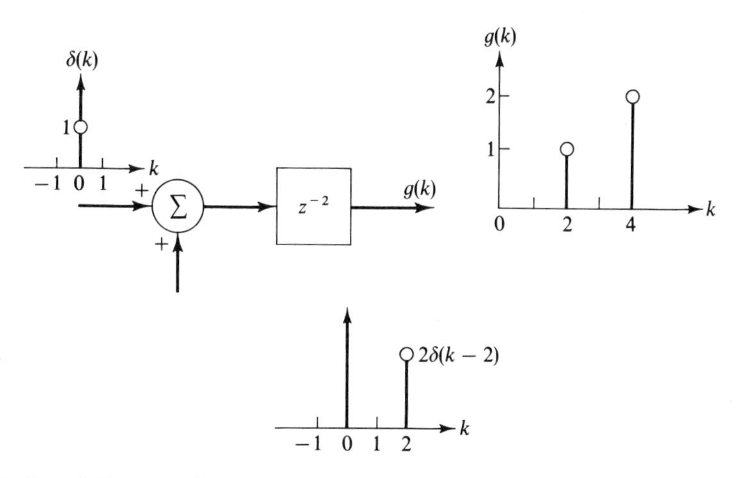

Figure 2.28 Simple Discrete System with a Delay Element

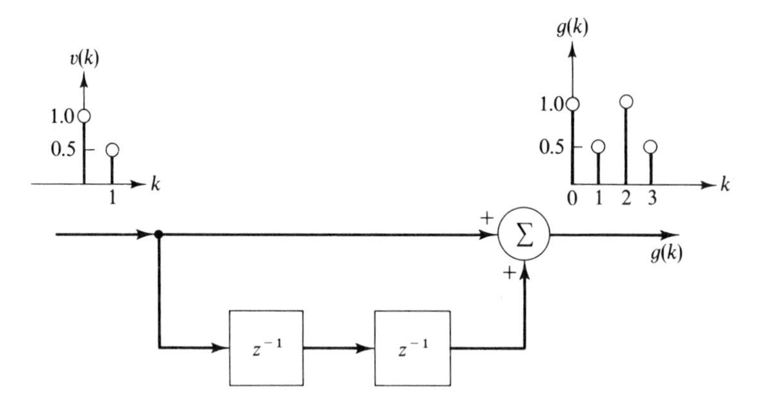

Figure 2.29 Single-Time Discrete Repeater

ments in the discrete system, the system is described by difference equations of different orders.

The following examples will help us understand how difference equations are developed. Also, an iteration method is adopted for the solution of such difference equations. Other methods are considered later in the text.

■ Example 2.12

Consider the system shown in Figure 2.30a. Find the difference equation that describes the system and deduce the output $g(k)$ if the input is $v(k) = u(k)$, the unit step sequence. The system is relaxed at $k = 0$, which implies that $g(-1) = 0$.

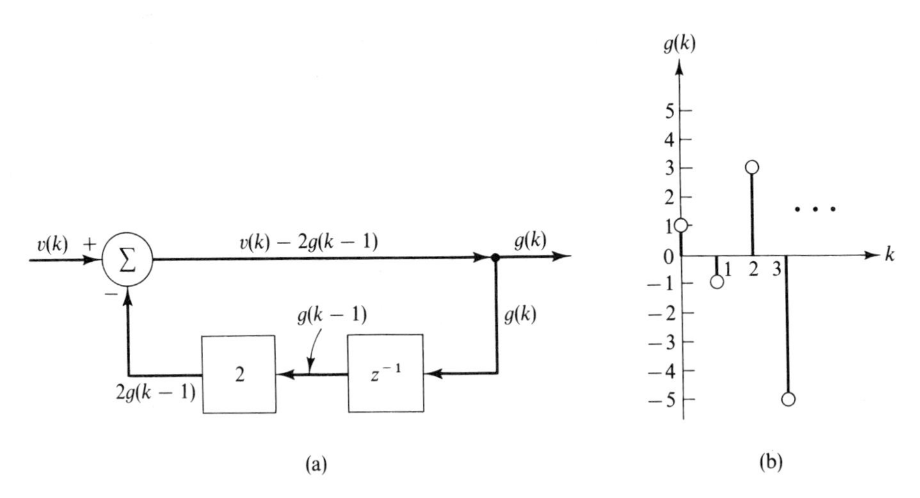

Figure 2.30 Illustrating Example 2.12

Solution From the figure we observe that

$$g(k) = v(k) - 2g(k-1) \tag{2.74}$$

where we note that a discrete function $g(k)$, if delayed by 1 unit, is $g(k-1)$, if delayed by 2 units, is $g(k-2)$, and so on. Additionally in this problem, since the difference of the independent variables k and $k-1$ belonging to the dependent variables $g(k)$ and $g(k-1)$, respectively, is 1, the difference equation is of **first order**.

To find a numerical solution, we proceed by successively introducing values of k into the difference equation, starting with $k = 0$ since the input function starts at time $k = 0$. We proceed iteratively thereafter. Thus,

$$\begin{aligned}
g(0) &= v(0) - 2g(-1) = 1 - (2 \times 0) = 1 \\
g(1) &= v(1) - 2g(0) \quad = 1 - (2 \times 1) = -1 \\
g(2) &= v(2) - 2g(1) \quad = 1 - 2(-1) = 3 \\
g(3) &= v(3) - 2g(2) \quad = 1 - (2 \times 3) = -5 \\
&\vdots
\end{aligned}$$

The function $g(k)$ is plotted in Figure 2.30b. ■

■ **Example 2.13**

Find the difference equation that describes the system shown in Figure 2.31a. Determine its output $g(k)$ if the input is $v(k) = u(k)$. The system is relaxed at $k = 0$, which implies that $g(-1) = 0$.

Solution From the figure we deduce that

$$g(k) = v(k) + 2v(k-1) - 4v(k-2) \tag{2.75}$$

Note that the output of the system is expressed only in terms of the input function. Such a system is called a **nonrecursive**, **transversal**, or **finite duration**

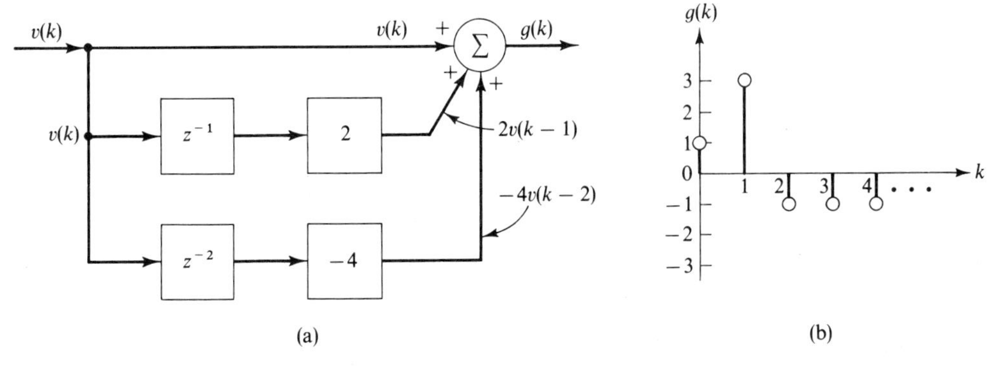

Figure 2.31 Illustrating Example 2.13

impulse response (FIR), system. To find the solution, we proceed by introducing successive values of k. Hence,

$$\begin{aligned} g(0) &= v(0) + 2v(-1) - 4v(-2) = 1 + (2 \times 0) - (4 \times 0) = 1 \\ g(1) &= v(1) + 2v(0) - 4v(-1) = 1 + (2 \times 1) - (4 \times 0) = 3 \\ g(2) &= v(2) + 2v(1) - 4v(0) = 1 + (2 \times 1) - (4 \times 1) = -1 \\ g(3) &= v(3) + 2v(2) - 4v(1) = 1 + (2 \times 1) - (4 \times 1) = -1 \\ &\vdots \end{aligned}$$

The function $g(k)$ is plotted in Figure 2.31b. ■

■ Example 2.14

Find the difference equation that describes the system shown in Figure 2.32a. Determine the output $g(k)$ for an input $v(k) = u(k)$. The system is relaxed at $k = 0$, which implies that $g(-1) = g(-2) = 0$.

Solution From the figure we see that

$$g(k) = v(k-1) - 2v(k-2) - 2g(k-2) \tag{2.76}$$

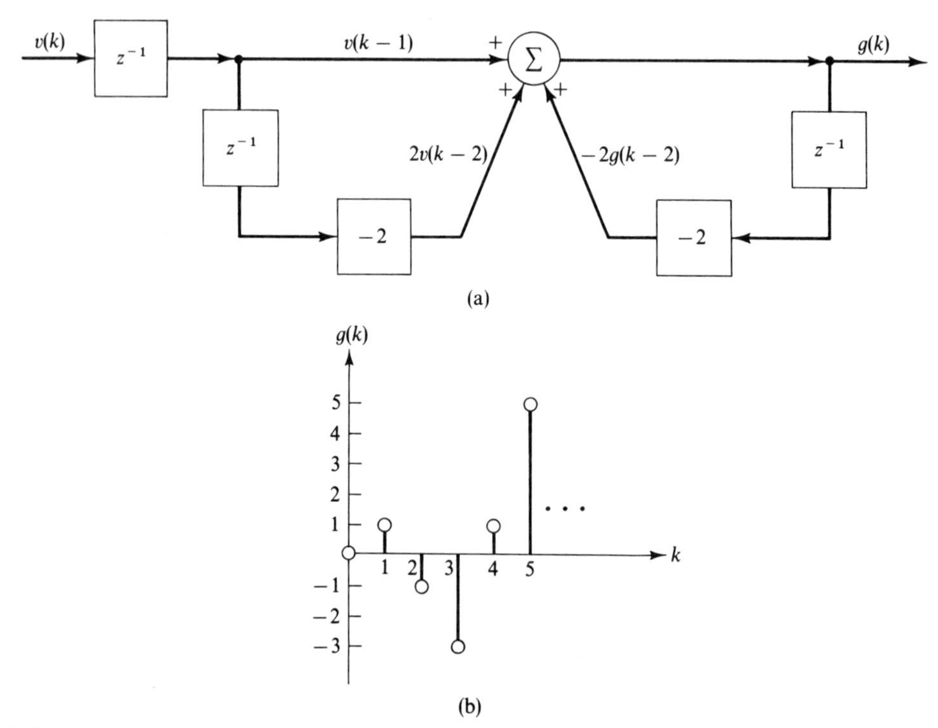

Figure 2.32 Illustrating Example 2.14

Because the difference between k and $k-2$ belonging to the dependent variables $g(k)$ and $g(k-2)$ is equal to 2, the difference equation is of **second order**. We note also that the output is the sum of both the input and delayed values of the output. Delayed values of the input might appear in such equations. Such systems are called **recursive**, or infinite impulse response (IIR), systems. The solution is built up as follows:

$$\begin{aligned}
g(0) &= v(-1) - 2v(-2) - 2g(-2) = 0 - (2 \times 0) - (2 \times 0) = 0 \\
g(1) &= v(0) - 2v(-1) - 2g(-1) \quad = 1 - (2 \times 0) - (2 \times 0) = 1 \\
g(2) &= v(1) - 2v(0) - 2g(0) \quad = 1 - (2 \times 1) - (2 \times 0) = -1 \\
g(3) &= v(2) - 2v(1) - 2g(1) \quad = 1 - (2 \times 1) - (2 \times 1) = -3 \\
&\vdots
\end{aligned}$$

The output is plotted in Figure 2.32b. ■

■ **Example 2.15** ***Banking***

The interest rate of a savings account is $r\%$ per year compounded n times per year ($n = 4$ would correspond to quarterly compounding). Determine what the total bank account balance $y(k)$ would be at the end of the kth compounding period if the total deposits during the kth compounding period are $x(k)$. Assume that deposits during any period earn no interest until the next compounding period.

Solution The interest is compounded at the rate $r/n\%$ for each compounding period. Therefore, at the end of any compounding period, the total bank account balance is equal to the sum of the following: the bank account balance at the start of the compounding period, the interest accrued on this balance, and the deposits made during the period. We can thus write

$$y(k) = y(k-1) + \frac{r}{n}\,y(k-1) + x(k) = \left(1 + \frac{r}{n}\right)y(k-1) + x(k)$$ ■

2.7 Digital Simulation of Analog Systems

If we wish to carry out continuous time systems analysis using digital computers, it is required that we determine a digital system whose output is equivalent to that of the continuous time or analog system. We refer to the digital equivalent as a digital simulator and require, of course, that the digital output closely approximate the output of the corresponding analog system. The objective of digital simulation is to determine a simulator of an analog system and to determine the class of signals that can be processed.

Because the analog systems that we are studying in this book are described by ordinary differential equations, the digital simulators will correspond to a recursive

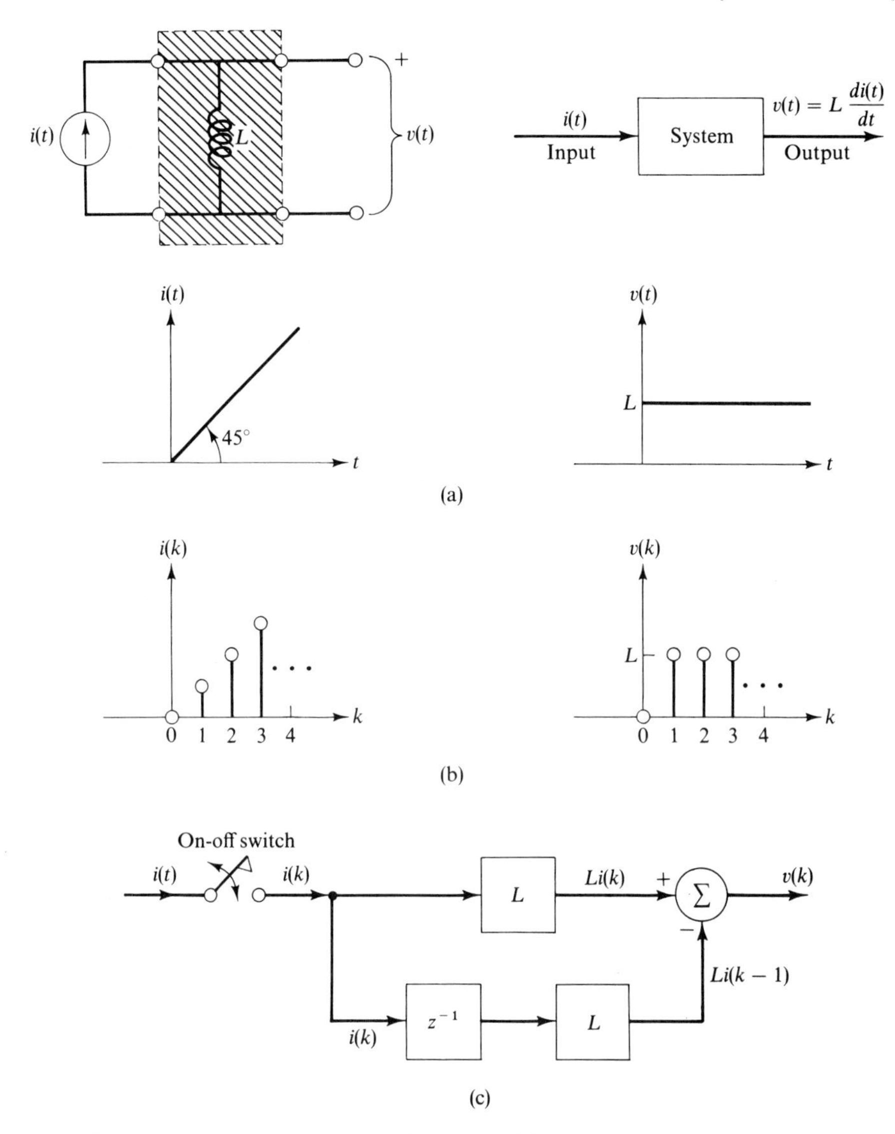

Figure 2.33 Analog to Digital Simulation of Electrical Circuits. (a) Simple analog circuit, input, and output. (b) Sampled input and output from digital equivalent system. (c) Simulator block diagram.

equation that can be represented by delay elements and scale multipliers. To accomplish these objectives, we must study how to create the digital simulators from their analog counterparts.

To understand the process, let us study the analog system shown in Figure 2.33a. We first replace the differential relationship $di(t)/dt$ by an approximately equivalent difference relationship. This transformation is accomplished by replacing the derivative by the approximate form

$$\boxed{\frac{di(t)}{dt} \doteq \frac{i(kT) - i[(k-1)T]}{T}} \tag{2.77a}$$

or

$$\frac{di(t)}{dt} \doteq i(k) - i(k-1) \qquad \text{for } T = 1 \tag{2.77b}$$

For our circuit, we multiply by L, which gives an approximation to the analog expression (the output voltage)

$$v(k) = L[i(k) - i(k-1)] \tag{2.77c}$$

Assume an initially relaxed system $v(-1) = 0$, and, for the discrete or sampled version of the analog input function $i(t)$ shown in Figure 2.33a, we obtain $i(k) = k$. The solution is built up as in previous examples as follows:

$$\begin{aligned}
v(0) &= L[i(0) - i(-1)] = L[0 - 0] = 0\\
v(1) &= L[i(1) - i(0)] \quad = L[1 - 0] = L\\
v(2) &= L[i(2) - i(1)] \quad = L[2 - 1] = L\\
v(3) &= L[i(3) - i(2)] \quad = L[3 - 2] = L\\
&\vdots
\end{aligned}$$

These data are shown in Figure 2.33b. The numerical process described by (2.77c) is shown in Figure 2.33c. Observe that the instantaneous on-off switch accomplishes the production of discrete signals from the analog one.

We now investigate the system shown in Figure 2.34a with a unit step input. We replace the integral relationship by an equivalent discrete form by writing the integral in the form

$$v(kT) = \frac{1}{M}\int_0^{kT} f(\tau)\,d\tau = \frac{1}{M}\int_0^{kT-T} f(\tau)\,d\tau + \frac{1}{M}\int_{kT-T}^{kT} f(\tau)\,d\tau \tag{2.78}$$

which becomes

$$\boxed{v(kT) = v(kT - T) + \frac{1}{M}\int_{kT-T}^{kT} f(\tau)\,d\tau} \tag{2.79}$$

However, the integral represents the area under the curve of $f(t)$ in the interval $kT - T \le t \le kT$, and this area is approximately equal to $Tf(kT)$. Equation (2.79) thus becomes

$$v(kT) \doteq v(kT - T) + \frac{1}{M}\,Tf(kT) \qquad k = 0, 1, 2, \ldots \tag{2.80}$$

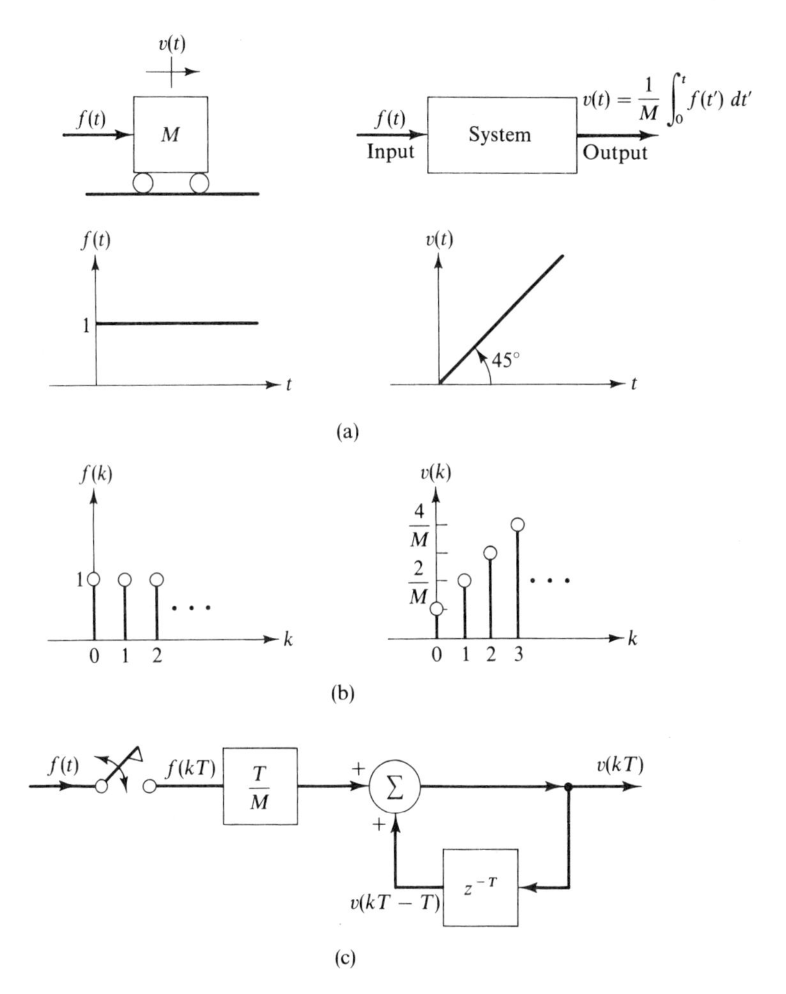

Figure 2.34 Analog to Digital Simulation of Mechanical System. (a) Mechanical system, step force input, and output velocity. (b) Sampled input and output from digital equivalent system. (c) Simulator block diagram.

For an initially relaxed system with unit step discrete input and for $T = 1$, we find

$$
\begin{aligned}
v(0) &= v(-1) + \frac{1}{M}f(0) = 0 + \frac{1}{M} \\
v(1) &= v(0) + \frac{1}{M}f(1) \quad = \frac{1}{M} + \frac{1}{M} = \frac{2}{M} \\
v(2) &= v(1) + \frac{1}{M}f(2) \quad = \frac{2}{M} + \frac{1}{M} = \frac{3}{M} \\
&\vdots
\end{aligned}
$$

These values are shown in Figure 2.34b. The numerical process described by (2.80) is shown in Figure 2.34c, which is the digital simulator for this problem.

■ Example 2.16

Find the output in analog and discrete form of the system shown in Figure 2.35a for a unit step input $v(t) = u(t)$. The system is initially relaxed at $t = 0$.

Solution The differential equation that describes the system is

$$\frac{di(t)}{dt} + 2i(t) = u(t) \qquad \text{and} \qquad v_o(t) = 2i(t)$$

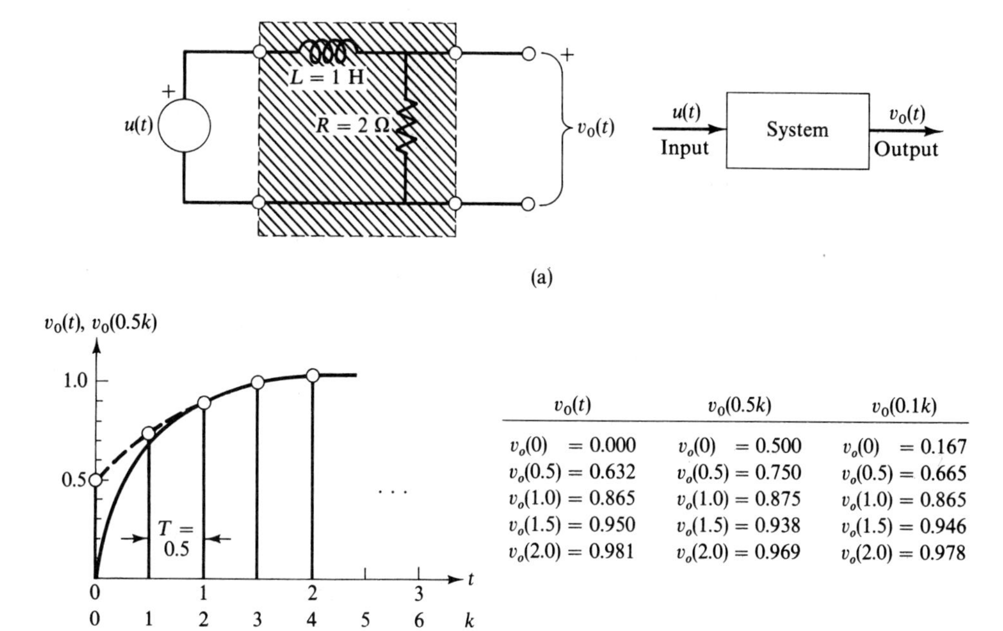

$v_o(t)$	$v_o(0.5k)$	$v_o(0.1k)$
$v_o(0) = 0.000$	$v_o(0) = 0.500$	$v_o(0) = 0.167$
$v_o(0.5) = 0.632$	$v_o(0.5) = 0.750$	$v_o(0.5) = 0.665$
$v_o(1.0) = 0.865$	$v_o(1.0) = 0.875$	$v_o(1.0) = 0.865$
$v_o(1.5) = 0.950$	$v_o(1.5) = 0.938$	$v_o(1.5) = 0.946$
$v_o(2.0) = 0.981$	$v_o(2.0) = 0.969$	$v_o(2.0) = 0.978$

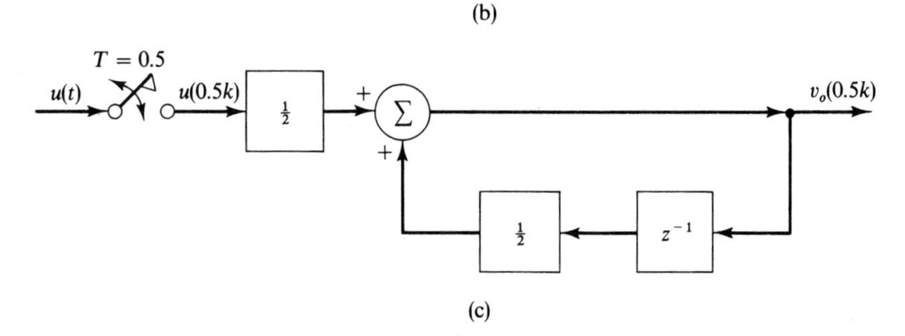

Figure 2.35 Illustrating Example 2.16

or

$$\frac{dv_o(t)}{dt} + 2v_o(t) = 2u(t) \tag{2.81}$$

By an application of the methods previously discussed for solving differential equations of the first order, we obtain the following solution:

$$v_o(t) = (1 - e^{-2t})u(t) \tag{2.82}$$

Next, we deduce the equivalent digital format of (2.81) using (2.77a). Equation (2.81) is approximated by

$$\frac{v_o(kT) - v_o[(k-1)T]}{T} + 2v_o(kT) = 2u(kT)$$

or

$$v_o(kT)(1 + 2T) - v_o[(k-1)T] = 2Tu(kT) \tag{2.83}$$

We consider the particular case for $T = 0.5$; hence, the equation under survey is

$$v_o(0.5k) = \frac{1}{2}\, v_o[0.5(k-1)] + \frac{1}{2}\, u(0.5k)$$

We develop the solution, which is

$$k = 0 \qquad v_o(0) = \frac{1}{2}\, v_o(-0.5) + \frac{1}{2}\, u(0) = \left(\frac{1}{2} \times 0\right) + \left(\frac{1}{2} \times 1\right) = \frac{1}{2}$$

$$k = 1 \qquad v_o(0.5) = \frac{1}{2}\, v_o(0) + \frac{1}{2}\, u(0.5) = \left(\frac{1}{2} \times \frac{1}{2}\right) + \frac{1}{2} = \frac{3}{4}$$

$$k = 2 \qquad v_o(1) = \frac{1}{2}\, v_o(0.5) + \frac{1}{2}\, u(1) = \left(\frac{1}{2} \times \frac{3}{4}\right) + \frac{1}{2} = \frac{7}{8}$$

$$k = 3 \qquad v_o(1.5) = \frac{1}{2}\, v_o(1) + \frac{1}{2}\, u(1.5) = \left(\frac{1}{2} \times \frac{7}{8}\right) + \frac{1}{2} = \frac{15}{16}$$

$$k = 4 \qquad v_o(2.0) = \frac{1}{2}\, v_o(1.5) + \frac{1}{2}\, u(2.0) = \left(\frac{1}{2} \times \frac{15}{16}\right) + \frac{1}{2} = \frac{31}{32}$$

Figure 2.35b gives plots of the system output and the output from its digital simulator. Figure 2.35c shows the block diagram representation of the simulated discrete system for the $T = 0.5$ sampling time in this example. The values of $v_o(k)$ for $T = 0.1$ are given. Observe the close agreement with the corresponding values of $v_o(t)$. ■

■ **Example 2.17**

Find the output of the analog and equivalent discrete form of the system shown in Figure 2.36a. The input to the system is the exponential function $v_i(t) = e^{-t}u(t)$. The system is initially relaxed at $t = 0$.

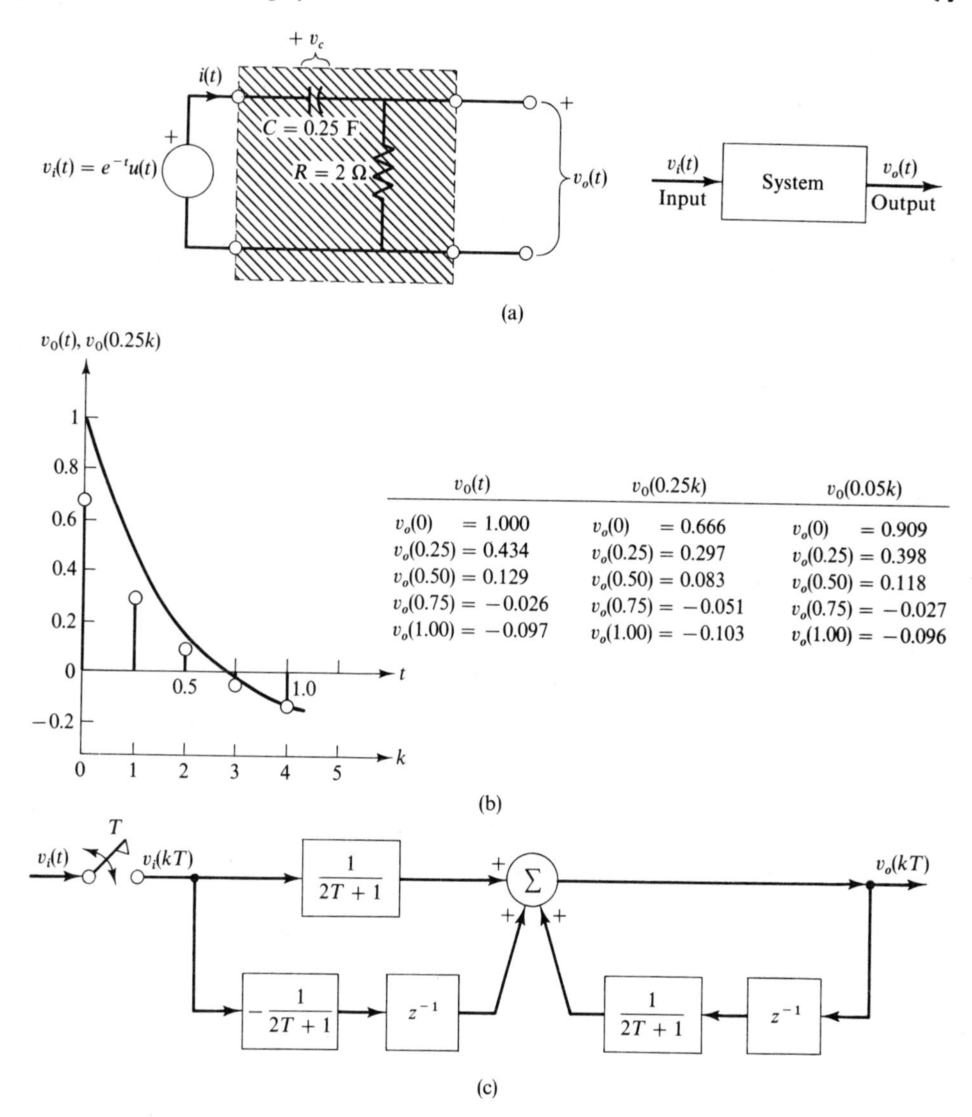

$v_0(t)$	$v_0(0.25k)$	$v_0(0.05k)$
$v_o(0) = 1.000$	$v_o(0) = 0.666$	$v_o(0) = 0.909$
$v_o(0.25) = 0.434$	$v_o(0.25) = 0.297$	$v_o(0.25) = 0.398$
$v_o(0.50) = 0.129$	$v_o(0.50) = 0.083$	$v_o(0.50) = 0.118$
$v_o(0.75) = -0.026$	$v_o(0.75) = -0.051$	$v_o(0.75) = -0.027$
$v_o(1.00) = -0.097$	$v_o(1.00) = -0.103$	$v_o(1.00) = -0.096$

Figure 2.36 Illustrating Example 2.17

Solution The integrodifferential equation describing the system is

$$4 \int i(t)\, dt + 2i(t) = v_i(t) \tag{2.84}$$

We make use of the fact that the current through the capacitor is $C\, dv_c/dt$ to obtain the equation

$$v_c(t) + 0.5 \frac{dv_c}{dt} = v_i(t) \tag{2.85}$$

For an exponential decaying input function and relaxed initial conditions, the solution is easily found to be

$$v_c(t) = 2e^{-t}(1 - e^{-t}) \qquad t > 0 \tag{2.86}$$

Further, the output voltage is

$$v_o(t) = RC\frac{dv_c}{dt} = 2e^{-2t} - e^{-t} \qquad t > 0 \tag{2.87}$$

A sketch of this function is given by the solid line in Figure 2.36b.

We now approximate (2.85) in discrete form. The resulting equation is

$$v_c(kT) + \frac{0.5}{T}[v_c(kT) - v_c(kT - T)] = v_i(kT) \tag{2.88}$$

Also, by inspection of Figure 2.36a, we write by Kirchhoff's voltage law,

$$v_i(kT) - v_c(kT) - v_o(kT) = 0 \tag{2.89}$$

Combine these two equations by eliminating $v_c(kT)$ and $v_c(kT - T)$, the latter by appropriately changing the time variable from kT to $kT - T$ in (2.89). The result is readily found to be

$$v_o(kT) = \frac{1}{2T + 1}[v_i(kT) - v_i(kT - T) + v_o(kT - T)] \tag{2.90}$$

For the particular case of $T = 0.25$ s, the solution is calculated as follows:

$$k = 0 \qquad v_o(0) = \frac{1}{1.5}[v_i(0) - v_i(-0.25) + v_o(-0.25)]$$
$$= \frac{1 - 0 + 0}{1.5} = 0.666$$

$$k = 1 \qquad v_o(0.25) = \frac{1}{1.5}[v_i(0.25) - v_i(0) + v_o(0)]$$
$$= \frac{0.779 - 2 + 0.666}{1.5} = 0.297$$

$$k = 2 \qquad v_o(0.50) = \frac{1}{1.5}[v_i(0.5) - v_i(0.25) + v_o(0.25)]$$
$$= \frac{0.607 - 0.779 + 0.297}{1.5} = 0.083$$

$$k = 3 \qquad v_o(0.75) = \frac{1}{1.5}[v_i(0.75) - v_i(0.5) + v_o(0.5)]$$
$$= \frac{0.472 - 0.606 + 0.083}{1.5} = -0.051$$

$$k = 4 \qquad v_o(1.0) = \frac{1}{1.5}[v_i(1.00) - v_i(0.75) + v_o(0.75)]$$

$$= \frac{0.368 - 0.472 - 0.51}{1.5} = -0.103$$

$\vdots$

Figure 2.36b shows the outputs for the continuous case and the digital simulated case. An interesting exercise is to repeat the calculations for $T = 0.05$. In this case, the reader will find that agreement between the continuous and the discrete calculation is considerably better than that shown for $T = 0.25$, the value at $k = 0$, $v_o(0)$ for $T = 0.05$ being 0.909 rather than the value of $v_o(0)$ for $T = 0.25$, which is 0.666. These data are given in Figure 2.36b. Figure 2.36c gives a block diagram representation of the simulated discrete system.

It is instructive to deduce the equivalent discrete form equation given by (2.89) by proceeding directly from the differential equation (2.84). We proceed by writing (2.84) in the form

$$\frac{1}{0.25}\int_0^{kT-T} i\,dt + \frac{1}{0.25}\int_{kT-T}^{kT} i\,dt + 2i = v_i$$

The equivalent difference equation is

$$\frac{q(kT-T)}{0.25} + \frac{1}{0.25}Ti(kT) + 2i(kT) = v_1(kT)$$

where $q(kT - T)$ is the charge accumulated in the capacitor up to time $(kT - T)$. Further, we have that

$$\frac{q(kT-T)}{0.25} = v_c(kT - T)$$

Also, from the circuit, we have

$$v_c(t) = v_i(t) - v_o(t)$$

which we write

$$v_c(kT - T) = v_i(kT - T) - v_o(kT - T)$$

The combination of the three discrete time equations yields (2.89). ■

■ **Example 2.18** ***Chemistry****

A large tank contains 81 gallons of brine that contains 20 pounds of dissolved salt. Additional brine containing 3 pounds of dissolved salt per gallon runs into the tank at the rate of 5 gallons per minute. The mixture, which is stirred to insure homogeneity, runs out of the tank at the rate of 2 gallons per minute.

* From N. Finizio and G. Ladas, *An Introduction to Differential Equations*, (Belmont, CA: Wadsworth Publishing Co., 1982), p.36.

How much salt is in the tank at the end of 37 minutes? Compare results using a continuous time and discrete time analysis.

Solution The rate of change of salt is given by

$$\dot{y}(t) = \text{rate in} - \text{rate out}$$

The rate in is given directly as

$$\text{rate in} = 3(\text{lb/gal}) \times 5(\text{gal/min}) = 15 \text{ lb/min}$$

To find the rate out, we must first find the concentration of salt at time t—that is, the amount of salt per gallon of the brine in the tank. Since

$$\text{concentration} = \frac{\text{pounds of salt in tank at time } t}{\text{gallons of brine in tank at time } t} = \frac{y(t)}{81 + (5 - 2)t}$$

hence,

$$\text{rate out} = \left[\frac{y(t)}{81 + 3t} \text{ lbs/gal}\right] 2(\text{gal/min}) = \frac{2y(t)}{81 + 3t} \text{ lbs/min}$$

Therefore, the differential equation that describes the mixture is

$$\frac{dy(t)}{dt} = 15 - \frac{2y(t)}{81 + 3t}$$

with the initial condition $y(0) = 20$.

To solve this differential equation, we employ the method of variation of parameters discussed in Section 2.3. Based on the solution of the homogeneous equation, we use the multiplying factor

$$\exp\left(\frac{2}{3} \int \frac{1}{27 + t}\right) dt = \exp \frac{2}{3} [\ln(27 + t)] = (27 + t)^{2/3}$$

Thus, we have

$$\frac{dy(t)}{dt} (27 + t)^{2/3} + \frac{2}{3} y(t)(27 + t)^{-1/3} = 15(27 + t)^{2/3}$$

This equation can be written

$$\frac{d}{dt} [y(t)(27 + t)^{2/3}] = 15(27 + t)^{2/3}$$

Integrate both sides with respect to t to obtain

$$y(t)(27 + t)^{2/3} = \frac{15(27 + t)^{5/3}}{5/3} + C$$

where C is the integration constant. This expression is written

$$y(t) = 9(27 + t) + C(27 + t)^{-2/3}$$

Applying the initial condition, we find that $C = -2007$. The final solution is

$$y(t) = 9(27 + t) - 2007(27 + t)^{-2/3}$$

For the special time $t = 37$, we find $y(37) = 450.6$ lb.

When this problem is converted into equivalent discrete form by writing $dy(t)/dt = [y(kT) - y(kT - T)]/T$, the discrete equivalent equation becomes

$$y(kT) = \frac{81 + 3kT}{81 + 2T + 3kT} 15T + \frac{81 + 3kT}{81 + 2T + 3kT} y(kT - T)$$

For comparison, the values obtained from the exact and the discrete equations are tabulated:

t min	$y(t)$	$y(k1)$	$y(k0.1)$
0	20.00	34.16	21.45
10	152.25	162.80	153.32
20	268.90	277.44	269.76
30	377.49	384.74	378.23

■

†2.8 Digital Simulation of Higher-Order Differential Equations

Because more complicated linear systems can be described by higher-order linear differential equations, it is desired to develop the equivalent digital representations of different-order derivatives. This development yields

$$\frac{dy(t)}{dt} \doteq \frac{y(kT) - y(kT - T)}{T} \tag{2.91a}$$

$$\frac{d^2y(t)}{dt^2} = \frac{d}{dt}\frac{dy(t)}{dt} \doteq \frac{y(kT) - 2y[(k-1)T] + 2y[(k-2)T]}{T^2} \tag{2.91b}$$

$$\frac{d^3y(t)}{dt^3} \doteq \frac{y(kT) - 3y[(k-1)T] + 3y[(k-2)T] - y[(k-3)T]}{T^3} \tag{2.91c}$$

In general, the nth derivative is approximated by the relationship

$$\left.\frac{d^ny(t)}{dt^n}\right|_{t=kT} \doteq \frac{1}{T^n} \sum_{i=0}^{n} (-1)^i \binom{n}{i} y[(k-i)T] \tag{2.91d}$$

where the bionomial coefficient is given by

$$\binom{n}{i} = \frac{n(n-1)(n-2)\cdots(n-i+1)}{i!} \tag{2.91e}$$

† Section is mathematically complex.

The values of initial conditions are determined from those values specified for the continuous system. For example, given the values of $y(t)$ and $dy(t)/dt$ at $t = 0$, the required value of $y(-1)$ can be obtained approximately from the relationship

$$\left.\frac{dy(t)}{dt}\right|_{t=0} = \frac{dy(0)}{dt} = \frac{y(0T) - y[(0-1)T]}{T}$$

or

$$y(-T) = y(0) - T\,\frac{dy(0)}{dt} \tag{2.92}$$

Following such a procedure, the value of $y(-nT)$ can be obtained from $d^n y(0)/dt^n$ by proceeding from the lower- to higher-order derivatives using those values already found for $y(0T), y(-T), \ldots, y(-n+1)T$.

■ **Example 2.19** ***Bioengineering***

The system shown in Figure 2.37a represents an idealized model of a stiff human limb as a step in assessing the passive control process of the locomotive action. It is required to find the movement of the system if the input torque is given by $\mathcal{T}(t) = e^{-t}u(t)$. We also assume that friction during the movement is specified by the friction constant D. The initial conditions of the system are zero—that is, $\theta(0) = d\theta(0)/dt = 0$. Compare the analog solution with the corresponding digital solution.

Solution By an application of D'Alembert's principle, which requires that the algebraic sum of torques must be zero at a node, we write

$$\mathcal{T} = \mathcal{T}_g + \mathcal{T}_D + \mathcal{T}_J \tag{2.93}$$

where

$$\mathcal{T} = \text{input torque}$$
$$\mathcal{T}_g = \text{gravity torque} = Mgl \sin\theta$$
$$\mathcal{T}_D = \text{frictional torque} = D\omega = D\,\frac{d\theta}{dt}$$
$$\mathcal{T}_J = \text{inertial torque} = J\,\frac{d\omega}{dt} = J\,\frac{d^2\theta}{dt^2}$$

The equation that describes the system is

$$J\,\frac{d^2\theta(t)}{dt^2} + D\,\frac{d\theta(t)}{dt} + Mgl \sin\theta(t) = \mathcal{T}(t) \tag{2.94}$$

This equation is seen to be nonlinear owing to the presence of the sin $\theta(t)$ term in the expression for $\mathcal{T}_g$. However, if we assume small deflections ($\theta \le 30°$), we can approximate sin θ by θ. Under these conditions, (2.94) becomes

$$J\,\frac{d^2\theta(t)}{dt^2} + D\,\frac{d\theta(t)}{dt} + Mgl\theta(t) = \mathcal{T}_{(t)} \tag{2.95}$$

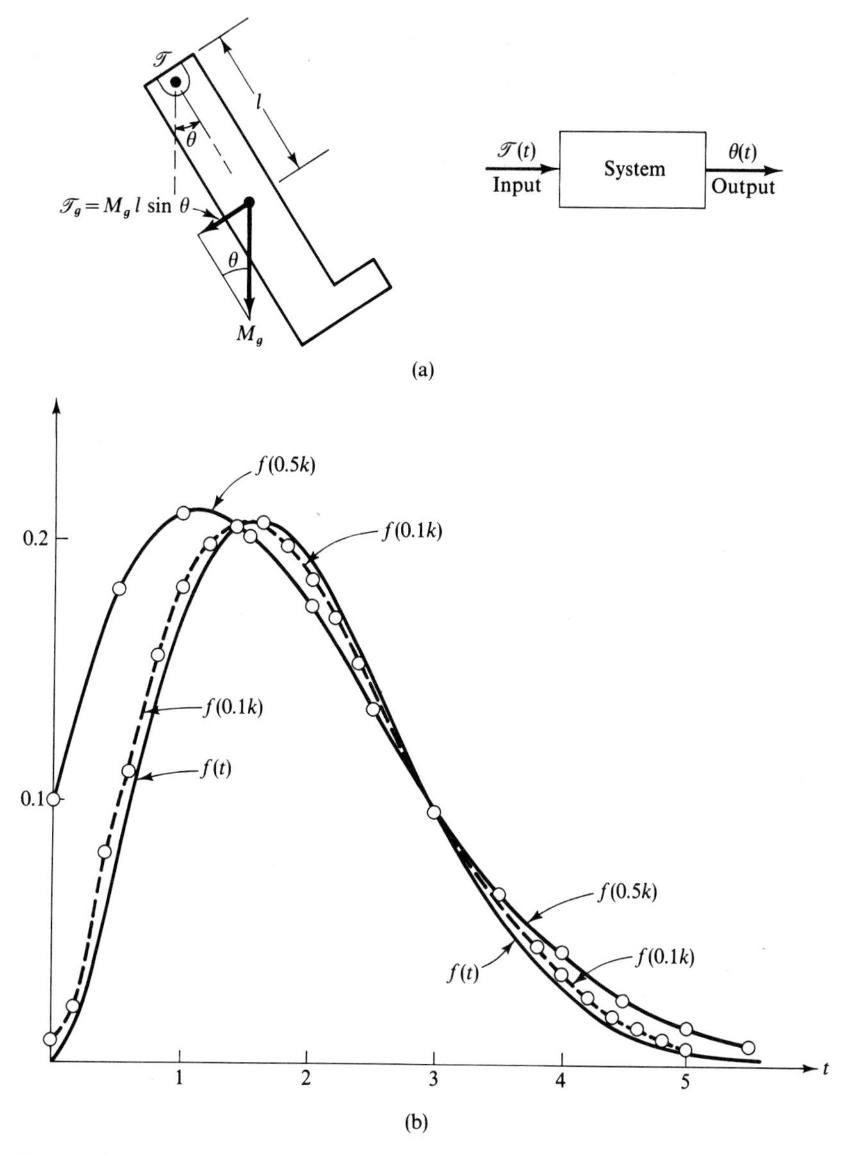

Figure 2.37 Model of Human Limb. (a) Modeling of the movement of a stiff human limb. (b) Continuous time and discrete simulation response for 0.1 and 0.5.

For the specific constants $J = 1$, $D = 2$, and $Mgl = 2$, the equation under survey becomes

$$\frac{d^2\theta(t)}{dt^2} + 2\frac{d\theta(t)}{dt} + 2\theta(t) = e^{-t}u(t) \qquad \textbf{(2.96)}$$

This is a second-order differential equation; hence, its solution must contain two arbitrary constants, the values of which will be determined from specified initial conditions.

We first find the homogeneous solution from the homogeneous equation. If we assume a solution of the form $\theta_h = Ce^{\lambda t}$, the solution requirement is

$$\lambda^2 + 2\lambda + 2 = 0$$

from which we find the roots $\lambda_1 = -1 + j$ and $\lambda_2 = -1 - j$. The homogeneous solution is, therefore,

$$\theta_h(t) = C_1 e^{\lambda_1 t} + C_2 e^{\lambda_2 t} \tag{2.97}$$

where C_1 and C_2 are the arbitrary constants of integration.

To find the particular solution, we assume a trial solution for (2.96) of the form $\theta_p(t) = Ae^{-t}$. By combining this assumed solution with (2.96), we obtain

$$Ae^{-t} - 2Ae^{-t} + 2Ae^{-t} = e^{-t} \qquad \text{Thus, } A = 1$$

The total solution is

$$\theta(t) = \theta_h(t) + \theta_p(t) = C_1 e^{\lambda_1 t} + C_2 e^{\lambda_2 t} + e^{-t} \tag{2.98}$$

We now apply the initial conditions that require

$$\theta(0) = C_1 e^{\lambda_1 0} + C_2 e^{\lambda_2 0} + e^{-0} = C_1 + C_2 + 1 = 0$$

$$\frac{d\theta(0)}{dt} = C_1 \lambda_1 e^{\lambda_1 0} + C_2 \lambda_2 e^{\lambda_2 0} - e^{-0} = C_1 \lambda_1 + C_2 \lambda_2 - 1 = 0$$

We solve these two equations for C_1 and C_2, with the results

$$C_1 = \frac{1 + \lambda_2}{\lambda_1 - \lambda_2} \qquad \text{and} \qquad C_2 = \frac{1 + \lambda_1}{\lambda_1 - \lambda_2}$$

Introduce these values into (2.98), and the final solution is

$$\theta(t) = -\frac{1}{2} e^{-t} e^{jt} - \frac{1}{2} e^{-t} e^{-jt} + e^{-t} = (1 - \cos t)e^{-t} \qquad t > 0 \tag{2.99}$$

The digital simulation of (2.96) is deduced by employing (2.91a) and (2.91b) in this expression. We obtain

$$\frac{\theta(kT) - 2\theta[(k-1)T] + \theta[(k-2)T]}{T^2} + 2\frac{\theta(kT) - \theta[(k-t)T]}{T} + 2\theta(kT) = e^{-kT} \qquad k = 0, 1, 2, \ldots \tag{2.100}$$

After rearrangement, this equation becomes

$$\theta(kT) = \frac{2 + 2T}{1 + 2T + 2T^2}\theta[(k-1)T] - \frac{1}{1 + 2T + 2T^2}\theta[(k-2)T] + \frac{T^2}{1 + 2T + 2T^2}e^{-kT} \qquad k = 0, 1, 2, \ldots \tag{2.101}$$

The solution to this equation is obtained recursively, as in previous examples. The continuous and simulated discrete solutions for $T = 0.5$ and $T = 0.1$ are shown in Figure 2.37b. ∎

Convolution and Correlation

2.9 Convolution of Continuous Time Signals

In the discussion earlier in the chapter of the response of systems to specified forcing functions, two techniques were discussed: the method of variation of parameters and standard methods of differential equations. Both methods are restricted to continuous time systems. It was noted at that time that convolution integral techniques also exist. For discrete time systems, we studied an iterative solution of the related difference equations. This section demonstrates that a discrete convolution solution is also possible.

Convolution plays a significant role in communications, signal detection, and in other fields, such as spectral analysis of atomic emission in physics and chemistry. The importance of the convolution integral in system studies stems from the fact that a knowledge of the output of a linear time-invariant system to an impulse (delta) function excitation allows us to find its output to any input function (subject to some mild restrictions). Further, we will later find that the convolution property can be used to find the Fourier transform of signals without taking their Fourier transform.

In an initial development of the convolution integral, let us begin with the properties of the delta function (see Section 1.3). The delta function allows any well-behaved function $f(t)$ to be represented by

$$f(t) = \int_{-\infty}^{\infty} f(\tau)\delta(t - \tau)\, d\tau \tag{2.102}$$

If we divide the time axis into intervals of width ΔT, then this integral is represented approximately by the sum

$$f(t) = \lim_{\Delta T \to 0} \sum_{k=-\infty}^{\infty} f(k\Delta T)\delta(t - k\Delta T)\Delta T \tag{2.103}$$

This expression states that the function $f(t)$, which is shown in Figure 2.38a, can be approximated by the pulse train with varying heights, which combine to $f_a(t)$, as shown in Figure 2.38b. In the limit, as $\Delta T \to 0$, then $f_a(t) \to f(t)$.

Now, we define response of a causal and LTI system to an impulse input $(t - k\Delta T)$ as $h(t - k\Delta T)$. Further, we define the output of a system as $g(t)$ if its input is $f(t)$. By (2.103) and the superposition property of LTI systems, we write

$$g(t) = \lim_{\Delta T \to 0} \sum_{k=-\infty}^{\infty} f(k\Delta T)h(t - k\Delta T)\, \Delta T$$

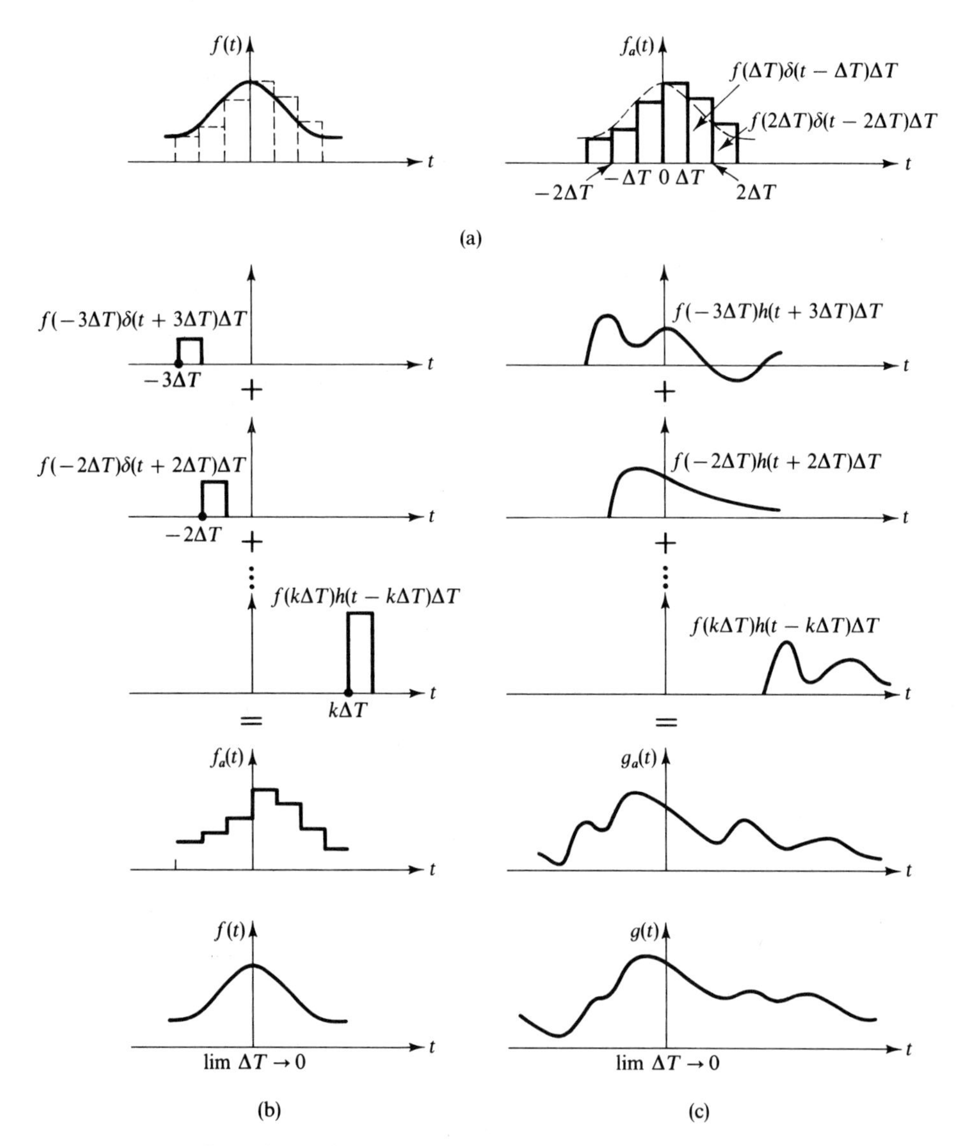

Figure 2.38 Illustrating the Convolution Integral and the Response of a Continuous Time LTI System

In the limit, as $\Delta T \to 0$, the summation becomes an integral of the form

$$g(t) = \int_{-\infty}^{\infty} f(\tau)h(t - \tau)\, d\tau \qquad \textbf{(2.104)}$$

This expression is the **convolution integral**. The process of building up the output given $f_a(t)$ and $h(t - k\Delta T)$ is shown graphically in Figure 2.38c.

The convolution process is now introduced in a more formal manner. Let us represent an LTI system as an equivalent operator $\mathcal{O}$. Clearly, the operator $\mathcal{O}$ denotes a linear process in the variable t that operates on the input function to yield the system response. In actual systems, the operator $\mathcal{O}\{\cdot\}$ can be a differentiator d/dt, an integrator $\int dt$, a multiplier (amplifier), or a combination of all. We write this operation

$$g(t) = \mathcal{O}\{f(t)\} \tag{2.105}$$

Further, we make use of (2.102), which specifies $f(t)$ as an infinite sum of weighted impulses. Thus,

$$g(t) = \mathcal{O}\left\{\int_{-\infty}^{\infty} f(\tau)\delta(t-\tau)\, d\tau\right\} = \int_{-\infty}^{\infty} f(\tau)\mathcal{O}\{\delta(t-\tau)\}\, d\tau$$

Observe that the integration is over the variable τ. Thus, finally,

$$g(t) = \int_{-\infty}^{\infty} f(\tau)h(t-\tau)\, d\tau$$

which is the convolution integral given by (2.104). This expression employed the definition $\mathcal{O}\{\delta(t)\} = h(t)$, the system response to an impulse function. Because the system is time invariant, $\mathcal{O}\{\delta(t-\tau)\} = h(t-\tau)$ for a shifted delta input, and the response to $f(\tau)\delta(t-\tau)$ is $f(t)h(t-\tau)$. By superposition, the response for all t is that given by (2.104).

Convolution is a general mathematical operation that applies when $h(t)$ and $f(t)$ are any two real-valued functions and need not necessarily be aspects of systems. Thus, for any two real-valued functions $h(t)$ and $f(t)$, their convolution, indicated mathematically by the asterisk between the functions, is given by

$$g(t) \triangleq f(t) * h(t) = \int_{-\infty}^{\infty} f(\tau)h(t-\tau)\, d\tau = \int_{-\infty}^{\infty} f(t-\tau)h(\tau)\, d\tau \tag{2.106}$$

Observe from this definition that $f(t) * h(t) = h(t) * f(t)$—that is, convolution is a commutative operation (see Problem 47).

■ Example 2.20

Deduce the convolution of the following two functions: $f(t) = e^{-t}u(t)$ and $h(t) = e^{-0.5t}u(t)$.

Solution First, we observe from (2.105) that one of the functions is unchanged when it is mapped from the t domain to the τ domain. The second function is reversed or folded over (mirrored with respect to the vertical axis) in the τ domain, and it is shifted by an amount t, which is just a parameter in the integrand. Figures 2.39a and 2.39b show the two functions in the t and τ

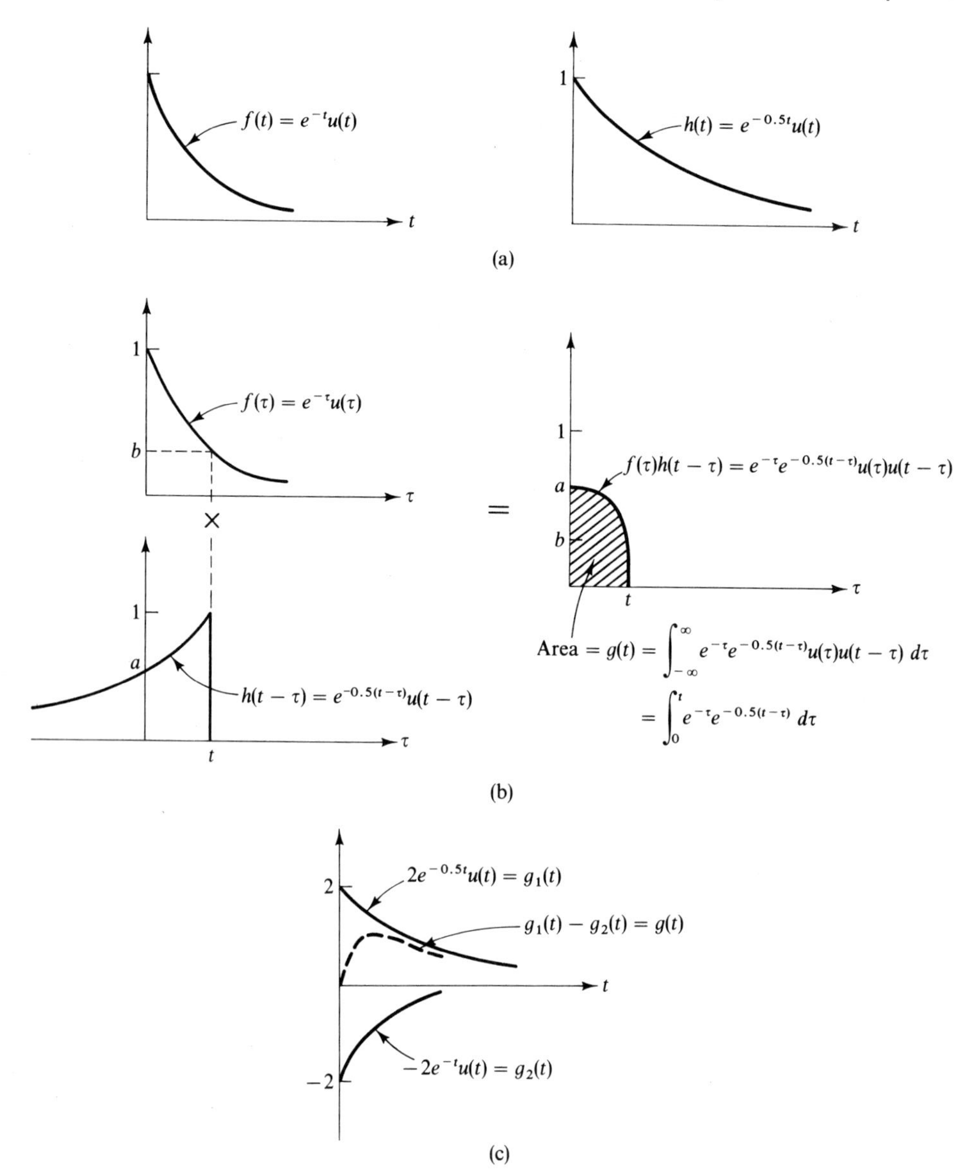

Figure 2.39 Illustrating Example 2.20

domains, respectively. We now write

$$g(t) = f(t) * h(t) = \int_{-\infty}^{\infty} e^{-\tau}u(\tau)e^{-0.5(t-\tau)}u(t-\tau)\,d\tau = \int_0^t e^{-\tau}e^{-0.5(t-\tau)}\,d\tau$$

$$= e^{-0.5t}\int_0^t e^{-0.5\tau}\,d\tau = 2(e^{-0.5t} - e^{-t})$$

This result is shown in Figure 2.39c. Observe that the resulting function is smoother than either of the two functions in the convolution process. This smoothing effect is a fundamental property of the convolution process. ■

■ Example 2.21

Discuss the convolution of the pulse functions $p_a(t)$ and $p_{2a}(t)$.

Solution Refer to Figure 2.40a, which shows the overlapping of the two pulse functions for different values of t. Figure 2.40b shows the resulting function $g(t)$. The points on the curve represent the values of the integrals at the values of t shown in Figure 2.40a. Since the two rectangular pulses have unit amplitudes, the value of $g(t)$ is equal to the area of overlap. Observe that the resulting function is smoother than either of the convolving functions, a feature already noted. ■

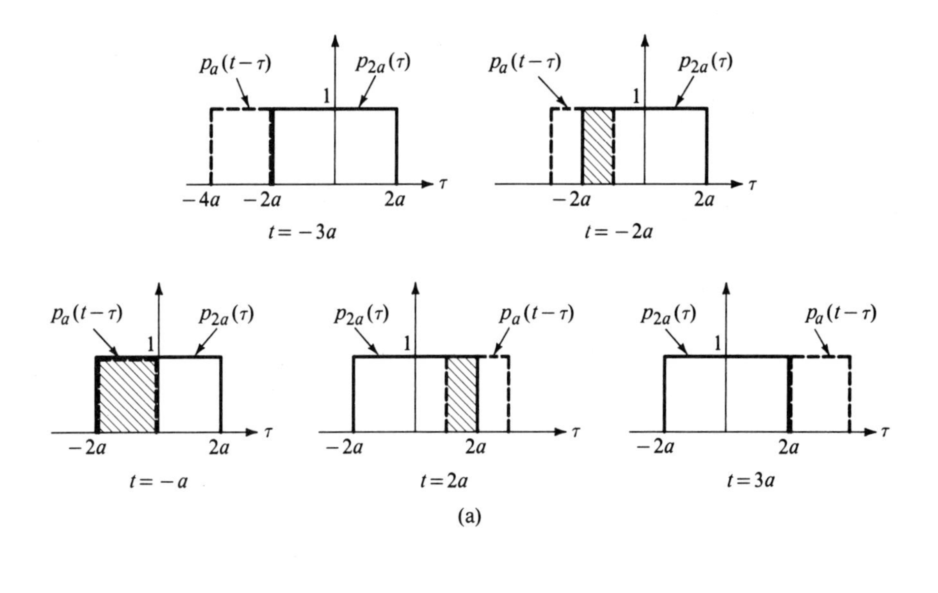

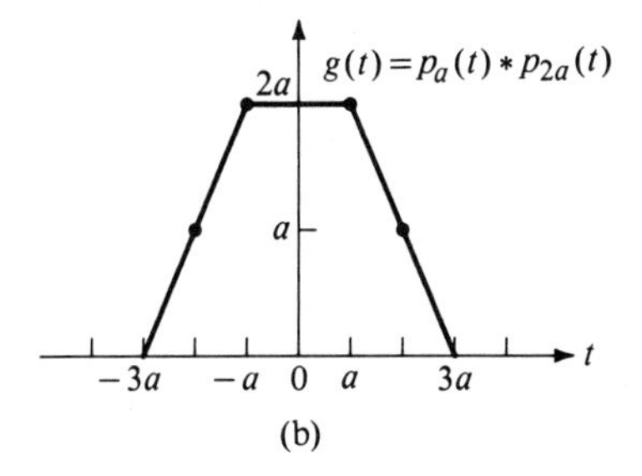

Figure 2.40 Graphical Representation of the Convolution of Two Unit Pulse Functions

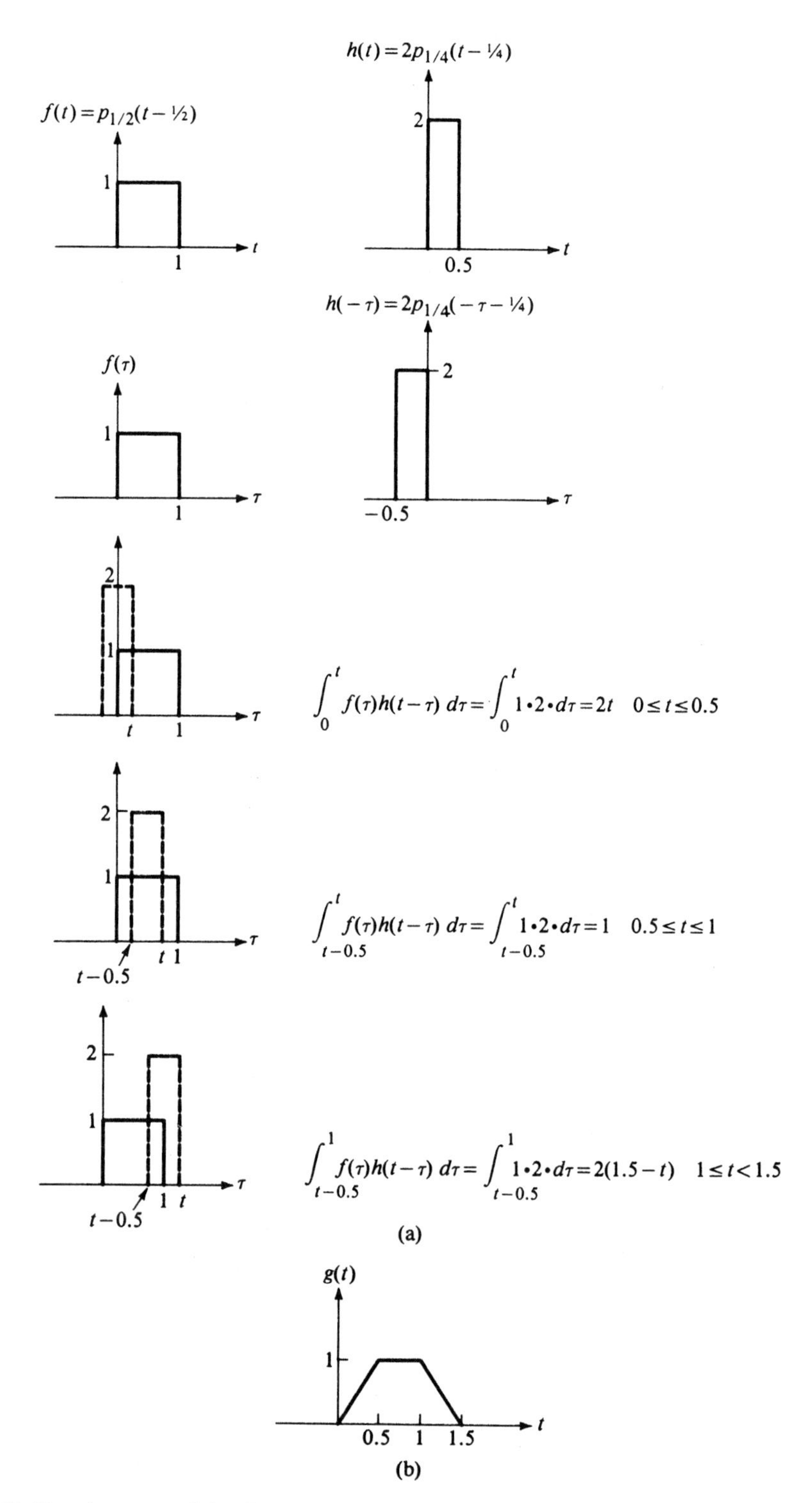

Figure 2.41 Development of the Convolution of Two Rectangular Pulses

Example 2.22

Determine the convolution $g(t) = p_a(t) * \delta(r - 2a)$.

Solution This convolution, in integral form, is

$$g(t) = \int_{-\infty}^{\infty} p_a(\tau)\delta(t - 2a - \tau)\, d\tau$$

By the use of the properties of the delta function, we proceed as follows: Set $t - 2a - \tau = 0$, from which $\tau = t - 2a$. Next, introduce this value into the $p_a(\tau)$ function. The resulting function is given by

$$g(t) = p_a(t - 2a)$$

This shows that we have recaptured the function $p_a(t)$, although it is shifted to the point where the delta function was located. ■

Example 2.23

Determine the convolution of the function $g(t) = p_{1/2}[t - (1/2)] * 2p_{1/2}[t - (1/4)]$.

Solution Figure 2.41 includes the details of the solution. ■

A number of important observations relative to convolution can be deduced:

1. If $f(t) = 0$ for $t < 0$, then $f(t) * h(t) = \int_0^\infty f(\tau)h(t - \tau)\, d\tau$ [see Figure 2.42a for the special case when $f(t) = e^{-t}u(t)$ and $h(t) = \text{sinc } t = \sin t/t$].

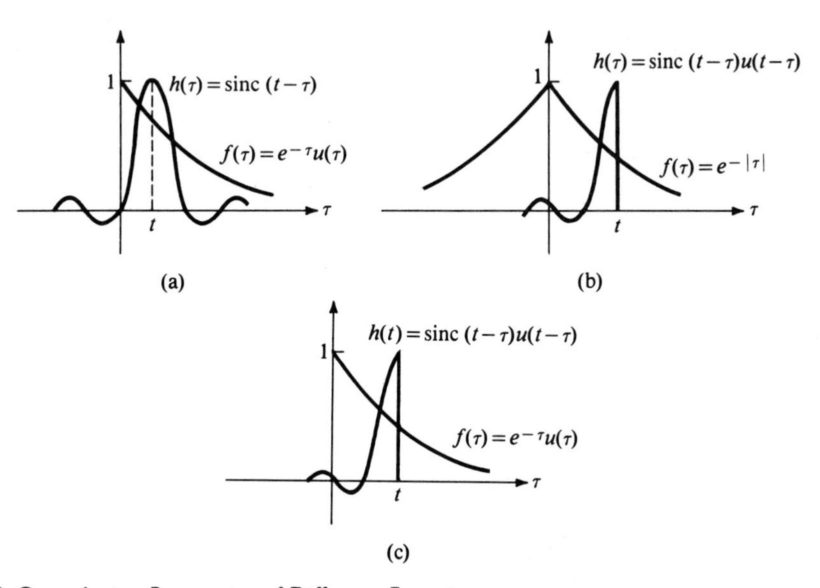

Figure 2.42 Convolution Properties of Different Functions

2. For $h(t-\tau)=0$ for $\tau > t$, the convolution integral is given by $\int_{-\infty}^{t} f(\tau)h(t-\tau)\,d\tau$ (see Figure 2.42b).
3. For causal systems, $h(t)=0$ for $t<0$ and $f(t)=0$ for $t<0$. Causality implies that $h(t-\tau)=0$ for $\tau>t$ and $h(\tau)=0$ for $\tau<0$. Their convolution is given by $\int_{0}^{t} f(\tau)h(t-\tau)\,d\tau$ (see Figure 2.42c).

When applied to a causal system, the response can never precede the input. In the manner discussed in connection with (2.106), we can split the convolution integral into two parts:

$$g(t) \triangleq f(t) * h(t) = \underbrace{\int_{-\infty}^{t_{0-}} f(\tau)h(t-\tau)\,d\tau}_{g_{zi}(t)} + \underbrace{\int_{t_{0-}}^{t} f(\tau)h(t-\tau)\,d\tau}_{g_{zs}(t)}$$
$$= g_{zi}(t) + g_{zs}(t) \tag{2.107}$$

The function $g_{zi}(t)$ is the *zero-input* response of the system, and $g_{zs}(t)$ is the *zero-state* response of the system, where t_0 is arbitrarily taken as the initial time. The symbol t_{0-} indicates that functions with finite discontinuities are included in the definition of the zero-state response.

The second convolution integral $g_{zs}(t)$ represents the zero-state response of the system. This integral specifies that at time $t=t_0$, the system was relaxed—that is, there were no charges on capacitors, no currents through inductors, no deformation of springs, no velocities of masses, and so on. However, if the initial state of the system is not zero, we must add a zero-input response produced by the initial state at $t=t_0$. That is, the first integral is the response at time t caused by the initial state (see also Section 2.3). This integral, $g_{zi}(t)$, specifies that the state at $t=t_0$ depends on the inputs prior to that time. Thus, if a force (input) is applied to a body (system) at time $t=t_0$, the motion of the body for $t \geq t_0$ is uniquely determined if we know its position and velocity at $t=t_0$, and it is immaterial how the body attained these initial values.

It is important to note that the convolution $g(t)=f(t) * h(t)$ does not exist for all possible functions $f(t)$ and $h(t)$. Any of the following conditions is sufficient to insure existence:

1. Both $f(t)$ and $h(t)$ must be absolutely integrable on the interval $(-\infty, 0]$.
2. Both $f(t)$ and $h(t)$ must be absolutely integrable on the interval $[0, \infty)$.
3. Either $f(t)$ or $h(t)$ (or both) must be absolutely integrable on the interval $(-\infty, \infty)$.

For example, the convolution $\cos\omega_0 t * \cos\omega_0 t$ does not exist.

■ Example 2.24

Show, by applying the convolution integral, that $[f_1(t) * f_2(t)] * f_3(t) = f_1(t) * [f_2(t) * f_3(t)] = h(t)$ for the functions shown in Figure 2.43a. This relationship is the *associative* property of the convolution integral.

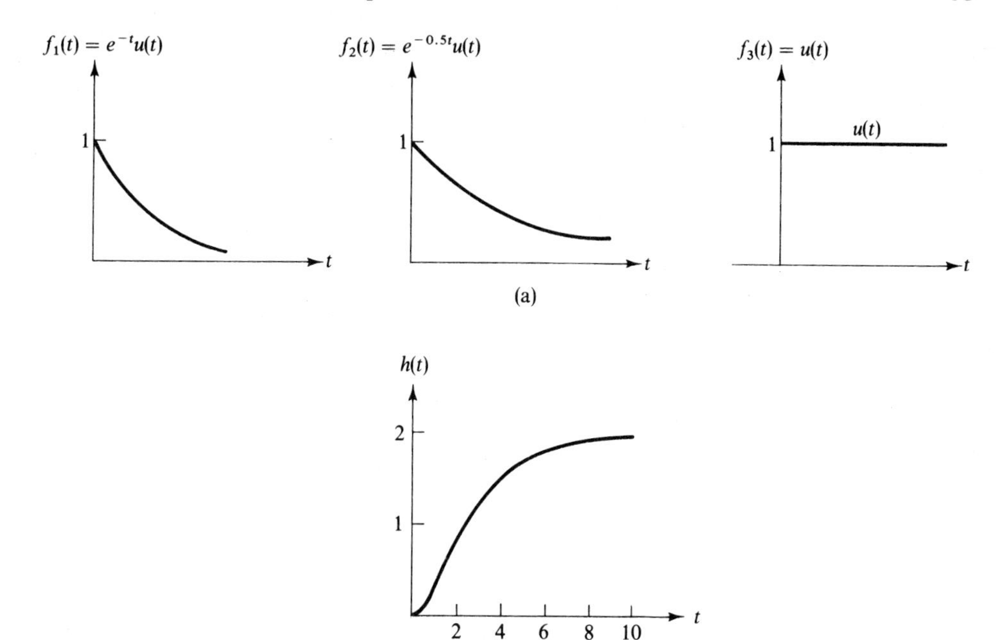

Figure 2.43 Illustrating Example 2.24

Solution We found in Example 2.20 that

$$g(t) = f_1(t) * f_2(t) = 2(e^{-0.5t} - e^{-t})u(t)$$

Therefore, $h(t) = g(t) * f_3(t)$ is given by

$$h(t) = \int_{-\infty}^{\infty} g(\tau)f_3(t - \tau)\, d\tau = 2\int_{-\infty}^{\infty} (e^{-0.5\tau} - e^{-\tau})u(\tau)u(t - \tau)\, d\tau$$

However, $u(t - \tau) = 0$ for $t < \tau$ and $u(\tau) = 0$ for $\tau < 0$, so this integral becomes

$$h(t) = 2\int_0^t (e^{-0.5\tau} - e^{-\tau})\, d\tau = (2 - 4e^{-0.5t} + 2e^{-t})u(t)$$

Now, we consider the alternate form. Begin with the convolution

$$f_2(t) * f_3(t) = \int_{-\infty}^{\infty} e^{-0.5\tau}u(\tau)u(t - \tau)\, d\tau = \int_0^t e^{-0.5\tau}\, d\tau = (2 - 2e^{-0.5t})u(t)$$

Then

$$h(t) = \int_{-\infty}^{\infty} (2 - 2e^{-0.5\tau})u(\tau)e^{-(t-\tau)}u(t - \tau)\, d\tau = e^{-t}\int_0^t (2e^{\tau} - 2e^{0.5\tau})\, d\tau$$

$$h(t) = (2 - 4e^{-0.5t} + 2e^{-t})u(t)$$

The two relationships for these particular functions are identical. It can be shown that the associative property is true for all functions obeying the sufficient conditions stated above. The resulting function $h(t)$ is shown in Figure 2.43b. ■

An important input function in system studies is $f(t) = e^{j\omega t}$. In this case, the output of a linear time-invariant system is

$$g(t) = \int_{-\infty}^{\infty} h(\tau)f(t-\tau)\,d\tau = \int_{-\infty}^{\infty} h(\tau)e^{j\omega t(t-\tau)}\,d\tau = e^{j\omega t}\int_{-\infty}^{\infty} h(\tau)e^{-j\omega\tau}\,d\tau$$

$$g_t = e^{j\omega t}H(\omega) \tag{2.108a}$$

where

$$H(\omega) = \int_{-\infty}^{\infty} h(\tau)e^{-j\omega t}\,d\tau \tag{2.108b}$$

and where $H(\omega)$ is the **system function**. This relation for $H(\omega)$ is called the Fourier transform of the impulse response of the system (discussed in Chapter 4). Also in this context, $e^{j\omega t}$ is the **eigenfunction** of the system and $H(\omega)$ is the **eigenvalue**.

This equation is of fundamental importance because it tells us that if we know the system function (eigenvalue) of a system, we can find its output to any input function by appropriately modifying the phase and amplitude of the sine and cosine functions that when added, construct the input function. In a linear time-invariant system that has a real-valued impulse response $h(t)$, the eigenvalues $H(\omega)$ are **Hermitian**—that is, the real part of $H(\omega)$ is even and the imaginary part is odd. This property is expressed by

$$H(\omega) = H^*(-\omega) \tag{2.109}$$

■ **Example 2.25**

Suppose that the input to a linear time-invariant system is the function $f(t) = \cos\omega t = \mathrm{Re}\{e^{j\omega t}\} = \mathrm{Re}\{\tilde{f}(t)\}$, where $\tilde{f}(t) = \cos\omega t + j\sin\omega t$ is a complex-valued function. Find the corresponding response for a given $h(t)$.

Solution By (2.106),

$$g(t) = \int_{-\infty}^{\infty} h(\tau)\cos\omega(t-\tau)\,d\tau = \int_{-\infty}^{\infty} h(\tau)\mathrm{Re}\{e^{j\omega(t-\tau)}\}\,d\tau$$

$$= \int \mathrm{Re}\left\{e^{j\omega t}\int_{-\infty}^{\infty} h(\tau)e^{-j\omega\tau}\,d\tau\right\} = Re\{e^{j\omega t}H(\omega)\}$$

To see that the exchange of the integral and Re{ } is valid, let us consider a specific example. We examine the expressions

$$\int \mathrm{Re}\{e^{j\omega t}\}\,dt = \int \cos\omega t\,dt = \frac{1}{\omega}\sin\omega t$$

and

$$\text{Re}\left\{\int e^{j\omega t}\, dt\right\} = \text{Re}\left\{\frac{1}{j\omega} e^{j\omega t}\right\} = \text{Re}\left\{-j\frac{1}{\omega}\cos\omega t + \frac{1}{\omega}\sin\omega t\right\} = \frac{1}{\omega}\sin\omega t$$

Even though this illustration is for a specific example, the principle applies to any integrable complex function. The reader should show that $(d/dt)[\text{Re}\{f(t)\}] = \text{Re}\{df(t)/dt\}$.

The system function $H(\omega)$ is a complex-valued function in general. It can be represented in the general form

$$H(\omega) = H_r(\omega) + jH_i(\omega) = |H(\omega)|\, e^{j\varphi(\omega)} \qquad \textbf{(2.110a)}$$

where $H_r(\omega)$ and $H_i(\omega)$ are real-valued functions and where

$$H(\omega) = [H_r^2(\omega) + H_i^2(\omega)]^{1/2} \qquad \textbf{(2.110b)}$$

$$\varphi(\omega) = \tan^{-1}[H_i(\omega)/H_r(\omega)] \qquad \textbf{(2.110c)}$$

The output is now written in the form

$$g(t) = \text{Re}\{e^{j\omega t}H(\omega)\} \triangleq \text{Re}\{\tilde{g}(t)\} = |H(\omega)| \cos[\omega t + \varphi(\omega)]$$

These results show that if

$$\tilde{f}(t) = e^{j\omega t} \qquad \text{then} \qquad \tilde{g}(t) = H(\omega)e^{j\omega t} = |H(\omega)|\, e^{j[\omega t + \varphi(\omega)]}$$

We see that if the input is a cosine function, the output is also a cosine function, but it has been effected by a change in amplitude and a shift in phase, as already suggested. ■

A reasonable question is whether, given $g(t)$ and $f(t)$, it would be possible to deduce $h(t)$. This process, known as *deconvolution*, is often encountered in electromagnetic measurements while measuring the impulse response of a system or device. However, deconvolution has no direct mathematical definition in the time domain and merely connotes the inverse of the convolution operation. Owing to errors and noise associated with practical measurements, the exact knowledge of deconvolved time signals is not possible, and approximation must be made. The deconvolution process lends itself to better interpretation in the frequency domain, where it becomes an approximation and filtering problem.

2.10 Impulse Response

As discussed above, we require a knowledge of $h(t)$ if we are to apply convolution techniques to the solution of system problems with general excitation functions. The following sequence arises from the system description:

$$g(t) = \mathcal{O}\{f(t)\} \qquad \textbf{(2.111)}$$

where $\mathscr{O}$ denotes the system operator, with $\mathscr{O}^{-1}\{g(t)\}$ denoting the controlling differential equation of the system. By definition, $h(t)$ is the response function when $f(t) = \delta(t)$ and the system is relaxed—that is,

$$h(t) = \mathscr{O}\{\delta(t)\} \tag{2.112}$$

However, $\delta(t)$ exists only at $t = 0$; then, we split the problem into two parts:

$$h(t)\Big|_{t=0} = \mathscr{O}\{\delta(t)\} \tag{2.113a}$$

$$h(t)\Big|_{t>0} = \mathscr{O}\{0\} \tag{2.113b}$$

Note that (2.113a) provides information about features of $h(t)$ only at $t = 0$ and so provides initial conditions on $h(t)$ that can be used in the solution of the resulting homogeneous differential equation in $h(t)$ specified by (2.113b).

A second approach is to use the fact that the impulse response $h(t)$ of a system is the time derivative of the response of the system to a unit step function $y_u(t)$. This response function is given the name **indicial response**. Symbolically,

$$y_u(t) = \mathscr{O}\{u(t)\} \tag{2.114a}$$

$$h(t) = \frac{d}{dt}\, y_u(t) \tag{2.114b}$$

Later chapters show that $h(t)$ can be determined by Fourier-transforming or Laplace-transforming the system differential equation with a delta function excitation and then finding the corresponding inverse transform. Here, examples are given of the methods of procedure specified by (2.113) and (2.114).

■ **Example 2.26**

Find the zero-input and zero-state response of the system described in Example 2.3. The initial condition for the velocity is $v(0) = 2$, the input force is $f(t) = e^{-100t}$ for $t > 0$, and the mass M and friction coefficient D are 1 and 0.1, respectively.

Solution The differential equation that describes the system is given by [see (2.33)]

$$\frac{dy}{dt} + 0.1v = f(t) \tag{2.115}$$

We apply the requirements of (2.113a) by multiplying all terms in the differential equation by dt and integrating from $0-$ to $0+$, with $f(t) = \delta(t)$. We obtain

$$\int_{0-}^{0+} \frac{dh}{dt}\, dt + \int_{0-}^{0+} 0.1h\, dt = \int_{0-}^{0+} \delta(t)\, dt \tag{2.116}$$

from which

$$h(0+) - h(0-) + 0.1 \int_{0-}^{0+} h(t)\, dt = \int_{0-}^{0+} \delta(t)\, dt = 1$$

using the known property of the delta function. The second term vanishes because $h(t)$ does not possess an infinite discontinuity at $t = 0$. Further, the system was relaxed at $t = 0$ and, therefore, $h(0-) = 0$. Thus, we have that

$$h(0+) = 1$$

An application of (2.113b) requires that we solve the differential equation

$$\frac{dh(t)}{dt} + 0.1h(t) = 0$$

This has the solution

$$h(t) = Ae^{-0.1t} \qquad t > 0$$

Using the known form for $h(0+)$, it follows that $A = 1$. The impulse response of the system is

$$h(t) = e^{-0.1t} \qquad t > 0 \tag{2.117}$$

The units of $h(t)$ are m/s. We adopted the letters $h(t)$ in order to conform to the accepted practice of representing the impulse response function by $h(t)$.

The zero-state response is given by [see (2.106)]

$$v_{zs}(t) = h(t) * f(t) = \int_0^t e^{-0.1\tau} e^{-100(t-\tau)}\, d\tau$$

$$= \frac{1}{99.9}(e^{-0.1t} - e^{-100t}) \qquad t > 0 \tag{2.118}$$

While v_{zi} is given in principle by the first term in (2.106), the forcing function $f(t)$ for $t < 0$ is not known, and we thus proceed directly from the controlling differential equation (2.115) with $f(t) = 0$. The solution to this homogeneous differential equation is

$$v = Be^{-0.1t}$$

Apply the given initial condition $v = 2$ for $t = 0$, which yields $B = 2$, so that

$$v_{zi}(t) = 2e^{-0.1t}u(t)$$

The total solution is [see (2.38)]

$$v(t) = 2e^{-0.1t} + \frac{1}{99.9}(e^{-0.1t} - e^{-100t}) \tag{2.119}$$

■

■ **Example 2.27**

Determine the output of the system shown in Figure 2.44a if the input is a pulse function.

Solution To determine the impulse response function of the system, we first write the controlling differential equation that describes the system. It is

$$\frac{di}{dt} + i = v(t) \qquad v_o(t) = i$$

For a delta function input, we obtain

$$\frac{dh(t)}{dt} + h(t) = \delta(t)$$

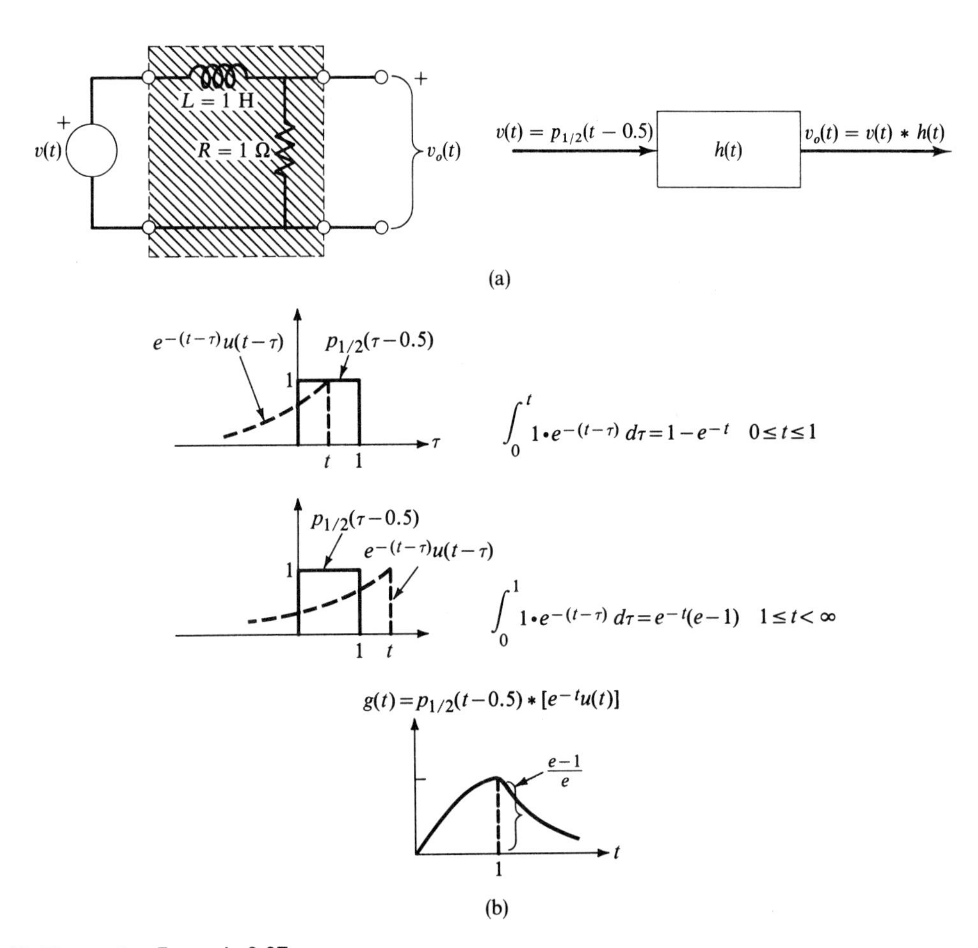

Figure 2.44 Illustrating Example 2.27

where $h(t)$ is actually the current in the circuit due to the delta voltage source. By following the procedure in Example 2.26, we readily obtain

$$h(t) = e^{-t}u(t)$$

By convolution, the system response is

$$y(t) = \begin{cases} 1 - e^{-t} & 0 \le t \le 1 \\ e^{-t}(e - 1) & 1 \le t < \infty \end{cases}$$

The essential details of the convolution evaluation are contained in Figure 2.44b. ■

■ †Example 2.28

Determine the impulse response of an initially relaxed RLC series circuit with $L = 1$ H, $R = 5\ \Omega$, and $C = 0.25$ F.

Solution The integrodifferential equation describing the system is

$$L\frac{di}{dt} + Ri + \frac{1}{C}\int i\, dt = v(t) \qquad \textbf{(2.120)}$$

We write this equation in differential equation form by writing $i = dq/dt$, with the result

$$\frac{d^2q}{dt^2} + 5\frac{dq}{dt} + 4q = v(t) \qquad \textbf{(2.121)}$$

For a δ function input, this equation becomes

$$\frac{d^2h}{dt^2} + 5\frac{dh}{dt} + 4h = \delta(t) \qquad \textbf{(2.122)}$$

First, we establish the initial conditions that permit a solution to this equation. The system is initially relaxed so that

$$\frac{dh(0-)}{dt} = h(0-) = 0 \qquad \textbf{(2.123)}$$

Now, let us integrate (2.122) between the limits $t = 0-$ and $t = 0+$. We thus write

$$\int_{0-}^{0+} \frac{d^2h}{dt^2}\, dt + 5\int_{0-}^{0+} \frac{dh}{dt}\, dt + 4\int_{0-}^{0+} h\, dt = \int_{0-}^{0+} \delta(t)\, dt \qquad \textbf{(2.124)}$$

The third integral is equal to zero because the area under a continuous function from $0-$ to $0+$ is zero. Also, the area under the δ function is unity. The result is

$$\left[\frac{dh(0+)}{dt} - \frac{dh(0-)}{dt}\right] + 5[h(0+) - h(0-)] = 1$$

which becomes, by (2.123),

$$\frac{dh(0+)}{dt} + 5h(0+) = 1 \tag{2.125}$$

Now, we integrate (2.122) twice, which yields

$$\int_{0-}^{0+} \frac{dh}{dt}\,dt + 5\int_{0-}^{0+} h\,dt + 4\iint_{0-}^{0+} h\,dt\,dt = \iint_{0-}^{0+} \delta(t)\,dt\,dt$$

All terms except the first are zero so that

$$h(0+) - h(0-) = 0 \qquad h(0+) = 0 \tag{2.126}$$

Combining (2.125) and (2.126) yields

$$\frac{dh(0+)}{dt} = 1 \tag{2.127}$$

This result indicates that the impulse source forces the current $dq/dt \triangleq dh/dt$ to jump instantaneously—in this case, from 0 to 1—while the charge remains at zero.

We now proceed with the solution of (2.122), noting, as before, that $\delta(t) = 0$ and $t > 0$. Thus, the equation under consideration is

$$\frac{d^2h}{dt^2} + 5\frac{dh}{dt} + 4h = 0 \qquad t > 0 \tag{2.128a}$$

subject to the conditions

$$h(0+) = 0 \qquad \frac{dh(0+)}{dt} = 1 \tag{2.128b}$$

For an assumed solution of the form $h(t) = Ae^{\lambda t}$, the characteristic equation becomes

$$(\lambda^2 + 5\lambda + 4) = 0$$

Thus, a solution exists when λ assumes the values

$$\lambda = \frac{-5 \pm \sqrt{25 - 16}}{2} = \frac{-5 \pm 3}{2} \qquad \lambda_1 = -4,\ \lambda_2 = -1$$

The solution of the homogeneous equation is

$$h(t) = Ae^{-4t} + Be^{-t} \tag{2.129}$$

Introduce the initial conditions into this expression to obtain

$$h(0+) = 0 = A + B$$

$$\frac{dh(0+)}{dt} = 1 = -4A - B$$

From these, we find that $A = -1/3$ and $B = 1/3$. The solution is

$$h(t) \triangleq q(t) = -\frac{1}{3}e^{-4t} + \frac{1}{3}e^{-t} \tag{2.130}$$

■

■ †Example 2.29

Repeat Example 2.28, but now proceeding from (2.120).

Solution We proceed now by writing the equation $[h(t) \triangleq i(t)]$

$$\frac{dh}{dt} + 5h + 4\int h\,dt = \delta(t) \tag{2.131}$$

We consider this equation at two specific instants of time, $t = 0-$ and $t = 0+$, and subtract the two. The result is

$$\left[\frac{dh(0+)}{dt} - \frac{dh(0-)}{dt}\right] + [5h(0+) - 5h(0-)] + 4\int_{0-}^{0+} h\,dt = \delta(t)\Big|_{0-}^{0+}$$

We recall that the δ function has a value only at $t = 0$; thus, $\delta(0+) = \delta(0-) = 0$. Further, the area under the $h(t)$ curve from $0-$ to $0+$ is zero since no impulse function exists in the interval. Because of the conditions $h(0-) = dh(0-)/dt = 0$, we now obtain

$$\frac{dh(0+)}{dt} + 5h(0+) = 0 \tag{2.132}$$

Now we consider the integral of (2.131) over the limits $t = 0-$ and $t = 0+$. This gives

$$\int_{0-}^{0+} \frac{dh}{dt}\,dt + 5\int_{0-}^{0+} h\,dt + 4\int_{0-}^{0+}\left(\int h\,dt\right)dt = \int_{0-}^{0+} \delta(t)\,dt$$

Remembering that the area under the δ function is unity and that $h(t)$ is a smooth function, we then have that

$$h(0+) - h(0-) = 1$$

from which, therefore,

$$h(0+) = 1 \tag{2.133a}$$

Combine this result with (2.132) to get

$$\frac{dh(0+)}{dt} = -5 \tag{2.133b}$$

To find the solution for $h(t)$ for $t > 0$, differentiate (2.131), which yields the differential equation

$$\frac{d^2h}{dt^2} + 5\frac{dh}{dt} + 4h = \frac{d\delta(t)}{dt} = 0$$

Since $\delta(t) = 0$ for $t > 0$, then, also, $d\delta(t)/dt = 0$ for $t > 0$. The resulting differential equation is precisely that given by (2.128a), with the general solution

$$h(t) = Ae^{-4t} + Be^{-t}$$

To find the constants A and B, introduce the initial conditions given by (2.133). This yields the values $A = 4/3$ and $B = -1/3$. The final solution for $h(t)$ is

$$h(t) \triangleq i(t) = \frac{4}{3}e^{-4t} - \frac{1}{3}e^{-t} \qquad t > 0 \tag{2.134}$$

Observe that the derivative of (2.130) yields (2.134), as it should, since $dq/dt = i$. ■

We now consider two examples that proceed in conformity with (2.114).

■ Example 2.30

The node equation describing the relaxed system shown in Figure 2.45a is

$$\frac{dv(t)}{dt} + \frac{v(t)}{RC} = \frac{1}{C}\,i(t) \tag{2.135}$$

Determine the general form of the solution and also the solution to a delayed impulse function current $i(t - t_0)$.

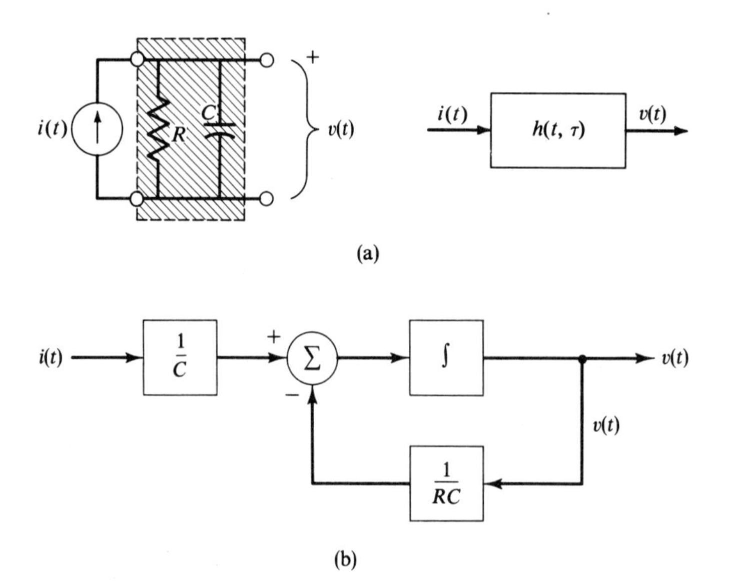

Figure 2.45 Low-Pass Filter

Solution We first consider the step function response of this circuit, which is the solution to

$$\frac{dv(t)}{dt} + \frac{v(t)}{RC} = \frac{1}{C}\,u(t) \tag{2.136}$$

The solution to the homogeneous equation

$$\frac{dv(t)}{dt} + \frac{v(t)}{RC} = 0 \tag{2.137}$$

is obtained by assuming a solution of the form $v_h(t) = Ae^{\lambda t}$. Combining this form with (2.137) yields the value for $\lambda = -1/RC$. Therefore, the homogeneous solution is

$$v_h(t) = Ae^{-t/RC} \tag{2.138}$$

where A is a constant that is to be found from the initial condition.

Now, we consider the particular solution to a step function excitation $u(t)$. This requires the solution of

$$\frac{dy(t)}{dt} + \frac{v(t)}{RC} = \frac{1}{C} \qquad t > 0 \tag{2.139}$$

We observe that the right-hand side is a constant. Hence, we assume that the particular solution is equal to some constant K—that is, $v_p(t) = K$. Introduce this value into (2.139); we obtain

$$\frac{K}{RC} = \frac{1}{C}$$

from which

$$v_p(t) = K = R \tag{2.140}$$

Attention is called to the fact that R is multiplied by unit current; hence, this result is dimensionally correct.

The total solution is

$$v(t) = v_h(t) + v_p(t) = Ae^{-t/RC} + R \tag{2.141}$$

The value of A is deduced by applying the initial condition $v(0+) = 0$ for the relaxed system. As a consequence, we have

$$v(0+) = 0 = Ae^{-(1/RC)0} + R \qquad \text{or} \qquad A = -R$$

The complete solution is

$$v(t) = R(1 - e^{-t/RC}) \qquad t > 0 \tag{2.142}$$

Now, making use of the fact that the impulse response is the time derivative of the step function response, we have

$$h(t) = \frac{dv(t)}{dt} = \frac{1}{C} e^{-t/RC} \qquad t > 0 \tag{2.143}$$

With a knowledge of the impulse response of the system, we can determine its response to an arbitrary input signal $i(t - t_0)$ using the convolution theorem. For the output, we find

$$\int_{-\infty}^{\infty} \frac{1}{C} e^{-(t-\tau)/RC} u(t - \tau) i(\tau - t_0) u(\tau - t_0)\, d\tau = \int_{t_0}^{t} \frac{1}{C} \times e^{-(t-\tau)/RC} u(t - \tau) i(\tau - t_0)\, d\tau$$

To carry out the integration, set $\tau - t_0 = x$, then $d\tau = dx$. In addition, at $\tau = t_0$, $x = 0$, and at $\tau = t$, $x = t - t_0$. We thus obtain

$$\frac{1}{C} \int_{0}^{t-t_0} e^{-[(t-t_0)-\tau]/RC} i(\tau)\, d\tau \triangleq v(t - t_0) \tag{2.144}$$

This equation indicates that the system is time invariant—that is, the quantity $t - t_0$ substitutes for t in (2.135). In other words, a shifted input of t_0 produces a shifted output of t_0. Figure 2.45b is a block diagram representation of (2.135). ■

■ Example 2.31

Find the impulse response of the system shown in Figure 2.46a. Use this result to find the output when the input is the function $p_1(t - 1)$.

Solution Initially, we wish to describe the system in its network representation. Thus, we create a diagram of velocity levels, as shown in Figure 2.46b. We connect the source (force) from the ground velocity to v_1. Since the mass element has a velocity v with respect to ground, we insert the mass element between v and v_g. Similarly, the relative velocity of the damper with respect to ground is v, so we insert the damper element between v and v_g. The resulting circuit is that shown in Figure 2.46c. Note that even though the system appears at first glance to be connected in series, it is actually a parallel combination of elements.

For mechanical circuits, D'Alembert's principle parallels the Kirchhoff current law in electrical circuits. This principle requires that each node be isolated in the analysis and that the $M(dv/dt)$ force be distinguished from the other forces. Doing this yields a **free body** diagram for each portion of the system. The appropriate free body diagram for this example is shown in Figure 2.46d. When using the equivalent network representation for mechanical circuits, it is more convenient to write the mechanical equilibrium equation by including f_M with other forces.

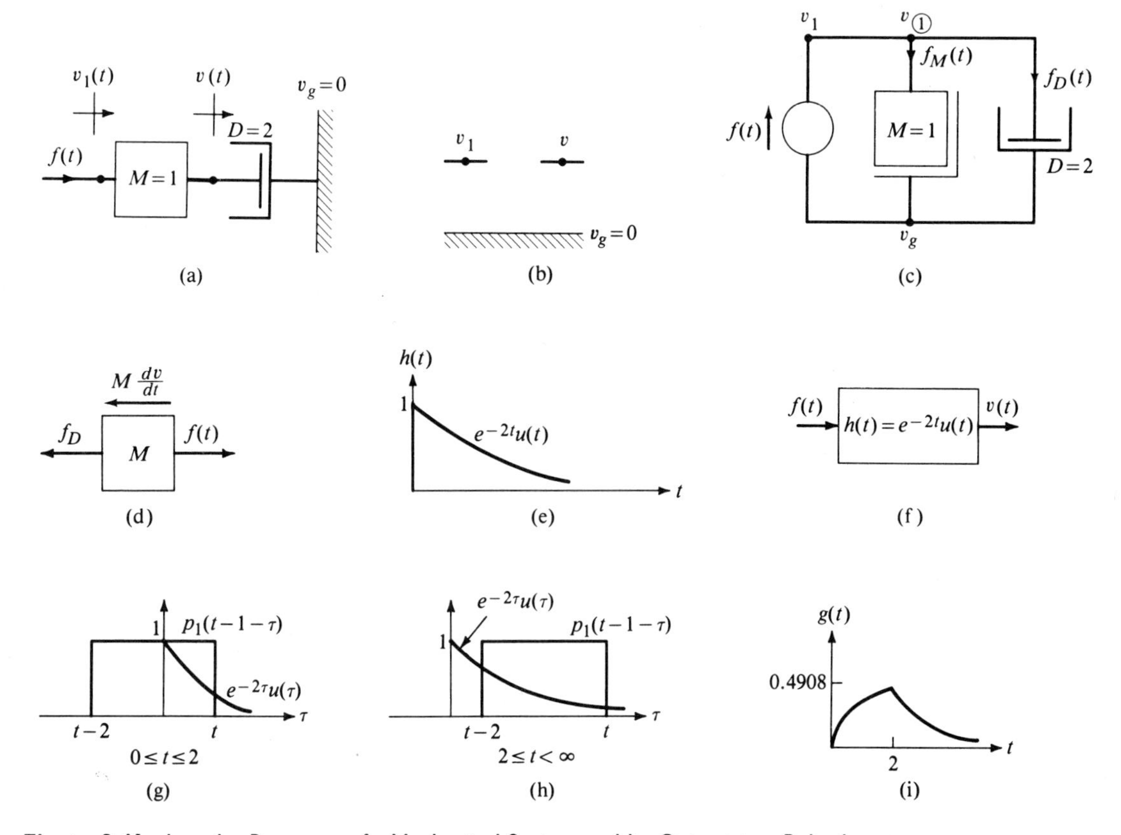

Figure 2.46 Impulse Response of a Mechanical System and Its Output to a Pulse Input

The equilibrium equation is obtained from an examination of Figure 2.46c by an application of the point law at node 1 (note that the *algebraic sum* of the forces equals zero):

$$-f(t) + f_M(t) + f_D(t) = 0 \tag{2.145}$$

Use the relationships for mechanical elements (see Section 2.2) to write this expression in the form

$$\frac{dv}{dt} + 2v = f(t) \tag{2.146}$$

We set $f(t) = u(t)$ and solve the first-order differential equation for initially relaxed conditions $v(0) = 0$. The solution is easily obtained (see Example 2.26) and is

$$v_u(t) = \frac{1}{2}(1 - e^{-2t})u(t) \tag{2.147}$$

The impulse response is then

$$h(t) = \frac{dv_u(t)}{dt} = e^{-2t}u(t) + \frac{1}{2}(1 - e^{-2t})\delta(t)$$

from which

$$h(t) = e^{-2t}u(t) \qquad t \geq 0+ \tag{2.148}$$

This function is shown in Figure 2.46e.

The input pulse to the system and the impulse response of the system are shown in Figures 2.46g and 2.46h. The output signal of the system, which is given by the convolution of these signals, is

$$g(t) = \begin{cases} \displaystyle\int_0^t 1 \cdot e^{-2\tau}\, d\tau = \frac{1}{2} e^{-2\tau}\Big|_0^t = \frac{1}{2}(1 - e^{-2t}) & 0 \leq t \leq 2 \\ \displaystyle\int_{t-2}^t 1 \cdot e^{-2\tau}\, d\tau = -\frac{1}{2} e^{-2\tau}\Big|_{t-2}^t = \frac{1}{2} e^{-2t}(e^4 - 1) & 2 \leq t < \infty \end{cases} \tag{2.149}$$

The output signal is shown in Figure 2.46i. ■

2.11 Convolution of Discrete Time Signals

The impulse response of discrete systems is defined in the same way as defined for continuous time systems. It specifies the output of a digital system $h(k)$ to a delta function excitation

$$\delta(k) = \begin{cases} 1 & k = 0 \\ 0 & \text{otherwise} \end{cases} \tag{2.150}$$

This process is represented by the input–output relationship of a discrete system in the form shown in Figure 2.47. Note that if the response to $\delta(k)$ is $h(k)$, then the response to a shifted delta function $\delta(k - k_0)$ is a shifted impulse response $h(k - k_0)$. Clearly, if the input is of the general form $\sum_{n=0}^{\infty} \delta(k - n)$, the output will be of the form $\sum_{n=0}^{\infty} h(k - n)$.

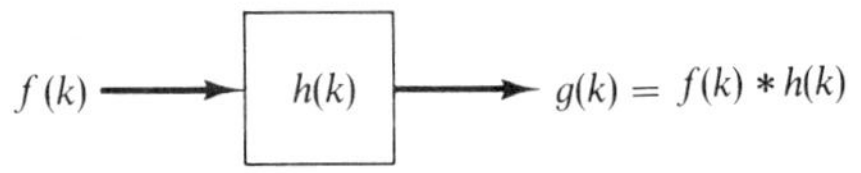

$f(k) \longrightarrow$ [$h(k)$] $\longrightarrow g(k) = f(k) * h(k)$

Figure 2.47 Diagrammatic Representation of the Input–Output Relationship of a Discrete System

We define discrete time convolution by the expression

$$g(k) = \sum_{n=-\infty}^{\infty} f(n)h(k-n) = \sum_{n=-\infty}^{\infty} f(k-n)h(n) \triangleq f(k) * h(k) \tag{2.151}$$

For LTI discrete systems, *causality*, *linearity*, and *stability* are defined in a manner analogous to their definitions in continuous systems. Therefore, we expect that we will not observe a response ahead of a discrete input, that the resulting output due to many inputs will be equal to the sum of the outputs to each input alone, and, finally, that the infinite sum of the impulse function values will converge to a noninfinite value, assuming, of course, that the input function is produced by a physical source. In the case when the sampling time is not unity, (2.151) becomes

$$\begin{aligned} g(kT) \triangleq f(kT) * h(kT) &= \sum_{n=-\infty}^{\infty} f(nT)h(kT-nT) \\ &= \sum_{n=-\infty}^{\infty} f(kT-nT)h(nT) \end{aligned} \tag{2.152}$$

Suppose that the input function to a system is

$$f(k) = e^{-0.5k}u(k) \tag{2.153}$$

and the system impulse response is $h(k) = \delta(k)$. The output of this system is

$$\begin{aligned} g(k) &= \sum_{n=-\infty}^{\infty} \delta(k-n)e^{-0.5n}u(n) = \sum_{n=0}^{\infty} \delta(k-n)e^{-0.5n} \\ &= \delta(k-0)e^{-0.5\times 0} + \delta(k-1)e^{-0.5} + \delta(k-2)e^{-0.5\times 2} + \cdots \end{aligned} \tag{2.154}$$

The output is, therefore,

$$\begin{aligned} g(0) &= 1 + 0 + 0 + \cdots && = 1 \\ g(1) &= 0 + e^{-0.5} + 0 + 0 + \cdots && = e^{-0.5} \\ g(2) &= 0 + 0 + e^{-1} + 0 + \cdots && = e^{-1} \\ &\vdots \end{aligned}$$

We observe that the output is identical with the input, an anticipated result since the impulse response was a delta function.

■ Example 2.32

Determine the output of the system shown in Figure 2.48a. The input to the system is the unit step function $u(k)$. Use the discrete convolution theorem.

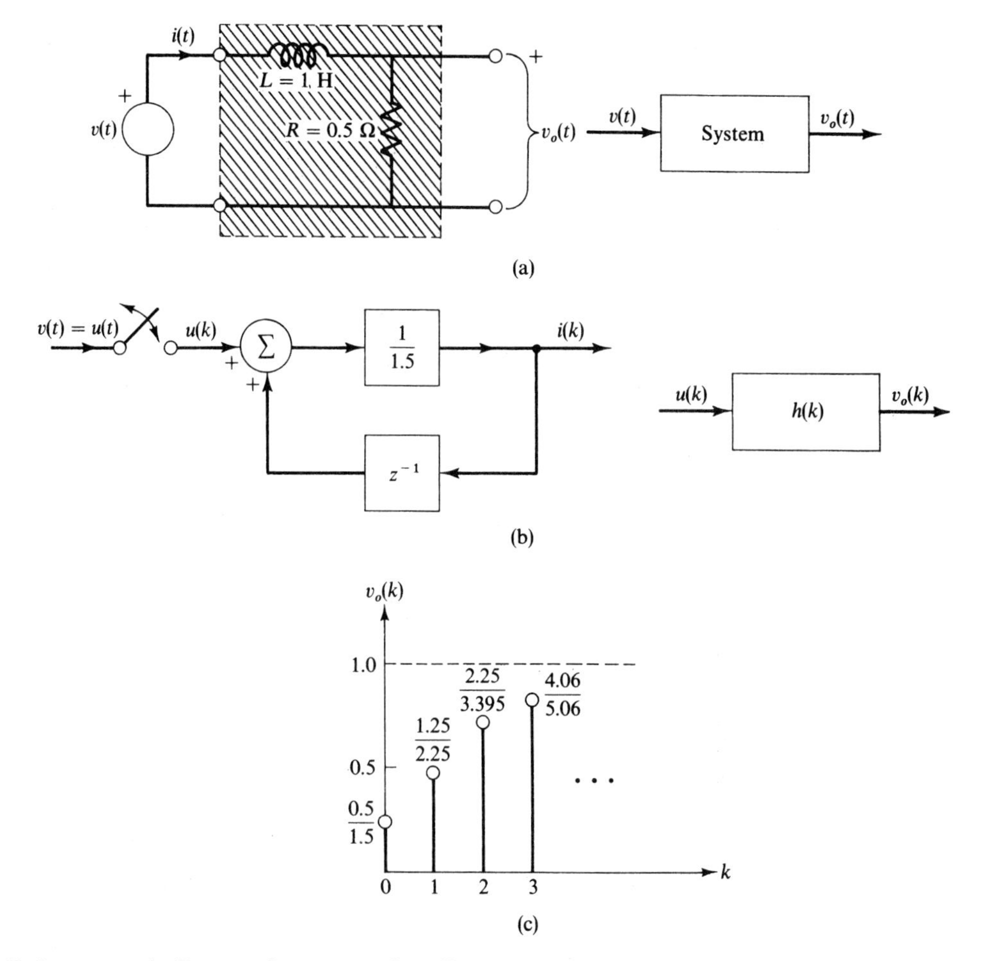

Figure 2.48 Response of a Discrete System to a Step Function

Solution An application of the Kirchhoff voltage law leads to the differential equation

$$\frac{di(t)}{dt} + 0.5i(t) = v(t) \tag{2.155}$$

Using (2.77) with $T = 1$, we have the corresponding difference equation

$$i(k) - i(k-1) + 0.5i(k) = v(k) \triangleq u(k)$$

from which

$$1.5i(k) - i(k-1) = u(k) \tag{2.156}$$

The equivalent discrete form of the system is shown in Figure 2.48b.

To apply convolution, we must first find the impulse response of the system. To do this, we write (2.156) in the form

$$h(k) = \frac{1}{1.5}\,\delta(k) + \frac{1}{1.5}\,h(k-1)$$

We obtain [since the system is initially relaxed, $h(-1) = 0$]

$$h(0) = \frac{1}{1.5}$$

$$h(1) = \frac{1}{1.5}\,h(1-1) = \frac{1}{1.5^2}$$

$$h(2) = \frac{1}{1.5}\,h(2-1) = \frac{h(1)}{1.5} = \frac{1}{1.5^3}$$

$$\vdots$$

$$h(k) = \frac{1}{1.5^{k+1}}$$

The output of the system is given by

$$v_o(k) = 0.5i(k) = 0.5u(k) * h(k)$$

$$= 0.5 \sum_{n=-\infty}^{\infty} u(k-n)h(n) = 0.5 \sum_{n=0}^{k} u(k-n)\,\frac{1}{1.5^{n+1}}$$

From this expression, we deduce the successive values

$$v_o(0) = 0.5 \sum_{n=0}^{0} u(0-n)\,\frac{1}{1.5^{n+1}} = 0.5u(0)\,\frac{1}{1.5} = \frac{0.5}{1.5}$$

$$v_o(1) = 0.5 \sum_{n=0}^{1} u(1-n)\,\frac{1}{1.5^{n+1}}$$

$$= 0.5\left[u(1)\,\frac{1}{1.5^1} + u(0)\,\frac{1}{1.5^2}\right] = 0.5\left(\frac{1}{1.5} + \frac{1}{1.5^2}\right) = \frac{1.25}{2.25}$$

$$v_o(2) = 0.5 \sum_{n=0}^{2} u(2-n)\,\frac{1}{1.5^{n+1}}$$

$$= 0.5\left[u(2)\,\frac{1}{1.5^1} + u(1)\,\frac{1}{1.5^2} + u(0)\,\frac{1}{1.5^3}\right]$$

$$= 0.5\left(\frac{1}{1.5} + \frac{1}{1.5^2} + \frac{1}{1.5^3}\right) = \frac{2.25}{3.325}$$

$$v_o(3) = 0.5 \sum_{n=0}^{3} u(3-n)\,\frac{1}{1.5^{n+1}}$$

$$= 0.5\left[u(3)\,\frac{1}{1.5^1} + u(2)\,\frac{1}{1.5^2} + u(1)\,\frac{1}{1.5^3} + u(0)\,\frac{1}{1.5^4}\right]$$

$$= 0.5\left(\frac{1}{1.5} + \frac{1}{1.5^2} + \frac{1}{1.5^3} + \frac{1}{1.5^4}\right) = \frac{4.0625}{5.0625}$$

$$\vdots$$

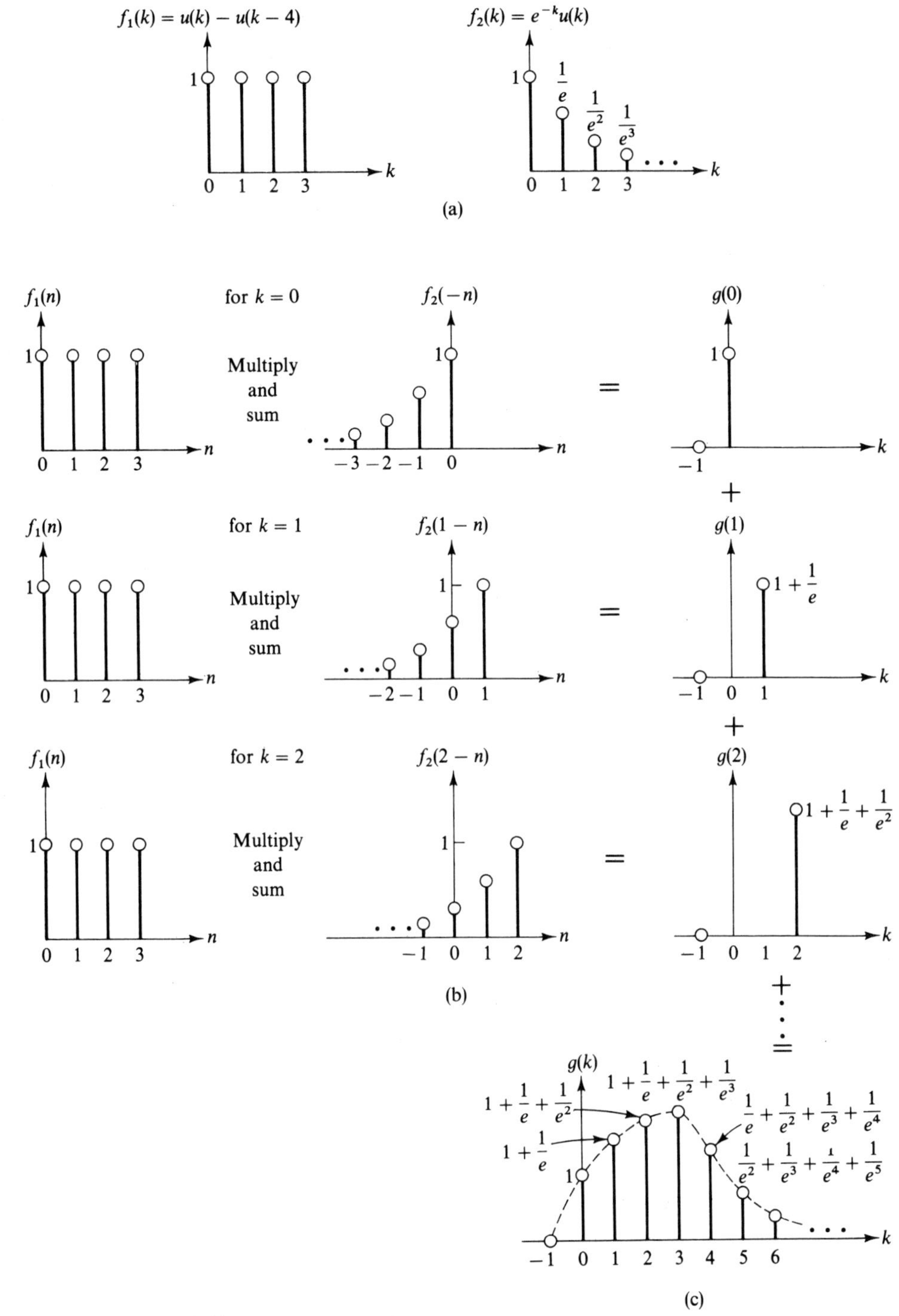

Figure 2.49 Illustrating Example 2.33

A sketch of the output is shown in Figure 2.48c. The results agree with what is expected for an RL circuit. ■

■ **Example 2.33**

Determine the convolution of the two discrete functions shown in Figure 2.49a.

Solution The two functions are shown in Figure 2.49b in the n domain for three different values of k. Now, apply the steps required in the convolution formula:

$$g(k) = \sum_{n=0}^{k} [u(n) - u(n-4)]e^{-(k-n)}u(k-n)$$

This can be accomplished by graphical construction. The resulting $g(k)$ is shown in Figure 2.49c. ■

2.12 Correlation

Correlation is an important concept in the study of random signals and serves to relate the average intensity (or power), an observable quantity, with specified time-average values of members of a family of functions defined on a probability space. In the case of optical signals, it relates irradiance with field intensity. Correlation techniques are also used in medicine when acoustic (ultrasonic) waves are used as probes to detect anomalies inside the human body. This technique also finds important applications in many areas of physics and technology.

Mathematically, correlation is a process somewhat like convolution. The **cross-correlation** of two different functions is defined by the relation

$$R_{fh}(t) \triangleq f(t) \bigstar h(t) = \int_{-\infty}^{\infty} f(\tau)h(\tau - t)\, d\tau = \int_{-\infty}^{\infty} f(\tau + t)h(\tau)\, d\tau \tag{2.157}$$

When $f(t) = h(t)$, the correlation operation is called **autocorrelation.**

Equation (2.157) shows that cross-correlation does not obey the commutative rule:

$$f(t) \bigstar h(t) \neq h(t) \bigstar f(t) \tag{2.158}$$

Using the Schwartz inequality, it can be shown that

$$|R_f(t)| \triangleq |f(t) \bigstar f(t)| \leq R_f(0) \tag{2.159}$$

This equation indicates that there is a time $t = 0$ at which the absolute value of the autocorrelation function is equal to or greater than at any other time. This fact is of great importance in signal detection. It is routinely used in radar signal detection when correlation is performed between the emitted signal and the signal returned from a target. A large peak indicates a resemblance between the returned signal and the emitted signal, from which it is inferred that a target is present.

■ Example 2.34

Find the correlation between a pulse transmitted by radar equipment, as shown in Figure 2.50a, and each of the two possible received pulses shown in Figures 2.50b and 2.50c.

Solution Employ (2.157) and the graphical approach discussed in Section 2.9 in connection with convolution. The correlation between $f(t)$ and $h_1(t)$ is shown in Figure 2.50d. The correlation between $f(t)$ and $h_2(t)$ can be accomplished by considering three independent correlations: the correlations between $f(t)$ and the three pulses of the function $h_2(t)$. The first pulse extends between 1.5 and 2, the second is between 2 and 2.5, and the third is between 2.5 and 3. The dotted lines in Figure 2.50e are the results of the three correlation operations, and the solid line is their total sum.

It is interesting to compare the resulting functions in Figures 2.50d and 2.50e. The first function results from the correlation of two similar pulses; the

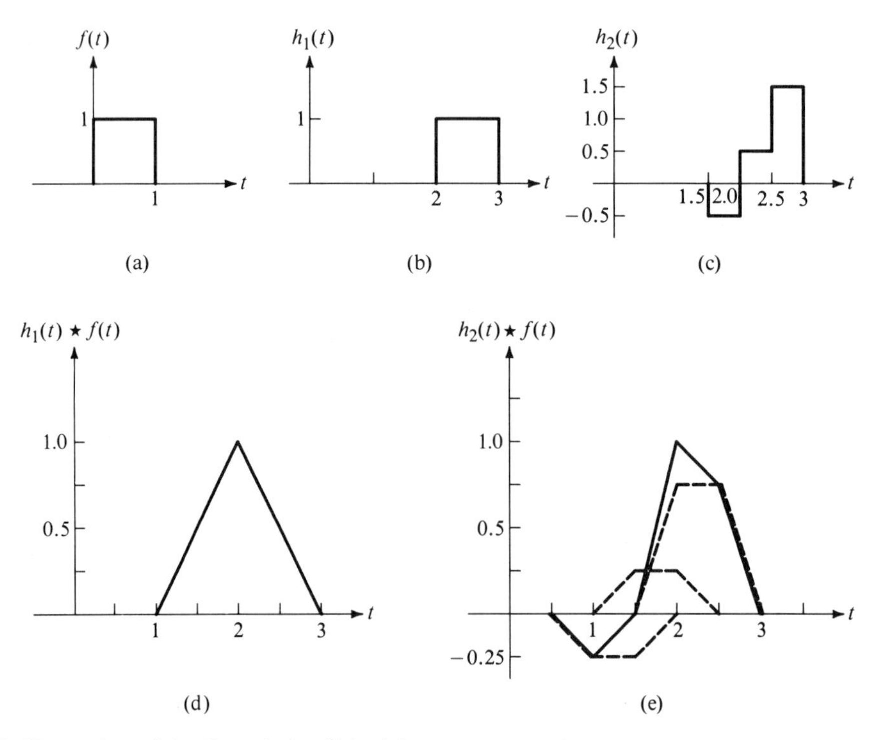

Figure 2.50 Illustration of the Correlation Principle

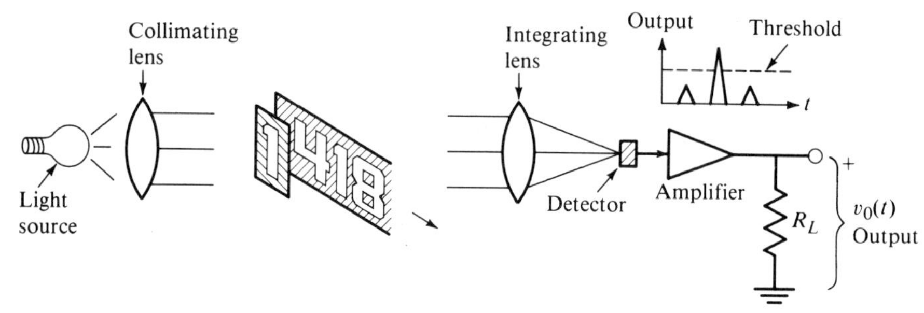

Figure 2.51 Simple Optical Correlating Device

second, from a pulse that might be considered to be distorted by noise. We see that if the detected signal is distorted by noise, the resulting output signal of the correlation operation is also distorted. However, if the noise is not severe, we can always assign a threshold value to specify whether or not the correlated output indicates the presence of a signal. An established threshold level provides a go–no-go situation. If the output of the correlator is larger than the threshold value, we say that the signal is present. ■

The idea of matching signals can take a completely different format. For example, Figure 2.51 illustrates a practical way of correlating shapes; in this case, recognizing numbers.

Problems

Section 2.1

1. Develop block diagram representations of the systems shown in Figure 2.52.

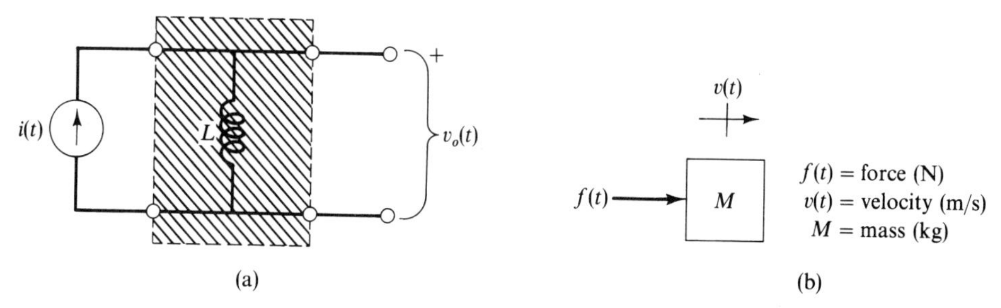

Figure 2.52

2. Develop block diagram representations of the systems shown in Figure 2.53.

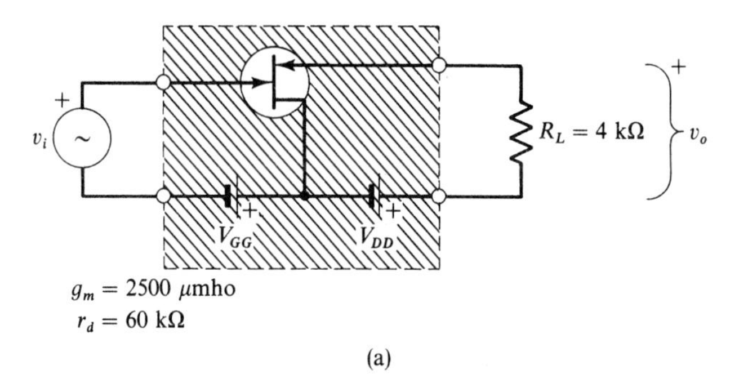

(a)

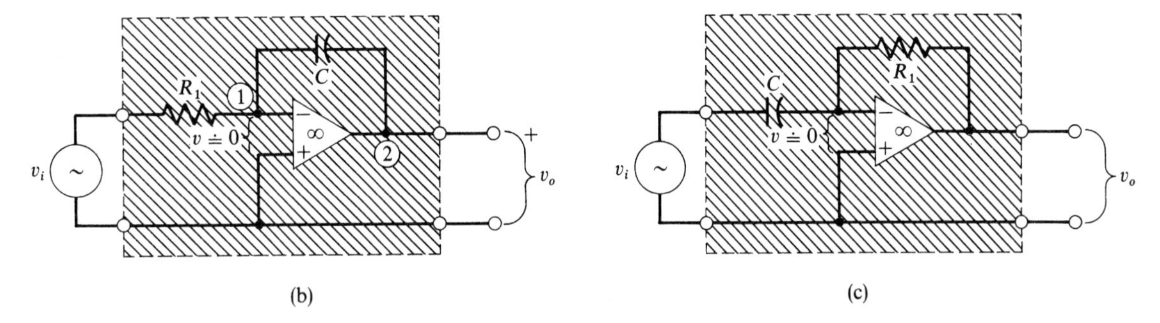

(b) (c)

Figure 2.53

Section 2.2

3. Find the current through an inductor of 1 H at $t = 0$ s and at $t = 2$ s if the voltage waveform across the inductor is that shown in Figure 2.54.

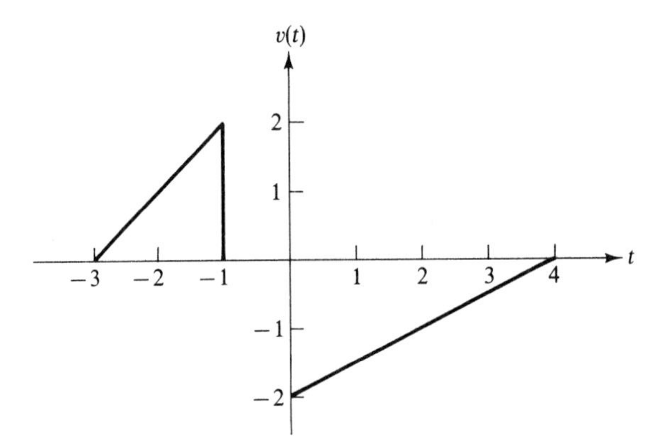

Figure 2.54

4. Find the energy dissipated by a resistor of 5 Ω for a current through it that has the waveform shown in Figure 2.55.

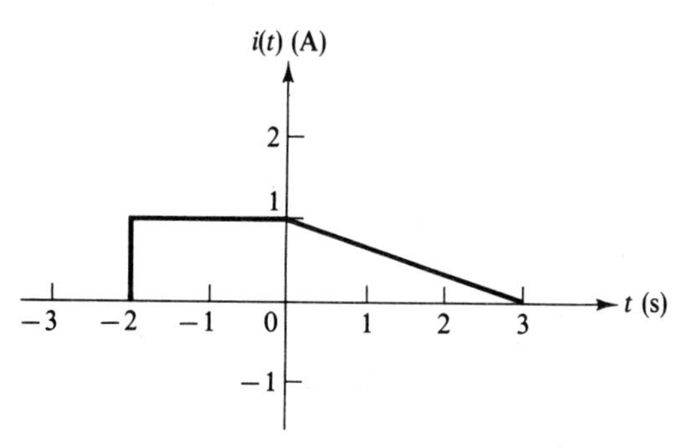

Figure 2.55

5. Forces of the form shown in Figure 2.56 are applied to a linear spring with spring constant $K = 2$. Determine the functional form of the velocity corresponding to these two forces.

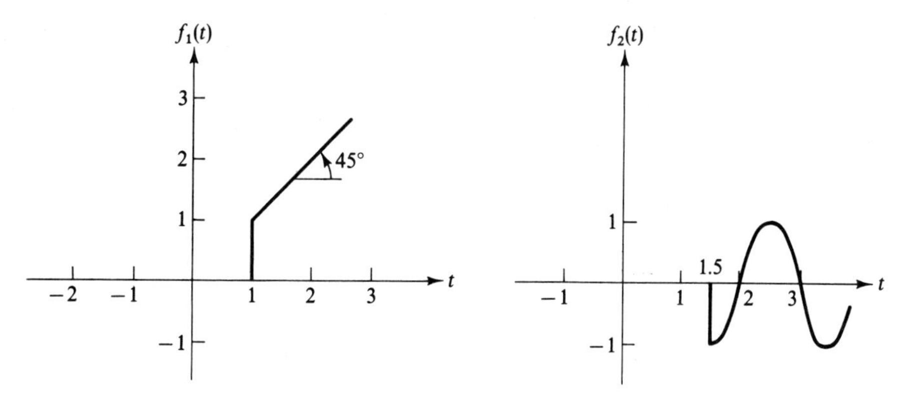

Figure 2.56

6. A time-varying torque is applied to a rotating body that has a polar moment of inertia of 2 kg-m². Plot the angular velocity of the rotating body if the torque is that shown in Figure 2.57.

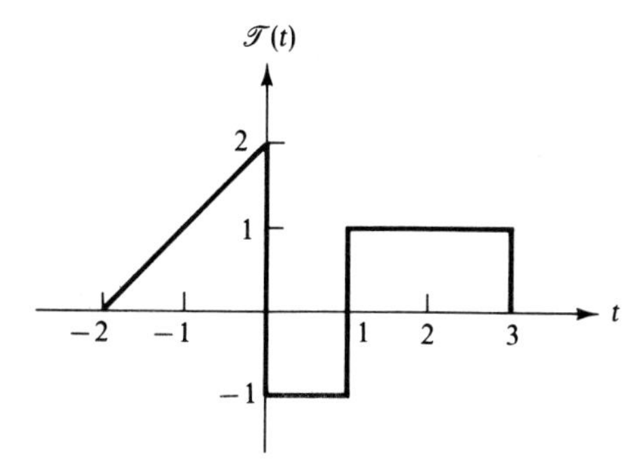

Figure 2.57

7. A current source having the functional form $i(t) = e^{-|t|}u(t + 2)$ is applied through a capacitor of 0.5 F. Find the voltage and charge across the capacitor if the current source remains applied for an infinite time.
8. ***Monte Carlo Method.*** A force having the functional form $f(t) = e^{-t}p_{1/2}(t - \frac{1}{2})$ is applied to a mass of 1 kg. Determine the velocity of the mass. Compare your answer with the result obtained by using the following numerical procedure, known as the Monte Carlo method. Here, because the curve lies within a unit square, use a random number generator supplied by your academic computer with values from 0 to 1. For any pair of numbers (t_i, τ_i), there corresponds a point inside the square. If the total number of trials is n (use $n = 1000$) and n' denotes the number of times that $f(t_i) = e^{-t_i} \geq \tau_i$ is satisfied, then the value of the integral is approximately equal to n'/n.
9. The energy delivered to each electrical element—resistor, inductor, and capacitor—between $t_1 \leq t \leq t_2$ is given by $E = \int_{t_1}^{t_2} v(\tau)i(r)\, d\tau$, where $v(\tau)$ is the voltage across the element and $i(\tau)$ is the current through it. Deduce expressions for the energies E_R, E_L, and E_C.
10. The switch to the relaxed circuit (zero initial conditions) shown in Figure 2.58 is closed at $t = 0$. The voltage across the RC parallel combination is $v(t) = 0.5(1 - e^{-10t})$. Determine **(a)** the energy delivered by the source at time t, **(b)** the energy dissipated in the resistor, and **(c)** the energy stored in the capacitor. From your answer, draw a fundamental conclusion.

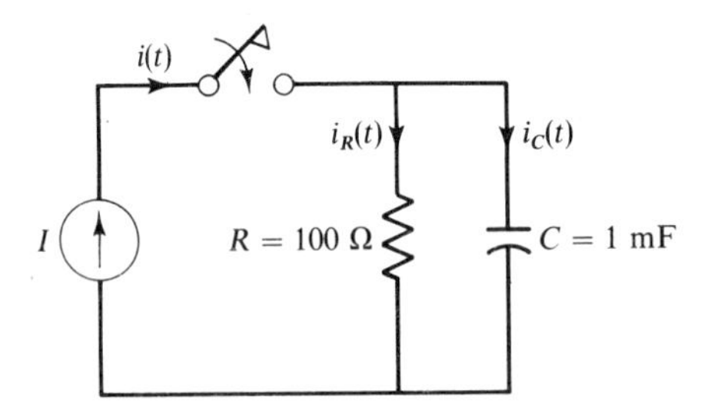

Figure 2.58

Section 2.3

11. Represent the following differential equations in block diagram form:
    a. $\frac{1}{2}(dy/dt) = 4y + e^{-t}u(t)$ **b.** $(dy/dt) - y - 2tu(t) = \sin tu(t)$
12. Write the equilibrium equations for each network shown in Figure 2.59. Specify the initial conditions, assuming that the situation shown existed for a long time before the switching operation was effected. The solutions are *not* required. What conclusions can be drawn from these results?

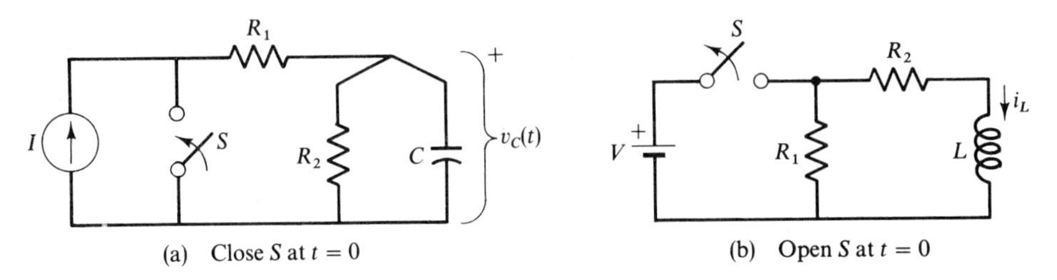

(a) Close S at $t = 0$ (b) Open S at $t = 0$

Figure 2.59

13. Find the transient and steady state (particular) solutions for the relaxed system given in Figure 2.60.

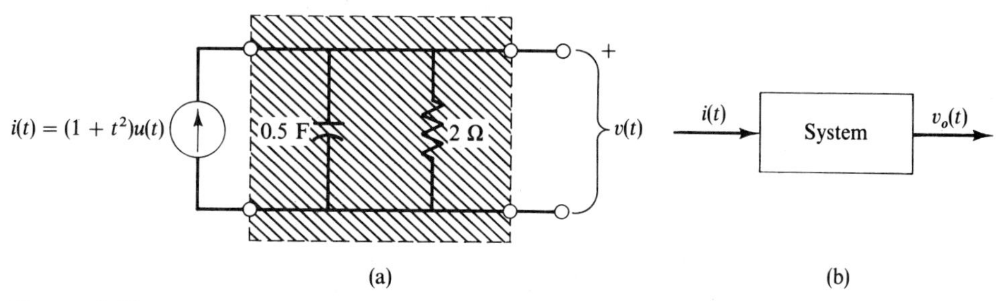

Figure 2.60

Hint: Assume a trial solution of the form $v(t) = a_0 + a_1 t + a_2 t^2$ in determining the particular solution.

14. A current is applied to the circuit shown in block diagram form in Figure 2.60. Determine the zero-input and the zero-state responses. Set $v(0) = 1$.

15. Repeat Problem 13 for the transient and steady state responses, but now by determining the zero-input and zero-state responses of the initially relaxed system. Compare these results with those obtained in Problem 13.

16. ***Heat Transfer.*** The temperature outside a digital chip is constant and equal to $T_0 = 22°C$. Because of currents in the chip, heat is generated uniformly at the rate Q. The temperature inside the chip is considered to be uniform throughout the chip at temperature T°C. The total rate of change of heat within the chip is equal to $mc_p(dT/dt)$, where m is the mass of the chip and c_p is its heat capacity. This heat equals the rate at which heat is supplied by the source Q plus the rate at which the heat is transferred to the chip from the surrounding air. Thus, we write $mc_p(dT/dt) = -K_0(T - T_0) + Q$, where $K_0(T - T_0)$ is the rate of heat transfer into the chip from the surrounding air (or heat sink). Given that $m = 50$ g, $c_p = 0.15$ cal/g-C°, $K_0 = 3$ cal/C°, and $Q = e^{-t} + \cos t$ cal for $t > 0$, determine the transient and steady state solutions for the chip temperature.
Hint: Find the particular solutions separately for e^{-t} and $\cos t$ and add the results. This superposition is valid because differentiation is a linear process.

17. The input voltage to the circuit shown in Figure 2.61 is $v(t) = (1 + e^{-t})u(t)$. Find how the charge on the capacitor varies with time. In your solution, indicate the zero-input, zero-state, transient, and steady state components of the charge given $q(0) = 2 \times 10^{-3}$ C. Also, draw the block diagram representation of the system.

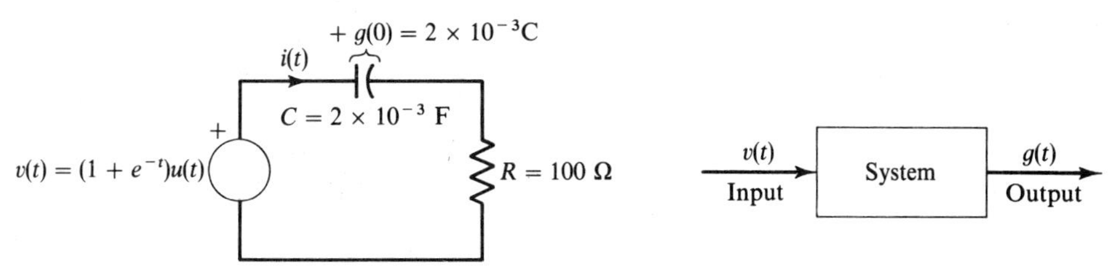

Figure 2.61

18. The current to the circuit shown in Figure 2.62 is $i(t) = 2(1 - e^{-2t})u(t)$. Deduce the input voltage.

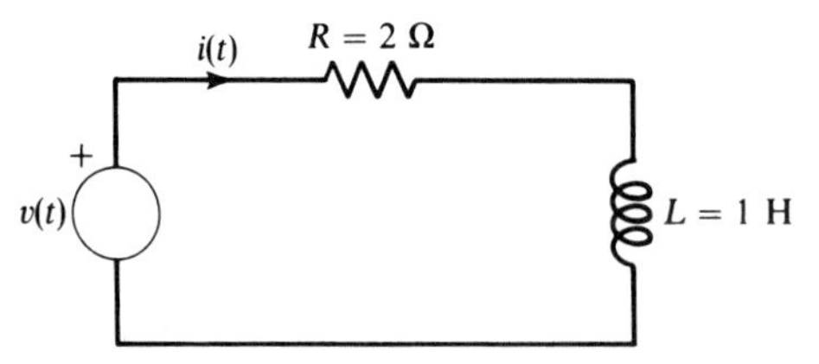

Figure 2.62

19. Determine the zero-input, zero-state, transient, and steady state solutions for the current in the circuit given in Figure 2.63. The input voltage is $v(t) = 4 + e^{-4t}$ for $t > 0$. The circuit is initially relaxed.

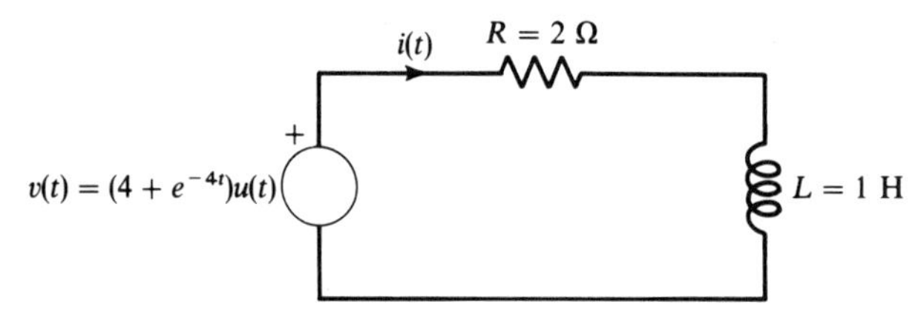

Figure 2.63

20. A force $f(t) = 2e^{-t}$ for $t > 0$ is applied to the system shown in Figure 2.64. This type of system is often used as a vibration isolator. Determine the distance x traveled by the top level of the initially relaxed system.

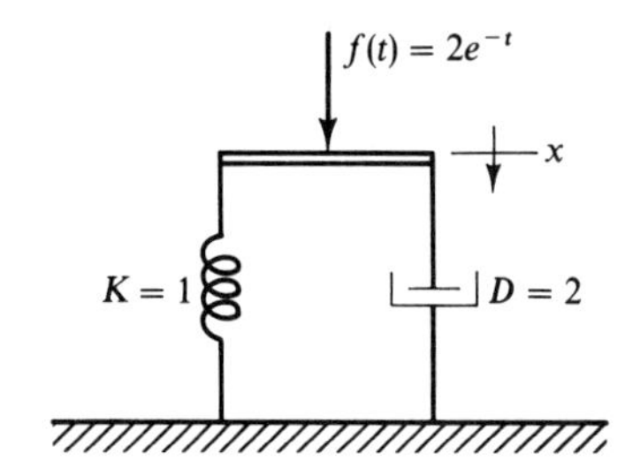

Figure 2.64

21. The voltage applied to the circuit of Figure 2.65 is $v = \cos \omega t$ for $t > 0$. The initial charge on the capacitor is zero.

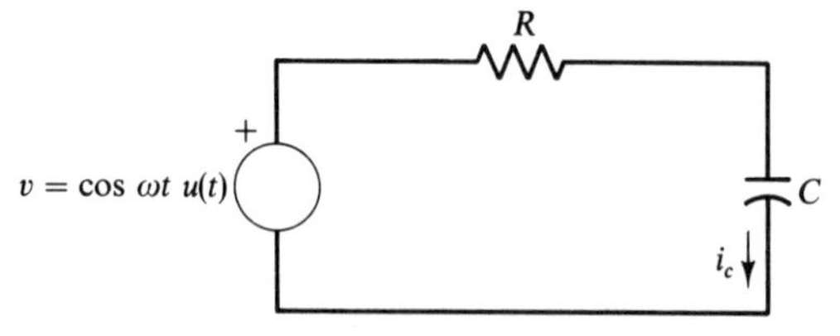

Figure 2.65

a. Find an expression for the current $i_c(t)$. **b.** Is there some value of $v_c(0-)$ for which the transient term is zero?

22. ***Biology.**** Assume that a colony of bacteria increases at a rate proportional to the number present. If the number of bacteria doubles in 5 hours, how long will it take for the number of bacteria to triple? Draw a block diagram that represents the system.

Section 2.4

23. The circuit shown in Figure 2.66 is initially in its quiescent state when the switch is opened.

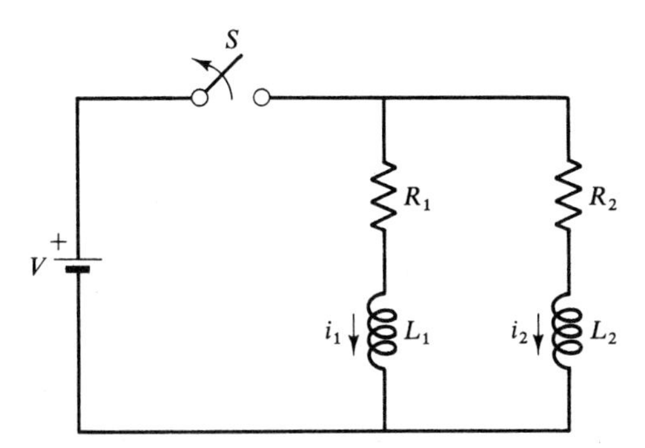

Figure 2.66

a. Deduce an expression for the inductor currents for $t > 0$. **b.** Determine the conditions for the current to be zero.

24. A pulse of height V and duration $T = RC$ is applied to the series RC circuit shown in Figure 2.67. The circuit is initially relaxed. Sketch the output voltage $v_o(t)$ as a function of time. Label all features of the curve.

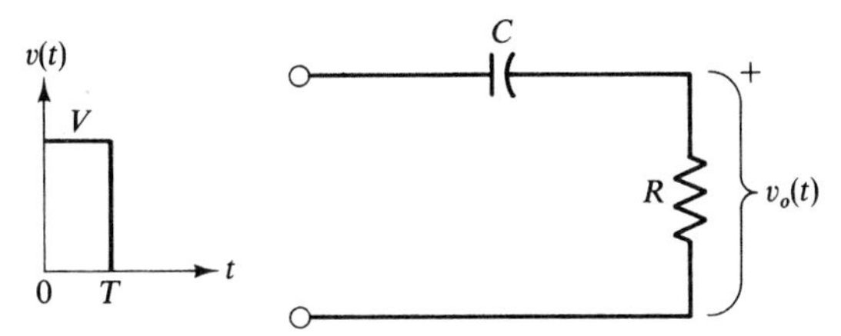

Figure 2.67

25. A two-pulse wavetrain is applied to the initially relaxed RC circuit shown in Figure 2.68.

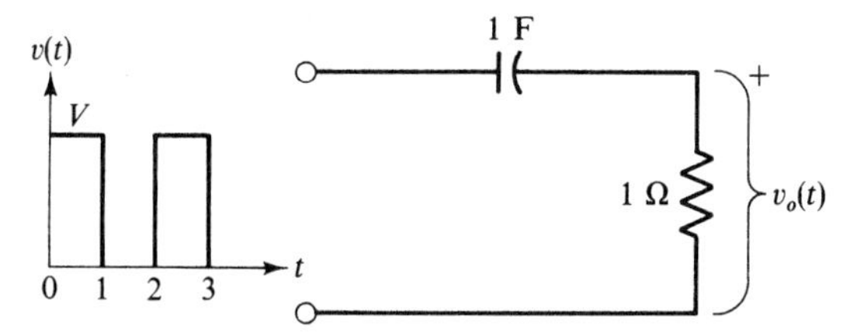

Figure 2.68

* From N. Finizio and G. Ladas, *An Introduction to Differential Equations* (Belmont, CA: Wadsworth Publishing Co., 1982), p. 20.

From a knowledge of the step function response of the *RC* circuit, deduce the voltage waveform $v_o(t)$.

Hint: Use a step-by-step procedure beginning at $t = 0$ and then determine the values of $v_o(t)$ at successive switching times.

26. In the circuit of Figure 2.69, $v_c(0-) = 0$. The switch is closed at time $t = 1$ s. Determine $v_c(t)$ and $i_c(t)$ and sketch the time variation.

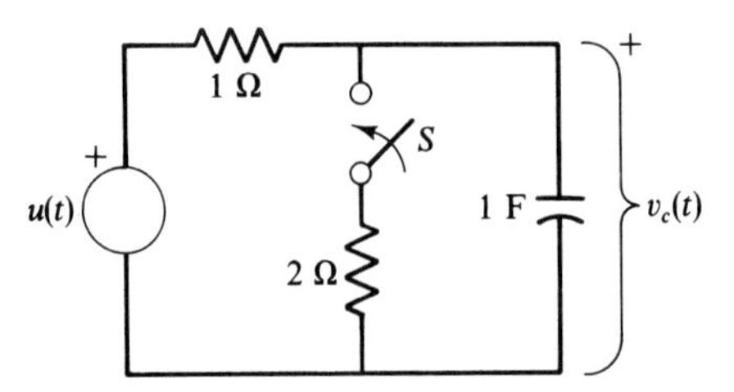

Figure 2.69

Section 2.5

27. Draw block diagram representations of the systems shown in Figure 2.70.

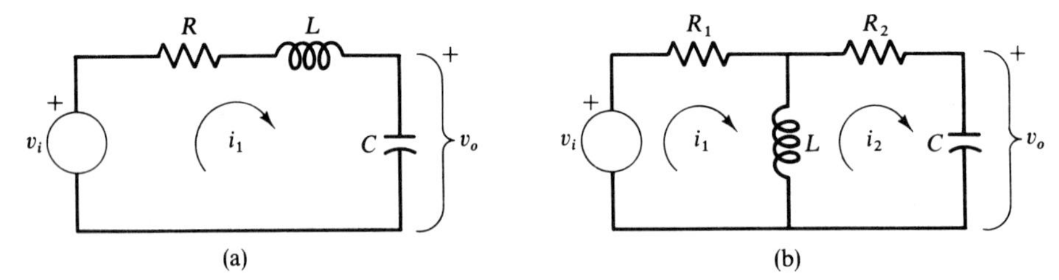

Figure 2.70

28. Draw block diagrams for the following sets of differential equations, where $p = d/dt$, $p^2 = d^2/dt^2$, and $p^3 = d^3/dt^3$:

a. $\begin{cases}(p^3 + 3p + 2)y = x + 7 \\ (p + 2)x = (3 - 2p)y\end{cases}$ **b.** $\begin{cases}(p^2 + 5)y = 3x \\ (p^2 + 7)x = 5y + 3\end{cases}$

29. Deduce the transmittances of the systems represented by the block diagrams shown in Figure 2.71.

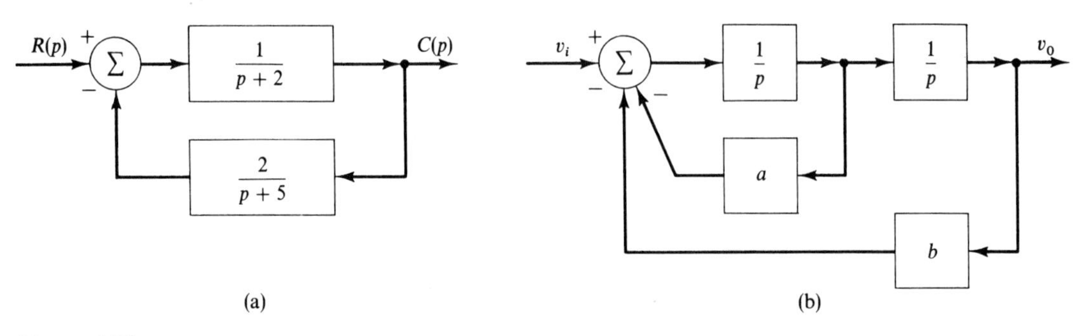

Figure 2.71

Section 2.6

30. A signal generator produces a signal specified by

$$v(k) = \begin{cases} 0 & k < 0 \\ 2k & 0 \le k \le 2 \\ 0 & k > 2 \end{cases}$$

With the signal source as a basic unit, draw block diagrams of the system that will produce the signals shown in Figure 2.72.

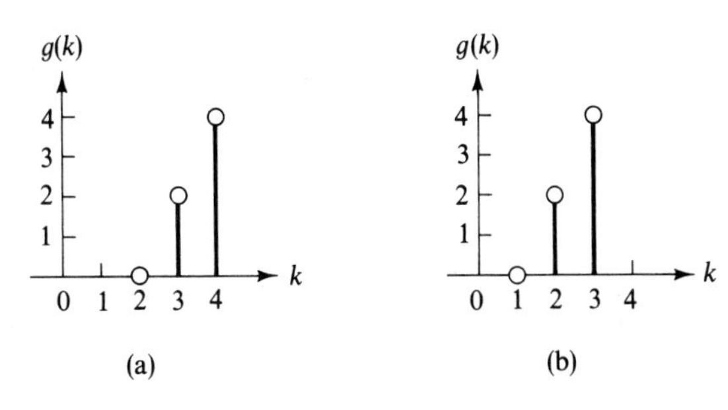

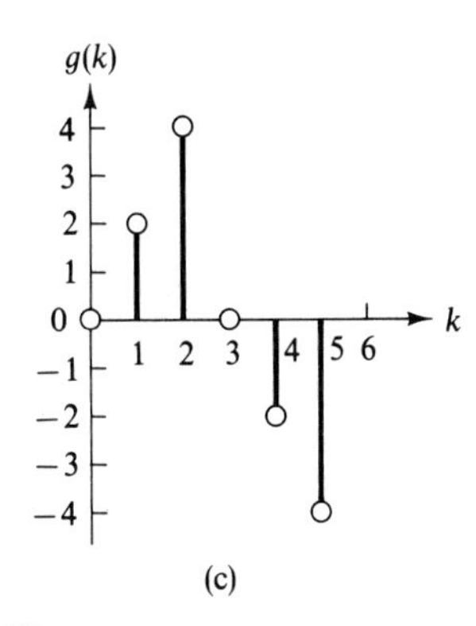

Figure 2.72

31. A discrete system is shown in Figure 2.73a. If the input function is that shown in Figure 2.73b, determine the output.

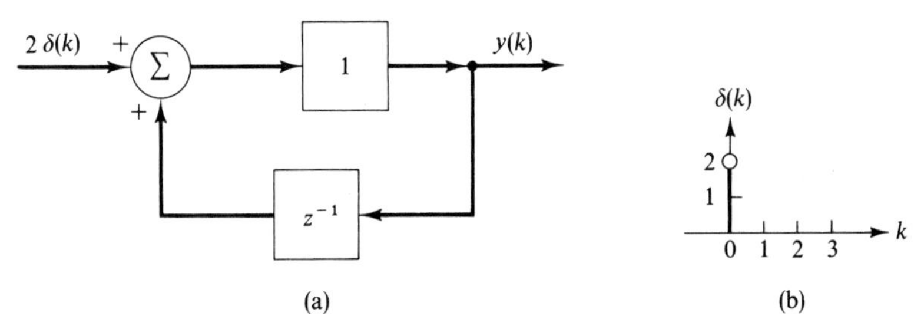

Figure 2.73

32. A discrete system is shown in Figure 2.74a. If the input is that shown in Figure 2.74b, find the output.

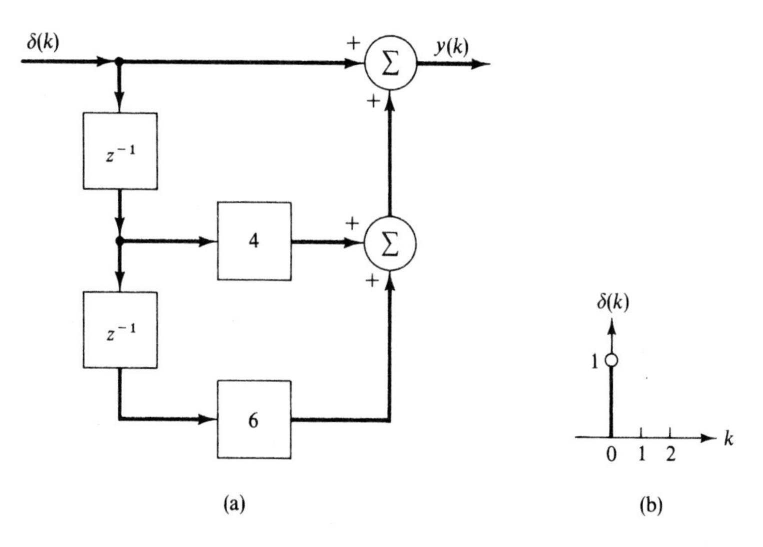

Figure 2.74

33. Refer to Figure 2.75. Deduce the difference equation and find its solution. Identify the system.

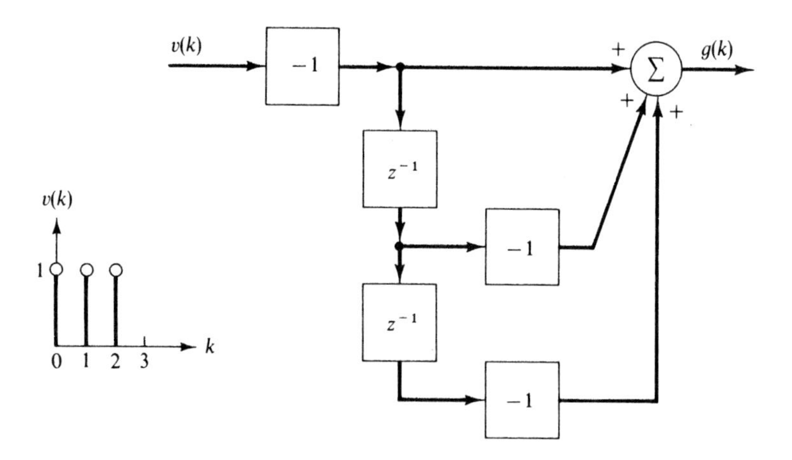

Figure 2.75

34. Deduce the difference equation and its solution for the system shown in Figure 2.76. What effect does this digital system have on the input data?

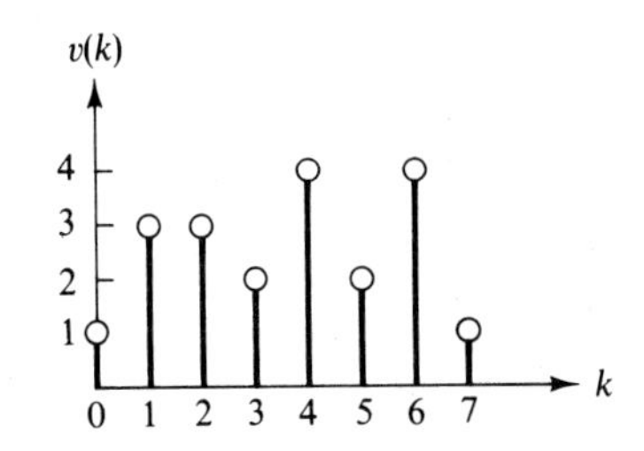

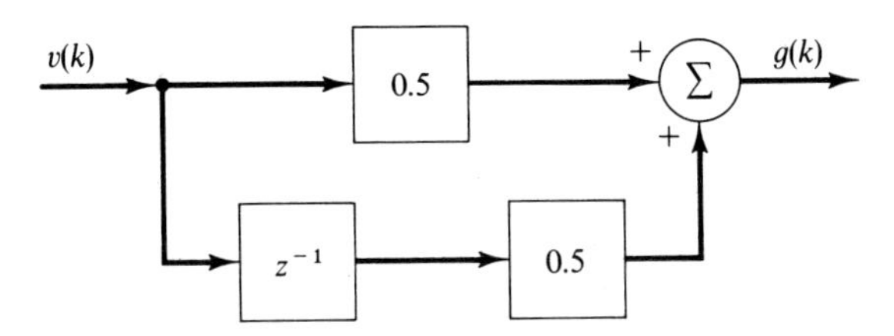

Figure 2.76

35. A unit step sequence is applied to the input of the system shown in Figure 2.77. Deduce the difference equation and its solution. Identify the nature of the output.

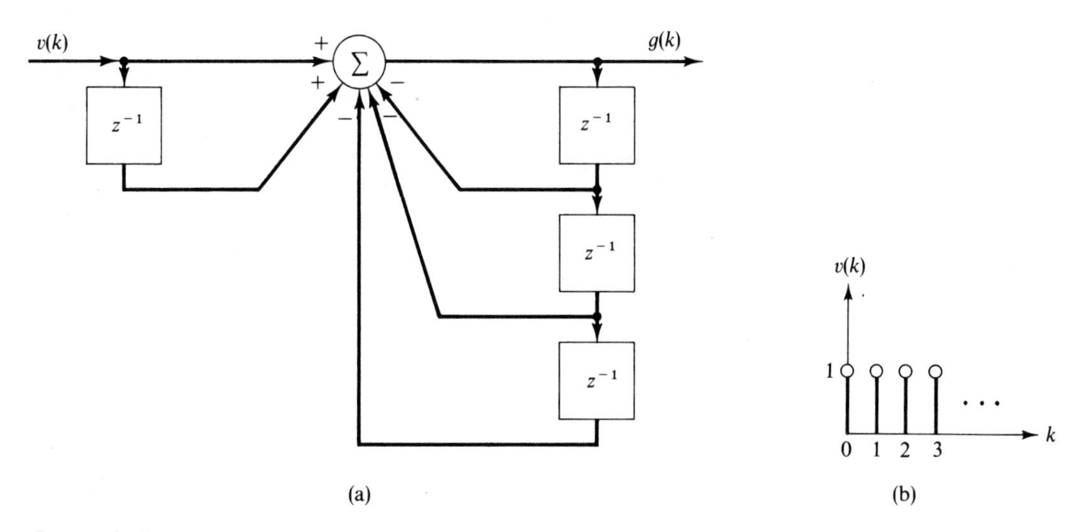

Figure 2.77

36. ***Banking.*** If a family invests \$500 per quarter at 12% interest for 20 years, how much money will the family have accumulated? Assume no initial money was in the account. Interest is compounded quarterly.

Section 2.7

37. The input to each system shown in Figure 2.78 is the ramp function $f(t) = 2r(t)$. Determine the outputs in analog form and in digital form for $T = 0.2$ s. Contrast the results. Draw analog and digital block diagram representations.

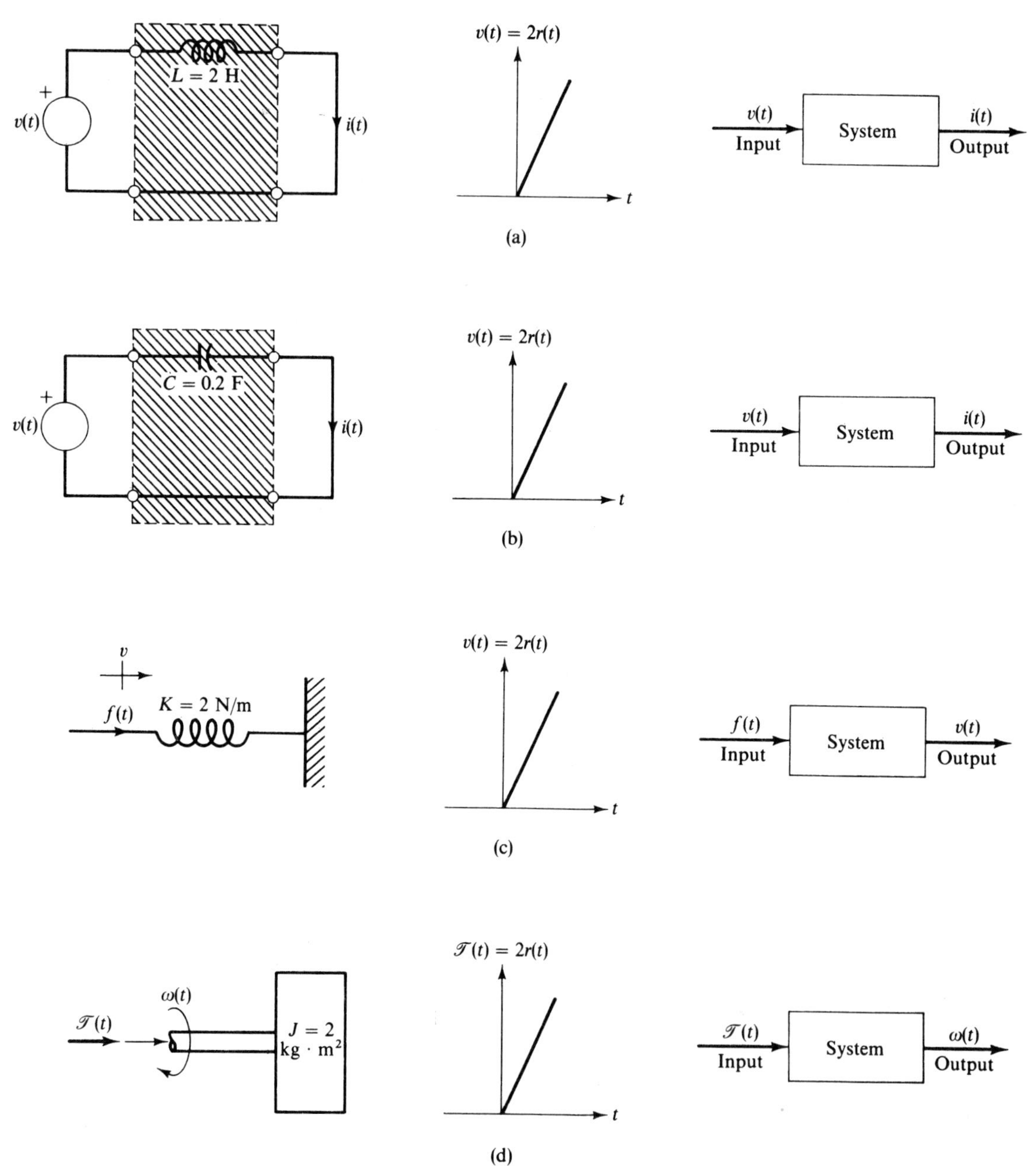

Figure 2.78

38. The initially relaxed system shown in Figure 2.79 is excited by a current source $i(t) = e^{-2t}u(t)$. Determine the output voltage in both analog and digital form for $T = 0.2$ s. Give block diagram representations for each case.

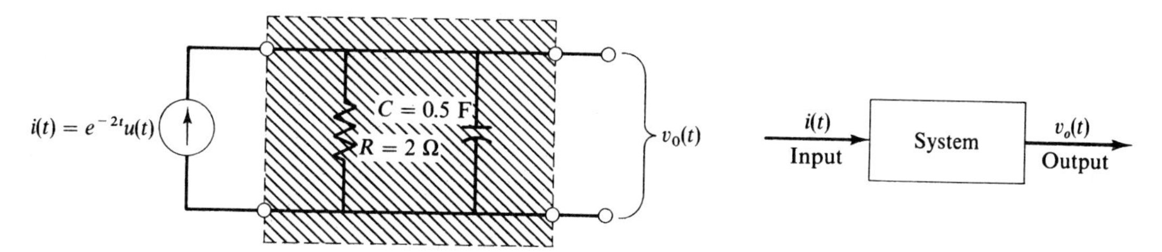

Figure 2.79

39. If $g(-1) = 0$ and $g(k) - 2g(k-1) - 4 = 0$ for $k \geq 0$, find a closed-form solution for $g(k)$. *Hint:* Use a recursive solution to identify the closed form.

40. If $g(-1) = 2$ and $g(k) - 2g(k-1) = \delta(k)$ for $k \geq 0$, find the closed-form solution for $g(k)$. *Hint:* Use a recursive solution to identify the closed form.

Section 2.8

41. Illustrated in Figure 2.80 is a ballistic pendulum that is initially at rest. A bullet of mass m traveling with a speed v is fired into the pendulum mass at time $t = 0$ and remains lodged therein. Determine the initial value $\omega(0+)$. Write the controlling equation for angle $\theta(t)$. Draw a network equivalent of the system.

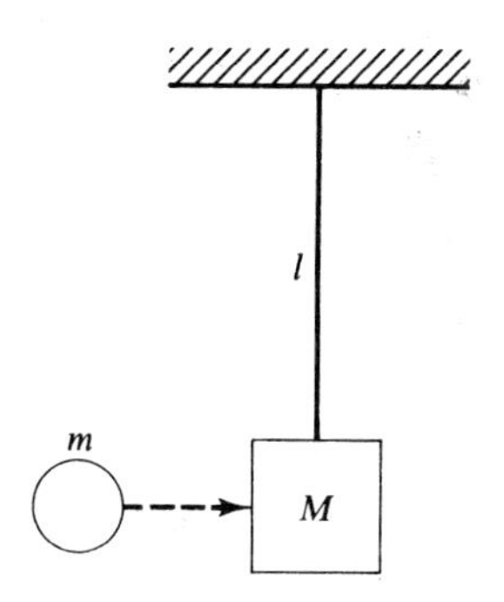

Figure 2.80

42. Determine the particular solution of the following differential equations:

a. $(d^2y/dt^2) + y = 2t \qquad t > 0$
Hint: Assume a solution of the form $y = A + Bt$.

b. $(d^2y/dt^2) - 4y = e^{2t} \qquad t > 0$
Hint: Since Ae^{2t} is a solution of the homogeneous equation, try $y = Ate^{2t}$.

c. $(d^2y/dt^2) - y = \sin t \qquad t > 0$
Hint: Assume a solution of the form $y = A \cos t + B \sin t$.

43. The capacitor of the *RLC* circuit shown in Figure 2.81 carries an initial charge $Q_0 = 2$ C. Determine the current in the circuit.

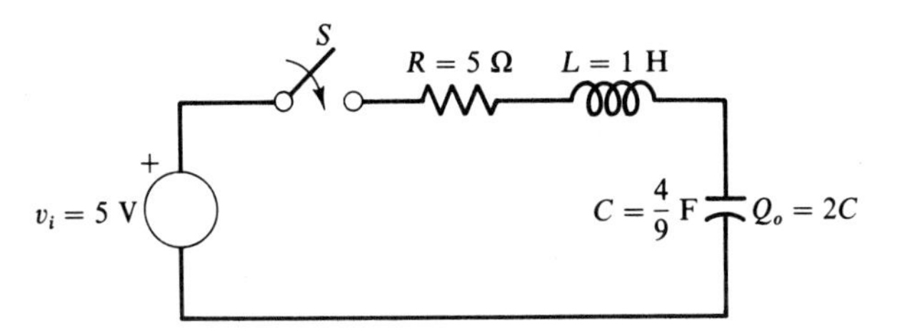

Figure 2.81

Hint: Use the fact that $i = dq/dt$ to solve an equation for q, with $dq(0)/dt = 0$. Use this solution to deduce the equation for $i = dq/dt$.

An alternate approach is to differentiate the KVL integrodifferential equation to obtain $L(d^2i/dt^2) + R(di/dt) + (1/C)i = dv_i/dt$.

Initial conditions are: From $q(0) = Q_0 =$ constant, then $i(0) = dq(0)/dt = 0$; from the integrodifferential equation $(di/dt)(0) = (1/L)[v_i(0) - (1/C)q(0)]$.

44. Solve the equations given in Problem 42 for zero initial conditions: $y(0) = 0$ and $dy(0)/dt = 0$. Then, simulate the equations in digital form and solve for $T = 0.1$. Compare the results.

Section 2.9

45. Determine the convolution of the following pairs of functions:
a. $f_1(t) = p_1(t), f_2(t) = p_1(t-2)$ **b.** $f_1(t) = p_1(t), f_2(t) = \delta(t)$
c. $f_1(t) = e^{-(t-2)}u(t-2), f_2(t) = \delta(t)$ **d.** $f_1(t) = u(t), f_2 = e^{-t}u(t)$

46. Determine the convolution of the following pairs of functions:
a. $f_1(t) = p_1(t) - p_1(t-2), f_2(t) = \delta(t)$ **b.** $f_1(t) = 2p_1(t-2), f_2(t) = e^{-t}u(t)$

47. Using the functions $f_1(t) = p_1(t-1)$ and $f_2(t) = e^{-t}u(t)$, verify the *commutative* property of the convolution illustrated in (2.106).

48. Determine the convolution of the following pairs of functions:
a. $f_1(t) = tu(t), f_2(t) = t^2u(t)$ **b.** $f_1(t) = t^2u(t), f_2(t) = t^3u(t)$

49. Show that if $h(t)$ is a real function and we define $[f_1(t) + jf_2(t)] * h(t) = g_1(t) + jg_2(t)$, then $f_1(t) * h(t) = g_1(t)$ and $f_2(t) * h(t) = g_2(t)$.

50. If $g(t) = f_1(t) * f_2(t)$, show that $dg(t)/dt = [df_1(t)/dt] * f_2(t) = f_1(t) * [df_2(t)/dt]$.

Section 2.10

51. Deduce the zero-input and zero-state responses of the system shown in Figure 2.82. The initial condition for the charge is $q(0) = 1$ and the input voltage source is $v(t) = tu(t)$. Use the convolution approach.

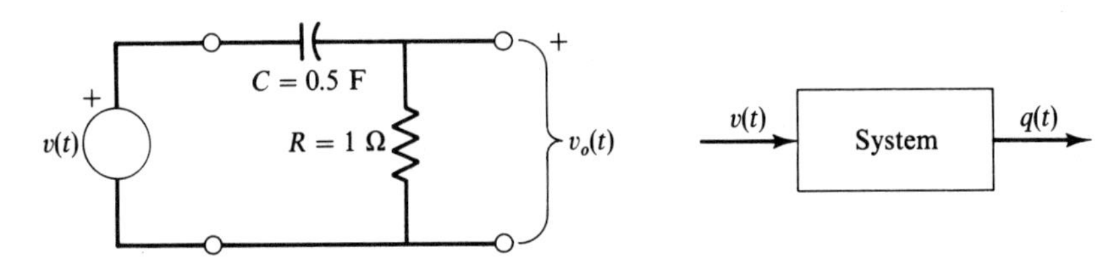

Figure 2.82

52. Determine the output of the initially relaxed systems shown in Figure 2.83 if the input is $v(t) = e^{-t}u(t)$. Use the convolution approach.

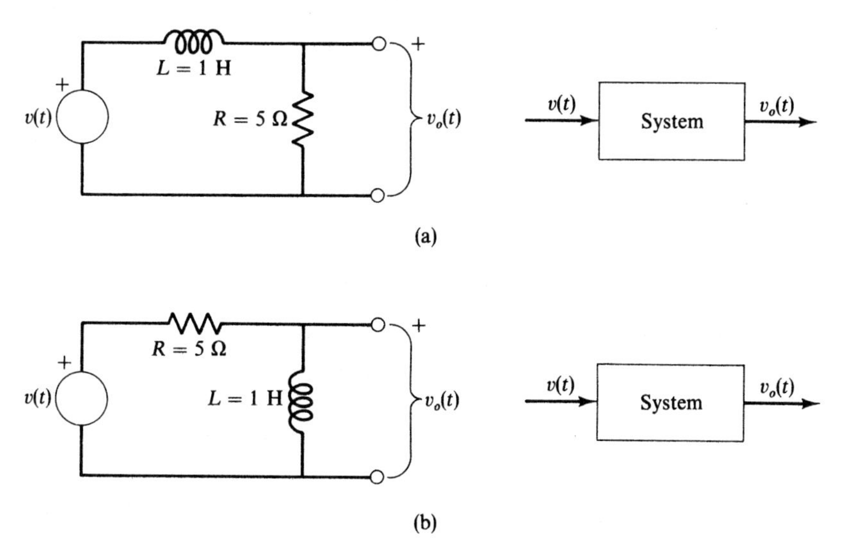

Figure 2.83

53. Determine the output of the initially relaxed systems shown in Figure 2.84 if the inputs are, respectively, $f(t) = p_1(t-1)$ and $\mathcal{T}(t) = e^{-1}u(t)$. Use convolution methods.

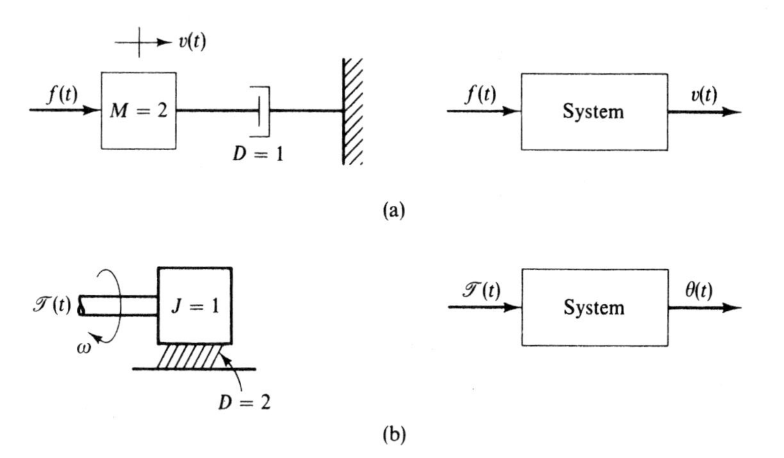

Figure 2.84

54. Find the impulse response of the initially relaxed systems shown in Figure 2.85. The charge on the capacitor is $q(t)$ for initial charge $q(0+) = 0$.

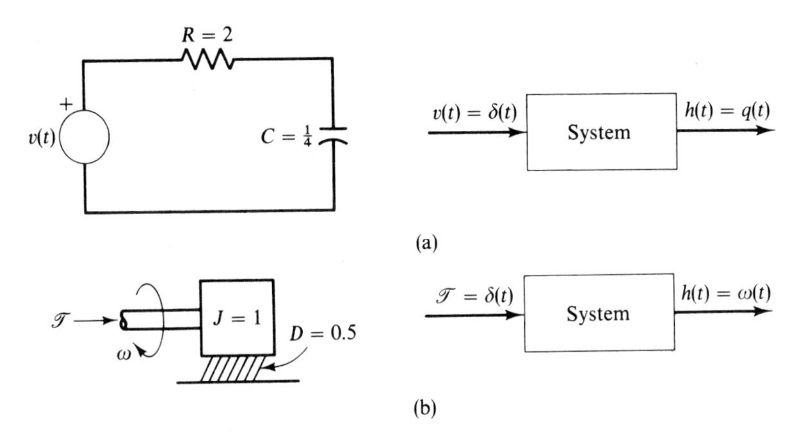

Figure 2.85

55. Find the output of the system described in Example 2.27 if the input is $v(t) = u(t-1) + \delta(t-3)$.
56. The input to the system discussed in Example 2.30 is $i(t) = p(t-4)$. Determine the output using convolution methods. Choose $C = 1$ and $R = 2$.
57. The input to the system discussed in Example 2.30 is $p(t-1) - p(t-5)$. Use convolution methods to deduce the output. Choose $C = 1$ and $R = 2$.
58. Determine the output of the initially relaxed system shown in Figure 2.86 if the following inputs are applied. Use convolution techniques.
    a. $i_1(t) = u(t-2)$ **b.** $i_2(t) = e^{-(t-4)}u(t-4)$

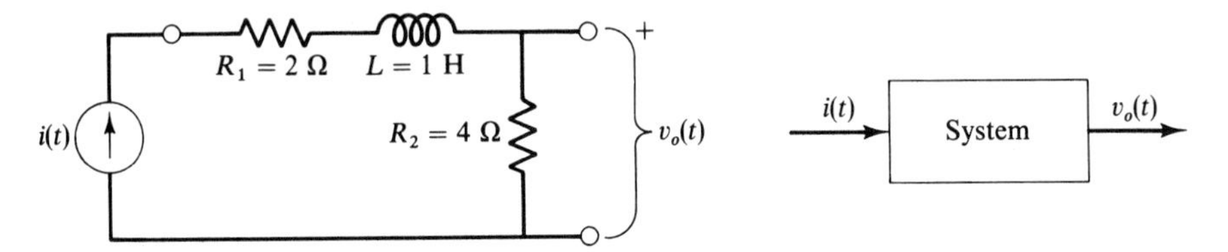

Figure 2.86

59. Determine the output of the system discussed in Example 2.29 if the input is a unit step function $v(t) = u(t)$.
60. Determine the output to the system shown in Figure 2.87 if the input is $f(t) = \cos tu(t)$. Use convolution methods.

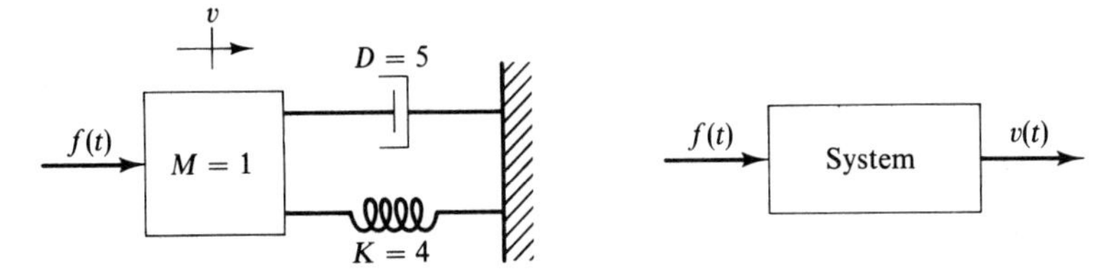

Figure 2.87

Section 2.11

61. Determine the convolution of the discrete signals shown in Figure 2.88.

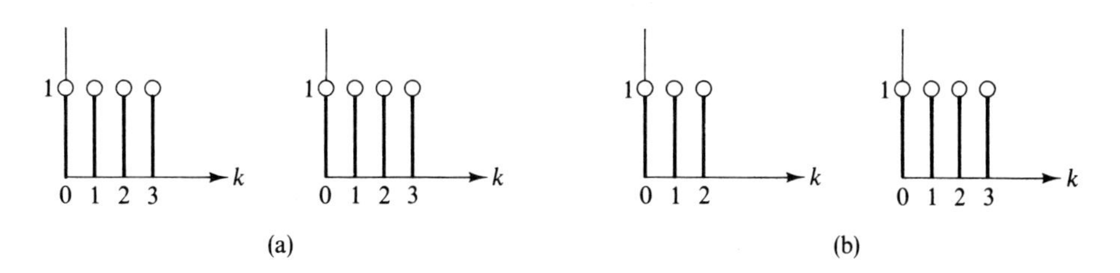

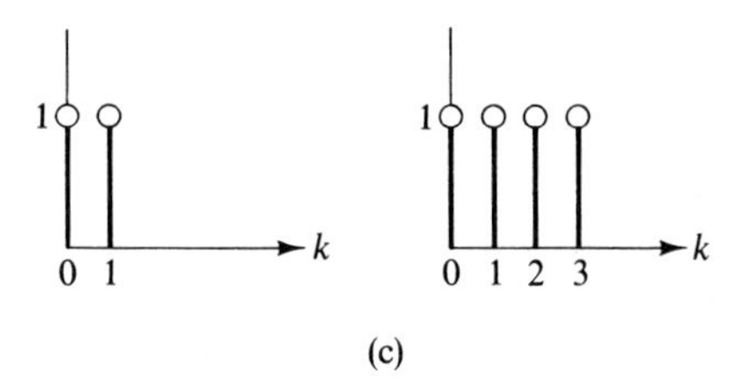

Figure 2.88

62. Deduce the output of the system shown in Figure 2.89 in discrete form using convolution methods. Assume a step function input $i(t) = u(t)$, a sampling time $T = 0.5$ s, $R = 0.5\ \Omega$, and $C = 1$ F.

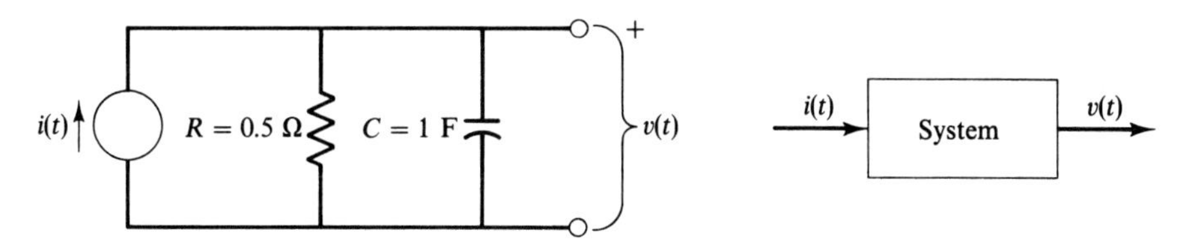

Figure 2.89

63. Deduce the convolution of the following pairs of functions:
a. $f_1(k) = 3^k u(k), f_2(k) = 4^k u(k)$ **b.** $f_1(k) = 0.8^k u(k), f_2(k) = u(k)$
c. $f_1(k) = u(k), f_2(k) = u(k)$

64. Determine the convolutions.
a. $g(k) = [2^k u(k)] * [2^k u(k)]$ **b.** $g(k) = [2^k u(k)] * [2^k u(k)] * [2^k u(k)]$

65. Determine the convolution of the functions shown in Figure 2.90.

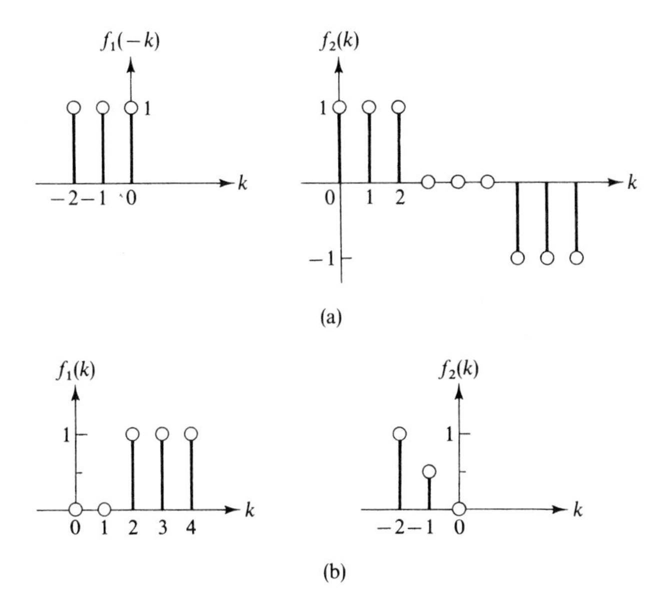

Figure 2.90

66. **a.** Show that $[f(k)u(k)] * u(k-k_0) = \sum_{k=0}^{k-k_0} f(k)$, where k_0 is a constant integer. **b.** Determine the convolution of the functions shown in Figure 2.91.

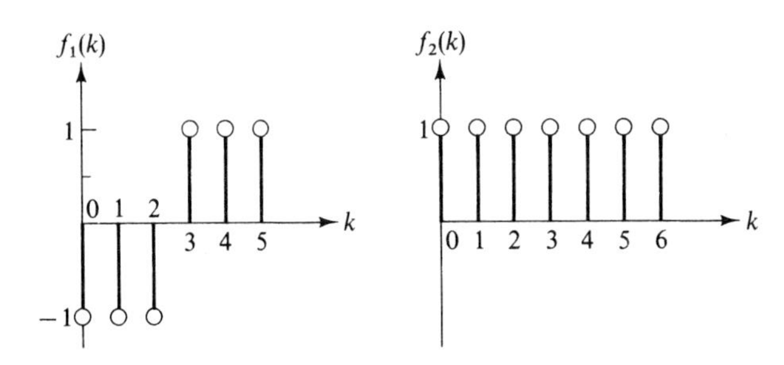

Figure 2.91

Section 2.12

67. Deduce the correlation between the functions given.
    a. $f(t) = p_1(t)$, $h(t) = e^{-t}u(t)$ **b.** $f(t) = p_1(t)$, $h(t) = \delta(t-1) + p_1(t-3)$
    c. $f(t) = e^{-t}u(t)$, $h(t) = e^{-t}u(t)$ **d.** $f(t) = tp_1(t-1)$, $h(t) = e^{-t}u(t)$
68. Verify that $f(t) \bigstar h(t) = f(t) \bigstar h(-t)$.

Periodic Signals and Their Spectrums

The study of periodic functions has had a long history. Bernoulli, around the middle of the eighteenth century, suggested that the physical motion of a clamped string, such as those in stringed instruments, could be represented by linear combinations of normal modes (sinusoids). Lagrange, at about the same time, strongly criticized the use of trigonometric series, arguing that it was not possible to represent functions that contain edges with such series. It was a half-century later that Jean Batiste Joseph Fourier, in conducting his studies on heat diffusion and propagation, developed the series now carrying his name that mathematically addressed such problems. His revolutionary discoveries have had a major impact on the development of mathematics. Fourier series are used extensively today in the fields of science and engineering.

As we will see in this chapter, many types of nonsinusoidal periodic functions can be represented as the sum of periodic complex exponential functions, or sinusoids, a property noted in Section 1.1. This important concept plays a significant role in our general studies. In particular, we will find that the output of a linear time-invariant (LTI) system to a periodic input signal composed of sinusoids is the sum of these same sinusoids, each of which is scaled and time shifted.

The representation of periodic functions in sampled form, a requirement when using a computer and in digital signal processing, will also be examined. Further, the conditions necessary for an acceptable approximation that lead to the discrete Fourier series (DFS) will be established.

3.1 Complex Functions

As a prelude to our studies of Fourier series, we consider the properties of signals (actually mathematical forms) in their complex form. Such signals are useful as building blocks or basis functions from which we can construct other signals (see Section 1.5). Both continuous time and discrete time functions are considered.

Continuous Time Signals. A general complex signal is of the form

$$y(t) = ce^{at} \tag{3.1}$$

where c and a are complex numbers in general. If c and a are real numbers, we have the well-known exponential signals. If c is a constant and $a = a_1 + ja_2$, we have the **complex exponential** of the form

$$y(t) = ce^{(a_1 + ja_2)t} = ce^{a_1 t}e^{ja_2 t} \tag{3.2}$$

A very important signal in our subsequent work is obtained by setting $c = 1$ and $a = j\omega_0$. This signal is

$$y(t) = e^{j\omega_0 t} = \cos \omega_0 t + j \sin \omega_0 t \tag{3.3}$$

where use is made of the **Euler relation** (1.6). The signal $y(t)$ can also be written in the form

$$y(t) = \sqrt{(\cos^2 \omega_0 t + \sin^2 \omega_0 t)}\, e^{j \tan^{-1} (\sin \omega_0 t/\cos \omega_0 t)} \tag{3.4}$$

The frequency is $\omega_0 = 2\pi/T$, where T is called the **period**.

A feature of the exponential signal is made evident by writing $t = t + T$ in (3.3). The signal now becomes

$$y(t + T) = e^{j\omega_0(t + T)} = e^{j\omega_0 t}e^{j\omega_0 T} = e^{j\omega_0 t}e^{j2\pi} = e^{j\omega_0 t} = y(t)$$

since $e^{j2\pi} = \cos 2\pi + j \sin 2\pi = 1$. This shows that $e^{j\omega_0 t}$ is periodic with period T. The smallest value of t that makes $e^{j\omega_0 t}$ equal to unity is known as the **fundamental period**. Further, if we plot $e^{j\omega_0 t}$ on the complex plane as t varies, we observe a unit vector that rotates counterclockwise at the rate of $\omega_0/2\pi$ rev/s. Figure 3.1 shows the function $e^{j\omega_0 t}$ in the complex plane for the particular value $\omega_0 = 4\pi$ rad/s and for different values of t. Similarly, the signal $e^{-j\omega_0 t}$ is also periodic, but it rotates in the clockwise direction as time t varies. Of course, the components of $e^{j\omega_0 t}$, $\sin \omega_0 t$, and $\cos \omega_0 t$ are also periodic.

A signal that is closely related to the complex one is the sinusoid of the form

$$y(t) = A \cos (\omega_0 t + \phi) \tag{3.5}$$

This can also be written in the forms

$$y(t) = \frac{Ae^{j(\omega_0 t + \phi)} + Ae^{-j(\omega_0 t + \phi)}}{2} \tag{3.6a}$$

$$y(t) = A \operatorname{Re}\{e^{j(\omega_0 t + \phi)}\} \tag{3.6b}$$

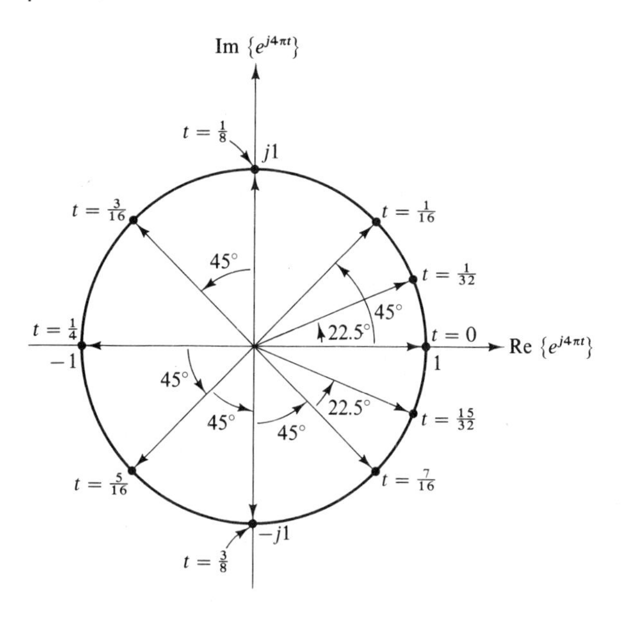

Figure 3.1 Complex Function $e^{j4\pi t}$ at Different Values of t

where Re{ } denotes the real part of the complex signal in the braces.

As already suggested, we can construct periodic nonsinusoidal signals using sinusoids at frequencies that are multiples of the **fundamental frequency** ω_0 (angular frequency). These sinusoids are of the form

$$y_k(t) = e^{jk\omega_0 t} \qquad k = 0, \pm 1, \pm 2, \ldots \tag{3.7}$$

We observe that for $k = 0$, $y_k(0) = 1$, a constant. Further, for any k, the signal $e^{jk\omega_0 t}$ has a frequency $|k|\omega_0/2\pi$ and fundamental period $2\pi/(|k|\omega_0) = 2\pi/(|k|2\pi/T) = T/|k|$. The real and imaginary parts of $y_1(t) = e^{j\omega_0 t}$, $y_2(t) = e^{j2\omega_0 t}$, and $y_4 = e^{j4\omega_0 t}$ are shown in Figure 3.2.

A feature of the complex functions $e^{jn\omega_0 t}$ for integral values of n $(-\infty < n < \infty)$ is that these functions constitute an orthogonal set over a full period (see Chapter 1). This means that

$$\int_0^T e^{jn\omega_0 t}(e^{jm\omega_0 t})^* \, dt = \int_0^T e^{j(n-m)\omega_0 t} \, dt = \begin{cases} T & n = m \\ 0 & n \neq m \end{cases} \tag{3.8}$$

Also, $\sin n\omega_0 t$ and $\cos n\omega_0 t$ constitute orthogonal sets, with

$$\int_0^T \cos(n\omega_0 t)\cos(m\omega_0 t)\, dt = \begin{cases} \dfrac{T}{2} & n = m \\ 0 & n \neq m \end{cases} \tag{3.9a}$$

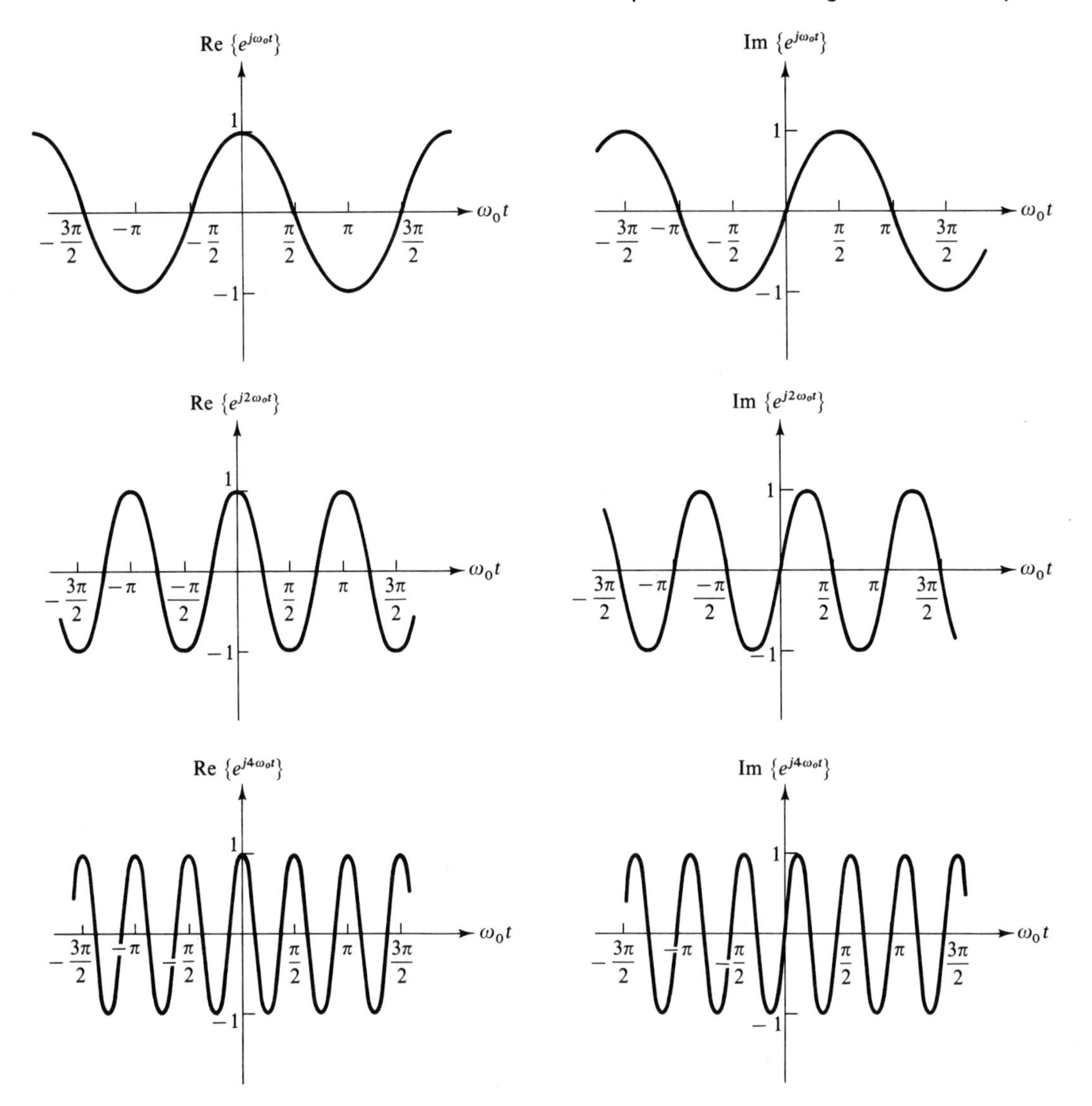

Figure 3.2 Real and Imaginary Parts of $e^{j\omega_0 t}$, $e^{j2\omega_0 t}$, and $e^{j4\omega_0 t}$

$$\int_0^T \sin(n\omega_0 t)\sin(m\omega_0 t)\,dt = \begin{cases} \dfrac{T}{2} & n = m \\ 0 & n \neq m \end{cases} \tag{3.9b}$$

These properties are of importance in the development of the Fourier series.

Discrete Time Signals. The equivalent exponential function in the discrete domain is

$$y(k) = e^{jk\Omega_0} \tag{3.10}$$

If we consider the new frequency $\Omega_0 + 2\pi$, we obtain

$$e^{j(\Omega_0 + 2\pi)k} = e^{j\Omega_0 k} e^{jk2\pi} = e^{jk\Omega_0} \tag{3.11}$$

This result indicates that the function at $\Omega_0 + 2\pi$ equals the same function at Ω_0. In fact, the functions are the same at Ω_0, $\Omega_0 + 2\pi$, $\Omega_0 + 4\pi$, and so forth. We thus conclude for discrete exponential signals that we need consider only the interval of length 2π, $0 \le \Omega_0 < 2\pi$ or $-\pi \le \Omega_0 < \pi$. This conclusion is different from that of the continuous case in which we have a different function for any distinct ω_0.

Figure 3.3 shows how $\sin k\Omega_0$ varies when Ω_0 is given different values in the range from 0 to π. Observe that $\sin k\Omega_0$ has the same values at $\Omega_0 = 0$ and π, as shown in Figures 3.3a and 3.3e. The values of $\sin k\Omega_0$ for Ω_0 equal to $3\pi/2 = 12\pi/8$, $7\pi/4 = 14\pi/8$, $15\pi/8$, and 2π are shown in Figures 3.3d, 3.3c, 3.3b, and 3.3a, respectively, with the difference that they will be reversed in polarity or sense. This polarity reversal results from the fact that the sine function is an odd function. This phenomenon does not occur if we plot the cosine function.

For the discrete function $e^{j\Omega_0 k}$ with period $K > 0$, we must have

$$e^{j\Omega_0(k+K)} = e^{j\Omega_0 k} e^{j\Omega_0 K} \tag{3.12}$$

which, for periodicity, requires that

$$e^{j\Omega_0 K} = 1 \tag{3.13}$$

This requires that

$$\Omega_0 K = n2\pi \qquad n = \text{integer} \tag{3.14}$$

or, equivalently,

$$\frac{\Omega_0}{2\pi} = \frac{n}{K} \tag{3.15}$$

This expression indicates that the ratio $\Omega_0/2\pi$ must be a rational number for the exponential function $e^{j\Omega_0 k}$ to be periodic.

When we wish to represent a continuous sinusoidal function by its discrete form representation, we must investigate whether or not the new function is periodic. For example, the function $f(t) = e^{j\omega_0 t}$ can be digitized to the form

$$f(kT) = e^{j(\omega_0 T)k} \tag{3.16}$$

which selects values of $f(t)$ at the time intervals $t = kT$. By comparing (3.16) with (3.13), we must conclude that the digitized function is periodic if

$$\frac{\omega_0 T}{2\pi} = \text{rational number} \tag{3.17}$$

This expression shows that although $e^{j\omega_0 t}$ is periodic, $e^{j\omega_0 kT}$ may not be.

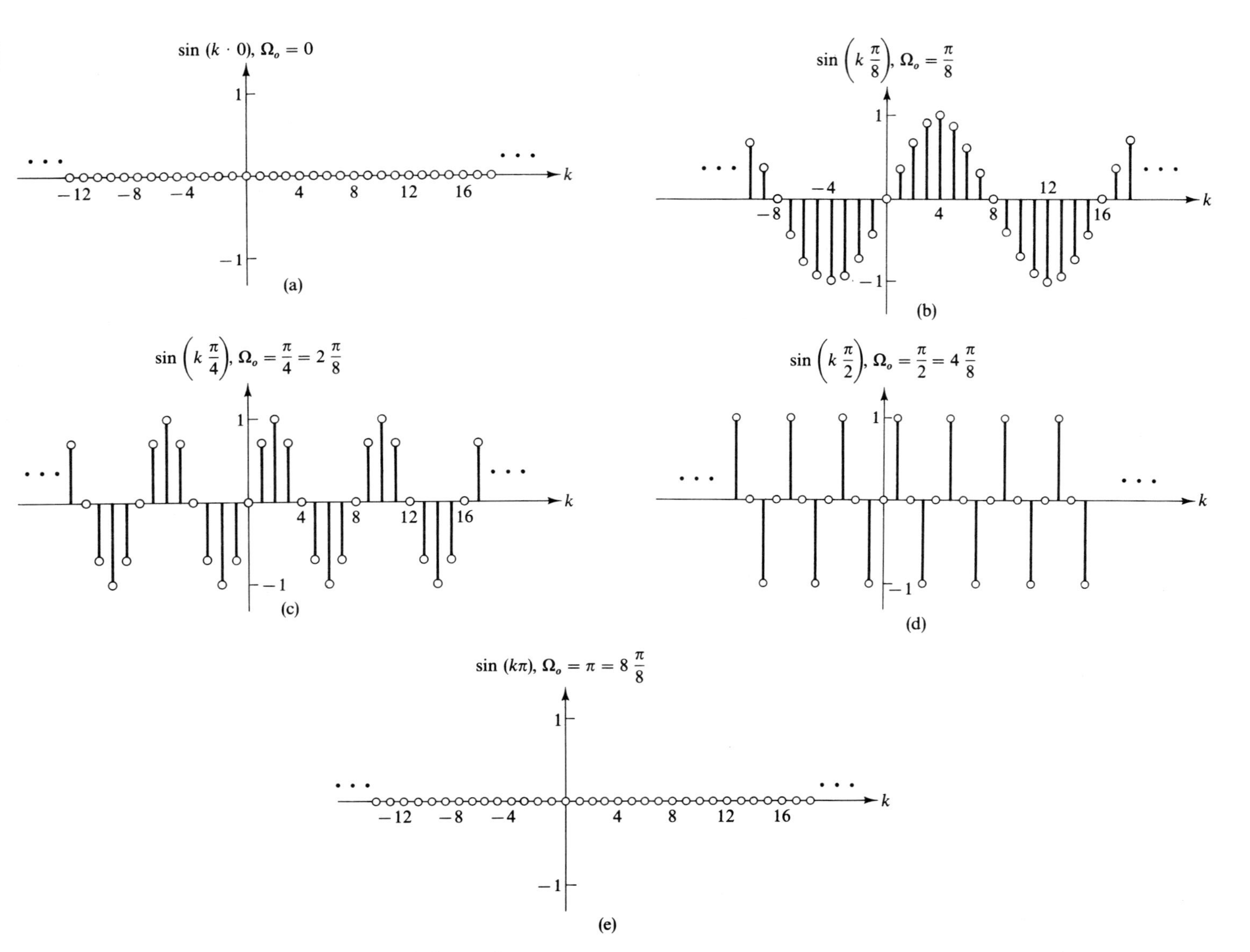

Figure 3.3 Discrete Sinusoidal Function for Different Frequencies

3.2 Fourier Series of Continuous Functions

One of the most frequent features of natural phenomena is **periodicity**. A wide range of periodic phenomena exist, such as the audible note of a mosquito, the beautiful patterns of crystal structures, the periodic vibrations of musical instruments, and acoustic and electromagnetic waves of most types. In all these phenomena, there is a pattern or displacement that repeats itself over and over again in time or in space. In some instances—for example, in wave patterns—the pattern itself moves in time. A periodic pattern might be a simple one, or it might be rather complicated, as shown in Figures 3.4a to 3.4e. It is important to our subsequent work that we understand the properties of periodic waves, or, equivalently, periodic functions.

Chapter 1 demonstrated that a function $f(t)$ (a physical pattern or phenomenon) is periodic with period T if it satisfies the condition

$$f(t + T) = f(t) \tag{3.18a}$$

or

$$f(t + nT) = f(t) \qquad n = 1, 2, \ldots \tag{3.18b}$$

for every t. We saw that $e^{j\omega_0 t}$ satisfied this condition of periodicity. Refer to Figure 3.5a, which shows a periodic or repetitive function, and to Figure 3.5b, which shows that we can create this periodic function by adding a basic functional form having a length equal to its period and appropriately displaced. We can write this latter function as the summation

$$f(t) = \sum_{n=-\infty}^{\infty} f_p(t - nT) \tag{3.19}$$

Chapter 1 stated that sine and cosine functions and, as a consequence, complex exponential functions constitute a set of orthogonal functions over one period and that these functions can be used to expand any periodic function in a series of such functions. This feature was emphasized again in Section 3.1. The use of complex exponential functions to study LTI system behavior is important since their response to such signals is easily obtained.

An important feature of a general periodic function is that it can be represented in terms of an infinite sum of sine and cosine functions that are themselves periodic. This series of sine and cosine terms is known as a **Fourier series**. For a function to be Fourier series transformable, it must possess properties known as the **Dirichlet conditions**, which ensure mathematical sufficiency, but not necessity. The Dirichlet conditions require that within a period:

1. Only a finite number of maximums and minimums can be present.
2. The number of discontinuities must be finite.
3. The discontinuities must be bounded. That is, the function must be absolutely integrable, which requires that $\int_0^T |f(t)|\, dt < \infty$.

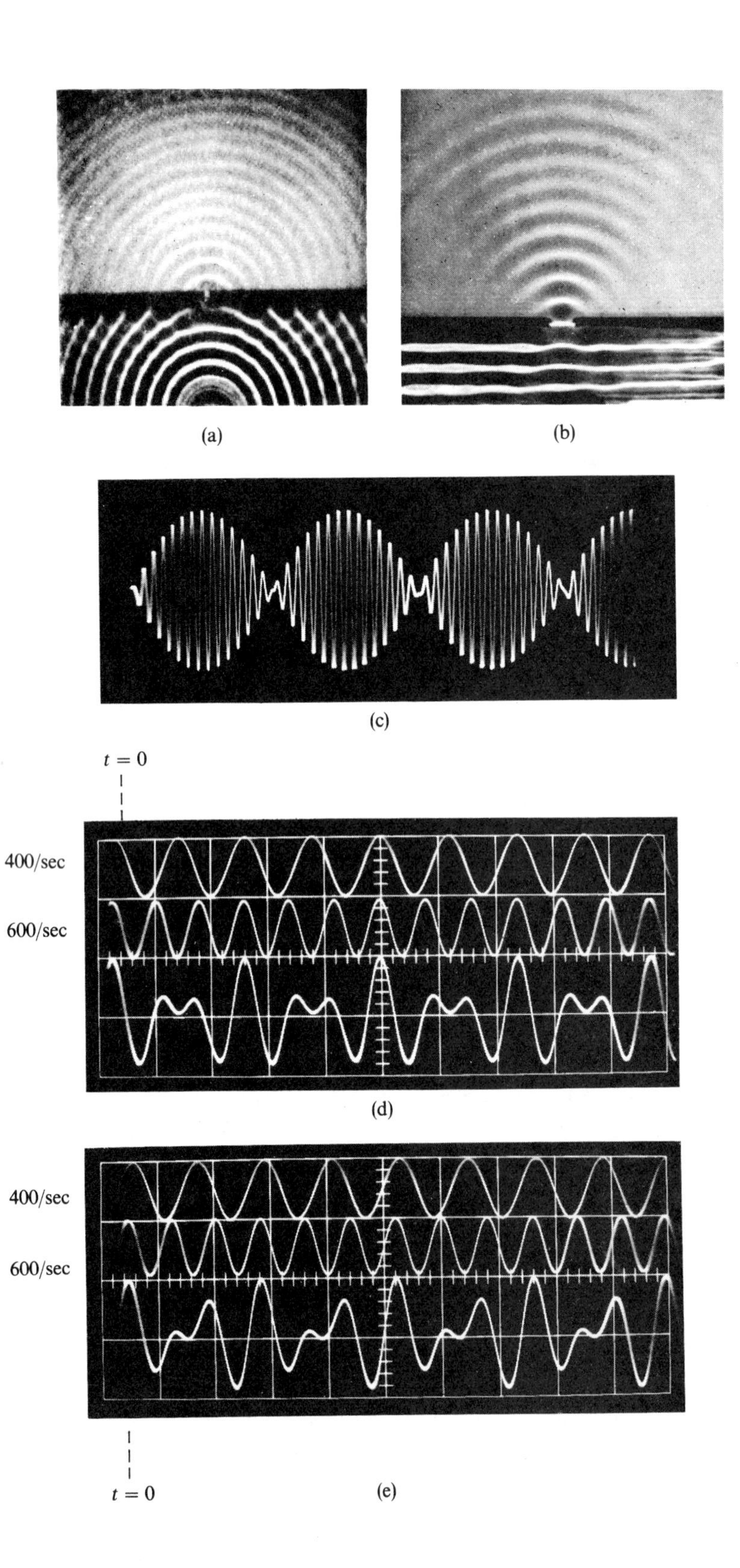
(a)
(b)
(c)
t = 0
400/sec
600/sec
(d)
400/sec
600/sec
t = 0
(e)

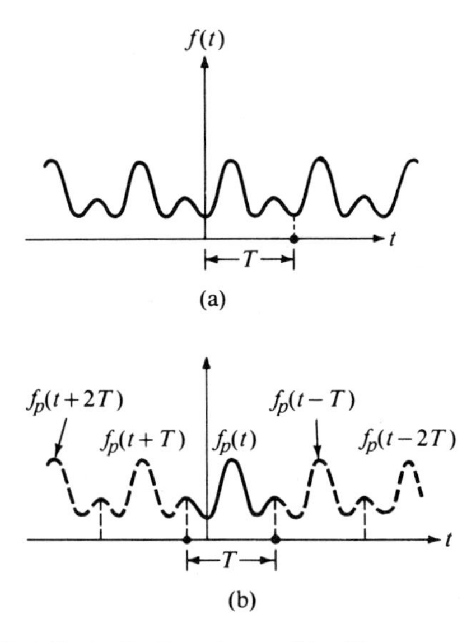

Figure 3.5 A Periodic Function and Its Elementary Representation

Fortunately, all of the periodic functions (phenomena) with which we deal in practice obey these conditions. The periodic functions shown in Figures 3.6a to 3.6c violate Dirichlet's conditions and are not amenable to Fourier series expansion.

A striking feature of the Fourier series is that it permits an arbitrary function, even a rough or discontinuous graph, defined over a finite interval to be represented as an infinite summation of sine and cosine terms, each of which is an analytic function. In this respect, the Fourier series is quite different from the Taylor series that allows us to find the value of an analytic function at a given point in terms of a knowledge of the value of the function an infinitesimal distance away. That is, the Fourier series gives a knowledge of the function over the entire range, whereas the Taylor series gives a strict prediction at a finite distance from a point. Another significant difference between the Fourier and Taylor expansions is that the coefficients of a Fourier series are obtained by integration, whereas the coefficients of a Taylor expansion are obtained by differentiation.

← **Figure 3.4** Examples of Periodic Signals. (a) and (b) Illustrating the generation of Huygens' wavelets at a narrow aperture in an advancing wavefront. (a) Circular primary waves. [From R.W. Pohl, *Physical Principles of Mechanics and Acoustics* (London: Blackie, 1932).] (b) Straight primary waves. (From the film "Ripple Tank Phenomena, Part II," Education Development Center, Newton, MA.) (c) Amplitude-modulated wave. (d) Superposition of two commensurable sinusoids of frequencies 400 s^{-1} and 600 s^{-1} whose maximums coincide at $t = 0$. (e) Superposition of same sinusoids if their zeros coincide at $t = 0$. [Photos (c), (d), and (e) by Jon Rosenfeld, Education Research Center, M.I.T., Cambridge, MA. Copyright © 1971 by The Massachusetts Institute of Technology.]

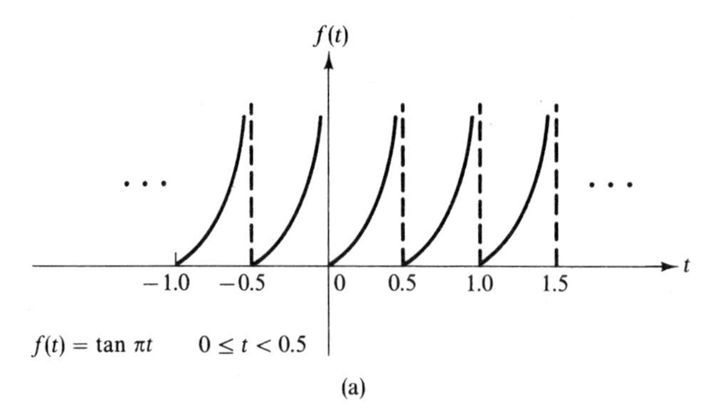

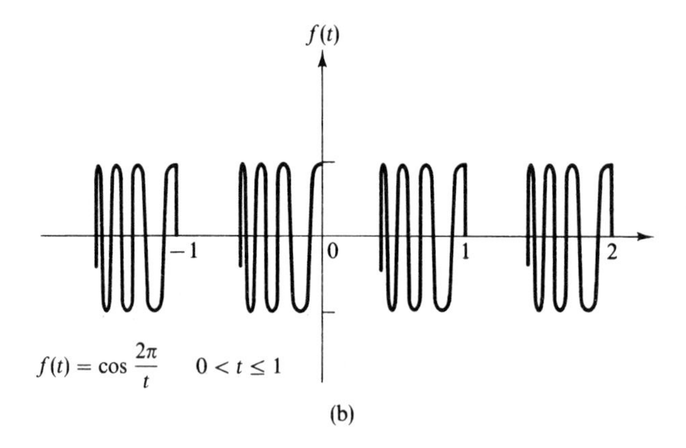

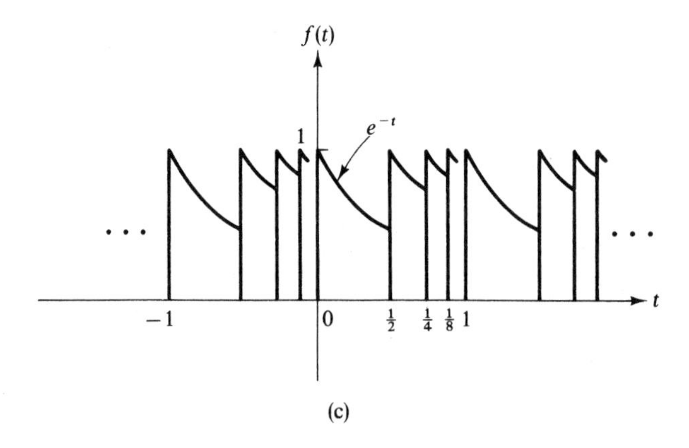

Figure 3.6 Signals That Violate Dirichlet Conditions. (a) Signal with infinite discontinuities. (b) Bounded signal with infinite variations. (c) Signal with infinite number of discontinuities.

Fourier Series in Complex Exponential Form. Any periodic signal $f(t)$ that satisfies the Dirichlet conditions can be expressed over an interval $t_0 \le t \le t_0 + T$, where T is the period, by the expansion

$$f(t) = \sum_{n=-\infty}^{\infty} \alpha_n e^{jn\omega_0 t} = \sum_{n=-\infty}^{\infty} |\alpha_n| e^{j(n\omega_0 t + \phi_n)} \qquad t_0 \le t \le t_0 + T \tag{3.20a}$$

where

$$\alpha_n = \frac{1}{T}\int_{t_0}^{t_0+T} f(t)e^{-jn\omega_0 t}\,dt = \text{complex constant} = |\alpha_n| e^{j\phi_n}$$

$$= |\alpha_n| \cos\phi_n + j|\alpha_n| \sin\phi_n \tag{3.20b}$$

$$\omega_0 = \frac{2\pi}{T}$$

Observe that the amplitudes α_n of the component terms in the Fourier series expansion of $f(t)$ are determined from the given $f(t)$. Correspondingly, $f(t)$ is determined from a knowledge of α_n. Often, these two related equations are referred to as a **Fourier series transform pair**—that is, knowing one equation, the second can be found, and vice versa. In addition, any periodic function that satisfies the Dirichlet conditions and is written in a Fourier series expansion converges at every point $t = t_0$ to $f(t_0)$ provided that the function is continuous at t_0. If $f(t)$ is discontinuous at $t = t_0$, the function $f(t_0)$ will converge to $f(t_0) = [f(t_0+) + f(t_0-)]/2$, the mean value at the point of discontinuity (the arithmetic mean of the left-hand and right-hand limits). If $f(t)$ is real, (3.20b) becomes

$$\alpha_{-n} = \frac{1}{T}\int_{t_0}^{t_0+T} f(t)e^{jn\omega_0 t}\,dt = \left[\frac{1}{T}\int_{t_0}^{t_0+T} f(t)e^{-jn\omega_0 t}\,dt\right]^* = \alpha_n^* \tag{3.21}$$

This result, when combined with (3.20a), yields

$$f(t) = \alpha_0 + \sum_{n=1}^{\infty} [(\alpha_n + \alpha_n^*) \cos n\omega_0 t + j(\alpha_n - \alpha_n^*)\sin n\omega_0 t] \tag{3.22}$$

■ **Example 3.1**

Find the coefficients α_n for the periodic function shown in Figure 3.7a.

Solution Apply (3.20b) to obtain

$$\alpha_n = \frac{1}{3.5}\int_{-0.5}^{3} f(t)e^{-jn\omega_0 t}\,dt = \frac{1}{3.5}\left[\int_{-0.5}^{1} 1e^{-jn\omega_0 t}\,dt + \int_{1}^{3} 0 \cdot e^{-jn\omega_0 t}\,dt\right]$$

$$= \frac{1}{3.5(-jn\omega_0)} e^{-jn\omega_0 t}\Big|_{-0.5}^{1} = \frac{1}{-j3.5n\omega_0}(e^{-jn\omega_0} - e^{j0.5n\omega_0})$$

To find the value of α_0, set $n = 0$ in (3.20b) and integrate; the value $\alpha_0 = 3/7$.

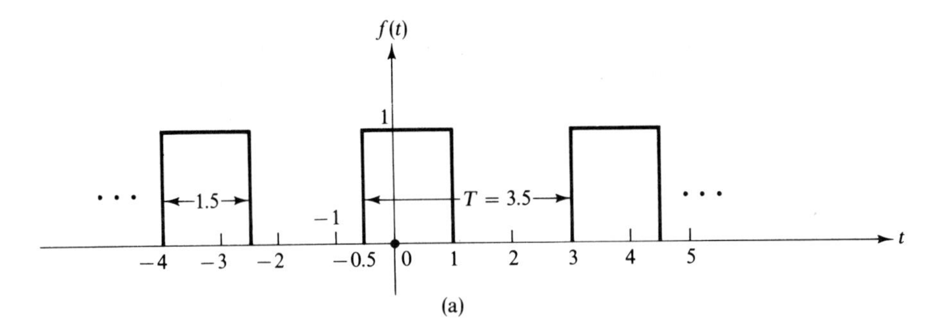

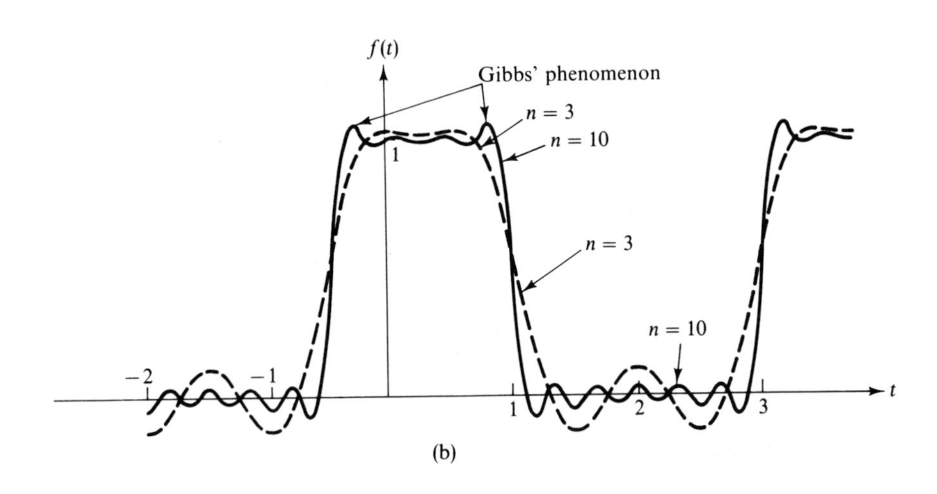

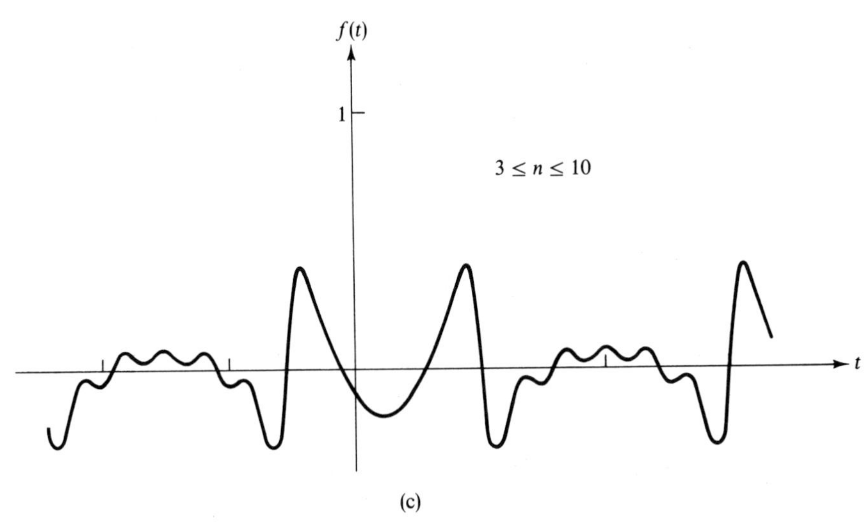

Figure 3.7 A Square Periodic Function and Its Fourier Representation

For the values α_{-n}, the complex conjugate values of α_n, it is only necessary to change the sign in front of each j in the equation for α_n. The result is

$$f(t) = \frac{3}{7} + \sum_{n=1}^{\infty} \left\{ \left[\frac{1}{-j3.5n\omega_0} (e^{-jn\omega_0} - e^{j0.5n\omega_0}) \right.\right.$$

$$\left. + \frac{1}{j3.5n\omega_0} (e^{jn\omega_0} - e^{-j0.5n\omega_0}) \right] \cos n\omega_0 t + j \left[\frac{1}{-j3.5n\omega_0} \right.$$

$$\left.\left. \times (e^{-jn\omega_0} - e^{+j0.5n\omega_0}) - \frac{1}{j3.5n\omega_0} (e^{jn\omega_0} - e^{-j0.5n\omega_0}) \right] \sin n\omega_0 t \right\}$$

$$= \frac{3}{7} + \sum_{n=1}^{\infty} \left[\frac{2}{3.5n\omega_0} (\sin n\omega_0 + \sin 0.5n\omega_0) \cos n\omega_0 t - \frac{2}{3.5n\omega_0} \right.$$

$$\left. \times (\cos n\omega_0 - \cos 0.5n\omega_0) \sin n\omega_0 t \right]$$

$$= \frac{3}{7} + \sum_{n=1}^{\infty} \left[\frac{4}{3.5n\omega_0} [(\sin 0.75n\omega_0 \cos 0.25n\omega_0) \cos n\omega_0 t \right.$$

$$\left. + (\sin 0.75n\omega_0 \sin 0.25n\omega_0) \sin n\omega_0 t] \right] \tag{3.23}$$

The plots in Figure 3.7b show (3.23) for $n = 3$ and $n = 10$.

We observe from Figure 3.7b that an overshoot occurs at each point of discontinuity. It was shown by Gibbs that the overshoot remains at about 10% at the edge, regardless of the number of terms included in the expansion, although the rest of the undulations decrease with increasing n. This property is known as the **Gibbs' phenomenon**. Figure 3.7c shows the deviation of the reconstructed wave from the original square wave based on the terms $n = 3$ through $n = 10$. Observe that the deviations are greatest at the points of discontinuity. Further, the number of undulations increases with the number of terms used in the expansion, although the resulting amplitudes of the deviations decrease with the number of terms. We conclude from this discussion that the high frequencies in the expansion contribute in building the discontinuities of the function. Thus, if a periodic nonsinusoidal signal is applied to a system and if the higher frequencies in the expansion are attenuated more than the lower frequencies, the output signal will be smoother than the input. This feature of frequency-selective attenuation is very important in our studies of signals and systems.

A similar phenomenon is observed when we look at a digitized picture closely and at a distance: The picture loses its sharpness as the observation distance increases (see Figure 8.2). The loss of sharpness is due to the fact that the high frequencies needed to reconstruct the image are lost as the image is transmitted through our own visual system—our eye–brain combination. ■

Fourier Series in Trigonometric Form. The Fourier series expansion given by (3.22) can be written

$$f(t) = \frac{A_0}{2} + \sum_{n=1}^{\infty} (A_n \cos n\omega_0 t + B_n \sin n\omega_0 t) \tag{3.24}$$

where

$$A_0 = 2\alpha_0 = \frac{2}{T} \int_{t_0}^{t_0+T} f(t)\, dt \tag{3.25a}$$

$$A_n = (\alpha_n + \alpha_n^*) = \frac{2}{T} \int_{t_0}^{t_0+T} f(t) \cos n\omega_0 t\, dt \tag{3.25b}$$

$$B_n = j(\alpha_n - \alpha_n^*) = \frac{2}{T} \int_{t_0}^{t_0+T} f(t) \sin n\omega_0 t\, dt \tag{3.25c}$$

These expressions for the coefficients A_n and B_n in (3.25) can be obtained directly from (3.24). Thus, to find A_0, multiply all terms in (3.24) by dt and integrate over a full period. The result is

$$\int_{t_0}^{t_0+T} f(t)\, dt = \frac{A_0}{2} \int_{t_0}^{t_0+T} dt + A_n \sum_{n=1}^{\infty} \int_{t_0}^{t_0+T} \cos n\omega_0 t\, dt$$
$$+ B_n \sum_{n=1}^{\infty} \int_{t_0}^{t_0+T} \sin n\omega_0 t\, dt$$

The trigonometric terms integrate to zero, leaving only

$$\int_{t_0}^{t_0+T} f(t)\, dt = \frac{A_0}{2} \int_{t_0}^{t_0+T} dt = A_0 \frac{T}{2}$$

which is (3.25a). To find A_n, multiply all terms in (3.24) by $\cos m\omega_0 t\, dt$ and integrate over a full period. This yields

$$\int_{t_0}^{t_0+T} f(t) \cos m\omega_0 t\, dt = \frac{A_0}{2} \int_{t_0}^{t_0+T} \cos m\omega_0 t\, dt$$
$$+ \sum_{n=1}^{\infty} A_n \int_{t_0}^{t_0+T} \cos n\omega_0 t \cos m\omega_0 t\, dt$$
$$+ \sum_{n=1}^{\infty} B_n \int_{t_0}^{t_0+T} \sin n\omega_0 t \cos m\omega_0 t\, dt$$

By the orthogonality relationships, every integral on the right-hand side becomes zero except the single expression for $n = m$ in the form

$$\int_{t_0}^{t_0+T} f(t) \cos n\omega_0 t\, dt = A_n \int_{t_0}^{t_0+T} \cos^2 n\omega_0 t\, dt = A_n \frac{T}{2}$$

Similarly, by multiplying all terms in (3.24) by $\sin m\omega_0 t\, dt$ and integrating over a full period, (3.25c) results.

Table 3.1 Forms of Fourier Series for Real Functions

Complex Form	Formulas for the Coefficients	
$f(t) = \sum_{n=-\infty}^{\infty} \alpha_n e^{jn\omega_0 t}$	$\omega_0 = \dfrac{2\pi}{T}$	$A_0 = 2\alpha_0$
$= \sum_{n=-\infty}^{\infty} \lvert\alpha_n\rvert e^{j(n\omega_0 t + \phi_n)}$	$\alpha_n = \lvert\alpha_n\rvert e^{j\phi_n}$	$A_n = \alpha_n + \alpha_n^* = 2\,\mathrm{Re}\{\alpha_n\}$
	$\alpha_n = \dfrac{1}{T}\int_{t_0}^{t_0+T} f(t)e^{-jn\omega_0 t}\,dt$	$B_n = j(\alpha_n - \alpha_n^*) = -2\,\mathrm{Im}\{\alpha_n\}$
	$t_0 \le t \le t_0 + T$	$C_n = [A_n^2 + B_n^2]^{1/2}$
Trigonometric Forms		$\phi_n = -\tan^{-1}[B_n/A_n]$
$f(t) = \dfrac{A_0}{2} + \sum_{n=1}^{\infty}(A_n \cos n\omega_0 t + B_n \sin n\omega_0 t)$	$A_n = \dfrac{2}{T}\int_{t_0}^{t_0+T} f(t)\cos n\omega_0 t\,dt$	$A_n = C_n \cos \phi_n$
	$n = 1, 2, \ldots$	$B_n = -C_n \sin \phi_n$
$f(t) = \dfrac{A_0}{2} + \sum_{n=1}^{\infty} C_n \cos(n\omega_0 t + \phi_n)$	$B_n = \dfrac{2}{T}\int_{t_0}^{t_0+T} f(t)\sin n\omega_0 t\,dt$	
	$n = 1, 2, \ldots$	

We can write (3.24) in a slightly different form:

$$f(t) = \frac{A_0}{2} + \sum_{n=1}^{\infty} A_n\left(\cos n\omega_0 t + \frac{B_n}{A_n}\sin n\omega_0 t\right)$$

$$= \frac{A_0}{2} + \sum_{n=1}^{\infty} A_n(\cos n\omega_0 t - \tan\phi_n \sin n\omega_0 t)$$

$$= \frac{A_0}{2} + \sum_{n=1}^{\infty} \frac{A_n}{\cos\phi_n}\cos(n\omega_0 t + \phi_n)$$

$$= \frac{A_0}{2} + \sum_{n=1}^{\infty} C_n \cos(n\omega_0 t + \phi_n) \tag{3.26a}$$

where

$$\phi_n = -\tan^{-1}(B_n/A_n) \qquad C_n = (A_n^2 + B_n^2)^{1/2} \tag{3.26b}$$

The foregoing results are summarized in Table 3.1.

■ Example 3.2

Develop the trigonometric forms of the Fourier series for the periodic function given in Example 3.1.

Solution By (3.25), we find

$$A_n = \frac{2}{3.5}\int_{-0.5}^{3} f(t)\cos n\omega_0 t\,dt = \frac{2}{3.5}\int_{-0.5}^{1} \cos n\omega_0 t\,dt$$

$$= \frac{2}{3.5n\omega_0}(\sin n\omega_0 + \sin 0.5n\omega_0)$$

$$A_0 = \frac{2}{3.5}\int_{-0.5}^{1} 1\,dt = \frac{3}{3.5}$$

$$B_n = \frac{2}{3.5}\int_{-0.5}^{3} f(t)\sin n\omega_0 t\,dt = \frac{2}{3.5}\int_{-0.5}^{1} \sin n\omega_0 t\,dt$$

$$= \frac{2}{3.5n\omega_0}(\cos 0.5n\omega_0 - \cos n\omega_0)$$

Introduce these constants in (3.24) to obtain (3.23).

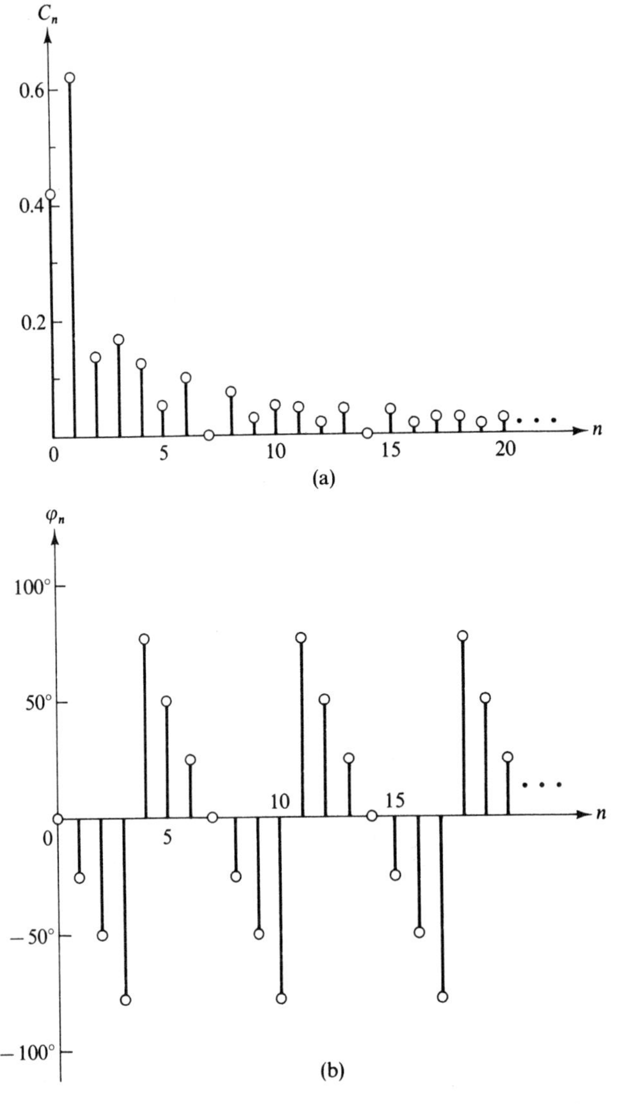

Figure 3.8 Amplitude and Phase Spectrums for the Signal Shown in Figure 3.7a

By (3.26a) and (3.26b), we obtain expressions for C_n and ϕ_n that are required for the alternate form of the Fourier series. These are

$$C_n = \left\{\left[\frac{2}{3.5n\omega_0}(\sin n\omega_0 + \sin 0.5n\omega_0)\right]^2 + \left[\frac{2}{3.5n\omega_0}(\cos 0.5n\omega_0 - \cos n\omega_0)\right]^2\right\}^{1/2}$$

$$\phi_n = -\tan^{-1}\left(\frac{\cos 0.5n\omega_0 - \cos n\omega_0}{\sin n\omega_0 + \sin 0.5n\omega_0}\right)$$

These are plotted in Figures 3.8a and 3.8b. The coefficients C_n are known as the **amplitude spectrum** and the phase ϕ_n is the **phase spectrum.** Specifying amplitude and phase spectrums is a very important concept in describing complex

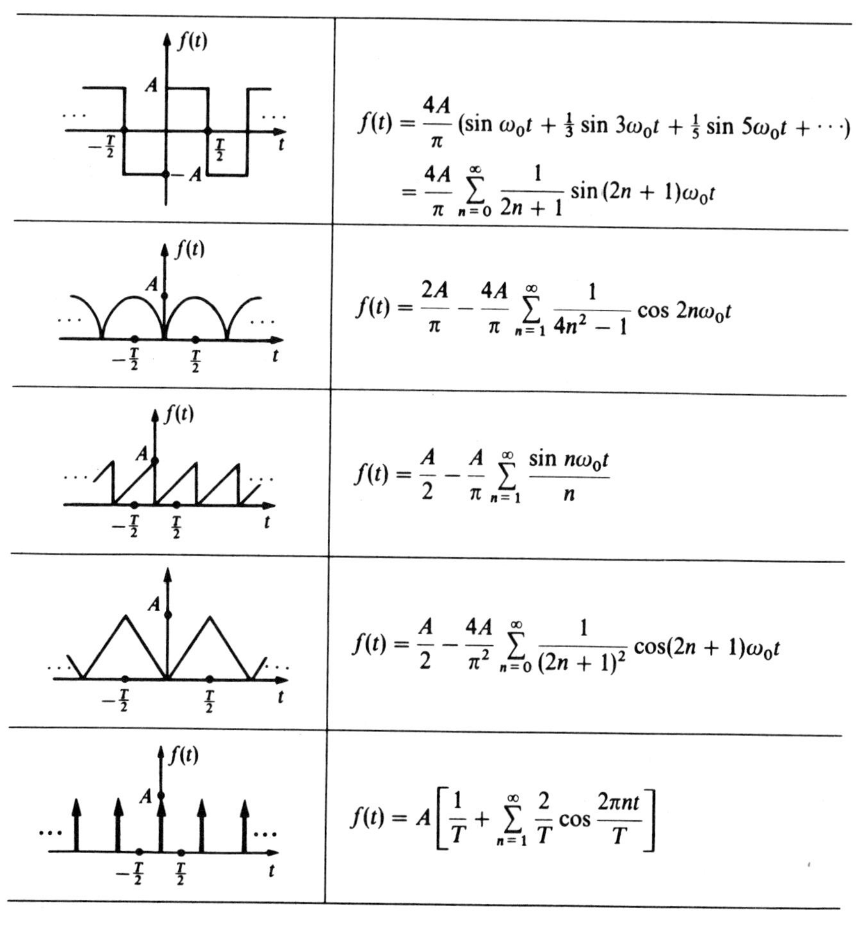

Figure 3.9 Examples of Fourier Series

waves, and the student should be familiar with it. We will find that the amplitude spectrum contains information about the energy content of a signal and the distribution of the energy among the different frequencies (see Section 3.3). A knowledge of the spectrum of a wave is important in many practical applications. For example, an electrocardiogram of the heart or a signal from an engine may reveal abnormal operation and possible imminent failure. ■

Figure 3.9 on page 149 contains a number of useful periodic functions and their Fourier series representations. Observe that the derivative of the fourth entry in this figure is the first entry, a result also confirmed by their respective Fourier series expansions. Ordinarily, however, the derivative of a Fourier series does not represent the derivative of the function itself.

3.3 Features of Periodic Continuous Functions

Parseval's Formula. One important property of continuous periodic functions is the energy relation known as the **Parseval formula**. Consider a periodic function $f(t)$ that is represented in its Fourier series expansion

$$f(t) = \frac{A_0}{2} + \sum_{n=1}^{\infty} C_n \cos(n\omega_0 t + \phi_n) \tag{3.27}$$

The mean value of $f^2(t)$ over a period is given by

$$\begin{aligned}\frac{1}{T}\int_{t_0}^{t_0+T} f(t)^2\, dt &= \int_{t_0}^{t_0+T} \frac{1}{T}\left[\frac{A_0}{2} + \sum_{n=1}^{\infty} C_n \cos(n\omega_0 t + \phi_n)\right] \\ &\quad \times \left[\frac{A_0}{2} + \sum_{m=1}^{\infty} C_m \cos(m\omega_0 t + \phi_m)\right] dt\end{aligned} \tag{3.28}$$

We can see that the terms in the integrand will be of the form $C_n C_m \cos(n\omega_0 t + \phi_m)\cos(m\omega_0 t + \phi_m)$. These terms are periodic within a period T, and the value of the integrals for $n \neq m$ will vanish. The remaining integrands for $n = m$ will be of the form $C_n^2 \cos^2(n\omega_0 t + \phi_n)$, and these integrals have the value $C_n^2/2$. Hence, (3.28) becomes

$$\boxed{\frac{1}{T}\int_{t_0}^{t_0+T} f(t)^2\, dt = \frac{A_0^2}{4} + \sum_{n=1}^{\infty} \frac{C_n^2}{2}} \tag{3.29}$$

This result is the **energy relation** and it can be considered as the energy dissipated during 1 period by a 1 Ω resistor when a voltage source $f(t)$ is applied to it. If $f(t)$ denotes a current, this result specifies that the root-mean-square (rms) value squared of the current is the sum of the dc component and the rms values of the ac components. In other words, the total power is the power of the dc component plus the power of all the ac components.

■ Example 3.3

Find the energy associated with the terms $n = 3$ to $n = \infty$ in the Fourier series expansion of the periodic function of Example 3.2.

Solution Use (3.29) and the results of Example 3.2 to write

$$\frac{1}{3.5}\int_{-0.5}^{1} dt - \frac{1}{4}\left(\frac{3}{7}\right)^2 - \frac{C_1^2}{2} - \frac{C_2^2}{2} = \sum_{n=3}^{\infty} \frac{C_n^2}{2}$$

or

$$\sum_{n=3}^{\infty} \frac{C_n^2}{2} = \frac{1.5}{3.5} - \frac{9}{196} - \frac{1}{2}\left[\left[\frac{2}{3.5(2\pi/3.5)}\left(\sin\frac{2\pi}{3.5} + \sin\frac{0.5\times 2\pi}{3.5}\right)\right]^2 + \left[\frac{2}{3.5(2\pi/3.5)}\left(\cos\frac{0.5\times 2\pi}{3.5} - \cos\frac{2\pi}{3.5}\right)\right]^2\right]$$
$$- \frac{1}{2}\left[\left[\frac{2}{3.5\times 2\times(2\pi/3.5)}\left(\sin\frac{4\pi}{3.5} + \sin\frac{2\pi}{3.5}\right)\right]^2 + \left[\frac{2}{3.5\times 2(2\pi/3.5)}\left(\cos\frac{2\pi}{3.5} - \cos\frac{4\pi}{3.5}\right)\right]^2\right] = 0.1805$$

This result shows that most of the energy is contained in the dc component and a few of the low-frequency harmonics. ■

Symmetric Functions. There are two very important symmetries of real periodic functions: **zero-axis** (even) symmetry and **zero-point** (odd) symmetry. An even function has symmetry about the axis $t = 0$, and an odd function has symmetry about the origin. These features are illustrated in Figure 3.10.

Even Function. An even periodic function is defined by $f(-t) = f(t) = f_e(t)$. It follows from (3.25c) that all coefficients B_n are zero since the integrand is (even × odd =) odd. The Fourier series expansion becomes

$$f_e(t) = \frac{A_0}{2} + \sum_{n=1}^{\infty} A_n \cos n\omega_0 t \qquad \textbf{(3.30a)}$$

where

$$A_n = \frac{4}{T}\int_{t_0}^{t_0+(T/2)} f_e(t) \cos n\omega_0 t \, dt \qquad \textbf{(3.30b)}$$

Odd Function. An odd periodic function is one for which $f(-t) = -f(-t) = f_0(t)$. From (3.25b), all $A_n = 0$, and the Fourier expansion becomes

$$f_0(t) = \sum_{n=1}^{\infty} B_n \sin n\omega_0 t \qquad \textbf{(3.31a)}$$

where

$$B_n = \frac{4}{T}\int_{t_0}^{t_0+(T/2)} f_0(t) \sin n\omega_0 t \, dt \qquad \textbf{(3.31b)}$$

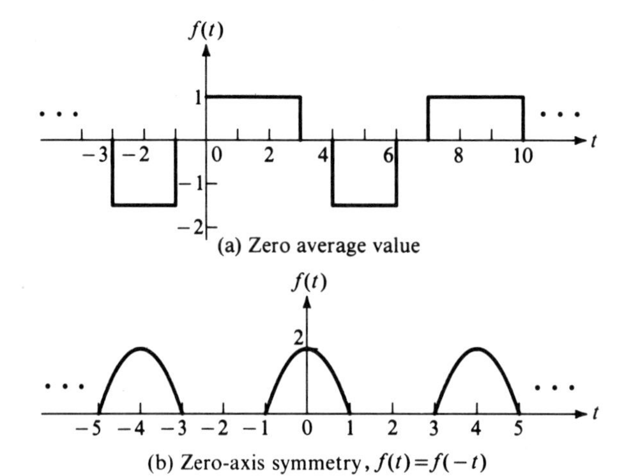

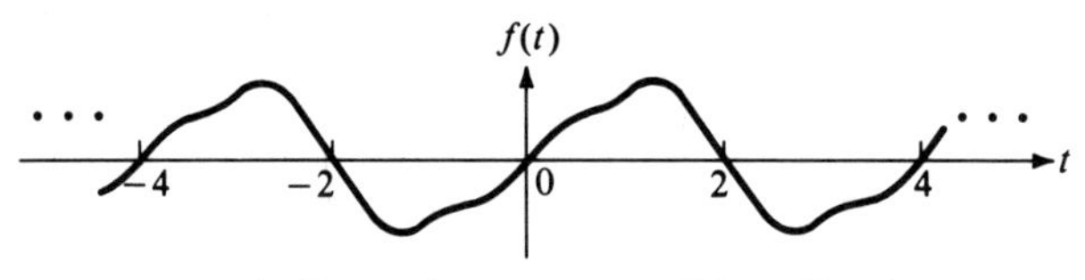

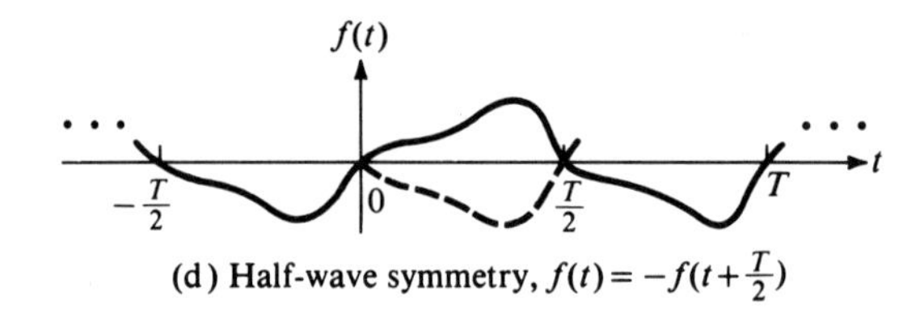

Figure 3.10 Illustrations of Types of Symmetry. (a) Zero average value. (b) Zero-axis symmetry, $f(t) = f(-t)$. (c) Zero-point symmetry, $f(t) = -f(-t)$. (d) Half-wave symmetry, $f(t) = -f[t + (T/2)]$.

Table 3.2 Symmetries and the Fourier Coefficients

Symmetry	Mathematical Requirements	A_0	A_n	B_n	Special Remarks
Even	$f(t) = f(-t)$	Exist	Exist	0	Integration required over half-cycle
Odd	$f(t) = -f(-t)$	0	0	Exist	Integration required over half-cycle
Half-wave	$f(t) = -f[t + (T/2)]$	0	Exist	Exist	Integration over half-cycle, no even terms in the expansion

Clearly, a recognition of the existence of one or more symmetries will result in the simplification of the computation of the harmonic coefficients. The consequences of these symmetries are given in Table 3.2.

It is important to realize that any periodic function can be resolved into even and odd parts. This follows because we can write $f(t)$ in the equivalent form

$$f(t) = \underbrace{\frac{f(t) + f(-t)}{2}}_{\text{even}} + \underbrace{\frac{f(t) - f(-t)}{2}}_{\text{odd}} \tag{3.32a}$$

The illustration in Figure 3.11 shows the construction of a function $f(t)$ from its even and odd parts. From (3.30) and (3.31), the series is

$$f(t) = \frac{A_0}{2} + \sum_{n=1}^{\infty} A_n \cos n\omega_0 t + \sum_{n=1}^{\infty} B_n \sin n\omega_0 t \tag{3.32b}$$

where the A_n's are deduced from (3.30b) and the B_n's from (3.31b).

Choice of Origin. The form of the Fourier series of a given wave is dependent on the origin about which the representation is to be developed. It is possible to use the series representation of a given wave specified about one origin to yield the series representation of the wave relative to another origin. This result is important, as it is often easier to find the Fourier series relative to one origin and then shift the origin to a previously specified point in the wave.

To examine the situation, refer to the square wave illustrated in Figure 3.12. The Fourier representation of this wave relative to an axis at point 0 is given by (see Figure 3.9)

$$f(x) = \frac{4}{\pi}\left(\sin x + \frac{1}{3}\sin 3x + \frac{1}{5}\sin 5x + \cdots\right) \tag{3.33}$$

If the Fourier series representation is desired relative to the axis at 0′, a distance $\pi/2$ to the right of point 0, we note that $f(x)$ relative to point 0′ is $f[x - (\pi/2)]$. The

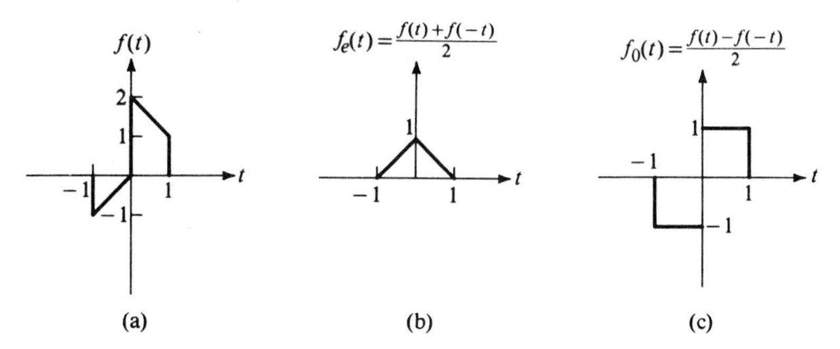

Figure 3.11 Construction of a Signal from Its Even and Odd Parts. (a) Given wave. (b) Even part. (c) Odd part.

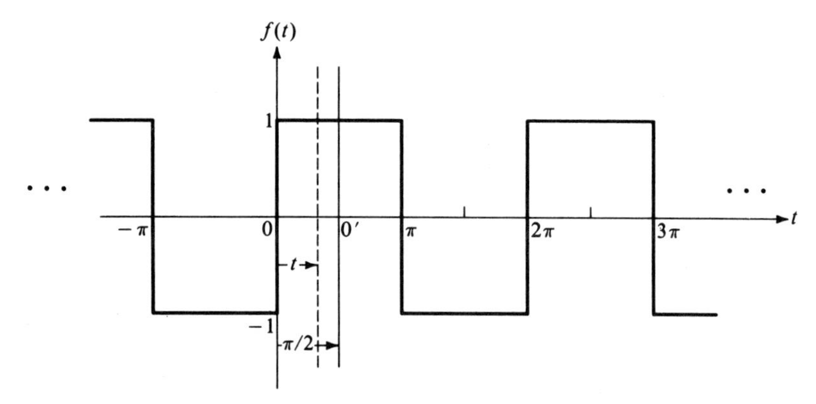

Figure 3.12 A Square Wave and the Reference Origins 0 and 0′

Fourier series for the square wave relative to point 0′ is obtained by replacing x by $x - \pi/2$ in (3.33). The result is

$$f(x) = \frac{4}{\pi}\left[\sin\,[x - (\pi/2)] + \frac{1}{3}\sin[3(x - \pi/2)] + \frac{1}{5}\sin\,5[x - (\pi/2)] + \cdots\right]$$

which can be written

$$f(x) = \frac{4}{\pi}\left[\cos x - \frac{1}{3}\cos 3x + \frac{1}{5}\cos 5x - \cdots\right] \tag{3.34}$$

These results can be generalized to the following statements:

1. If the Fourier series of a periodic wave $f(x)$ is known relative to one origin, the Fourier series relative to another origin at an angle θ to the *left* is obtained from the first series by writing $x + \theta$ for x in each term of the series.
2. If the new origin is to the *right* by an angle θ, write $x - \theta$ in each term of $f(x)$.

Note that by shifting, we find that new terms may occur since, for example, $\cos(x - \theta) = \cos x \cos \theta + \sin x \sin \theta$.

■ Example 3.4

Deduce the Fourier series expansion of the square wave in Figure 3.7a relative to an axis centered in the square wave. From this result, show the relation to the original axis.

Solution For the specified origin, the wave possesses even symmetry; hence, $B_n = 0$. We then have

$$A_0 = \frac{2}{3.5}\int_{-0.75}^{0.75} dt = \frac{2}{3.5} \times 1.5 = \frac{3}{3.5}$$

$$A_n = \frac{4}{3.5}\int_0^{0.75} 1 \times \cos n\omega_0 t \, dt = \frac{4}{3.5n\omega_0} \sin n\omega_0 t \Big|_0^{0.75}$$
$$= \frac{4}{3.5n\omega_0} \sin 0.75n\omega_0$$

and the Fourier series representation is

$$f(t) = \frac{3}{7} + \sum_{n=1}^{\infty} \left(\frac{4}{3.5n\omega_0} \sin 0.75n\omega_0 \right) \cos n\omega_0 t$$

To refer this expression to the original zero axis, we replace t by $t + 0.25$. The result is

$$f(t) = \frac{3}{7} + \sum_{n=1}^{\infty} \left(\frac{4}{3.5n\omega_0} \sin 0.75n\omega_0 \right) \cos n\omega_0(t + 0.25) \tag{3.35}$$

It can be shown that this form is the same as (3.23). ■

Finite Signals. It can be shown that a continuous function $f(t)$ within an interval $t_0 \leq t \leq t_0 + T$ can be approximated by a trigonometric polynomial of the form given in (3.24) to any degree of accuracy specified in advance. To approximate function $f(t)$ shown in Figure 3.13a, the periodic function $f_p(t)$ shown in Figure 3.13b is created. The expansion then proceeds as before for the periodic function, but the final range of applicability is limited to the range of the original function. The solution is then specified as

$$f(t) = \begin{cases} \sum_{n=-\infty}^{\infty} \alpha_n e^{jn\omega_0 t} & -a \leq t \leq c \\ 0 & t < -a \quad t > c \end{cases} \tag{3.36}$$

where

$$\alpha_n = \frac{1}{T}\int_{t_0}^{t_0+T} f_p(t) e^{-jn\omega_0 t} \, dt$$

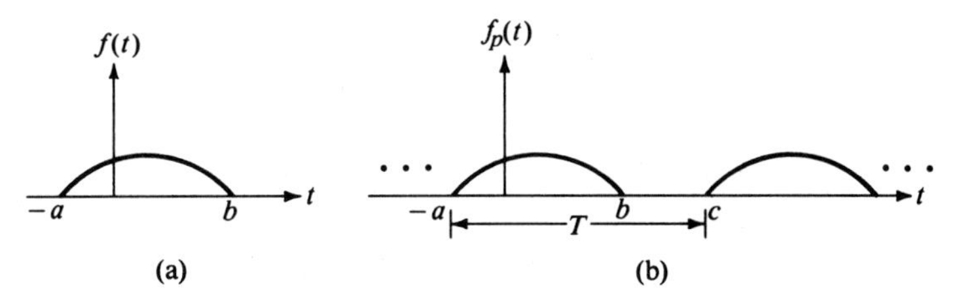

Figure 3.13 Representation of a Nonperiodic Function by a Fourier Series

Convolution. As a continuation of the discussion of convolution begun in Section 2.9, let us consider the special case when $f(t)$ and $h(t)$ are periodic functions with the same period. We will find that the convolution integral assumes special properties. **Periodic,** or **cyclic, convolution** is defined by the integral

$$g(t) = \frac{1}{T} \int_0^T f(\tau)h(t - \tau)\, d\tau \tag{3.37}$$

where the integral is taken over one period. In this case, $g(t)$ is also periodic. To show that $g(t)$ is periodic, consider the integral

$$g_p(t) = \frac{1}{T} \int_c^{c+T} f(\tau)h(t - \tau)\, d\tau \tag{3.38}$$

and choose $c = kT + a$ with $0 \leq a \leq T$. Equation (3.38) then becomes

$$\begin{aligned} g_p(t) &= \frac{1}{T} \int_{kT+a}^{kT+a+T} f(\tau)h(t - \tau)\, d\tau \\ &= \frac{1}{T} \int_0^T f(\tau' + kT + a)h[t - (\tau' + kT + a)]\, d\tau' \\ &= \frac{1}{T} \int_0^T f(\tau')h(t - \tau')\, d\tau' = g(t) \end{aligned}$$

Since $f(t)$ and $h(t)$ are periodic, this result shows that $g(t)$ is periodic.

Now, since $g(t)$ is periodic, we can express it in a Fourier series expansion with coefficients:

$$\alpha_n = \frac{1}{T} \int_{-T/2}^{T/2} g(t)e^{-jn\omega_0 t}\, dt = \frac{1}{T^2} \iint_{-T/2}^{T/2} f(\tau)h(t - \tau)e^{-jn\omega_0 t}\, dt\, d\tau$$

We write this

$$\alpha_n = \frac{1}{T} \int_{-T/2}^{T/2} f(\tau)e^{-jn\omega_0 \tau}\, d\tau \cdot \frac{1}{T} \int_{-T/2}^{T/2} h(t - \tau)e^{-jn\omega_0 (t-\tau)}\, dt \tag{3.39}$$

Write $t - \tau = \tau'$ in the second integral, and so

$$\alpha_n = \frac{1}{T} \int_{-T/2}^{T/2} f(\tau)e^{-jn\omega_0 \tau}\, d\tau \times \frac{1}{T} \int_{(-T/2)+\tau}^{(T/2)-\tau} h(\tau')e^{-jn\omega_0 \tau'}\, d\tau'$$

However, for periodic functions, the integration of the second integral is independent of a shift τ. Then

$$\alpha_n = \beta_n \gamma_n \tag{3.40}$$

where the coefficients β_n and γ_n belong to the functions $f(t)$ and $h(t)$, respectively.

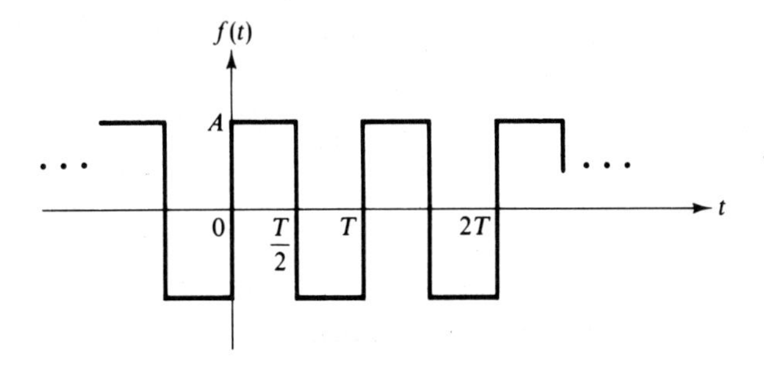

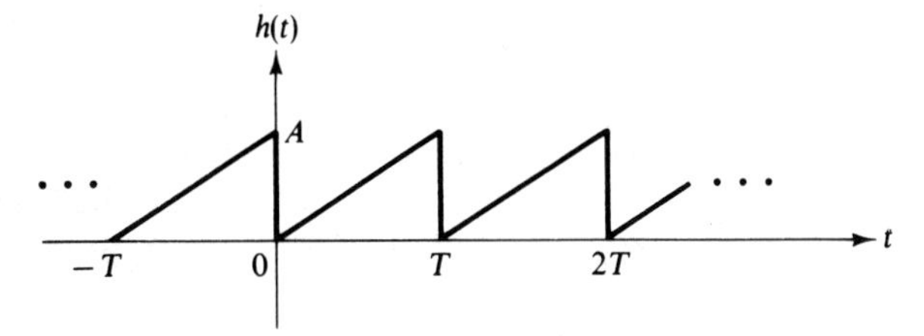

Figure 3.14 Waveforms for Example 3.5

Therefore, we have that

$$g(t) = \sum_{n=-\infty}^{\infty} \alpha_n e^{jn\omega_0 t} = \sum_{n=-\infty}^{\infty} \beta_n \gamma_n e^{jn\omega_0 t} = \frac{1}{T} \int_{-T/2}^{T/2} f(\tau)h(t-\tau)\, d\tau \qquad (3.41)$$

■ **Example 3.5**

Deduce the coefficients α_n for the convolution of the two periodic functions shown in Figure 3.14.

Solution From Figure 3.9, the coefficients β_n for $f(t)$ and γ_n for $h(t)$ are

$$\beta_n = \frac{4A}{\pi n} \quad n \text{ odd} \qquad \gamma_0 = \frac{A}{2} \qquad \gamma_n = -\frac{A}{\pi n} \qquad n = 1, 2, 3, \ldots$$

Thus, the Fourier coefficients for the convolution function α_n follow from (3.40):

$$\alpha_n = -4\left(\frac{A}{\pi n}\right)^2 \qquad n \text{ odd}$$ ■

Another important property of (3.37) is that cyclic convolution is commutative, so that

$$f(t) * h(t) = h(t) * f(t) \qquad (3.42)$$

To show this commutative property, substitute $t - \tau = \tau'$ in (3.37). We write

$$g(t) = -\int_{t}^{t-T} f(t-\tau')h(\tau')\,d\tau' = -\int_{T}^{0} f(t-\tau')h(\tau')\,d\tau' = \int_{0}^{T} f(t-\tau')h(\tau')\,d\tau'$$

which proves the assertion.

3.4 Linear Systems with Periodic Inputs

As discussed, it is always possible for bounded periodic signals with finite range to be expanded as the sum of an infinite number of sine and cosine functions. We can therefore consider the total effect of an LTI filter to these signals as the sum of the individual effect on each sine and cosine term. Let us explore these notions.

Refer to the system shown in Figure 3.15a. It is assumed that the driving system produces a force $f(t) = f_0 \sin \omega_0 t$, where f_0 is the peak amplitude. To develop the equivalent circuit representation of this mechanical system, we draw two levels that correspond to the velocity v of the mass and damper and to the reference velocity v_g, or ground velocity. Now, we connect the mass element between these two levels. The damping element is also connected between these two velocity levels. Finally, we connect the force source between v_g and v. The circuit representation is shown in Figure 3.15d. Figure 3.15b shows the force equilibrium diagram, and Figure 3.15c shows the input–output relationships of the system.

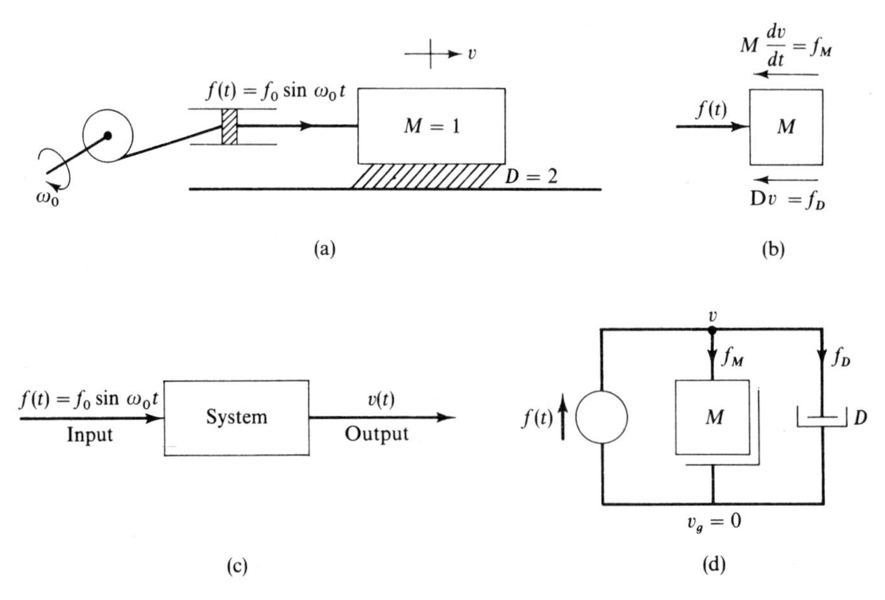

Figure 3.15 Linear Time-Invariant System Excited by a Sinusoidal Time Function

An application of D'Alembert's principle at node v yields

$$-f(t) + f_M + f_D = 0 \qquad \text{or} \qquad f_M + f_D = f(t) \tag{3.43}$$

The resulting differential equation that describes the system behavior is

$$M\frac{dv(t)}{dt} + Dv(t) = f(t)$$

For the specified parameters, this differential equation becomes

$$\frac{dv(t)}{dt} + 2v(t) = f_0 \sin \omega_0 t \tag{3.44}$$

To find the particular (steady state) solution of this differential equation, we assume a solution of the form $v(t) = A \cos \omega_0 t + B \sin \omega_0 t$. Introduce this solution into (3.44), from which we obtain the identity

$$(2A + B\omega_0) \cos \omega_0 t + (2B - A\omega_0) \sin \omega_0 t = f_0 \sin \omega_0 t$$

Equating coefficients of like functions on both sides of this equation, we obtain

$$2A + B\omega_0 = 0 \qquad -\omega_0 A + 2B = f_0$$

From these, we find that

$$A = -\frac{\omega_0 f_0}{4 + \omega_0^2} \qquad B = \frac{2f_0}{4 + \omega_0^2}$$

Thus, the velocity of the system is given by

$$v(t) = -f_0 \frac{\omega_0}{4 + \omega_0^2} \cos \omega_0 t + f_0 \frac{2}{4 + \omega_0^2} \sin \omega_0 t$$

or

$$v(t) = -f_0 \frac{\omega_0}{4 + \omega_0^2}\left(\cos \omega_0 t - \frac{2}{\omega_0} \sin \omega_0 t\right) \tag{3.45}$$

If we set $\tan \phi_0 = 2/\omega_0$ in (3.45), we obtain the equation

$$\begin{aligned} v(t) &= -\frac{\omega_0}{4 + \omega_0^2} \frac{f_0}{\cos \phi_0} (\cos \omega_0 t \cos \phi_0 - \sin \omega_0 t \sin \phi_0) \\ &= \frac{\omega_0}{4 + \omega_0^2} \frac{f_0}{\cos \phi_0} \cos(\omega_0 t + \phi_0 + \pi) \\ &= \frac{\omega_0}{4 + \omega_0^2} \frac{f_0}{\cos \phi_0} \sin\left(\omega_0 t + \phi_0 + \frac{3\pi}{2}\right) \end{aligned} \tag{3.46}$$

For the particular case for $\omega_0 = 1$ rad/s, the phase shift is 333.435° and the amplitude factor is $0.447 f_0$.

We observe from this LTI system that when the input is a sine function, the output is the same sine function, but with a phase shift of $\phi_0 + (3\pi/2)$ and with an

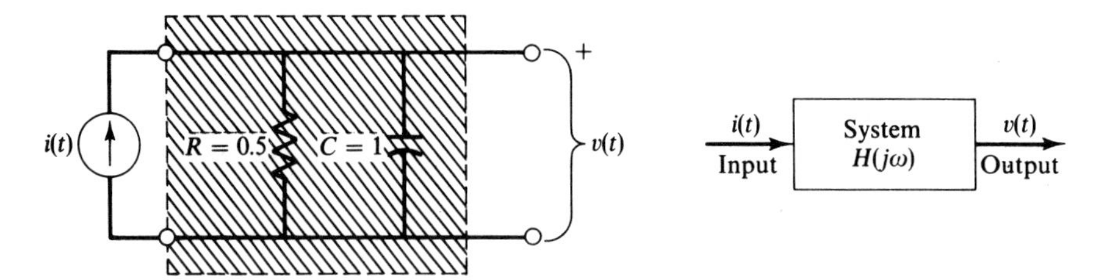

Figure 3.16 Simple Electric System

amplitude change of $\omega_0/[(4+\omega_0^2)\cos\phi_0]$. A similar result would be found when the input is a cosine function. Similar conclusions apply for all LTI systems. Notice also that the phase and amplitude changes are functions of the frequency. That is, when the input is a sinusoidal function, the output is also sinusoidal, but with different amplitude and phase. Thus, if the signal is made up of many sinusoidal functions of different frequencies, each component will experience different phase and amplitude shifts.

Now, refer to the system shown in Figure 3.16. The equation that describes this system is

$$C\frac{dv}{dt} + \frac{v}{R} = i(t)$$

which is, for the specified parameters,

$$\frac{dv}{dt} + 2v = i(t) \tag{3.47}$$

If we assume that the input is an exponential of the form $\boldsymbol{i}(t) = i_o e^{j\omega_0 t}$, the output will be of the same form: $\boldsymbol{v}(t) = \boldsymbol{v}_o e^{j\omega_0 t}$. Here, i_o is assumed constant, and so $\boldsymbol{v}_o$ (a complex quantity) specifies the output amplitude. In particular, if we include both forms in (3.47), we have

$$\boldsymbol{v}_o j\omega_0 e^{j\omega_0 t} + 2\boldsymbol{v}_o e^{j\omega_0 t} = i_o e^{j\omega_0 t}$$

We define $H(j\omega_0)$, the system function,

$$H(j\omega_0) \triangleq \frac{i_o}{\boldsymbol{v}_o} = \frac{1}{2+j\omega_0} = \frac{1}{\sqrt{4+\omega_0^2}} \underline{/\tan^{-1}(\omega_0/2)} \tag{3.48}$$

which, in this case, is the admittance function $Y(j\omega_0)$. Thus,

$$H(j\omega_0) = \frac{1}{\sqrt{4+\omega_0^2}} e^{-j(\tan^{-1}0.5\omega_0)} = |H(j\omega_0)|\, e^{j\phi(\omega_0)} \tag{3.49}$$

The output is given by

$$\boldsymbol{v}(t) = \frac{i_o}{\sqrt{4+\omega_0^2}} e^{j(\omega_0 t - \tan^{-1}0.5\omega_0)} \tag{3.50}$$

If we had assumed that the input was $i_o \sin \omega_0 t = \text{Im}\{i_o e^{j\omega_0 t}\}$, the output would be

$$v(t) = \text{Im}\{\boldsymbol{v}(t)\} = \frac{i_o}{\sqrt{4 + \omega_0^2}} \sin(\omega_0 t - \tan^{-1} 0.5\omega_0) \tag{3.51}$$

Observe that the amplitude and phase of the output are dictated by the amplitude and phase characteristics of the system function $H(j\omega_0)$.

We compare the mathematical descriptions of the systems shown in Figures 3.15 and 3.16. Note that these are identical and, further, that their output forms are identical for the same input functions. These systems are **analogs** of each other. As a practical matter, we observe from the second example that the solution is more easily deduced using the complex periodic representation of the input function than by using the trigonometric form.

■ Example 3.6

Deduce the steady state output (the current) for the system shown in Figure 3.17 for an input voltage $v(t) = 3 \cos \omega_0 t$.

Solution Apply the Kirchhoff voltage law to write the controlling system equation

$$2 \frac{di(t)}{dt} + i(t) + \int i(t)\, dt = v(t) \tag{3.52}$$

The input is written $v(t) = \text{Re}\{3e^{j\omega_0 t}\}$, and the output is assumed to be of the form $i(t) = \text{Re}\{\boldsymbol{i}_o e^{j\omega_0 t}\}$. Equation (3.52) leads to

$$2j\omega_0 \boldsymbol{i}_o e^{j\omega_0 t} + \boldsymbol{i}_o e^{j\omega_0 t} + \frac{1}{j\omega_0} \boldsymbol{i}_o e^{j\omega_0 t} = 3e^{j\omega_0 t}$$

from which the system function $H(j\omega_0)$ is (an admittance function)

$$H(j\omega_0) = \frac{\boldsymbol{i}_o}{\boldsymbol{v}_o} = \frac{1}{1 + 2j\omega_0 + \dfrac{1}{j\omega_0}} = \frac{j\omega_0}{1 - 2\omega_0^2 + j\omega_0}$$

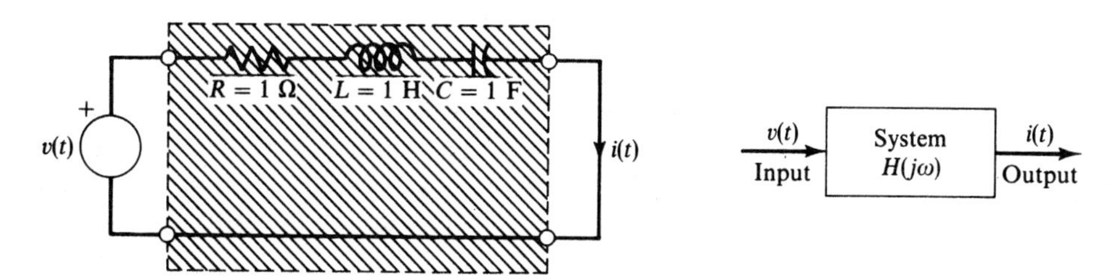

Figure 3.17 *RLC* Electric System

Thus,

$$\begin{aligned}
\mathbf{i}_o = H(j\omega)\mathbf{v}_o &= \frac{3j\omega_0}{1 - 2\omega_0^2 + j\omega_0} \\
&= \frac{3\omega_0\, e^{j\pi/2}}{\sqrt{(1 - 2\omega_0^2)^2 + \omega_0^2}\, \exp[j \tan^{-1}[\omega_0/(1 - 2\omega_0^2)]]} \\
&= \frac{3\omega_0}{[(1 - 2\omega_0^2)^2 + \omega_0^2]^{1/2}}\, e^{j[\pi/2 - \tan^{-1}[\omega_0/(1 - 2\omega_0^2)]]}
\end{aligned} \tag{3.53}$$

The output current is then

$$\begin{aligned}
i(t) &= \mathrm{Re}\{\mathbf{i}(t)\} = \mathrm{Re}\{\mathbf{i}_o\, e^{j\omega_0 t}\} \\
&= \frac{3\omega_0}{[(1 - 2\omega_0^2)^2 + \omega_0^2]^{1/2}} \cos\left(\omega_0 t + \frac{\pi}{2} - \tan^{-1}\frac{\omega_0}{1 - 2\omega_0^2}\right)
\end{aligned} \tag{3.54}$$

As in the previous discussion, we observe that the amplitude and phase of the output signal are dictated by the amplitude and phase of the system function, a somewhat complicated function. ■

We observe from our analysis above that when the input is a sinusoidal input $e^{j\omega_0 t}$, the transfer function is $H(j\omega_0)$ and the output is $H(j\omega_0)e^{j\omega_0 t}$. Of course, if the input frequency is $n\omega_0$ so that the input is $e^{jn\omega_0 t}$, the transfer function is $H(jn\omega_0)$ and the output is $H(jn\omega_0)e^{jn\omega_0 t}$. Clearly, when the input is the sum of sinusoids, the output will consist of each component sinusoid multiplied by the appropriately chosen transfer function. Thus, for an input

$$f_i(t) = \sum_{n=-\infty}^{\infty} \alpha_n e^{jn\omega_0 t}$$

the output will be

$$\boxed{f_o(t) = \sum_{n=-\infty}^{\infty} \alpha_n H(jn\omega_0) e^{jn\omega_0 t}} \tag{3.55}$$

Therefore, if the input to an LTI system is a periodic nonsinusoidal function, the output is a periodic function with Fourier series coefficients defined by the expression $\alpha_n H(jn\omega_0)$. This conclusion presupposes, of course, that the input function has been applied for a long time so that all transient effects have disappeared.

If we expand the input periodic function in the form

$$f_i(t) = \frac{A_0}{2} + \sum_{n=1}^{\infty} (A_n \cos n\omega_0 t + B_n \sin n\omega_0 t)$$

the output $f_o(t)$ will have the form

$$f_o(t) = \frac{A_0}{2}|H(j0)| + \sum_{n=1}^{\infty} |H(jn\omega_0)| \times (A_n \cos[n\omega_0 t + \phi(n\omega_0)] + B_n \sin[n\omega_0 t + \phi(n\omega_0)]) \tag{3.56}$$

■ **Example 3.7**

The periodic signal $f_i(t) = 2\sin(\pi/100)t + 0.1\sin(5\pi/100)t$ is applied to a system with transfer function $H(j\omega) = 1/(1 + 2j\omega)$. Determine the output $f_o(t)$ of the system.

Solution The amplitude and phase functions of the transfer function are

$$|H(j\omega)| = \frac{1}{\sqrt{1 + 4\omega^2}} \qquad \phi(\omega) = -\tan^{-1} 2\omega$$

By (3.56) with $A_0 = A_n = 0$, we obtain

$$f_o(t) = 2\frac{1}{\sqrt{1 + 4\left(\frac{\pi}{100}\right)^2}} \sin\left(\frac{\pi}{100}t - \tan^{-1} 2\frac{\pi}{100}\right) + 0.1\frac{1}{\sqrt{1 + 4\left(\frac{5\pi}{100}\right)^2}} \sin\left(\frac{5\pi t}{100} - \tan^{-1} 2\frac{5\pi}{100}\right)$$

■

3.5 Discrete Time Fourier Series

It is important that we be able to represent periodic functions in sampled form, a requirement when we use a computer or when we wish to approximate an analog filter characteristic for digital filter realization. This need forces us to

1. Substitute finite sums for infinite sums.
2. Approximate integrals by finite sums.
3. Use the values of functions only at the sampled points.

If these conditions are imposed, the question that arises is, Is it possible to introduce these approximations and still approximate the continuous time periodic function within any prescribed error limits? This can be done, but we must examine whether any restrictions must be imposed.

We wish to determine a discrete time approximation for a periodic function $f(t)$ that we have expanded in a Fourier series

$$f(t) = \sum_{n=\infty}^{\infty} \alpha_n e^{jn\omega_0 t} \tag{3.57}$$

where

$$\alpha_n = \frac{1}{T}\int_0^T f_T(t)e^{-jn\omega_0 t}\, dt \tag{3.58}$$

where $f_T(t)$ denotes the periodic function within the period. To effect this approximation, we define a set of relations that apply to the discrete case, with the proviso that we must prove its validity and its ability to approximate the initial continuous function. These relations are

$$f(m\tau) \triangleq f(mT/N) = \sum_{n=0}^{N-1} \tilde{\alpha}_n e^{jn\omega_0 m\tau} \tag{3.59a}$$

$$\tilde{\alpha}_n = \frac{1}{N}\sum_{m=0}^{N-1} f(m\tau)e^{-jn\omega_0 m\tau} \tag{3.59b}$$

These expressions are written

$$f(m\tau) = \sum_{n=0}^{N-1} \tilde{\alpha}_n W^{-nm} \tag{3.60a}$$

$$\tilde{\alpha}_n = \frac{1}{N}\sum_{n=0}^{N-1} f(m\tau)W^{+nm} \tag{3.60b}$$

where

$$W = e^{-j\omega_0\tau} = e^{-j[(2\pi/T)(T/N)]} = e^{-j(2\pi/N)} = \cos\frac{2\pi}{N} - j\sin\frac{2\pi}{N} \tag{3.61}$$

We observe that W is a complex number with unity amplitude and phase $2\pi/N$. Its representation in the complex plane for the case $N = 8$ is shown in Figure 3.18.

From (3.61), we obtain the properties of W shown in Table 3.3.

Table 3.3 Properties of the Complex Number W

1. $W^N = (e^{-j2\pi/N})^N = e^{-j2\pi} = 1$.
2. $W^{m+N} = W^m W^N = W^m\, 1 = W^m$, a quantity that is periodic with period N.
3. $1, W, W^2, \ldots, W^{N-1}$ specify equidistant points around the unit circle on the complex plane.
4. $e^{-jn\omega_0 m\tau} = e^{-jn(2\pi/T)m(T/N)} = (e^{-j2\pi/N})^{nm} = W^{nm}$.

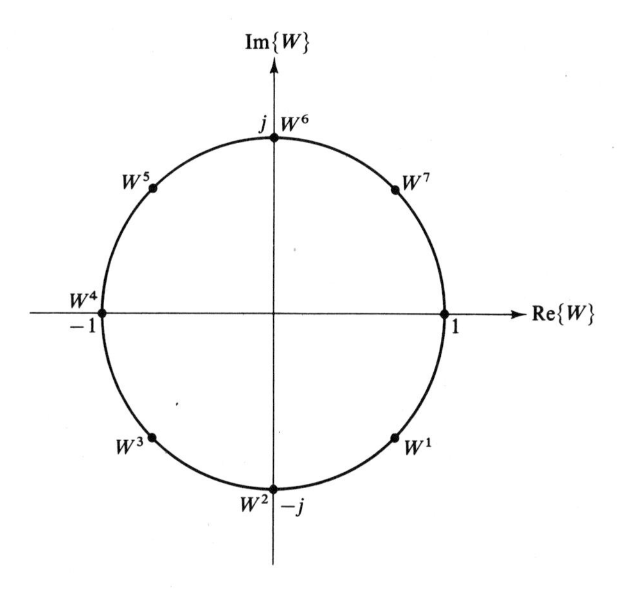

Figure 3.18 Graphical Representation of the Complex Number $W = e^{-j2\pi/N}$ for $N = 8$

To show that the equations of (3.60) constitute the reciprocal pair for the discrete Fourier series, substitute (3.60a) into (3.60b) and, to avoid confusion, substitute q for n in (3.60a). We obtain

$$\tilde{\alpha}_n = \frac{1}{N} \sum_{m=0}^{N-1} \sum_{q=0}^{N-1} \tilde{\alpha}_q W^{-qm} W^{nm} = \frac{1}{N} \sum_{q=0}^{N-1} \tilde{\alpha}_q \sum_{m=0}^{N-1} W^{(n-q)m} \tag{3.62}$$

The second summation in this expression is a geometric progression that can be written

$$\sum_{m=0}^{N-1} W^{(n-q)m} = \frac{1 - W^{(n-q)N}}{1 - W^{(n-q)}} = \begin{cases} N & q = n \\ 0 & q \neq n \end{cases} \tag{3.63}$$

where L'Hospital's rule was applied for the case $q = n$. Therefore, (3.62) becomes an identity, and the equations of (3.60) form a consistent pair.

It still remains to be shown that the defined discrete Fourier series pair will approximate (3.57) and (3.58) when the periodic function is a continuous time function. Let us look at (3.57) at times $t = m\tau = mT/N$, which means that we sample the function $f(t)$ at equidistant points separated by the time distance $\tau = T/N$. Thus, we write

$$f(m\tau) = \sum_{n=-\infty}^{\infty} \alpha_n e^{jn\omega_0 m\tau} = \sum_{n=-\infty}^{\infty} \alpha_n e^{j[n(2\pi/T)m(T/N)]} = \sum_{n=-\infty}^{\infty} \alpha_n W^{-mn} \tag{3.64}$$

This equation indicates that the value of the periodic function at each point $m\tau$ is equal to an infinite sum of the powers of W, an essential property for the numerical evaluation of the Fourier series. However, we note $W^{(m+N)n} = W^{mn}$ and $f[(m+N)\tau] = f(m\tau + T) = f(m\tau)$ since $f(t)$ is periodic; then, only N of these values generates new equations.

Let us look at the integral in (3.58), which we approximate by the finite sum

$$\tilde{\alpha}_n \doteq \frac{1}{T}\sum_{m=0}^{N-1}\left(\frac{T}{N}\right)f(m\tau)e^{-jn\omega_0 m\tau} = \frac{1}{N}\sum_{m=0}^{N-1} f(m\tau)W^{mn} \tag{3.65}$$

This expression shows that the $\tilde{\alpha}_n$'s deduced using the finite summation are not exactly equal to those found by integration. However, for regular functions, as $N \to \infty$, the approximation becomes exact. A comparison of (3.64) and (3.65) with (3.60) shows that they are identical and, hence, constitute acceptable pairs for **periodic sequences**.

We note, of course, that using the values of the function at a specified number of points and using finite sums yields α_n's and $f(m\tau)$'s that are approximate. However, we can increase the value of N within practical limits to obtain improved approximations. The value of N to be selected will depend on how smooth the function is to be. That is, if the function contains high frequencies (and this would be the case for functions with discontinuities), the value of N must be large. Therefore, the values of α_n's and $f(m\tau)$'s obtained from (3.59) and (3.60) will be different from those that are deduced from (3.57) and (3.58). The difference

$$\boxed{\varepsilon_n \triangleq \text{error} = \tilde{\alpha}_n - \alpha_n} \tag{3.66}$$

is called the **aliasing error**, a quantity that is not always zero.

Suppose that the frequency components of a periodic function $f(t)$ do not extend beyond some known value—that is, the function is **band limited**. Suppose that we choose M to be the highest harmonic in the expansion. In this case, from (3.57),

$$f(t) = \sum_{n=-M}^{M} \alpha_n e^{jn\omega_0 t} = \sum_{n=-M}^{M} \alpha_n e^{jn(2\pi/T)t} \tag{3.67}$$

This expansion is exact. By (3.64), the corresponding form is

$$f(m\tau) = \sum_{n=-M}^{M} \tilde{\alpha}_n e^{j2\pi mn/N} \tag{3.68}$$

By comparing these two equations, we see that $f(mT/N)$ of $f(t)$ and its coefficients $\tilde{\alpha}_n$ satisfy a set of N equations in one case and $(2M+1)$ equations in the other. If the number of coefficients $(2M+1)$ is less than or equal to N—that is,

$$\boxed{2M + 1 \le N} \tag{3.69}$$

then the set of equations can be solved for the unknown α_n's. Clearly, if $f(t)$ is a trigonometric polynomial (the sum of cosine and sine terms) of order $M < N/2$, the coefficients α_n can be found exactly. However, if the inequality is not true, then **undersampling** will occur and an aliasing error will arise. The following examples elucidate these assertions.

Example 3.8

Deduce the Fourier coefficients for the periodic function $f(t) = 4\cos 2\omega_0 t$ for $N = 3$ and $N = 5$.

Solution We write $f(t)$ in the form

$$f(t) = 2e^{j2\omega_0 t} + 2e^{-j2\omega_0 t}$$

This equation indicates that $M = 2$ and, specifically, that $\alpha_{-2} = 2$, $\alpha_0 = 0$, $\alpha_2 = 2$. All remaining α_n's are zero.

Case 1. For the case $N = 3$, the relationship $(2M + 1) = (2 \cdot 2 + 1) > 3$. This value contradicts (3.69), and an aliasing error will result. Hence, the coefficients that are found will not be equal to the exact values given above.

Specifically, for the case $N = 3$ and $T = 1$, we obtain

$$f(m\tau) = f\left(m\frac{T}{N}\right) = f\left[m \cdot 2\left(\frac{2\pi}{T}\right)\left(\frac{T}{N}\right) = 4\cos\left(m\frac{4\pi}{3}\right)\right]$$

By (3.65), we obtain the following:

$$\tilde{\alpha}_0 = \frac{1}{3}\sum_{m=0}^{2} f(m\tau)e^{-j0(2\pi/3)m} = \frac{4}{3}\left[1 - \frac{1}{2} - \frac{1}{2}\right] = 0$$

$$\tilde{\alpha}_1 = \frac{1}{3}\sum_{m=0}^{2} f(m\tau)e^{-j1(2\pi/3)m} = \frac{4}{3}\left[1 - \frac{1}{2}\left(-\frac{1}{2} - j\frac{\sqrt{3}}{2}\right) - \frac{1}{2}\left(-\frac{1}{2} + j\frac{\sqrt{3}}{2}\right)\right]$$
$$= \frac{8}{3}$$

$$\tilde{\alpha}_2 = \frac{1}{3}\sum_{m=0}^{2} f(m\tau)e^{-j2(2\pi/3)m} = \frac{4}{3}\left[1 - \frac{1}{2}\left(-\frac{1}{2} + j\frac{\sqrt{3}}{2}\right) - \frac{1}{2}\left(-\frac{1}{2} - j\frac{\sqrt{3}}{2}\right)\right]$$
$$= \frac{8}{3}$$

From these values of α, we see that $\tilde{\alpha}_{-1} = \tilde{\alpha}_{1-2} \neq \tilde{\alpha}_1$; $\tilde{\alpha}_{-2} = \tilde{\alpha}_{0-2} \neq \tilde{\alpha}_2$, which supports the assertion above.

Case 2. For the case $N = 5$, the relationship $(2M + 1) = (2 \cdot 2 + 1) = 5 = N$, which means that we are sampling at the minimum rate. The sampled function now becomes

$$f(n\tau) = 4\cos\left(2\frac{2\pi}{T}n\frac{T}{5}\right) = 4\cos\left(n\frac{4\pi}{5}\right)$$

By (3.65), we obtain

$$\begin{aligned}
\tilde{\alpha}_0 &= \frac{1}{5}\sum_{m=0}^{4} f(m\tau)e^{-j(2\pi/5)m\cdot 0} \\
&= \frac{4}{5}[1 - 0.809 + 0.309 + 0.309 - 0.809] \\
&= 0 \\
\tilde{\alpha}_1 &= \frac{1}{5}\sum_{m=0}^{4} f(m\tau)e^{-j(2\pi/5)m\cdot 1} \\
&= \frac{4}{5}[1 - 0.809e^{-j(2\pi/5)} + 0.309e^{-j(4\pi/5)} + 0.309e^{-j(6\pi/5)} - 0.809e^{-j(8\pi/5)}] \\
&= 0 \\
\tilde{\alpha}_2 &= \frac{1}{5}\sum_{m=0}^{4} f(m\tau)e^{-j(2\pi/5)m\cdot 2} \\
&= \frac{4}{5}[1 - 0.809e^{-j(4\pi/5)} + 0.309e^{-j(8\pi/5)} \\
&\quad + 0.309e^{-j(12\pi/5)} - 0.809e^{-j(16\pi/5)}] \\
&= 2 \\
\tilde{\alpha}_3 &= \frac{1}{5}\sum_{m=0}^{4} f(m\tau)e^{-j(2\pi/5)m\cdot 3} \\
&= \frac{4}{5}[1 - 0.809e^{-j(6\pi/5)} + 0.309e^{-j(12\pi/5)} \\
&\quad + 0.309e^{-j(18\pi/5)} - 0.809e^{-j(24\pi/5)}] \\
&= 0 \\
\tilde{\alpha}_4 &= \frac{1}{5}\sum_{m=0}^{4} f(m\tau)e^{-j(2\pi/5)m\cdot 4} \\
&= \frac{4}{5}[1 - 0.809e^{-j(8\pi/5)} + 0.309e^{-j(16\pi/5)} \\
&\quad + 0.309e^{-j(24\pi/5)} - 0.809e^{-j(32\pi/5)}] \\
&= 0
\end{aligned}$$

Because $\tilde{\alpha}_{-2} = \tilde{\alpha}_{2-4} = 2$, $\tilde{\alpha}_{-1} = \tilde{\alpha}_{3-4} = 0$; then, $\tilde{\alpha}_{-2} = \alpha_{-2}$, $\tilde{\alpha}_0 = \alpha_0$, and $\tilde{\alpha}_2 = \alpha_2$, the exact values.

This set of equations for the $\tilde{\alpha}_n$'s can be written in matrix form and is given by

$$\tilde{\boldsymbol{\alpha}}_n = \frac{1}{5}\mathbf{W}\mathbf{f}(m\tau) \tag{3.70}$$

which, in expanded form, is

$$\begin{bmatrix} \tilde{\alpha}_0 \\ \tilde{\alpha}_1 \\ \tilde{\alpha}_2 \\ \tilde{\alpha}_3 \\ \tilde{\alpha}_4 \end{bmatrix} = \frac{1}{5} \begin{bmatrix} 1 & 1 & 1 & 1 & 1 \\ 1 & e^{-j(2\pi/5)} & e^{-j(4\pi/5)} & e^{-j(6\pi/5)} & e^{-j(8\pi/5)} \\ 1 & e^{-j(4\pi/5)} & e^{-j(8\pi/5)} & e^{-j(12\pi/5)} & e^{-j(16\pi/5)} \\ 1 & e^{-j(6\pi/5)} & e^{-j(12\pi/5)} & e^{-j(18\pi/5)} & e^{-j(24\pi/5)} \\ 1 & e^{-j(8\pi/5)} & e^{-j(16\pi/5)} & e^{-j(24\pi/5)} & e^{-j(32\pi/5)} \end{bmatrix} \times \begin{bmatrix} 1.0 \\ -0.809 \\ 0.309 \\ 0.309 \\ -0.809 \end{bmatrix}$$ ■

■ **Example 3.9**

Find the discrete Fourier series for the function shown in Figure 3.19a.

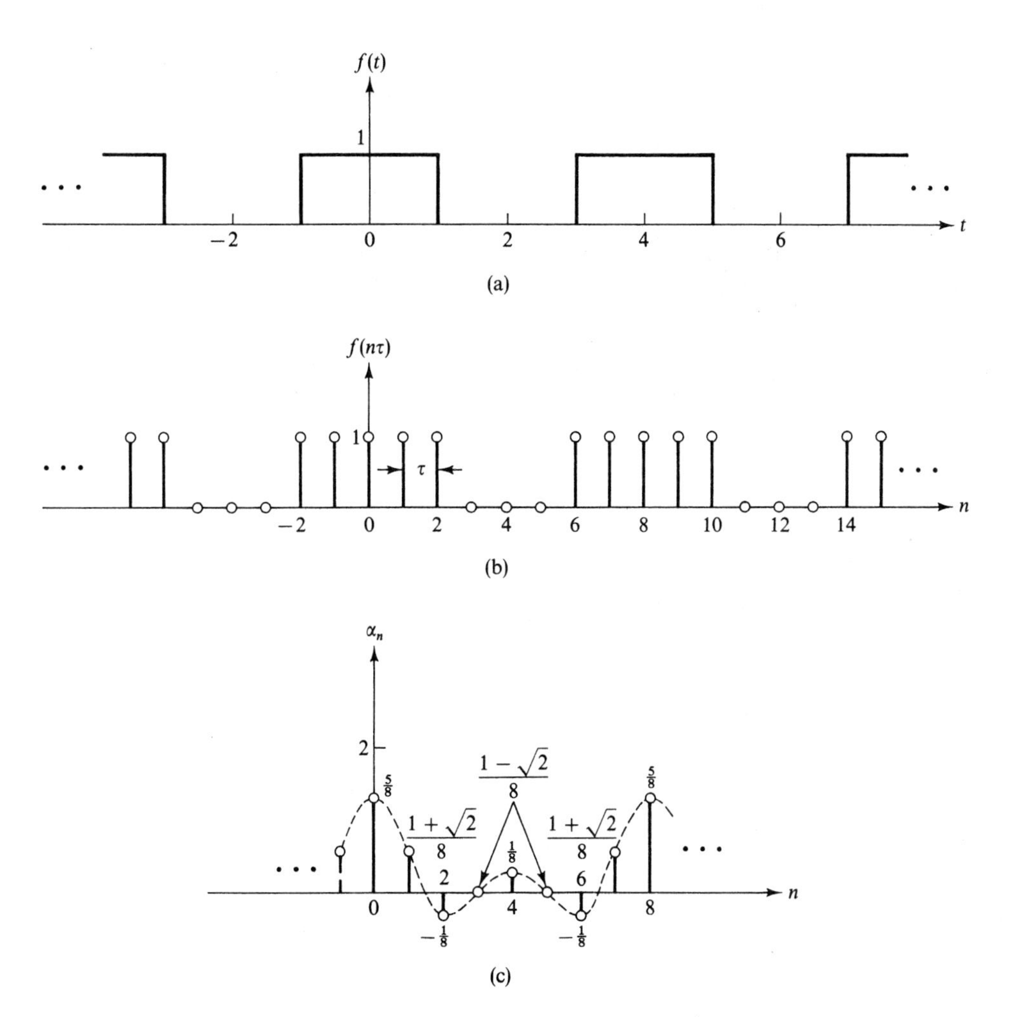

Figure 3.19 Development of the Discrete Fourier Series Coefficients

Solution From Figures 3.19a and 3.19b, we observe that $T = 4$, $N = 8$ and, therefore, $\tau = T/N = 1/2$. By (3.59b), the approximate values of the Fourier coefficients are

$$\tilde{\alpha}_0 = \frac{1}{8}\sum_{m=0}^{7} f(m\tau)e^{-jn(2\pi/4)m(4/8)} = \frac{1}{8}\sum_{m=0}^{7} f(m\tau)e^{-j(\pi/4)m(0)}$$
$$= \frac{1}{8}(1+1+1+0+0+0+1+1) = \frac{5}{8} = 0.625$$

$$\tilde{\alpha}_1 = \frac{1}{8}\sum_{m=0}^{7} f(m\tau)e^{-j(\pi/4)m(1)} = \frac{1}{8}(1 + e^{-j(\pi/4)} + e^{-j(2\pi/4)}$$
$$+ 0\cdot e^{-j(3\pi/4)} + 0\cdot e^{-j(4\pi/4)} + 0\cdot e^{-j(5\pi/4)} + e^{-j(6\pi/4)} + e^{-j(7\pi/4)})$$
$$= 0.3018$$

$$\tilde{\alpha}_2 = \frac{1}{8}\sum_{m=0}^{7} f(m\tau)e^{-j(\pi/4)m(2)} = -0.125$$

$$\tilde{\alpha}_3 = \frac{1}{8}\sum_{m=0}^{7} f(m\tau)e^{-j(\pi/4)m(3)} = -0.518$$

$$\tilde{\alpha}_4 = 0.125 \qquad \tilde{\alpha}_5 = -0.0518 \qquad \tilde{\alpha}_6 = -0.125 \qquad \tilde{\alpha}_7 = 0.3018$$

The spectrum is shown in Figure 3.19c.

Now, apply (3.58) to obtain the exact Fourier coefficients. We obtain

$$\alpha_n = \frac{1}{4}\int_{-2}^{2} f_T(t)e^{-jn(2\pi/4)t}\,dt = \frac{1}{4}\int_{-1}^{1} e^{-jn(\pi/2)t}\,dt$$
$$= \frac{1}{4}\frac{1}{-jn\dfrac{\pi}{2}}e^{-jn(\pi/2)t}\bigg|_{-1}^{1} = \frac{\sin n\dfrac{\pi}{2}}{n\pi}$$

The values for the different values of n are

$$\alpha_0 = \frac{1}{2}\ \text{(L'Hospital's rule was used)} \qquad \alpha_1 = \frac{1}{\pi} = 0.3183 \qquad \alpha_2 = 0$$

$$\alpha_3 = -\frac{1}{3\pi} = -0.1061 \qquad \alpha_4 = 0 \qquad \alpha_5 = \frac{1}{5\pi} = 0.0636$$

$$\alpha_6 = 0 \qquad \alpha_7 = \frac{1}{7\pi} = 0.0455$$

Because the $\tilde{\alpha}_n$'s are periodic, we can find the aliasing errors using the first four values of α_n. We find

$$\varepsilon_0 = 0.125 \qquad \varepsilon_1 = -0.0165 \qquad \varepsilon_2 = -0.125 \qquad \varepsilon_3 = -0.412$$

■

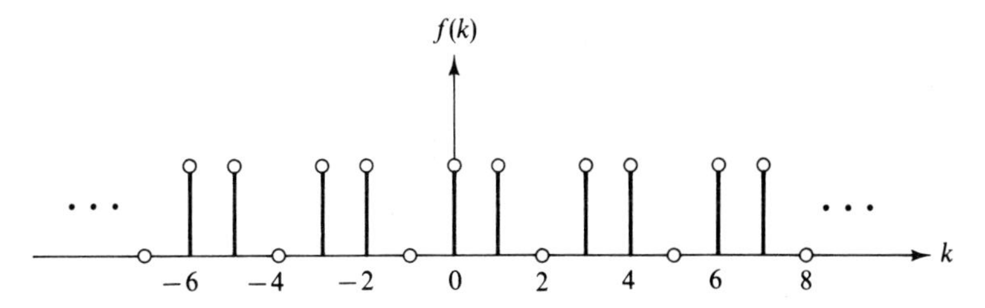

Figure 3.20 A Periodic Discrete Signal

A rather different situation exists if we wish to express a discrete periodic signal in terms of a discrete Fourier series form. In this case, (3.59) and (3.60) are written

$$f(m) = \sum_{n=0}^{N-1} \tilde{\alpha}_n e^{jmn(2\pi/N)} = \sum_{n=0}^{N-1} \tilde{\alpha}_n W^{-nm} \tag{3.71a}$$

$$\tilde{\alpha}_n = \frac{1}{N} \sum_{n=0}^{N-1} f(m) W^{nm} \tag{3.71b}$$

The value of n can start at any integer just so long as the N terms are included.

The Fourier coefficients for the periodic discrete function in Figure 3.20 are, by an application of (3.71b), for $N = 3, f(0) = 1, f(1) = 1, f(2) = 0$, and $W = e^{-j(2/3)} = e^{-j120^\circ}$,

$$\tilde{\alpha}_0 = \frac{1}{3}[1 + 1] = \frac{2}{3}$$

$$\tilde{\alpha}_1 = \frac{1}{3}[1 + e^{-j120^\circ}] = \frac{1}{6} - j\frac{\sqrt{3}}{6}$$

$$\tilde{\alpha}_2 = \frac{1}{3}[1 + e^{-j240^\circ}] = \frac{1}{6} + j\frac{\sqrt{3}}{6}$$

■ **Example 3.10**

Determine the Fourier series coefficients for the periodic discrete function shown in Figure 3.21a. Plot the amplitude spectrum $|\tilde{\alpha}_n|$.

Solution An application of (3.71b) yields the following values ($N = 6$):

$$\tilde{\alpha}_0 = \frac{1}{6}(1 + 1) = \frac{2}{3} \qquad \tilde{\alpha}_1 = \frac{1}{6}(1 + e^{-j60^\circ}) = \frac{3}{12} - j\frac{\sqrt{3}}{12}$$

$$\tilde{\alpha}_2 = \frac{1}{6}(1 + e^{-j120^\circ}) = \frac{1}{12} - j\frac{\sqrt{3}}{12} \qquad \tilde{\alpha}_3 = \frac{1}{6}(1 - 1) = 0$$

$$\tilde{\alpha}_4 = \frac{1}{6}(1 + e^{-j240^\circ}) = \frac{1}{12} + j\frac{\sqrt{3}}{12} \qquad \tilde{\alpha}_5 = \frac{3}{12} + j\frac{\sqrt{3}}{12}$$

The spectrum $|\tilde{\alpha}_n|$ is shown in Figure 3.21b. ■

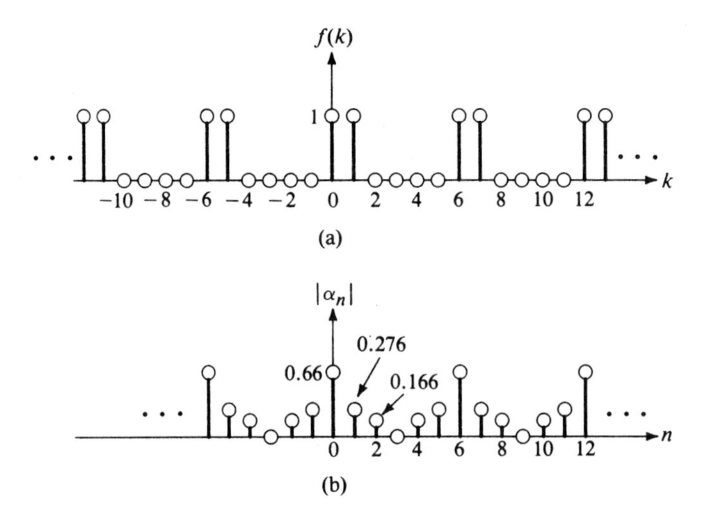

Figure 3.21 A Periodic Discrete Signal and Its Amplitude Spectrum

3.6 Convolution of Periodic Discrete Sequences

Just as there were special properties of the convolution of periodic analog signals relative to that of general functions, as discussed in Section 3.3, there are certain special properties of convolution of periodic discrete series. We begin with (2.106) for discrete time convolution

$$g(k) = \sum_{n=-\infty}^{\infty} f(n)h(k-n) = \sum_{n=-\infty}^{\infty} f(k-n)h(n) \tag{3.72}$$

where $h(n)$ and $f(n)$ are discrete sequences. When $h(n)$ and $f(n)$ are periodic sequences, so that

$$\left.\begin{aligned} f(n) &= f(n+pN) \\ h(n) &= h(n+pN) \end{aligned}\right\} \quad p = 0, \pm 1, \pm 2, \ldots \tag{3.73}$$

then (3.72) denotes periodic or cyclic convolution.

Consider the case of two periodic sequences $f(k) = \{1, 2, 3\}$ and $h(k) = \{1, 1, 0\}$. Figure 3.22 shows graphically their convolution. An alternate approach in cyclic convolution is shown in Figure 3.23. This shows how we can arrange the two sequences in a cyclic manner before proceeding with the convolution process.

Ordinarily, we are interested in linear rather than circular convolution. We can modify the two sequences in such a manner that circular convolution gives identical results with those achieved by linear convolution. If we have two finite and unequal sequences $f(k)$ and $h(k)$, we select the period for each function according to the relation

$$N = F + H - 1 \tag{3.74}$$

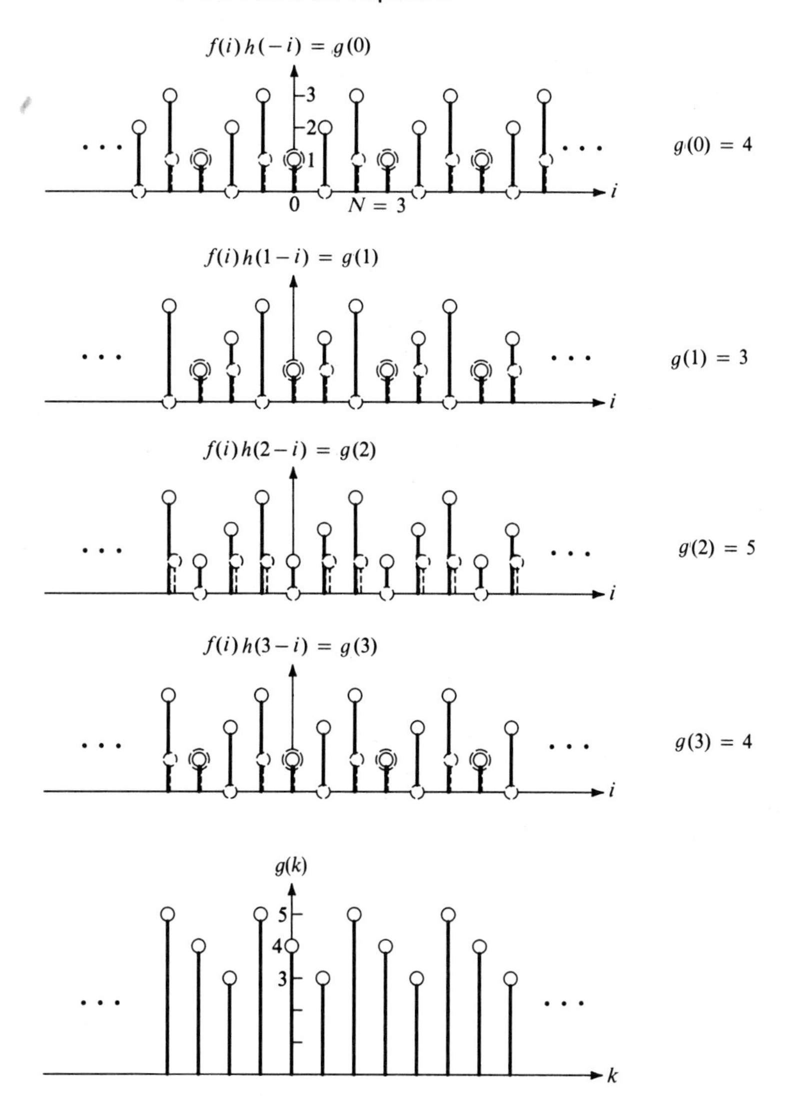

Figure 3.22 Convolution of Two Periodic Sequences

where F denotes the number of samples in the $f(k)$ sequence and H denotes the number of samples in the $h(k)$ sequence. Under this modification, both the linear and circular convolutions give identical results. Since F and H are each less than N, we pad the sequences with zeros. Padding has the effect of improving frequency resolution and avoids circular convolution artifacts. If one of the signals has infinite extent, end effects will occur. Note, however, that it is not possible to convolve two discrete sequences of infinite extent. We will find, when considering the discrete

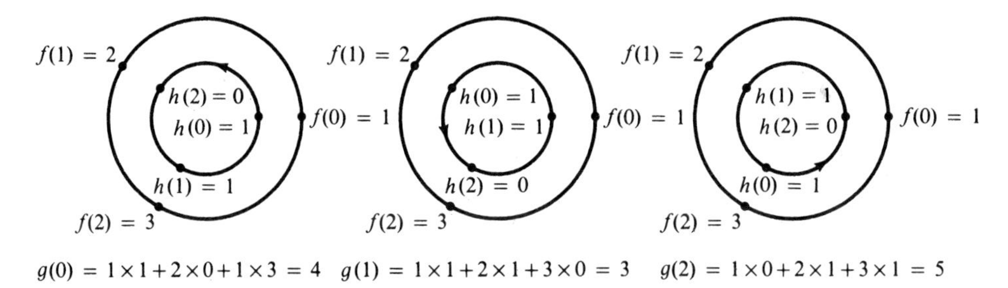

Figure 3.23 Arrangement of Sequences for Cyclic Convolution

Fourier transform (DFT), also a discrete periodic process, that an advantage in using circular convolution lies in the fact that we can use fast Fourier transform (FFT) techniques in the convolution process.

Problems

Section 3.1

1. Draw the following functions: $y_1(t) = ce^{at}$ and $y_2(t) = ce^{-at}$, given that c and a are real numbers.
2. Plot the real and imaginary parts of the signal $y = ce^{-at}$ for $c = 2 + j$ and $a = 2 - j2$.
3. Using Euler's relation, show the following:
   a. $\cos \omega_0 t = (e^{j\omega_0 t} + e^{-j\omega_0 t})/2$ **b.** $\sin \omega_0 t = (e^{j\omega_0 t} - e^{-j\omega_0 t})/2j$
   c. $\cos^2 \omega_0 t = \frac{1}{2}(1 + \cos 2\omega_0 t)$ **d.** $\sin \omega_1 t \sin \omega_2 t = \frac{1}{2}\cos(\omega_1 - \omega_2)t - \frac{1}{2}\cos(\omega_1 + \omega_2)t$
4. Any complex number z can be represented by a point in the complex plane with $z = a + jb = \sqrt{a^2 + b^2}\, e^{j\tan^{-1}(b/a)} \triangleq re^{j\theta} = r\cos\theta + jr\sin\theta$, as shown in Figure 3.24. Show the following points on the complex plane:
   a. $z = 2 + j3$ **b.** $z = -2e^{j30°}$ **c.** $z = 3e^{-j140°}$
   d. $z = -1 - j$ **e.** $z = -1 + j$ **f.** $z = 3e^{j140°}$

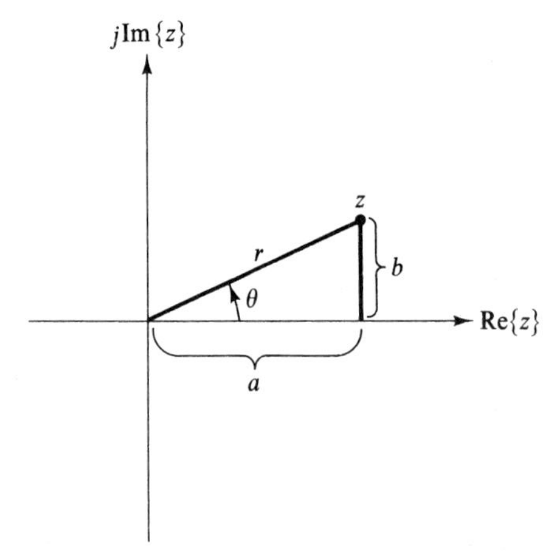

Figure 3.24

5. Corresponding to the complex number $z = a + jb = re^{j\theta}$ is the **complex conjugate** $z^* = a - jb = re^{-j\theta}$. If $z_1 = a_1 + jb_1$, $z_2 = a_2 + jb_2$, and $z_3 = a_3 + jb_3$, determine the following relationships:
   a. $z_1 z_1^*$ **b.** $z_2/(z_2 + z_2^*)$ **c.** $z_3 + z_3^*$
   d. $(z_1 + z_2)^*$ **e.** $(z_1 + z_1^*)/(z_2 + z_2^*)$ **f.** $(3z_1 z_2)^*$
6. Express each relation by a complex number in its polar form ($re^{j\theta}$).
   a. $(2 + j4)/(1 + j)$ **b.** $[2e^{j30°}/(1 + j)]$ **c.** $[2e^{j30°}/(1 + j)]^*$
   d. $\sqrt{3}\, e^{j30°}(2 + j6)^*$ **e.** $e^{-j\pi/2} - e^{j\pi}$ **f.** $j(3 + j4)^* e^{j30°}$
   g. $[(2 - 6j)/(2 + j6)]^*$ **h.** $(1 - j)^5$ **i.** $(2 + j)^*(2 - j)^* e^{j45°}$
7. The quantities z_1 and z_2 are complex numbers. Prove the following relationships:
   a. $|z_1| = r_1$ **b.** $|z_1 z_2| = |z_1||z_2|$ **c.** $(|z_1| - |z_2|)^2 \le |z_1 + z_2|^2 \le (|z_1| + |z_2|)^2$
8. Prove the following orthogonality relations:
   a. $\int_0^T \cos n\omega_0 t \sin m\omega_0 t\, dt = 0$ **b.** $\int_0^T \cos n\omega_0 t \cos m\omega_0 t\, dt = 0$ for $n \ne m$; $= T/2$ for $n = m$.
9. Plot $\cos \Omega_0 k$ for the following values of Ω_0: 0, $\pi/8$, $\pi/4$, $\pi/2$, π, $3\pi/2$, $7\pi/4$, $15\pi/8$, and 2π. Comment on the difference between your results and those shown in Figure 3.2.
10. Determine the fundamental period of the following signals. If any signals are not periodic, give reasons.
    a. $f(k) = \cos[(8/7)k + 30°]$ **b.** $f(k) = \cos[(\pi/4)k + 30°]$ **c.** $f(k) = e^{j[(k/4) - (\pi/2)]}$
    d. $f(k) = \cos(k/8)\cos(\pi k/16)$
11. The continuous function $\cos \omega_0 t$ is sampled at $t = kT$. Specify the condition that enables $\cos k\omega_0 T$ to be periodic.

Section 3.2

12. Show the following relations:
    a. $A_0 = 2\alpha_0$ **b.** $A_n = 2\,\mathrm{Re}\{\alpha_n\}$ **c.** $B_n = -2\,\mathrm{Im}\{\alpha_n\}$.
13. Show that $C_n = \sqrt{A_n^2 + B_n^2}$.
14. Deduce the Fourier series in trigonometric form for the periodic function shown in Figure 3.25a. Find and plot the amplitude and phase spectrums of the series. This function is known as the **half-wave rectified** signal, and it is produced by the circuit shown in Figure 3.25b.

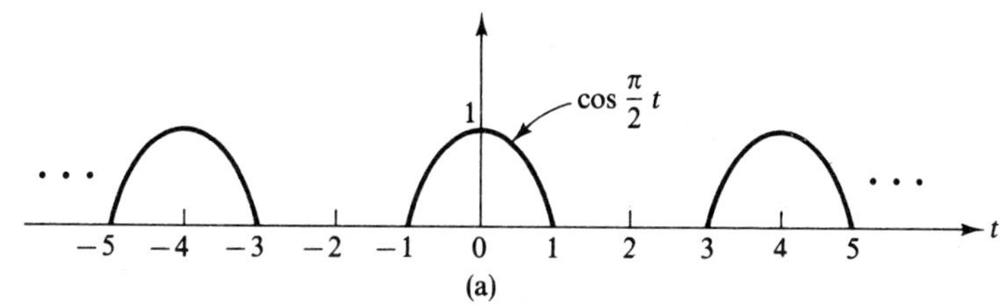

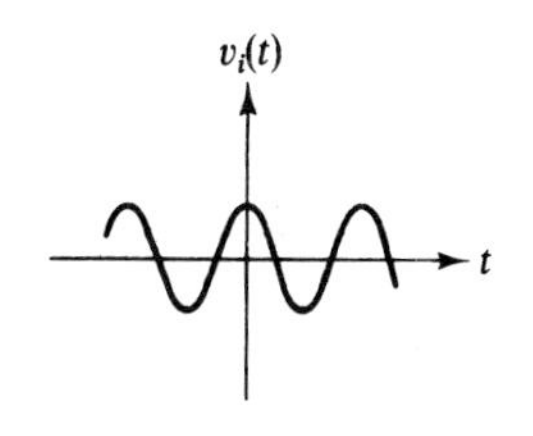

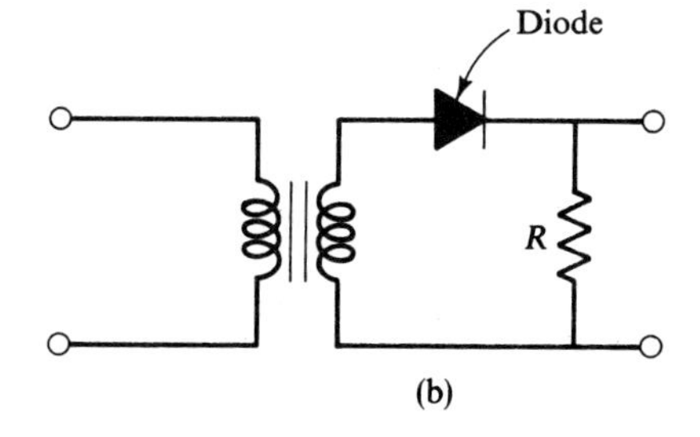

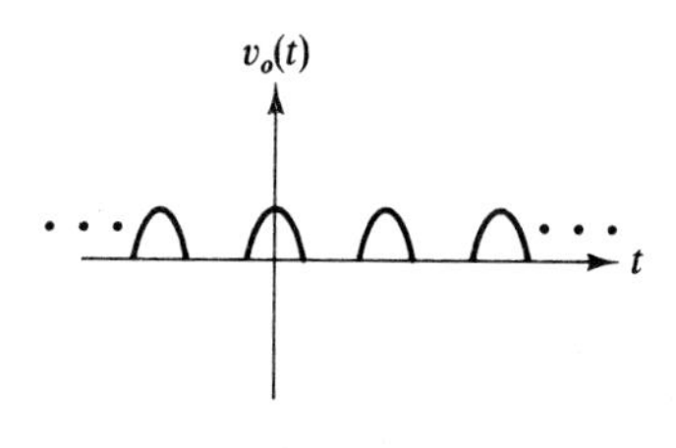

Figure 3.25

15. Show that the Fourier series of the **full-wave rectified** signal shown in Figure 3.26a is given by $f(t) = (2A/\pi) - (4A/\pi) \sum_{n=1}^{\infty}[1/(4n^2 - 1)]\cos 2n\omega_0 t$. Carry out the solution in the following three ways:

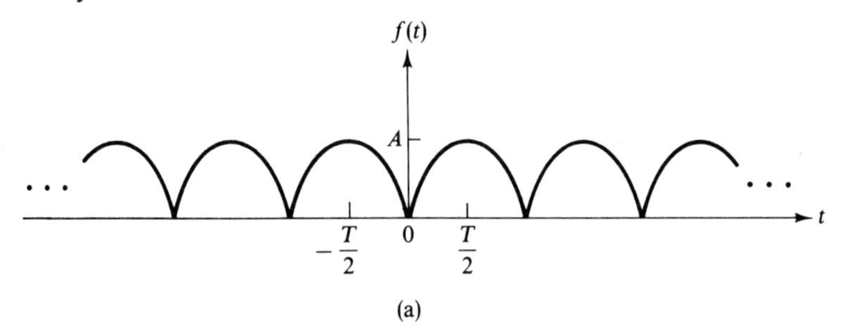

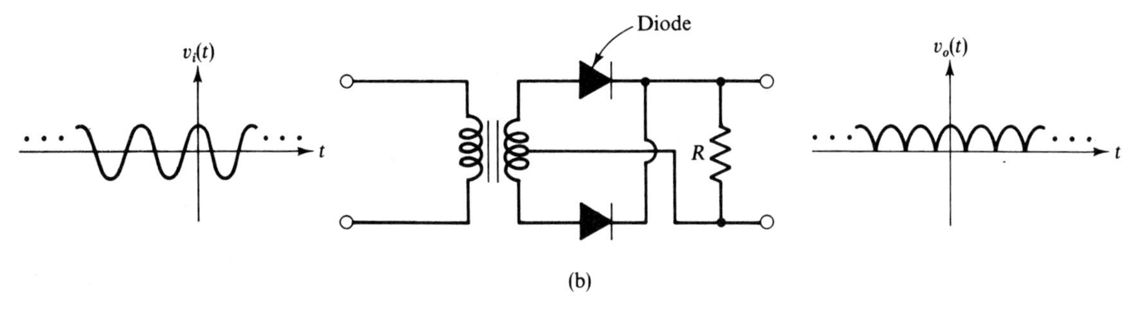

Figure 3.26

a. Evaluate the coefficients in the Fourier series. **b.** Use the fact that this wave is the summation of two waves of the form in Figure 3.25 with one wave shifted by 2 units relative to the other. **c.** Use the fact that the wave is the product of $\sin \omega_0 t$ and a square wave centered at $\omega t = \pi/2$.

16. The **ripple factor** of a half-wave (or full-wave) rectified signal is defined by $r = \sqrt{(f_{\text{rms}}/f_{\text{dc}}) - 1}$, where f_{rms} is the rms value and the ac components of the signal within a period and f_{dc} is the average value of the periodic signal. Show that r for the half- and full-wave signals are 1.21 and 0.48, respectively.

17. Verify the entries of Figure 3.9.

18. Compute the Fourier series of the following functions:
a. $f(t) = t^2 \quad -\pi \le t \le \pi,\ T = 2\pi$ **b.** $f(t) = t \quad -1 \le t \le 1,\ T = 2$

19. Compute the Fourier series of the following functions:
a. $f(t) = t \quad -t_0 \le t \le t_0;\ f(t + 2t_0) = f(t)$
b. $f(t) = 1 + e^t \quad -1 \le t \le 1$

Section 3.3

20. If the Fourier series expansion of a periodic function $f(t)$ is written in its exponential form, $f(t) = \sum_{n=-\infty}^{\infty} \alpha_n e^{jn\omega_0 t}$, show that $1/T \int_{t_0}^{t_0+T} f(t)f^*(t)\,dt \triangleq 1/T \int_{t_0}^{t_0+T} |f(t)|^2\,dt = \sum_{n=-\infty}^{\infty} |\alpha_n|^2$. This is another form of the Parseval energy relation.

21. Show that the Parseval energy relation can be written in the form $(1/T) \int_{t_0}^{t_0+T} |f(t)|^2\,dt = A_0^2/4 + \sum_{n=1}^{\infty}(A_n^2/2 + B_n^2/2)$.

22. Deduce the Fourier series expansions for the waves shown in Figure 3.27.

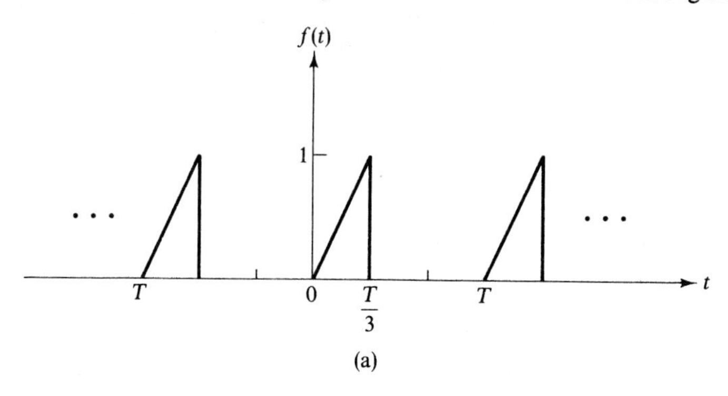

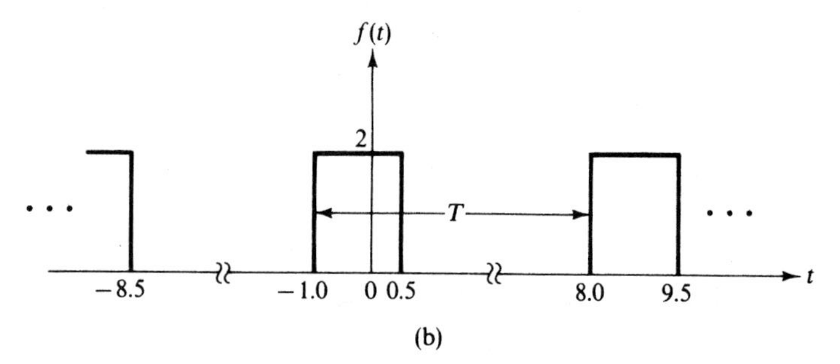

Figure 3.27

23. Find the Fourier series for the functions shown in Figure 3.28.

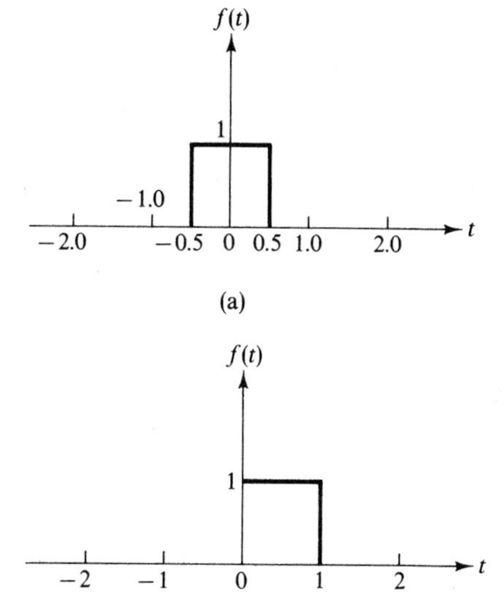

Figure 3.28

24. Verify that (3.23) and (3.35) are identical.
25. Determine the Fourier series of the periodic functions shown in Figure 3.9 if they are shifted by a half-period $T/2$ to the right.
26. Deduce the Fourier series for the functions shown in Figure 3.29. Comment on the amplitude and phase spectrums of these waves.

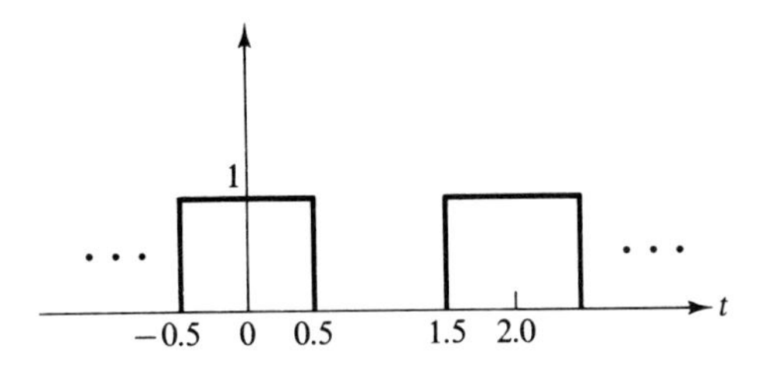

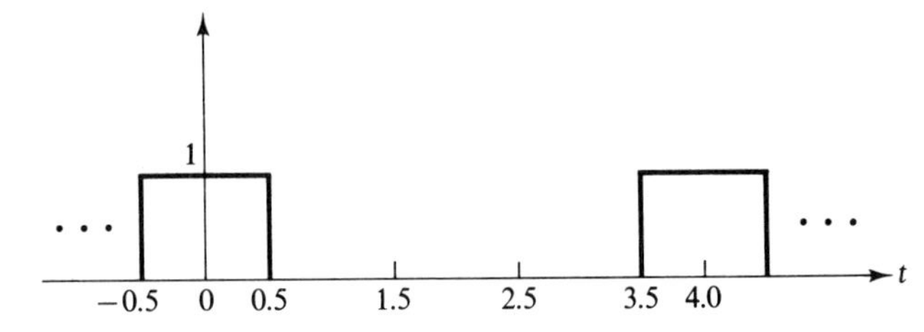

Figure 3.29

27. Deduce the coefficients α_n for the convolution of the pairs of periodic functions shown in Figure 3.30.

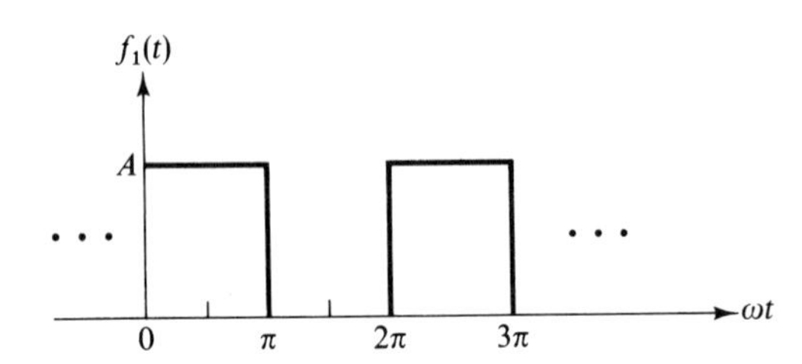

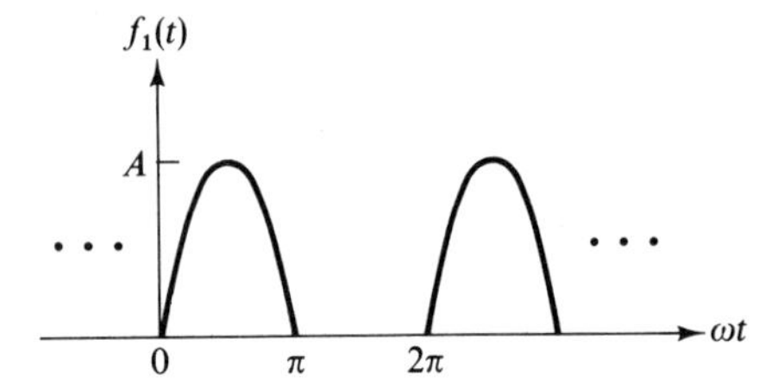

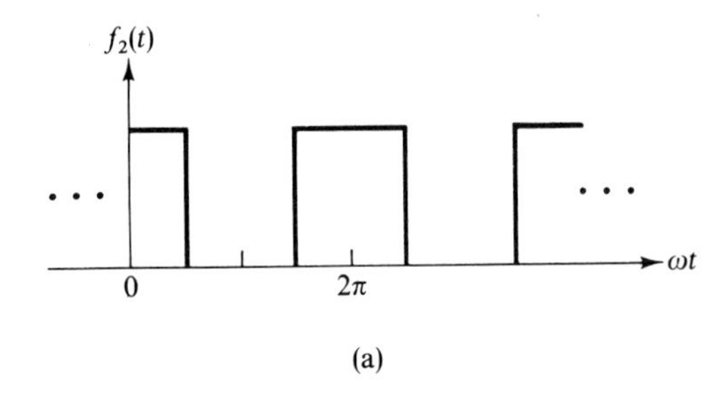

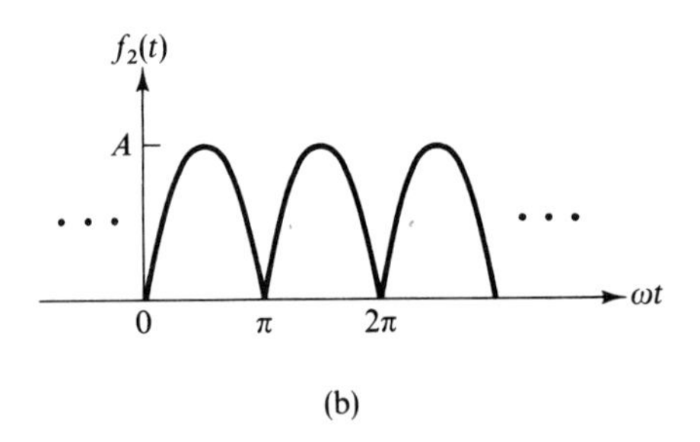

Figure 3.30

Section 3.4

28. Determine the output for the systems shown in Figure 3.31 if the input is $\sin \omega_0 t$. State your observations about the output as ω_0 varies from zero to infinity.

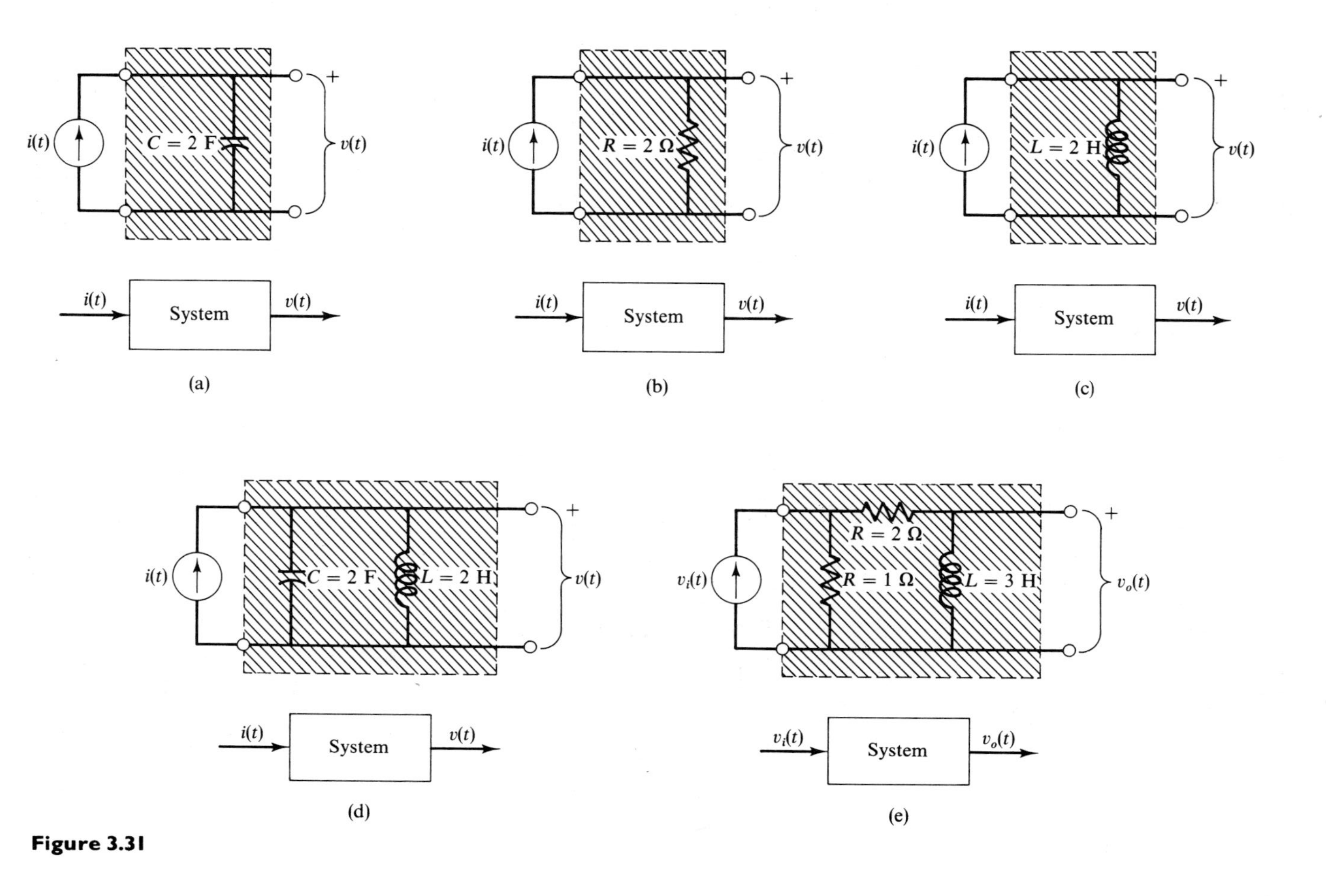

i(t)
C = 2 F
+
v(t)
i(t)
System
v(t)
(a)
i(t)
R = 2 Ω
+
v(t)
i(t)
System
v(t)
(b)
i(t)
L = 2 H
+
v(t)
i(t)
System
v(t)
(c)
i(t)
C = 2 F
L = 2 H
+
v(t)
i(t)
System
v(t)
(d)
$v_i(t)$
R = 2 Ω
R = 1 Ω
L = 3 H
+
$v_o(t)$
$v_i(t)$
System
$v_o(t)$
(e)

Figure 3.31

29. Determine the output for the systems shown in Figure 3.32 if the input is $\sin \omega_1 t + \cos \omega_2 t$.

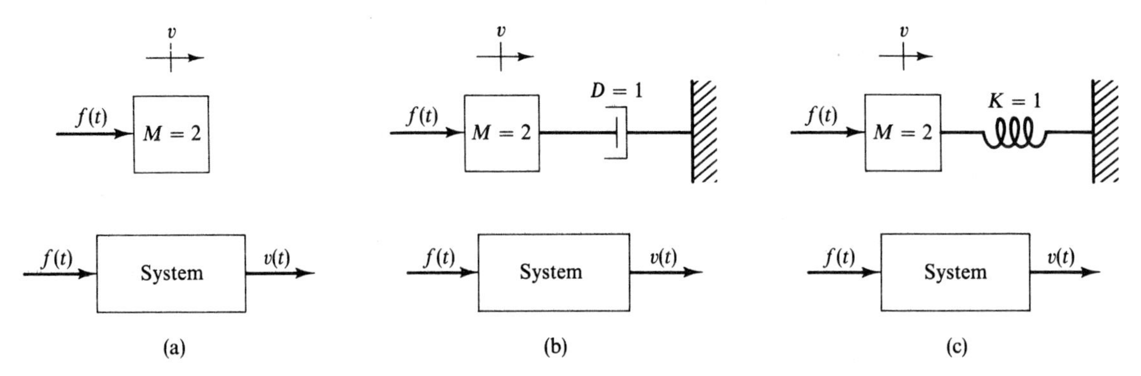

Figure 3.32

Hint: Remember that the systems are linear; thus, define the system function $H(j\omega)$ appropriate to each ω.

30. **a.** Deduce the output voltage $v_o(t)$ for the system shown in Figure 3.33a. **b.** Deduce the velocity $v_2(t)$ for the system shown in Figure 3.33b.

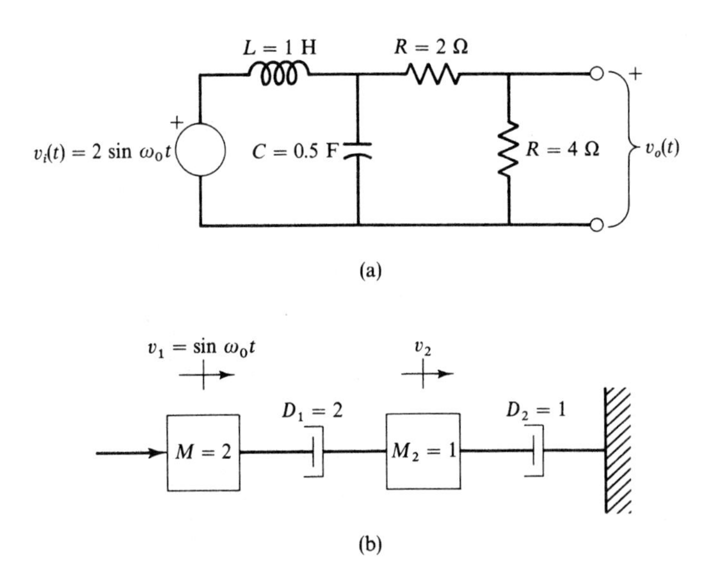

Figure 3.33

31. A full-wave rectified signal (see Figure 3.9) with period $T = 4$ ms, amplitude $A = 2$, and fundamental frequency $\omega_0 = 2\pi/T = 5\pi \times 10^2$ rad/s is the input to an ideal low-pass filter. The cutoff frequency of the filter is $\omega_c = 8 \times 10^3$ rad/s. Deduce the output.
Hint: an ideal low-pass filter is one that passes all frequencies up to cutoff value without amplitude and phase variations and eliminates all higher frequencies.

Section 3.5

32. Plot the complex numbers W^2, W^5, and W^8 in the complex plane for the following:
a. $N = 16$ **b.** $N = 32$

33. Find the Fourier series coefficients for the harmonic function $f(t) = 5 \cos 2\pi t$ for $N = 2$, $N = 3$, and $N = 4$. Assume $T = 1$, which implies that $M = 1$.

34. Plot the complex discrete signals $e^{jk(2\pi/8)n}$ in the complex plane over the range $n = 0, 1, 2, \ldots 7$ for different values of k.

35. Find the Fourier coefficients of the periodic sequences shown in Figure 3.34 and plot their spectrums.

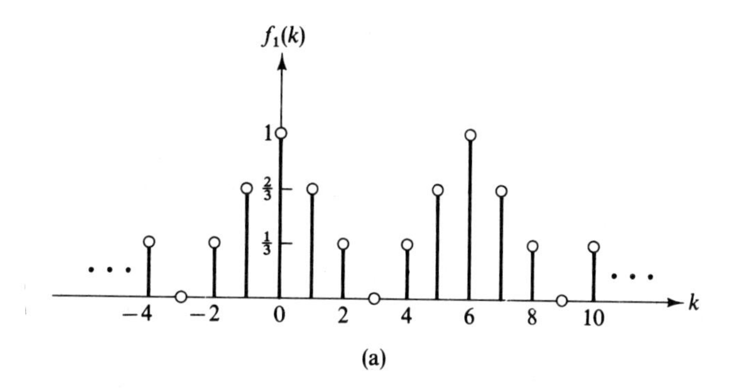

(a)

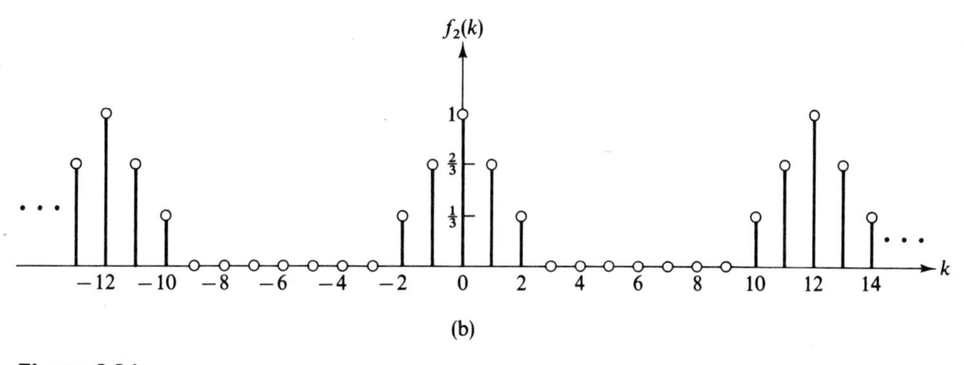

(b)

Figure 3.34

36. Show that the matrixes [see (3.70)]

$$\mathbf{W} = \begin{bmatrix} 1 & 1 & 1 \\ 1 & e^{-j2(\pi/3)} & e^{-j4\pi/3} \\ 1 & e^{-j4\pi/3} & e^{-j8\pi/3} \end{bmatrix} \qquad \mathbf{W}^* = \begin{bmatrix} 1 & 1 & 1 \\ 1 & e^{j2\pi/3} & e^{j4\pi/3} \\ 1 & e^{j4\pi/3} & e^{j8\pi/3} \end{bmatrix}$$

are orthogonal—that is $\mathbf{WW}^* = 3\mathbf{I}$, where $\mathbf{I}$ is the identity matrix. This development is easily extended to $N \times N$ dimensional matrixes. What is the result for the $N \times N$ case? Use this result to determine $\mathbf{W}^*\tilde{\boldsymbol{\alpha}}_n$ where $\tilde{\boldsymbol{\alpha}}_n$ is given by the form specified in (3.70); from this result, write an expression for $\mathbf{f}(m\tau)$ in matrix form.

Section 3.6

37. Use circular convolution to find the linear convolution of the two signals shown in Figure 3.35.

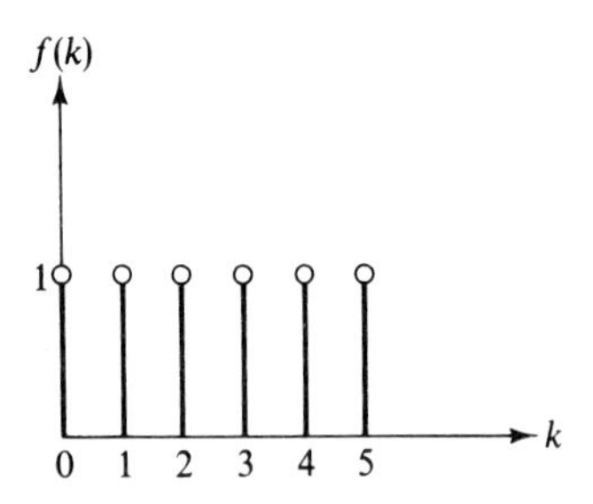

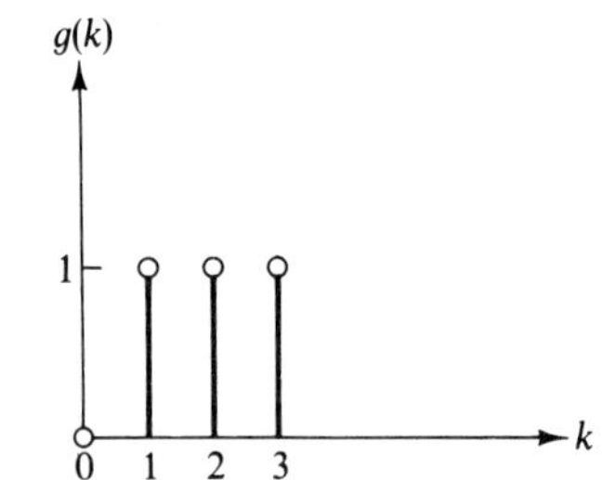

Figure 3.35

38. Find the circular convolution of the two sequences shown in Figure 3.36 so that it is identical with their linear convolution.

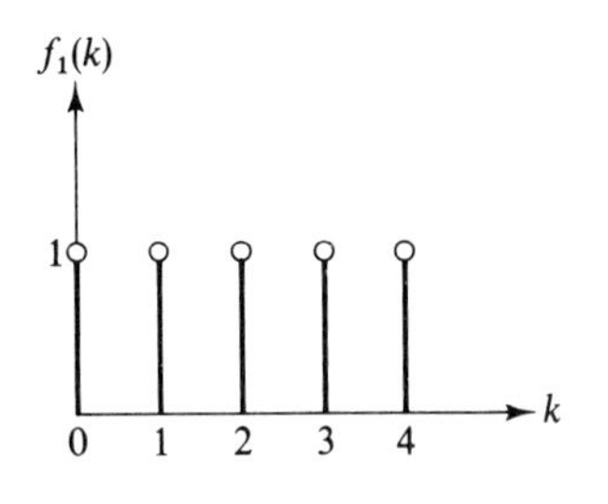

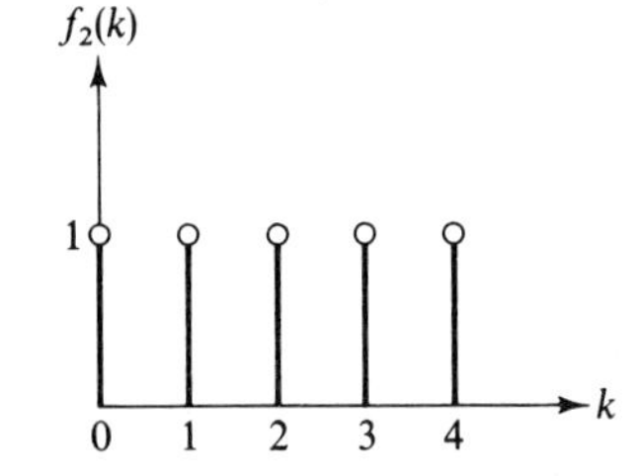

Figure 3.36

39. Show that the convolution of two periodic sequences with $N = 3$ is given by the matrix relationship

$$\begin{bmatrix} y(0) \\ y(1) \\ y(2) \end{bmatrix} = \begin{bmatrix} f(0) & f(1) & f(2) \\ f(1) & f(2) & f(0) \\ f(2) & f(0) & f(1) \end{bmatrix} \begin{bmatrix} g(0) \\ g(2) \\ g(1) \end{bmatrix}$$

Write the matrix form for $N = 4$; then, generalize the result for $N = N$.

Nonperiodic Signals and Fourier Transforms

Unlike the Fourier series that is essentially oriented towards periodic functions, the Fourier integral permits a description of nonperiodic functions. The Fourier integral bears a close relationship to the Fourier series. The fact that a Fourier transform pair exists is of importance to our work. The transform pair permits a frequency domain function $F(\omega)$ to be deduced from a knowledge of the time domain function $f(t)$, and vice versa: A knowledge of $F(\omega)$ permits a determination of the corresponding $f(t)$.

This chapter considers the properties of the Fourier transform, with examples of the calculations of some elementary transform pairs. Among the important applications of the Fourier transform are analytically representing nonperiodic functions, solving differential equations, aiding in the analysis of LTI systems, and analyzing and processing signals in engineering, medical, optical, metallographic, and seismic problems.

For the case where signals are experimentally derived, analytic forms are not available for the integrations involved. The approach now is to replace the continuous Fourier transform by an equivalent **discrete Fourier transform** (DFT) (a form that is closely related to the discrete Fourier series) and then evaluate the DFT using the discrete data. While the process is straightforward in principle, the number of calculations involved can become extremely large, even in relatively small problems. It is the use of the **fast Fourier transform** (FFT), a computational algorithm that greatly reduces the number of calculations in the use of the DFT, that makes the DFT a viable procedure. This chapter includes discussions of the DFT and the FFT.

Continuous Time Functions

4.1 Direct and Inverse Fourier Transforms

The Fourier transform of a function $f(t)$, written $\mathscr{F}\{f(t)\}$, and the inverse Fourier transform, written $\mathscr{F}^{-1}\{F(\omega)\}$, are defined by the integral relations

$$\mathscr{F}\{f(t)\} \triangleq F(\omega) = \int_{-\infty}^{\infty} f(t)e^{-j\omega t}\, dt$$

direct, or forward, Fourier transform **(4.1a)**

$$\mathscr{F}^{-1}\{F(\omega)\} \triangleq f(t) = \frac{1}{2\pi}\int_{-\infty}^{\infty} F(\omega)e^{j\omega t}\, d\omega$$

inverse Fourier transform **(4.1b)**

The function $F(\omega)$ is known as the **spectrum** function. If $F(\omega)$ is a complex function of the form $F(\omega) = F_r(\omega) + jF_i(\omega)$, we would ordinarily plot the absolute value $|F(\omega)| = \sqrt{F_r^2(\omega) + F_i^2(\omega)}$ and the argument $\text{Arg}\, F(\omega) = \tan^{-1}[F_i(\omega)/F_r(\omega)]$ versus ω, or the real and imaginary parts versus ω.

Not all functions $f(t)$ are Fourier transformable. Sufficiency conditions for a function $f(t)$ to be Fourier transformable are called the **Dirichlet conditions**, which are as follows:

1. $\int_{-\infty}^{\infty} |f(t)|\, dt < \infty$.
2. $f(t)$ has finite maximums and minimums within any finite interval.
3. $f(t)$ has a finite number of discontinuities within any finite interval.

If these conditions are met, $f(t)$ can be transformed uniquely. Some functions exist that do not possess Fourier transforms in the strict sense since they violate one or another of the Dirichlet conditions. Yet, in many cases, it is still possible to deduce the Fourier transform if the function under consideration belongs to a set known as **generalized functions**. One such function is the **delta function** $\delta(t)$, which is considered below.

■ Example 4.1

Determine the Fourier transform of the function $f(t) = e^{-at}u(t)$ and, from this result, plot the following versus ω:

a. The real part of its Fourier spectrum.
b. The imaginary part of its Fourier spectrum.
c. The absolute value and phase of the Fourier spectrum.

Solution By an application of (4.1a),

$$F(\omega) \triangleq \mathscr{F}\{f(t)\} = \int_{-\infty}^{\infty} e^{-at}u(t)e^{-j\omega t}\,dt$$

$$= \int_{0}^{\infty} e^{-(a+j\omega)t}\,dt = \frac{1}{a+j\omega} \qquad a > 0$$

The real and imaginary parts of the spectrum are

$$F_r(\omega) = \operatorname{Re}\left\{\frac{1}{a+j\omega}\right\} = \operatorname{Re}\left\{\frac{a-j\omega}{a^2+\omega^2}\right\} = \frac{a}{a^2+\omega^2}$$

$$F_i(\omega) = \operatorname{Im}\left\{\frac{1}{a+j\omega}\right\} = \operatorname{Im}\left\{\frac{a-j\omega}{a^2+\omega^2}\right\} = -\frac{\omega}{a^2+\omega^2}$$

The function $F(\omega)$ can also be written in the form

$$F(\omega) = \frac{1}{\sqrt{a^2+\omega^2}}\, e^{-j\tan^{-1}(\omega/a)}$$

Thus, the absolute value and phase of the spectrum are

$$|F(\omega)| = \frac{1}{\sqrt{a^2+\omega^2}} \qquad \operatorname{Arg} F(\omega) = -\tan^{-1}(\omega/a)$$

Plots of these several functions are given in Figure 4.1. Observe particularly the relationship between the time function durations and their corresponding spectrums. Clearly, *as the time function duration becomes shorter, its spectrum becomes wider.* ■

■ **Example 4.2**

Determine and plot the spectrums of the following functions:

a. $f_1(t) = \delta(t)$

b. $f_2(t) = \delta(t-a)$

Solution Employ the properties of the delta function to obtain

$$F_1(\omega) \triangleq \mathscr{F}\{\delta(t)\} = \int_{-\infty}^{\infty} \delta(t)e^{-j\omega t}\,dt = e^{-j\omega\cdot 0} = 1$$

$$F_2(\omega) \triangleq \mathscr{F}\{\delta(t-a)\} = \int_{-\infty}^{\infty} \delta(t-a)e^{-j\omega t}\,dt = e^{-j\omega a}$$

The functions and their spectrums are shown in Figure 4.2. ■

We next examine the features of $F(\omega)$ under various special conditions on $f(t)$.

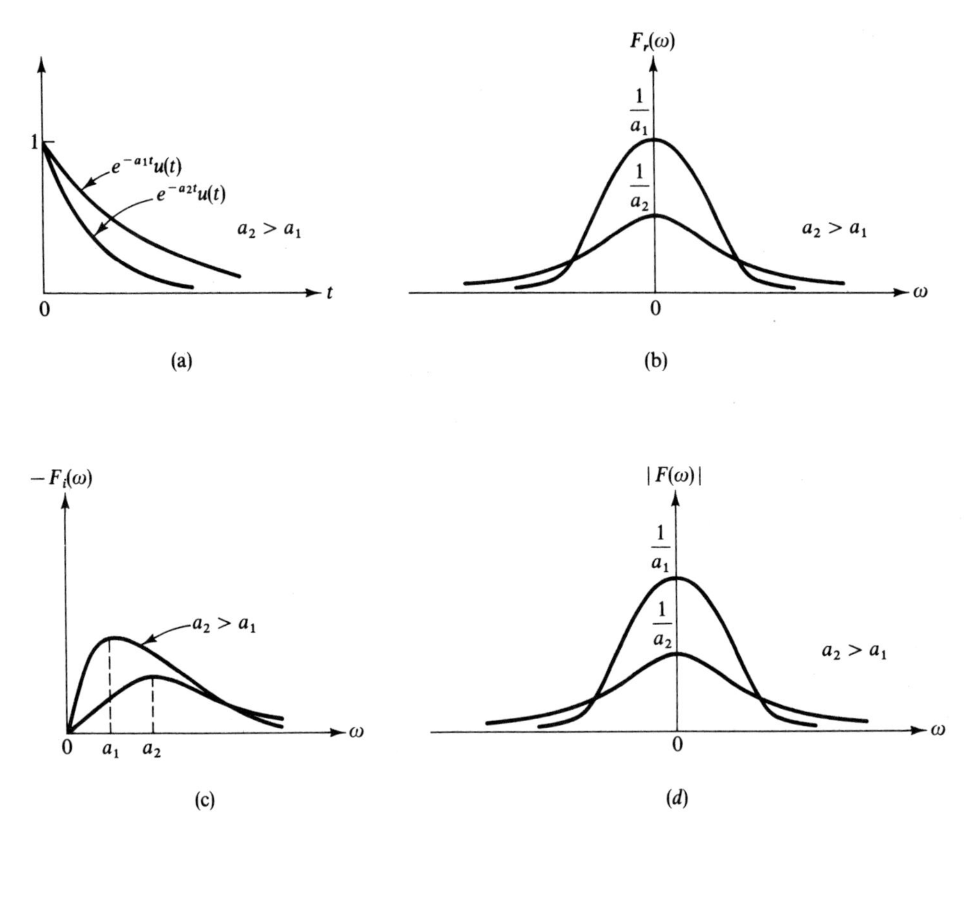

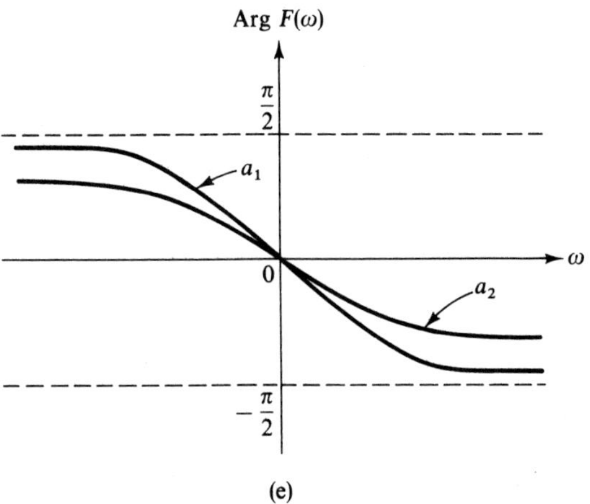

Figure 4.1 Time and Frequency Functions. (a) Time functions. (b) Corresponding real parts of their spectrums. (c) Corresponding imaginary parts of their spectrums. (d) The $|F(\omega)|$ values of the spectrums. (e) Arguments of the spectrums.

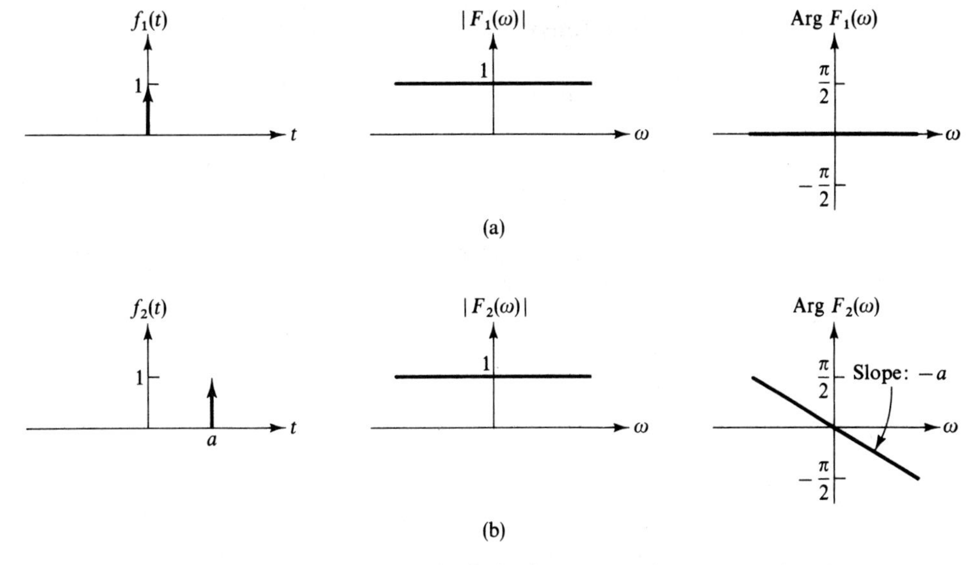

Figure 4.2 Delta Function and Its Representations. (a) Delta function at the origin and its Fourier spectrum. (b) Shifted delta function and its Fourier spectrum.

Real Functions. Suppose that $f(t)$ is real. We obtain the relationship

$$F(-\omega) = \int_{-\infty}^{\infty} f(t)e^{j\omega t}\, dt = \left[\int_{-\infty}^{\infty} f(t)e^{-j\omega t}\, dt\right]^* = F^*(\omega) \tag{4.2}$$

This result indicates that the reflected form of the function $F(\omega)$ is equal to the conjugate of $F(\omega)$. To prove this result, we write

$$\begin{aligned}\left[\int_{-\infty}^{\infty} f(t)\cos\omega t\, dt - j\int_{-\infty}^{\infty} f(t)\sin\omega t\, dt\right]^* &\\ = \int_{-\infty}^{\infty} f(t)\cos\omega t\, dt + j\int_{-\infty}^{\infty} f(t)\sin\omega t\, dt &\\ = \int_{-\infty}^{\infty} [f(t)e^{j\omega t}]\, dt = \int_{-\infty}^{\infty} f(t)e^{-j(-\omega)t}\, dt = F(-\omega)&\end{aligned}$$

This result, when applied to Example 4.1, shows that

$$F(-\omega) = \frac{1}{a - j\omega} = \left(\frac{1}{a + j\omega}\right)^* = F^*(\omega)$$

in accord with the above results.

Real and Even Functions. For $f(t)$ even and real, we obtain,

$$F(\omega) \triangleq F_r(\omega) + jF_i(\omega) = \int_{-\infty}^{\infty} f(t)e^{-j\omega t}\,dt$$

$$= \int_{-\infty}^{\infty} f(t)\cos\omega t\,dt - j\int_{-\infty}^{\infty} f(t)\sin\omega t\,dt = \int_{-\infty}^{\infty} f(t)\cos\omega t\,dt \quad \textbf{(4.3a)}$$

Here, the integrand $f(t)\sin\omega t$ is an odd function, and the integral in the range $(-\infty, \infty)$ is zero. We can write (4.3a)

$$F_r(\omega) = \int_{-\infty}^{\infty} f(t)\cos\omega t\,dt = 2\int_{0}^{\infty} f(t)\cos\omega t\,dt \quad \textbf{(4.3b)}$$

$$F_i(\omega) = 0 \quad \textbf{(4.3c)}$$

■ **Example 4.3**

Deduce and plot the Fourier spectrum of the even function $f(t) = e^{-2|t|}$ illustrated in Figure 4.3a. Show that this spectrum verifies (4.3).

Solution The Fourier transform of the given function is

$$F(\omega) = \int_{-\infty}^{\infty} e^{-2|t|}e^{-j\omega t}\,dt = \int_{-\infty}^{0} e^{2t}e^{-j\omega t}\,dt + \int_{0}^{\infty} e^{-2t}e^{-j\omega t}\,dt$$

$$= \int_{-\infty}^{0} e^{(2-j\omega)t}\,dt + \int_{0}^{\infty} e^{-(2+j\omega)t}\,dt = \frac{1}{2-j\omega} + \frac{1}{2+j\omega} = \frac{4}{4+\omega^2}$$

This final expression shows that $F_i(\omega) = 0$, and the even function is shown in Figure 4.3b. Now, we examine

$$F_r(\omega) = 2\int_{0}^{\infty} e^{-2t}\cos\omega t\,dt = \int_{0}^{\infty} e^{-2t}(e^{j\omega t} + e^{-j\omega t})\,dt$$

$$= \frac{1}{-2-j\omega} + \frac{1}{-2+j\omega} = \frac{4}{4+\omega^2}$$

which agrees with the above. ■

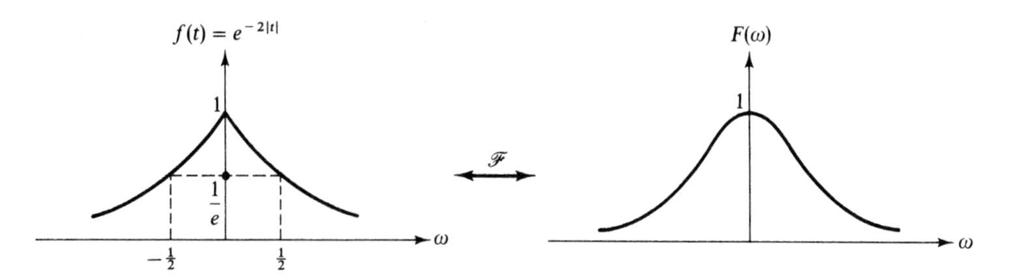

Figure 4.3 Illustrating Example 4.3

Real and Odd Functions. For $f(t)$ odd and real, we obtain

$$F(\omega) = \int_{-\infty}^{\infty} f(t)e^{-j\omega t}\,dt = \int_{-\infty}^{\infty} f(t)\cos\omega t\,dt - j\int_{-\infty}^{\infty} f(t)\sin\omega t\,dt$$

$$= -j\int_{-\infty}^{\infty} f(t)\sin\omega t\,dt \tag{4.4a}$$

Thus,

$$F_r(\omega) = 0 \tag{4.4b}$$

$$F_i(\omega) = -j\int_{-\infty}^{\infty} f(t)\sin\omega t\,dt$$

Interpretation of the Fourier Transform. To interpret the defining Fourier integral of (4.1a), we assume that the function $f(t)$ is real and even. We further assume that $f(t) = p_{0.5}(t)$, the pulse function having limits -0.5 to 0.5. For this function, the integral becomes

$$F(\omega) = \int_{-\infty}^{\infty} p_{0.5}(t)\cos\omega t\,dt = \int_{-0.5}^{0.5} \cos\omega t\,dt$$

$$= 2\left(\frac{\sin\dfrac{\omega}{2}}{\omega}\right) = 2\,\text{sinc}_{0.5}\,\omega \tag{4.5}$$

At any particular frequency $\omega = \omega_1$, this equation assumes the form

$$F(\omega_i) = \int_{-\infty}^{\infty} p_{0.5}(t)\cos\omega_i t\,dt$$

where the number $F(\omega_i)$ is the area under the product function $p_{0.5}(t)\cos\omega_i t$. Figure 4.4a illustrates this assertion in graphical form for specific values of ω. If we imagine that this process is repeated for an infinite number of ω's, the continuous curve $F(\omega)$ will result. Figure 4.4b shows how the function $f(t)$ is constructed. Each $f(t_i)$ is equal to the area under the product function curve $2\,\text{sinc}_{0.5}\,\omega\cos\omega t_i$, which is the integrand of the inverse transform of the function $2\,\text{sinc}_{0.5}\,\omega$. This follows because $\text{sinc}\,\omega$ is real and symmetric.

4.2 Properties of Fourier Transforms

Fourier transforms possess a number of very important properties. These properties are developed next.

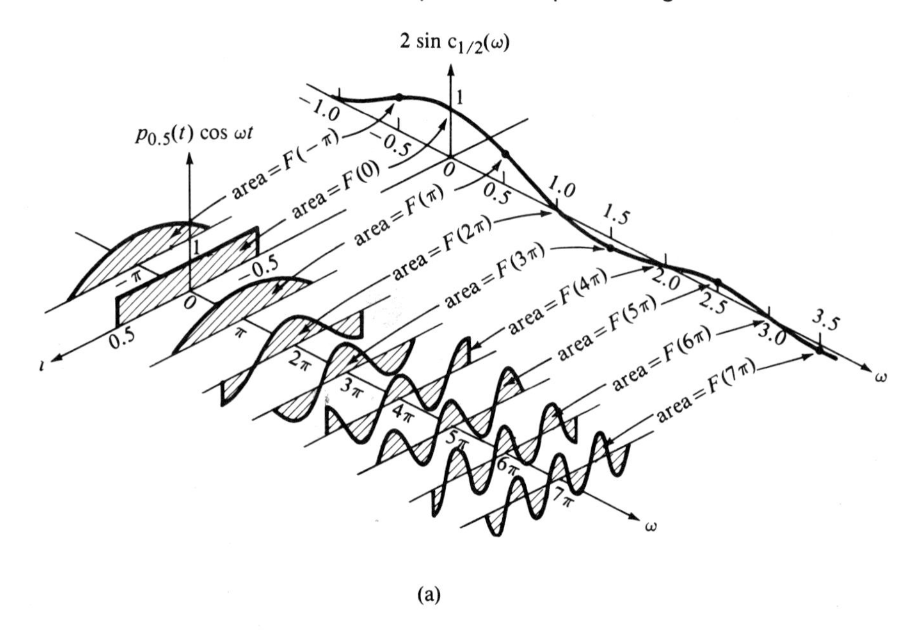

(a)

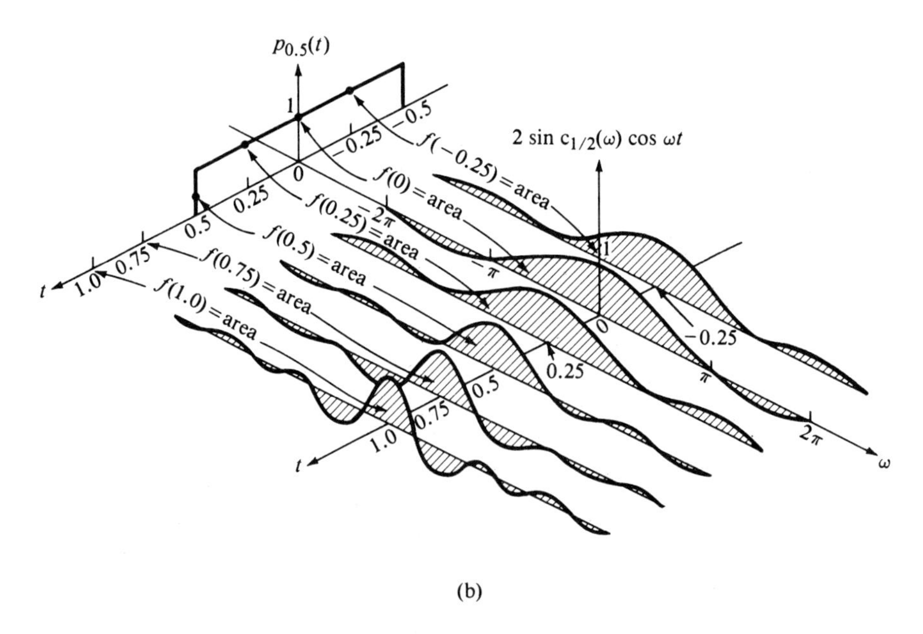

(b)

Figure 4.4 Illustration of the Fourier Integral Pair. (a) Shows $p_{0.5}(t)$ and successive values of cos ωt for $\omega t = \pi, 2\pi, 3\pi, \ldots$ and the corresponding value of the Fourier transform, $F(\omega)$. (b) Shows the variation of $F(\omega)$ cos ωt for successive values of t. (Gaskill, *Linear Systems, Fourier Transforms, and Optics*. Copyright © 1978 John Wiley & Sons. Reprinted by permission of John Wiley & Sons, Inc.)

Linearity. Consider the Fourier integral of the function $[a_1 f_1(t) + bf_2(t)]$

$$\mathscr{F}\{af_1(t) + bf_2(t)\} = a\mathscr{F}\{f_1(t)\} + b\mathscr{F}\{f_2(t)\} = aF_1(\omega) + bF_2(\omega) \tag{4.6}$$

where a and b are constants. This property is a direct result of the linear operation of integration.

Symmetry. If $\mathscr{F}\{f(t)\} = F(\omega)$, then

$$2\pi f(-\omega) = \int_{-\infty}^{\infty} F(t)e^{-j\omega t}\, dt \tag{4.7}$$

Proof Begin with the inverse Fourier integral

$$2\pi f(t) = \int_{-\infty}^{\infty} F(\omega)e^{j\omega t}\, d\omega$$

Now, interchange the symbols ω and t and this equation becomes

$$2\pi f(\omega) = \int_{-\infty}^{\infty} F(t)e^{j\omega t}\, dt$$

By introducing the change from ω to $-\omega$, the result is (4.7). This symmetry property can be used to extend the tables of Fourier transforms.

■ **Example 4.4**

Examine the symmetry property of the pulse function $p_a(t)$ and the impulse function (delta function) $\delta(t)$.

Solution The Fourier transform of the pulse function is

$$\mathscr{F}\{p_a(t)\} = \int_{-\infty}^{\infty} p_a(t)e^{-j\omega t}\, dt = \int_{-a}^{a} e^{-j\omega t}\, dt$$

$$= 2\,\frac{\sin \omega a}{\omega} = 2 \operatorname{sinc}_a \omega \tag{4.8}$$

From the symmetry property, we write

$$2\pi p_a(-\omega) = \mathscr{F}\left\{2\,\frac{\sin at}{t}\right\} \tag{4.9}$$

The graphical representations of these formulas are given in Figure 4.5a. To prove this result requires the use of the integral (the integrand is an even function)

$$2\int_0^{\infty} 2\,\frac{\sin at}{t} \cos \omega t\, dt = 2\pi \qquad -a \le \omega \le a$$

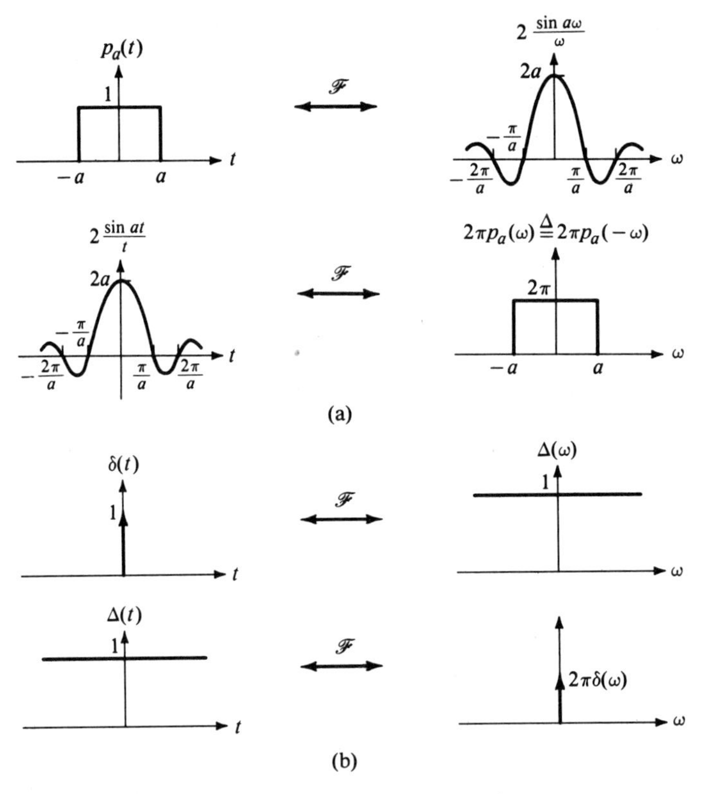

Figure 4.5 Symmetry Properties. (a) Illustration of the symmetry property of the pulse function. (b) Illustration of the symmetry property of the delta function.

For the delta function, we have

$$\mathscr{F}\{\delta(t)\} = \int_{-\infty}^{\infty} \delta(t)e^{-j\omega t}\,dt = e^{-j\omega 0} = 1 \triangleq \Delta(\omega) \tag{4.10a}$$

By the symmetry property and because the delta function is even,

$$2\pi\delta(-\omega) = 2\pi\delta(\omega) = \mathscr{F}\{\Delta(t)\} = \mathscr{F}\{1\} \tag{4.10b}$$

These relationships are shown in Figure 4.5b. ■

Time Shifting. For any real time t_0,

$$\mathscr{F}\{f(t \pm t_0)\} = e^{\pm j\omega t_0}\mathscr{F}\{f(t)\} = e^{\pm j\omega t_0}F(\omega) \tag{4.11}$$

■ **Example 4.5**

Find the Fourier transform of the function $f(t - t_0) = e^{-(t-t_0)}u(t - t_0)$.

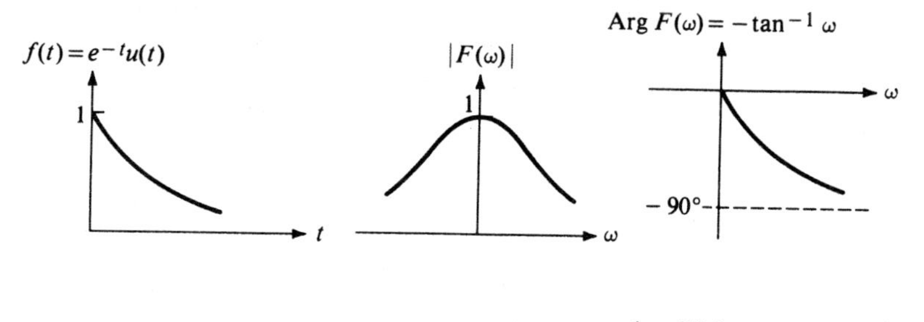

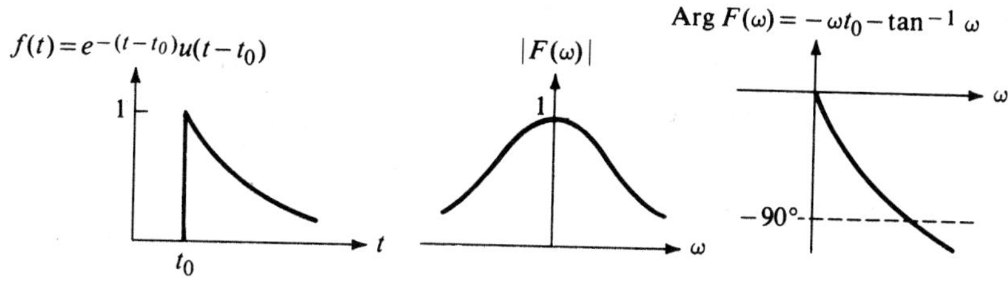

Figure 4.6 The Function $\exp(-t)u(t)$ and Effect of Shifting in the Time Domain

Solution Use (4.11) to write (see also Example 4.1)

$$\mathscr{F}\{f(t-t_0)\} = e^{-j\omega t_0}\mathscr{F}\{f(t)\} = e^{-j\omega t_0}\mathscr{F}\{e^{-t}u(t)\} = \frac{e^{-j\omega t_0}}{1+j\omega}$$

The effect of time shifting is shown in Figure 4.6. Observe that only the phase spectrum is modified. ■

Scaling. If $\mathscr{F}\{f(t)\} = F(\omega)$, then

$$\mathscr{F}\{f(at)\} = \frac{1}{|a|}F\left(\frac{\omega}{a}\right) \tag{4.12a}$$

and from this, we see that

$$\mathscr{F}\{f(-t)\} = F(-\omega) \tag{4.12b}$$

This equation indicates that if a time function is reflected, its Fourier spectrum is also reflected.

■ **Example 4.6**

Discuss the Fourier transform of the pulse function $f_b(t) = p_a(bt)$, where $b > a$.

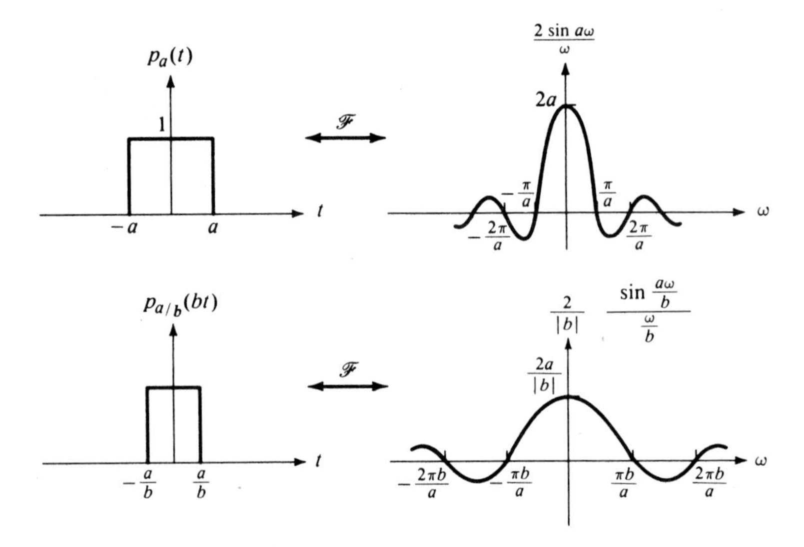

Figure 4.7 Effect of Scaling in Time and in Frequency Domains, $b > a$

Solution By Example 4.4, the Fourier transform of $f_a(t) = p_a(t)$ is $2(\sin a\omega/\omega)$. By (4.12a), the Fourier transform of $p_{a/b}(bt)$ is

$$\mathscr{F}\{p_{a/b}(bt)\} = \frac{1}{|b|} F_a(\omega)\bigg|_{\omega=(\omega/b)} = \frac{1}{|b|} \frac{2 \sin \frac{a}{b}\omega}{\frac{\omega}{b}}$$

The respective functions are shown in Figure 4.7. Note that as the pulse narrows in time, the spectrum broadens although the amplitude decreases. ■

Central Ordinate. By setting $\omega = 0$ and $t = 0$ in (4.1a) and (4.1b), respectively, the resulting expressions are

$$F(0) = \int_{-\infty}^{\infty} f(t)\, dt \tag{4.13a}$$

$$f(0) = \frac{1}{2\pi} \int_{-\infty}^{\infty} F(\omega)\, d\omega \tag{4.13b}$$

The first of these equations shows that the area under the $f(t)$ curve is equal to the central ordinate of the Fourier transform. The second of these equations shows that the area under the $F(\omega)$ curve is 2π times the value of the function at $t = 0$.

■ **Example 4.7**

Find $F(0)$ and $f(0)$ for the function $f(t) = 2p_a(t)$ using (4.13).

Solution From Example 4.4, the Fourier integral of $2p_a(t)$ is

$$\mathcal{F}\{2p_a(t)\} = 4\,\frac{\sin a\omega}{\omega}$$

For $\omega = 0$, by an application of L'Hospital's rule, $F(0) = 4a$.
From (4.13a), we also have

$$F(0) = \int_{-\infty}^{\infty} 2p_a(t)\,dt = 2\int_{-a}^{a} dt = 4a$$

For $f(0)$, we use the inverse Fourier integral

$$f(0) = \frac{1}{2\pi}\int_{-\infty}^{\infty} 4\,\frac{\sin a\omega}{\omega}\,d\omega = \frac{2}{\pi}\int_{-\infty}^{\infty} \frac{\sin a\omega}{a\omega}\,d(a\omega)$$
$$= \frac{2}{\pi}\int_{-\infty}^{\infty} \frac{\sin \tau}{\tau}\,d\tau = \frac{2}{\pi} \times \tau = 2$$

where use has been made of mathematical tables for the value of the integral. ■

Frequency Shifting. If $\mathcal{F}\{f(t)\} = F(\omega)$, then

$$\mathcal{F}\{e^{\pm j\omega_0 t}f(t)\} = F(\omega \mp \omega_0) \tag{4.14}$$

Modulation. If $\mathcal{F}\{f(t)\} = F(\omega)$, then

$$\mathcal{F}\{f(t)\cos\omega_0 t\} = \frac{1}{2}\,[F(\omega + \omega_0) + F(\omega - \omega_0)] \tag{4.15a}$$

$$\mathcal{F}\{f(t)\sin\omega_0 t\} = \frac{1}{2j}\,[F(\omega - \omega_0) - F(\omega + \omega_0)] \tag{4.15b}$$

Equation (4.15a) is shown graphically in Figure 4.8a. Equation (4.15) indicates that the spectrum of a modulated signal $f(t)$ is halved and shifted to the carrier frequency ω_0.

These formulas are easily derived by expanding the cosine and sine terms into their equivalent exponential forms, given by (1.8), and then by using (4.14).

The results of (4.15) constitute the fundamental properties of modulation and are basic to the field of communications. Figure 4.8b shows that modulation is present in some biological signals. Observe also that the resulting spectrum is equal to the convolution of the spectrums of the product functions (see *Frequency Convolution*).

■ Example 4.8

Find the spectrum of the modulated signal $\mathcal{F}(t)\cos\omega_c t$ shown in Figure 4.9.

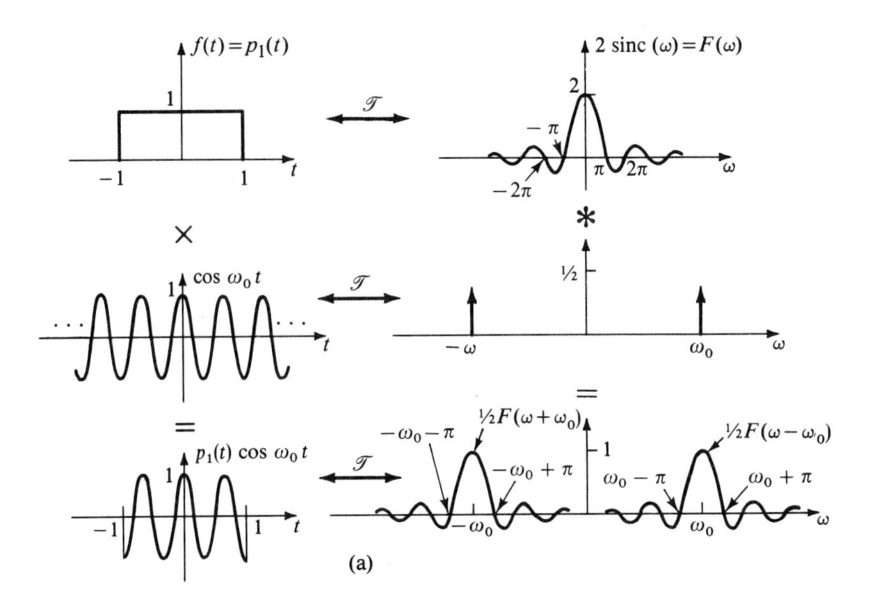

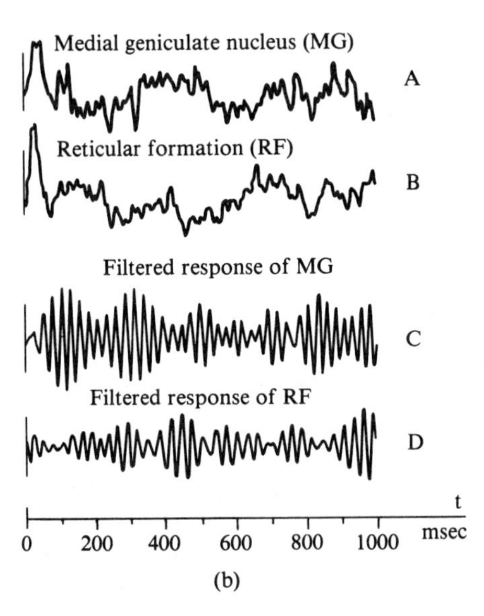

Figure 4.8 Modulated Signals. (a) Illustration of the spectrum shift of a modulated signal $f(t) = p_1(t)$. (b) Simultaneously recorded evoked response (AEPs) of the medial geniculate nucleus and the reticular formation in the same cat (A and B). The same AEPs filtered with bandpass filters of 33 Hz–42 Hz are shown below (C and D). (From E. Basar, *Biophysical and Physiological Systems Analysis*, © 1976. Addison-Wesley, Reading, MA. Reprinted with permission.)

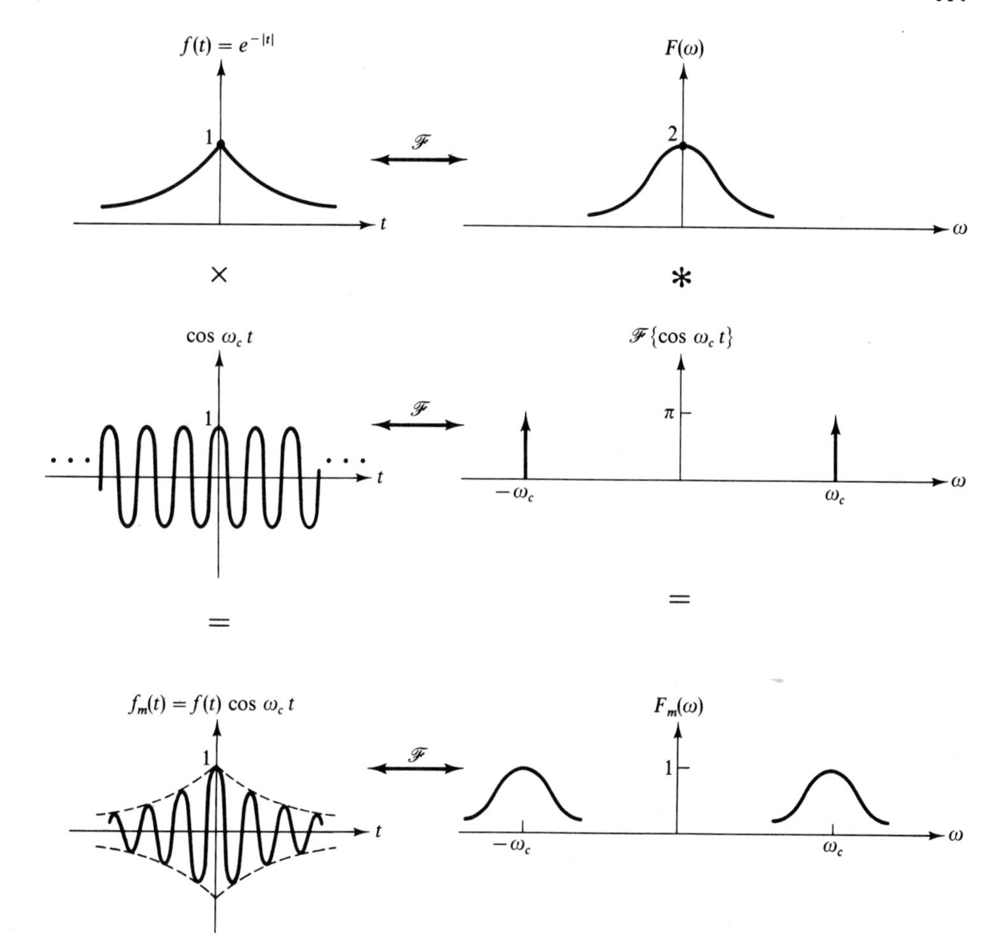

Figure 4.9 Illustrating Example 4.8

Solution Initially, we find the Fourier spectrums of $\cos \omega_c t$ and $f(t)$. These are

$$\mathscr{F}\{\cos \omega_c t\} = \mathscr{F}\left\{\frac{e^{j\omega_c t} + e^{-j\omega_c t}}{2}\right\} = \frac{1}{2}\int_{-\infty}^{\infty} e^{-j(\omega - \omega_c)t}\, dt + \frac{1}{2}\int_{-\infty}^{\infty} e^{-j(\omega + \omega_c)t}\, dt$$

$$= \pi\delta(\omega - \omega_c) + \pi\delta(\omega + \omega_c)$$

$$\mathscr{F}\{e^{-|t|}\} = \int_{-\infty}^{\infty} e^{-|t|}e^{-j\omega t}\, dt = \int_{-\infty}^{0} e^{t}e^{-j\omega t}\, dt + \int_{0}^{\infty} e^{-t}e^{-j\omega t}\, dt = \frac{2}{1 + \omega^2}$$

The spectrums are shown in Figure 4.9.

The spectrum of $f_m(t)$ is deduced as follows:

$$F_m(\omega) \triangleq \mathscr{F}\{e^{-|t|} \cos \omega_c t\} = \mathscr{F}\left\{\frac{e^{-|t|}e^{j\omega_c t}}{2} + \frac{e^{-|t|}e^{-j\omega_c t}}{2}\right\}$$

$$= \frac{1}{2}\int_{-\infty}^{0} e^{-(j\omega - j\omega_c - 1)t}\, dt + \frac{1}{2}\int_{0}^{\infty} e^{-(j\omega + j\omega_c + 1)t}\, dt$$

$$+ \frac{1}{2}\int_{-\infty}^{\infty} e^{-(j\omega + j\omega_c - 1)t}\, dt + \frac{1}{2}\int_{0}^{\infty} e^{-(j\omega - j\omega_c + 1)t}\, dt$$

$$= -\frac{1}{2}\frac{1}{j(\omega - \omega_c) - 1} + \frac{1}{2}\frac{1}{j(\omega + \omega_c) + 1}$$

$$-\frac{1}{2}\frac{1}{j(\omega + \omega_c) - 1} + \frac{1}{2}\frac{1}{j(\omega + \omega_c) + 1}$$

$$= \frac{1}{1 + (\omega - \omega_c)^2} + \frac{1}{1 + (\omega - \omega_c)^2}$$

The spectrum of $F_m(\omega)$ is also shown in Figure 4.9. Observe from Figures 4.8 and 4.9 that when a signal is modulated by a cosine function of frequency ω_c, its spectrum is shifted in the frequency domain by ω_c, the carrier frequency. This process is used in communications and is known as **amplitude modulation** (AM) (see Section 1.4). It is created by controlling the amplitude of one signal by a second signal. ■

The need for modulation in communication systems arises from practical considerations. For transmission through space, the question of the antenna length, as discussed in Section 1.4, is an important consideration. Without some form of modulation, the antenna problem is impracticable. A second consideration arises if we want to use a given **channel** to transmit a number of messages simultaneously without interference. We are familiar with the many broadcasting stations within the allowed broadcast band that use free space as the channel. In fact, this same free-space channel is used for FM, TV, and many other forms of communication.

In the amplitude-modulated (AM) system, the carrier signal is easily produced by a stable oscillator with power amplifiers to establish the desired power level. The carrier signal is of the form $v_c(t) = V_c \cos \omega_c t$, where ω_c is the **carrier frequency**. The modulating signal (tone modulation) in its simplest form is $v_m(t) = V_m \cos \omega_m t$ and may denote one component of a complex signal pattern, where ω_m is the modulating frequency and where $\omega_m \ll \omega_c$. The general form of the modulation process is specified by the equation

$$v(t) = V_c[1 + mv_m(t)] \cos \omega_c t \tag{4.16}$$

where m is the **modulation index** and is defined as $m = V_m/V_c$. The maximum value of $mv_m(t)$ must be less than unity if distortion of the envelope is to be avoided. For the case of simple sinusoidal modulation, this equation can be expanded to

$$v(t) = V_c \cos \omega_c t + V_c m \cos \omega_c t \cos \omega_m t$$

or

$$v(t) = V_c\left\{\cos \omega_c t + \frac{m}{2}\left[\cos(\omega_c + \omega_m)t + \cos(\omega_c - \omega_m)t\right]\right\} \tag{4.17}$$

The amplitude spectrums of the three waveforms are given in Figure 4.10a. Figure 4.10b shows the system of an AM generator in schematic form. Observe from Figure 4.10 that the amplitude-modulated signal has twice the bandwidth of the original signal and, in addition, that the carrier is also present.

Suppose that we had used a modulated signal of the form

$$\begin{aligned} v(t) &= mv_m(t) \cos \omega_c t = m \cos \omega_m t \cos \omega_c t \\ &= \frac{m}{2}\left[\cos(\omega_c + \omega_m)t + \cos(\omega_c - \omega_m)t\right] \end{aligned}$$

In such a system, the carrier frequency is not present. This type of modulation is known as **double-sideband suppressed carrier** (DSBSC) modulation. While such modulation does save the energy of the carrier in the transmitted signal and the carrier component carries no information, subsequent extraction of the information component is rather difficult. Moreover, the information is contained redundantly in each sideband; hence, it is desirable to remove one or the other sideband to yield **single-sideband** (SSB) modulation.

■ Example 4.9

Consider a band-limited modulating signal $v_m(t)$ that has a bandwidth ω_b, as shown in Figure 4.11a. Sketch the frequency spectrum of the signal. This signal modulates a carrier $v_c(t) = \cos \omega_c t$; therefore, the modulated signal is $v(t) = v_m(t) \cos \omega_c t$. Sketch its form in the time domain and in the frequency domain.

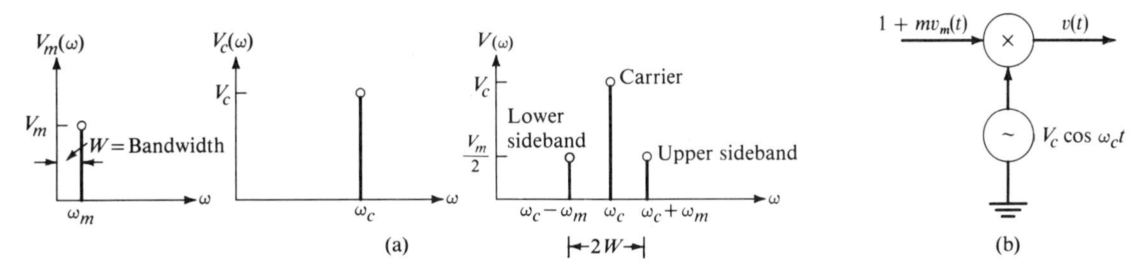

Figure 4.10 Amplitude Modulation. (a) Frequency spectrum of an AM signal modulated by $V_m \cos \omega_m t$. (b) A schematic representation of an ideal generator of an AM signal.

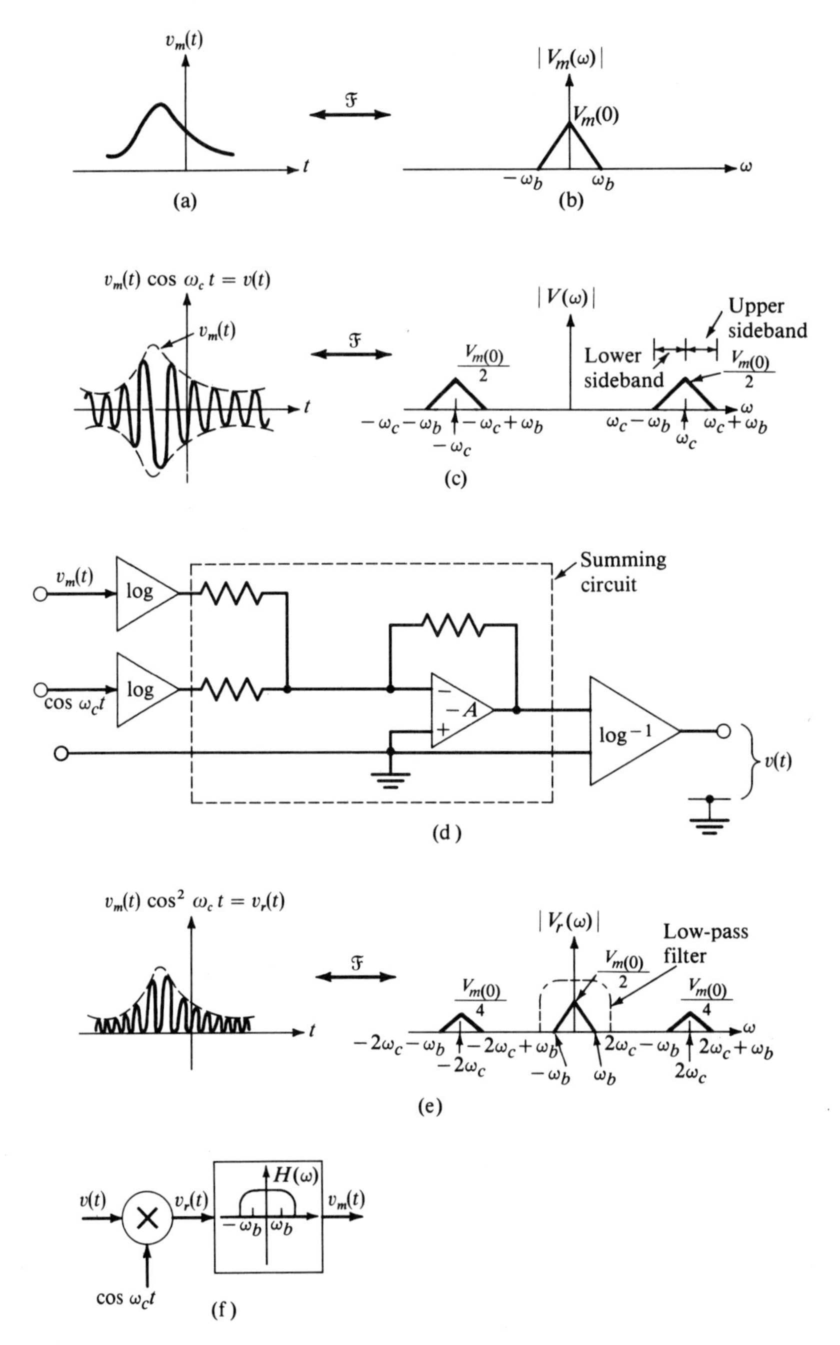

Figure 4.11 AM Modulation and Demodulation. (a) Information-carrying signal $v_m(t)$. (b) Fourier spectrums of $v_m(t)$. (c) Modulated signal and its Fourier spectrums. (d) One type of multiplier circuit. (e) Received signal multiplied by $\cos\,\omega_c t$ and its Fourier spectrum. (f) Demodulation scheme.

Finally, multiply the received signal by a signal $\cos \omega_c t$ and show that the modulating signal is recovered in this process, called **demodulation**.

Solution We suppose that the signal is that shown in Figure 4.11a and that its Fourier spectrum is that shown in Figure 4.11b. The Fourier spectrum of $v(t)$, the modulated signal, is

$$\mathscr{F}\{v(t)\} = \mathscr{F}\left\{v_m(t)\,\frac{e^{j\omega_c t} + e^{-j\omega_c t}}{2}\right\}$$
$$= \frac{1}{2}\left[\int_{-\infty}^{\infty} v_m(t)e^{-j(\omega+\omega_c)t}\,dt + \int_{-\infty}^{\infty} v_m(t)e^{-j(\omega-\omega_c)t}\,dt\right]$$
$$= \frac{1}{2}\,V_m(\omega+\omega_c) + \frac{1}{2}\,V_m(\omega-\omega_c)$$

using the frequency shifting property (4.14). This spectrum is shown in Figure 4.11c.

The Fourier spectrum of the received signal is given by

$$\mathscr{F}\{v_r(t) = v(t)\cos\omega_c t\} = \mathscr{F}\left\{v_m(t)\left[\frac{e^{j\omega_c t} + e^{-j\omega_c t}}{2}\right]^2\right\}$$
$$= \mathscr{F}\left\{\frac{v_m(t)}{2} + v_m(t)\,\frac{e^{j2\omega_c t}}{4} + v_m(t)\,\frac{e^{-j2\omega_c t}}{4}\right\}$$
$$= \frac{V_m(\omega)}{2} + \frac{V_m(\omega-2\omega_c)}{4} + \frac{V_m(\omega+2\omega_c)}{4}$$

where the Fourier transform frequency shifting theorem was used. Now, we use a low-pass filter with cutoff ω_b to pass frequencies equally well up to ω_b and to reject all higher frequencies than ω_b and we recover $V_m(\omega)$, the desired signal. ■

The ability to shift the frequency spectrum of the information-carrying signal by means of amplitude modulation allows us to transmit many different signals simultaneously through a given channel, such as a transmission line, telephone line, microwave link, radio broadcast, and the like. This scheme is known as **frequency division multiplexing** (FDM). Of course, the ability to extract a given signal from the channel is equally essential, and a variety of demodulation or detection schemes exist. The sum of the frequency bands of the transmitted signals plus the frequency guard bands separating different signals must be less than or equal to the bandwidth of the channel for undistorted transmission.

A schematic representation of frequency division mutiplexing for three signals is shown in Figure 4.12. Only the positive part of the total spectrum is presented here since the other part appears on the negative ω-axis and is an exact mirror-image reflection of the positive portion of the spectrum relative to the origin. Bear in mind that negative frequencies do not exist physically, but they do play an important role in our mathematical formulations. Figure 4.12b shows the schematic representation for detecting the combined signal and separating it into its three components.

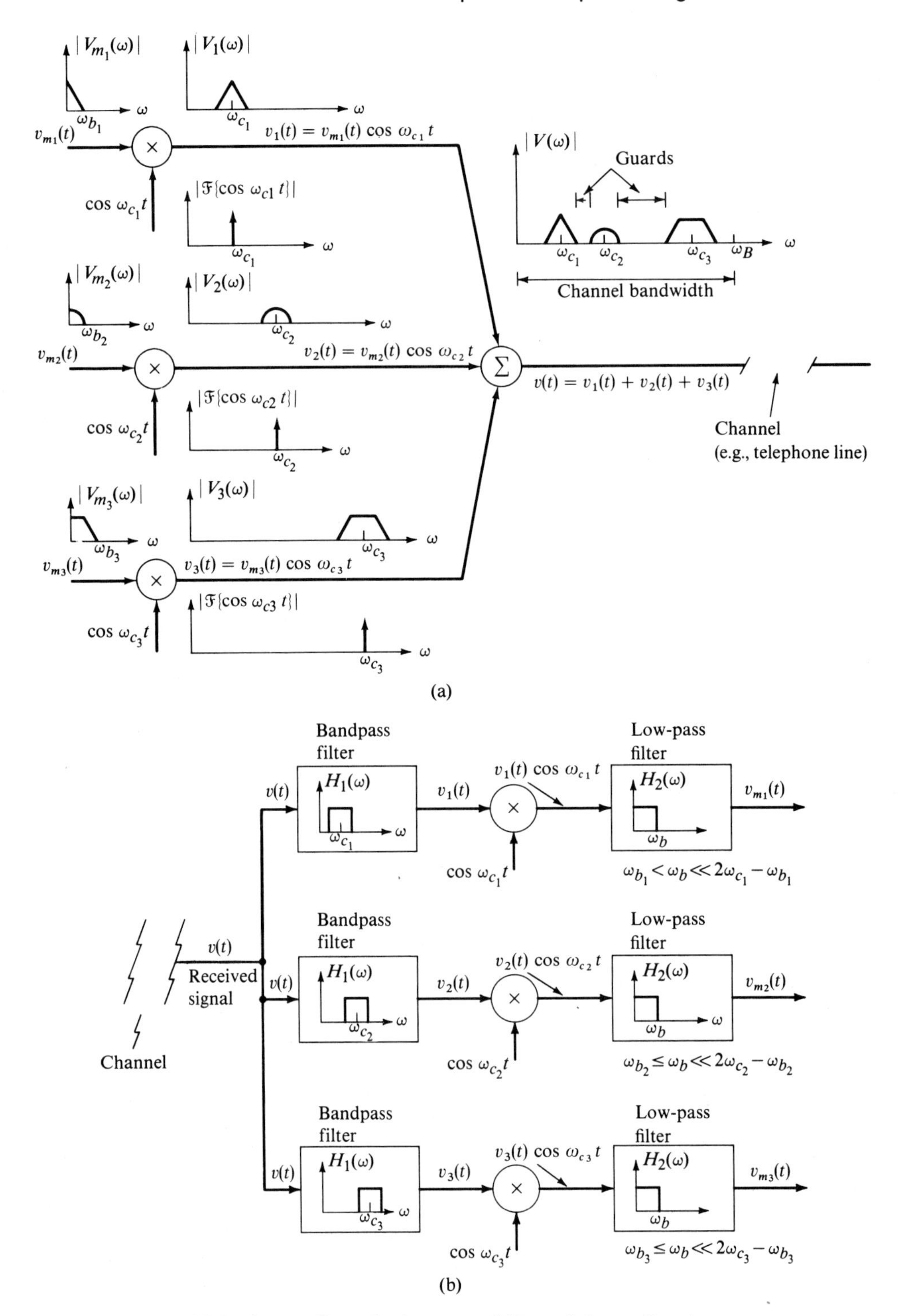

Figure 4.12 Frequency Multiplexing, Demultiplexing, and Demodulating Signals

For purposes of classification, the frequency spectrum is roughly divided as follows: 3 kHz to 300 kHz for telephony, navigation, industrial communication, and long-range navigation; 0.3 MHz to 30 MHz for AM broadcasting, military communication, and amateur and citizen-band radio; 30 MHz to 300 MHz for FM broadcasting, TV broadcasting, and land transportation; and 0.3 GHz to 3 GHz for UHF TV, radar, and military applications. The frequencies above 30 GHz are used mostly for research purposes and radio astronomy.

Derivatives. If $\mathscr{F}\{f(t)\} = F(\omega)$, then

$$\mathscr{F}\left\{\frac{df(t)}{dt}\right\} = j\omega F(\omega) \tag{4.18a}$$

$$\mathscr{F}\left\{\frac{d^n f(t)}{dt^n}\right\} = (j\omega)^n F(\omega) \tag{4.18b}$$

■ **Example 4.10**

Find the transformed input–output relationship of the system shown in Figure 4.13a, with block representations shown in Figure 4.13b.

Solution It is first necessary to write the differential equation of the system in the time domain. This equation is readily seen to be

$$\frac{v(t)}{R} + C\frac{dv(t)}{dt} = i(t)$$

Because of the linearity property, the Fourier transform of both sides of this equation becomes

$$\left(\frac{1}{R} + j\omega C\right)V(\omega) = I(\omega)$$

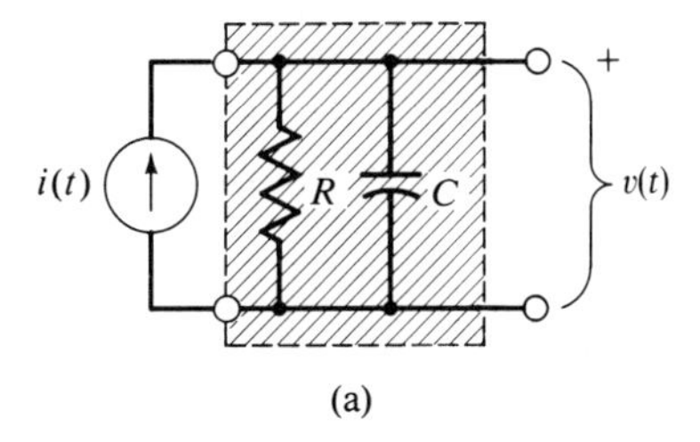

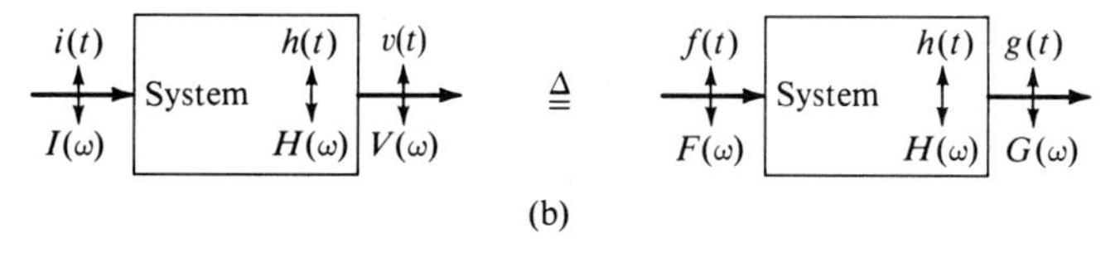

Figure 4.13 An Electrical System and Its Schematic Representation

from which,

$$\underbrace{V(\omega)}_{\text{Output}} = \underbrace{\frac{1}{\frac{1}{R} + j\omega C}}_{\substack{\text{System}\\\text{function}}} \underbrace{I(\omega)}_{\text{Input}} = \frac{1}{Y(\omega)} I(\omega) = Z(\omega)I(\omega) = \underbrace{H(\omega)}_{\substack{\text{System}\\\text{function}}} \underbrace{I(\omega)}_{\text{Input}}$$

where, in this case, the system function $H(\omega) = Z(\omega)$. This expression shows that the input–output relationship for any LTI system is given by

$$\boxed{\underbrace{G(\omega)}_{\text{Output}} = \underbrace{H(\omega)}_{\substack{\text{System}\\\text{function}}} \underbrace{F(\omega)}_{\text{Input}}} \tag{4.19}$$

If the input to the system is an impulse function, the impulse response $h(t)$ of the system is deduced from the differential equation

$$\frac{h(t)}{R} + C\frac{dh(t)}{dt} = \delta(t) \tag{4.20}$$

Our first step is to find $h(t)$ at $t = 0$, following the procedure discussed in Section 2.10. Thus, we integrate this equation from $t = 0-$ to $t = 0+$, which yields

$$\frac{1}{R}\int_{0-}^{0+} h(t)\,dt + C\int_{0-}^{0+} \frac{dh(t)}{dt}\,dt = \int_{0-}^{0+} \delta(t)\,dt$$

or

$$\frac{1}{R} \times 0 + C[h(0+) - h(0-)] = 1$$

since $h(t)$ is assumed to be continuous at $t = 0$. This condition is true because $h(t)$ is the response of a physical system and $h(t)$ is not expected to be impulsive. Further, for a causal system, $h(0-) = 0$; hence, $h(0+) = 1/C$.

The solution to the homogeneous equation

$$\frac{dh(t)}{dt} + \frac{1}{RC}h(t) = 0$$

is easily found to be (see Chapter 2)

$$h(t) = Ae^{-t/RC} \qquad t \geq 0$$

where A is an unknown constant. However, we have already found that $h(0+) = 1/C$; therefore, from the last equation, $A = 1/C$. Thus,

$$h(t) = \frac{1}{C}e^{-t/RC} \qquad t > 0$$

The Fourier transform of this function is given by

$$H(\omega) = \frac{1}{C}\int_0^\infty e^{-t/RC}e^{-j\omega t}\,dt = -\frac{1}{C}\frac{1}{j\omega + \dfrac{1}{RC}}e^{-(j\omega+1/RC)t}\Bigg|_0^\infty = \frac{1}{j\omega C + \dfrac{1}{R}}$$

which is identical with $H(\omega)$ above, but which was found by a different approach. ■

We conclude from this example that the impulse response of a system can be deduced by the following steps:

1. Fourier-transform the differential equation that describes the system assuming a delta function input and zero initial conditions.

$$\mathscr{F}\left\{\frac{h(t)}{R} + C\,\frac{dh(t)}{dt}\right\} = \mathscr{F}\{\delta(t)\}$$

from which,

$$\left(j\omega C + \frac{1}{R}\right)H(\omega) = 1$$

2. Solve for the output function.

$$H(\omega) = \frac{R}{1 + jRC\omega} = \frac{1}{C}\frac{1}{\dfrac{1}{RC} + j\omega}$$

3. Take the inverse Fourier transform.

$$\mathscr{F}^{-1}\{H(\omega)\} \triangleq h(t) = \frac{1}{2\pi C}\int_{-\infty}^{\infty}\frac{1}{\dfrac{1}{RC} + j\omega}e^{j\omega t}\,d\omega = \frac{1}{C}e^{-t/RC}$$

This result is obtained using Figure 4.26.

■ **Example 4.11**

Deduce the impulse response of the system shown in Figure 4.14a from a knowledge of the system response to the voltage $v = e^{j\omega t}$. Indicate the response to a general voltage $v(t)$.

Solution By an application of the Kirchhoff voltage law, we write

$$\frac{di(t)}{dt} + \frac{R}{L}\,i(t) = \frac{1}{L}\,v(t)$$

If we set $v = e^{j\omega t}$, the current is

$$\tilde{i}(t) = H(\omega)e^{j\omega t}$$

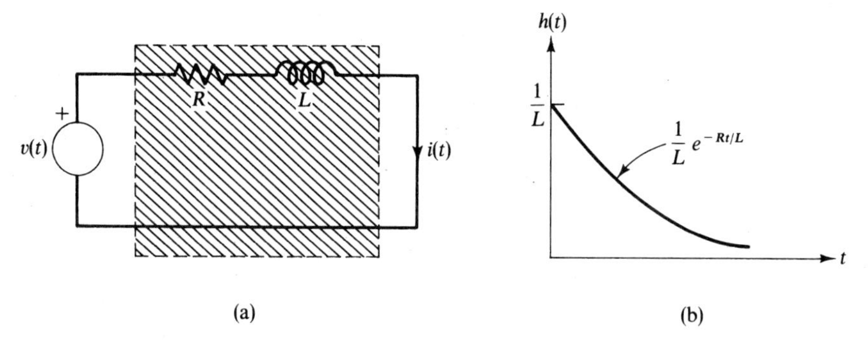

Figure 4.14 Simple Linear Time-Invariant System

Observe that $\tilde{\imath}(t)$ is a complex function. $H(\omega)$ is also a complex function that we can find by combining the foregoing two equations. Combining these equations, we obtain

$$j\omega H(\omega)e^{j\omega t} + \frac{R}{L}\,H(\omega)e^{j\omega t} = \frac{1}{L}\,e^{j\omega t}$$

From this, we obtain

$$H(\omega) = \frac{1}{L}\,\frac{1}{\dfrac{R}{L} + j\omega}$$

The value $H(\omega)$ is the value that would be obtained by using the Fourier transform on the controlling differential equation. The impulse response is obtained by taking the inverse Fourier transform of this function:

$$h(t) \triangleq \mathscr{F}^{-1}[H(\omega)] = \frac{1}{L}\int_{-\infty}^{\infty} \frac{1}{\dfrac{R}{L} + j\omega}\,e^{j\omega t}\,d\omega = \frac{1}{L}\,e^{-Rt/L} \qquad t > 0$$

This function is shown in Figure 4.14b. Thus, the solution for $v(t)$ is given by

$$i(t) = h(t) * v(t) = \frac{1}{L}\,e^{-Rt/L}\int_{-\infty}^{t} v(\tau)e^{R\tau/L}\,d\tau$$ ■

The results of these examples indicate that the transform of a differential equation that describes a physical system will be of the form

$$\sum_{n=0}^{N} a_n \frac{d^n g(t)}{dt^n} = \sum_{m=0}^{M} b_m \frac{d^m f(t)}{dt^m} \tag{4.21}$$

and will be the algebraic equation

$$\sum_{n=0}^{N} a_n(j\omega)^n G(\omega) = \sum_{m=0}^{M} b_m(j\omega)^m F(\omega)$$

from which it follows that

$$\underbrace{G(\omega)}_{\text{Output}} = \underbrace{\frac{\sum_{m=0}^{M} b_m(j\omega)^m}{\sum_{n=0}^{N} a_n(j\omega)^n}}_{\text{System function}} \underbrace{F(\omega)}_{\text{Input}} = H(\omega)F(\omega) \qquad (4.22)$$

The output in the time domain then follows from the inverse transform

$$g(t) = \frac{1}{2\pi}\int_{-\infty}^{\infty} H(\omega)F(\omega)e^{j\omega t}\, d\omega \qquad (4.23)$$

■ **Example 4.12**

Deduce the transfer function for the system shown in Figure 4.15.

Solution By an application of Kirchhoff's equation to the two loops,

$$L\frac{di_1(t)}{dt} + R_1 i_1(t) - L\frac{di_2(t)}{dt} = v(t)$$

$$L\frac{di_1(t)}{dt} - (R_2 + R_3)i_2(t) - L\frac{di_2(t)}{dt} = 0$$

The Fourier transform of these equations yields

$$(j\omega L + R_1)I_1(\omega) - j\omega L I_2(\omega) = V(\omega)$$

$$j\omega L I_1(\omega) - (R_2 + R_3 + j\omega L)I_2(\omega) = 0$$

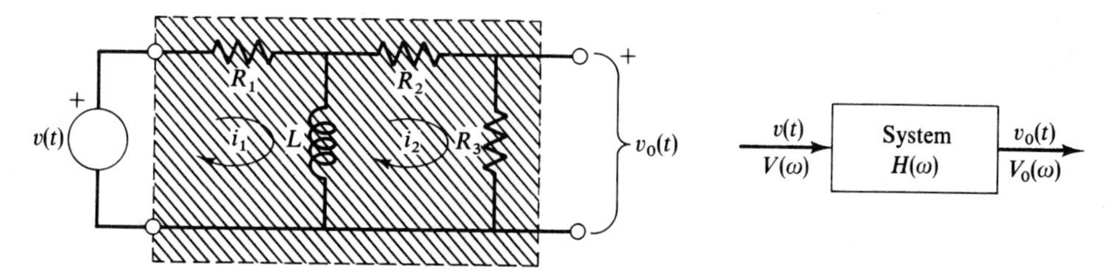

Figure 4.15 Illustrating Example 4.12

Solve this system of equations to find $I_2(\omega)$. The result is

$$I_2(\omega) = \frac{j\omega L}{(R_1 + j\omega L)(R_2 + R_3 + j\omega L) + \omega^2 L^2} V(\omega)$$

Since the output

$$V_o(\omega) = R_3 I_2(\omega)$$

then

$$\frac{V_o(\omega)}{V(\omega)} \triangleq H(\omega) = \frac{j\omega L R_3}{(R_1 + j\omega L)(R_2 + R_3 + j\omega L) + \omega^2 L^2}$$
$$= \frac{j\omega L R_3}{R_1(R_2 + R_3) + j\omega L(R_1 + R_2 + R_3)}$$

As an interesting exercise, we now solve this problem when it is cast in the form given in (4.21). We first subtract the two equations deduced by an application of the Kirchhoff laws. This yields

$$i_1(t) = -\frac{R_2 + R_3}{R_1} i_2(t) + \frac{v(t)}{R_1}$$

Differentiate this equation and then substitute the results into the second of the Kirchhoff equations. This yields

$$L(R_2 + R_3 + R_1)\frac{di_2(t)}{dt} + R_1(R_2 + R_3)i_2(t) = L\frac{dv(t)}{dt}$$

which has the form of (4.21). The Fourier transform of this equation is

$$[j\omega L(R_1 + R_2 + R_3) + R_1(R_2 + R_3)]I_2(\omega) = j\omega L\, V(\omega)$$

By combining the quantity $V_o(\omega) = R_3 I_2(\omega)$ with the foregoing equation, we obtain

$$H(\omega) \triangleq \frac{V_o(\omega)}{V(\omega)} = \frac{j\omega L R_3}{R_1(R_2 + R_3) + j\omega L(R_1 + R_2 + R_3)}$$

which is identical with the expression found by operations on the two-equation representation. ■

Parseval's Theorem. As an extension of the discussion in Section 3.3, let us consider the Parseval theorem in the Fourier transform domain. This review will show that

$$E = \int_{-\infty}^{\infty} |f(t)|^2\, dt = \frac{1}{2\pi}\int_{-\infty}^{\infty} |F(\omega)|^2\, d\omega \triangleq \int_{-\infty}^{\infty} f(t)f^*(t)\, dt$$
$$= \frac{1}{2\pi}\int_{-\infty}^{\infty} F(\omega)F^*(\omega)\, d\omega \tag{4.24}$$

Proof Proceed as follows:

$$\int_{-\infty}^{\infty} |f(t)|^2\, dt = \int_{-\infty}^{\infty} f(t)f^*(t)\, dt = \int_{-\infty}^{\infty}\left[\frac{1}{2\pi}\int_{-\infty}^{\infty} F(\omega)e^{j\omega t}\, d\omega\right] f^*(t)\, dt$$
$$= \frac{1}{2\pi}\int_{-\infty}^{\infty} F(\omega)\left[\int_{-\infty}^{\infty} f(t)e^{-j\omega t}\, dt\right]^* d\omega = \frac{1}{2\pi}\int_{-\infty}^{\infty} F(\omega)F^*(\omega)\, d\omega$$
$$= \frac{1}{2\pi}\int_{-\infty}^{\infty} |F(\omega)|^2\, d\omega$$

This shows that the energy of the time domain signal is equal to the energy of the frequency domain transform. This is a statement of the conservation of energy.

If the **power density** spectrum of a signal is defined by

$$W(\omega) = \frac{1}{2\pi} |F(\omega)|^2 \tag{4.25}$$

then the energy in an infinitesimal band of frequencies $d\omega$ is $W(\omega)\, d\omega$, and the energy contained within a band $\omega_1 \le \omega \le \omega_2$ is

$$\Delta E = \int_{\omega_1}^{\omega_2} \frac{1}{2\pi} |F(\omega)|^2\, d\omega \tag{4.26}$$

The fraction of the total energy that is contained within the band $\Delta\omega$ is

$$\frac{\Delta E}{E} = \frac{\text{energy in band}}{\text{total energy}} = \frac{\dfrac{1}{2\pi}\displaystyle\int_{\omega_1}^{\omega_2} |F(\omega)|^2\, d\omega}{\dfrac{1}{2\pi}\displaystyle\int_{-\infty}^{\infty} |F(\omega)|^2\, d\omega} = \frac{\displaystyle\int_{\omega_1}^{\omega_2} |F(\omega)|^2\, d\omega}{\displaystyle\int_{-\infty}^{\infty} |F(\omega)|^2\, d\omega} \tag{4.27}$$

The interpretation of energy and power of signals in this manner is possible because $f(t)$ may be a voltage, so that $f(t)/1\ \Omega$ = current and, thus, $f(t)^2$ is proportional to power.

■ Example 4.13

Determine the total energy associated with the function $f(t) = e^{-t}u(t)$.

Solution From (4.24), the total energy is

$$E = \int_{-\infty}^{\infty} (e^{-t})^2 u(t)\, dt = \int_{0}^{\infty} e^{-2t}\, dt = \frac{1}{2}$$

By using the results of Example 4.1, we can also proceed from a frequency viewpoint:

$$E = \frac{1}{2\pi}\int_{-\infty}^{\infty}\left(\frac{1}{1+j\omega}\right)\left(\frac{1}{1-j\omega}\right) d\omega = \frac{1}{2\pi}\int_{-\infty}^{\infty} \frac{1}{1+\omega^2}\, d\omega$$
$$= \frac{1}{\pi}\int_{0}^{\infty} \frac{1}{1+\omega^2}\, d\omega = \frac{1}{\pi}\frac{\pi}{2} = \frac{1}{2}$$

■

Another important form follows using the spectrum between input and output, specified by

$$G(\omega) = F(\omega)H(\omega)$$

so that

$$|G(\omega)|^2 = |F(\omega)H(\omega)|^2 = |F(\omega)|^2|H(\omega)|^2 \tag{4.28}$$

In general, $H(\omega)$ is a complex quantity that can be written

$$H(\omega) = H_0(\omega)e^{j\theta(\omega)} \tag{4.29}$$

where $H_0(\omega)$ is a real quantity, and (4.28) becomes

$$\boxed{|G(\omega)|^2 = H_0^2(\omega)|F(\omega)|^2} \tag{4.30}$$

This equation shows that the power density spectrum of the response of an LTI system is the product of the power density spectrum of the input function and the squared amplitude function of the system (network). The phase characteristic of the network does not affect the energy density of the output.

■ Example 4.14

Find the input–output power density spectrum of the system shown in Figure 4.16a. Also, find the fractional energy ratio of the input and output signals.

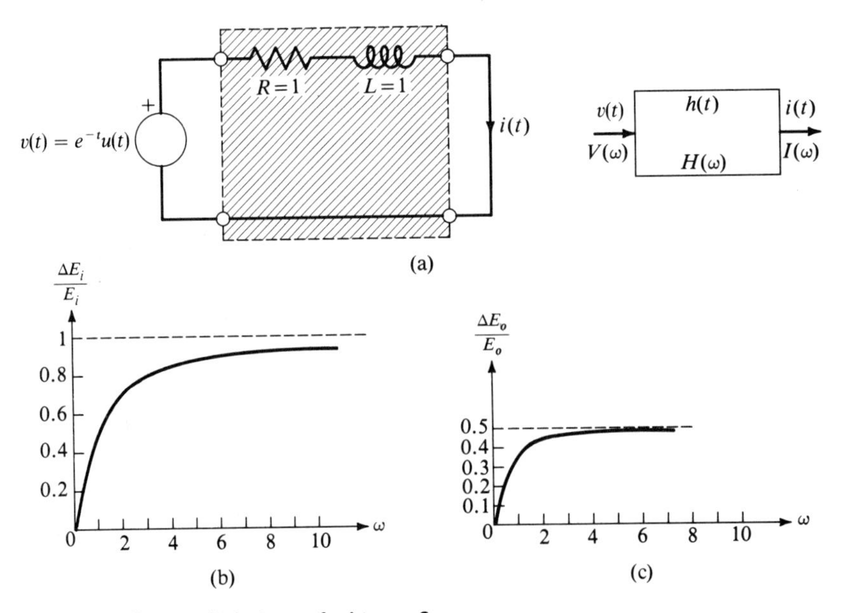

Figure 4.16 Fractional Energy Relations of a Linear System

Solution By an application of the Kirchhoff voltage law,

$$v(t) = L\frac{di}{dt} + Ri$$

The Fourier transform of this equation permits writing

$$I(\omega) = \frac{1}{R + j\omega L}V(\omega) = \frac{1}{1 + j\omega}V(\omega) = H(\omega)V(\omega)$$

The transfer function $H(\omega)$ can be written in the form

$$H(\omega) = H_0(\omega)e^{j\theta} = \frac{1}{(1 + \omega^2)^{1/2}}e^{-j\tan^{-1}\omega}$$

so that

$$H_0(\omega) = \frac{1}{(1 + \omega^2)^{1/2}}$$

Furthermore,

$$V(\omega) = \mathscr{F}\{v(t)\} = \mathscr{F}\{e^{-t}u(t)\} = \frac{1}{1 + j\omega}$$

and so

$$|V(\omega)|^2 = \frac{1}{1 + \omega^2}$$

The fractional energy of the input signal is given by

$$\frac{\Delta E_i}{E_i} = \frac{\dfrac{2}{2\pi}\displaystyle\int_0^{\omega}\frac{1}{1 + \omega'^2}\,d\omega'}{\dfrac{2}{2\pi}\displaystyle\int_0^{\infty}\frac{1}{1 + \omega'^2}\,d\omega'} = \frac{2}{\pi}\tan^{-1}\omega$$

The fractional energy of the output is given by

$$\frac{\Delta E_o}{E_o} = \frac{\displaystyle\int_0^{\omega}\left(\frac{1}{1 + \omega'^2}\right)\left(\frac{1}{1 + \omega'^2}\right)d\omega'}{\pi/2} = \frac{2}{\pi}\left[\frac{\omega}{2(1 + \omega^2)} + \frac{1}{2}\tan^{-1}\omega\right]$$

$$= \frac{\omega}{\pi(1 + \omega^2)} + \frac{1}{\pi}\tan^{-1}\omega$$

These fractional energy relations are plotted in Figures 4.16b and 4.16c. ■

■ **Example 4.15**

Find the frequency response of an LTI system given that the input is $f(t) = e^{-t}u(t)$ and the output is $g(t) = 2e^{-t}u(t)$. Determine the impulse response of the system.

Solution From (4.19), we write the relation

$$H(\omega) = \frac{\text{output spectrum}}{\text{input spectrum}} = \frac{2/(2 + j\omega)}{1/(1 + j\omega)} = 2\,\frac{1 + j\omega}{2 + j\omega} = 2 - \frac{2}{2 + j\omega}$$

The impulse response, which is the inverse transform of this expression, is

$$h(t) = 2\delta(t) - 2e^{-2t}$$

■

Time Convolution. If $F(\omega)$ and $H(\omega)$ denote the Fourier transforms of $f(t)$ and $h(t)$, respectively, then

$$\mathscr{F}\{f(t) * h(t)\} = \mathscr{F}\left\{\int_{-\infty}^{\infty} f(\tau)h(t - \tau)\,d\tau\right\} = F(\omega)H(\omega) \tag{4.31}$$

Proof The Fourier transform

$$\mathscr{F}\{f(t) * h(t)\} = \int_{-\infty}^{\infty} [f(t) * h(t)]e^{-j\omega t}\,dt = \int_{-\infty}^{\infty} f(\tau)\,d\tau \int_{-\infty}^{\infty} h(t - \tau)e^{-j\omega t}\,dt$$
$$= \int_{-\infty}^{\infty} f(\tau)e^{-j\omega\tau}\,d\tau \int_{-\infty}^{\infty} h(s)e^{-j\omega s}\,ds = F(\omega)H(\omega)$$

where we have written $t - \tau = s$. This result agrees with (4.19).

If (4.31) is written in the form [see also (4.23)]

$$g(t) = \int_{-\infty}^{\infty} f(\tau)h(t - \tau)\,dt = \mathscr{F}^{-1}\{F(\omega)H(\omega)\}$$
$$= \frac{1}{2\pi}\int_{-\infty}^{\infty} F(\omega)H(\omega)e^{j\omega t}\,d\omega \tag{4.32}$$

This expression shows that the output of an LTI system in the time domain is equal to the inverse Fourier transform of the convolution of its transfer function and the input signal. Figure 4.17 shows this relationship in graphical form.

■ **Example 4.16**

Determine the Fourier transform of the function $f(t) = te^{-t}u(t)$.

Solution We observe that $f(t)$ is the convolution of $f_1(t) = e^{-t}u(t)$ and $f_2(t) = e^{-t}u(t)$. (Refer to Example 2.20 for the procedure in carrying out the con-

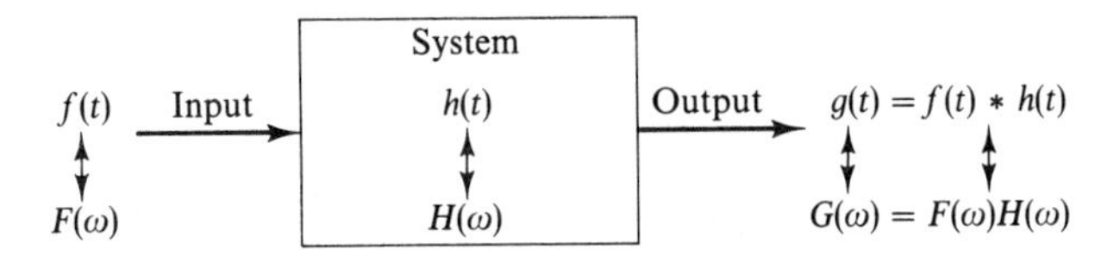

Figure 4.17 Graphical Representation of LTI Response

volution relation.) However, the Fourier transform of $e^{-t}u(t)$ is $1/(1 + j\omega)$, so that

$$F(\omega) = \frac{1}{(1 + j\omega)^2}$$

Readers should use the frequency differentiation property to verify their result. ∎

■ Example 4.17

Determine the frequency spectrum of the output for the system shown in Figure 4.18.

Solution By an application of the Kirchhoff current law, the controlling differential equation is

$$\frac{dv_o(t)}{dt} + 5v_o(t) = 5p(t)$$

The impulse response of the system is obtained from the equation

$$\frac{dh(t)}{dt} + 5h(t) = \delta(t)$$

The Fourier transform of this equation is

$$j\omega H(\omega) + 5H(\omega) = 1$$

From this,

$$H(\omega) = \frac{1}{5 + j\omega}$$

from which

$$h(t) = e^{-5t}u(t)$$

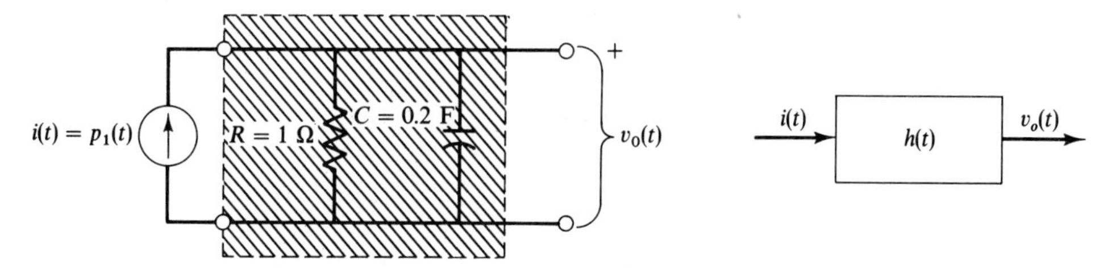

Figure 4.18 Illustrating Example 4.17

However, the output is the convolution of the system input and its impulse response, and the frequency spectrum of the output is given by the product

$$V_o(\omega) = \mathcal{F}\{5p(t)\}\mathcal{F}\{e^{-5t}u(t)\} = 10\,\frac{\sin\omega}{\omega}\,\frac{1}{5+j\omega}$$

We could also proceed by Fourier-transforming the first equation. This yields

$$j\omega V_o(\omega) + 5V_o(\omega) = 10\,\frac{\sin\omega}{\omega}$$

from which we have

$$V_o(\omega) = 10\,\frac{\sin\omega}{\omega}\,\frac{1}{5+j\omega}$$

which is identical with our previous result. ■

Frequency Convolution. If $f(t)$ and $h(t)$ are Fourier-transformable functions, then

$$\mathcal{F}\{f(t)h(t)\} = \frac{1}{2\pi}\int_{-\infty}^{\infty} F(\tau)H(\omega-\tau)\,d\tau = \frac{1}{2\pi}\,F(\omega) * H(\omega) \tag{4.33}$$

Proof We proceed by writing

$$\begin{aligned}\mathcal{F}^{-1}\{\mathcal{F}\{f(t)h(t)\}\} &= f(t)h(t) = \mathcal{F}^{-1}\left\{\frac{1}{2\pi}\,F(\omega) * H(\omega)\right\}\\ &= \frac{1}{2\pi}\,\frac{1}{2\pi}\iint_{-\infty}^{\infty} F(\tau)H(\omega-\tau)e^{j\omega t}\,d\tau\,d\omega\\ &= \frac{1}{2\pi}\int_{-\infty}^{\infty} F(\tau)e^{j\tau t}\,d\tau\,\frac{1}{2\pi}\int_{-\infty}^{\infty} H(s)e^{jst}\,ds = f(t)h(t)\end{aligned}$$

where we have written $\omega - \tau = s$—that is, $\omega = \tau + s$ and $d\omega = ds$.

■ **Example 4.18**

Verify the results of Example 4.8 by using the frequency convolution property of the Fourier transform.

Solution The Fourier transform of the function $\cos\omega_c t$ is given by (see also Figure 4.26)

$$\begin{aligned}\mathcal{F}\{\cos\omega_c t\} &= \mathcal{F}\left\{\frac{e^{j\omega_c t} + e^{-j\omega_c t}}{2}\right\} = \frac{1}{2}\int_{-\infty}^{\infty} e^{-j(\omega-\omega_c)t}\,dt + \frac{1}{2}\int_{-\infty}^{\infty} e^{-j(\omega+\omega_c)t}\,dt\\ &= \pi\delta(\omega-\omega_c) + \pi\delta(\omega+\omega_c)\end{aligned}$$

Further, we know that

$$\mathscr{F}\{e^{-|t|}\} = \frac{2}{1+\omega^2}$$

Now, use (4.33) and apply the properties of the delta function. Thus,

$$\begin{aligned}\mathscr{F}\{\cos \omega_c t\, e^{-|t|}\} &= \frac{1}{2\pi}\int_{-\infty}^{\infty} [\pi\delta(\tau-\omega_c)+\pi\delta(\tau+\omega_c)]\,\frac{2}{1+(\omega-\tau)^2}\,d\tau \\ &= \int_{-\infty}^{\infty} \delta(\tau-\omega_c)\,\frac{1}{1+(\omega-\tau)^2}\,d\tau \\ &\quad + \int_{-\infty}^{\infty} \delta(\tau+\omega_c)\,\frac{1}{1+(\omega-\tau)^2}\,d\tau \\ &= \frac{1}{1+(\omega-\omega_c)^2}+\frac{1}{1+(\omega+\omega_c)^2}\end{aligned}$$

■

A number of important Fourier transform properties are summarized in Table 4.1. Figures 4.19, 4.20, and 4.21 show Fourier spectrums of representative nonelectrical signals. This widespread applicability of Fourier techniques in analyzing and understanding different types of signals and systems is indicative of the power of this technique.

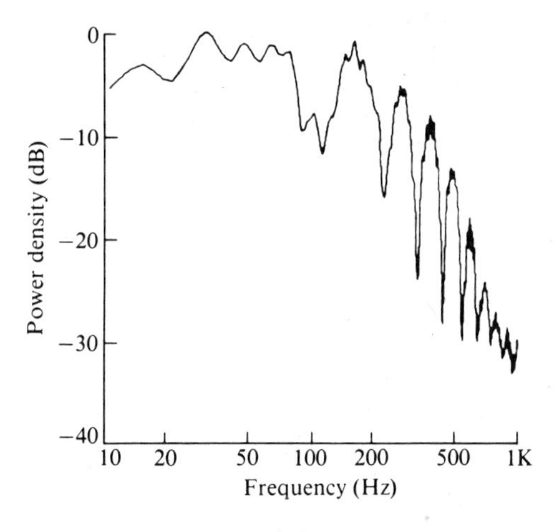

Figure 4.19 Power Spectrum of Myoelectric Signal from the Biceps Brachii Muscle (Single Motor Unit). [From Lindstöm and Magnusson, "Interpretation of Myoelectric Power Spectra: A Model and Its Applications," *IEEE Proceedings*, vol. 65 (1977), p. 653. © 1977 IEEE.]

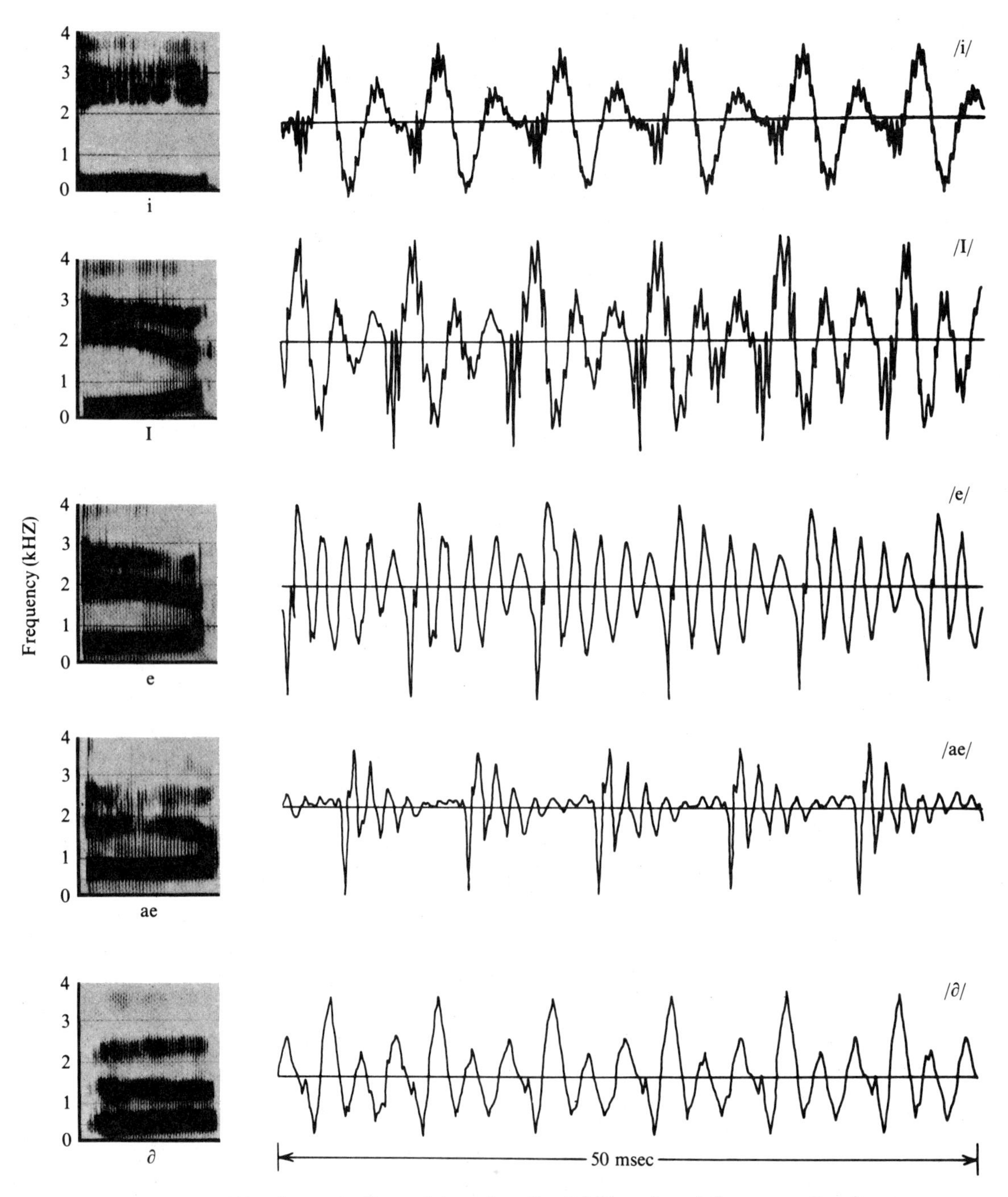

Figure 4.20 Acoustic Waveforms for Several American English Vowels and Corresponding Spectrograms. (Rabiner and Schafer, *Digital Processing of Speech Signals*, © 1978, pp. 46–47. Reprinted by permission of Prentice-Hall, Inc., Englewood Cliffs, New Jersey.)

Table 4.1 Properties of Fourier Transform

Operation	$f(t)$	$F(\omega)$
Direct transform	$f(t)$	$\int_{-\infty}^{\infty} f(t)e^{-j\omega t}\,dt$
Inverse transform	$\frac{1}{2\pi}\int_{-\infty}^{\infty} F(\omega)e^{j\omega t}\,d\omega$	$F(\omega)$
Linearity	$af_1(t) + bf_2(t)$	$aF_1(\omega) + bF_2(\omega)$
Symmetry	$F(t)$	$2\pi f(-\omega)$
Time shifting	$f(t \pm t_0)$	$e^{\pm j\omega t_0}F(\omega)$
Scaling	$f(at)$	$\frac{1}{\lvert a\rvert} F\left(\frac{\omega}{a}\right)$
Time reversal	$f(-t)$	$F(-\omega)$
Frequency shifting	$e^{\pm j\omega_0 t}f(t)$	$F(\omega \mp \omega_0)$
Modulation	$f(t)\cos\omega_0 t$	$\frac{1}{2}[F(\omega + \omega_0) + F(\omega - \omega_0)]$
	$f(t)\sin\omega_0 t$	$\frac{1}{2j}[F(\omega - \omega_0) - F(\omega + \omega_0)]$
Time differentiation	$\frac{d^n}{dt^n}f(t)$	$(j\omega)^n F(\omega)$
Frequency differentiation	$(-jt)f(t)$	$\frac{dF(\omega)}{d\omega}$
	$(-jt)^n f(t)$	$\frac{d^n F(\omega)}{d\omega^n}$
Time convolution	$f(t) * h(t) = \int_{-\infty}^{\infty} f(\tau)h(t - \tau)\,d\tau$	$F(\omega)H(\omega)$
Frequency convolution	$f(t)h(t)$	$\frac{1}{2\pi}F(\omega) * H(\omega) = \frac{1}{2\pi}\int_{-\infty}^{\infty} F(\tau)H(\omega - \tau)\,d\tau$
Autocorrelation	$f(t) \bigstar f(t) = \int_{-\infty}^{\infty} f(\tau)f^*(\tau - t)\,d\tau$	$F(\omega)F^*(\omega) = \lvert F(\omega)\rvert^2$
Central ordinate	$f(0) = \frac{1}{2\pi}\int_{-\infty}^{\infty} F(\omega)\,d\omega$	$F(0) = \int_{-\infty}^{\infty} f(t)\,dt$
Parseval's theorem	$E = \int_{-\infty}^{\infty} f(t)^2\,dt$	$E = \frac{1}{2\pi}\int_{-\infty}^{\infty} \lvert F(\omega)\rvert^2\,d\omega$
Moments formula	$m_n = \int_{-\infty}^{\infty} t^n f(t)\,dt = \frac{F^{(n)}(0)}{(-j)^n}$	$F^{(n)}(0) = \left.\frac{d^n F(\omega)}{d\omega^n}\right\rvert_{\omega=0}$

Figure 4.21 Spectrogram of the Word " READ " Computed from Contiguous 8 msec Speech Segments. [Reprinted, by permission, from Tufts, Levinson, and Rao, " Measuring Pitch and Format Frequencies for Speech Understanding System," *IEEE International Conference on Acoustics, Speech, and Signals Proceedings* (1976), p. 314. ©1976 IEEE.]

4.3 Some Special Fourier Transform Pairs

As has already been noted, we can often employ generalized functions and limiting processes to find the Fourier transform of a function that does not satisfy the Dirichlet conditions. We consider a number of such special functions.

Example 4.19

Find the Fourier transform of $\delta(t)$ illustrated in Figure 4.22 and defined here by the limiting formula for different positive values of ε.

$$\delta(t) = \lim_{\varepsilon \to 0} \frac{1}{|\varepsilon|} p_{\varepsilon/2}(t)$$

Solution The Fourier transform of this equation is

$$\mathscr{F}\{\delta(t)\} = \mathscr{F}\left\{\lim_{\varepsilon \to 0} \frac{1}{|\varepsilon|} p_{\varepsilon/2}(t)\right\} = \lim_{\varepsilon \to 0} \mathscr{F}\left\{\frac{1}{|\varepsilon|} p_{\varepsilon/2}(t)\right\}$$

$$= \lim_{\varepsilon \to 0} \frac{\sin \varepsilon\omega}{\varepsilon\omega} = 1 \tag{4.34}$$

where the limit is found by using L'Hospital's rule. ■

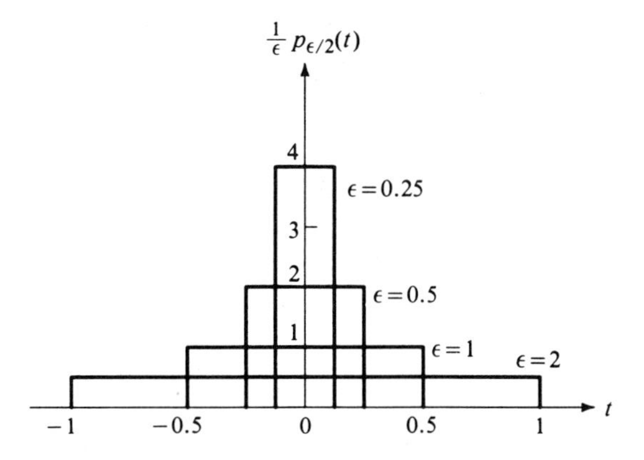

Figure 4.22 A Delta Function Sequence

■ **Example 4.20**

Find the Fourier transform of the function $sgn(t)$ shown in Figure 4.23a.

Solution We proceed by writing the $sgn(t)$ function as $\lim_{\varepsilon\to 0}\exp[-\varepsilon|t|]$ $sgn(t)$, as shown in Figure 4.23b. The procedure is now direct and yields

$$\begin{aligned}\mathscr{F}\{sgn(t)\} &= \mathscr{F}\left\{\lim_{\varepsilon\to 0} e^{-\varepsilon|t|}sgn(t)\right\} = \lim_{\varepsilon\to 0}\int_{-\infty}^{\infty} e^{-\varepsilon|t|}sgn(t)e^{-j\omega t}\,dt \\ &= \lim_{\varepsilon\to 0}\left[\int_{-\infty}^{0} - e^{(\varepsilon-j\omega)t}\,dt + \int_{0}^{\infty} e^{-(\varepsilon+j\omega)t}\,dt\right] \\ &= \lim_{\varepsilon\to 0}\left(-\frac{1}{\varepsilon-j\omega}+\frac{1}{\varepsilon+j\omega}\right) = \frac{2}{j\omega} = \frac{2}{\omega}e^{-j\pi/2} \triangleq SGN(\omega)\end{aligned} \tag{4.35}$$

The Fourier amplitude and phase spectrums of $sgn(t)$ are shown in Figures 4.23c and 4.23d. In this proof, we changed the order of limit taking and integration. Such an interchange requires mathematical justification that is beyond the scope of this text. ■

■ **Example 4.21**

Find the Fourier transform of $e^{j\omega_0 t}$.

Solution This result can be written down on the basis of (4.10b) and the shifting property. The result is

$$\mathscr{F}\{e^{j\omega_0 t}\} = \mathscr{F}\{1\cdot e^{j\omega_0 t}\} = 2\pi\delta(\omega-\omega_0) \tag{4.36}$$

■

■ **Example 4.22**

Find the Fourier transform of the unit step function $u(t)$.

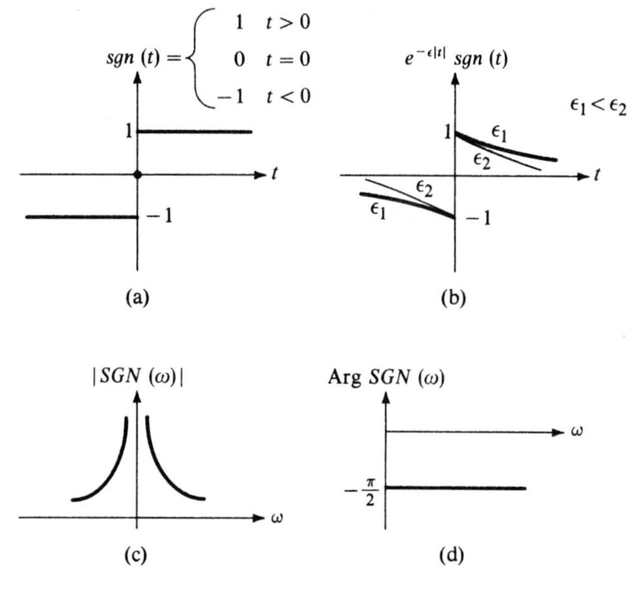

Figure 4.23 The *sgn* Function and Its Fourier Representation

Solution Begin by writing $u(t)$ in its equivalent representation involving the $sgn(t)$ function:

$$u(t) = \frac{1}{2} + \frac{1}{2}\, sgn(t) \tag{4.37}$$

From Examples 4.21 and 4.20, we find that

$$U(\omega) \triangleq \mathscr{F}\{u(t)\} = \frac{2\pi}{2}\,\delta(\omega) + \frac{2}{2j\omega} = \pi\delta(\omega) + \frac{1}{j\omega} \tag{4.38}$$

The unit step function and its transform are shown in Figure 4.24. ■

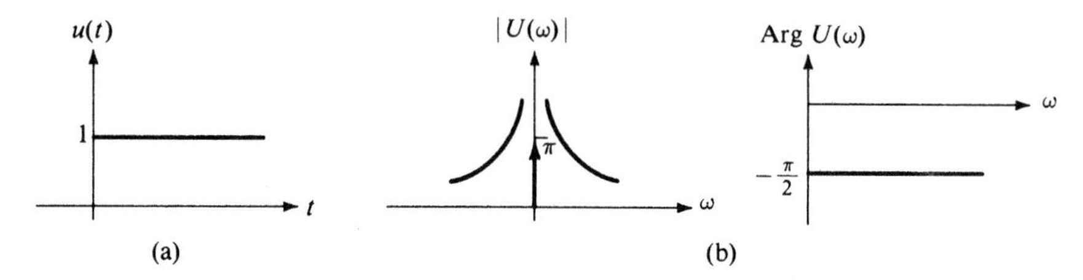

Figure 4.24 Unit Step Function and Its Fourier Transform Representation

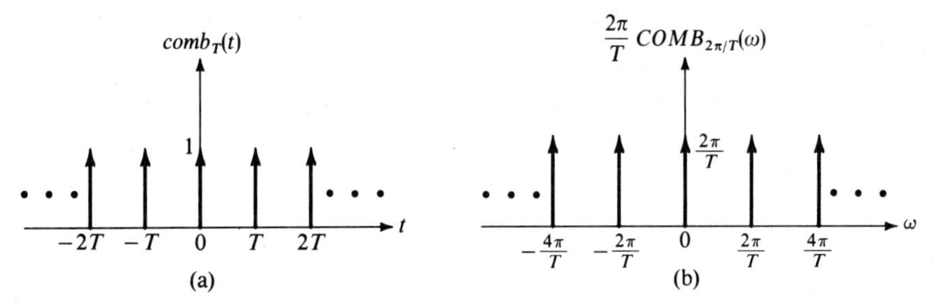

Figure 4.25 Fourier Transform of the $comb_T(t)$ Function

■ **Example 4.23**

Find the Fourier transform of the $comb_T(t)$ function shown in Figure 4.25a.

Solution Carrying out this problem requires that the $comb_T(t)$ function first be represented in its Fourier series expansion, which is given by

$$comb_T(t) = \sum_{n=-\infty}^{\infty} \delta(t - nT) \triangleq \sum_{n=-\infty}^{\infty} \alpha_n e^{jn\omega_0 t} = \frac{1}{T} \sum_{n=-\infty}^{\infty} e^{jn\omega_0 t} \tag{4.39}$$

where

$$\alpha_n = \frac{1}{T}\int_{-T/2}^{T/2} \delta(t)e^{-jn\omega_0 t}\, dt = \frac{1}{T} \qquad \omega_0 = \frac{2\pi}{T}$$

The Fourier transform is then

$$\begin{aligned}\mathscr{F}\{comb_T(t)\} &= \frac{1}{T}\sum_{n=-\infty}^{\infty} \mathscr{F}\{e^{jn\omega_0 t}\} = \frac{1}{T}\sum_{n=-\infty}^{\infty} 2\pi\delta(\omega - n\omega_0) \\ &= \frac{2\pi}{T}\sum_{n=-\infty}^{\infty} \delta\left(\omega - n\frac{2\pi}{T}\right) \triangleq \frac{2\pi}{T} COMB_{2\pi/T}(\omega)\end{aligned} \tag{4.40}$$

The spectrum of the function is shown in Figure 4.25b.

The foregoing shows that any periodic function of the form

$$f(t) = \sum_{n=-\infty}^{\infty} \alpha_n e^{jn\omega_0 t}$$

has a Fourier transform of the form

$$\mathscr{F}\{f(t)\} \triangleq F(\omega) = 2\pi \sum_{n=-\infty}^{\infty} \alpha_n \delta(\omega - n\omega_0) \tag{4.41}$$

■

By proceeding in the manner of the examples given, a table of transforms can be developed; such a table is given in Figure 4.26. Note that owing to the uniqueness

Figure 4.26 Fourier Transforms of Signals

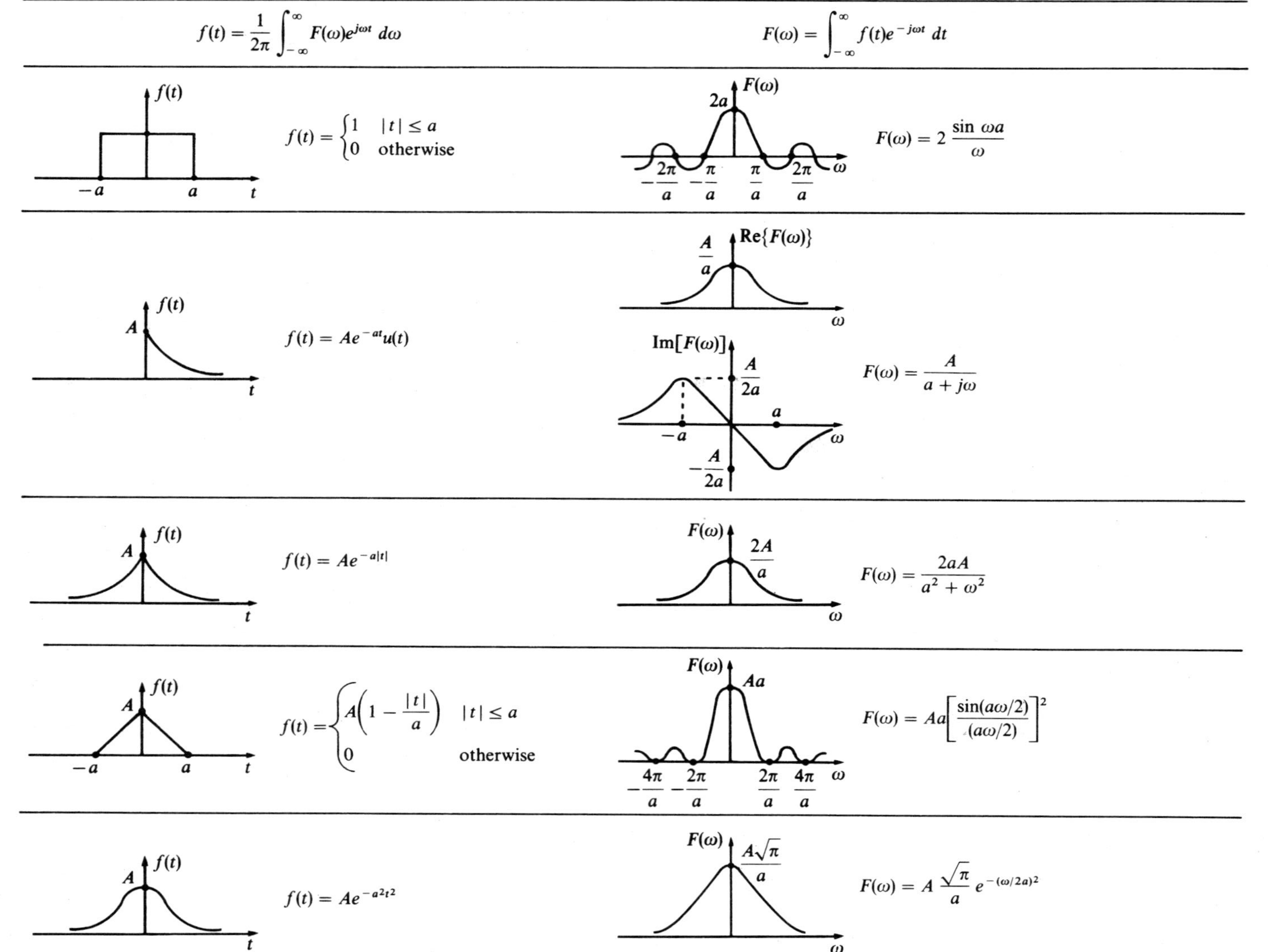

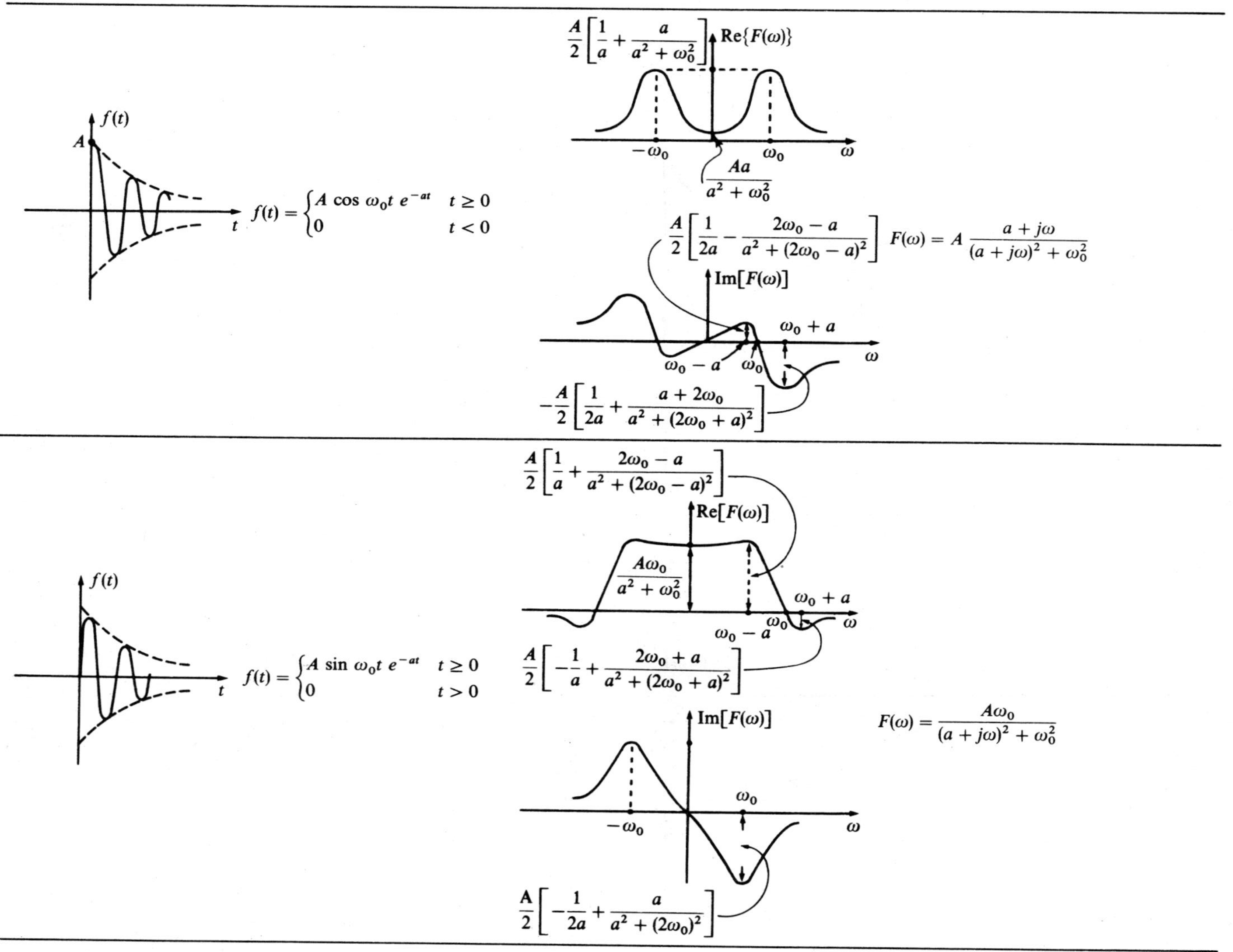
$f(t)$
A
t
$f(t) = \begin{cases} A \cos \omega_0 t\, e^{-at} & t \geq 0 \\ 0 & t < 0 \end{cases}$
$\frac{A}{2}\left[\frac{1}{a} + \frac{a}{a^2 + \omega_0^2}\right]$
$\mathrm{Re}\{F(\omega)\}$
$-\omega_0$
ω_0
ω
$\frac{Aa}{a^2 + \omega_0^2}$
$\frac{A}{2}\left[\frac{1}{2a} - \frac{2\omega_0 - a}{a^2 + (2\omega_0 - a)^2}\right]$
$F(\omega) = A\,\frac{a + j\omega}{(a + j\omega)^2 + \omega_0^2}$
$\mathrm{Im}[F(\omega)]$
$\omega_0 + a$
$\omega_0 - a$
ω_0
ω
$-\frac{A}{2}\left[\frac{1}{2a} + \frac{a + 2\omega_0}{a^2 + (2\omega_0 + a)^2}\right]$
$f(t)$
t
$f(t) = \begin{cases} A \sin \omega_0 t\, e^{-at} & t \geq 0 \\ 0 & t > 0 \end{cases}$
$\frac{A}{2}\left[\frac{1}{a} + \frac{2\omega_0 - a}{a^2 + (2\omega_0 - a)^2}\right]$
$\mathrm{Re}[F(\omega)]$
$\frac{A\omega_0}{a^2 + \omega_0^2}$
$\omega_0 + a$
$\omega_0 - a$
ω_0
ω
$\frac{A}{2}\left[-\frac{1}{a} + \frac{2\omega_0 + a}{a^2 + (2\omega_0 + a)^2}\right]$
$\mathrm{Im}[F(\omega)]$
$F(\omega) = \frac{A\omega_0}{(a + j\omega)^2 + \omega_0^2}$
ω_0
$-\omega_0$
ω
$\frac{A}{2}\left[-\frac{1}{2a} + \frac{a}{a^2 + (2\omega_0)^2}\right]$

(continues)

Figure 4.26 *(continued)*

$$f(t) = \frac{1}{2\pi}\int_{-\infty}^{\infty} F(\omega)e^{j\omega t}\,d\omega \qquad\qquad F(\omega) = \int_{-\infty}^{\infty} f(t)e^{-j\omega t}\,dt$$

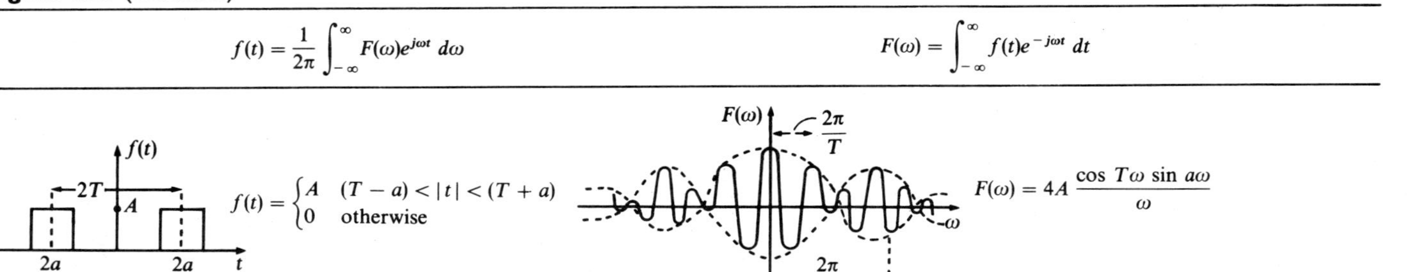

$$f(t) = \begin{cases} A & (T-a) < |t| < (T+a) \\ 0 & \text{otherwise} \end{cases} \qquad F(\omega) = 4A\,\frac{\cos T\omega \sin a\omega}{\omega}$$

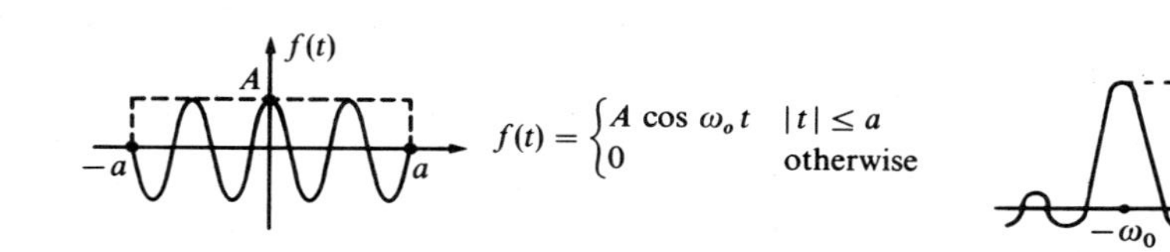

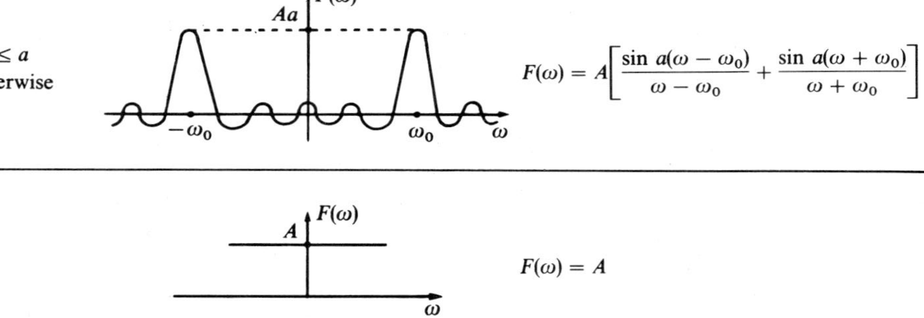

$$f(t) = \begin{cases} A\cos\omega_o t & |t| \le a \\ 0 & \text{otherwise} \end{cases} \qquad F(\omega) = A\left[\frac{\sin a(\omega-\omega_0)}{\omega-\omega_0} + \frac{\sin a(\omega+\omega_0)}{\omega+\omega_0}\right]$$

$$f(t) = A\,\delta(t) \qquad F(\omega) = A$$

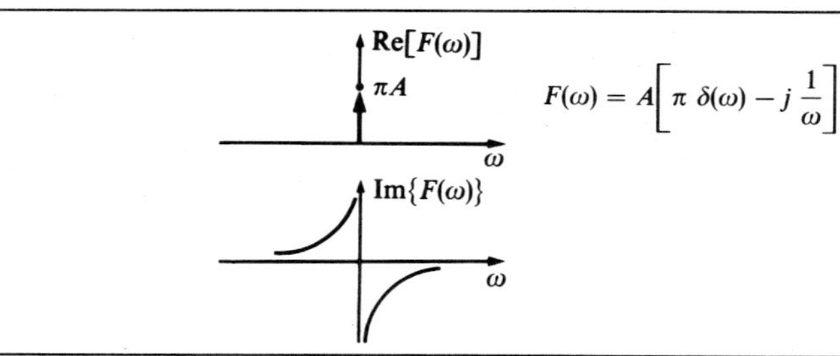

$$f(t) = \begin{cases} A & t > 0 \\ 0 & \text{otherwise} \end{cases} \qquad F(\omega) = A\left[\pi\,\delta(\omega) - j\,\frac{1}{\omega}\right]$$

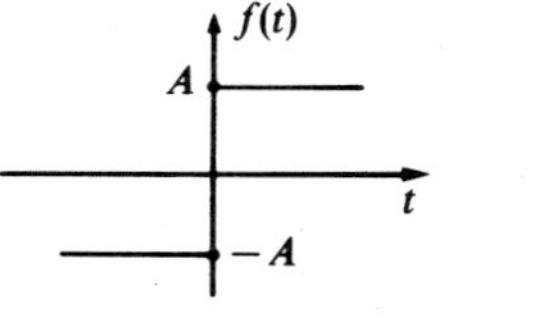

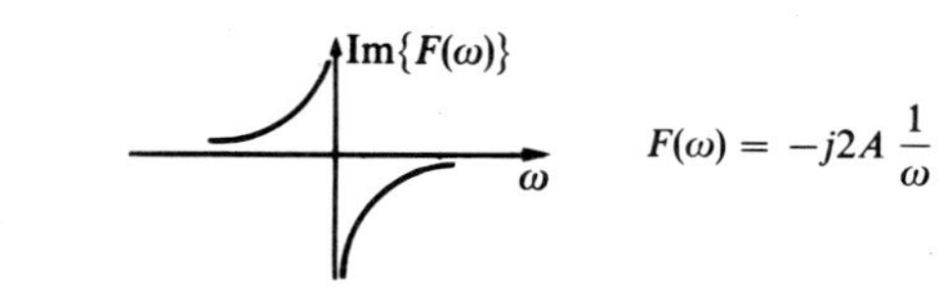

$$f(t) = \begin{cases} A & t > 0 \\ 0 & t = 0 \\ -A & t < 0 \end{cases} \qquad F(\omega) = -j2A\,\frac{1}{\omega}$$

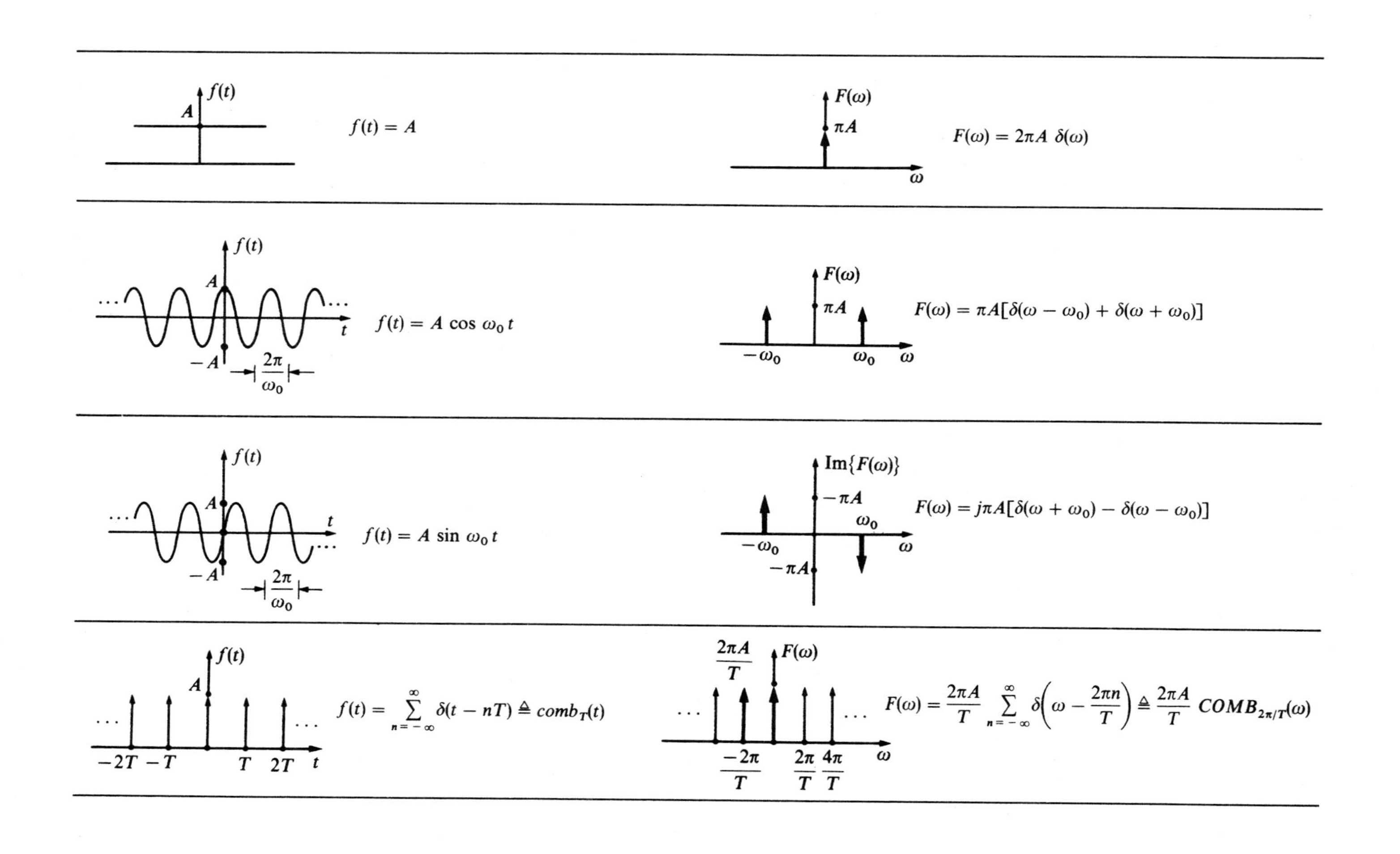

$f(t)$
A
$f(t) = A$
$F(\omega)$
πA
ω
$F(\omega) = 2\pi A\,\delta(\omega)$
$f(t)$
A
$-A$
t
$\frac{2\pi}{\omega_0}$
$f(t) = A\cos\omega_0 t$
$F(\omega)$
πA
$-\omega_0$
ω_0
ω
$F(\omega) = \pi A[\delta(\omega - \omega_0) + \delta(\omega + \omega_0)]$
$f(t)$
A
$-A$
t
$\frac{2\pi}{\omega_0}$
$f(t) = A\sin\omega_0 t$
$\mathrm{Im}\{F(\omega)\}$
$-\pi A$
πA
$-\omega_0$
ω_0
ω
$F(\omega) = j\pi A[\delta(\omega + \omega_0) - \delta(\omega - \omega_0)]$
$f(t)$
A
$-2T$ $-T$ T $2T$ t
$f(t) = \sum_{n=-\infty}^{\infty} \delta(t - nT) \triangleq comb_T(t)$
$F(\omega)$
$\frac{2\pi A}{T}$
$\frac{-2\pi}{T}$ $\frac{2\pi}{T}$ $\frac{4\pi}{T}$ ω
$F(\omega) = \frac{2\pi A}{T} \sum_{n=-\infty}^{\infty} \delta\left(\omega - \frac{2\pi n}{T}\right) \triangleq \frac{2\pi A}{T}\, COMB_{2\pi/T}(\omega)$

property of the Fourier transform, there is a one-to-one correspondence between the direct and the inverse transform. That is, corresponding to a function $f(t)$, the transform $F(\omega)$ is unique, and vice versa. Consequently, we can use Figure 4.26 to write the function $f(t)$ appropriate to a given $F(\omega)$. If the available tables do not include a given $F(\omega)$ and if the $F(\omega)$ cannot be reduced to available forms, recourse to the inversion integral might be necessary.

Sampling of Signals and the Fourier Transform

4.4 Fundamentals of Sampling

The sampling of continuous signals at periodic intervals has become a very important practical, as well as an important, mathematical operation. One of the main concerns when signals are sampled is the accuracy with which the sampled function is represented by its sampled values. Also, what must the sampling interval be in order that an optimum recovery of the original signal can be accomplished from the sampled values?

Important in the sampling operation is the fact that most engineering systems have frequency response limitations—that is, they respond only to some upper frequency limit. As a result, the output signal of these systems is band limited. We have already seen that the ordinary house telephone set has an upper frequency limit of about 4 kHz and that television signals have an upper frequency limit of about 4 MHz. An important consequence of a finite bandwidth signal is that it can be accurately represented by a narrow time-duration sampling sequence, with samples taken at discrete and periodic instants. As already noted, the time space between the samples of one signal can be used to accommodate (multiplex) without interference the samples of a different signal when transmitted through some transmitting channel. Often the samples are digitized, and this digitizing is readily accomplished with an analog-to-digital (A/D) converter, the output being amplitude information in digital form. It is in this form that sampled and digitized signals enter a computer for further processing.

The values of the function at the sampling points are called **sampled values.** The time that separates the sampling points is called the **sampling interval,** and the reciprocal of the sampling interval is the **sampling frequency,** or **sampling rate**. The value of any continuous function $f(t)$ at the point nT_s, where T_s is the sampling interval, is specified by

$$f(t)\delta(t - nT_s) = f(nT_s)\delta(t - nT_s) \tag{4.42}$$

This relationship is easily proven by integrating both sides of the equation. The sampling interval T_s is here chosen to be constant, and $n = 0, \pm 1, \pm 2, \ldots$. The choice of T_s is critical if aliasing, a matter to be discussed in detail in Section 4.5, is to be avoided. The sampled signal is (see also Figure 1.12)

$$f_s(t) \triangleq f(t) \sum_{n=-\infty}^{\infty} \delta(t - nT_s) = f(t)comb_{T_s}(t)$$
$$= \sum_{n=-\infty}^{\infty} f(nT_s)\delta(t - nT_s) \tag{4.43}$$

The Fourier transform of this quantity is

$$F_s(\omega) \triangleq \mathscr{F}\{f_s(t)\} = \sum_{n=-\infty}^{\infty} f(nT_s)\mathscr{F}\{\delta(t - nT_s)\}$$
$$= \sum_{n=-\infty}^{\infty} f(nT_s)e^{-jn\omega T_s} \tag{4.44}$$

since the Fourier transform of the shifted delta function is $e^{-jn\omega T_s}$.

Now, consider the Fourier transform of the term $f_s(t) = f(t)\ comb_{T_s}(t)$, which appears in (4.43) and which is the equivalent of the quantity involving the shifted delta function. By Figure 4.26 and (4.40), we have

$$F_s(\omega) = \mathscr{F}\{f(t)comb_{T_s}(t)\} = \frac{1}{2\pi} F(\omega) * \mathscr{F}\{comb_{T_s}(t)\}$$
$$= \frac{1}{2\pi} F(\omega) * \left[\frac{2\pi}{T_s} \sum_{n=-\infty}^{\infty} \delta(\omega - n\omega_s)\right]$$
$$= \frac{1}{T_s} \sum_{n=-\infty}^{\infty} \int_{-\infty}^{\infty} F(\tau)\delta(\omega - \tau - n\omega_s)\, d\tau$$
$$= \frac{1}{T_s} \sum_{n=-\infty}^{\infty} F(\omega - n\omega_s) = \frac{1}{T_s} \sum_{n=-\infty}^{\infty} F(\omega + n\omega_s) \tag{4.45}$$

By (4.44) and (4.45),

$$F_s(\omega) = \sum_{n=-\infty}^{\infty} f(nT_s)e^{-jn\omega T_s} = \frac{1}{T_s} \sum_{n=-\infty}^{\infty} F(\omega + n\omega_s) \qquad \omega_s = 2\pi/T_s \tag{4.46}$$

This discussion shows that if we know the Fourier transform of $f(t)$, its sampled version $f_s(t)$ is uniquely determined. Moreover, if we set $-\omega = \omega + m\omega_s$ in (4.46), we obtain

$$F_s(\omega + m\omega_s) = \frac{1}{T_s} \sum_{n=-\infty}^{\infty} F[\omega + (n + m)\omega_s]$$
$$= \frac{1}{T_s} \sum_{k=-\infty}^{\infty} F(\omega + k\omega_s) = F_s(\omega) \tag{4.47}$$

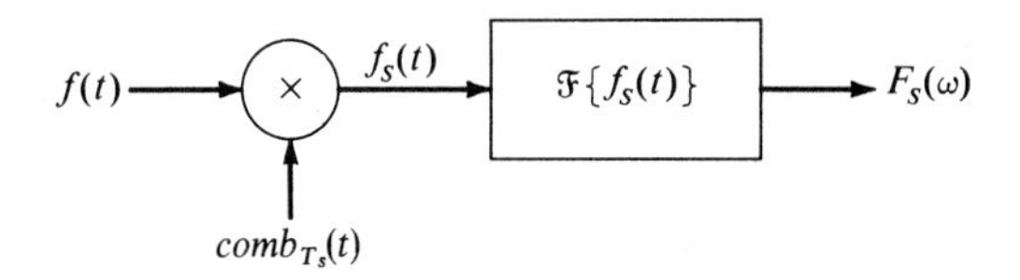

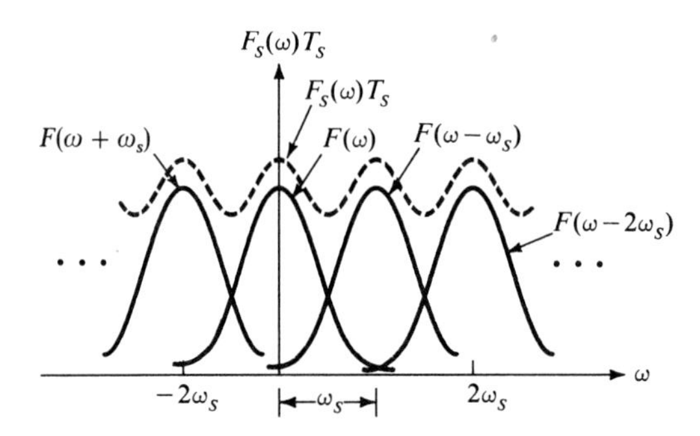

Figure 4.27 Fourier Spectrum of a Sampled Signal

This shows that $F_s(\omega)$ is periodic in the frequency domain, as shown in Figure 4.27. Here, $F_s(\omega)$ accurately represents the sampled function provided successive periods do not overlap; otherwise, aliasing occurs.

When the function $f(t)$ is causal (positive time), $f(t) = 0$ for $t < 0$; then

$$f_s(t) = \sum_{n=0}^{\infty} f(nT_s)\delta(t - nT_s) \tag{4.48a}$$

which can be shown to yield

$$F_s(\omega) = \sum_{n=0}^{\infty} f(nT_s)e^{-jn\omega T_s} = \frac{f(0+)}{2} + \frac{1}{T_s}\sum_{n=-\infty}^{\infty} F(\omega + n\omega_s) \tag{4.48b}$$

■ **Example 4.24**

Find the Fourier transform of the sampled functions.

a. $f_s(t) = e^{-|t|}comb_{T_s}(t)$

b. $f_s(t) = e^{-t}u(t)comb_{T_s}(t)$

Solution By (4.46) and (4.48) and Figure 4.26, we obtain, respectively,

$$\mathscr{F}\{e^{-|t|}comb_{T_s}(t)\} \triangleq F_s(\omega) = \frac{1}{T_s}\sum_{n=-\infty}^{\infty} \frac{2}{1 + (\omega + n\omega_s)^2}$$

$$\omega_s = \frac{2\pi}{T_s} \tag{4.49a}$$

$$\mathscr{F}\{e^{-t}u(t)comb_{T_s}(t)\} \triangleq F_s(\omega) = \frac{1}{2} + \frac{1}{T_s}\sum_{n=-\infty}^{\infty} \frac{1}{1 + j(\omega + n\omega_s)}$$

$$\omega_s = \frac{2\pi}{T_s} \quad \textbf{(4.49b)}$$

■

■ Example 4.25

Consider three functions: $f_1(t)$, $f_2(t)$, and $f_3(t)$, with respective frequency characteristics $F_1(\omega)$, $F_2(\omega)$, and $F_3(\omega)$, as shown in Figure 4.28b. Find the maximum sampling interval T_s in order that the function $f(t) = f_1(t) + f_2(t)f_3(t)$ shown in Figure 4.28a is recovered from its sampled version $f_s(t)$ using a low-pass filter.

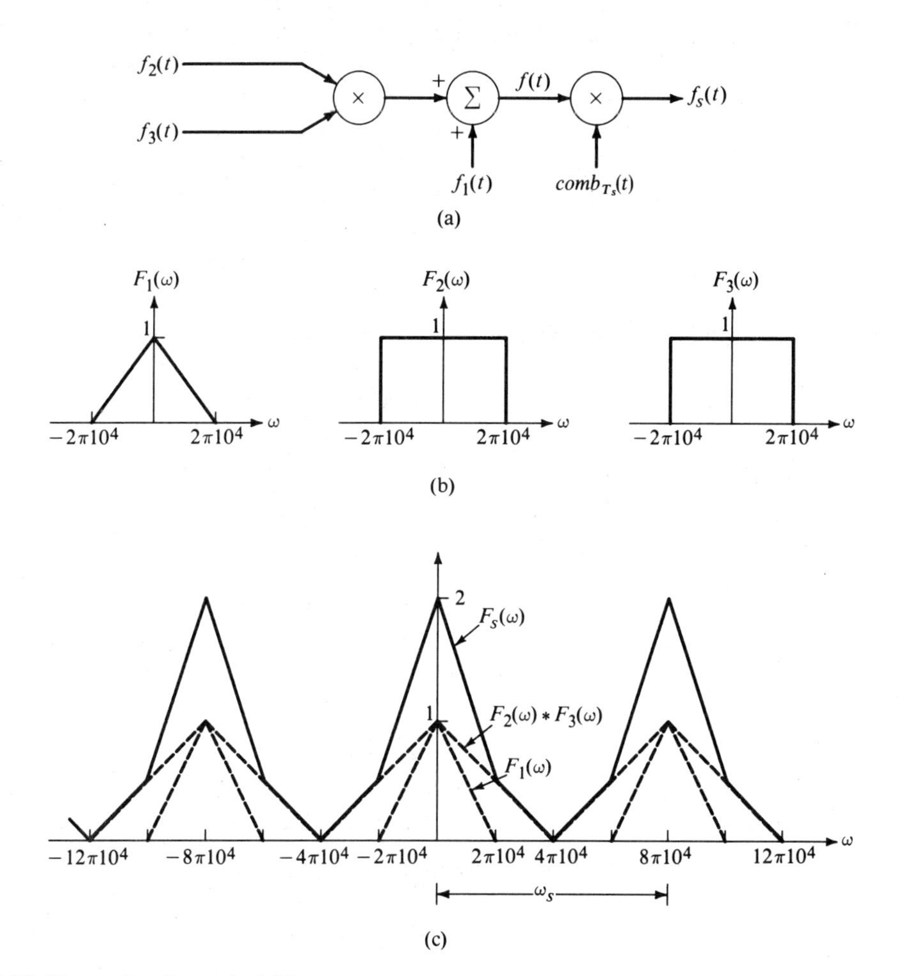

Figure 4.28 Illustrating Example 4.25

Solution The Fourier transform of the sampled function is given by

$$F_s(\omega) = \mathscr{F}\{f_1(t)comb_T(t) + f_2(t)f_3(t)comb_T(t)\}$$

By entry 11 in Table 4.1,

$$F_s(\omega) = \frac{1}{2\pi} F_1(\omega) * \frac{2\pi}{T_s} COMB_{\omega_s}(\omega) + \frac{1}{2\pi} F_2(\omega) * F_3(\omega) * \frac{2\pi}{T_s} COMB_{\omega_s}(\omega)$$

The convolution of $F_1(\omega)$ and $COMB_{\omega_s}(\omega)$ gives us a periodic repetition of the spectrum $F_1(\omega)$. The convolution of $F_2(\omega) * F_3(\omega)$ with $COMB_{\omega_s}(\omega)$ gives us a periodic repetition of the spectrum $F_2(\omega) * F_3(\omega)$. However, the spectral width of $F_2(\omega) * F_3(\omega)$ is equal to the sum of the spectral widths of $F_2(\omega)$ and $F_3(\omega)$; hence, in the present case, $\omega_N = \omega_{N_2} + \omega_{N_3} = 2\pi \times 10^4 + 2\pi \times 10^4 = 4\pi \times 10^4$. The spectrum of $F_s(\omega)$ is shown in Figure 4.28c. We observe that the minimum ω_s in order that the spectrums of $F_2(\omega) * F_3(\omega)$ do not overlap is $8\pi \times 10^4$ or, equivalently, the maximum $T_s = 2\pi/\omega_s = 2\pi/8\pi \times 10^4 = 0.25 \times 10^{-4}$ s. Because the spectral width of $F_2(\omega) * F_3(\omega)$ is greater than the spectral width of $F_1(\omega)$, the value of T_s is determined by the spectral width of $F_2(\omega) * F_3(\omega)$. However, if the spectral width of $F_1(\omega)$ were greater than the spectral width of $F_2(\omega) * F_3(\omega)$, the value of T_s must be determined from the spectral width of $F_1(\omega)$. The spectrums in Figure 4.28c have been normalized to unity. ■

4.5 Sampling Theorem

We next show that it is possible for a band-limited signal $f(t)$ to be exactly specified by its sampled values provided that the time distance between sampled values does not exceed a critical sampling interval. A limited view of sampling was discussed in Section 3.5 for periodic, band-limited signals. The sampling theorem follows.

■ **Theorem 4.1**

A finite energy function $f(t)$ having a band-limited Fourier spectrum—that is, $F(\omega) = 0$ for $|\omega| \geq \omega_N$—can be completely reconstructed from its sampled values $f(nT_s)$ (see Figure 4.29), with

$$f(t) = \sum_{n=-\infty}^{\infty} T_s f(nT_s) \frac{\sin[\omega_s(t - nT_s)/2]}{\pi(t - nT_s)} \qquad \omega_s = \frac{2\pi}{T_s} \tag{4.50a}$$

provided that the sampling time is selected to satisfy

$$\frac{2\pi}{\omega_s} \triangleq T_s = \frac{\pi}{\omega_N} = \frac{\pi}{2\pi f_N} = \frac{1}{2f_N} \triangleq \frac{T_N}{2} \tag{4.50b}$$

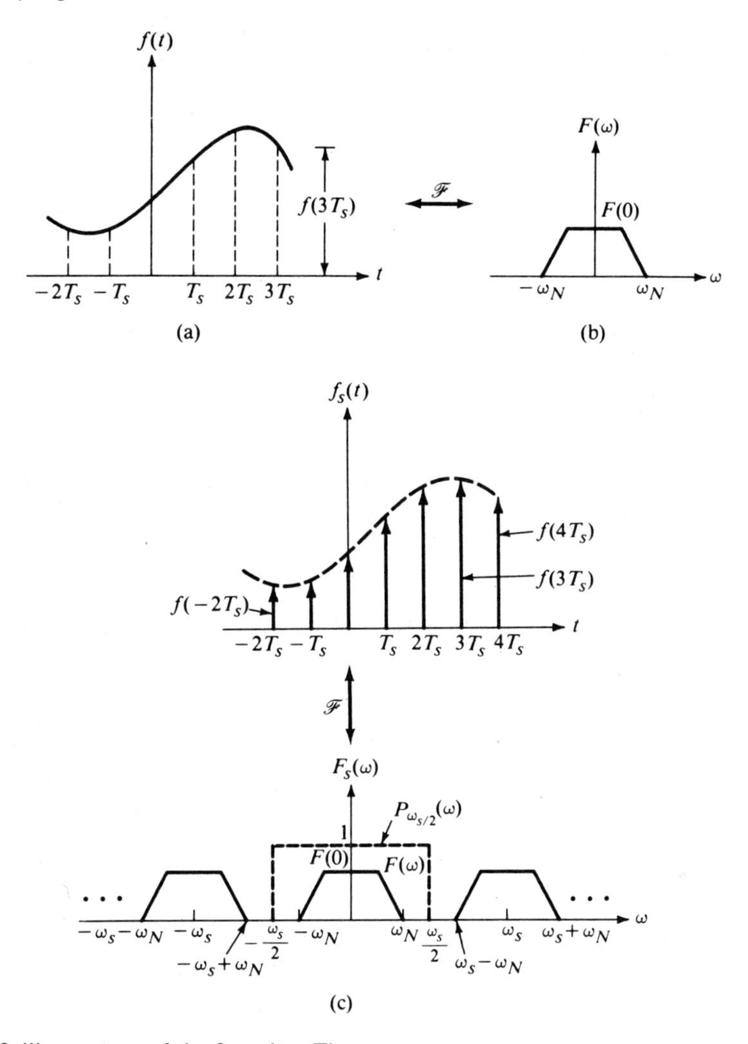

Figure 4.29 Illustrations of the Sampling Theorem

This theorem states that no loss of information is incurred through the sampling process if the signal is sampled at a rate that is at least twice as fast as the highest period contained in the signal. For band-limited signals, the sampling process introduces no error since, in theory, we can recover the original continuous time signal from the sampled version. The function within the braces, which is a sinc function, is known as the **interpolation function** to indicate that it allows an interpolation between the sampled values to find $f(t)$ for all t.

Proof Employ (4.46) and Figure 4.29b to write ($n = 0$)

$$F(\omega) = p_{\omega_s/2}(\omega) T_s F_s(\omega) \tag{4.51}$$

By (4.44), this equation becomes

$$F(\omega) = p_{\omega_s/2}(\omega) T_s \sum_{n=-\infty}^{\infty} f(nT_s) e^{-jn\omega T_s} \tag{4.52}$$

From this, we have that

$$f(t) = \mathscr{F}^{-1}\{F(\omega)\} = \mathscr{F}^{-1}\{p_{\omega_s/2}(\omega) T_s \sum_{n=-\infty}^{\infty} f(nT_s) e^{-j\omega n T_s}\}$$

$$= T_s \sum_{n=-\infty}^{\infty} f(nT_s) \mathscr{F}^{-1}\{p_{\omega_s/2}(\omega) e^{-j\omega n T_s}\} \tag{4.53}$$

By an application of the frequency-shift property of Fourier transforms, it is seen that this equation proves the theorem.

As can be appreciated from (4.50), the generation of $f(t)$ from the sequence $\{f(nT)\}$ is a complex task. This equation is reserved mainly for theoretical considerations. It is useful when the sampling rate is limited.

Example 4.26

Can the given function $f(t)$ be uniformly sampled without a significant loss of information in the transition?

$$f(t) = \begin{cases} e^{-t} & t \geq 0 \\ 0 & t < 0 \end{cases}$$

Solution The Fourier transform of this function yields

$$F(\omega) = \frac{1}{1 + j\omega} \qquad \text{Thus, } |F(\omega)| = \frac{1}{\sqrt{1 + \omega^2}}$$

This function is not band limited, and the sampling theorem would require a sampling period of zero—that is, continuous sampling—to incur no loss of information in the sampling process. Suppose, therefore, that we choose a sampling plan that will contain 99% of the energy of $F(\omega)$. This will establish an upper frequency ω_N, such that

$$\int_0^{\omega_N} |F(\omega)|^2 \, d\omega = 0.99 \int_0^{\infty} |F(\omega)|^2 \, d\omega$$

Incorporating the known expression for $F(\omega)$, then

$$\int_0^{\omega_N} \frac{1}{1 + \omega^2} \, d\omega = 0.99 \int_0^{\infty} \frac{1}{1 + \omega^2} \, d\omega$$

which leads to

$$\tan^{-1} \omega \Big|_0^{\omega_N} = 0.99 \tan^{-1} \omega \Big|_0^{\infty}$$

or

$$\tan^{-1}\omega_N = 0.99\frac{\pi}{2} \qquad \omega_N = \tan\left(0.99\frac{\pi}{2}\right) = 63.657$$

It has been found in practice that little loss in information occurs through sampling if the sampling period is chosen in the range $0.2\pi/\omega_N$ to $0.5\pi/\omega_N$ (see Section 4.6). In our example, $\pi/\omega_N = \pi/63.657 = 0.05$, and the sampling period should be chosen in the range $0.01 \leq T_s \leq 0.025$. ■

To avoid frequencies beyond ω_N, a low-pass filter is included. If the frequency width of the filter ω_1 is other than $\omega_s/2$, (4.51) must be appropriately modified. This modification involves substituting this frequency value for $\omega_s/2$, the result being that the sine term within the braces of (4.50a) becomes $\sin[\omega_1(t - nT_s)]$ and $p_{\omega_s/2}(\omega)$ becomes $p_{\omega_1/2}(\omega)$.

For the case when $\omega_s = 2\omega_N$, (4.50a) becomes (see Problem 34)

$$f(t) = \sum_{n=-\infty}^{\infty} f(nT_s)\frac{\sin[\omega_N(t - nT_s)]}{\omega_N(t - nT_s)} \tag{4.54}$$

and the spectrum of $F_s(\omega)$ is the same as that shown in Figure 4.31d, but with the spectrum for $F_s(\omega)$ just touching the successive replicas of $F(\omega)$.

The sampling time

$$\boxed{T_s = \frac{T_N}{2} = \frac{1}{2f_N}} \tag{4.55}$$

is called the **Nyquist interval.** It is the longest time interval that can be used for sampling a band-limited signal while still permitting us to recover the signal without distortion. Figure 4.30 shows how a signal can be reconstructed from its samples

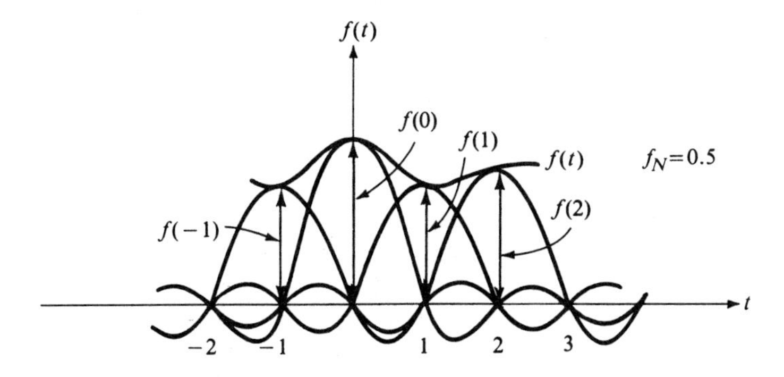

Figure 4.30 Reconstruction of a Signal from Its Samples

using (4.50a). Observe that the sinc functions tend to cancel between the sampling times and to reinforce at the sampling points. In the limit, as $n \to \infty$, the recovery of the signal is complete.

Figure 4.31a shows the overall procedure of delta function sampling and transform representation of a band-limited signal. Note, however, that if the sampling time interval T_s is taken too large, the product $F(\omega) * COMB_{\omega_s}(\omega)$ would look like Figure 4.31b. The overlapping of spectrums is known as **aliasing**. Aliasing disappears if the sampling time diminishes at least to the value $T_s = 1/2f_N$, where f_N is the highest frequency component belonging to the signal. It is clear from Figure 4.31b that there is no filter available that is capable of extracting the frequency content of the signal without including additional frequencies not contained in the signal itself. The recovery of the signal with aliasing present results in a signal with artifacts, as shown in Figure 4.31c for a two-dimensional periodic signal (spokewheel) that has been undersampled.

The effect of aliasing can be used to our advantage in some cases. Suppose that we want to stop optically a repetitive action—for example, the wing undulation of a bee or the turning of a wheel. To accomplish this optical effect, we flash the object with a strobe light. If we adjust the repetition of the strobe flashes to equal the wing repetition rate or the wheel rotation rate, these events will appear to be stationary. If the strobe frequency is much higher than twice that of the periodic phenomenon, the speed of the phenomenon does not appear to change. However, if the frequency of the strobe flashes is less than twice the frequency of the phenomenon under observation, the repetition slows down; thus, we observe a slow-flying bee or a slow rotating wheel. This phenomenon is commonly observed in the movies when we observe a moving stagecoach, with the wheels appearing to be stationary or turning slowly (sometimes backwards). In the movies, the sampling rate is about 1/20 s because the frame rate of the film is about 20 frames per second.

Figure 4.31d shows the product $F(\omega) * COMB_{\omega_s}(\omega)$ when the sampling time $T_s = 1/2f_N$ is just at the Nyquist rate. Figure 4.31e shows the procedure to recover the signal. In this case, we write

$$
\begin{aligned}
\mathscr{F}^{-1}\{F(\omega)\} \triangleq f(t) &= \mathscr{F}^{-1}\left\{\left[\frac{1}{2\pi} F(\omega) * COMB_{\omega_s}(\omega)\right] p_{\omega_s/2}(\omega)\right\} \\
&= \mathscr{F}^{-1}\left\{\frac{1}{2\pi} F(\omega) * COMB_{\omega_s}(\omega)\right\} * \mathscr{F}^{-1}\{p_{\omega_s/2}(\omega)\} \\
&= [f(t) comb_{T_s}(t)] * \frac{T_s}{\pi} \frac{\sin(\omega_s t/2)}{t} \\
&= \frac{T_s}{\pi}\left[\sum_{n=-\infty}^{\infty} f(nT_s)\delta(t - nT_s)\right] * \frac{\sin(\omega_s t/2)}{t} \\
&= T_s \sum_{n=-\infty}^{\infty} f(nT_s) \frac{\sin[\omega_s(t - nT_s)/2]}{\pi(t - nT_s)}
\end{aligned}
$$

which is identical with (4.50a).

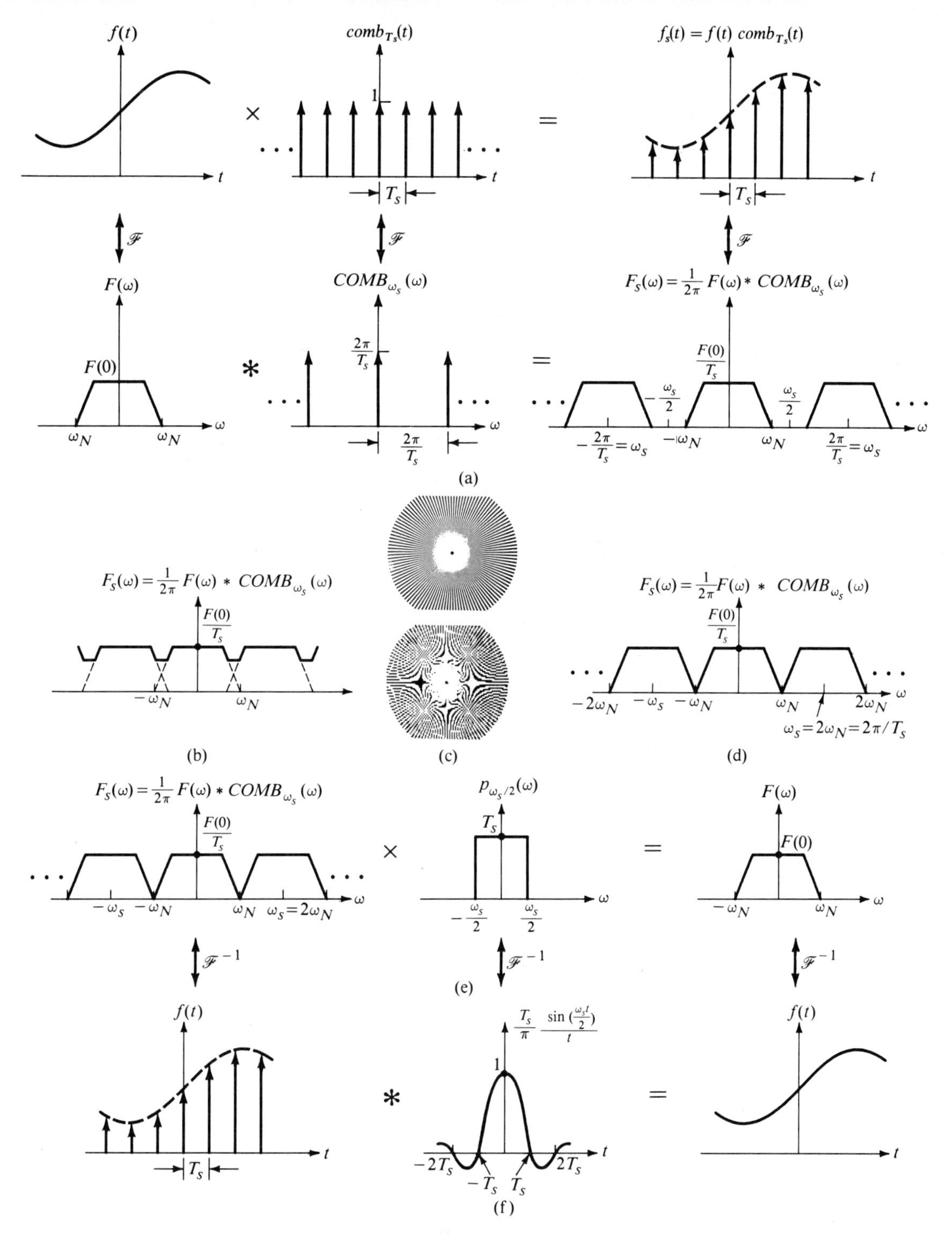

Figure 4.31 Delta Sampling, Representation, and Recovery of Signals. (c) shows original image of spokewheel and its undersampled image. The effect of aliasing appears clearly. [(c) is from Leger and Lee, "Signal Processing Using Hybrid Systems," in H. Stark, ed., *Applications of Optical Fourier Transforms* (New York: Academic Press, 1982). Reprinted by permission.]

Example 4.27

Show the aliasing phenomenon by decreasing ω_s or, equivalently, by increasing the sampling time T_s, associated with a pure cosine function $f(t) = \cos \omega_0 t$. Use a low-pass filter of bandwidth ω_s in the output.

Solution The Fourier transform of $f(t)$ is $F(\omega) = \pi\delta(\omega - \omega_0) + \pi\delta(\omega + \omega_0)$. Thus, the Fourier transform of the sampled function $f_s(t)$ is

$$
\begin{aligned}
F_s(\omega) &= \frac{1}{T_s} F(\omega) * COMB_{\omega_s}(\omega) \\
&= \frac{\pi}{T_s} [\delta(\omega - \omega_0) * COMB_{\omega_s}(\omega) + \delta(\omega + \omega_0) * COMB_{\omega_s}(\omega)]
\end{aligned}
$$

Figure 4.32a shows the spectrum of $F_s(\omega)$ when $\omega_s \gg \omega_0$ or, equivalently, when $T_s \ll T_0 = 2\pi/\omega_0$. Figure 4.32b is the result of the convolution of $\delta(\omega - \omega_0)$ and $COMB_{\omega_s}(\omega)$. Figure 4.32d shows the convolution of $\delta(\omega + \omega_0)$ and $COMB_{\omega_s}(\omega)$. By adding the spectrums of Figures 4.32d and 4.32e, we obtain the total spec-

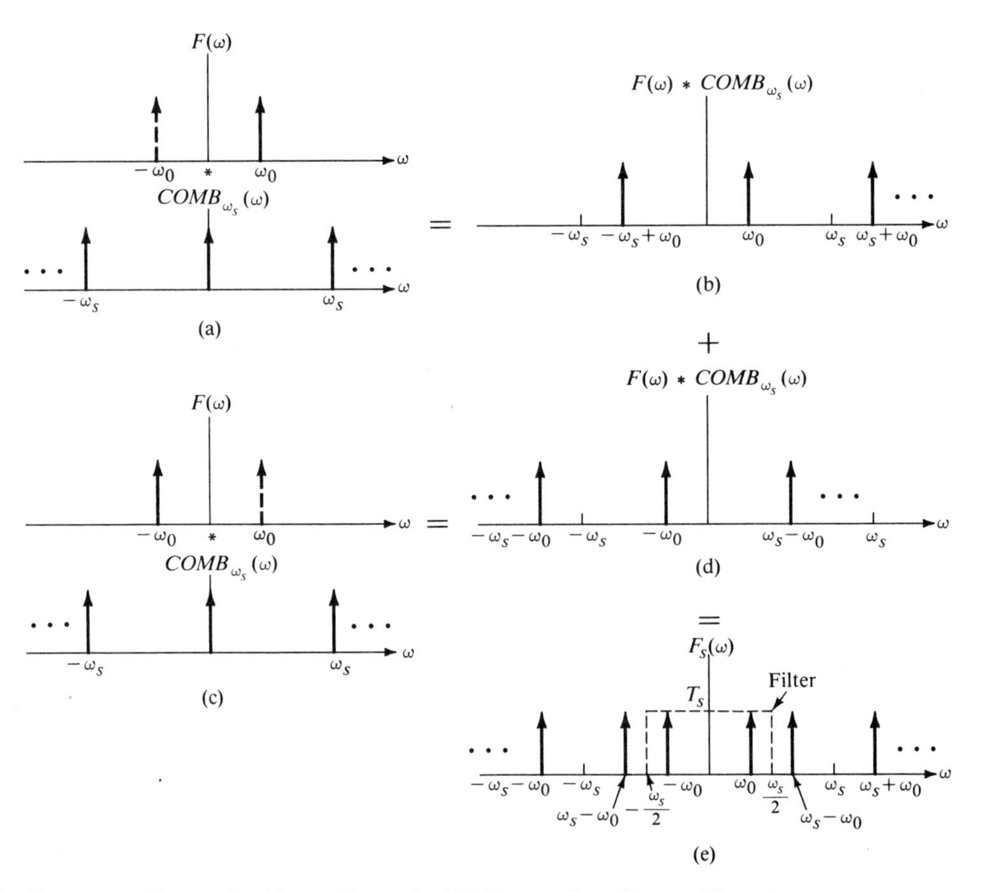

Figure 4.32 Illustrating Aliasing Problem of Example 4.27 Using a Pure Sinusoid Function

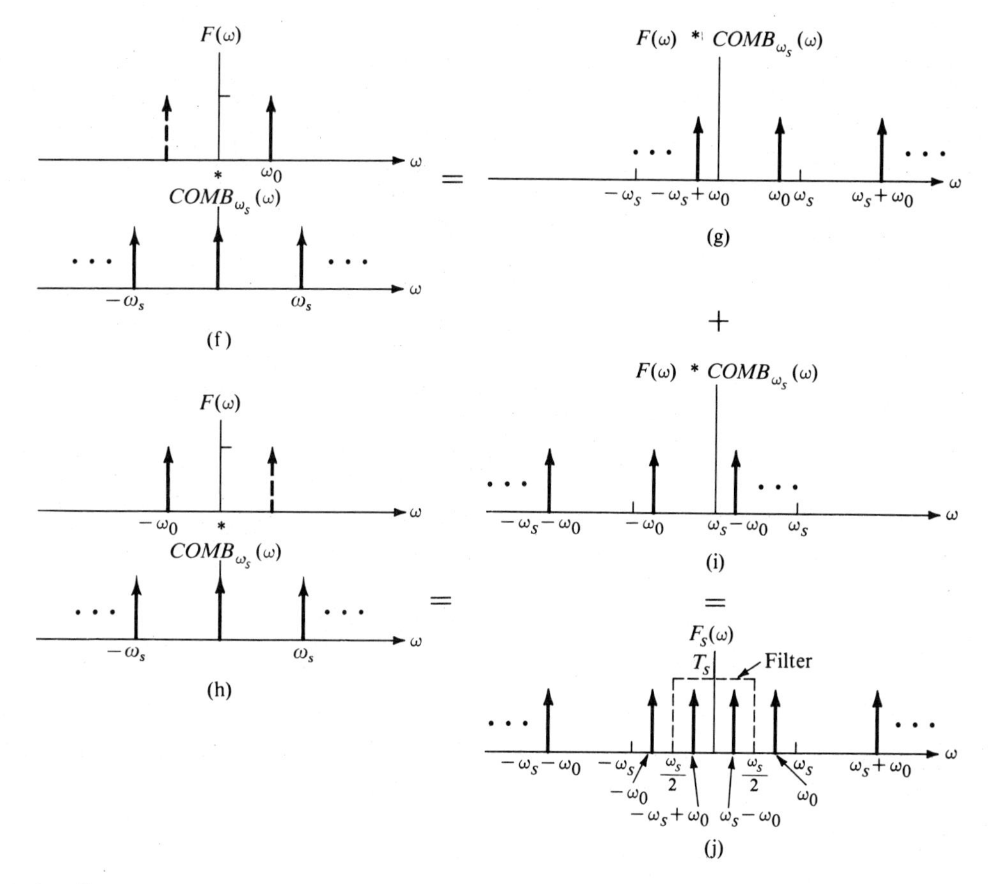

Figure 4.32 *(continued)*

trum of $F_s(\omega)$ as specified by the above equation. If we incorporate a filter having a frequency bandwidth of $\omega_s/2$, we regain our signal since

$$\frac{\pi}{2\pi}\frac{T_s}{T_s}\int_{-\infty}^{\infty} p_{\omega_s/2}(\omega)F_s(\omega)e^{j\omega t}\,d\omega = \frac{1}{2}\int_{-\omega_s/2}^{\omega_s/2}[\delta(\omega+\omega_0)+\delta(\omega-\omega_0)]e^{j\omega t}\,d\omega$$

$$= \frac{1}{2}\left[e^{j\omega_0 t} + e^{-j\omega_0 t}\right] = \cos\omega_0 t$$

We follow the same procedure for the steps shown in Figures 4.32f through 4.32j and develop the function $\cos(\omega_s - \omega_0)t$, a function that is quite different from $\cos\omega_0 t$. Hence, when aliasing occurs, the original frequency ω_0 assumes another identity at a lower frequency $\omega_s - \omega_0$, which is the *alias* of ω_0. ■

4.6 Reconstruction of Sampled Signals

We have found that if a signal is band limited, we can always sample it at such a rate that its periodic Fourier spectrum is without overlap. Under these conditions, a low-pass filter will permit all the harmonics contained in the signal to be recaptured, thereby permitting the signal to be reproduced exactly. Also, the reproduction is noncausal. As a practical matter, all the signals that are of interest possess spectrums of infinite extent, and it is impossible to reconstruct them without some aliasing. One possible solution in this case is first to pass the signal through a low-pass filter to band-limit it and then sample it appropriately. This sequence will distort the signal, of course, and we must impose some kind of quality factor that will ensure acceptable results. One such factor is the amount of energy rejected during the band-limiting process.

To clarify the foregoing discussion, let us consider the Gaussian signal shown in Figure 4.33a and its Fourier spectrum shown in Figure 4.33b (see Figure 4.26). Our purpose is to establish an appropriate bandwidth ω_N of the signal, such that the energy error

$$\Delta E = \frac{1}{2\pi}\int_{-\infty}^{\infty} |F(\omega) - \hat{F}(\omega)|^2 \, d\omega \tag{4.56}$$

is, say, 2% of the energy of the signal $f(t)$. In this expression, $\hat{F}(\omega)$ is the truncated Fourier spectrum of $F(\omega)$ shown in Figure 4.33c. The rejected spectrum $F(\omega) - \hat{F}(\omega)$ is shown in Figure 4.33d.

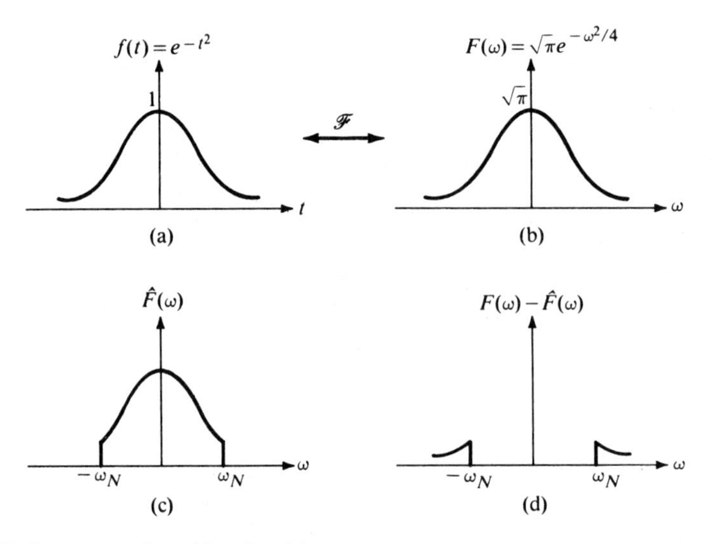

Figure 4.33 Estimating Signal Bandwidth

Because of symmetry, (4.56) becomes

$$\Delta E = \frac{1}{\pi}\int_0^{\infty} |F(\omega) - \hat{F}(\omega)|^2\,d\omega = \frac{1}{\pi}\int_{\omega_N}^{\infty} (\sqrt{\pi}\,e^{-\omega^2/4})^2\,d\omega = \int_{\omega_N}^{\infty} e^{-\omega^2/2}\,d\omega$$

$$= \int_0^{\infty} e^{-\omega^2/2}\,d\omega - \int_0^{\omega_N} e^{-\omega^2/2}\,d\omega = \sqrt{\frac{\pi}{2}} - \sqrt{\frac{\pi}{2}}\,\mathrm{erf}\left(\frac{\omega_N}{2}\right) \tag{4.57}$$

where erf is the *error function.*

The **error function** is defined by the expressions

$$\mathrm{erf}(t) = \frac{2}{\sqrt{\pi}}\int_0^{t} e^{-\tau^2}\,d\tau = \frac{2}{\sqrt{\pi}}\sum_{n=0}^{\infty}\frac{(-1)^n t^{2n+1}}{n!(2n+1)} \tag{4.58a}$$

Table 4.2 $\mathrm{erf}(t) = \frac{2}{\sqrt{\pi}}\int_0^t e^{-\tau^2}\,d\tau$

t	erf(t)	t	erf(t)
0.00	0.00000	0.65	0.64203
0.02	0.02256	0.70	0.67780
0.04	0.04511	0.75	0.71115
0.06	0.06762	0.80	0.74210
0.08	0.09008	0.85	0.77067
0.10	0.11246	0.90	0.79691
0.12	0.13476	0.95	0.82089
0.14	0.15695	1.00	0.84270
0.16	0.17901	1.05	0.86244
0.18	0.20093	1.10	0.88020
0.20	0.22270	1.15	0.89612
0.22	0.24429	1.20	0.91031
0.24	0.26570	1.25	0.92290
0.26	0.28690	1.30	0.93401
0.28	0.30788	1.35	0.94376
0.30	0.32863	1.40	0.95228
0.32	0.34913	1.45	0.95969
0.34	0.36936	1.50	0.96610
0.36	0.38933	1.55	0.97162
0.38	0.40901	1.60	0.97635
0.40	0.42839	1.65	0.98037
0.42	0.44747	1.70	0.98379
0.44	0.46622	1.75	0.98667
0.46	0.48465	1.80	0.98909
0.48	0.50275	1.85	0.99111
0.50	0.52050	1.90	0.99279
0.55	0.56332	1.95	0.99418
0.60	0.60386	2.00	0.99532

and the **complementary error function** is a related function defined by

$$\text{erf } c(t) = 1 - \text{erf}(t) = \frac{2}{\sqrt{\pi}} \int_t^{\infty} e^{-\tau^2}\, d\tau \tag{4.58b}$$

Further,

$$\int_0^{\infty} e^{-\tau^2}\, d\tau = \frac{\sqrt{\pi}}{2}$$

Therefore,

$$\text{erf}(\infty) = 1 \qquad \text{Also, erf}(0) = 0$$

Table 4.2 (page 239) gives values of erf(t) for different values of t.

The total energy of the function $f(t)$ is given by

$$\lim_{\omega_N \to 0} \Delta E = \sqrt{\frac{\pi}{2}} = E_f$$

Therefore,

$$\frac{\Delta E}{E} = 1 - \text{erf}\left(\frac{\omega_N}{2}\right) \tag{4.59}$$

From Table 4.2, we see that when $\omega_N/2 = 1.65$, erf$(1.65) = 0.98037$, giving an energy error of $\Delta E/E = 1 - 0.98037 = 0.01963$, which is approximately equal to 2%. Hence, for $\omega_N \geq 3.30$, the error will be maintained within $\Delta E \leq 0.02E_f$.

Discrete Time Transform

4.7 Discrete Fourier Transforms

The foregoing sections have included discussion of the use of Fourier transform techniques in continuous time signal processing and signal sampling studies. However, in many problems, the signals may be experimentally derived, and analytic functions are not available for the integrations involved. There are two general approaches that might be adopted in such cases. One method calls for approximating the functions and carrying out the integrations by numerical means. A second method, and one that is used extensively, calls for replacing the continuous Fourier transform by an equivalent **discrete Fourier transform** (DFT) and then evaluating the DFT using the discrete data. Now, instead of integrations, the direct solution of the DFT requires, for each sample, N complex multiplications, N complex additions, and the access to N coefficients $\exp(-j\Omega Tnk)$ that appear in the DFT; hence, with 10^4 samples (a small number in many cases), more than 10^8 mathematical operations are required in the solution. It was the development of the **fast Fourier transform** (FFT), a computational technique that reduces the number of mathematical operations in the evaluation of the DFT to $N \log_2 N$, that makes the DFT a useful transform (in digital filter design, for example).

The DFT is particularly suitable for describing phenomena related to a discrete time series. It can be developed from the Fourier integral transform of the continuous waveform from which samples are taken to form the time series. Thus, there is a close parallel in the relation of the DFT and the Fourier transform that is not unlike the relation between the discrete Fourier series (DFS) and the Fourier series discussed in Chapter 3. (The DFT can also relate to the DFS.) First, however, the DFT is defined; its relationship to the continuous Fourier transform is shown later. Further, the mathematical properties of the DFT are analogous to those of the Fourier integral transform.

We found in Section 4.4 that if a time function is sampled uniformly in time, its Fourier spectrum is a periodic function. Therefore, corresponding to any sampled function in the frequency domain, a periodic function exists in the time domain. As a result, the sampled signal values can be related in both domains.

As a practical matter, we are only able to manipulate a certain length of signal. That is, suppose that the data sequence is available only within a finite time window from $n = 0$ to $n = N - 1$. The transform is discretized for N values by taking samples at the frequencies $2\pi/NT$, where T is the time interval between sample points. Hence, we define the discrete Fourier transform (DFT), written $\mathscr{D}$, of a sequence of N samples $\{f(kT)\}$ for $0 \leq k \leq N - 1$ by the relation

$$F(n\Omega) \triangleq \mathscr{D}\{f(kT)\} = \sum_{k=0}^{N-1} f(kT)e^{-j2\pi nkT/NT} = \sum_{k=0}^{N-1} f(kT)e^{-j\Omega Tnk} \qquad n = 0, 1, \ldots N - 1 \tag{4.60}$$

where

$$\begin{aligned} N &= \text{number of sample values (even number)} \\ T &= \text{sampling time interval} \\ (N-1)T &= \text{signal length} \\ \Omega &= \frac{\omega_s}{N} = \frac{2\pi}{NT} = \text{the frequency sampling interval} \\ e^{-j\Omega T} &= N\text{th principal root of unity} \end{aligned}$$

Observe that with this specification of Ω, there are only N distinct values computable by (4.60).

The inverse discrete Fourier transform (IDFT), written $\mathscr{D}^{-1}$, is related to the direct DFT in much the same way that the direct Fourier transform is related to the inverse Fourier integral. We will see that the IDFT is given by

$$f(kT) \triangleq \mathscr{D}^{-1}\{F(n\Omega)\} = \frac{1}{N} \sum_{n=0}^{N-1} F(n\Omega)e^{j\Omega Tnk} \qquad k = 0, 1, \ldots N - 1 \tag{4.61}$$

Proof The relationship between (4.60) and (4.61) is proved as follows:

$$\frac{1}{N}\sum_{n=0}^{N-1} F(n\Omega)e^{j2\pi nkT/NT} = \frac{1}{N}\sum_{n=0}^{N-1}\left[\sum_{m=0}^{N-1} f(mT)e^{-j2\pi nmT/NT}\right]e^{j2\pi nkT/NT}$$
$$= \frac{1}{N}\sum_{m=0}^{N-1} f(mT)\sum_{n=0}^{N-1} e^{-j2\pi(m-k)nT/NT} \tag{4.62}$$

However, we have already established that

$$\sum_{n=0}^{N-1} e^{-j2\pi(m-k)n/N} = \begin{cases} N & m = k \\ 0 & m \neq k \end{cases}$$

Equation (4.62) thus yields

$$\frac{1}{N}\sum_{n=0}^{N-1} F(n\Omega)e^{j2\pi nkT/NT} = \frac{1}{N}\sum_{n=0}^{N-1} F(n\Omega)e^{j\Omega Tnk} = f(kT)$$

Hence, we have the DFT pair

$$\mathscr{D}\{f(kT)\} \triangleq F(n\Omega) = \sum_{k=0}^{N-1} f(kT)e^{-j2\pi nkT/NT}$$
$$= \sum_{k=0}^{N-1} f(kT)e^{-jn\Omega kT} \qquad k = 0, 1, \ldots N-1 \tag{4.63a}$$
$$\mathscr{D}^{-1}\{F(n\Omega)\} \triangleq f(kT) = \frac{1}{N}\sum_{n=0}^{N-1} F(n\Omega)e^{j2\pi nkT/NT}$$
$$= \frac{1}{N}\sum_{n=0}^{N-1} F(n\Omega)e^{jn\Omega kT} \qquad n = 0, 1, \ldots N-1 \tag{4.63b}$$

with both the time and the frequency domain sequences being **periodic**. The periodicity of these sequences stems from the fact that the functions $e^{-j2\pi nk/N}$ are periodic, that is,

$$e^{-j\pi nk/N} = e^{-j\pi(n+N)k/N} \qquad k, n = 0, \pm 1, \pm 2, \ldots \tag{4.64}$$

In general, $F(n\Omega)$ is complex and can be written in the form

$$F(n\Omega) = |F(n\Omega)|\, e^{j\phi(n\Omega)}$$

where $|F(n\Omega)|$ and $\phi(n\Omega) = \text{Arg } F(n\Omega)$ are discrete frequency functions. The plots of $|F(n\Omega)|$ and $\phi(n\Omega)$ versus $n\Omega$ are referred to as the **amplitude** and **phase** spectrums of the sequence $f(kT)$.

A comparison of (4.63) with (3.59) shows that the DFT is simply the sampled DFS. It follows, therefore, that the DFS can be obtained from the DFT by interpolation.

4.8 Properties of the DFT

Since the DFT is related to the Fourier transform, it is anticipated that many of the properties of the DFT will parallel those of the Fourier transform. The important properties are discussed here. For convenience of notation, kT is replaced by k and $n\Omega$ is replaced by n in the functional forms that follow.

Linearity. For a function $af_1(k) + bf_2(k)$, its DFT is

$$\begin{aligned}\mathscr{D}\{af_1(k) + bf_2(k)\} &= a\mathscr{D}\{f_1(k)\} + b\mathscr{D}\{f_2(k)\} \\ &= aF_1(n) + bF_2(n)\end{aligned} \tag{4.65}$$

This property is the direct result of (4.63).

Symmetry. If $f(k)$ and $F(n)$ are a DFT pair, then

$$\mathscr{D}\left\{\frac{1}{N}F(k)\right\} = f(-n) \tag{4.66}$$

Proof Rewrite (4.63b) in the form

$$f(-k) = \frac{1}{N}\sum_{n=0}^{N-1} F(n)e^{jn(-k)}$$

Now, interchange the parameters k and n, which yields

$$f(-n) = \frac{1}{N}\sum_{k=0}^{N-1} F(k)e^{-jnk} \triangleq \mathscr{D}\left\{\frac{1}{N}F(k)\right\}$$

Time Shifting. For any real integer,

$$\mathscr{D}\{f(k-i)\} = F(n)e^{-jni} \tag{4.67}$$

Proof Substitute $m = k - i$ into (4.63b) so that

$$f(m) = \frac{1}{N}\sum_{n=0}^{N-1} F(n)e^{jnm}$$

$$\begin{aligned}f(k-i) &= \frac{1}{N}\sum_{n=0}^{N-1} F(n)e^{jn(k-i)} = \frac{1}{N}\sum_{n=0}^{N-1} [F(n)e^{-jni}]e^{jnk} \\ &\triangleq \mathscr{D}^{-1}\{F(n)e^{-jni}\}\end{aligned}$$

■ **Example 4.28**

Deduce the DFT of the two sequences shown in Figure 4.34a.

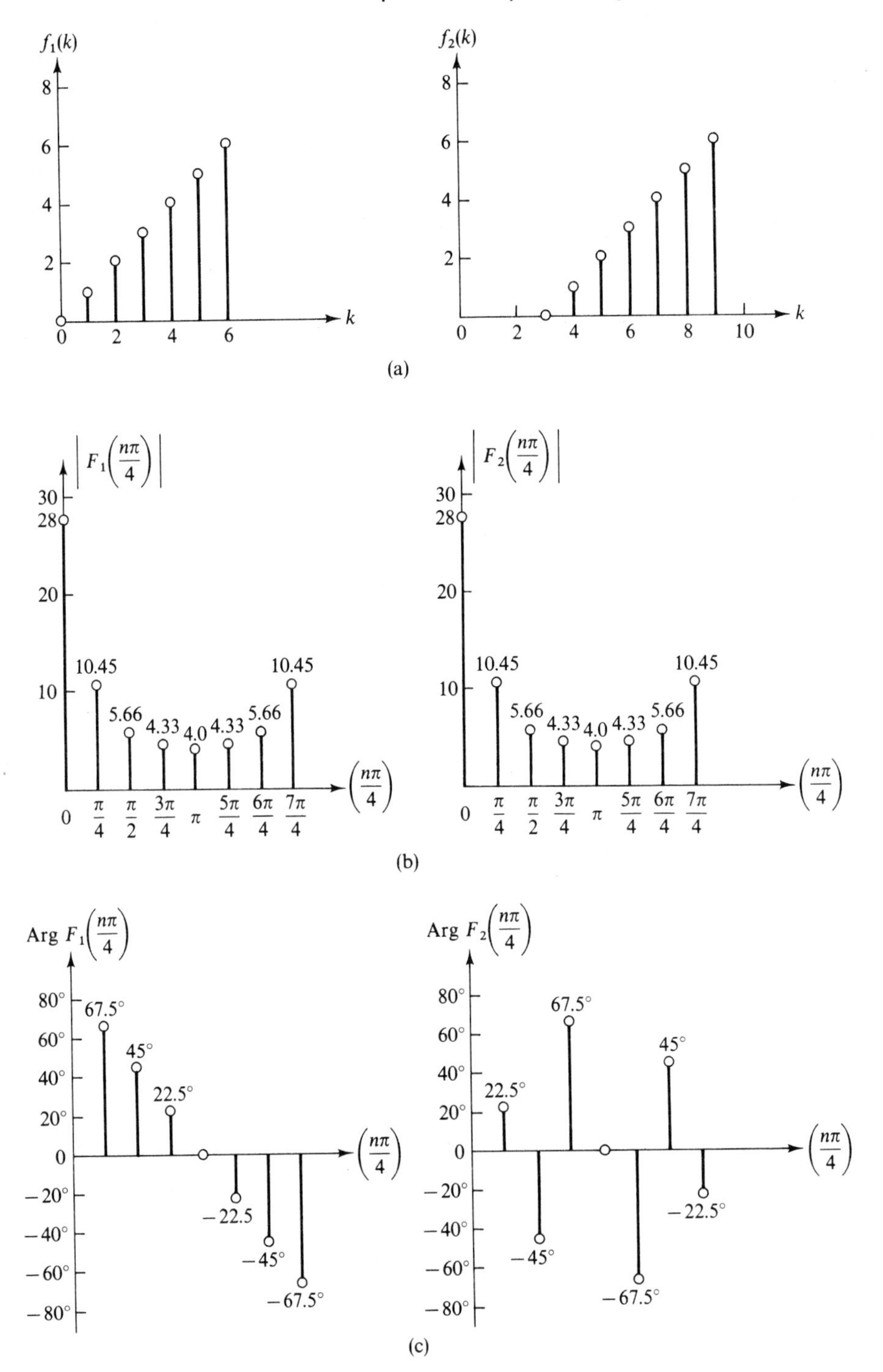

Figure 4.34 Illustrating the Time-Shift Property

Solution From (4.63a) we obtain, respectively,

$$F_1\left(n\frac{\pi}{4}\right) = \sum_{k=0}^{7} f_1(k)e^{-jn(\pi/4)k} \qquad F_2\left(n\frac{\pi}{4}\right) = \sum_{k=3}^{10} f_2(k)e^{-jn(\pi/4)k}$$

The specific expansions are

$$\begin{aligned}
F_1\left(0\frac{\pi}{4}\right) = {} & 0\cos\left(0\frac{\pi}{4}0\right) + 1\cos\left(0\frac{\pi}{4}1\right) + 2\cos\left(0\frac{\pi}{4}2\right) + 3\cos\left(0\frac{\pi}{4}3\right) \\
& + 4\cos\left(0\frac{\pi}{4}4\right) + 5\cos\left(0\frac{\pi}{4}5\right) + 6\cos\left(0\frac{\pi}{4}6\right) + 7\cos\left(0\frac{\pi}{4}7\right) \\
& - j\left[0\sin\left(0\frac{\pi}{4}0\right) + 1\sin\left(0\frac{\pi}{4}1\right) + 2\sin\left(0\frac{\pi}{4}2\right) + 3\sin\left(0\frac{\pi}{4}3\right)\right. \\
& \left. + 4\sin\left(0\frac{\pi}{4}4\right) + 5\sin\left(0\frac{\pi}{4}5\right) + 6\sin\left(0\frac{\pi}{4}6\right) + 7\sin\left(0\frac{\pi}{4}7\right)\right] \\
= {} & 28.0 + j0
\end{aligned}$$

$$\begin{aligned}
F_1\left(1\frac{\pi}{4}\right) = {} & 0\cos\left(1\frac{\pi}{4}0\right) + 1\cos\left(1\frac{\pi}{4}1\right) + 2\cos\left(1\frac{\pi}{4}2\right) + 3\cos\left(1\frac{\pi}{4}3\right) \\
& + 4\cos\left(1\frac{\pi}{4}4\right) + 5\cos\left(1\frac{\pi}{4}5\right) + 6\cos\left(1\frac{\pi}{4}6\right) + 7\cos\left(1\frac{\pi}{4}7\right) \\
& - j\left[0\sin\left(1\frac{\pi}{4}0\right) + 1\sin\left(1\frac{\pi}{4}1\right) + 2\sin\left(1\frac{\pi}{4}2\right)\right. \\
& + 3\sin\left(1\frac{\pi}{4}3\right) + 4\sin\left(1\frac{\pi}{4}4\right) + 5\sin\left(1\frac{\pi}{4}5\right) + 6\sin\left(1\frac{\pi}{4}6\right) \\
& \left. + 7\sin\left(1\frac{\pi}{4}7\right)\right] = -4.0 - j9.657
\end{aligned}$$

$$\begin{aligned}
F_1\left(2\frac{\pi}{4}\right) = {} & 0\cos\left(2\frac{\pi}{4}0\right) + 1\cos\left(2\frac{\pi}{4}1\right) + \cdots - j\left[0\sin\left(2\frac{\pi}{4}0\right)\right. \\
& \left. + 1\sin\left(2\frac{\pi}{4}1\right) + \cdots\right] = -4.0 - j4.0
\end{aligned}$$

$$F_1\left(3\frac{\pi}{4}\right) = -4.00 - j1.657 \qquad F_1\left(4\frac{\pi}{4}\right) = -4.00 + j0.00$$

$$F_1\left(5\frac{\pi}{4}\right) = -4.00 + j1.657$$

$$F_1\left(6\frac{\pi}{4}\right) = -4.00 + j4.00 \qquad F_1\left(7\frac{\pi}{4}\right) = -4.00 + j9.657$$

By the same procedure, we find

$$F_2\left(0\frac{\pi}{4}\right) = 0\cos\left(0\frac{\pi}{4}3\right) + 1\cos\left(0\frac{\pi}{4}4\right) + \cdots - j\left[0\sin\left(0\frac{\pi}{4}3\right) + 1\sin\left(0\frac{\pi}{4}4\right) + \cdots\right] = 28.00 + j0.0$$

$$F_2\left(1\frac{\pi}{4}\right) = 9.657 + j4.00 \qquad F_2\left(2\frac{\pi}{4}\right) = -4.00 + j4.00$$

$$F_2\left(3\frac{\pi}{4}\right) = -1.657 - j4.00$$

$$F_2\left(4\frac{\pi}{4}\right) = 4.00 + j0.00 \qquad F_2\left(5\frac{\pi}{4}\right) = -1.657 + j4.00$$

$$F_2\left(6\frac{\pi}{4}\right) = -4.00 - j4.00$$

$$F_2\left(7\frac{\pi}{4}\right) = 0.657 - j4.00$$

The amplitude and phase spectrums are shown in Figure 4.34b. Observe that the procedure parallels that in Example 3.8 for the discrete Fourier pairs. ■

Frequency Shifting. For any real integer,

$$\boxed{f(k)e^{jki} = \mathscr{D}^{-1}\{F(n-i)\}} \tag{4.68}$$

Proof Write (4.63a) as

$$F(m) = \sum_{k=0}^{N-1} f(k)e^{-jmk}$$

Now, write $m = n - i$ in this expression:

$$F(n-i) = \sum_{k=0}^{N-1} f(k)e^{-j(n-i)k} = \sum_{k=0}^{N-1} [f(k)e^{jik}]e^{-jnk}$$

Alternative Inversion Formula. The inversion formula of (4.63b) can also be written in the form

$$f(k) = \frac{1}{N}\left[\sum_{k=0}^{N-1} F^*(n)e^{-jnk}\right]^* = \frac{1}{N}[\mathscr{D}\{F^*(n)\}]^* = \mathscr{D}^{-1}\{F(n)\} \tag{4.69}$$

Proof The proof proceeds by writing $F(n) = R(n) + jI(n)$ in terms of its real and imaginary parts, and so $F^*(n) = R(n) - jI(n)$ in (4.69). By carrying out the successive steps, it will lead to

$$f(k) = \frac{1}{N} \sum_{k=0}^{N-1} F(n)e^{jnk}$$

The usefulness of (4.69) is that it shows that we can obtain the IDFT using a DFT algorithm on the conjugate value of $F(n)$, scale the results by $1/N$, and then take their conjugate value.

Time Convolution. Discrete convolution is defined by the expression [see (2.112)]

$$y(k) = f(k) * g(k) = \sum_{i=0}^{N-1} f(i)g(k-i) \tag{4.70a}$$

where $f(k)$ and $g(k)$ are periodic and of the same period N:

$$f(k) = f(k + pN) \qquad p = 0, \pm 1, \pm 2, \ldots \tag{4.70b}$$

$$g(k) = g(k + pN) \qquad p = 0, \pm 1, \pm 2, \ldots \tag{4.70c}$$

This is circular or cyclic convolution and was discussed in Section 3.6. The DFT of this expression yields

$$\boxed{Y(n) = \mathscr{D}\{f(k) * g(k)\} = F(n)G(n)} \tag{4.70d}$$

The function $g(k-i)$ is a shifted version of $g(i)$ by k time intervals and is reversed with respect to the $g(i)$ axis. The function $g(k-i)$ is shifted any time we change k. Thus, the discrete convolution of two functions is obtained by multiplying, point by point, one function with the reflected form of the other and summing the products. This process continues for different values of k. The resulting values are the values of $y(k)$ corresponding to a particular k.

Proof Begin with the function

$$\sum_{i=0}^{N-1} f(i)g(k-i) = \sum_{i=0}^{N-1} \frac{1}{N} \sum_{n=0}^{N-1} F(n)e^{jin} \frac{1}{N} \sum_{m=0}^{N-1} G(m)e^{jm(k-i)}$$

This is rearranged to

$$= \frac{1}{N} \sum_{n=0}^{N-1} \sum_{m=0}^{N-1} F(n)G(m)e^{jmk}\left[\frac{1}{N} \sum_{i=0}^{N-1} e^{jin}e^{-jim}\right]$$

However, as already discussed in connection with 4.62,

$$\frac{1}{N} \sum_{i=0}^{N-1} e^{jin}e^{-jim} = \begin{cases} 1 & \text{for } n = m \\ 0 & \text{for } n \neq m \end{cases}$$

Hence, for $n = m$ in the second sum, we find, finally,

$$y(k) = \sum_{i=0}^{N-1} f(i)g(k-i) = \frac{1}{N}\sum_{n=0}^{N-1} F(n)G(n)e^{jnk} \triangleq \mathscr{D}^{-1}\{F(n)G(n)\}$$

which implies (4.70d).

■ **Example 4.29**

Consider the two periodic sequences

$$f(k) = \{1, -1, 4\} \qquad g(k) = \{0, 1, 3\}$$

Verify (4.70) by showing that for $T = 1$,

$$y(2) = \sum_{i=0}^{N-1} f(i)g(2-i) = \mathscr{D}^{-1}\{F(n)G(n)\} = \frac{1}{N}\sum_{n=0}^{N-1} F(n)G(n)e^{j2\pi n2/N}$$

Solution First, find the summation:

$$\sum_{i=0}^{2} f(i)g(2-i) = f(0)g(2) + f(1)g(1) + f(2)g(0)$$

$$= 1 \times 3 + (-1) \times 1 + 4 \times 0 = 2$$

Next, obtain $F(n)$ and $G(n)$ using (4.63a):

$$F(0) = \sum_{k=0}^{2} f(k)e^{-j0k2\pi/3} = f(0) + f(1) + f(2) = 1 - 1 + 4 = 4$$

$$F(1) = \sum_{k=0}^{2} f(k)e^{-jk2\pi/3} = f(0) + f(1)e^{-j2\pi/3} + f(2)e^{-j4\pi/3}$$

$$= -0.5 + j5 \times 0.866$$

$$F(2) = \sum_{k=0}^{2} f(k)e^{-j2k2\pi/3} = f(0) + f(1)e^{-j4\pi/3} + f(2)e^{-j8\pi/3}$$

$$= -0.5 - j5 \times 0.866$$

Similarly, we obtain

$$G(0) = 4 \qquad G(1) = -2 + j2 \times 0.866 \qquad G(2) = -2 - j2 \times 0.866$$

The second summation given above becomes

$$\frac{1}{3}\sum_{n=0}^{2} F(n)G(n)e^{jn4\pi/3} = \frac{1}{3}[16 + 11.55e^{j115.7^\circ} + 11.55e^{j604.3^\circ}] = 2$$

This shows the validity of (4.70). ■

From this discussion, it follows that to obtain the convolution of two nonperiodic sequences $f_1(k)$ and $f_2(k)$ with N_1 and N_2 elements, respectively, the procedure, or algorithm, is:

1. Calculate the DFTs of the sequences $f_1(k)$ and $f_2(k)$ to deduce $F_1(n)$ and $F_2(n)$ using (4.63a).
2. Multiply these DFTs to obtain $F_0(n) = F_1(n)F_2(n)$.
3. Calculate the inverse DFT of $F_0(n)$. The result is the desired convolution $f_0(k) = f_1(k) * f_2(k)$.

Note: The only constraint in following this procedure is that the DFT is one for which $N \geq N_1 + N_2 - 1$, the condition discussed in Section 3.6 to avoid circular convolution artifacts.

Steps 1 and 3 can be done efficiently using the fast Fourier transform, as discussed later in Section 4.9. Thus, the overall algorithm represents an extremely efficient procedure for calculating the convolution of fine-duration signals.

Frequency Convolution. Consider the frequency convolution

$$Y(n) = \sum_{i=0}^{N-1} F(i)G(n-i) = F(n) * G(n)$$

The inverse DFT of this expression yields

$$\mathscr{D}^{-1}\{Y(n)\} = \mathscr{D}^{-1}\left[\frac{1}{N}\sum_{i=0}^{N-1} F(i)G(n-i)\right] = f(k)g(k) \tag{4.71}$$

Proof Substitute known forms into

$$\begin{aligned}\sum_{i=0}^{N-1} F(i)G(n-i) &= \sum_{i=0}^{N-1}\left[\sum_{m=0}^{N-1} f(m)e^{-jmi}\right]\left[\sum_{k=0}^{N-1} g(k)e^{-jk(n-i)}\right] \\ &= \sum_{m=0}^{N-1}\sum_{k=0}^{N-1} f(m)g(k)e^{-jkn}\left[\sum_{i=0}^{N-1} e^{-jmi}e^{jki}\right]\end{aligned}$$

The bracketed term is the orthogonality relationship and is equal to N if $m = k$. Therefore,

$$\sum_{i=0}^{N-1} F(i)G(n-i) = N\sum_{k=0}^{N-1} f(k)g(k)e^{-jnk} \triangleq N\mathscr{D}\{f(k)g(k)\}$$

from which (4.71) follows by taking the inverse DFT of both sides of the equation. Because $F(n)$ and $G(n)$ are periodic, (4.71) indicates a circular convolution in the frequency plane.

■ **Example 4.30**

Use the values of $F(n)$ and $G(n)$ of Example 4.29 to verify the frequency convolution property.

Solution Figure 4.35 shows the circular convolution of $F(n)$ and $G(n)$, with the values obtained from Example 4.29. From (4.71), we obtain the periodic

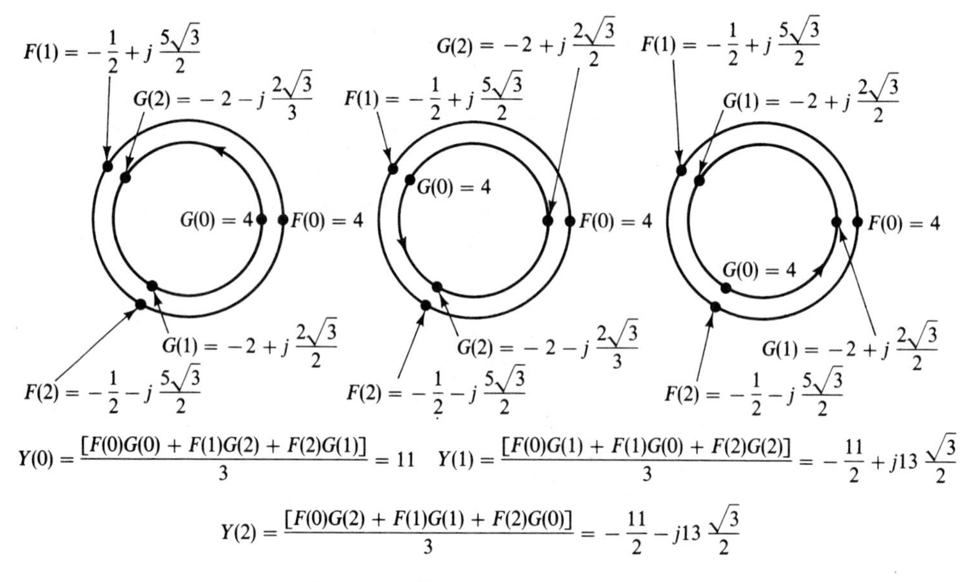

Figure 4.35 Circular Convolution in the Frequency Domain

sequence $y(k)$ from the relation

$$y(k) = \mathscr{D}^{-1}\{Y(n)\} \qquad \text{or} \qquad \{y(k)\} = \{f(k)g(k)\} = \{0, -1, 12\}$$

Thus, from the results of Figure 4.35, we obtain

$$\begin{aligned}
y(0) &= \mathscr{D}^{-1}\{Y(n)\} = \frac{1}{3}\sum_{n=0}^{N-1} Y(n)e^{jn(2\pi/3)0} \\
&= \frac{1}{3}\left[11 - \frac{11}{2} - \frac{11}{2} + j13\frac{\sqrt{3}}{2} - j13\frac{\sqrt{3}}{2}\right] = 0 \\
y(1) &= \mathscr{D}^{-1}\{Y(n)\} = \frac{1}{3}\left[11 + \left(-\frac{11}{2} + j13\frac{\sqrt{3}}{2}\right)\left(\cos\frac{2\pi}{3} + j\sin\frac{2\pi}{3}\right)\right. \\
&\quad \left. + \left(-\frac{11}{2} - j13\frac{\sqrt{3}}{2}\right)\left(\cos\frac{4\pi}{3} + j\sin\frac{4\pi}{3}\right)\right] = -1 \\
y(2) &= \mathscr{D}^{-1}\{Y(n)\} = \frac{1}{3}\left[11 + \left(-\frac{11}{2} + j13\frac{\sqrt{3}}{2}\right)\left(\cos\frac{4\pi}{3} + j\sin\frac{4\pi}{3}\right)\right. \\
&\quad \left. + \left(-\frac{11}{2} - j13\frac{\sqrt{13}}{2}\right)\left(\cos\frac{8\pi}{3} + j\sin\frac{8\pi}{3}\right)\right] = 12
\end{aligned}$$

The results obtained thus verify (4.71). ∎

Parseval's Theorem. For discrete functions, Parseval's relationship between power computed in the time domain and in the frequency domain is

$$\sum_{k=0}^{N-1} f^2(k) = \frac{1}{N} \sum_{n=0}^{N-1} |F(n)|^2 \tag{4.72}$$

Proof To prove this relationship, let $y(k) = f(k)f(k)$. By (4.71), this is given by

$$\sum_{k=0}^{N-1} f^2(k)e^{-jnk} = \frac{1}{N} \sum_{i=0}^{N-1} F(i)F(n-i)$$

Now, set $n = 0$ in this expression. Therefore,

$$\sum_{k=0}^{N-1} f^2(k) = \frac{1}{N} \sum_{i=0}^{N-1} F(i)F(-i) = \frac{1}{N} \sum_{i=0}^{N-1} |F(i)|^2$$

From this, we may define a discrete energy spectral density or periodogram spectral estimate:

$$S(n) = |F(n)|^2 \qquad 0 \leq n \leq N-1 \tag{4.73}$$

Note, however, that $S(n)$ and $F_s(\omega)$ in (4.44), when evaluated at $\omega = 2\pi n/NT$ for $n = 0, 1, \ldots (N-1)$, do not yield identical values. $S(n)$ is, in effect, a sampled version of a spectrum determined from the convolution of $F(\omega)$ with the transform of the rectangular window that contains the data sampled. Thus, the discrete spectrum $S(n)$ based on a finite data set is a distorted version of the continuous spectrum $S_s(\omega)$ based on an infinite data set.

■ **Example 4.31**

Verify Parseval's theorem using the sequence $f(k) = \{1, -1, 4\}$.

Solution We have directly that

$$\sum_{k=0}^{2} f^2(k) = 1 + 1 + 16 = 18$$

The values of $F(n)$ for this sequence are given in Example 4.28, so that

$$\frac{1}{3} \sum_{n=0}^{2} |F(n)|^2 = \frac{1}{3} [16 + |-0.5 + j5 \times 0.866|^2 + |-0.5 - j5 \times 0.866|^2]$$

$$= \frac{1}{3} [16 + 19 + 19] = 18$$

■

Time Reversal. For negative k,

$$\mathscr{D}\{f(-k)\} = F(-n) \tag{4.74}$$

This property tells us that if we reverse the time function, its spectrum is also reversed.

Proof From (4.63b), we have

$$f(-k) = \frac{1}{N} \sum_{n=0}^{N-1} f(n)e^{-jnk}$$

Now, set $n = -m$ on the right. Then

$$f(-k) = \frac{1}{N} \sum_{m=0}^{-(N-1)} F(-m)e^{jmk}$$

Because of the periodic nature of $F(-m)$ and e^{jmk}, the sum over $(-N + 1, 0)$ and $(0, N - 1)$ is the same. Thus,

$$f(-k) = \frac{1}{N} \sum_{m=0}^{N-1} F(-m)e^{jmk} = \mathscr{D}^{-1}\{F(-m)\}$$

which proves (4.74).

Conjugate Functions. For conjugate functions $f^*(k)$ and $f^*(-k)$,

$$\mathscr{D}\{f^*(k)\} = F^*(-n) \tag{4.75a}$$

$$\mathscr{D}\{f^*(-k)\} = F^*(n) \tag{4.75b}$$

Proof From (4.63b), we obtain

$$f^*(k) = \frac{1}{N} \sum_{n=0}^{N-1} F^*(n)e^{-jnk}$$

Set $n = -m$ and use the periodicity property, as was done in *Time Reversal*, to find

$$f^*(k) = \frac{1}{N} \sum_{m=0}^{-(N-1)} F^*(-m)e^{jmk} = \frac{1}{N} \sum_{m=0}^{N-1} F^*(-m)e^{jmk} = \mathscr{D}^{-1}\{F^*(-m)\}$$

This proves the first identity. The second identity is easily proved using (4.74).

Delta Function. For the delta function $\delta(k)$,

$$\mathscr{D}\{\delta(k)\} = 1 \tag{4.76}$$

Proof This relationship is deduced directly from (4.63a).

Central Ordinate. Specific values of $f(0)$ and $F(0)$ corresponding to (4.13) are

$$f(0) = \frac{1}{N}\sum_{n=0}^{N-1} F(n)$$
$$F(0) = \sum_{k=0}^{N-1} f(k) \tag{4.77}$$

Proof These relationships are the direct consequence of (4.63). Table 4.3 contains the essential properties of the discrete Fourier transform.

■ Example 4.32

Find the DFT of the function shown in Figure 4.36a discretized with $T = 1, 0.5$.

Table 4.3 Properties of Discrete Fourier Transforms

Property	Function	Transform
Linearity	$af_1(kT) + bf_2(kT)$	$aF_1(n\Omega) + bF_2(n\Omega)$
Symmetry	$(1/N)F(kT)$	$f(-n\Omega)$
Time shifting	$f(kT - iT)$	$F(n\Omega)e^{-jm\Omega iT}$
Frequency shifting	$f(kT)e^{\pm jkTi\Omega}$	$F(n\Omega \mp i\Omega)$
Even functions	$f_e(kT)$	$\sum_{k=0}^{N-1} f_e(kT)\cos(kTn\Omega)$
Odd functions	$f_o(kT)$	$-j\sum_{k=0}^{N-1} f_o(kT)\sin(kTn\Omega)$
Time convolution	$f(kT) * g(kT)$	$F(n\Omega)G(n\Omega)$
Frequency convolution	$f(kT)g(kT)$	$F(n\Omega) * G(n\Omega)$
Time reversal	$f(-kT)$	$F(-n\Omega)$
Conjugate functions	$f^*(kT)$	$F^*(-n\Omega)$
	$f^*(-kT)$	$F^*(n\Omega)$
Delta function	$\delta(kT)$	1
Central ordinate		$f(0) = \frac{1}{N}\sum_{n=0}^{N-1} F(n\Omega)$
		$F(0) = \sum_{n=0}^{N-1} f(kT)$
Parseval's theorem		$\sum_{k-0}^{N-1} f^2(kT) = \frac{1}{N}\sum_{n=0}^{N-1} \lvert F(n\Omega)\rvert^2$
Relation to continuous FT		$F_s(\omega)\rvert_{\omega=n\Omega} = F(n\Omega)$
		$= FT$ of the sampled function $f_s(t)$
Relation to Fourier series		$\alpha_k = F(n\Omega)/N$

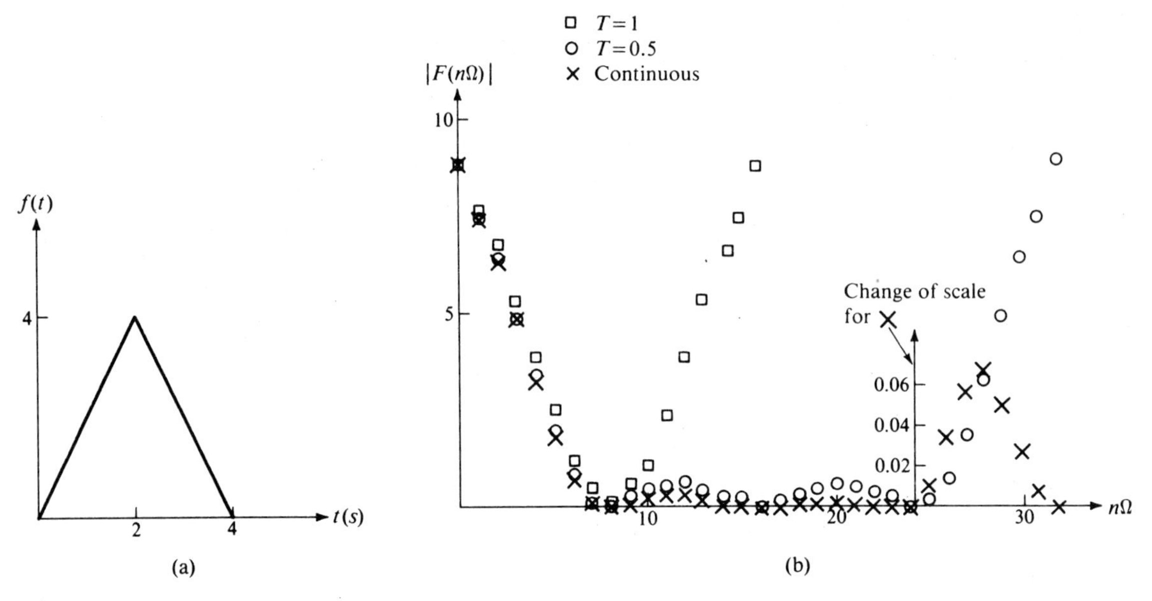

Figure 4.36 Illustrating Example 4.32. (a) The signal. (b) Its discrete Fourier transform.

Solution For the case $T = 0.5$ and $NT = 16$, we obtain $N = 32$. There are eight discrete values from the triangular function. The value of Ω is $2\pi/NT = 2\pi/16 = \pi/8$ rad/s, and the values of $F(n\Omega)$ for different values of n are

$$
\begin{aligned}
F(0\Omega) &= (0 + 1 + 2 + 3 + 4 + 3 + 2 + 1) \times 0.5 = 8 \\
F(1\Omega) &= [0 + 1\cos(\pi/16) + 2\cos(2\pi/16) + 3\cos(3\pi/16) + 4\cos(4\pi/16) \\
&\quad + 3\cos(5\pi/16) + 2\cos(6\pi/16) + 1\cos(7\pi/16)] \times 0.5 \\
&\quad - j[0 + 1\sin(\pi/16) + 2\sin(2\pi/16) + 3\sin(3\pi/16) + 4\sin(4\pi/16) \\
&\quad + 3\sin(5\pi/16) + 2\sin(6\pi/16) + 1\sin(7\pi/16)] \times 0.5 \\
&= 5.389 - j5.389 \\
F(2\Omega) &= [0 + 1\cos(2\pi/16) + 2\cos(4\pi/16) + 3\cos(6\pi/16) + 4\cos(8\pi/16) \\
&\quad + 3\cos(10\pi/16) + 2\cos(12\pi/16) + 1\cos(14\pi/16)] \times 0.5 \\
&\quad - j[0 + 1\sin(2\pi/16) + 2\sin(4\pi/16) + 3\sin(6\pi/16) + 4\sin(8\pi/16) \\
&\quad + 3\sin(10\pi/16) + 2\sin(12\pi/16) + 1\sin(14\pi/16)] \times 0.5 \\
&= 0 - j6.568
\end{aligned}
$$

and so on, for subsequent values of n. The values of $F(n\Omega)$ are summarized in Table 4.4. Figure 4.36b shows the discrete Fourier transform for $T = 1$ and $T = 0.5$, and it also shows a comparison with the values obtained from a continuous Fourier transform at the same values of ω.

Table 4.4 Values of $F(n\Omega)$ in Example 4.32

n	$\omega = n\pi/8$	$\mathrm{Re}\{F(n\Omega)\}$	$\mathrm{Im}\{F(n\Omega)\}$	$\lvert F(n\Omega) \rvert$
0	0	8.0000	0.0000	8.0000
1	$\pi/8$	5.3892	−5.3892	7.6215
2	$2\pi/8$	0.0000	−6.5685	6.5685
3	$3\pi/8$	−3.5812	−3.5812	5.0646
4	$4\pi/8$	−3.4142	0.0000	3.4142
5	$5\pi/8$	−1.3580	1.3580	1.9205
6	$6\pi/8$	0.0000	0.8099	0.8099
7	$7\pi/8$	0.1286	0.1286	0.1819
8	$8\pi/8$	0.0000	0.0000	0.0000
9	$9\pi/8$	0.0866	−0.0866	0.1225
10	$10\pi/8$	0.0000	−0.3616	0.3616
11	$11\pi/8$	−0.3879	−0.3880	0.5487
12	$12\pi/8$	−0.5857	0.0000	0.5857
13	$13\pi/8$	−0.3295	0.3295	0.4660
14	$14\pi/8$	0.0000	0.2598	0.2598
15	$15\pi/8$	0.0522	0.0522	0.0739
16	$16\pi/8$	0.0000	0.0000	0.0000
17	$17\pi/8$	0.0522	−0.0522	0.0739
18	$18\pi/8$	0.0000	−0.2598	0.2598
19	$19\pi/8$	−0.3295	−0.3295	0.4660
20	$20\pi/8$	−0.5857	0.0000	0.5857
21	$21\pi/8$	−0.3880	0.3879	0.5487
22	$22\pi/8$	0.0000	0.3616	0.3616
23	$23\pi/8$	0.0866	0.0866	0.1225
24	$24\pi/8$	0.0000	0.0000	0.0000
25	$25\pi/8$	0.1286	−0.1286	0.1819
26	$26\pi/8$	0.0000	−0.8099	0.8099
27	$27\pi/8$	−1.3579	−1.3580	1.9205
28	$28\pi/8$	−3.4141	−0.0001	3.4141
29	$29\pi/8$	−3.5813	3.5811	5.0646
30	$30\pi/8$	−0.0002	6.5684	6.5684
31	$31\pi/8$	5.3890	5.3894	7.6215
32	$32\pi/8$	8.0000	0.0002	8.0000

■

The following example clarifies the effect of changing both the sampling time T and the product NT.

■ **Example 4.33**

Deduce the discrete Fourier transform of the function

$$f(t) = \begin{cases} 2 & 0 \le t < 6 \\ 0 & \text{otherwise} \end{cases}$$

for the following three cases

a. $T = 1.0, NT = 16$
b. $T = 1.0, NT = 32$
c. $T = 0.2, NT = 16$

Solution We readily find the Fourier transform of the continuous time function to be

$$|F(\omega)| = \frac{4 \sin 3\omega}{\omega}$$

The results of the DFT for the three cases are contained in the tables.

Case a: Table 4.5 gives the results of the DFT with $T = 1$ and $NT = 16$. For $T = 1$, $N = 16/1 = 16$ and the frequency spectrum folds at $N = 8$, or at $8 \times 2\pi/16 = \pi$ rad/s.

Case b: Table 4.6 gives the results of the DFT with $T = 1$ and $NT = 32$. In this case, for $T = 1$, $N = 32/1 = 32$ and the frequency spectrum folds at $N = 16$, or at $16 \times 2\pi/32 = \pi$ rad/s. A comparison of Tables 4.4 and 4.5 shows that increasing the product NT (doubling in this case) adds more discrete values (twice as many in this case) within the frequency span of π rad/s. However, the accuracy remains the same. From these results, we conclude that the sampling frequency T controls the accuracy of the operation.

Table 4.5 DFT with $T = 1$ and $NT = 16$

n	$\|F(n\Omega)\|$	$\|F(\omega)\|$	$\|F(n\Omega) - F(\omega)\|$
0	12.000000	12.000000	$8.88178e - 16$
1	9.471301	9.410560	$6.07409e - 02$
2	3.695518	3.601265	$9.42529e - 02$
3	1.377624	1.299327	$7.82968e - 02$
4	2.828427	2.546479	$2.81948e - 01$
5	0.920499	0.779596	$1.40903e - 01$
6	1.530734	1.200422	$3.30312e - 01$
7	1.883959	1.344366	$5.39593e - 01$
8	0.000000	0.000000	$7.82676e - 09$
9	1.883959	1.045618	$8.38341e - 01$
10	1.530734	0.720253	$8.10481e - 01$
11	0.920499	0.354362	$5.66137e - 01$
12	2.828427	0.848826	$1.97960e + 00$
13	1.377624	0.299845	$1.07778e + 00$
14	3.695518	0.514466	$3.18105e + 00$
15	9.471300	0.627371	$8.84393e + 00$
16	12.000000	0.000000	$1.20000e + 01$

Table 4.6 DFT with $T = 1$ and $NT = 32$

n	$\lvert F(n\Omega)\rvert$	$\lvert F(\omega)\rvert$	$\lvert F(n\Omega) - F(\omega)\rvert$
0	12.000000	12.000000	$8.88178e-16$
1	11.336185	11.317984	$1.82015e-02$
2	9.471301	9.410560	$6.07409e-02$
3	6.757403	6.660131	$9.72718e-02$
4	3.695518	3.601265	$9.42529e-02$
5	0.827712	0.794869	$3.28423e-02$
6	1.377624	1.299327	$7.82968e-02$
7	2.621306	2.419794	$2.01512e-01$
8	2.828427	2.546479	$2.81948e-01$
9	2.151251	1.882062	$2.69188e-01$
10	0.920499	0.779596	$1.40903e-01$
11	0.442421	0.361304	$8.11169e-02$
12	1.530734	1.200422	$3.30312e-01$
13	2.049836	1.536953	$5.12882e-01$
14	1.883959	1.344366	$5.39593e-01$
15	1.116517	0.754532	$3.61985e-01$
16	0.000000	0.000000	$7.82676e-09$
17	1.116517	0.665764	$4.50753e-01$
18	1.883959	1.045618	$8.38341e-01$
19	2.049836	1.051600	$9.98236e-01$
20	1.530734	0.720253	$8.10481e-01$
21	0.442421	0.189255	$2.53167e-01$
22	0.920499	0.354362	$5.66137e-01$
23	2.151251	0.736459	$1.41479e+00$
24	2.828427	0.848826	$1.97960e+00$
25	2.621306	0.677542	$1.94376e+00$
26	1.377624	0.299845	$1.07778e+00$
27	0.827712	0.147198	$6.80514e-01$
28	3.695518	0.514466	$3.18105e+00$
29	6.757403	0.688979	$6.06842e+00$
30	9.471300	0.627371	$8.84393e+00$
31	11.336185	0.365096	$1.09711e+01$
32	12.000000	0.000000	$1.20000e+01$

Case c: Table 4.7 gives the results of the DFT with $T = 0.2$ and $NT = 16$. Now, $N = 16/0.2 = 80$ and the frequency spectrum folds at $N = 40$, or at $40 \times 2\pi/16 = 5\pi$ rad/s. From comparison of this table with the other two tables, we observe: (1) The accuracy has increased by a factor approximately equal to 10, and (2) the useful frequency range has increased to 5π rad/s.

Table 4.7 DFT with $T = 0.2$ and $NT = 16$

n	$\lvert F(n\Omega)\rvert$	$\lvert F(\omega)\rvert$	$\lvert F(n\Omega) - F(\Omega)\rvert$
0	12.000000	12.000000	$4.44089e-16$
1	9.412979	9.410560	$2.41915e-03$
2	3.604970	3.601265	$3.70507e-03$
3	1.302338	1.299327	$3.01046e-03$
4	2.556981	2.546479	$1.05022e-02$
5	0.784628	0.779596	$5.03194e-03$
6	1.211601	1.200422	$1.11796e-02$
7	1.361447	1.344366	$1.70814e-02$
8	0.000000	0.000000	$2.28178e-10$
9	1.067708	1.045618	$2.20899e-02$
10	0.739104	0.720253	$1.88506e-02$
11	0.365627	0.354362	$1.12652e-02$
12	0.881076	0.848826	$3.22493e-02$
13	0.313276	0.299845	$1.34314e-02$
14	0.541327	0.514466	$2.68608e-02$
15	0.665176	0.627371	$3.78050e-02$
16	0.000000	0.000000	$9.45570e-10$
17	0.596924	0.553562	$4.33613e-02$
18	0.435512	0.400141	$3.53719e-02$
19	0.225506	0.205157	$2.03487e-02$
20	0.565685	0.509296	$5.63896e-02$
21	0.208455	0.185618	$2.28371e-02$
22	0.371963	0.327388	$4.45750e-02$
23	0.470577	0.409155	$6.14219e-02$
24	0.000000	0.000000	$2.26202e-09$
25	0.444456	0.376422	$6.80338e-02$
26	0.331726	0.277020	$5.47054e-02$
27	0.175443	0.144370	$3.10734e-02$
28	0.448930	0.363783	$8.51478e-02$
29	0.168556	0.134413	$3.41433e-02$
30	0.306147	0.240084	$6.60624e-02$
31	0.393898	0.303566	$9.03317e-02$
32	0.000000	0.000000	$4.40575e-09$
33	0.383968	0.285168	$9.87993e-02$
34	0.290880	0.211839	$7.90406e-02$
35	0.156072	0.111371	$4.47014e-02$
36	0.404986	0.282942	$1.22044e-01$
37	0.154142	0.105351	$4.87910e-02$
38	0.283717	0.189540	$9.41770e-02$
39	0.369837	0.241296	$1.28541e-01$
40	0.000000	0.000000	$7.82676e-09$
41	0.369837	0.229526	$1.40311e-01$
42	0.283717	0.171489	$1.12229e-01$
43	0.154142	0.090651	$6.34911e-02$
44	0.404986	0.231498	$1.73488e-01$

Table 4.7 *(continued)*

n	$\lvert F(n\Omega)\rvert$	$\lvert F(\omega)\rvert$	$\lvert F(n\Omega) - F(\Omega)\rvert$
45	0.156072	0.086622	6.94505e − 02
46	0.290880	0.156577	1.34303e − 01
47	0.383968	0.200225	1.83743e − 01
48	0.000000	0.000000	1.34646e − 08
49	0.393898	0.192052	2.01846e − 01
50	0.306147	0.144051	1.62096e − 01
51	0.168556	0.076431	9.21254e − 02
52	0.448930	0.195883	2.53047e − 01
53	0.175443	0.073547	1.01896e − 01
54	0.331726	0.133380	1.98346e − 01
55	0.444456	0.171101	2.73355e − 01
56	0.000000	0.000000	2.35607e − 08
57	0.470577	0.165098	3.05479e − 01
58	0.371963	0.124182	2.47781e − 01
59	0.208455	0.066067	1.42388e − 01
60	0.565685	0.169765	3.95920e − 01
61	0.225506	0.063901	1.61604e − 01
62	0.435512	0.116170	3.19343e − 01
63	0.596924	0.149374	4.47550e − 01
64	0.000000	0.000000	4.49183e − 08
65	0.665176	0.144778	5.20398e − 01
66	0.541327	0.109129	4.32198e − 01
67	0.313276	0.058179	2.55097e − 01
68	0.881076	0.149793	7.31283e − 01
69	0.365627	0.056492	3.09135e − 01
70	0.739104	0.102893	6.36210e − 01
71	1.067708	0.132543	9.35165e − 01
72	0.000000	0.000000	1.11750e − 07
73	1.361447	0.128912	1.23254e + 00
74	1.211601	0.097332	1.11427e + 00
75	0.784628	0.051973	7.32655e − 01
76	2.556981	0.134025	2.42296e + 00
77	1.302338	0.050623	1.25171e + 00
78	3.604970	0.092340	3.51263e + 00
79	9.412978	0.119121	9.29386e + 00
80	12.000000	0.000000	1.20000e + 01

■

Because the DFT uses a finite number of samples, we must be concerned about the effect that trunction has on the Fourier spectrum, even if the original function extends to infinity. Specifically, if the signal $f(t)$ extends beyond the total sampling period NT, the resulting frequency spectrum is an approximation of the exact one. If, for example, we take the DFT of a truncated sinusoidal signal, we find that the Fourier spectrum consists of additional lines that are the result of the truncation process. Therefore, if N is small and the sampling covers neither a large number nor an integral number of cycles of the signal, a large error in spectral representation can occur. This phenomenon is known as **leakage** and is the direct result of truncation. Since the truncated portion of the signal is equal to $f(t)p_a(t)$, the leakage is the result of the rectangular window $p_a(t)$. To reduce leakage, a number of different window functions have been devised.

■ **Example 4.34**

Find the DFT of the exponential function shown in Figure 4.37a for times $t = 1$ s and $t = 1.5$ s.

Solution The results are shown in Figure 4.37b; these were obtained by a direct application of the DFT expression. We observe that as NT increases—that is, as we incorporate more and more of the function in our calculations—the variations (or noise) on its spectrum decreases. ■

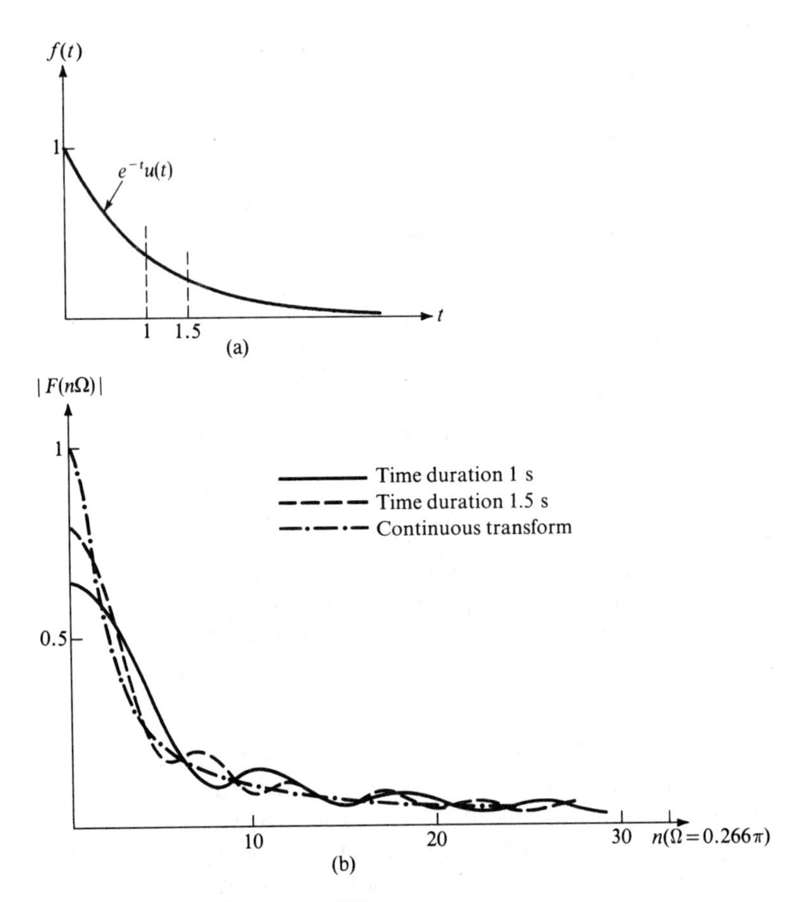

Figure 4.37 Illustration of the Truncation Effect

As noted, before taking the DFT, leakage can be reduced by multiplying the length of the data record by a window that does not have the sharp cutoff of the rectangular window. That is, we determine $\mathscr{D}\{f(k)w(k)\}$ rather than $\mathscr{D}\{f(k)p_a(k)\}$. A number of important window functions exist, including the following.

Hann function:

$$w(t) = \frac{1}{2} - \frac{1}{2}\cos\frac{2\pi t}{NT} \qquad 0 < t < NT \tag{4.78a}$$

or, in discrete form,

$$w(k) = \frac{1}{2} - \frac{1}{2}\cos\frac{2\pi k}{N-1} \qquad 0 \leq k \leq N-1 \tag{4.78b}$$

Figure 4.38a shows the Hann function that has zero first-order derivatives at its two end points. In addition to the Hann window, Figure 4.38 also shows some additional windows that are commonly used in practice.

Hamming window (Figure 4.38b):

$$w(k) = 0.54 - 0.46\cos\frac{2\pi k}{N-1} \qquad k = 0, 1, 2, \ldots N-1 \tag{4.79}$$

Blackman window (Figure 4.38c):

$$w(k) = 0.42 - 0.5\cos\frac{2\pi k}{N-1} + 0.08\cos\frac{4\pi k}{N-1} \qquad k = 0, 1, \ldots N-1 \tag{4.80}$$

Hann-Poisson (Figures 4.38d and 4.38e):

$$w(k) = 0.5\left[1 - \cos\left(\frac{2\pi k}{N-1}\right)\right]e^{-(\alpha \times 2|k-N/2|)/N} \qquad k = 0, 1, \ldots N-1 \tag{4.81}$$

Triangle (not shown):

$$w(k) = \begin{cases} \dfrac{k}{N/2} & k = 0, 1, \ldots \dfrac{N}{2} \\ w(N-k) & k = \dfrac{N}{2}, \ldots N-1 \end{cases} \tag{4.82}$$

$\operatorname{Sin}^{\alpha}(k)$ type (not shown):

$$w(k) = \sin^{\alpha}\left(\frac{k\pi}{N}\right) \qquad k = 0, 1, \ldots N-1 \tag{4.83}$$

$$w(k) = \sin^{2}\left(\frac{k\pi}{N}\right) = 0.5\left(1 - \cos\frac{2\pi k}{N}\right) \qquad k = 0, 1, \ldots N-1 \tag{4.84}$$

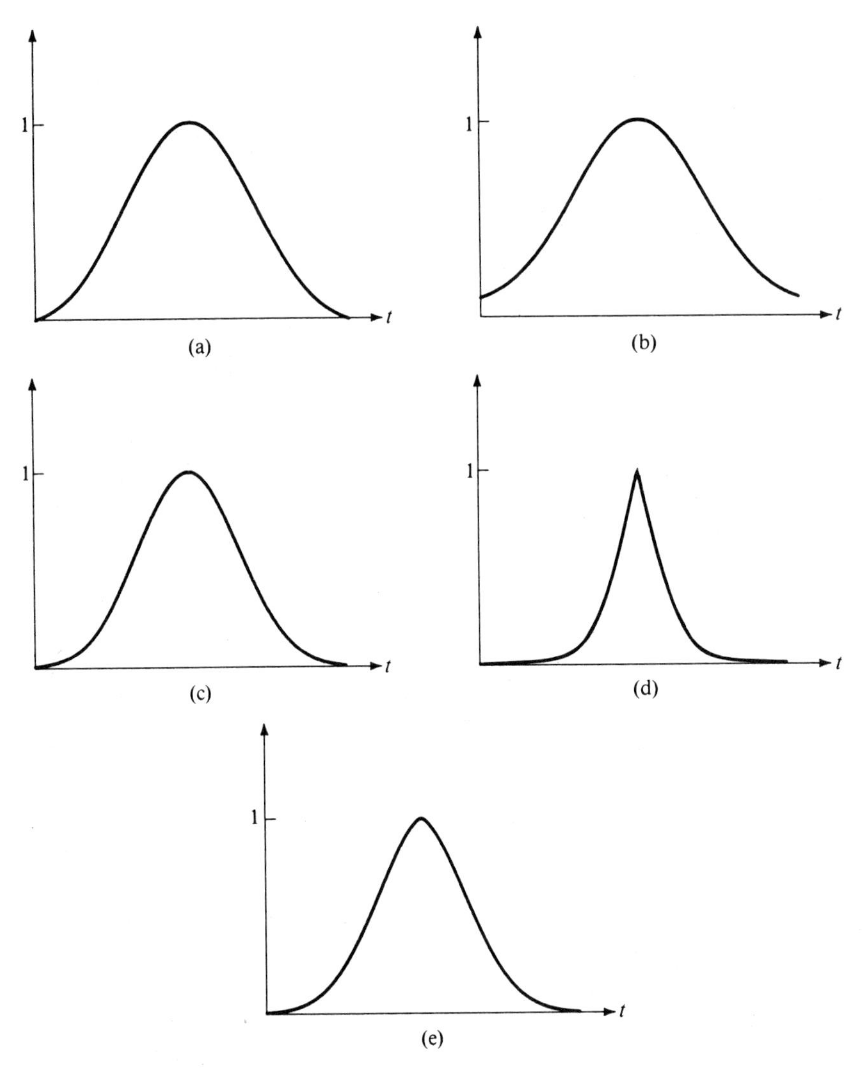

Figure 4.38 Different Truncating Windows. (a) Hann. (b) Hamming. (c) Blackman. (d) Hann-Poisson with $\alpha = 3$. (e) Hann-Poisson with $\alpha = 0.5$.

4.9 Fast Fourier Transform

As already noted, the fast Fourier transform (FFT) is a computational algorithm that reduces the number of multiplications and additions required for determining the coefficients of the DFT. We will consider one approach to the FFT, but note that a number of FFT algorithms have been programmed. The FFT method, first developed by Cooley and Tukey, has produced major changes in the computational techniques used in digital spectral analysis, filter simulation, and related fields.

For purposes of computation, it is convenient to define the quantity

$$W = e^{-j2\pi/N} = e^{-j\Omega T} \tag{4.85}$$

which denotes a unit distance at the angle $-2\pi/N$. With this notation, the DFT pair given in (4.63) are written

$$F(n) = \sum_{k=0}^{N-1} f(k)W^{nk} \tag{4.86a}$$

$$f(k) = \frac{1}{N}\sum_{n=0}^{N-1} F(n)W^{-nk} \tag{4.86b}$$

Observe that W^n denotes N equally spaced points on the unit circle.

One FFT procedure replaces the equations in (4.86) by their matrix equivalents. We can write $F(n)$, say for $N = 4$, in the form

$$\begin{bmatrix} F(0) \\ F(1) \\ F(2) \\ F(3) \end{bmatrix} = \begin{bmatrix} W^0 & W^0 & W^0 & W^0 \\ W^0 & W^1 & W^2 & W^3 \\ W^0 & W^2 & W^4 & W^6 \\ W^0 & W^3 & W^6 & W^9 \end{bmatrix} \begin{bmatrix} f(0) \\ f(1) \\ f(2) \\ f(3) \end{bmatrix} \tag{4.87a}$$

or

$$\mathbf{F}(n) = \mathbf{W}\mathbf{f}(k) \tag{4.87b}$$

The next step is to replace $\mathbf{W}$ by a number of carefully chosen factorized matrixes $\mathbf{W}_1, \mathbf{W}_2 \ldots$. In this process, the number of multiplications and additions in the expansion

$$\mathbf{F}(n) = \mathbf{W}_1\mathbf{W}_2 \cdots \mathbf{f}(k) \tag{4.88}$$

is considerably less than in the expansion of (4.87). We will consider a theoretical basis for developing the matrix factorization involved in this process.

Consider the quantity W^{nk} for $N = 2^\gamma$ so that both n and k are γ-bit binary numbers that can be written in binary form. Specifically, attention is given to the respective weights of the binary digits making up the number. Thus, if $N = 12$, k would range from 0 to 11; in binary notation, k would take on the values 0000, 0001, ... 1011, where the least significant bit has a weight of 1 and the most significant bit has a weight of 8. If k is written in binary form,

$$k = k_3 k_2 k_1 k_0$$

then the effective weights permit k to be written

$$k = 2^3k_3 + 2^2k_2 + 2^1k_1 + 2^0k_0 = 8k_3 + 4k_2 + 2k_1 + k_0 \tag{4.89}$$

A similar writing exists for n.

We carry out the calculations for $N = 4$. Specifically, therefore,

$$F(n) = \sum_{k=0}^{N-1} f_0(k) W^{nk} = \sum_{k_0=0}^{1} \sum_{k_1=0}^{1} f_0(k_1, k_0) W^{(2n_1+n_0)(2k_1+k_0)} \tag{4.90}$$

We focus our attention on the factor W and write this

$$\begin{aligned} W^{(2n_1+n_0)(2k_1+k_0)} &= W^{(2n_1+n_0)2k_1} \cdot W^{(2n_1+n_0)k_0} \\ &= W^{4n_1k_1} \cdot W^{2n_0k_1} \cdot W^{(2n_1+n_0)k_0} \end{aligned}$$

Note that the factor

$$W^{4n_1k_1} = W^{4(n_1k_1)} = 1^{n_1k_1} = 1$$

because $W^4 = [e^{-j2\pi/4}]^4 = e^{-j2\pi} = 1$. Equation (4.90) is thus written

$$F(n_1, n_0) = \sum_{k_0=0}^{1} \left[\sum_{k_1=0}^{1} f_0(k_1, k_0) W^{2n_0k_1} \right] W^{(2n_1+n_0)k_0} \tag{4.91}$$

This equation is the keystone for the FFT algorithm. We apply it to the specific case already considered.

Consider the inner summation included in the brackets as

$$f_1(n_0, k_0) = \sum_{k_1=0}^{1} f_0(k_1, k_0) W^{2n_0k_1} \tag{4.92}$$

Expand this summation, which yields

$$\begin{aligned} f_1(0, 0) &= f_0(0, 0) + f_0(1, 0)W^0 \\ f_1(0, 1) &= f_0(0, 1) + f_0(1, 1)W^0 \\ f_1(1, 0) &= f_0(0, 0) + f_0(1, 0)W^2 \\ f_1(1, 1) &= f_0(0, 1) + f_0(1, 1)W^2 \end{aligned} \tag{4.93}$$

Observe that wherever $k_1 \neq 0$, we kept the quantity W^0 although it is equal to 1. The steps in this expansion are shown graphically in Figure 4.39, which is often called a **butterfly** chart. We have changed the notation from binary to decimal.

Equation (4.93) in matrix formulation is

$$\begin{bmatrix} f_1(0, 0) \\ f_1(0, 1) \\ f_1(1, 0) \\ f_1(1, 1) \end{bmatrix} = \begin{bmatrix} 1 & 0 & W^0 & 0 \\ 0 & 1 & 0 & W^0 \\ 1 & 0 & W^2 & 0 \\ 0 & 1 & 0 & W^2 \end{bmatrix} \begin{bmatrix} f_0(0, 0) \\ f_0(0, 0) \\ f_0(1, 0) \\ f_0(1, 1) \end{bmatrix} \tag{4.94}$$

Now, consider the outer summation of (4.91), which is written

$$f_2(n_0, n_1) = \sum_{k_0=0}^{1} f_1(n_0, k_0) W^{(2n_1+n_0)k_0} \tag{4.95}$$

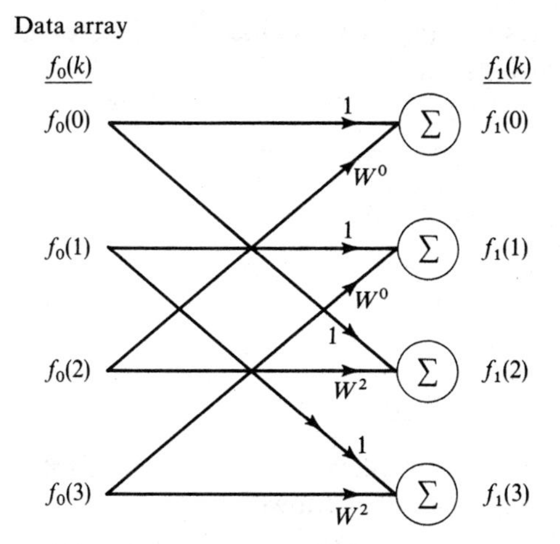

Figure 4.39 A Step in the FFT Algorithm

Next, expand this summation as in (4.93) and write it in matrix form. The result is

$$\begin{bmatrix} f_2(0, 0) \\ f_2(0, 1) \\ f_2(1, 0) \\ f_2(1, 1) \end{bmatrix} = \begin{bmatrix} 1 & W^0 & 0 & 0 \\ 1 & W^2 & 0 & 0 \\ 0 & 0 & 1 & W^1 \\ 0 & 0 & 1 & W^3 \end{bmatrix} \begin{bmatrix} f_1(0, 0) \\ f_1(0, 1) \\ f_1(1, 0) \\ f_1(1, 1) \end{bmatrix} = \begin{bmatrix} F(0, 0) \\ F(1, 0) \\ F(0, 1) \\ F(1, 1) \end{bmatrix} \tag{4.96}$$

The steps in the expansion of this matrix equation are shown in Figure 4.40. From (4.89) and (4.95), it follows that

$$F(n_1, n_0) = f_2(n_0, n_1) \tag{4.97}$$

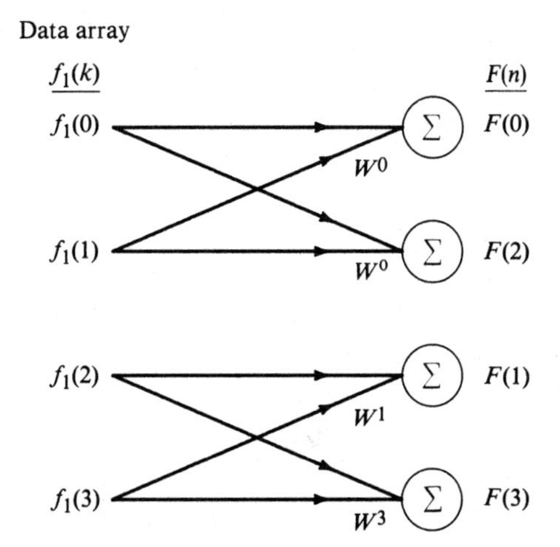

Figure 4.40 A Second Step in the FFT Algorithm

This shows that the final result $f_2(n_0, n_1)$ obtained from the outer sum is the bit-reversed form of the desired $F(n_1, n_0)$.

The key result of this development is the set of equations

$$
\begin{aligned}
f_1(n_0, k_0) &= \sum_{k_1=0}^{1} f_0(k_1, k_0) W^{2n_0k_1} \\
f_2(n_0, n_1) &= \sum_{k_0=0}^{1} f_1(n_0, k_0) W^{(2n_1+n_0)k_0} \\
F(n_1, n_0) &= f_2(n_0, n_1)
\end{aligned}
\qquad \textbf{(4.98)}
$$

This represents the Cooley-Tukey formulation for $N = 4$. The total process is given in data flow graph form in Figure 4.41. It shows that the four-point DFT has been reduced to complex multiplications and additions by repeated **decimations**.

It is of interest to determine the exact number of multiplications and additions involved in the expansion of (4.94). We note that $f_1(0)$ is determined by one complex multiplication and one addition since

$$f_1(0) = f_0(0) + W^0 f_0(2) \qquad \textbf{(4.99)}$$

To find $f_1(1)$ also requires one complex multiplication and one addition. To find $f_1(2)$, we examine the expansion

$$
\begin{aligned}
f_1(2) &= f_0(0) + W^2 f_0(2) \\
&= f_0(0) - W^0 f_0(2)
\end{aligned}
\qquad \textbf{(4.100)}
$$

since $W^2 = -W^0$. But, $W^0 f_0(2)$ has already been performed in carrying out (4.99), and carrying out this expansion requires one additional complex addition. By the

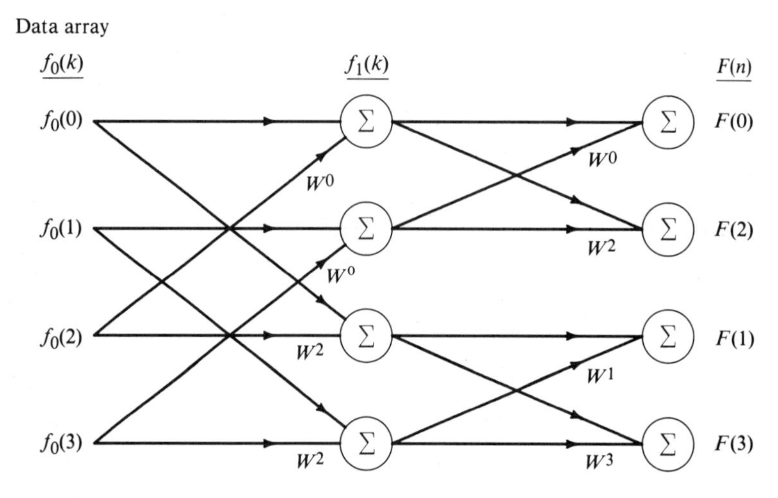

Figure 4.41 FFT Algorithm for Evaluating $\mathbf{F}(n) = \mathbf{W}^{nk}\mathbf{f}(k)$

same reasoning, $f_1(3)$ requires one complex addition. Thus, the evaluation of the vector $\mathbf{f}_1(k)$ requires a total of two multiplications and four additions.

In the next step, we determine the number of computations involved in carrying out the requirements of (4.96). We consider the expansion for $F(0)$:

$$F(0) = f_1(0) + W^0 f_1(1) \tag{4.101}$$

This determination involves one multiplication and one addition. The determination of $F(2)$ requires one addition because $W^2 = -W^0$. Continuing with this procedure, we find that $F(1)$ requires one multiplication and one addition, and $F(3)$ requires one addition. In total, therefore, determining all elements of the vector $\mathbf{F}(n)$ requires $Ni/2 = 4$ complex multiplications and $Ni = 8$ additions for a total of 12 complex multiplications and additions, as compared with $N^2 = 16$ complex multiplications and $N(N-1)$ complex additions for finding $\mathbf{F}(n)$ by a direct DFT evaluation. For large N, the savings in time and effort are huge. For example, a 1,024 sequence requires 1,048,576 multiplications and 1,047,552 additions when a DFT is applied and only 5,120 multiplications and 10,240 additions when an FFT is used.

In its more general form, the Cooley-Tukey FFT algorithm can be considered a method for factoring an $N \times N$ matrix into $iN \times n$ matrixes ($N = 2^i$) so that each of the factored matrixes has the special property of minimizing the number of complex multiplications. This optimum matrix factoring process rearranges the $\mathbf{F}(n)$ and is readily accomplished by replacing the argument in the $\mathbf{F}(n)$ of (4.96) by its binary equivalent and then effecting a bit reversal.

We extend the results for the case $N = 8 = 2^3$. For this case,

$$\begin{aligned} n &= 4n_2 + 2n_1 + n_0 \\ k &= 4k_2 + 2k_1 + k_0 \end{aligned} \tag{4.102}$$

Now, (4.91) becomes

$$\begin{aligned} F(n_2, n_1, n_0) = &\sum_{k_0=0}^{1} \sum_{k_1=0}^{1} \sum_{k_2=0}^{1} f_0(k_2, k_1, k_0) \\ &\times W^{(4n_1+2n_2+n_0)(4k_2+2k_1+k_0)} \end{aligned} \tag{4.103}$$

Expand the W function:

$$\begin{aligned} W^{(4n_2+2n_1+n_0)(4k_2+2k_1+k_0)} = &\; W^{(4n_2+2n_1+n_0)4k_2} W^{(4n_2+2n_1+n_0)2k_1} \\ &\times W^{(4n_2+2n_1+n_0)k_0} \end{aligned}$$

However, since $W^8 = (e^{j2\pi/8})^8 = 1$, then

$$\begin{aligned} W^{(4n_2+2n_1+n_0)4k_2} &= W^{8(2n_2k_2)} W^{8(n_1k_2)} W^{4n_0k_2} = W^{4(n_0k_2)} \\ W^{(4n_2+2n_1+n_0)2k_1} &= W^{8(n_2k_1)} W^{(2n_1+n_0)2k_1} = W^{(2n_1+n_0)2k_1} \end{aligned}$$

and (4.103) can be written

$$\begin{aligned} F(n_2, n_1, n_0) = &\sum_{k_0=0}^{1} \sum_{k_1=0}^{1} \sum_{k_2=0}^{1} f_0(k_2, k_1, k_0) \\ &\times W^{4n_0k_2} W^{(2n_1+n_0)2k_1} W^{(4n_2+2n_1+n_0)k_0} \end{aligned} \tag{4.104}$$

This can be reduced to the set of equations

$$f_1(n_0, k_1, k_0) = \sum_{k_2=0}^{1} f_0(k_2, k_1, k_0) W^{4n_0k_2} \quad \textbf{(4.105a)}$$

$$f_2(n_0, n_1, k_0) = \sum_{k_1=0}^{1} f_1(n_0, k_1, k_0) W^{(2n_1+n_0)2k_1} \quad \textbf{(4.105b)}$$

$$f_3(n_0, n_1, n_2) = \sum_{k_0=0}^{1} f_2(n_0, n_1, k_0) W^{(4n_2+2n_1+n_0)k_0} \quad \textbf{(4.105c)}$$

$$F(n_2, n_1, n_0) = f_3(n_0, n_1, n_2) \quad \textbf{(4.105d)}$$

The factorization given by these equations is shown graphically in Figure 4.42. This Cooley–Tukey procedure can be extended to the formulation of the FFT for $N = 2^{\gamma}$.

Other FFTs are available—for example, the Sande FFT. In this FFT, the matrix W is separated into components of n instead of into components of k. The Sande and other FFTs can be considered variations of the Cooley–Tukey procedure and are not pursued further in this text.

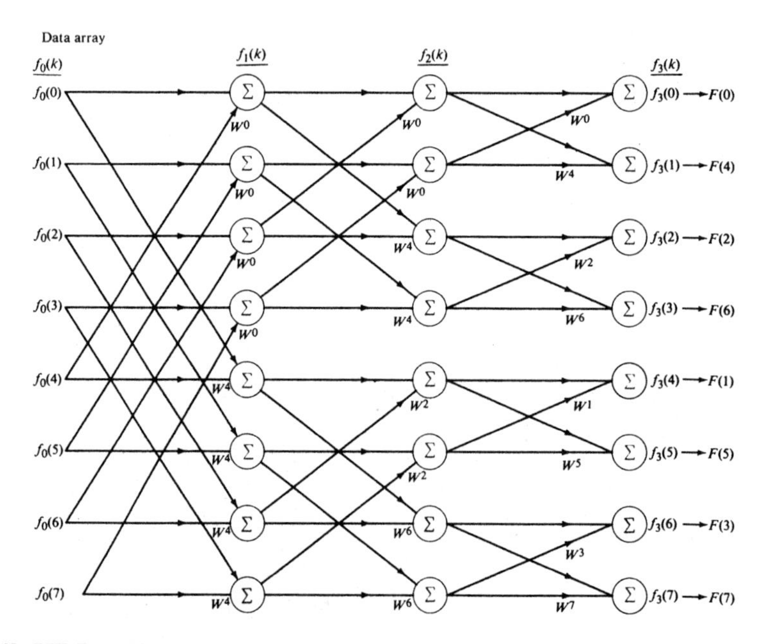

Figure 4.42 FFT Data Flow Graph for $N = 8$

Problems

Section 4.1

1. **a.** Deduce the spectrum functions of the time functions shown in Figure 4.43a.
   b. Deduce the spectrum function of Figure 4.43b by two methods: (1) by using the Fourier integral, and (2) by combining the results under part (a). Compare the results.

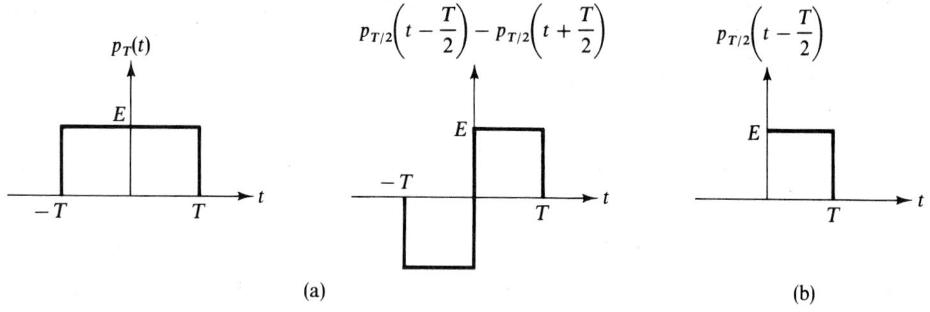

Figure 4.43

2. Refer to Figure 4.44.

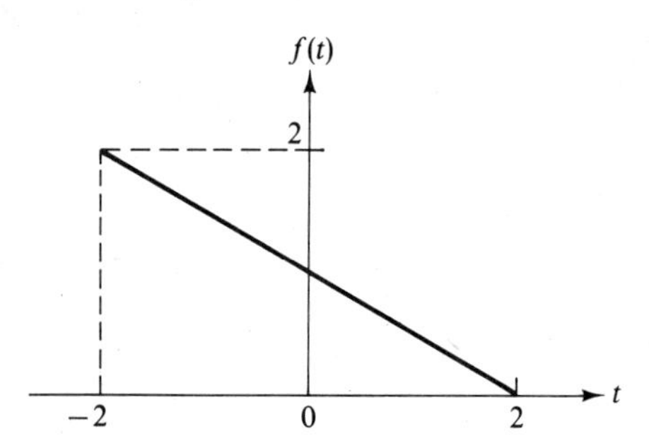

Figure 4.44

   a. Deduce the even and odd functions $F_r(\omega)$ and $F_i(\omega)$ for this function.
   b. Decompose the given function into two functions with even and odd parts and again find $F_r(\omega)$ and $F_i(\omega)$. Compare these results with the results in part (a).

3. Deduce the Fourier transform of the odd function

$$f(t) = \begin{cases} e^{-t}u(t) \\ -e^{t}u(-t) \end{cases}$$

   and verify the odd and real function properties of the Fourier transform.

4. Determine the Fourier transform of the following functions and give the value of $|F(\omega)|$ as $\omega \to \infty$.
   a. $f(t) = p_{0.5}(t) + \delta(t+1)$ **b.** $f(t) = e^{-t}u(t) + \delta(t-2)$

Section 4.2

5. Prove (4.11), (4.12), (4.14), and (4.15).
6. Find the Fourier transforms of the following functions and sketch their amplitude and phase spectrums.

a. $f(t) = p_3(t-2)$ **b.** $f(t) = p_2(t-2) + p_2(t+2)$ **c.** $f(t) = e^{-|t|} \cos \omega_0 t$
d. $f(t) = e^{j3t} p_1(t)$ **e.** $f(t) = e^{j2t} p_2(3t)$

7. Find the Fourier transforms of the following functions:
a. $1/(a + jt)$ **b.** $1/(1 + t^2)$ **c.** $(\sin at)/t$ **d.** t^2

8. Explain, on the basis of (4.12), what to expect when a voice recording is played back at (a) a higher speed and (b) a lower speed than the speed at which it was recorded.

9. The frequency spectrum of the modulating signal of an AM carrier is $G(\omega)$ and is shown in Figure 4.45. Determine the Fourier transform of the AM signal.

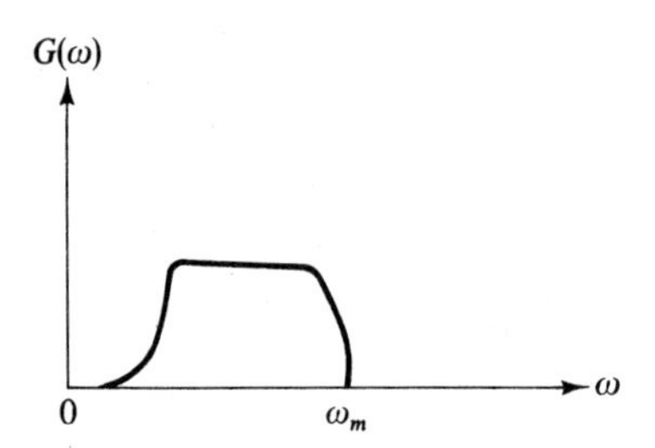

Figure 4.45

10. A signal $f(t) = e^{-t}u(t)$ is applied to a system that has an impulse response $h(t) = e^{-3t}u(t)$. Specify the system output.

11. Systems are given in block diagram form in Figure 4.46. Find the transfer function of these systems and the Fourier outputs.

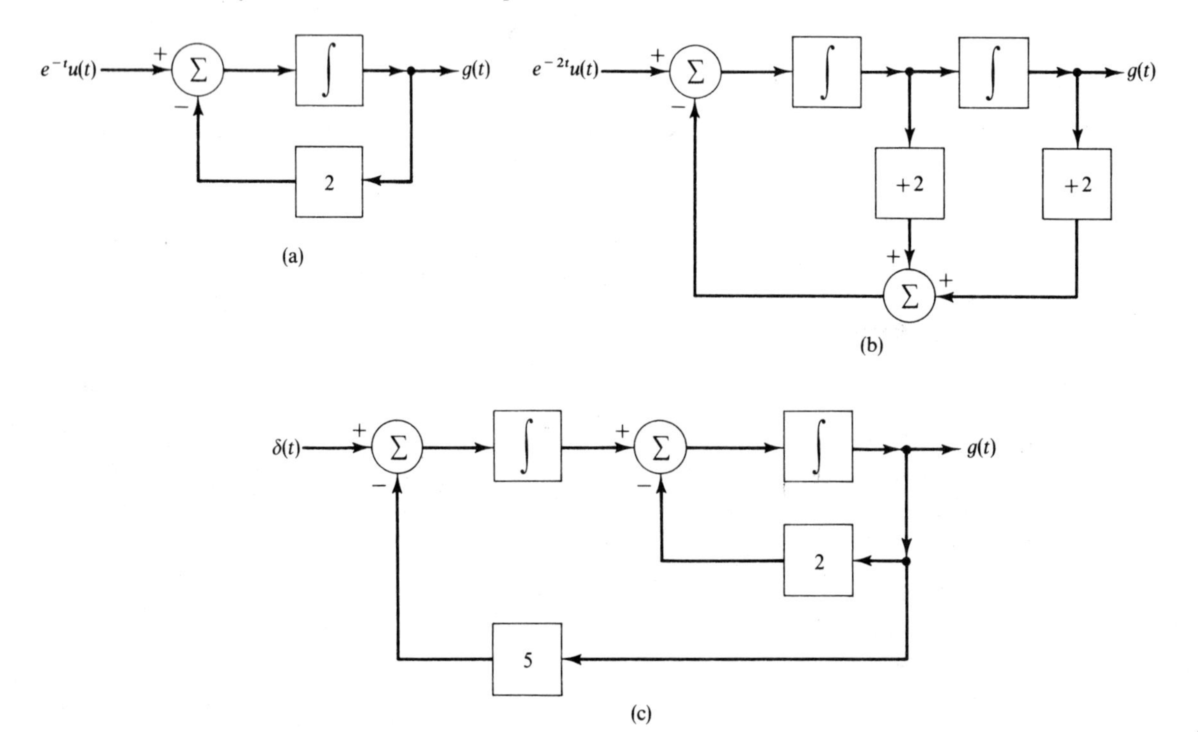

Figure 4.46

12. Deduce $H(\omega)$ for the systems shown in Figure 4.47: (a) by a direct application of the Fourier transform, and (b) by first finding $h(t)$ and then using the Fourier transform to find $H(\omega)$. Compare the results. The systems are relaxed at $t = 0$.

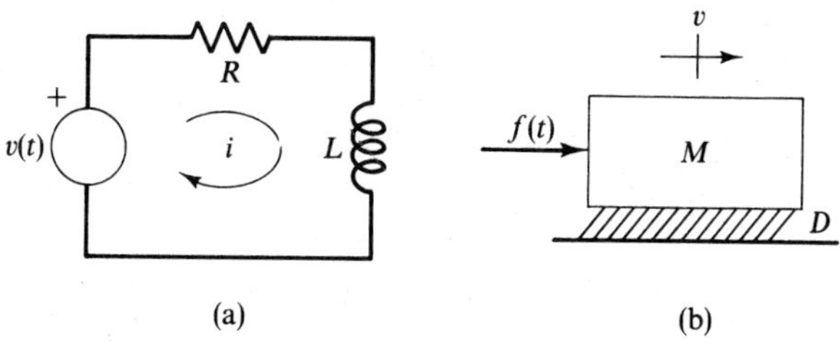

Figure 4.47

13. The impulse response of a network is given as $h(t) = p_2(t) - 0.5p_4(t)$. Deduce $H(\omega)$ and, from the spectrum, indicate the effect on input signals.
14. Prove the following identities, where a, b, and ω_0 are constant.
    a. $\mathscr{F}\{f_1(t) * f_2(t) * f_3(t)\} = F_1(\omega)F_2(\omega)F_3(\omega)$ **b.** $\mathscr{F}^{-1}\{F_1(\omega) * F_2(\omega)\} = 2\pi f_1(t)f_2(t)$
    c. $\mathscr{F}\{f(t)\delta(t-a)\} = f(a)e^{-j\omega a}$ **d.** $\mathscr{F}\{f(t) * \delta[(t/a) - b]\} = |a|F(\omega)e^{-jab\omega}$
15. Find the Fourier transforms of the functions given and sketch their amplitude and phase spectrums.
    a. $f(t) = p_1(t) * p_3(t-3)$ **b.** $f(t) = p_2(t+2) * p_1(t-2)$
    c. $f(t) = \text{sinc } t \text{ sinc}_3\, t$ **d.** $f(t) = e^{-|t|} \cos \omega t$
16. A 1 microsecond (10^{-6} s) pulse modulates a carrier wave with frequency $\omega_c = 10^9$ rad/s. Locate the frequencies at which the resulting output spectrum becomes zero.
17. Deduce the spectrum of the output for the systems shown in Figure 4.48 for a delta function input.

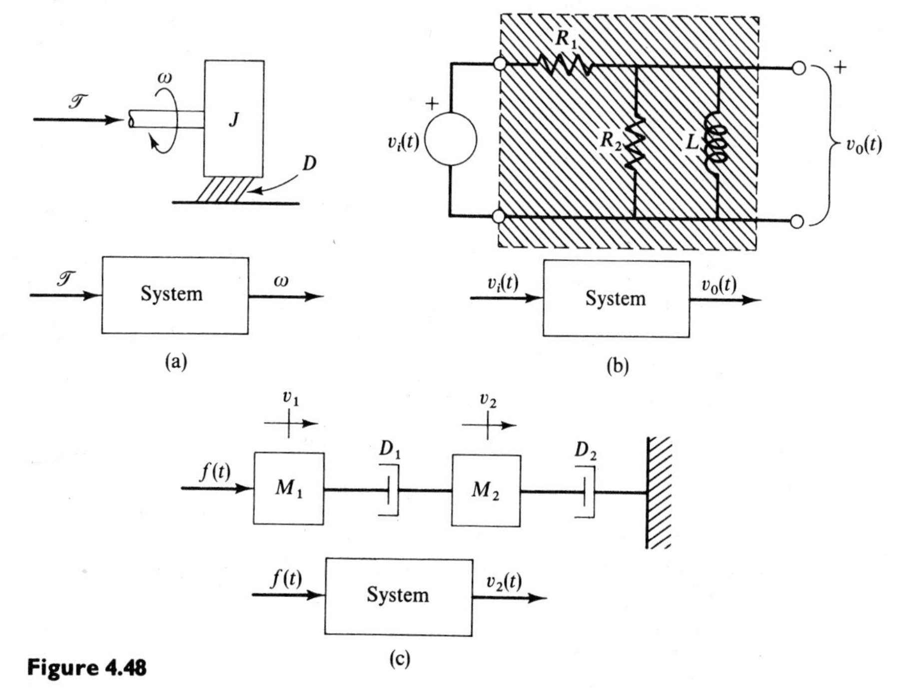

Figure 4.48

18. Compare the amplitude and phase spectrums of the following sets of functions:
a. $p(t)$, $p(t-2)$, $p(t+2)$ **b.** $p(t)$, $p(2t-2)$

19. The impulse response of a system is $h(t) = e^{-(2-j\omega_0)t}u(t)$. Find the spectrum of the output if the input is $p(t)$.

20. Square-Law Modulator. Assume that a nonlinear resistive device has the voltage–current characteristic given by $v = a_1 i + a_2 i^2$. Suppose that the input is $i = I_m \cos \omega_0 t + Bm(t)$, where $m(t)$ has a band-limited spectrum. Find the spectrum of $v(t)$.

21. Using the convolution property, find the frequency spectrum of the function $p_a(t) * p_a(t) = 2a\Lambda_{2a}(t)$. Verify your result by evaluating $2a\mathscr{F}\{\Lambda_{2a}(t)\}$.

22. Determine the Fourier transform of the function $f(t) = p_1(t) \cos 2\pi t$.

Section 4.3

23. Find the Fourier transforms of the following functions:
a. $f(t) = \sin \omega_0(t - t_0) + \cos \omega_0(t - 3t_0)$ **b.** $f(t) = e^{-t} \sin \omega_0 t\, u(t)$
c. $f(t) = \cos \omega_1 t \cos \omega_2 t$ **d.** $f(t) = (1 + \cos \omega_m t) \cos \omega_c t$

24. Find the Fourier transforms of the periodic functions shown in Figure 4.49.

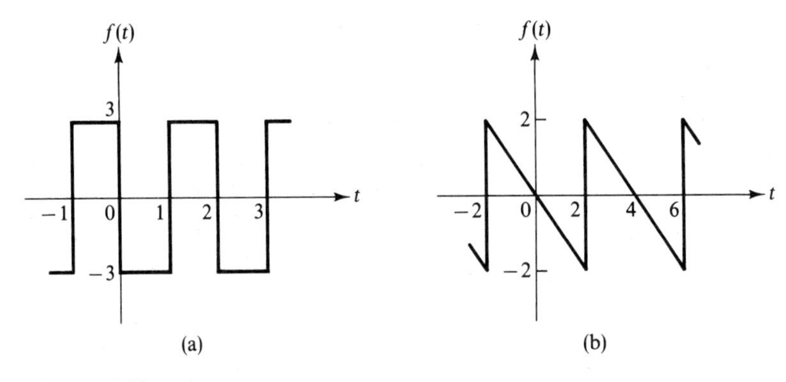

Figure 4.49

25. Show that for periodic functions, $\sum_{n=-\infty}^{\infty} \alpha(nT)e^{-jn\omega_0 T} = (1/T)\sum_{n=-\infty}^{\infty} F(n\omega_0)$.

26. We may often want to find the spectrum of a function taken from an oscilloscope trace. Also, there are certain closed-form functions for which the Fourier transform cannot be found. One method of approach is to approximate the function by piecewise polynomial approximations and/or straight-line segments. Compare the Fourier spectrums of the function $p(t)$ with those of $(1 - t^2)p(t)$ and $(1 - t^4)p(t)$. Discuss your results.

27. Prove the frequency differentiation property of the Fourier transform

$$\mathscr{F}\{(-jt)f(t)\} = \frac{dF(\omega)}{d\omega} \qquad \mathscr{F}\{(-jt)^n f(t)\} = \frac{d^n F(\omega)}{d\omega^n}$$

28. Prove the *reversal property* of the Fourier transform $\mathscr{F}\{f(-t)\} = F(-\omega)$, in the case where $F(\omega) = \mathscr{F}\{f(t)\}$.

29. Determine the Fourier transform of the signals shown in Figure 4.50 by employing Fourier transform properties in conjunction with $f_0(t) = e^{-t}u(t)$. All the curves shown in the figure decay as e^{-t}.

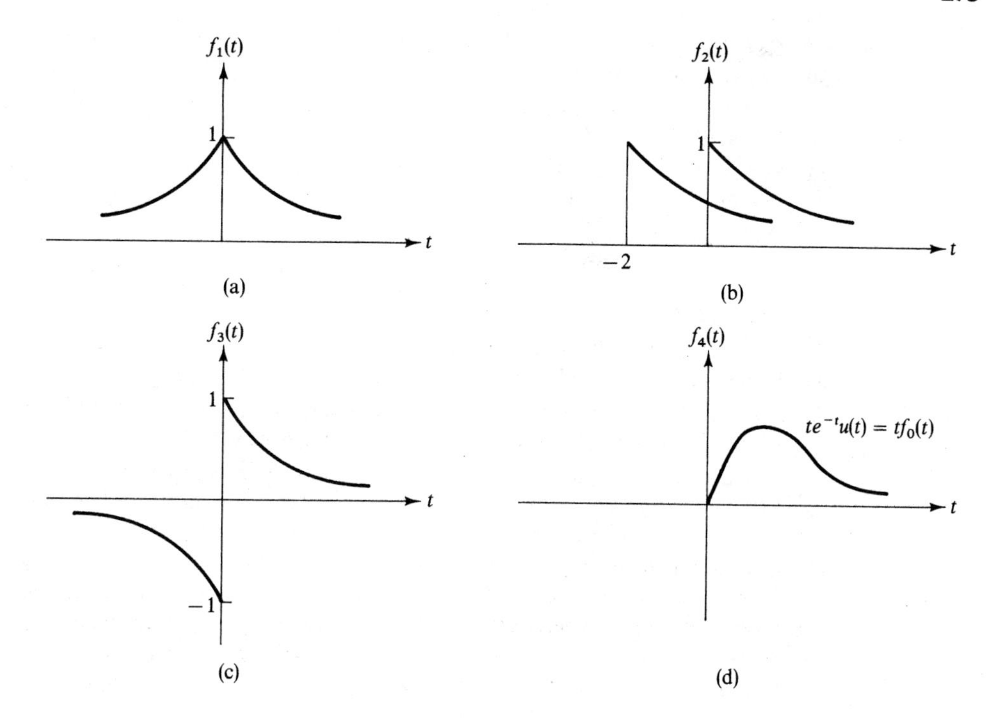

Figure 4.50

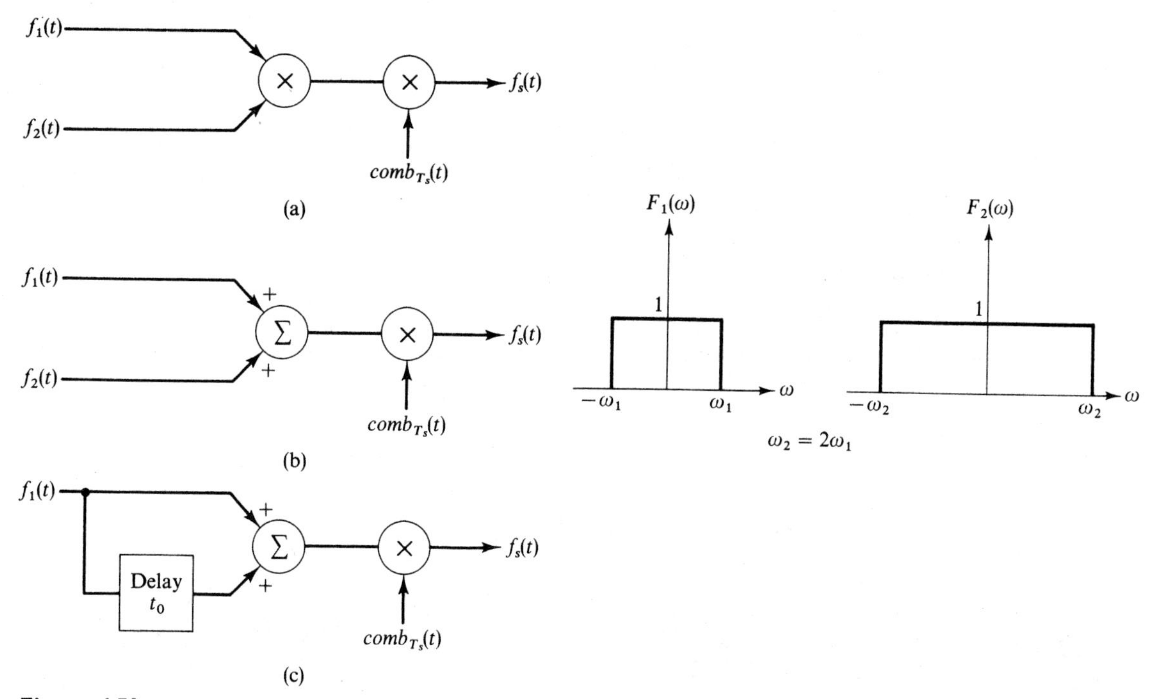

Figure 4.51

Section 4.4

30. Prove the identities.
    a. $\delta(\omega + n\omega_s) = (1/\omega_s) \sum_{n=-\infty}^{\infty} e^{-n\omega T_s} \qquad T_s = 2\pi/\omega_s$
    b. $F_s(\omega) = (1/T_s) \sum_{n=-\infty}^{\infty} F(\omega + n\omega_s)$ [(4.46)]
31. Sketch the amplitude Fourier spectrum of $f_s(t)$ for the systems shown in Figure 4.51. Assume that ω_s is sufficiently large that no overlap of repeated spectrums occurs.
32. Determine the Fourier transform of the product $f_1(t)f_2(t)f_3(t)$. Based on this answer, deduce the Fourier transform of the product $f_1(t)f_2(t) \cdots f_n(t)$.

Section 4.5

33. Verify (4.50) using (4.53).
34. Prove (4.54) by expanding the band-limited $F(\omega)$ with $|\omega| \leq \omega_N$ in a Fourier series.
35. A signal $f(t) = 2(\sin t/t)^2$ is to be sampled at such a rate that 92% of the energy is contained within the bandwidth $-\omega_N \leq \omega \leq \omega_N$. Determine the sampling time.
36. A signal $f(t)$ is sampled with pulses. The sampled signal is represented by $f_s(t) = f(t)s(t)$, where $s(t) = \sum_{n=-\infty}^{\infty} p_{\tau/2}(t - nT_s)$. Use the Fourier representation of $s(t)$ to find the Fourier spectrum of $f_s(t)$. Sketch the Fourier spectrum of $f_s(t)$ if $f(t)$ is a band-limited function.
37. Consider that we have a time function $f(t) = 1 - |t|/a)$ for $|t| \leq a$ with the spectrum function $F(\omega) = a[\sin(a\omega/2)/(a\omega/2)]^2$. Determine the value of ω_N for a truncated function $\hat{F}(\omega)$ having an energy difference between the two functions $F(\omega) - \hat{F}(\omega)$ of less than 0.05.
38. A signal $f(t)$ that has the spectrum shown in Figure 4.52 has been sampled to yield $f_s(t)$. Determine the maximum sampling time T_s, the filter type, and its bandwidth in order for the signal to be completely recovered from its sampled version.

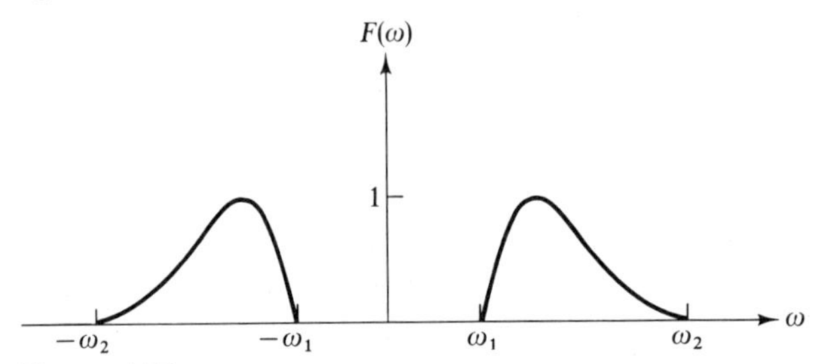

Figure 4.52

Section 4.7

39. Prepare time and frequency sketches that show the steps in obtaining the DFT of the waveform given in Figure 4.53.

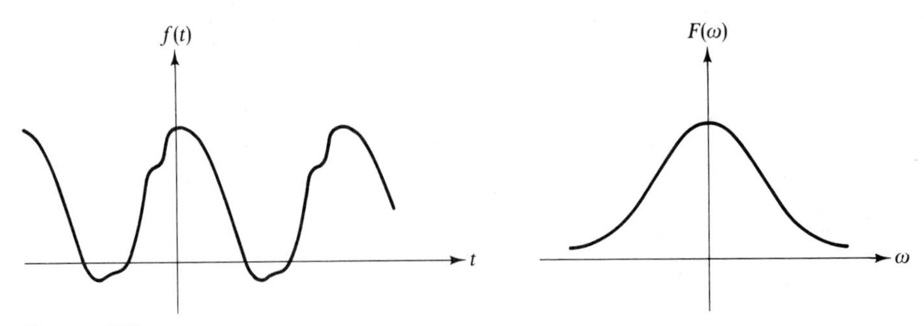

Figure 4.53

40. Write several terms to verify the relationship

$$\sum_{k=0}^{N-1} e^{-j[2\pi(m-n)k]/N} = \begin{cases} N & m = n \\ 0 & m \neq n \end{cases}$$

41. The function $f(t) = \cos t\, u(t)$ is sampled at $T = 1/4$ s intervals. Write the DFT of $N = 16$ and $N = 32$. Compare and discuss the results.

42. Show that $F(n\Omega)$ and $f(kT)$ are periodic. Determine their periods.

43. Deduce the DFT of the function $f(kT) = \cos(k\omega_0 T)$. Compare the result with the Fourier transform of $f(t) = \cos(\omega_0 t)$ when $\omega_0 = m \cdot 2\pi/NT$.

44. Deduce the DFT of the sequence shown in Figure 4.54.

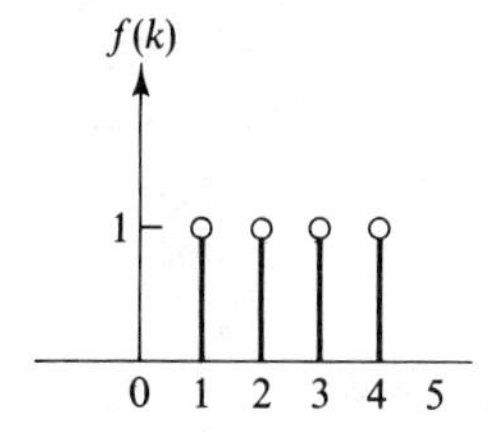

Figure 4.54

45. Deduce the DFT of the signals shown in Figure 4.55.

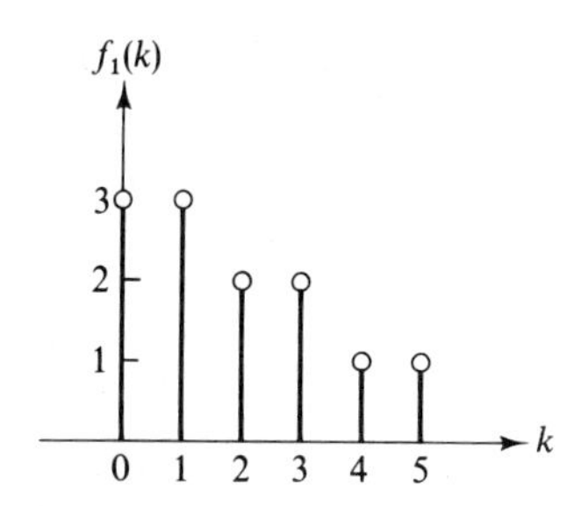

$f_2(k)$

3 2 1

0 1 2 3 4 5 6 k

Figure 4.55

Section 4.8

46. Evaluate $\mathscr{D}\{f(k-3)\}$. Compare the results with (4.67).

47. Evaluate $\mathscr{D}^{-1}\{F(n-4)\}$. Compare the results with (4.63).

48. A sequence $f(n)$ with period N is diluted with zeros between each member of the sequence to produce a "stretched" sequence $\hat{f}(n)$ with period $2N$, where $\hat{f}(n) = f(n/2)$, n even and $\hat{f}(n) = 0$, n odd. Show that $\hat{F}(k)$ is $F(k)$ with twice the number of terms, thereby providing interpolation midway between $F(k)$ samples. Sketch a sequence $f(n)$ and $\hat{f}(n)$ for $N = 4$. Generalize the results.

49. Given two 4-period sequences $f(k) = \{1, 0, 1, 1\}$ and $g(k) = \{1, 1, 0, 1\}$, verify (4.70) by considering each side of the equation

$$y(k) = \sum_{i=0}^{3} f(i)g(k-i) = 1/N \sum_{n=0}^{3} F(n)G(n)e^{j(2\pi nk)/N}$$

50. Show that Parseval's theorem holds for the discretized function shown in Figure 4.56. Use the results to check the equations in (4.77).

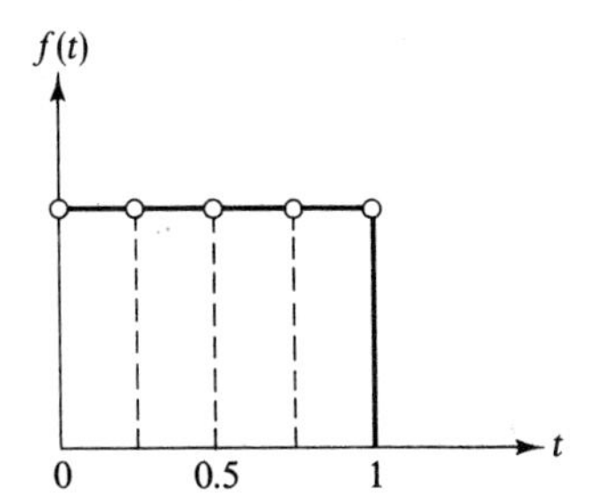

Figure 4.56

51. Find the Fourier coefficients of the periodic sequences shown in Figure 4.57. Compare the results. Discuss the results in Figures 4.57a and 4.57c and in the light of Problem 49.

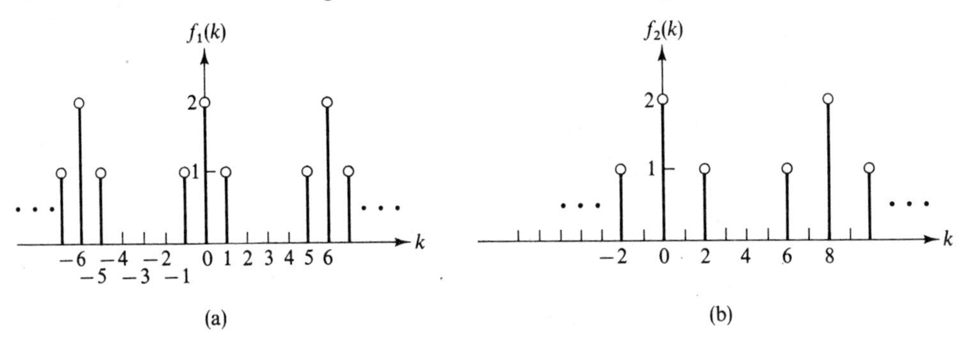

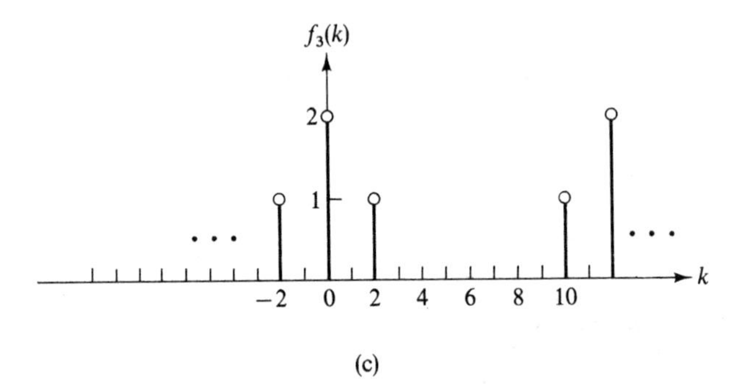

Figure 4.57

52. Verify the time-shift property of the DFT by using the functions $f_1(k) = k^2$, $k = 0, 1, 2, \ldots 7$ and $f_2(k) = (k - 3)^2$, $k = 3, 4, \ldots 10$.

Section 4.9

53. Consider the sequence $f(k) = \{2, 1, 4, 3\}$.

a. Deduce the DFT of this sequence using (4.60) and note the number of additions and multiplications in this process.

b. Repeat the calculations using the FFT discussed in Section 4.9.

c. Compare the number of additions and multiplications by each method.

State Variables and State Equations

One important formulation of a system of connected elements is by means of a set of first-order equations in matrix form that describes unique relationships among the input, output, and state of the system. The **state** of a system is a fundamental concept. It denotes a minimum set of variables that enables us to calculate the outputs of the system for times greater than t_0 if the variables' values are known at time t_0 and if all inputs are known for times greater than t_0. The state of the system might be considered to be the system's memory; thus, the state at any time t_0 summarizes the effect of all past inputs and any initial state or memory.

The representation of systems in state equation form has many advantages, some of which are:

1. This form of system differential equations has been extensively investigated and used.
2. It can be extended to time-varying and nonlinear systems.
3. The state variables are part of the solution, and often it is very important to know these variables.
4. This form is compact in its representation and is suitable for analog and digital computer solution.
5. The form of the solution is common for all systems.

We will find that the selection of state variables is not a unique process; many acceptable state variables exist for any given system. However, systematic procedures exist for deducing state variables. In general, different acceptable state variables can be deduced from each other.

In this chapter, we study the formulation of systems in state equation form and the solution of the state equations. We also examine the entirely parallel formulation of the state description of discrete systems and their solution.

State Representation of Continuous Time Systems

5.1 State Equation Formulation

A state variable description of a system is written in the general form

$$\dot{\mathbf{x}} = \mathbf{A}\mathbf{x} + \mathbf{B}\mathbf{w} \tag{5.1a}$$

$$\mathbf{y} = \mathbf{C}\mathbf{x} + \mathbf{D}\mathbf{w} \tag{5.1b}$$

where the coefficient matrixes **A**, **B**, **C**, and **D** are prescribed by the system; **x** is a column matrix that denotes the set of state variables; $\dot{\mathbf{x}}$ denotes the time derivative of **x**; **w** is the source, or driver, matrix; and **y** is the output matrix. **A** is an $n \times n$ square matrix that may be time dependent in some applications; **B**, **C**, and **D** are not usually square matrixes and might be time dependent. Here, consideration is limited to systems in which **A**, **B**, **C**, and **D** have constant elements. If **y** depends only on **w**, the system is said to be **memoryless**.

The examples that follow show how to develop the state variable descriptions of systems. A critical element in the description is the selection of the state variables. In one-dimensional, rigid-body mechanics (Newtonian), we know that if an external force (input to the system) is applied to a body (system) at time t_0, the motion (output of the system) of the body for $t \geq t_0$ is uniquely defined if we know the position and its velocity at $t = t_0$. Hence, **position** and **velocity** can be used as state variables. For electrical circuits, the situation is a little more complicated. However, if we assume that there are no loops made up exclusively of voltage sources and capacitors and no nodes made up exclusively of current sources and inductors, we can write the state equations if we

1. Choose all **capacitor voltages** and **inductor currents** as state variables.
2. Write relationships among mesh currents and state variables.
3. Write mesh equations.
4. Eliminate all variables except the state variables from the two sets of equations.

We will find that when systems are represented in block diagram form, these rules translate into choosing the outputs of integrators as state variables. A similar set of procedures is employed for node equations.

■ **Example 5.1**

Develop the state model representation for the system shown in Figure 5.1a.

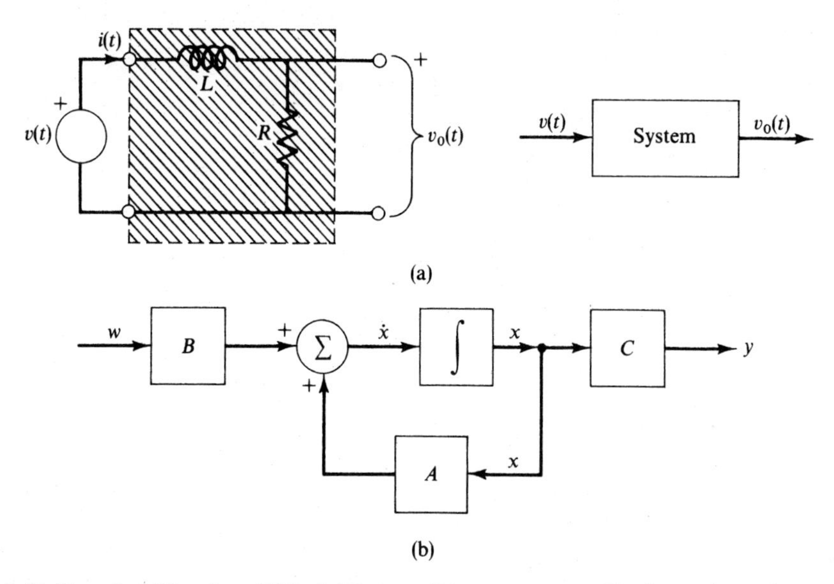

Figure 5.1 *RL* Electrical Circuit and Block Diagram Representation of Its Space State Form

Solution The Kirchhoff voltage law around the loop and Ohm's law for the output voltage yield the expressions

$$\frac{di}{dt} = -\frac{R}{L}i + \frac{1}{L}v$$
$$v_o = Ri \tag{5.2}$$

If we set the current through the inductor as the state variable, where $x = i$, $y = v_o$, $A = -R/L$, $B = 1/L$, $C = R$, and $v = w$, the resulting equations attain the standard form of state variable representation. The transformed equations are

$$\frac{dx}{dt} = Ax + Bw$$
$$y = Cx \tag{5.3}$$

Here, since the system is of order one, the vector functions become simple functions and the matrixes become constant numbers. Figure 5.1b shows the implicit feedback structure of the state equations. ■

■ **Example 5.2**
Develop the state model representation of the system shown in Figure 5.2a.

Solution We observe that the applied force will produce at the same instant three opposing forces whose total algebraic sum must equal zero. These

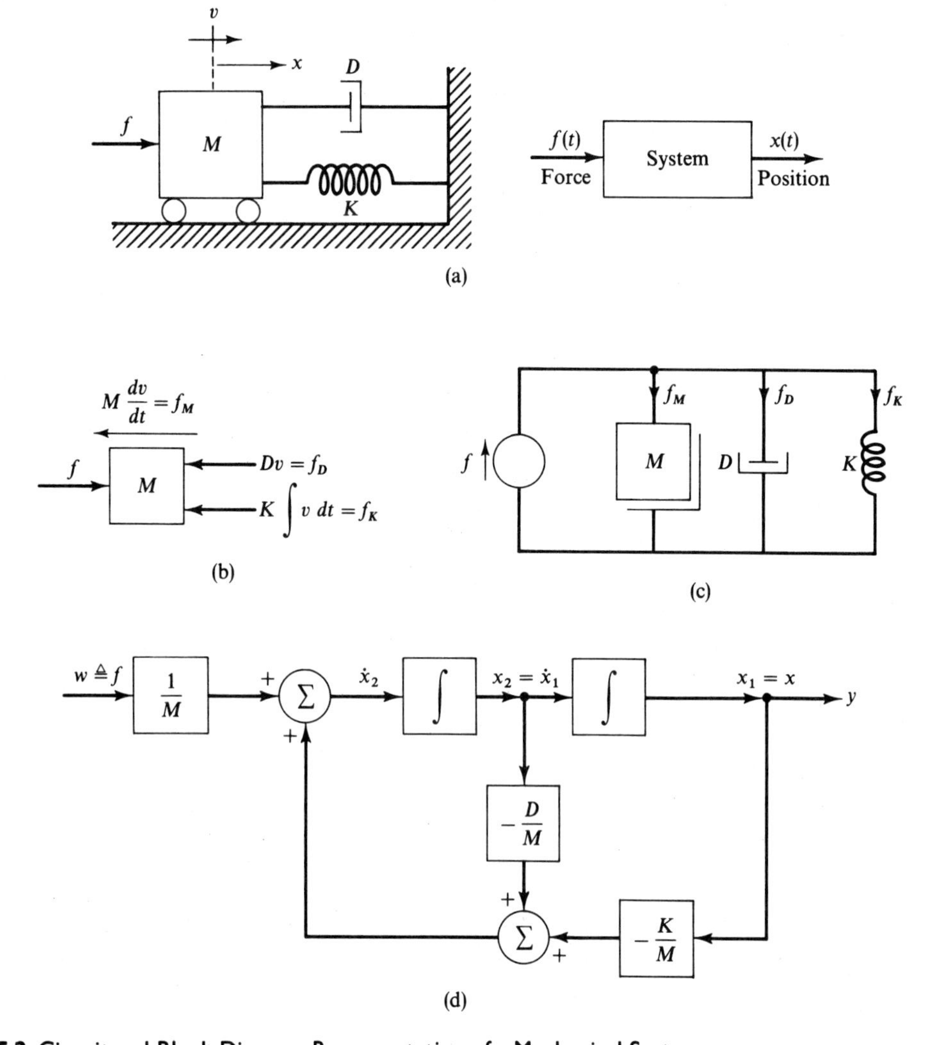

Figure 5.2 Circuit and Block Diagram Representation of a Mechanical System

forces are inertia $M\,dv/dt = f_M$, friction $Dv = f_D$, and spring deformation $K \int v\,dt = f_K$. The equivalent circuit diagram representation is shown in Figure 5.2c, which is developed in the manner discussed in connection with Example 2.3. Here, the elements move with velocity v with respect to ground-zero velocity, and all elements are connected in parallel, as shown in Figure 5.2c. A free body diagram for the mass element is given in Figure 5.2b.

The algebraic sum of the forces at the node must be equal to zero. We write

$$\frac{dv}{dt} = -\frac{D}{M}v - \frac{K}{M}\int v\,dt + \frac{1}{M}f \tag{5.4}$$

This expression is written in terms of x, the displacement, with $v = dx/dt$:

$$\frac{d^2x}{dt^2} = -\frac{D}{M}\frac{dx}{dt} - \frac{K}{M}x + \frac{1}{M}f \tag{5.5}$$

Now, make the following substitutions

$$x = x_1$$
$$\frac{dx}{dt} = \frac{dx_1}{dt} = x_2$$
$$f = w$$

and write (5.5) in terms of two first-order state equations:

$$\dot{x}_1 = \frac{dx_1}{dt} = 0x_1 + x_2 = x_2$$
$$\dot{x}_2 = \frac{dx_2}{dt} = \frac{d^2x}{dt^2} = -\frac{D}{M}x_2 - \frac{K}{M}x_1 + \frac{1}{M}w \tag{5.6}$$
$$y = x_1$$

This set of equations is written in matrix form:

$$\dot{\mathbf{x}} = \begin{bmatrix} \dot{x}_1 \\ \dot{x}_2 \end{bmatrix} = \begin{bmatrix} 0 & 1 \\ -\dfrac{K}{M} & -\dfrac{D}{M} \end{bmatrix} \begin{bmatrix} x_1 \\ x_2 \end{bmatrix} + \begin{bmatrix} 0 \\ \dfrac{1}{M} \end{bmatrix} w \tag{5.7a}$$

$$y = [1 \quad 0] \begin{bmatrix} x_1 \\ x_2 \end{bmatrix} \tag{5.7b}$$

In this example, **position** and the **velocity** were used as state variables. Figure 5.2d gives the block diagram representation of the system. ■

■ Example 5.3

Develop the state equations for the electric circuit shown in Figure 5.3a.

Solution We follow the general guide for the state description of an electric circuit:

a. Choose the current through the inductor $i_2 = x_1$ as one state variable and the voltage across the capacitor $v_C = x_2$ as a second state variable.

b. Next, write the relationships between the mesh currents i_1 and i_2 and the state variables:

$$x_1 = i_2 \tag{5.8a}$$

$$C\frac{dx_2}{dt} = i_1 - i_2 \tag{5.8b}$$

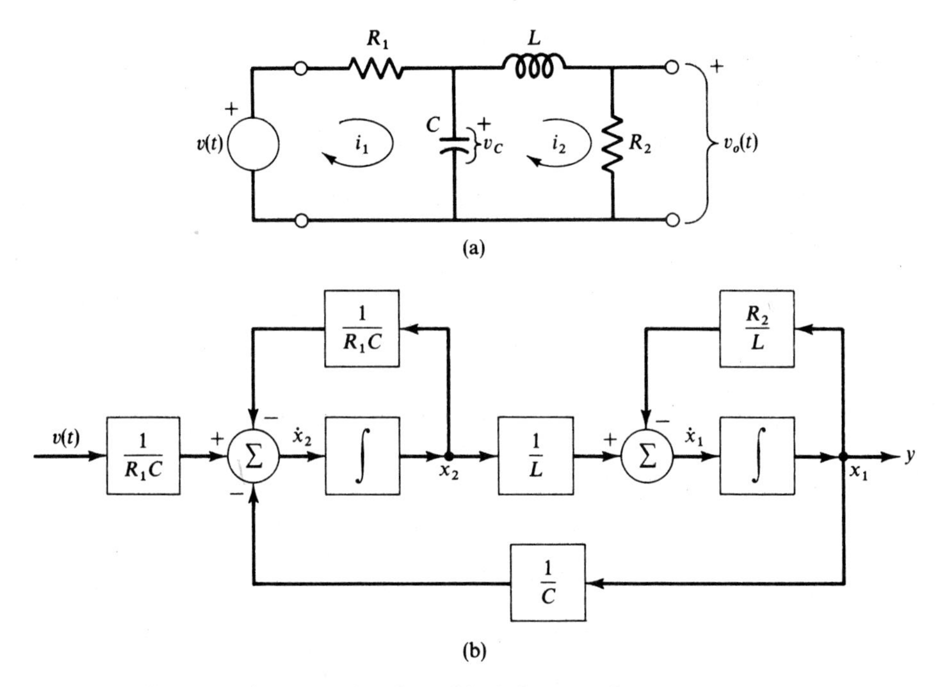

Figure 5.3 Two-Loop Electrical Circuit and Its State Block Diagram Representation

c. The loop equations yield the following equations:

$$v - R_1 i_1 - x_2 = 0 \tag{5.9a}$$

$$-L\frac{dx_1}{dt} - R_2 x_1 + x_2 = 0 \tag{5.9b}$$

d. Eliminate i_1 from (5.8b) and (5.9a) to obtain

$$\dot{x}_1 = -\frac{R_2}{L}x_1 + \frac{1}{L}x_2 \tag{5.10a}$$

$$\dot{x}_2 = -\frac{1}{C}x_1 - \frac{1}{R_1 C}x_2 + \frac{1}{R_1 C}v \tag{5.10b}$$

These equations are shown in block diagram representation in Figure 5.3b. Their matrix form representation is

$$\dot{\mathbf{x}} = \begin{bmatrix} \dot{x}_1 \\ \dot{x}_2 \end{bmatrix} = \begin{bmatrix} -\dfrac{R_2}{L} & \dfrac{1}{L} \\ \dfrac{1}{C} & -\dfrac{1}{R_1 C} \end{bmatrix} \begin{bmatrix} x_1 \\ x_2 \end{bmatrix} + \begin{bmatrix} 0 \\ \dfrac{1}{R_1 C} \end{bmatrix} v \tag{5.11}$$

$$y = [R_2 \quad 0] \begin{bmatrix} x_1 \\ x_2 \end{bmatrix} = v_o$$

■

■ **Example 5.4** ***Nuclear Physics***
Develop the state space representation of a radioactive material of mass M to which additional radioactive material is added at the rate $r(t) = Ku(t)$, where K is a constant.

Solution We know from nuclear physics for simple radioactive decay that the mass decay is proportional to the mass present. Thus, because additional radioactive material is added at the rate $r(t)$, the mass change is specified by

$$\frac{dM(t)}{dt} = -QM(t) + Ku(t) \tag{5.12}$$

where Q is a constant depending on the particular radioactive material, and the value of Q indicates the rate of decay of the substance. Writing x for M and recognizing that the output $y = x$, we can then write

$$\frac{dx}{dt} = Ax + Bw \tag{5.13a}$$

$$y = Cx \tag{5.13b}$$

where $A = -Q$; $B = K$, and $C = 1$. ■

5.2 State Equations in First Canonical Form

A procedure exists for writing the state equations in **first canonical form**. The procedure is developed by the examples that follow. A second state equation formulation is discussed in a later section. Note that the different procedures in writing state equations lead to different state space representations, but they are all equivalent and can be derived from each other. Thus, although the individual states in these different forms possess mathematical significance, they have no physical significance in themselves.

■ **Example 5.5**
Deduce a state space representation of the system that is described by the differential equation

$$\frac{d^2y(t)}{dt^2} + 3\frac{dy(t)}{dt} + 2y(t) = 4\frac{dw(t)}{dt} \tag{5.14}$$

Solution Write this equation in the form

$$\frac{d^2y(t)}{dt^2} = -3\frac{dy(t)}{dt} - 2y(t) + 4\frac{dw(t)}{dt} \tag{5.15}$$

Integrate this equation twice, writing the result

$$y(t) = \int\left[-3y(t) - \int 2y(t)\,dt + 4w(t)\right]dt \tag{5.16}$$

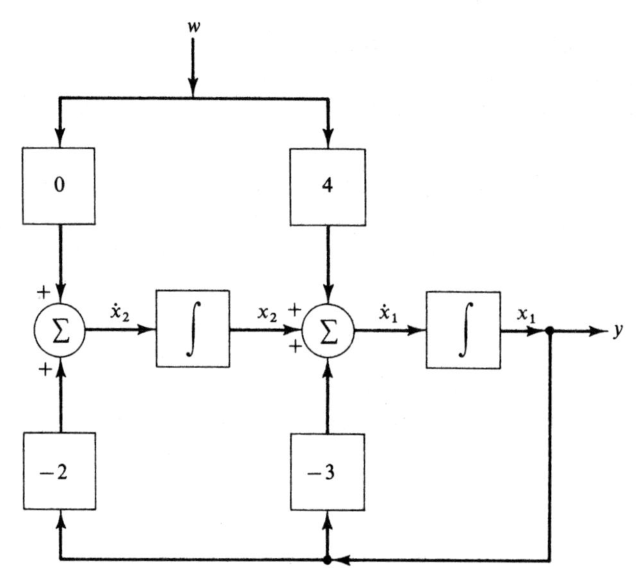

Figure 5.4 Block Diagram Representation of (5.16) or (5.17)

The block diagram that simulates this equation is shown in Figure 5.4. As a note, it may be easier for some readers to use (5.17) to develop the block diagram representation of the system.

We choose the outputs of the integrators as state variables, which yield

$$\frac{dx_1}{dt} = -3x_1(t) + x_2(t) + 4w(t) \tag{5.17a}$$

$$\frac{dx_2}{dt} = -2x_1(t) \tag{5.17b}$$

$$y(t) = x_1(t) \tag{5.17c}$$

The matrix representation of this set of equations is

$$\dot{\mathbf{x}}(t) = \begin{bmatrix} -3 & 1 \\ -2 & 0 \end{bmatrix} \mathbf{x}(t) + \begin{bmatrix} 4 \\ 0 \end{bmatrix} \mathbf{w}(t) \qquad \mathbf{y}(t) = [1 \quad 0]\mathbf{x}(t) \tag{5.18}$$

This is in **first canonical** form.

If we were to select the output of the integrators to be the state variables, but reversed the labeling—that is, we set $x_2 = x_1$ and $x_1 = x_2$—we would find, beginning with (5.16), that the equation set is

$$\dot{x}_1 = -2x_2 \tag{5.19a}$$

$$\dot{x}_2 = x_1 - 3x_2 + 4w \tag{5.19b}$$

$$y = x_2 \tag{5.19c}$$

These equations can be written in matrix form:

$$\dot{\mathbf{x}}(t) = \begin{bmatrix} 0 & -2 \\ 1 & -3 \end{bmatrix}\mathbf{x}(t) + \begin{bmatrix} 0 \\ 4 \end{bmatrix}w(t) \qquad y(t) = [0 \quad 1]\mathbf{x}(t) \tag{5.20}$$

These results should be compared with (5.18). ■

To develop the general features of the first canonical form, consider the second-order differential equation given by

$$\frac{d^2y}{dt} + \frac{a_1}{a_2}\frac{dy}{dt} + \frac{a_0}{a_2}y = \frac{b_2}{a_2}\frac{d^2w}{dt^2} + \frac{b_1}{a_2}\frac{dw}{dt} + \frac{b_0}{a_2}w \tag{5.21}$$

where the equation has been divided by the constant a_2, the coefficient of the highest derivative. We define the state variables as follows:

$$x_1 = y - \frac{b_2}{a_2}w \equiv \int\int\left[\frac{d^2y}{dt^2} - \frac{b_2}{a_2}\frac{d^2w}{dt^2}\right]dt\,dt \tag{5.22a}$$

$$\begin{aligned} x_2 &= \frac{dy}{dt} - \frac{b_2}{a_2}\frac{dw}{dt} + \frac{a_1}{a_2}y - \frac{b_1}{a_2}w \\ &\equiv \int\left[\frac{d^2y}{dt^2} - \frac{b_2}{a_2}\frac{d^2w}{dt^2}\right]dt + \int\left[\frac{a_1}{a_2}\frac{dy}{dt} - \frac{b_1}{a_2}\frac{dw}{dt}\right]dt \end{aligned} \tag{5.22b}$$

These equations can be written in the form

$$x_1 = y - \frac{b_2}{a_2}w \tag{5.23a}$$

$$x_2 = \dot{x}_1 + \frac{a_1}{a_2}y - \frac{b_1}{a_2}w \tag{5.23b}$$

Now, differentiate (5.22b) to get

$$\dot{x}_2 = \frac{d^2y}{dt^2} - \frac{b_2}{a_2}\frac{d^2w}{dt^2} + \frac{a_1}{a_2}\frac{dy}{dt} - \frac{b_1}{a_2}\frac{dw}{dt}$$

However, by (5.21), this expression can be written

$$\dot{x}_2 = -\frac{a_0}{a_2}y + \frac{b_0}{a_2}w \tag{5.24}$$

Further, from (5.23a) and (5.23b),

$$\dot{x}_1 = -\frac{a_1}{a_2}y + x_2 + \frac{b_1}{a_2}w = -\frac{a_1}{a_2}\left(x_1 + \frac{b_2}{a_2}w\right) + x_2 + \frac{b_1}{a_2}w \tag{5.25}$$

Thus, we see that (5.24) and (5.25), using (5.23a), can be written

$$\dot{x}_1 = -\frac{a_1}{a_2}x_1 + x_2 + \left[\frac{b_1}{a_2} - \frac{a_1b_2}{a_2^2}\right]w \tag{5.26a}$$

$$\dot{x}_2 = -\frac{a_0}{a_2} x_1 + \left[\frac{b_0}{a_2} - \frac{a_0 b_2}{a_2^2}\right] w \tag{5.26b}$$

$$y = x_1 + \frac{b_2}{a_2} w \tag{5.26c}$$

These equations, given in first canonical form, are, in matrix form,

$$\dot{\mathbf{x}} = \begin{bmatrix} \dot{x}_1 \\ \dot{x}_2 \end{bmatrix} = \begin{bmatrix} -\dfrac{a_1}{a_2} & 1 \\ -\dfrac{a_0}{a_2} & 0 \end{bmatrix} \begin{bmatrix} x_1 \\ x_2 \end{bmatrix} + \begin{bmatrix} \dfrac{b_1}{a_2} - \dfrac{a_1 b_2}{a_2^2} \\ \dfrac{b_0}{a_2} - \dfrac{a_0 b_2}{a_2^2} \end{bmatrix} w \tag{5.27a}$$

$$y = [1 \quad 0] \begin{bmatrix} x_1 \\ x_2 \end{bmatrix} + \begin{bmatrix} \dfrac{b_2}{a_2} \end{bmatrix} w \tag{5.27b}$$

We observe that (5.26) can also be written in the form

$$\dot{x}_1 = x_2 + \frac{b_1}{a_2} w - \frac{a_1}{a_2} y \tag{5.28a}$$

$$\dot{x}_2 = x_3 + \frac{b_0}{a_2} w - \frac{a_0}{a_2} y \qquad \text{(in our case, } x_3 = 0\text{)} \tag{5.28b}$$

$$y = x_1 + \frac{b_2}{a_2} w \tag{5.28c}$$

We develop the block diagram representation of these equations—the customary form for the first canonical equations. Set $d/dt = p$ and $\int dt = p^{-1}$. Equation (5.21) assumes the form

$$p^2 y = -\frac{a_1}{a_2} py - \frac{a_0}{a_2} y + \frac{b_2}{a_2} p^2 w + \frac{b_1}{a_2} pw + \frac{b_0}{a_2} w$$

from which

$$y = -\frac{a_1}{a_2} p^{-1} y - \frac{a_0}{a_2} p^{-2} y + \frac{b_2}{a_2} w + \frac{b_1}{a_2} p^{-1} w + \frac{b_0}{a_2} p^{-2} w$$

This equation is rearranged as follows:

$$y = \frac{b_2}{a_2} w + \underbrace{p^{-1}\overbrace{\left[\left(-\frac{a_1}{a_2} y + \frac{b_1}{a_2} w\right) + \underbrace{p^{-1}\overbrace{\left(-\frac{a_0}{a_2} y + \frac{b_0}{a_2} w\right)}^{\dot{x}_2}}_{x_2}\right]}^{\dot{x}_1}}_{x_1} \tag{5.29}$$

We display this expression in the diagram shown in Figure 5.5. Here, we start with the output y at the right and work to the left.

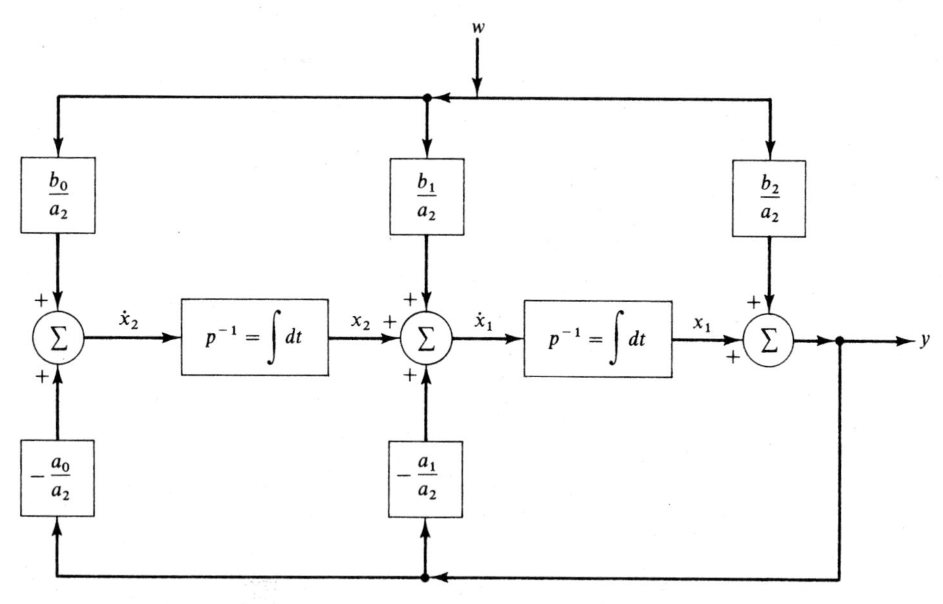

Figure 5.5 Block Diagram Representation of a Second-Order System in First Canonical Form Configuration

If we consider a third-order system specified by the differential equation

$$a_3 \frac{d^3y}{dt^3} + a_2 \frac{d^2y}{dt^2} + a_1 \frac{dy}{dt} + a_0 y = b_3 \frac{d^3w}{dt^3} + b_2 \frac{d^2w}{dt^2} + b_1 \frac{dw}{dt} + b_0 w \quad \textbf{(5.30)}$$

and proceed as above, the state variables would be written

$$\begin{bmatrix} \dot{x}_1 \\ \dot{x}_2 \\ \dot{x}_3 \end{bmatrix} = \begin{bmatrix} -\frac{a_2}{a_3} & 1 & 0 \\ -\frac{a_1}{a_3} & 0 & 1 \\ -\frac{a_0}{a_3} & 0 & 0 \end{bmatrix} \begin{bmatrix} x_1 \\ x_2 \\ x_3 \end{bmatrix} + \begin{bmatrix} \frac{b_2}{a_3} - \frac{a_2 b_3}{a_3^2} \\ \frac{b_1}{a_3} - \frac{a_1 b_3}{a_3^2} \\ \frac{b_0}{a_3} - \frac{a_0 b_3}{a_3^2} \end{bmatrix} w \quad \textbf{(5.31a)}$$

$$y = [1 \quad 0 \quad 0] \begin{bmatrix} x_1 \\ x_2 \\ x_3 \end{bmatrix} + \left[\frac{b_3}{a_3}\right] w \quad \textbf{(5.31b)}$$

or, by the corresponding set of equations,

$$\dot{x}_1 = x_2 + \frac{b_2}{a_3} w - \frac{a_2}{a_3} y \quad \textbf{(5.32a)}$$

$$\dot{x}_2 = x_3 + \frac{b_1}{a_3} w - \frac{a_1}{a_3} y \quad \textbf{(5.32b)}$$

$$\dot{x}_3 = x_4 + \frac{b_0}{a_3} w - \frac{a_0}{a_3} y \qquad \text{(in our case, } x_4 = 0\text{)} \tag{5.32c}$$

$$y = x_1 + \frac{b_3}{a_3} w \tag{5.32d}$$

Example 5.6

Find a first canonical form state space representation of the system shown in Figure 5.6a. The charge on the capacitor is to be considered as the output.

Solution An application of the Kirchhoff voltage law gives

$$L\frac{di}{dt} + Ri + \frac{1}{C}\int i\,dt = v(t)$$

and, since $i = dq/dt$, we obtain

$$L\frac{d^2q}{dt^2} + R\frac{dq}{dt} + \frac{1}{C}q = v(t)$$

By comparing this equation with (5.21), we observe the following correspondences:

$$L = a_2 \qquad R = a_1 \qquad a_0 = \frac{1}{C} \qquad b_0 = 1 \qquad b_2 = 0 \qquad b_1 = 0$$

The desired equations follow from (5.27):

$$\begin{bmatrix} \dot{x}_1 \\ \dot{x}_2 \end{bmatrix} = \frac{1}{L}\begin{bmatrix} -R & L \\ -\dfrac{1}{C} & 0 \end{bmatrix}\begin{bmatrix} x_1 \\ x_2 \end{bmatrix} + \begin{bmatrix} 0 \\ \dfrac{1}{L} \end{bmatrix} w$$

$$y = [1 \quad 0]\begin{bmatrix} x_1 \\ x_2 \end{bmatrix}$$

Its block diagram representation is given in Figure 5.6b (compare with Figure 5.5).

If we were required to find the first canonical form with i as the output, we would write the Kirchhoff equation in the form ($y \triangleq i$, $w \triangleq v$, and $p^{-1} \triangleq \int dt$)

$$\frac{dy}{dt} = -\frac{R}{L}y + \frac{1}{L}w - \frac{1}{LC}\int y\,dt$$

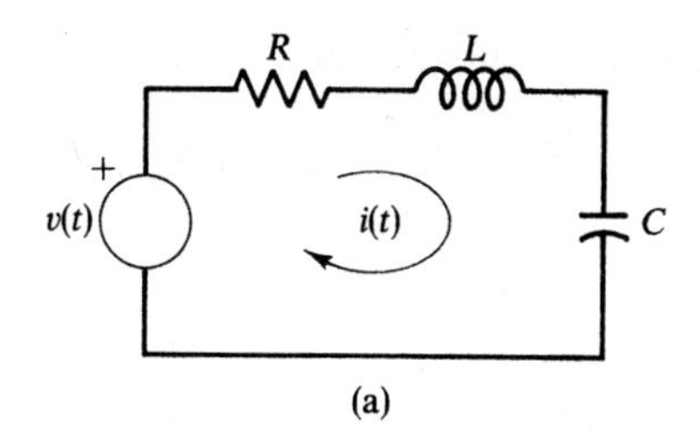

(a)

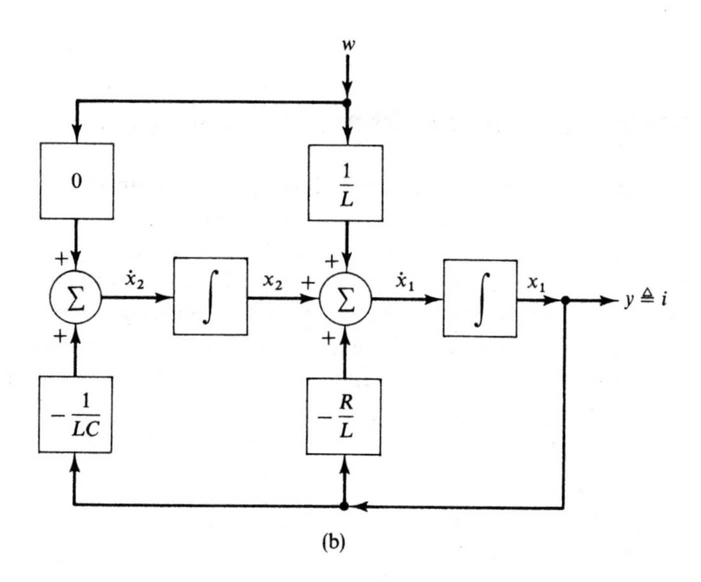

(b)

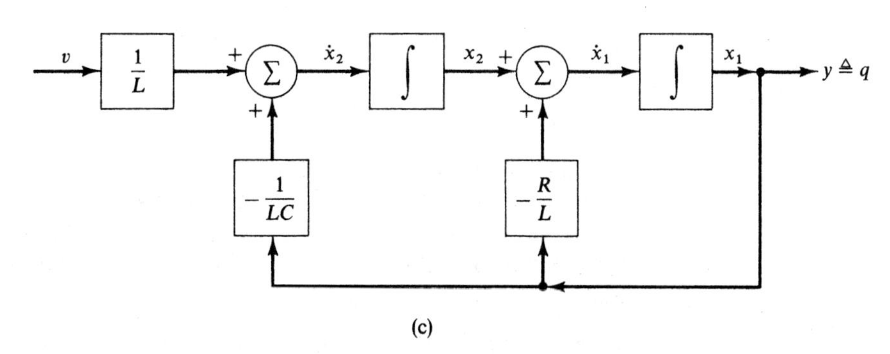

(c)

Figure 5.6 Electrical Circuit. (a) Physical system. (b) First canonical form block diagram representation with $y \triangleq q$. (c) First canonical form block diagram representation with $y \triangleq i$.

which becomes, on integration,

$$y = p^{-1}\underbrace{\left[-\frac{R}{L} y + \frac{1}{L} w - \underbrace{\frac{1}{LC} \underbrace{p^{-1} y}_{\dot{x}_2}}_{x_2} \right]}_{\dot{x}_1}$$

The block diagram representation is shown in Figure 5.6c. ■

5.3 State Equations in Phase Variable Form

Consider the input–output description of a system to be given in terms of an nth order differential equation or in terms of a set of second-order differential equations as deduced by an application of the Kirchhoff current or voltage law. It is readily possible to convert these higher-order differential equations into a set of first-order differential equations. In this case, the higher-order differential equation is transformed into **normal** form. This form expressed in state matrix form is known as the **phase variable** form. We will later find that a parallel procedure applies to difference equations.

■ **Example 5.7**

Deduce the normal form of the differential equation

$$4 \frac{d^2 y}{dt^2} + 3 \frac{dy}{dt} - 2y = 2 \frac{dw}{dt} + 5w \tag{5.33}$$

where y is the output and w is the input to the system.

Solution We first focus our attention on the reduced equation

$$4 \frac{d^2 \eta}{dt^2} + 3 \frac{d\eta}{dt} - 2\eta = w \tag{5.34}$$

Observe that this reduced equation has the same form on the left as (5.33), but it has a simple function w on the right. Note specifically that if $\eta(t)$ is the response of (5.34) to the excitation $w(t)$, then the response to the input $d^r w/dt^r$ will be $d^r \eta/dt^r$. This conclusion follows by a straightforward differentiation of (5.34), with the result

$$4 \frac{d^2}{dt^2}\left(\frac{d^r \eta}{dt^r}\right) + 3 \frac{d}{dt}\left(\frac{d^r \eta}{dt^r}\right) - 2\left(\frac{d^r \eta}{dt^r}\right) = \frac{d^r w}{dt^r} \tag{5.35}$$

This is an important property of linear differential equations.

We now multiply (5.34) by 5 and multiply the derivative of this equation by 2. The two resulting equations are

$$4 \times 5 \frac{d^2\eta}{dt^2} + 3 \times 5 \frac{d\eta}{dt} - 2 \times 5\eta = 5w \tag{5.36a}$$

$$4 \times 2 \frac{d^2}{dt^2}\left(\frac{d\eta}{dt}\right) + 3 \times 2 \frac{d}{dt}\left(\frac{d\eta}{dt}\right) - 2 \times 2\left(\frac{d\eta}{dt}\right) = 2 \frac{dw}{dt} \tag{5.36b}$$

Add these two equations to obtain

$$4 \frac{d^2}{dt^2}\left(2 \frac{d\eta}{dt} + 5\eta\right) + 3 \frac{d}{dt}\left(2 \frac{d\eta}{dt} + 5\eta\right) - 2\left(2 \frac{d\eta}{dt} + 5\eta\right) = 2 \frac{dw}{dt} + 5w \tag{5.37}$$

By comparing (5.37) with (5.33), we see that

$$y = 2 \frac{d\eta}{dt} + 5\eta \tag{5.38}$$

We now write in (5.34) and (5.38),

$$x_1 = \eta \tag{5.39a}$$

$$x_2 = \dot{x}_1 = \frac{d\eta}{dt} \tag{5.39b}$$

$$\dot{x}^2 = \frac{d^2\eta}{dt^2} = -\frac{3}{4}\frac{d\eta}{dt} + \frac{2\eta}{4} + \frac{w}{4} \tag{5.39c}$$

These equations attain the form

$$\dot{x}_1 = x_2 \tag{5.40a}$$

$$\dot{x}_2 = -\frac{3}{4} x_2 + \frac{2}{4} x_1 + \frac{1}{4} w \tag{5.40b}$$

$$y = 2x_2 + 5x_1 \tag{5.40c}$$

In matrix form, these equations are

$$\begin{bmatrix} \dot{x}_1 \\ \dot{x}_2 \end{bmatrix} = \begin{bmatrix} 0 & 1 \\ \frac{2}{4} & -\frac{3}{4} \end{bmatrix} \begin{bmatrix} x_1 \\ x_2 \end{bmatrix} + \begin{bmatrix} 0 \\ \frac{1}{4} \end{bmatrix} w \tag{5.41a}$$

$$y = [5 \quad 2] \begin{bmatrix} x_1 \\ x_2 \end{bmatrix} \tag{5.41b}$$

The block diagram representation of (5.40) is given in Figure 5.7a. When (5.41) is written in the form

$$\begin{aligned} \dot{\mathbf{x}} &= \mathbf{A}\mathbf{x} + \mathbf{B}w \\ y &= \mathbf{C}\mathbf{x} \end{aligned} \tag{5.42}$$

it may be represented in the vector matrix form shown in Figure 5.7b. ■

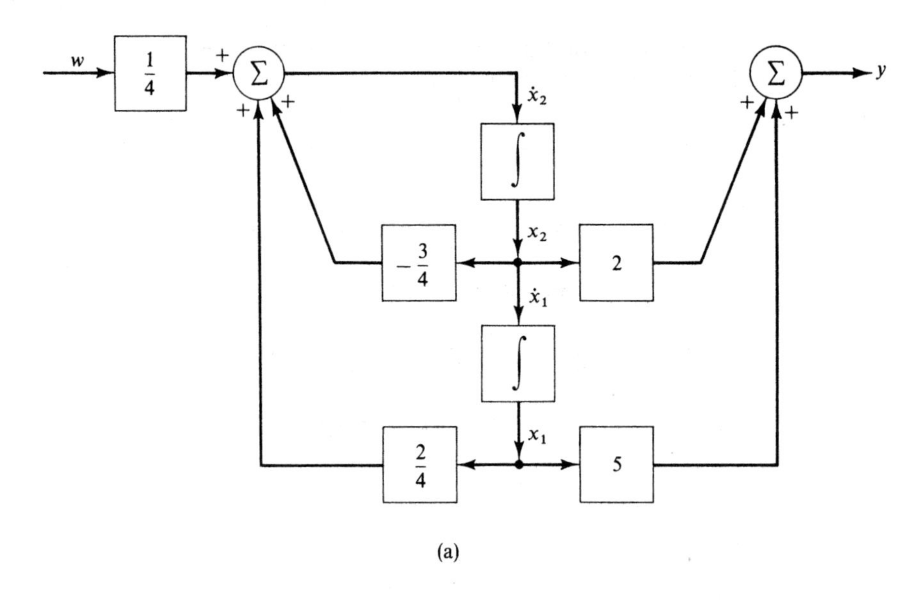

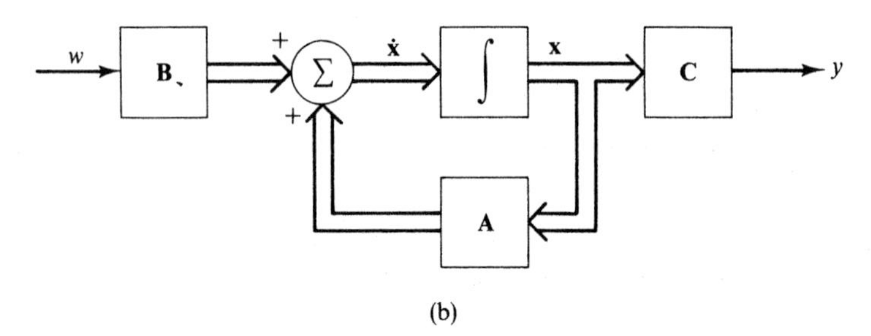

Figure 5.7 (a) Block diagram representation in phase variable form of (5.40). (b) Block diagram representation of the vector matrix form of (5.42).

■ **Example 5.8**

Develop the phase variable form of the state equations given that the system is represented by the differential equation

$$\frac{d^3y}{dt^3} + 2\frac{d^2y}{dt^2} + 4\frac{dy}{dt} + y = \frac{d^2w}{dt^2} + 3\frac{dw}{dt}$$

Compare this representation with the first canonical form of (5.31).

Solution Consider the reduced equation

$$\frac{d^3\eta}{dt^3} + 2\frac{d^2\eta}{dt^2} + 4\frac{d\eta}{dt} + \eta = w$$

Now, proceed as in Example 5.5, which leads to

$$x_1 = \eta$$

$$x_2 = \dot{x}_1 = \frac{d\eta}{dt}$$

$$x_3 = \dot{x}_2 = \frac{d^2\eta}{dt^2}$$

$$\dot{x}_3 = \frac{d^3\eta}{dt^3} = -2\frac{d^2\eta}{dt^2} - 4\frac{d\eta}{dt} - \eta + w = -2x_3 - 4x_2 - x_1 + w$$

These equations are written in matrix form:

$$\begin{bmatrix} \dot{x}_1 \\ \dot{x}_2 \\ \dot{x}_3 \end{bmatrix} = \begin{bmatrix} 0 & 1 & 0 \\ 0 & 0 & 1 \\ -1 & -4 & -2 \end{bmatrix} \begin{bmatrix} x_1 \\ x_2 \\ x_3 \end{bmatrix} + \begin{bmatrix} 0 \\ 0 \\ 1 \end{bmatrix} w$$

Further, the output is written

$$y = \frac{d^2\eta}{dt^2} + 3\frac{d\eta}{dt} = x_3 + 3x_2$$

which is, in matrix form,

$$y = [0 \quad 3 \quad 1] \begin{bmatrix} x_1 \\ x_2 \\ x_3 \end{bmatrix}$$

To express the given differential equation in first canonical form, we compare it with (5.30). We obtain the correspondences

$$a_3 = 1 \qquad a_2 = 2 \qquad a_1 = 4 \qquad a_0 = 1 \qquad b_3 = 0 \qquad b_2 = 1 \qquad b_1 = 3$$

$$b_0 = 0$$

These values are substituted in (5.31) to obtain

$$\begin{bmatrix} \dot{x}_1 \\ \dot{x}_2 \\ \dot{x}_3 \end{bmatrix} = \begin{bmatrix} -2 & 1 & 0 \\ -4 & 0 & 1 \\ -1 & 0 & 0 \end{bmatrix} \begin{bmatrix} x_1 \\ x_2 \\ x_3 \end{bmatrix} + \begin{bmatrix} 1 \\ 3 \\ 0 \end{bmatrix} w$$

$$y = [1 \quad 0 \quad 0] \begin{bmatrix} x_1 \\ x_2 \\ x_3 \end{bmatrix}$$

Observe that the **A** matrix in the phase variable and the first canonical forms are rearranged forms of each other, and this simple rearrangement ensures that the eigenvalues of the system are unchanged with the system formulation. Block diagram representations of both decomposition forms are shown in Figure 5.8. ■

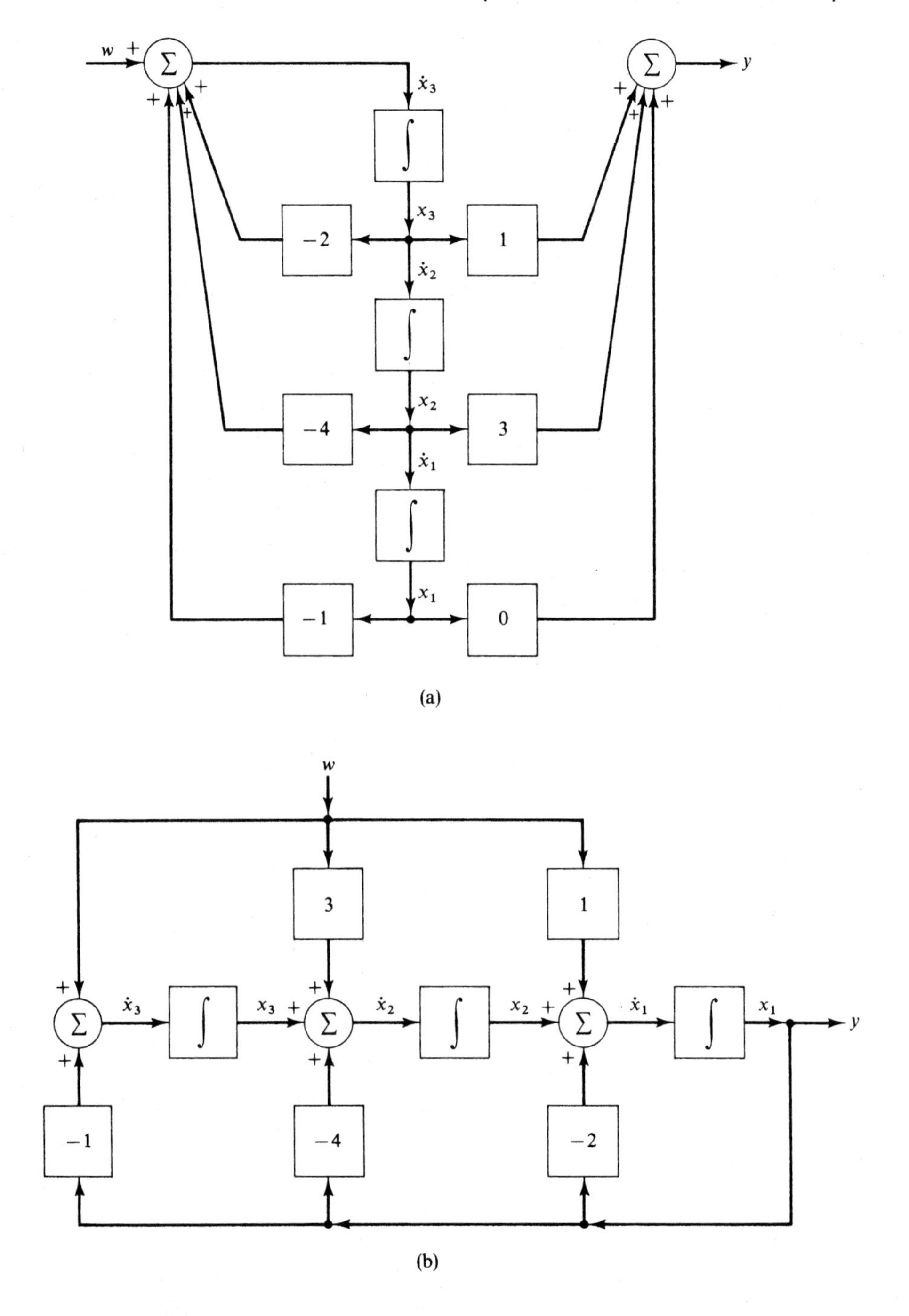

Figure 5.8 (a) Block diagram representation in phase variable form. (b) Block diagram representation in first canonical form.

5.4 Solution of Continuous Time State Equations: Force-Free Conditions

We consider the solution of the state equations

$$\dot{\mathbf{x}}(t) = \mathbf{A}\mathbf{x}(t) + \mathbf{B}\mathbf{w}(t) \tag{5.43a}$$

$$\mathbf{y}(t) = \mathbf{C}\mathbf{x}(t) + \mathbf{D}\mathbf{w}(t) \tag{5.43b}$$

in two steps. Initially we consider the force-free (homogeneous) equation

$$\dot{\mathbf{x}} = \mathbf{A}\mathbf{x} \tag{5.44}$$

with known initial conditions $\mathbf{x}(0)$ at $t_0 = 0$. In this connection, we examine the matrix function

$$\mathbf{\Phi}(t) \triangleq e^{\mathbf{A}t} = I + \mathbf{A}t + \mathbf{A}^2 \frac{t^2}{2!} + \cdots = \sum_{k=0}^{\infty} \mathbf{A}^k \frac{t^k}{k!} \tag{5.45}$$

This function is called the **fundamental matrix** and is often referred to as the **state transition matrix** of the system. It can be shown by a term-by-term differentiation of (5.45) that

$$\frac{d}{dt} e^{\mathbf{A}t} = \mathbf{A}e^{\mathbf{A}t} = e^{\mathbf{A}t}\mathbf{A} \tag{5.46}$$

By direct substitution, it is found that the solution of (5.44) is

$$\mathbf{x}(t) = e^{\mathbf{A}t}\mathbf{x}(0) \tag{5.47}$$

or, more generally, with $\mathbf{\Phi}(t) \triangleq e^{\mathbf{A}t}$,

$$\mathbf{x}(t) = \mathbf{\Phi}(t)\mathbf{x}(0) \tag{5.48}$$

This result can be generalized to initial time $t = t_0$ instead of $t = 0$. The solution is written

$$\boxed{\mathbf{x}(t) = e^{\mathbf{A}(t-t_0)}\mathbf{x}(t_0) = \mathbf{\Phi}(t - t_0)\mathbf{x}(t_0)} \tag{5.49}$$

As defined, *the fundamental matrix relates the state at time t with the state at time t_0.*

A physical interpretation is possible that provides some insight into the meaning of (5.48). Specifically, consider a second-order system with the description

$$\begin{bmatrix} x_1(t) \\ x_2(t) \end{bmatrix} = \begin{bmatrix} \phi_{11}(t) & \phi_{12}(t) \\ \phi_{21}(t) & \phi_{22}(t) \end{bmatrix} \begin{bmatrix} x_1(0) \\ x_2(0) \end{bmatrix} \tag{5.50}$$

If we set $x_1(0) = 1$ and $x_2(0) = 0$, then $x_1(t) = \phi_{11}(t)$. That is, $\phi_{11}(t)$ is the response at the output of integrator 1 to an impulse at the input of this integrator when the initial condition to integrator 2 is zero. In general, $\phi_{ij}(t)$ is the response at the output of the ith integrator to an impulse at the input of the jth integrator, with the initial conditions to all other integrators being zero.

Example 5.9

A system is specified by the fundamental matrix $e^{\mathbf{A}t}$ with

$$\mathbf{A} = \begin{bmatrix} 0 & 1 \\ -1 & -1 \end{bmatrix}$$

Determine the response of the system to a specified initial condition vector $\mathbf{x}(0)$.

Solution We employ (5.45) in the solution. The factors $\mathbf{A}$ are given by

$$\mathbf{A}^2 = \begin{bmatrix} -1 & -1 \\ 1 & 0 \end{bmatrix} \quad \mathbf{A}^3 = \begin{bmatrix} 1 & 0 \\ 0 & 1 \end{bmatrix} \quad \mathbf{A}^4 = \begin{bmatrix} 0 & 1 \\ -1 & -1 \end{bmatrix} \cdots$$

The solution is

$$\mathbf{\Phi}(t) \triangleq e^{\mathbf{A}t} = \begin{bmatrix} 1 - \dfrac{t^2}{2} + \dfrac{t^3}{3!} + \cdots & t - \dfrac{t^2}{2!} + \dfrac{t^4}{4!} + \cdots \\ -t + \dfrac{t^2}{2!} - \dfrac{t^4}{4!} + \cdots & 1 - t + \dfrac{t^3}{3!} - \dfrac{t^4}{4!} + \cdots \end{bmatrix}$$

It is usually not possible to recognize a closed form corresponding to these series, although such series solutions are often very acceptable. We will find in Chapter 6 that the use of Laplace transform methods leads to closed-form solutions. ■

Example 5.10

Find the zero-input response to the circuit shown in Figure 5.9a using the state space method. Show a block diagram representation of the system.

Solution By an application of the Kirchhoff voltage law to the left-hand loop

$$v_1(t) - v_{R_1}(t) - L\frac{di_L(t)}{dt} - R_2 i_L(t) = 0$$

However,

$$v_{R_1}(t) = v_1(t) - v_c(t) - v_2(t)$$

Combine these equations to write

$$\frac{di_L(t)}{dt} = -\frac{R_2}{L} i_L(t) + \frac{1}{L} v_c(t) + \frac{1}{L} v_2(t)$$

In state space form, this expression is written

$$\dot{x}_1(t) = -\frac{R_2}{L} x_1(t) + \frac{1}{L} x_2(t) + \frac{1}{L} w_2(t) \tag{5.51}$$

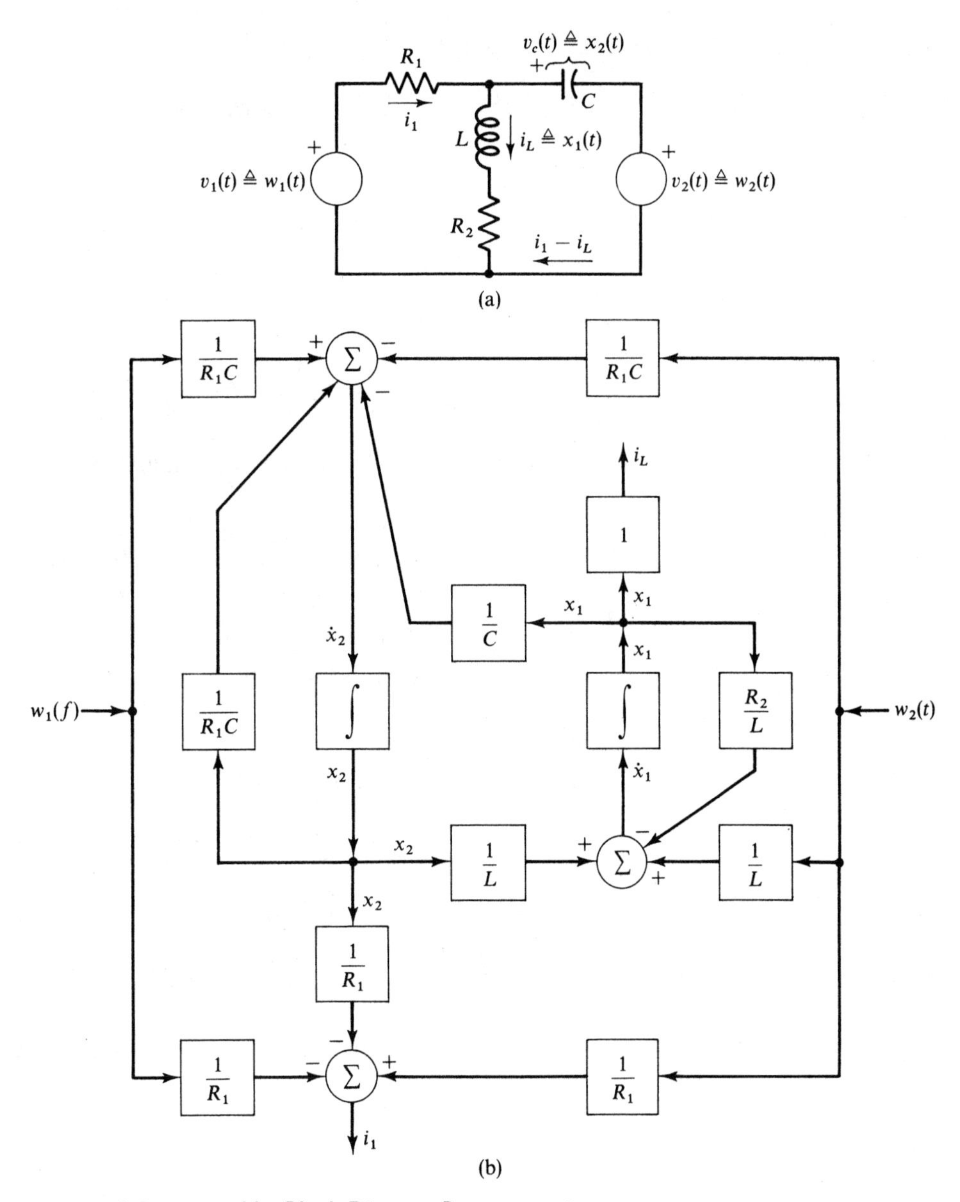

Figure 5.9 Electrical Circuit and Its Block Diagram Representation

For the outside loop, the voltage equation is

$$v_1(t) - i_1(t)R_1 - v_c(t) - v_2(t) = 0$$

However,

$$C\,\frac{dv_c(t)}{dt} = i_1(t) - i_L(t)$$

Combine these equations to get

$$v_1(t) - R_1\left[C\,\frac{dv_c(t)}{dt} + i_L(t)\right] - v_c(t) - v_2(t) = 0$$

or

$$\frac{dv_c(t)}{dt} = -\frac{1}{C}\,i_L(t) - \frac{1}{R_1C}\,v_c(t) + \frac{1}{R_1C}\,v_1(t) - \frac{1}{R_1C}\,v_2(t)$$

In state variable form, this equation is

$$\dot{x}_2(t) = -\frac{1}{C}\,x_1(t) - \frac{1}{R_1C}\,x_2(t) + \frac{1}{R_1C}\,w_1(t) - \frac{1}{R_1C}\,w_2(t) \tag{5.52}$$

We combine (5.51) and (5.52) and write the result in matrix form. Thus,

$$\begin{bmatrix}\dot{x}_1(t)\\ \dot{x}_2(t)\end{bmatrix} = \begin{bmatrix} -\dfrac{R_2}{L} & \dfrac{1}{L}\\ -\dfrac{1}{C} & -\dfrac{1}{R_1C}\end{bmatrix}\begin{bmatrix}x_1(t)\\ x_2(t)\end{bmatrix} + \begin{bmatrix} 0 & \dfrac{1}{L}\\ \dfrac{1}{R_1C} & -\dfrac{1}{R_1C}\end{bmatrix}\begin{bmatrix}w_1(t)\\ w_2(t)\end{bmatrix} \tag{5.53}$$

If we select the currents i_1 and i_L as the outputs, the output equations become

$$i_L(t) = x_1(t)$$
$$i_1(t) = -\frac{1}{R_1}\,x_2(t) + \frac{w_2(t)}{R_1} - \frac{w_1(t)}{R_1}$$

In matrix form, these equations are written

$$\begin{bmatrix}i_L(t)\\ i_1(t)\end{bmatrix} = \begin{bmatrix}1 & 0\\ 0 & -\dfrac{1}{R_1}\end{bmatrix}\begin{bmatrix}x_1(t)\\ x_2(t)\end{bmatrix} + \begin{bmatrix}0 & 0\\ -\dfrac{1}{R_1} & \dfrac{1}{R_1}\end{bmatrix}\begin{bmatrix}w_1(t)\\ w_2(t)\end{bmatrix} \tag{5.54}$$

Equations (5.53) and (5.54) are included in the block diagram representation in Figure 5.9b.

Let us now choose the following numerical values for the circuit parameters:

$$R_2 = 0 \qquad L = 1\text{ H} \qquad C = 0.5\text{ F} \qquad \frac{1}{CR_1} = 3\text{ s}$$

Now, find the quantities $\mathbf{A}$, $\mathbf{A}^2$, $\mathbf{A}^3$, $\mathbf{A}^4$, and so on. These quantities are

$$\mathbf{A} = \begin{bmatrix}0 & 1\\ -2 & -3\end{bmatrix} \qquad \mathbf{A}^2 = \begin{bmatrix}-2 & -3\\ 6 & 7\end{bmatrix} \qquad \mathbf{A}^3 = \begin{bmatrix}6 & 7\\ -14 & -15\end{bmatrix}$$

$$\mathbf{A}^4 = \begin{bmatrix}-14 & -15\\ 30 & 31\end{bmatrix}\cdots$$

The fundamental matrix has the form [from (5.45)]

$$\mathbf{\Phi}(t) = e^{\mathbf{A}t}$$
$$= \begin{bmatrix} 1 - \dfrac{2t^2}{2!} + 6\dfrac{t^3}{3!} - 14\dfrac{t^4}{4!} \cdots & t - 3\dfrac{t^2}{2!} + 7\dfrac{t^3}{3!} - 15\dfrac{t^4}{4!} \cdots \\ -2t + 6\dfrac{t^2}{2!} - 14\dfrac{t^3}{3!} + 30\dfrac{t^4}{4!} \cdots & 1 - 3t + 7\dfrac{t^2}{2!} - 15\dfrac{t^3}{3!} + 31\dfrac{t^4}{4!} \cdots \end{bmatrix} \tag{5.55}$$

While the likelihood of identifying these series is doubtful, other techniques to solve this problem—for example, Laplace transform methods—yield the closed-form expression

$$\mathbf{\Phi}(t) = \begin{bmatrix} 2e^{-t} - e^{-2t} & e^{-t} - e^{-2t} \\ -2e^{-t} + 2e^{-2t} & -e^{-t} + 2e^{-2t} \end{bmatrix}$$ ■

■ **Example 5.11** ***Medicine****

A drug taken orally is ingested at a rate r. The mass of the drug in the gastrointestinal tract is denoted by m_1; m_2 denotes the mass in the bloodstream of the individual. The rate of change of the mass of the drug in the gastrointestinal tract is equal to the rate at which the drug is ingested minus the rate at which the drug enters the bloodstream, a rate that is taken to be proportional to the mass present. The rate of change of the mass in the bloodstream is proportional to the amount coming from the gastrointestinal tract minus the rate at which mass is lost by metabolism; the latter is proportional to the mass present in the blood. Develop the state space representation of this system. Determine the zero-input response for $K_1 = 1$ and $K_2 = 1$.

Solution The rate of change of the mass of the drug in the gastrointestinal tract is given by

$$\frac{dm_1}{dt} = -K_1 m_1 + r \tag{5.56}$$

where K_1 is a positive constant that is characteristic of each individual. The rate of change of the mass of the drug in the bloodstream is

$$\frac{dm_2}{dt} = K_1 m_1 - K_2 m_2 \tag{5.57}$$

The positive constant K_2 characterizes the metabolic and excretory processes of the individual.

An obvious choice of state variables is the mass of the drug in the gastrointestinal tract $x_1 = m_1$ and the mass of the drug in the bloodstream $x_2 = m_2$.

* From N. H. McClamroch, *State Models of Dynamic Systems* (New York: Springer-Verlag, 1980), p. 38.

Thus, the controlling equations in state variable form are

$$\frac{dx_1}{dt} = -K_1 x_1 + r = -x_1 + w \tag{5.58a}$$

$$\frac{dx_2}{dt} = K_1 x_1 - K_2 x_2 = x_1 - x_2 \tag{5.58b}$$

$$y = x_2 \tag{5.58c}$$

where we have set $r \triangleq w$ as the input variable. For zero input $w = 0$, the equations in state matrix form become

$$\begin{bmatrix} \dot{x}_1 \\ \dot{x}_2 \end{bmatrix} = \begin{bmatrix} -1 & 0 \\ 1 & -1 \end{bmatrix} \begin{bmatrix} x_1 \\ x_2 \end{bmatrix} = \mathbf{A}\mathbf{x} \tag{5.59}$$

To deduce the fundamental matrix, we determine the quantities $\mathbf{A}$, $\mathbf{A}^2$, $\mathbf{A}^3$, ... :

$$\mathbf{A} = \begin{bmatrix} -1 & 0 \\ 1 & -1 \end{bmatrix} \qquad \mathbf{A}^2 = \begin{bmatrix} 1 & 0 \\ -2 & 1 \end{bmatrix} \qquad \mathbf{A}^3 = \begin{bmatrix} -1 & 0 \\ 3 & -1 \end{bmatrix}$$

$$\mathbf{A}^4 = \begin{bmatrix} 1 & 0 \\ -4 & 1 \end{bmatrix} \cdots$$

The fundamental matrix has the form

$$\mathbf{\Phi}(t) = e^{\mathbf{A}t} = \begin{bmatrix} \left(1 - t + \frac{1}{2!}t^2 - \frac{1}{3!}t^3 + \frac{1}{4!}t^4 + \cdots\right) & 0 \\ \left(t - \frac{2}{2!}t^2 + \frac{3}{3!}t^3 - \frac{4}{4!}t^4 \cdots\right) & \left(1 - t + \frac{1}{2!}t^2 - \frac{1}{3!}t^3 + \frac{1}{4}t^4 \cdots\right) \end{bmatrix}$$

$$= \begin{bmatrix} \sum_{n=0}^{\infty} \frac{(-1)^n}{n!} t^n & 0 \\ \sum_{n=1}^{\infty} \frac{(-1)^{n+1} n}{n!} t^n & \sum_{n=0}^{\infty} \frac{(-1)^n}{n!} t^n \end{bmatrix} = \begin{bmatrix} e^{-t} & 0 \\ te^{-t} & e^{-t} \end{bmatrix} \tag{5.60}$$

If we assume that the masses were initially $m_1(0) \triangleq x_1(0) = 1$ and $m_2(0) \triangleq x_2(0) = 0$, then the masses at any time are given by

$$\begin{bmatrix} x_1(t) \\ x_2(t) \end{bmatrix} = \mathbf{\Phi}(t)\mathbf{x}(0) = \begin{bmatrix} \sum_{n=0}^{\infty} \frac{(-1)^n}{n!} t^n \\ \sum_{n=1}^{\infty} \frac{(-1)^{n+1} n}{n!} t^n \end{bmatrix} = \begin{bmatrix} e^{-t} \\ te^{-t} \end{bmatrix} \tag{5.61}$$

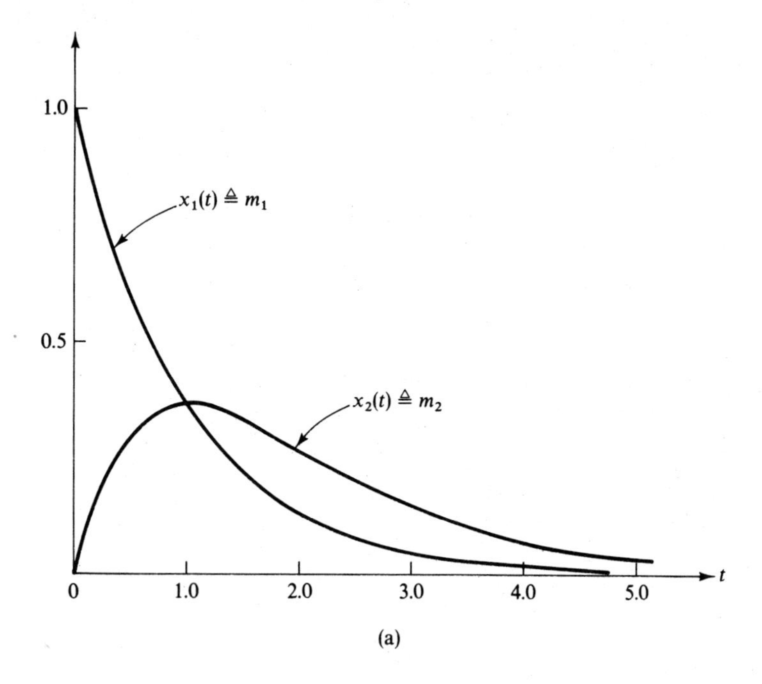

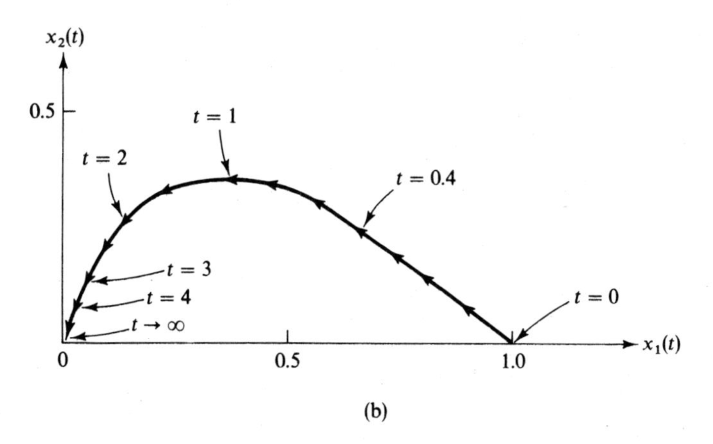

Figure 5.10 (a) Change of the drug masses with respect to time. (b) Phase-plane representation.

The time variations $x_1(t)$ and $x_2(t)$ are shown graphically in Figure 5.10. Figure 5.10a shows how each mass of drug is changing with time. Figure 5.10b shows the dependence between the two state variables by exhibiting a typical trajectory in the phase plane. The trajectory corresponds to the time responses illustrated in Figure 5.10a. ■

5.5 Complete Solution of Continuous Time State Equations

We now seek a solution to the general state equation given by (5.62):

$$\dot{\mathbf{x}}(t) = \mathbf{A}\mathbf{x}(t) + \mathbf{B}\mathbf{w}(t) \tag{5.62}$$

Multiply each term in this equation by the factor $e^{-\mathbf{A}t}$, a procedure suggested by the method of variation of parameters. The result is

$$e^{-\mathbf{A}t}\dot{\mathbf{x}}(t) = e^{-\mathbf{A}t}\mathbf{x}(t) + e^{-\mathbf{A}t}\mathbf{B}\mathbf{w}(t)$$

Rearrange this equation to the form

$$e^{-\mathbf{A}t}\dot{\mathbf{x}} - e^{-\mathbf{A}t}\mathbf{A}\mathbf{x} = e^{-\mathbf{A}t}\mathbf{B}\mathbf{w}$$

which is

$$\frac{d}{dt}(e^{-\mathbf{A}t}\mathbf{x}) = e^{-\mathbf{A}t}\mathbf{B}\mathbf{w}$$

Multiply by dt and integrate over the interval t_0 to t. Also, to avoid confusion, a change of variable is made. The result is

$$\int_{t_0}^{t} \frac{d}{d\tau}(e^{-\mathbf{A}\tau}\mathbf{x})\, d\tau = \int_{t_0}^{t} e^{-\mathbf{A}\tau}\mathbf{B}\mathbf{w}\, d\tau$$

This expression yields

$$e^{-\mathbf{A}t}\mathbf{x}(t) - e^{-\mathbf{A}t_0}\mathbf{x}(t_0) = \int_{t_0}^{t} e^{-\mathbf{A}\tau}\mathbf{B}\mathbf{w}\, d\tau$$

Now, premultiply all terms in this equation by $e^{\mathbf{A}t}$, with the result

$$\mathbf{x}(t) = e^{\mathbf{A}(t-t_0)}\mathbf{x}(t_0) + \int_{t_0}^{t} e^{\mathbf{A}(t-\tau)}\mathbf{B}\mathbf{w}(\tau)\, d\tau \tag{5.63}$$

When written terms of the fundamental matrix, this expression becomes

$$\boxed{\mathbf{x}(t) = \mathbf{\Phi}(t - t_0)\mathbf{x}(t_0) + \int_{t_0}^{t} \mathbf{\Phi}(t - \tau)\mathbf{B}\mathbf{w}(\tau)\, d\tau} \tag{5.64}$$

The first term on the right specifies the contribution to the total response that arises from the free or natural response of the system to initial conditions. The second term is the contribution due to the applied drivers, or forcing functions, and appears in a matrix convolution integral. Be advised that obtaining a solution to this general matrix equation is usually a complicated task.

The corresponding expression for the output $\mathbf{y}(t)$ involves combining the general form

$$\mathbf{y}(t) = \mathbf{C}\mathbf{x}(t) + \mathbf{D}\mathbf{w}(t) \tag{5.65}$$

with the expression for $\mathbf{x}(t)$ given by (5.64). The result is

$$\mathbf{y}(t) = \mathbf{C}e^{\mathbf{A}(t-t_0)}\mathbf{x}(t_0) + \int_{t_0}^{t} \mathbf{C}e^{\mathbf{A}(t-\tau)}\mathbf{B}\mathbf{w}(\tau)\,d\tau + \mathbf{D}\mathbf{w}(t)$$

or

$$\boxed{\mathbf{y}(t) = \mathbf{C}e^{\mathbf{A}(t-t_0)}\mathbf{x}(t_0) + \int_{t_0}^{t} [\mathbf{C}e^{\mathbf{A}(t-\tau)}\mathbf{B} + \mathbf{D}\delta(t-\tau)]\mathbf{w}(\tau)\,d\tau} \quad (5.66)$$

Note that the entity $\mathbf{C}e^{\mathbf{A}t}\mathbf{B} + \mathbf{D}\delta(t)$ is the impulse response function $h(t)$; $\mathbf{w}(\tau)$ is the input, with $\mathbf{D}$ denoting the straight-through paths from input to output. Specifically, we set the initial conditions to zero—that is, $\mathbf{x}(t_0) = \mathbf{0}$—with the result

$$\mathbf{h}(t) = \begin{cases} \mathbf{C}\mathbf{\Phi}(t)\mathbf{B} + \mathbf{D}\delta(t) & t \geq 0 \\ 0 & \text{otherwise} \end{cases} \quad (5.67)$$

If we define two functions as follows [see (5.64)]:

$$\mathbf{x}_1(t;\, t_0,\, \mathbf{0},\, \mathbf{w}) \triangleq \int_{t_0}^{t} \mathbf{\Phi}(t-\tau)\mathbf{B}\mathbf{w}(\tau)\,d\tau \quad (5.68a)$$

$$\mathbf{x}_2(t;\, t_0,\, \mathbf{x}(t_0),\, \mathbf{0}) \triangleq \mathbf{\Phi}(t-t_0)\mathbf{x}(t_0) \quad (5.68b)$$

then we observe that $\mathbf{x}_1(\ )$ is a solution to (5.62) with zero initial state vector $\mathbf{x}(t_0) = \mathbf{0}$, and it is the **zero-state response**. We observe also that $\mathbf{x}_2(\ )$ is the solution to the same equation to zero input, and it is the **zero-input response**. Therefore, the output of any system is the sum of these two responses.

■ **Example 5.12**

Find a state representation and the impulse response of the network shown in Figure 5.11.

Solution We choose the voltages across the capacitors as the state variables. However, since $q = Cv$, then for $C = 1$, $q = v$; we can then choose the

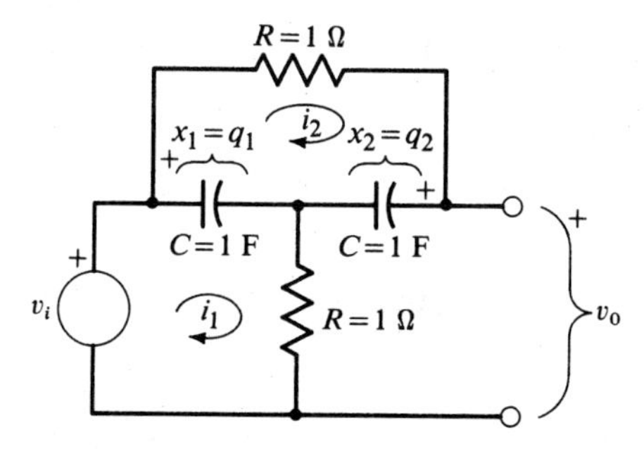

Figure 5.11 Illustrating Example 5.12

charge q as the state variable, as shown in Figure 5.11. Moreover, since $C\,dv/dt = i_c$, we can then use the mesh current equations to write a relation between the mesh currents and the state variables. Thus,

$$\frac{dq_1}{dt} = i_1 - i_2$$

$$\frac{dq_2}{dt} = i_2$$

From the mesh voltage equations for the two loops, we write

$$v_i - \frac{q_1}{1} - i_1 \cdot 1 = 0$$

$$-\frac{q_1}{1} + \frac{q_2}{1} + i_2 \cdot 1 = 0$$

Eliminate i_1 and i_2 from the foregoing equations and incorporate the state variable notation, with $v_i = w$, and $y = v_0$. We obtain the following set:

$$\frac{dx_1}{dt} = -2x_1 + x_2 + w$$

$$\frac{dx_2}{dt} = x_1 - x_2$$

or, in matrix form,

$$\frac{d}{dt}\begin{bmatrix} x_1 \\ x_2 \end{bmatrix} = \begin{bmatrix} -2 & 1 \\ 1 & -1 \end{bmatrix}\begin{bmatrix} x_1 \\ x_2 \end{bmatrix} + \begin{bmatrix} 1 \\ 0 \end{bmatrix} w$$

The output equation becomes $v_o = -q_1 + q_2 + v_i$, and its state representation is

$$y = -x_1 + x_2 + w = \begin{bmatrix} -1 & 1 \end{bmatrix}\begin{bmatrix} x_1 \\ x_2 \end{bmatrix} + w$$

To write the fundamental matrix, we evaluate

$$\mathbf{A} = \begin{bmatrix} -2 & 1 \\ 1 & -1 \end{bmatrix} \quad \mathbf{A}^2 = \begin{bmatrix} 5 & -3 \\ -3 & 2 \end{bmatrix} \quad \mathbf{A}^3 = \begin{bmatrix} -13 & 8 \\ 8 & -5 \end{bmatrix}$$

$$\mathbf{A}^4 = \begin{bmatrix} 34 & -21 \\ -21 & 13 \end{bmatrix} \cdots$$

Thus,

$$\mathbf{\Phi}(t) = \begin{bmatrix} 1 - 2t + \dfrac{5t^2}{2!} - \dfrac{13t^3}{3!} + \dfrac{34t^4}{4!} + \cdots & t - \dfrac{3t^2}{2!} + \dfrac{8t^3}{3!} - \dfrac{21t^4}{4!} + \cdots \\ t - \dfrac{3t^2}{2!} + \dfrac{8t^3}{3!} - \dfrac{21t^4}{4!} + \cdots & 1 - t + \dfrac{2t^2}{2!} - \dfrac{5t^3}{3!} + \dfrac{13t^4}{4!} + \cdots \end{bmatrix}$$

and

$$h(t) = \mathbf{C\Phi B} + \mathbf{D}\delta(t) = [-1 \quad 1]\mathbf{\Phi}(t)\begin{bmatrix}1\\0\end{bmatrix}$$

$$= -1 + 3t - \frac{8t^2}{2!} + \frac{21t^3}{3!} - \frac{55t^4}{4!} + \cdots \qquad t > 0$$

■

■ **Example 5.13** ***Ecology****

Consider two species that coexist in a given region and that interact in a specific way. Denote the number of each species at time t by $N_1(t)$ and $N_2(t)$, respectively. Assume that the rate of change of their numbers is proportional to the number present. Find the change in their numbers if the proportionality constants are $a = -1$, $b = 0$, $c = 2$, and $d = -1$.

Solution If the species were in isolation, their number at time t would be

$$\frac{dN_1}{dt} = aN_1 \qquad \frac{dN_2}{dt} = dN_2 \tag{5.69}$$

Setting a and d equal to -1 implies that both species in isolation decay with time. Now, because of the interaction of the species, we write

$$\frac{dN_1}{dt} = aN_1 + bN_2 \tag{5.70a}$$

$$\frac{dN_2}{dt} = cN_1 + dN_2 \tag{5.70b}$$

The given conditions are: $b = 0$ means that the second species does not compete with the first species and $c = 2$ implies that the first species competes with the second. By writing $x_1 = N_1$ and $x_2 = N_2$, the equations of (5.70) in state matrix form become

$$\begin{bmatrix}\dot{x}_1\\\dot{x}_2\end{bmatrix} = \begin{bmatrix}-1 & 0\\2 & -1\end{bmatrix}\begin{bmatrix}x_1\\x_2\end{bmatrix}$$

We evaluate

$$\mathbf{A} = \begin{bmatrix}-1 & 0\\2 & -1\end{bmatrix} \quad \mathbf{A}^2 = \begin{bmatrix}1 & 0\\-4 & 1\end{bmatrix} \quad \mathbf{A}^3 = \begin{bmatrix}-1 & 0\\6 & -1\end{bmatrix}$$

$$\mathbf{A}^4 = \begin{bmatrix}1 & 0\\-8 & 1\end{bmatrix} \cdots$$

* From N. Finizio and G. Ladas, *An Introduction to Differential Equations* (Belmont, CA: Wadsworth Publishing Co., 1980), p. 153.

The fundamental matrix has the form

$$\Phi(t) \triangleq e^{\mathbf{A}t} = \begin{bmatrix} \sum_{n=0}^{\infty} (-1)^n \frac{t^n}{n!} & 0 \\ \sum_{n=1}^{\infty} (-1)^{n+1} \frac{t^n}{n!}(2n) & \sum_{n=0}^{\infty} (-1)^n \frac{t^n}{n!} \end{bmatrix}$$

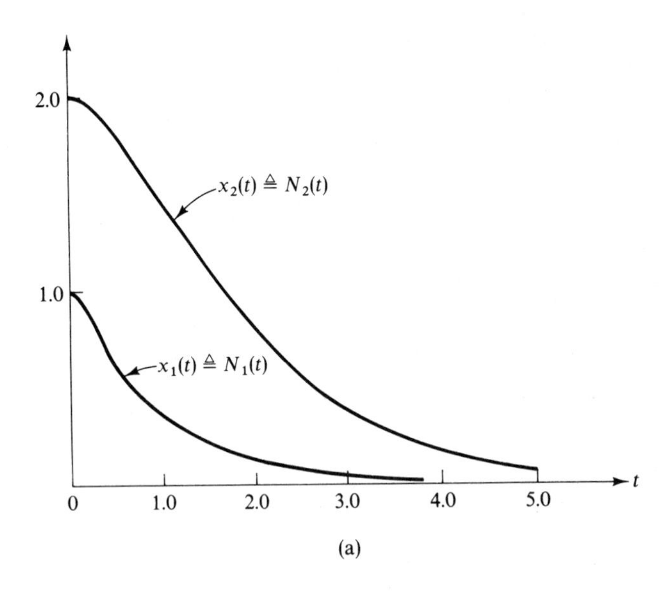

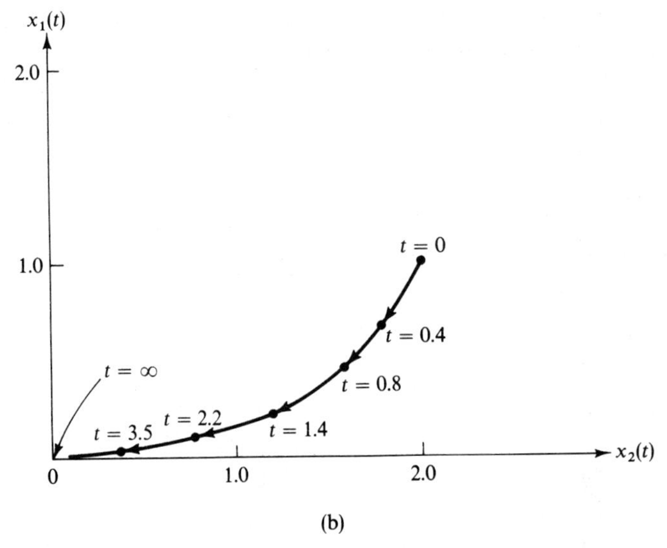

Figure 5.12 Illustrating Example 5.13

Recall that $0! = 1$. If we assume that the normalized number of species initially were $N_1(0) = x_1(0) = 1$ and $N_2(0) = x_2(0) = 2$, their numbers at time t are given by

$$\begin{bmatrix} x_1(t) \\ x_2(t) \end{bmatrix} = \mathbf{\Phi}(t)\mathbf{x}(0) = \begin{bmatrix} \sum_{n=0}^{\infty} (-1)^n \frac{t^n}{n!} \\ 2\left[1 - \sum_{n=1}^{\infty} (-1)^n \frac{t^n}{n!}(n-1)\right] \end{bmatrix}$$

These variations are shown graphically in Figure 5.12a. Figure 5.12b shows the locus of $x_1(t)$, $x_2(t)$ in the phase plane. ■

5.6 State Response to Periodic Inputs

We wish to examine the form acquired by (5.64) when the input $\mathbf{w}$ is a periodic function—that is, when $\mathbf{w}(t) = \mathbf{w}(t + T)$, where T is the period. For the periodic case, we require that $\mathbf{x}(0)$ at $t = 0$ must be equal to $\mathbf{x}(t)|_{t=T} = \mathbf{x}(T)$. This requires that

$$\mathbf{x}(T) = \mathbf{x}(0) = e^{\mathbf{A}T}\mathbf{x}(0) + \int_0^T e^{\mathbf{A}(T-\tau)}\mathbf{B}\mathbf{w}(\tau)\,d\tau$$

Solve this expression for $\mathbf{x}(0)$ to find

$$\mathbf{x}(0) = [\mathbf{I} - e^{\mathbf{A}T}]^{-1} \int_0^T e^{\mathbf{A}(T-\tau)}\mathbf{B}\mathbf{w}(\tau)\,d\tau \tag{5.71}$$

Combine this expression with (5.64) to obtain

$$\mathbf{x}(t) = e^{\mathbf{A}t}[\mathbf{I} - e^{\mathbf{A}T}]^{-1} \int_0^T e^{\mathbf{A}(T-\tau)}\mathbf{B}\mathbf{w}(\tau)\,d\tau + \int_0^t e^{\mathbf{A}(t-\tau)}\mathbf{B}\mathbf{w}(\tau)\,d\tau$$

or

$$\mathbf{x}(t) = e^{\mathbf{A}t}\left\{[\mathbf{I} - e^{\mathbf{A}T}]^{-1}e^{\mathbf{A}T} \int_0^T e^{-\mathbf{A}\tau}\mathbf{B}\mathbf{w}(\tau)\,d\tau + \int_0^t e^{-\mathbf{A}\tau}\mathbf{B}\mathbf{w}(\tau)\,d\tau\right\} \tag{5.72}$$

For the special case when the input is sinusoidal of the form $\mathbf{w} = [e^{j\omega t}]$, the complete solution, given by (5.72) with $T = 2\pi$, becomes

$$\mathbf{x}(t) = e^{\mathbf{A}t}\left\{[\mathbf{I} - e^{2\pi\mathbf{A}}]^{-1}e^{2\pi\mathbf{A}} \int_0^{2\pi} e^{-\mathbf{A}(-j\omega+1)\tau}\mathbf{B}\,d\tau + \int_0^t \mathbf{B}e^{-\mathbf{A}(-j\omega+1)\tau}\,d\tau\right\} \tag{5.73}$$

By carrying out the integrations and rearranging the results, we find that

$$\mathbf{x}(t) = \frac{-\mathbf{B}\mathbf{A}^{-1}e^{-\mathbf{A}t}}{(-j\omega+1)} \{e^{-\mathbf{A}(-j\omega+1)t} + [\mathbf{I} - e^{2\pi\mathbf{A}}]^{-1}e^{2\pi\mathbf{A}}[e^{-\mathbf{A}(-j\omega+1)2\pi} - 1] - 1\} \tag{5.74}$$

In this form, an interpretation is not readily apparent. However, we can approach this matter from a slightly different direction.

From past considerations, we know that for an LTI system, the output $\mathbf{y}(t)$ to a sinusoidal function is of the form $y(j\omega)e^{j\omega t} = H(j\omega)e^{j\omega t}$. Correspondingly, the steady state solution for the state $\mathbf{x}(t)$ is $\mathbf{x}(j\omega)e^{j\omega t}$. The state equation becomes

$$j\omega\mathbf{x}(j\omega)e^{j\omega t} = \mathbf{A}\mathbf{x}(j\omega)e^{j\omega t} + \mathbf{B}e^{j\omega t}$$

This leads to

$$[j\omega\mathbf{x}(j\omega) - \mathbf{A}\mathbf{x}(j\omega)]e^{j\omega t} = \mathbf{B}e^{j\omega t}$$

Cancel the common factor $e^{j\omega t}$ that appears on both sides of the equation, and so

$$[j\omega\mathbf{I} - \mathbf{A}]\mathbf{x}(j\omega) = \mathbf{B}$$

from which

$$\mathbf{x}(j\omega) = [j\omega\mathbf{I} - \mathbf{A}]^{-1}\mathbf{B} \tag{5.75}$$

Combine this value of $\mathbf{x}(j\omega)$ with the second state equation, which then becomes

$$\mathbf{y}(j\omega)e^{j\omega t} = \mathbf{C}\mathbf{x}(j\omega)e^{j\omega t} + \mathbf{D}e^{j\omega t}$$

from which we find

$$\mathbf{y}(j\omega) = \mathbf{C}[j\omega\mathbf{I} - \mathbf{A}]^{-1}\mathbf{B} + \mathbf{D} \tag{5.76}$$

5.7 Initial State Vectors and Initial Conditions

A knowledge of the initial state vector is essential to the solution of the state equations. The initial state vector $\mathbf{x}(0+)$, written $\mathbf{x}(0)$ for ease in writing, is found from the specified initial conditions that apply in any given case. The procedure for relating the physical initial conditions with the initial state vector requires special consideration. This matter is discussed in terms of a particular example.

Consider a system that is described by the state equations

$$\begin{bmatrix} \dot{x}_1 \\ \dot{x}_2 \\ \dot{x}_3 \end{bmatrix} = \begin{bmatrix} -2 & 1 & 0 \\ -3 & 0 & 1 \\ 0 & 0 & -5 \end{bmatrix} \begin{bmatrix} x_1 \\ x_2 \\ x_3 \end{bmatrix} + \begin{bmatrix} 0 \\ 1 \\ 3 \end{bmatrix} w \tag{5.77}$$

$$y = [1 \quad 0 \quad 0] \begin{bmatrix} x_1 \\ x_2 \\ x_3 \end{bmatrix}$$

subject to a set of specified initial conditions $y(0)$, $\dot{y}(0)$, and $\ddot{y}(0)$. In expanded form, the state equations are

$$\dot{x}_1 = -2x_1 + x_2 \tag{5.78a}$$

$$\dot{x}_2 = -3x_1 + x_3 + w \tag{5.78b}$$

$$\dot{x}_3 = -5x_3 + 3w \tag{5.78c}$$

$$y = x_1 \tag{5.78d}$$

The initial conditions translate by (5.78d) into the equivalent conditions

$$y(0) = x_1(0) \qquad \dot{y}(0) = \dot{x}_1(0) \qquad \ddot{y}(0) = \ddot{x}_1(0) \tag{5.79}$$

Combine (5.79) with (5.78a) to get

$$x_2(0) = \dot{x}_1(0) + 2x_1(0) = \dot{y}(0) + 2y(0) \tag{5.80}$$

Further, by differentiating (5.78a), we find that

$$\dot{x}_2(0) = \ddot{y}(0) + 2\dot{y}(0) \tag{5.81}$$

Combine this equation with (5.79) and apply this result to (5.78b). The quantity w is omitted because it is not involved in the initial state. The result is

$$x_3(0) = \dot{x}_2(0) + 3x_1(0) = \ddot{y}(0) + 2\dot{y}(0) + 3y(0) \tag{5.82}$$

These results are

$$\begin{aligned} x_1(0) &= y(0) \\ x_2(0) &= \dot{y}(0) + 2y(0) \\ x_3(0) &= \ddot{y}(0) + 2\dot{y}(0) + 3y(0) \end{aligned} \tag{5.83}$$

State Space Representation of Discrete Systems

5.8 State Representation of Discrete Time Systems

Discrete time systems can also be represented in state space by a set of matrix equations

$$\mathbf{x}(k+1) = \mathbf{A}\mathbf{x}(k) + \mathbf{B}\mathbf{w}(k) \tag{5.84a}$$

$$\mathbf{y}(k) = \mathbf{C}\mathbf{x}(k) + \mathbf{D}\mathbf{w}(k) \tag{5.84b}$$

where the matrixes **A**, **B**, **C**, and **D** are constants for time-invariant systems, the systems on which we focus our attention. The general discussion of the comparable set of equations for continuous time systems is generally applicable for discrete systems. We develop an understanding by means of a number of examples.

■ Example 5.14

Find the state space representation of the discrete system described by the difference equation

$$y(k) + \alpha_1 y(k-1) + \alpha_2 y(k-2) = \beta_0 w(k) \tag{5.85}$$

Solution To deduce a set of state variables from this difference equation, we proceed in a manner that parallels the discussion in Section 5.3. That is, we

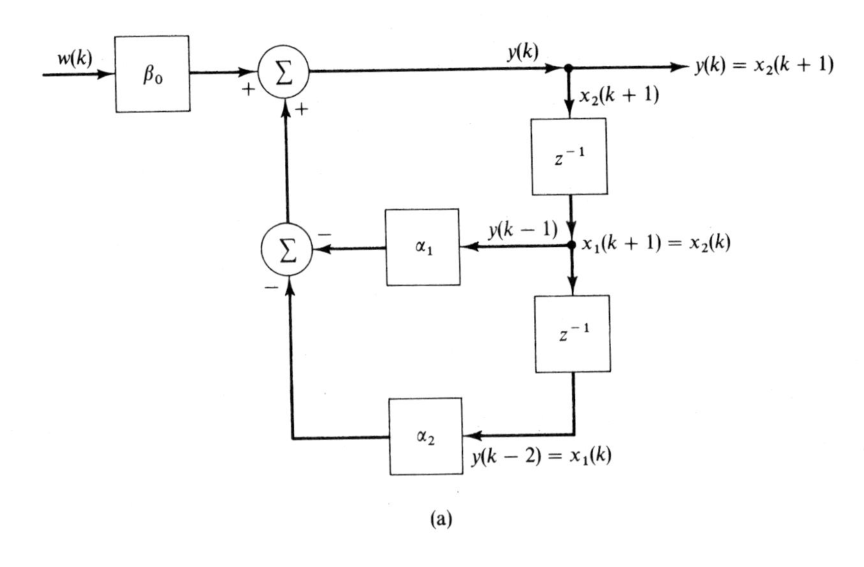

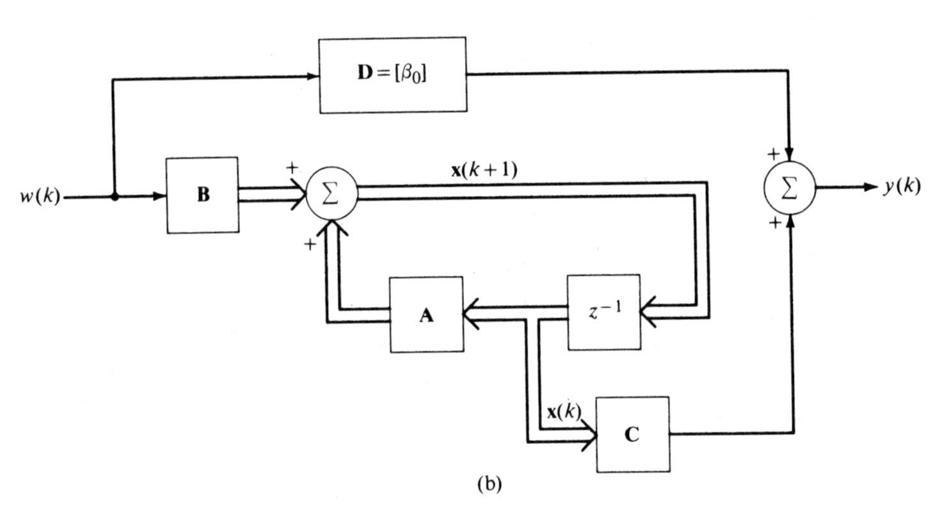

Figure 5.13 Illustrating Example 5.14

convert this difference equation into normal form. We write

$$x_1(k) = y(k-2) \tag{5.86a}$$

$$x_2(k) = x_1(k+1) = y(k-1) \tag{5.86b}$$

$$\begin{aligned} x_2(k+1) = y(k) &= -\alpha_1 y(k-1) - \alpha_2 y(k-2) + \beta_0 w(k) \\ &= -\alpha_1 x_2(k) - \alpha_2 x_1(k) + \beta_0 w(k) \end{aligned} \tag{5.86c}$$

The block diagram representation of these equations is shown in Figure 5.13a. Observe that we again use the symbol z^{-1} to denote a time delay of 1 unit, z^{-2}

for a time delay of 2 units, and so on. We write these equations in matrix form:

$$\begin{bmatrix} x_1(k+1) \\ x_2(k+1) \end{bmatrix} = \begin{bmatrix} 0 & 1 \\ -\alpha_2 & -\alpha_1 \end{bmatrix} \begin{bmatrix} x_1(k) \\ x_2(k) \end{bmatrix} + \begin{bmatrix} 0 \\ \beta_0 \end{bmatrix} w(k) \tag{5.87a}$$

$$[y(k)] = [-\alpha_2 \quad -\alpha_1] \begin{bmatrix} x_1(k) \\ x_2(k) \end{bmatrix} + [\beta_0] w(k) \tag{5.87b}$$

The vector matrix block diagram representation is shown in Figure 5.13b. ∎

As an extension of Example 5.14, we consider a third-order difference equation

$$\begin{aligned} \alpha_3 y(k+3) + \alpha_2 y(k+2) + \alpha_1 y(k+1) + \alpha_0 y(k) \\ = \beta_2 w(k+2) + \beta_1 w(k+1) + \beta_0 w(k) \end{aligned} \tag{5.88}$$

We expect that we can express this difference equation in state equation form. Particularly, we first wish to formulate the state equations in **phase variable** form. We begin with the reduced equation

$$\alpha_3 \eta(k+3) + \alpha_2 \eta(k+2) + \alpha_1 \eta(k+1) + \alpha_0 \eta(k) = w(k) \tag{5.89}$$

Now, define the quantities

$$\begin{aligned} x_1(k) &= \eta(k) \\ x_2(k) &= \eta(k+1) = x_1(k+1) \\ x_3(k) &= \eta(k+2) = x_2(k+1) \end{aligned} \tag{5.90}$$

and, from (5.89),

$$x_3(k+1) = \eta(k+3) = \frac{1}{\alpha_3}[w(k) - \alpha_2 x_3(k) - \alpha_1 x_2(k) - \alpha_0 x_1(k)] \tag{5.91}$$

This set is written in matrix form:

$$\begin{bmatrix} x_1(k+1) \\ x_2(k+1) \\ x_3(k+1) \end{bmatrix} = \begin{bmatrix} 0 & 1 & 0 \\ 0 & 0 & 1 \\ -\dfrac{\alpha_0}{\alpha_3} & -\dfrac{\alpha_1}{\alpha_3} & -\dfrac{\alpha_2}{\alpha_3} \end{bmatrix} \begin{bmatrix} x_1(k) \\ x_2(k) \\ x_3(k) \end{bmatrix} + \begin{bmatrix} 0 \\ 0 \\ \dfrac{1}{\alpha_3} \end{bmatrix} w(k) = \mathbf{A}\mathbf{x}(k) + \mathbf{B}\mathbf{w}(k) \tag{5.92}$$

Now, multiply (5.89) in succession by β_0, β_1, β_2, and β_3 and shift the successive expressions to the left by an amount equal to that indicated by the subscript of the β's. Upon adding the resulting expressions, we obtain

$$\begin{aligned} \beta_0[\alpha_0 \eta(k) + \alpha_1 \eta(k+1) + \alpha_2 \eta(k+2) + \alpha_3 \eta(k+3)] \\ + \beta_1[\alpha_0 \eta(k+1) + \alpha_1 \eta(k+2) + \alpha_2 \eta(k+3) + \alpha_3 \eta(k+4)] \\ + \beta_2[\alpha_0 \eta(k+2) + \alpha_1 \eta(k+3) + \alpha_2 \eta(k+4) + \alpha_3 \eta(k+5)] \\ = \beta_0 w(k) + \beta_1 w(k+1) + \beta_2 w(k+2) \end{aligned}$$

From this, we write

$$y(k) = \beta_0 \eta(k) + \beta_1 \eta(k + 1) + \beta_2 \eta(k + 2)$$

That is, if we substitute this expression in the above, we recapture (5.88). This equation is combined with (5.90) to yield

$$y(k) = \beta_2 x_3(k) + \beta_1 x_2(k) + \beta_0 x_1(k) \tag{5.93}$$

which, in matrix form, is

$$y(k) = [\beta_0\, \beta_1\, \beta_2] \begin{bmatrix} x_1(k) \\ x_2(k) \\ x_3(k) \end{bmatrix} = \mathbf{C}\mathbf{x}(k) \tag{5.94}$$

Equations (5.92) and (5.94) are the phase variable equivalent of (5.88). These equations are shown in block diagram form in Figure 5.14a and in matrix form in Figure 5.14b.

These results are readily extended to an nth order difference equation specified by

$$\begin{aligned} \alpha_n y(k + n) + \alpha_{n-1} y(k + n - 1) + \cdots + \alpha_0 y(k) \\ = \beta_n w(k + n) + \beta_{n-1} w(k + n - 1) + \cdots + \beta_0 w(k) \end{aligned} \tag{5.95}$$

The final matrix coefficients are

$$\mathbf{A} = \begin{bmatrix} 0 & 1 & 0 & \cdots & 0 \\ 0 & 0 & 1 & \cdots & 0 \\ \vdots & \vdots & \vdots & & \vdots \\ 0 & 0 & 0 & & 1 \\ -\dfrac{\alpha_0}{\alpha_n} & -\dfrac{\alpha_1}{\alpha_n} & -\dfrac{\alpha_2}{\alpha_n} & & -\dfrac{\alpha_{n-1}}{\alpha_n} \end{bmatrix}; \mathbf{B} = \begin{bmatrix} 0 \\ 0 \\ \vdots \\ 0 \\ \dfrac{1}{\alpha_n} \end{bmatrix}; \mathbf{C} = [\beta_0\, \beta_1 \beta_2 \cdots \beta_n]; \mathbf{D} = [0] \tag{5.96}$$

Suppose that the original difference equation, instead of the form given in (5.88), is given as

$$\begin{aligned} \xi_0 y(k) + \xi_1 y(k - 1) + \xi_2 y(k - 2) + \xi_3 y(k - 3) \\ = \zeta_0 w(k) + \zeta_1 w(k - 1) + \zeta_2 w(k - 2) + \zeta_3 w(k - 3) \end{aligned} \tag{5.97}$$

which we rewrite as

$$\begin{aligned} y(k) + a_1 y(k - 1) + a_2 y(k - 2) + a_3 y(k - 3) \\ = b_0 w(k) + b_1 w(k - 1) + b_2 w(k - 2) + b_3 w(k - 3) \end{aligned} \tag{5.98}$$

where

$$b_j = \frac{\zeta_j}{\xi_0} \qquad a_j = \frac{\xi_j}{\xi_0}$$

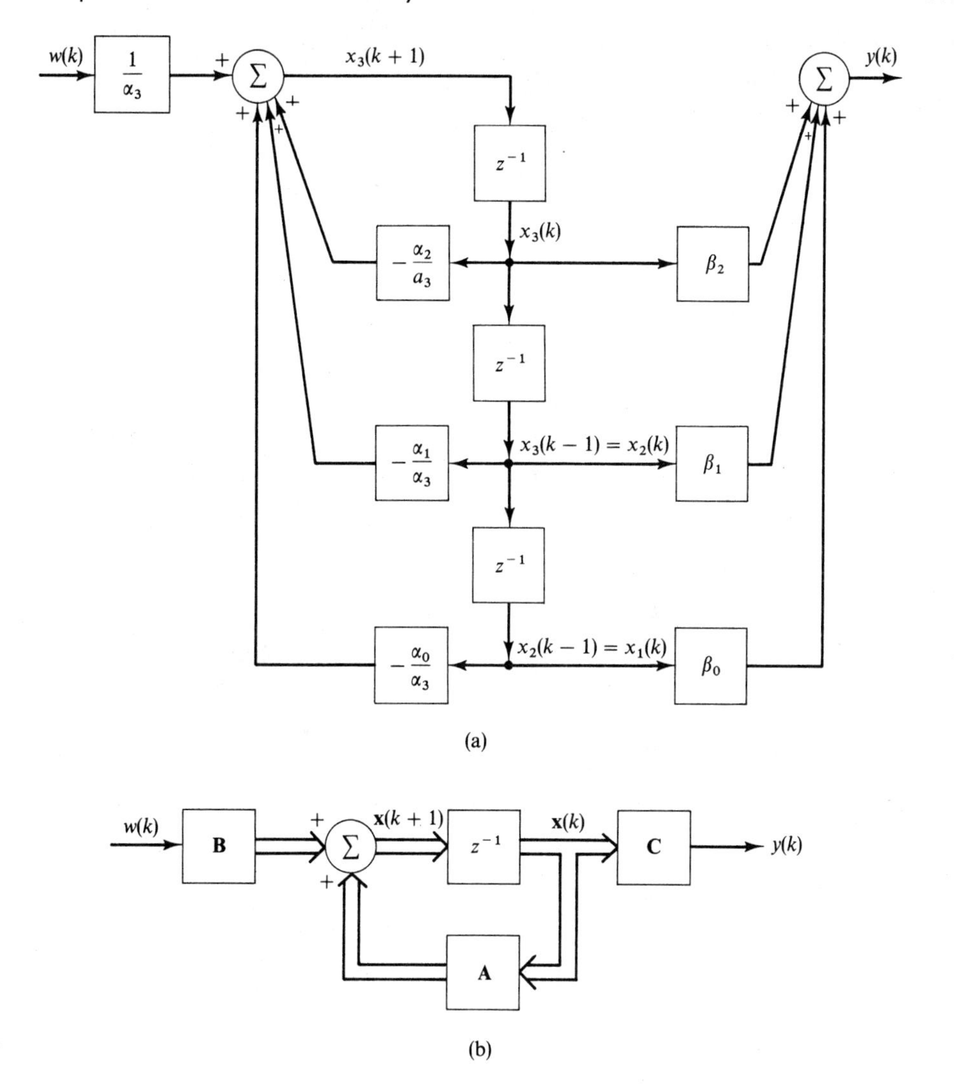

Figure 5.14 Representation of a Third-Order Discrete System in Phase Variable Form. (a) Block diagram. (b) Matrix form.

Clearly, if all a_j's are zero, $y(k)$ is a linear weighting of the previous samples of the input. Thus, $y(k)$ is a nonrecursive summation of the present and previous samples of the input—that is, an FIR system.

We proceed as before by considering the reduced equation

$$\eta(k) + a_1\eta(k-1) + a_2\eta(k-2) + a_3\eta(k-3) = w(k) \tag{5.99}$$

Using this equation, we write four related equations. In the first, we multiply by b_0; in the second, we multiply by b_1 and shift the order of the equation by one; in the third, we multiply by b_2 and shift the order of the equation by two; in the fourth, we multiply by b_3 and shift the order of the equation by three. The resulting equations are

$$\begin{aligned}
b_0\,\eta(k) + b_0\,a_1\eta(k-1) + b_0\,a_2\,\eta(k-2) + b_0\,a_3\,\eta(k-3) &= b_0\,w(k)\\
b_1\eta(k-1) + b_1a_1\eta(k-2) + b_1a_2\,\eta(k-3) + b_1a_3\,\eta(k-4) &= b_1w(k-1)\\
b_2\,\eta(k-2) + b_2\,a_1\eta(k-3) + b_2\,a_2\,\eta(k-4) + b_2\,a_3\,\eta(k-5) &= b_2\,w(k-2)\\
b_3\,\eta(k-3) + b_3\,a_1\eta(k-4) + b_3\,a_2\,\eta(k-5) + b_3\,a_3\,\eta(k-6) &= b_3\,w(k-3)
\end{aligned}$$

Add these three equations to obtain

$$\begin{aligned}
&[b_0\,\eta(k) + b_1\eta(k-1) + b_2\,\eta(k-2) + b_3\,\eta(k-3)]\\
&\quad + a_1[b_0\,\eta(k-1) + b_1\eta(k-2) + b_2\,\eta(k-3) + b_3\,\eta(k-4)]\\
&\quad + a_2[b_0\,\eta(k-2) + b_1\eta(k-3) + b_2\,\eta(k-4) + b_3\,\eta(k-5)]\\
&\quad + a_3[b_0\,\eta(k-3) + b_1\eta(k-4) + b_2\,\eta(k-5) + b_3\,\eta(k-6)]\\
&= b_0\,w(k) + b_1w(k-1) + b_2\,w(k-2)
\end{aligned}$$

Observe that if we set

$$y(k) = b_0\,\eta(k) + b_1\eta(k-1) + b_2\,\eta(k-2) + b_3\,\eta(k-3) \tag{5.100}$$

in this equation, we recapture the original difference equation. Therefore, (5.99) and (5.100) represent the original difference equation (5.98). Now, we write as state variables

$$x_1(k) = \eta(k-3) \tag{5.101a}$$

$$x_2(k) = x_1(k+1) = \eta(k-2) \tag{5.101b}$$

$$x_3(k) = x_2(k+1) = \eta(k-1) \tag{5.101c}$$

and, from (5.99),

$$\begin{aligned}
x_3(k+1) = \eta(k) &= w(k) - a_1\eta(k-1) - a_2\,\eta(k-2) - a_3\,\eta(k-3)\\
&= w(k) - a_1x_3(k) - a_2\,x_2(k) - a_3\,x_1(k)
\end{aligned} \tag{5.101d}$$

Also, from (5.100), we have

$$\begin{aligned}
y(k) &= b_0[w(k) - a_1x_3(k) - a_2\,x_2(k) - a_3\,x_1(k)]\\
&\quad + b_1x_3(k) + b_2\,x_2(k) + b_3\,x_1(k)\\
&= b_0\,w(k) + (b_1 - a_1b_0)x_3(k)\\
&\quad + (b_2 - a_2\,b_0)x_2(k) + (b_3 - a_3\,b_0)x_1(k)
\end{aligned} \tag{5.102}$$

From (5.101) and (5.102), we can write the coefficient matrixes

$$\mathbf{A} = \begin{bmatrix} 0 & 1 & 0\\ 0 & 0 & 1\\ -a_3 & -a_2 & -a_1 \end{bmatrix} \qquad \mathbf{B} = \begin{bmatrix} 0\\ 0\\ 1 \end{bmatrix}$$

$$\mathbf{C} = [(b_3 - b_0\,a_3)(b_2 - a_2\,b_0)(b_1 - a_1b_0)] \qquad \mathbf{D} = [b_0] \tag{5.103}$$

■ **Example 5.15**

Deduce a state space representation of the finite impulse (FIR) system specified by

$$y(k) = \beta_0 w(k) + \beta_1 w(k-1) + \beta_2 w(k-2) + \beta_3 w(k-3)$$

Solution A direct application of (5.103) yields

$$\begin{bmatrix} x_1(k+1) \\ x_2(k+1) \\ x_3(k+1) \end{bmatrix} = \begin{bmatrix} 0 & 1 & 0 \\ 0 & 0 & 1 \\ 0 & 0 & 0 \end{bmatrix} \begin{bmatrix} x_1(k) \\ x_2(k) \\ x_3(k) \end{bmatrix} + \begin{bmatrix} 0 \\ 0 \\ 1 \end{bmatrix} w(k)$$

$$y(k) = [\beta_3 \quad \beta_2 \quad \beta_1] \begin{bmatrix} x_1(k) \\ x_2(k) \\ x_3(k) \end{bmatrix} + [\beta_0] w(k)$$

■

■ **Example 5.16**

Repeat Example 5.14 employing a first canonical selection of states.

Solution Begin with (5.85), which is written

$$y(k) = -\alpha_1 y(k-1) - \alpha_2 y(k-2) + \beta_0 w(k) \tag{5.104}$$

Define a state variable

$$x_2(k) = -\alpha_2 y(k-2) - \alpha_1 y(k-1) \tag{5.105}$$

Combine this with (5.104) to get

$$y(k) = x_2(k) + \beta_0 w(k) \tag{5.106}$$

Increase the index k by 1 in (5.105) and write

$$x_2(k+1) = -\alpha_2 y(k-1) - \alpha_1 y(k) \tag{5.107}$$

Select as a second state variable

$$x_1(k) = -\alpha_2 y(k-1) \tag{5.108}$$

Combine (5.107) and (5.108):

$$\begin{aligned} x_2(k+1) &= x_1(k) - \alpha_1 y(k) = x_1(k) - \alpha_1[x_2(k) + \beta_0 w(k)] \\ &= x_1(k) - \alpha_1 x_2(k) - \alpha_1 \beta_0 w(k) \end{aligned} \tag{5.109}$$

However, from (5.108), by increasing the index by 1 and using (5.106),

$$x_1(k+1) = -\alpha_2 y(k) = -\alpha_2 x_2(k) - \alpha_2 \beta_0 w(k) \tag{5.110}$$

Equations (5.109) and (5.110) are combined into the matrix expression

$$\begin{bmatrix} x_1(k+1) \\ x_2(k+1) \end{bmatrix} = \begin{bmatrix} 0 & -\alpha_2 \\ 1 & -\alpha_1 \end{bmatrix} \begin{bmatrix} x_1(k) \\ x_2(k) \end{bmatrix} + \begin{bmatrix} -\alpha_2 \beta_0 \\ -\alpha_1 \beta_0 \end{bmatrix} [w(k)] = \mathbf{A}\mathbf{x}(k) + \mathbf{B}\mathbf{w}(k) \tag{5.111a}$$

The output $y(k)$ is given by (5.106), which we write as

$$[y(k)] = [0 \quad 1]\begin{bmatrix} x_1(k) \\ x_2(k) \end{bmatrix} + [\beta_0][w(k)] = \mathbf{C}\mathbf{x}(k) + \mathbf{D}\mathbf{w}(k) \tag{5.111b}$$

If we reverse the indexes of the state variables—that is, by setting $x_1(k) = -\alpha_2 y(k-2) - \alpha_1 y(k-1)$ in (5.105) and $x_2(k) = -\alpha_2 y(k-1)$ in (5.108)—and proceed as above, we obtain another form of the canonical representation:

$$\mathbf{x}(k+1) = \begin{bmatrix} -\alpha_1 & 1 \\ -\alpha_2 & 0 \end{bmatrix}\mathbf{x}(k) + \begin{bmatrix} -\alpha_1\beta_0 \\ -\alpha_2\beta_0 \end{bmatrix}\mathbf{w}(k) \tag{5.111c}$$

$$\mathbf{y}(k) = [1 \quad 0]\mathbf{x}(k) + [\beta_0]\mathbf{w}(k) \tag{5.111d}$$

■

■ Example 5.17

Obtain a first canonical state space form for the third-order system given by the difference equation

$$y(k) + \alpha_1 y(k-1) + \alpha_2 y(k-2) + \alpha_3 y(k-3) = \beta_0 w(k) + \beta_1 w(k-1) + \beta_2 w(k-2) + \beta_3 w(k-3) \tag{5.112}$$

Solution Write the equation in the form

$$y(k) = [\beta_3 w(k-3) - \alpha_3 y(k-3)] + [\beta_2 w(k-2) - \alpha_2 y(k-2)] + [\beta_1 w(k-1) - \alpha_1 y(k-1)] + \beta_0 w(k) \tag{5.113}$$

We define the state variable $x_3(k)$:

$$x_3(k) = [\beta_3 w(k-3) - \alpha_3 y(k-3)] + [\beta_2 w(k-2) - \alpha_2 y(k-2)] + [\beta_1 w(k-1) - \alpha_1 y(k-1)] \tag{5.114}$$

Thus, the output is

$$y(k) = x_3(k) + \beta_0 w(k) \tag{5.115}$$

Now, increase the index k in (5.114) by 1 and write

$$x_3(k+1) = [\beta_3 w(k-2) - \alpha_3 y(k-2)] + [\beta_2 w(k-1) - \alpha_2 y(k-1)] + [\beta_1 w(k) - \alpha_1 y(k)] \tag{5.116}$$

We select as a second state variable

$$x_2(k) = [\beta_3 w(k-2) - \alpha_3 y(k-2)] + [\beta_2 w(k-1) - \alpha_2 y(k-1)] \tag{5.117}$$

Combine (5.117) with (5.116) to get

$$\begin{aligned} x_3(k+1) &= x_2(k) + \beta_1 w(k) - \alpha_1 y(k) \\ &= x_2(k) - \alpha_1[x_3(k) + \beta_0 w(k)] + \beta_1 w(k) \end{aligned}$$

or, using (5.115), we can write

$$x_3(k+1) = x_2(k) - \alpha_1 x_3(k) + [\beta_1 - \alpha_1\beta_0]w(k) \tag{5.118}$$

Proceed by increasing k by 1 in (5.117), which gives

$$x_2(k+1) = [\beta_3 w(k-1) - \alpha_3 y(k-1)] + [\beta_2 w(k) - \alpha_2 y(k)] \tag{5.119}$$

We select the next state variable:

$$x_1(k) = \beta_3 w(k-1) - \alpha_3 y(k-1) \tag{5.120}$$

Combine (5.120) with (5.119) and use (5.115):

$$x_2(k+1) = x_1(k) - \alpha_2 x_3(k) + [\beta_2 - \alpha_2 \beta_0]w(k) \tag{5.121}$$

We can write, using (5.120),

$$x_1(k+1) = \beta_3 w(k) - \alpha_3 y(k) = -\alpha_3[x_3(k) + \beta_0 w(k)] + \beta_3 w(k)$$

or

$$x_1(k+1) = -\alpha_3 x_3(k) + [\beta_3 - \alpha_3 \beta_0]w(k) \tag{5.122}$$

Equations (5.122), (5.121), and (5.118) are combined and written in matrix form:

$$\begin{bmatrix} x_1(k+1) \\ x_2(k+1) \\ x_3(k+1) \end{bmatrix} = \begin{bmatrix} 0 & 0 & -\alpha_3 \\ 1 & 0 & -\alpha_2 \\ 0 & 1 & -\alpha_1 \end{bmatrix} \begin{bmatrix} x_1(k) \\ x_2(k) \\ x_3(k) \end{bmatrix} + \begin{bmatrix} \beta_3 - \alpha_3 \beta_0 \\ \beta_2 - \alpha_2 \beta_0 \\ \beta_1 - \alpha_1 \beta_0 \end{bmatrix} w(k) \tag{5.123a}$$

The output $y(k)$ is, from (5.115),

$$y(k) = [0 \quad 0 \quad 1] \begin{bmatrix} x_1(k) \\ x_2(k) \\ x_3(k) \end{bmatrix} + [\beta_0]w(k) \tag{5.123b}$$

A block diagram realization of this system is shown in Figure 5.15a. The matrix diagram, obtained by writing (5.123) in the form

$$\mathbf{x}(k+1) = \mathbf{A}\mathbf{x}(k) + \mathbf{B}w(k) \tag{5.124a}$$

$$y(k) = \mathbf{C}\mathbf{x}(k) + \mathbf{D}w(k) \tag{5.124b}$$

is given in Figure 5.15b.

The initial state from which we can find the state of the system at any subsequent time is given by the set of equations—that is, (5.114), (5.117), and (5.120)—in the form

$$x_1(0) = -\alpha_3 y(-1) + \beta_3 w(-1) \tag{5.125a}$$

$$x_2(0) = -\alpha_2 y(-1) - \alpha_3 y(-2) + \beta_2 w(-1) + \beta_3 w(-2) \tag{5.125b}$$

$$\begin{aligned} x_3(0) = &-\alpha_1 y(-1) - \alpha_2 y(-2) - \alpha_3 y(-3) \\ &+ \beta_1 w(-1) + \beta_2 w(-2) + \beta_3 w(-3) \end{aligned} \tag{5.125c}$$

The matrix format of these equations is

$$\begin{bmatrix} x_1(0) \\ x_2(0) \\ x_3(0) \end{bmatrix} = \begin{bmatrix} -\alpha_3 & 0 & 0 \\ -\alpha_2 & -\alpha_3 & 0 \\ -\alpha_1 & -\alpha_2 & -\alpha_3 \end{bmatrix} \begin{bmatrix} y(-1) \\ y(-2) \\ y(-3) \end{bmatrix} + \begin{bmatrix} \beta_3 & 0 & 0 \\ \beta_2 & \beta_3 & 0 \\ \beta_1 & \beta_2 & \beta_3 \end{bmatrix} \begin{bmatrix} w(-1) \\ w(-2) \\ w(-3) \end{bmatrix} \tag{5.126a}$$

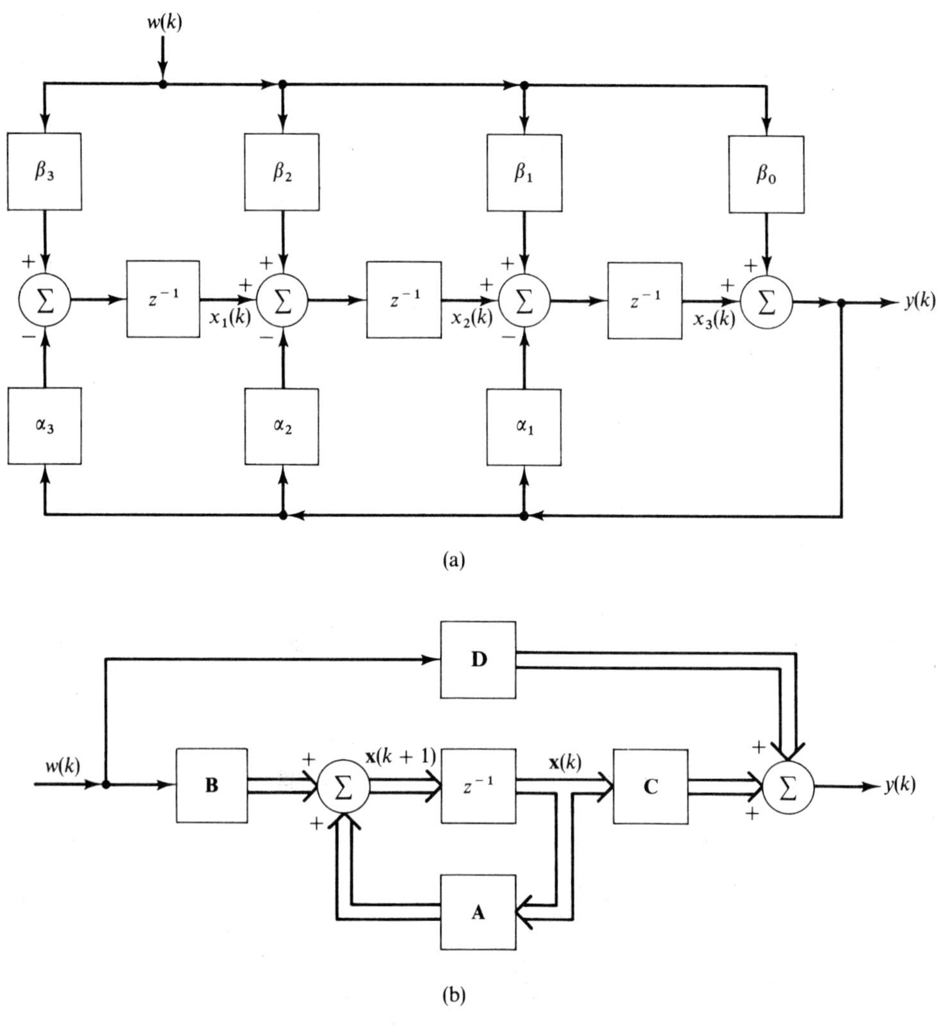

Figure 5.15 Canonical Decomposition Realization Form of the Third-Order Discrete System Described by (5.123)

which can be written in the form

$$\mathbf{x}(0) = \mathbf{E}\mathbf{y}_0 + \mathbf{F}\mathbf{w}_0 \tag{5.126b}$$

■

By following the same procedure for an nth order discrete system specified by

$$y(k) + \alpha_1 y(k-1) + \alpha_2\, y(k-2) + \cdots + \alpha_n\, y(k-n)$$
$$= \beta_0\, w(k) + \beta_1 w(k-1) + \cdots + \beta_n\, w(k-n) \tag{5.127}$$

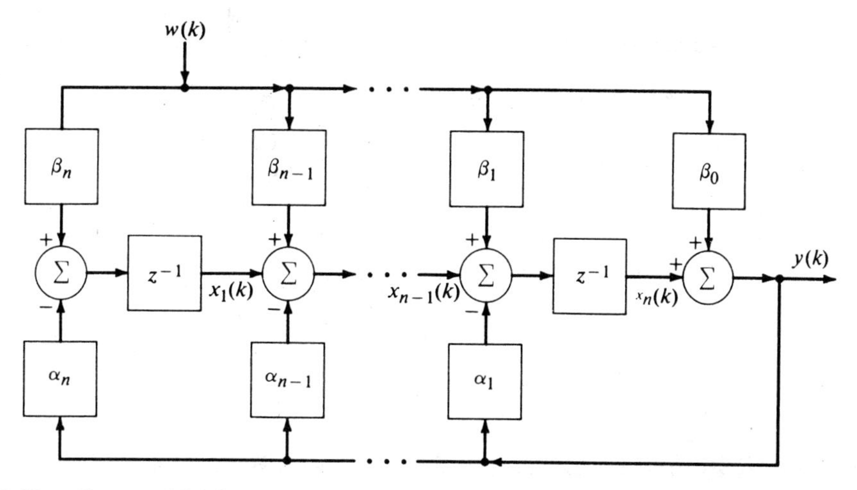

Figure 5.16 First Canonical Realization of the nth Order Discrete System Described by (5.127)

we will obtain the following matrixes:

$$\mathbf{A} = \begin{bmatrix} 0 & 0 & 0 & \cdots & 0 & 0 & -\alpha_n \\ 1 & 0 & 0 & & 0 & 0 & -\alpha_{n-1} \\ 0 & 1 & 0 & & 0 & 0 & -\alpha_{n-2} \\ & & & \vdots & & & \vdots \\ 0 & 0 & 0 & & 1 & 0 & -\alpha_2 \\ 0 & 0 & 0 & & 0 & 1 & -\alpha_1 \end{bmatrix} \quad \mathbf{B} = \begin{bmatrix} \beta_n - \alpha_n \beta_0 \\ \beta_{n-1} - \alpha_{n-1}\beta_0 \\ \beta_{n-2} - \alpha_{n-2}\beta_0 \\ \vdots \\ \beta_2 - \alpha_2 \beta_0 \\ \beta_1 - \alpha_1 \beta_0 \end{bmatrix} \tag{5.128}$$

$$\mathbf{C} = [0 \quad 0 \quad 0 \quad \cdots \quad 0 \quad 1] \qquad \mathbf{D} = [\beta_0]$$

The realization of this system is shown in Figure 5.16.

■ Example 5.18

Write the state space coefficients for the system shown in Figure 5.17 in both first canonical and phase variable form.

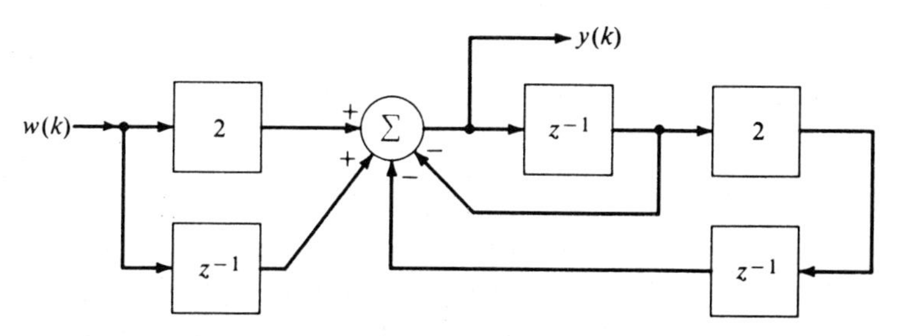

Figure 5.17 Second-Order Discrete System

Solution The difference equation specified in this figure is

$$y(k) + y(k-1) + 2y(k-2) = 2w(k) + w(k-1)$$

By choosing the states according to (5.128), the state matrixes are

$$\mathbf{A} = \begin{bmatrix} 0 & -2 \\ 1 & -1 \end{bmatrix} \quad \mathbf{B} = \begin{bmatrix} -4 \\ -1 \end{bmatrix} \quad \mathbf{C} = [0 \quad 1] \quad \mathbf{D} = [2]$$

According to (5.103), the state matrixes are

$$\mathbf{A} = \begin{bmatrix} 0 & 1 \\ -2 & -1 \end{bmatrix} \quad \mathbf{B} = \begin{bmatrix} 0 \\ 1 \end{bmatrix} \quad \mathbf{C} = [-4 \quad -1] \quad \mathbf{D} = [2]$$

■

5.9 Solution to Discrete Time State Equations

We initially focus our attention on the solution of the homogeneous state equation

$$\mathbf{x}(k+1) = \mathbf{A}\mathbf{x}(k) \tag{5.129}$$

For the case of an initial state $\mathbf{x}(k_0)$ at time k_0, the successive states of the system are obtained by direct iteration as follows:

$$\begin{aligned} \mathbf{x}(k_0+1) &= \mathbf{A}\mathbf{x}(k_0) \\ \mathbf{x}(k_0+2) &= \mathbf{A}\mathbf{x}(k_0+1) = \mathbf{A}\mathbf{A}\mathbf{x}(k_0) = \mathbf{A}^2\mathbf{x}(k_0) \\ &\vdots \\ \mathbf{x}(k_0+n) &= \mathbf{A}^n\mathbf{x}(k_0) \end{aligned} \tag{5.130}$$

If we set $k_0 + n = k$ in this last iterative element, we have

$$\mathbf{x}(k) = \mathbf{A}^{k-k_0}\mathbf{x}(k_0) \tag{5.131a}$$

and, for $k_0 = 0$,

$$\boxed{\mathbf{x}(k) = \mathbf{A}^k\mathbf{x}(0)} \tag{5.131b}$$

We write these

$$\mathbf{x}(k) = \mathbf{\Phi}(k, k_0)\mathbf{x}(k_0) \tag{5.132a}$$

and

$$\boxed{\mathbf{x}(k) = \mathbf{\Phi}(k)\mathbf{x}(0)} \tag{5.132b}$$

Here, the state transition matrix (also the fundamental matrix) is written $\mathbf{\Phi}(k, k_0)$, an $n \times n$ matrix such that the equations of (5.132) are specified.

We now consider the solution of the general state equations given by (5.129) for the initial vector specified at $k = k_0$. We develop the solutions by noting that

$$\begin{aligned}
\mathbf{x}(k_0+1) &= \mathbf{A}\mathbf{x}(k_0) + \mathbf{B}\mathbf{w}(k_0) \\
\mathbf{x}(k_0+2) &= \mathbf{A}\mathbf{x}(k_0+1) + \mathbf{B}\mathbf{w}(k_0+1) = \mathbf{A}^2\mathbf{x}(k_0) + \mathbf{A}\mathbf{B}\mathbf{w}(k_0) \\
&\quad + \mathbf{B}\mathbf{w}(k_0+1) \\
\mathbf{x}(k_0+3) &= \mathbf{A}\mathbf{x}(k_0+2) + \mathbf{B}\mathbf{w}(k_0+2) = \mathbf{A}^3\mathbf{x}(k_0) + \mathbf{A}^2\mathbf{B}\mathbf{w}(k_0) \\
&\quad + \mathbf{A}\mathbf{B}\mathbf{w}(k_0+1) + \mathbf{B}\mathbf{w}(k_0+2) \\
&\ \ \vdots \\
\mathbf{x}(k_0+q) &= \mathbf{A}^q\mathbf{x}(k_0) + \sum_{m=k_0}^{k_0+q-1} \mathbf{A}^{k_0+q-m-1}\mathbf{B}\mathbf{w}(m)
\end{aligned}$$

If we set $k_0 + q = k$, this final expression becomes

$$\boxed{\mathbf{x}(k) = \mathbf{A}^{k-k_0}\mathbf{x}(k_0) + \sum_{m=k_0}^{k-1} \mathbf{A}^{k-m-1}\mathbf{B}\mathbf{w}(m)} \tag{5.133}$$

or, equivalently,

$$\boxed{\mathbf{x}(k) = \mathbf{\Phi}(k-k_0)x(k_0) + \sum_{m=k_0}^{k-1} \mathbf{\Phi}(k-m-1)\mathbf{B}\mathbf{w}(m)} \tag{5.134}$$

This equation specifies the state vector at times $k \geq k_0$ and shows it to be the sum of two terms: one representing the contributions due to the initial state $\mathbf{x}(k_0)$ and the second representing the contributions due to the input $\mathbf{w}(k)$ over the interval $(k_0, k-1)$.

Introduce the value of $\mathbf{x}(k)$ given by (5.134) into (5.84b) to obtain

$$\boxed{\mathbf{y}(k) = \mathbf{C}\mathbf{\Phi}(k-k_0)\mathbf{x}(k_0) + \sum_{m=k_0}^{k-1} \mathbf{C}\mathbf{\Phi}(k-m-1)\mathbf{B}\mathbf{w}(m) + \mathbf{D}\mathbf{w}(k)} \tag{5.135}$$

When we set the initial conditions equal to zero, $\mathbf{x}(0) = \mathbf{0}$, and use an input $w(k) = \delta(k)$, the output is the impulse response function

$$h(k) = \sum_{m=0}^{k-1} \mathbf{C}\mathbf{\Phi}(k-m-1)\mathbf{B}\delta(m) + \mathbf{D}\delta(k) \tag{5.136}$$

However, since $\delta(k)$ is zero for $k \neq 0$, the second term is equal to $\mathbf{D}$ when $k = 0$.

When $k \neq 0$, the sum has zero value. Hence, the expression for $h(k)$ is

$$h(k) = \begin{cases} \mathbf{D} & k = 0 \\ \sum_{m=0}^{k-1} \mathbf{C\Phi}(k-m-1)\mathbf{B}\delta(m) = \mathbf{C\Phi}(k-1)\mathbf{B} & k > 0 \\ 0 & k < 0 \end{cases} \tag{5.137}$$

where

$$\mathbf{\Phi}(k-1) = \mathbf{A}^{k-1}$$

■ **Example 5.19**

Deduce the solution to the system shown in Figure 5.18 for $k \geq 0$ and $w(k) = u(k)$.

Solution From the figure, we obtain the following state equations:

$$\begin{bmatrix} x_1(k+1) \\ x_2(k+1) \end{bmatrix} = \begin{bmatrix} 0 & 1 \\ 0 & 2 \end{bmatrix} \begin{bmatrix} x_1(k) \\ x_2(k) \end{bmatrix} + \begin{bmatrix} 0 \\ 1 \end{bmatrix} w(k)$$

$$y(k) = [1 \quad 0] \begin{bmatrix} x_1(k) \\ x_2(k) \end{bmatrix}$$

The respective powers of matrix $\mathbf{A}$ are found to be

$$\mathbf{A}^2 = \begin{bmatrix} 0 & 2 \\ 0 & 2^2 \end{bmatrix} \quad \mathbf{A}^3 = \begin{bmatrix} 0 & 2^2 \\ 0 & 2^3 \end{bmatrix} \quad \mathbf{A}^4 = \begin{bmatrix} 0 & 2^3 \\ 0 & 2^4 \end{bmatrix} \cdots$$

Combine these equations with (5.133) to get

$$\begin{bmatrix} x_1(k) \\ x_2(k) \end{bmatrix} = \begin{bmatrix} 0 & 2^{k-1} \\ 0 & 2^k \end{bmatrix} \begin{bmatrix} x_1(0) \\ x_2(0) \end{bmatrix} + \sum_{m=0}^{k-1} \begin{bmatrix} 0 & 2^{k-m-2} \\ 0 & 2^{k-m-1} \end{bmatrix} \begin{bmatrix} 0 \\ 1 \end{bmatrix} w(m)$$

$$= \begin{bmatrix} 0 & 2^{k-1} \\ 0 & 2^k \end{bmatrix} \begin{bmatrix} x_1(0) \\ x_2(0) \end{bmatrix} + \begin{bmatrix} 2^{k-2} + 2^{k-3} + \cdots + 2^{-1} \\ 2^{k-1} + 2^{k-2} + \cdots + 2^0 \end{bmatrix}$$

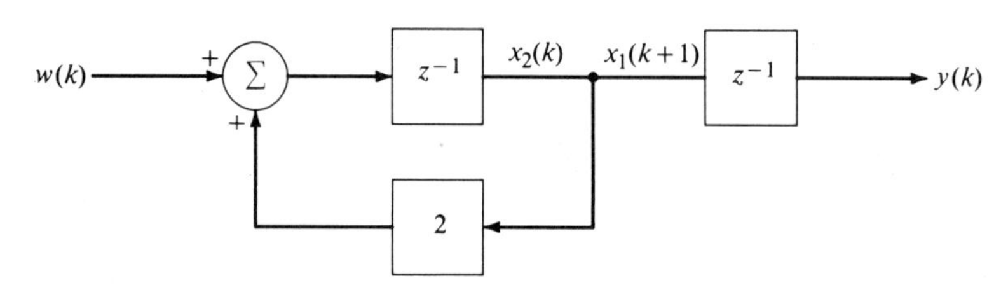

Figure 5.18 Simple Discrete System

The output of the system is given by

$$y(k) = 2^{k-1}x_2(0) + \sum_{m=0}^{k-1} 2^{k-2}2^{-m} = 2^{k-1}x_2(0) + 2^{k-2}\sum_{m=0}^{k-1}\left(\frac{1}{2}\right)^m$$

$$= 2^{k-1}x_2(0) + 2^{k-2}\frac{1-(1/2)^k}{1-(1/2)} = 2^{k-1}x_2(0) + 2^{k-1}[1-(1/2)^k]$$

$k = 0, 1, 2, 3, \ldots$ ■

■ Example 5.20

Find the solution to the system shown in Figure 5.19 for $k \geq 0$ and $w(k) = \delta(k)$.

Solution The difference equation that describes this system is

$$y(k) + 4y(k-1) + 2y(k-2) = w(k)$$

From (5.123) with $\alpha_1 = 4$, $\alpha_2 = 2$, $\beta_0 = 1$, the appropriate state matrixes are

$$\mathbf{A} = \begin{bmatrix} 0 & -2 \\ 1 & -4 \end{bmatrix} \quad \mathbf{B} = \begin{bmatrix} -2 \\ -4 \end{bmatrix} \quad \mathbf{C} = [0 \quad 1] \quad \mathbf{D} = [1]$$

The respective powers of matrix **A** are found to be

$$\mathbf{A} = \begin{bmatrix} 0 & -2 \\ 1 & -4 \end{bmatrix} \quad \mathbf{B} = \begin{bmatrix} -2 \\ -4 \end{bmatrix} \quad \mathbf{C} = [0 \quad 1] \quad \mathbf{D} = [1]$$

Using other methods, it is found that $\mathbf{\Phi}(k-1) = \mathbf{A}^{k-1}$ can be written in the following form:

$$\mathbf{\Phi}(k-1) = \frac{1}{\sqrt{2}}\begin{bmatrix} (-1)^k[(2+\sqrt{2})^k - (2-\sqrt{2})^k] & 2(-1)^k[(5+2\sqrt{2})(2+\sqrt{2})^k + (3+2+\sqrt{2})(2-\sqrt{2})^{k-1}] \\ \frac{1}{2}(-1)^k[(2+\sqrt{2})^{k+1} - (2-\sqrt{2})^{k+1}] & (-1)^k[(5+2\sqrt{2})(2+\sqrt{2})^k + (3+2\sqrt{2})(2-\sqrt{2})^k] \end{bmatrix}$$

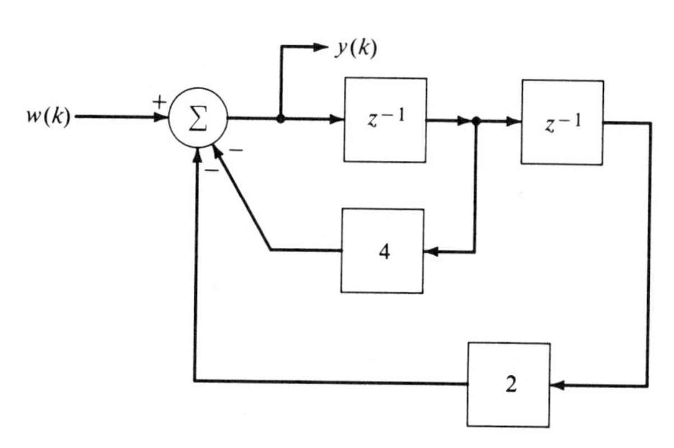

Figure 5.19 Illustrating Example 5.20

By (5.137), we find that

$$h(k) = \begin{cases} 1 & k = 0 \\ -\dfrac{1}{\sqrt{2}}(-1)^k[(2+\sqrt{2})^{k+1} - (2-\sqrt{2})^{k+1}] \\ \qquad -\dfrac{4}{\sqrt{2}}(-1)^k[(5+2\sqrt{2})(2+\sqrt{2})^k + (3+2\sqrt{2})(2-\sqrt{2})^k] & k > 1 \\ 0 & k < 0 \end{cases}$$

This solution requires that we find $\mathbf{A}^k$ for all values of k. This type of solution, although correct, does not always yield a closed-form solution; hence, it does not offer any insight into the structure of the solution. Appendix A provides the structure for a matrix function approach. ■

5.10 Continuous Time Systems with Sampled Inputs

Suppose that the system inputs are replaced by stepwise approximations with transition times T. At two successive time intervals, we obtain from (5.47) at $t = NT$,

$$\mathbf{x}(nT) = e^{\mathbf{A}nT}\mathbf{x}(0) \tag{5.138}$$

and for $t = (n+1)T$,

$$\mathbf{x}[(n+1)]T = e^{\mathbf{A}(n+1)]T}\mathbf{x}(0) \tag{5.139}$$

From these two expressions, it follows that

$$\mathbf{x}[(n+1)]T = e^{\mathbf{A}T}\mathbf{x}(nT) \tag{5.140}$$

For the complete solution given by (5.63) under these same sampled conditions, we find for $t = nT$ that

$$\mathbf{x}(nT) = e^{\mathbf{A}nT}\mathbf{x}(0) + e^{\mathbf{A}nT}\int_0^{nT} e^{-\mathbf{A}\tau}\mathbf{B}\mathbf{w}(\tau)\,d\tau \tag{5.141}$$

and for $t = (n+1)T$,

$$\mathbf{x}[(n+1)T] = e^{\mathbf{A}(n+1)T}\mathbf{x}(0) = e^{\mathbf{A}(n+1)T}\int_0^{(n+1)T} e^{-\mathbf{A}\tau}\mathbf{B}\mathbf{w}(\tau)\,d\tau \tag{5.142}$$

Now, multiply (5.141) by $e^{\mathbf{A}T}$ and subtract from (5.142). The result is

$$\mathbf{x}[(n+1)T] = e^{\mathbf{A}T}\mathbf{x}(nT) + e^{\mathbf{A}(n+1)T}\int_{nT}^{(n+1)T} e^{-\mathbf{A}\tau}\mathbf{B}\mathbf{w}(\tau)\,d\tau \tag{5.143}$$

Suppose that $\mathbf{w}(t)$ is stepwise constant during the interval $nT \le t \le (n+1)T$. The integrations can be carried out under these conditions. The result is, after some algebraic manipulation,

$$\mathbf{x}[(n+1)T] = e^{\mathbf{A}T}\mathbf{x}(nT) + (e^{\mathbf{A}T} - 1)\mathbf{A}^{-1}\mathbf{B}\mathbf{w}(nT) \tag{5.144}$$

Let us write this expression as

$$\mathbf{x}[(n+1)T] = \mathbf{F}\mathbf{x}(nT) + \mathbf{G}\mathbf{w}(nT) \tag{5.145a}$$

where

$$\mathbf{F} = e^{\mathbf{A}T} \tag{5.145b}$$

$$\mathbf{G} = (e^{\mathbf{A}T} - 1)\mathbf{A}^{-1}\mathbf{B} \tag{5.145c}$$

It is observed that both **F** and **G** are constants that can be evaluated at the start of a computation.

This development shows that a system that is described by (5.143) with piecewise constant inputs at regular sampling intervals is equivalent, at the sampling instants, to a system that is given by the difference equation (5.145a). This form is identical to (5.84a), with the solution given by (5.133).

Problems

Section 5.1

1. Develop state model representations for the systems shown in Figure 5.20.

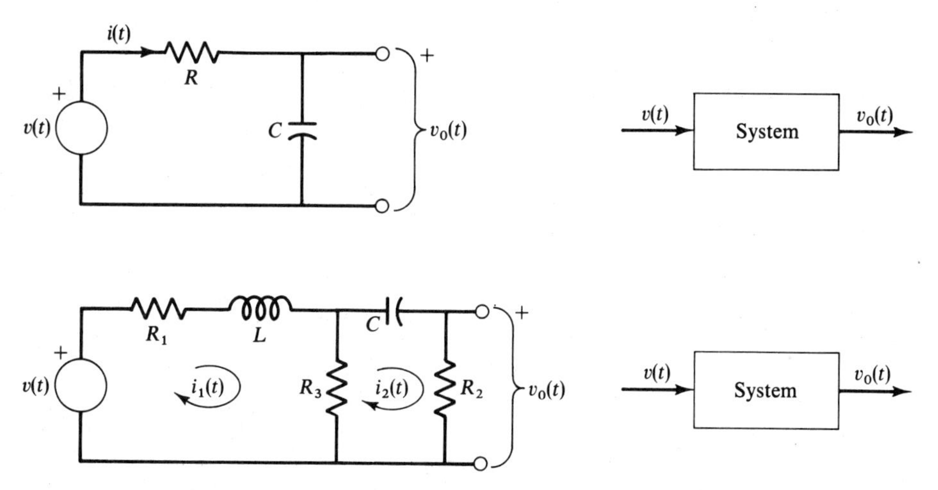

Figure 5.20

2. Develop the network representation and a state model description of the system shown in Figure 5.21.

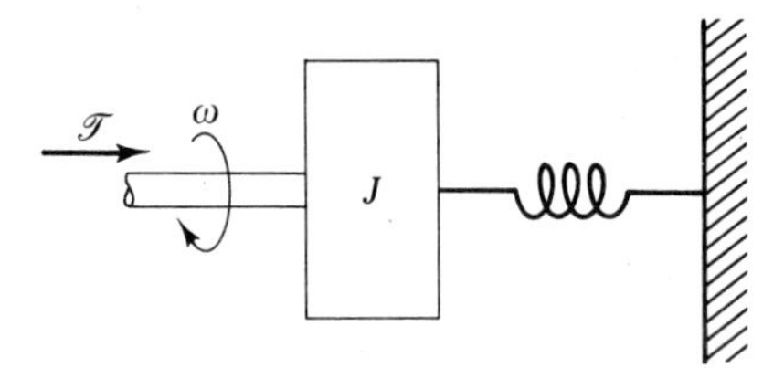

Figure 5.21

3. Develop a state model description of the electrical filter shown in Figure 5.22.

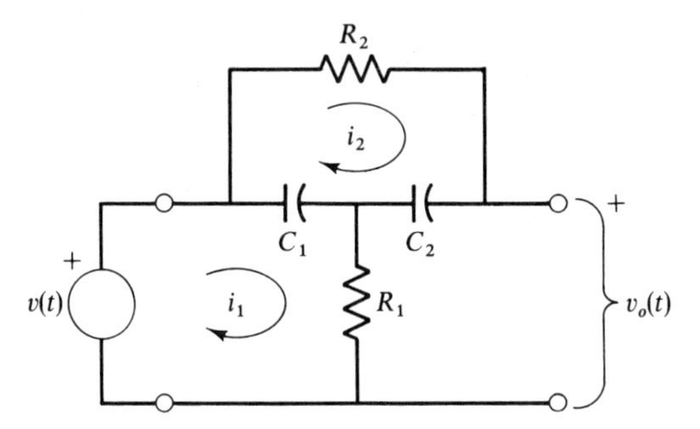

Figure 5.22

4. Deduce state models for the circuits shown in Figure 5.23.

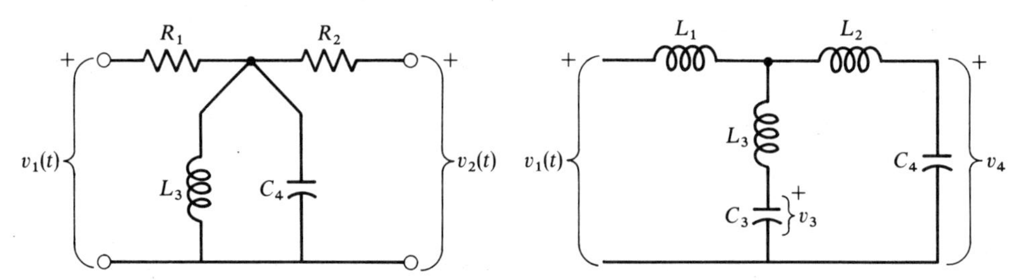

Figure 5.23

5. ***Aerospace.*** A source in a spaceship produces heat at the rate Q. From physics, we know that the rate of change of heat within the spaceship is given by $mC_p(dT/dt)$, where m is the air mass and C_p is its heat capacity. The rate of heat loss to space is equal to $K(T - T_0)$, where K is a constant, T is the interior temperature, and T_0 is the outside temperature, assumed to be constant. Determine the state space representation of the system and its block diagram representation. Use state variable $x = (T - T_0)$ with output $y = T$.
6. Shown in Figure 5.24 is a dc motor with a connected mechanical load. The controlling equations are field circuit $v_f = R_f i_f + L_f(di_f/dt)$; armature circuit $v_a = R_a i_a + L_a(di_a/dt) + G\omega i_f$, where G is the electromechanical constant for the motor and relates the voltage induced in the armature windings due to their rotation in the magnetic field produced by the field current; mechanical torque $\mathcal{T} = D\omega + J(d\omega/dt)$ for damping and inertial effects; and electrical torque $\mathcal{T} = Gi_f i_a$. The system operates under constant armature current. Give a block

diagram description of this electromechanical system and develop a state model representation.

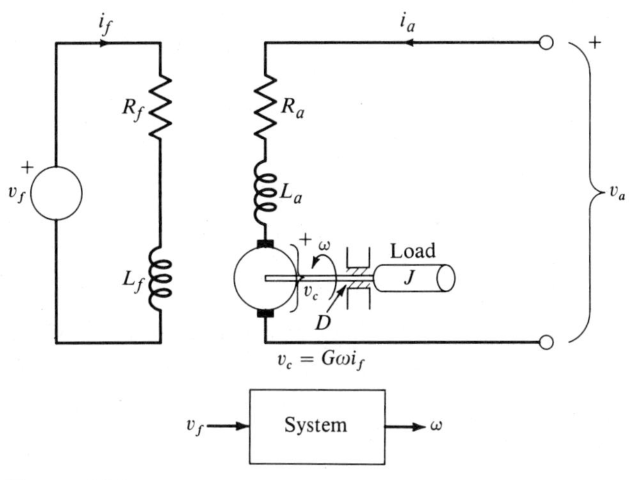

Figure 5.24

Section 5.2

7. Develop state space representations in first canonical form for the systems specified by the following differential equations. Draw block diagrams of each.
   a. $[dy(t)/dt] + ay(t) = W(t)$
   b. $[dy(t)/dt] + ay(t) = [dw(t)/dt] + bw(t)$
   c. $[d^2y(t)/dt^2] + 2[dy(t)/dt] + y(t) = 2[dw(t)/dt] + 5w(t)$
   d. $(d^3y/dt^3) + (d^2y/dt^2) + (dy/dt) + y = (dw/dt) + w$
8. Repeat Problem 7 for the following differential equations:
   a. $(3p^2 + 2p + 1)y = w + 2$ **b.** $(p^3 + 2p^2 + 3p + 1)y = (1 + p)w$
   c. $(2p^3 + 3p^2 + p + 4)y = (p^2 + 2p + 3)w$
9. Refer to the circuit given in Figure 5.25.
   a. Write the differential equations for i_1 and i_2.
   b. Deduce a state model in first canonical form.
   c. Draw a block diagram of the system.

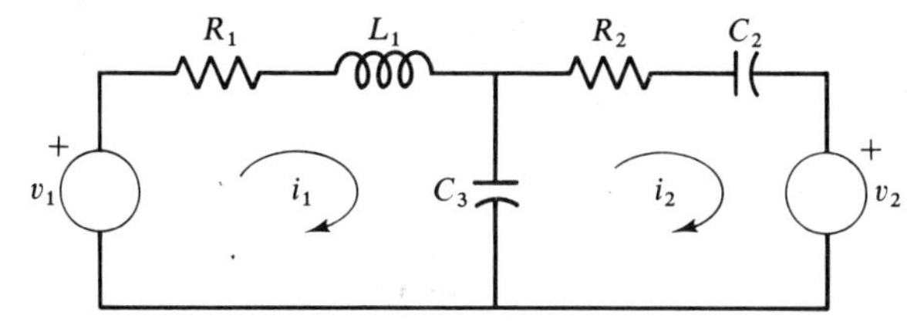

Figure 5.25

10. ***Sociology.*** Rashevsky,* in his study of riots by oppressed groups, developed the following second-order differential equation to describe the performance: $(d^2y/dt^2) - a_0 y = b_0 u(t)$. Develop the first canonical form for this equation and draw its block diagram.

* From N. Rashevsky, *Bull. Math. Biophys.*, Vol. 30 (1968), pp. 501–518.

11. Draw the block diagram representation for the system described by (5.30).

Section 5.3

12. Repeat Problem 7, but now express the results in phase variable form. Draw block diagrams of each.
13. Repeat Problem 8, but write the results in phase variable form.

Section 5.4

14. Deduce expressions for $\mathbf{A}^k$ by induction by evaluating $\mathbf{A}^2$, $\mathbf{A}^3$, ... for the following:

    a. $\mathbf{A} = \begin{bmatrix} \alpha & 0 \\ 0 & \alpha \end{bmatrix}$ **b.** $\mathbf{A} = \begin{bmatrix} 0 & \beta \\ \beta & 0 \end{bmatrix}$ **c.** $\mathbf{A} = \begin{bmatrix} \alpha & 1 \\ 0 & \alpha \end{bmatrix}$

15. Show that (5.49) follows from (5.47).
16. Determine the conditions on **A** and **B** (both are $n \times n$ matrixes) for which $e^{\mathbf{A}+\mathbf{B}} = e^{\mathbf{A}}e^{\mathbf{B}}$. *Hint:* Compare $e^{\mathbf{A}+\mathbf{B}}$ and $e^{\mathbf{A}}e^{\mathbf{B}}$ on a term-by-term basis in the series expansion of the exponentials [see (5.45)].
17. Given the fundamental matrix of a system

$$\mathbf{\Phi}(t) = e^{-t/2}\begin{bmatrix} \cos t/2 + \sin t/2 & 2 \sin t/2 \\ -\sin t/2 & \cos t/2 - \sin t/2 \end{bmatrix} \quad \text{where } \mathbf{A} = \begin{bmatrix} 0 & -1 \\ -1/2 & -1 \end{bmatrix}$$

    a. Develop an expression for the partial derivative $\partial\mathbf{\Phi}(t)/\partial t$.
    b. Find $\mathbf{\Phi}(0)$ and $\partial\mathbf{\Phi}/\partial t$ for $t = 0$.

18. Refer to the circuit of Figure 5.26.

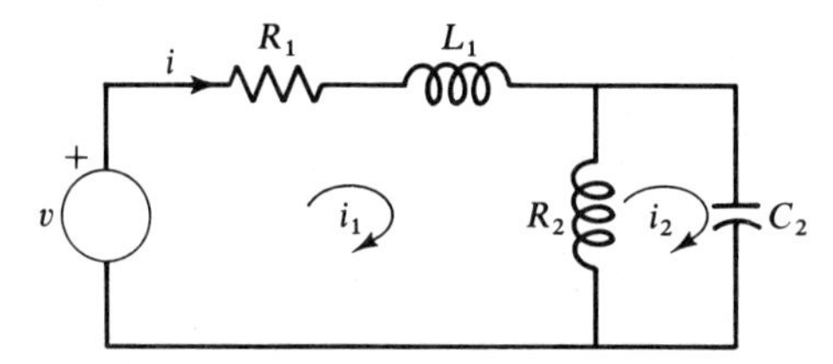

Figure 5.26

    a. Write the differential equation that relates i to v.
    b. Draw a block diagram of the network.
    c. Deduce a state model from the differential equation.
    d. Deduce a state model from the circuit.
    e. Compare the **A** matrixes obtained in (c) and (d).

Section 5.5

19. The inputs to the system in Example 5.10 are $w_1(t) = u(t)$ and $w_2(t) = 0$. The initial conditions are specified by $\mathbf{x}(0) = [1 \quad 0]^T$. Find the outputs $\mathbf{y}(t) = [i_L(t) \quad i_1(t)]^T$ and also determine the impulse response of the system.
20. Find the impulse response of the system given in Example 5.10 with $R_1 = 1$.
21. Find the impulse response for the system of Example 5.11.
22. Determine the solution of the following system:

$$\begin{bmatrix} \dot{x}_1 \\ \dot{x}_2 \end{bmatrix} = \begin{bmatrix} -1 & 0 \\ 0 & -2 \end{bmatrix}\begin{bmatrix} x_1 \\ x_2 \end{bmatrix} + \begin{bmatrix} 1 \\ 1 \end{bmatrix}u(t) \qquad x_1(0) = 1,\ x_2(0) = 1$$

    Determine the impulse response if $y = x_1$.

Section 5.8

23. Deduce the first canonical form for the difference equation $a_2 y(k+2) + a_1 y(k+1) + a_0 y(k) = b_2 w(k+2) + b_1 w(k+1) + b_0 w(k)$.

24. Discrete time systems are specified by the difference equations $2y(k+2) + 5y(k+1) + y(k) = w(k)$ and $3y(k+2) + 2y(k+1) + 5y(k) = 2w(k+1) + 3w(k)$. Draw block diagrams for each equation. Express each system in phase variable and first canonical state representations.

25. Deduce the first canonical form for the third-order difference equation $a_3 y(k+3) + \cdots + a_0 y(k) = b_3 w(k+3) + \cdots + b_0 w(k)$.

26. The block diagram for a specified discrete time system is given in Figure 5.27.

a. Write the difference equations of the system.

b. Express the difference equations in state variable form.

c. Determine difference equations in $y_1(k)$ and $y_2(k)$.

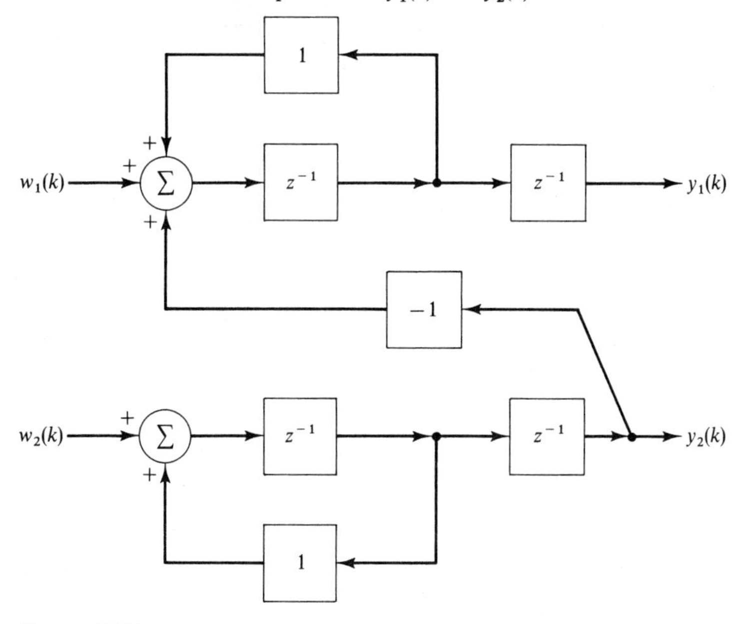

Figure 5.27

Section 5.9

27. Obtain a numerical solution of the state equations for k from 1 to 10 and sketch the results.

$$\begin{bmatrix} x_1(k+1) \\ x_2(k+1) \\ x_3(k+1) \end{bmatrix} = \begin{bmatrix} 2 & -1 & -1 \\ 1 & 0 & -1 \\ 0 & 0 & 1 \end{bmatrix} \begin{bmatrix} x_1(k) \\ x_2(k) \\ x_3(k) \end{bmatrix} \qquad x(0) = \begin{bmatrix} 1 \\ 1 \\ 1 \end{bmatrix}$$

28. Determine the solution to the following systems:

a. $y(k) - y(k-1) + y(k-2) = w(k)$

b. $$\begin{bmatrix} x_1(k+1) \\ x_2(k+1) \end{bmatrix} = \begin{bmatrix} 0 & -2 \\ 0 & 1 \end{bmatrix} \begin{bmatrix} x_1(k) \\ x_2(k) \end{bmatrix} + \begin{bmatrix} 0 \\ 1 \end{bmatrix} w(k)$$

$$y(k) = [1 \quad 0] \begin{bmatrix} x_1(k) \\ x_2(k) \end{bmatrix} + 2w(k)$$

29. Deduce the output for the discrete system specified by the state equation

$$\begin{bmatrix} x_1(k+1) \\ x_2(k+1) \end{bmatrix} = \begin{bmatrix} 0 & 1 \\ 0 & b \end{bmatrix} \begin{bmatrix} x_1(k) \\ x_2(k) \end{bmatrix} + \begin{bmatrix} 0 \\ 1 \end{bmatrix} w(k) \qquad w(k) = u(k)$$

30. A system is described by the block diagram shown in Figure 5.28.

a. Determine the fundamental matrix of the system.

b. Give the unit step response of the system.

c. Give the impulse response of the system.

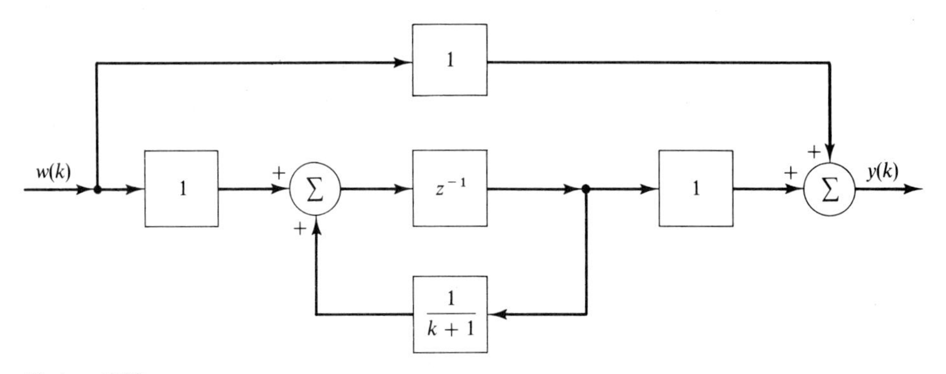

Figure 5.28

Laplace Transform

The use of the Fourier transform in systems analysis involves the decomposition of the excitation function $f(t)$ into a function $F(\omega)$ over an infinite band of frequencies. The excitation function $F(\omega)$, together with the appropriate system function $H(\omega)$, leads, through the inverse Fourier transform, to the response of the system to the prescribed excitation or excitations. Despite its general importance in system studies, the Fourier integral is not generally useful in determining the transient response of networks. Among the shortcomings of the Fourier transform for transient analysis are:

1. The Fourier integral does not converge for some functions, such as the unit step.
2. The response function appears as an integral that may be difficult to evaluate.
3. The circuit must be initially relaxed.

The discussion of the Fourier transform showed that we could represent a function $f(t)$ by a continuous sum of weighted exponential functions of the form $f(t)e^{-j\omega t}$. These exponentials are restricted to the $j\omega$-axis in the complex plane. This restriction proves to be undesirable in many cases. We will find that it can be removed by representing $f(t)$ by a continuous sum of weighted damped exponential functions of the form $f(t)e^{-st}$, where $s = \sigma + j\omega$ with σ a constant. The choice of s moves the path off the $j\omega$-axis in the complex plane. The resultant Laplace transform is well adapted to linear time domain systems analysis. Another feature of the Laplace transform is that it automatically provides for initial conditions in the system.

This chapter develops the Laplace transform from the Fourier transform. The properties of the Laplace transform are discussed. Also, applications of the Laplace transform to systems analysis and to the solution of state equations are examined.

6.1 Preliminary Comments

The foregoing chapters discussed a number of methods for solving the differential equations that described systems problems. The method of variation of parameters is a two-step procedure involving the zero-input response and the zero-state response. The standard techniques of differential equations require finding the homogeneous solution and the steady state, or particular, solution. Both procedures directly involve the differential equations. The convolution integral is also a two-step process: First, we find the system response to an impulse function and then use this response in the convolution integral to find the response to the specified excitation function.

Even though the Fourier series decomposition of periodic, nonsinusoidal functions permits a solution only to the steady state, or particular, response, it does emphasize the use of the system function in systems problems. Applying a Fourier series approach is also a two-step process, involving as it does the determination of the system function $H(\omega)$ and then the response. It leads to a response that is the superposition of the response of each component excitation, but it involves the system function appropriate to each component.

The use of the Fourier integral in systems analysis with nonperiodic excitations involves the decomposition of the excitation function $f(t)$ into a function $F(\omega)$ over an infinite band of frequencies. The function $F(\omega)$, together with the appropriate system function, then leads, through the inverse Fourier transform, to the response of the system to the prescribed excitation. Further, the use of the Fourier integral shows that if the steady state response of a network is known over an infinite band of frequencies, its transient response is uniquely specified: To specify one response is to imply the other, and to change one is to change the other. As noted above, the shortcomings of the Fourier integral in network analysis serve as a useful starting point for a discussion of the Laplace transform. This situation is reviewed first.

Suppose that a circuit is excited by a function $v(t)$. Additionally, suppose that $v(t)$ is a positive time function—that is, it is zero until time $t = 0$. This time function can be represented by the frequency function given by the Fourier transform

$$V(\omega) = \mathscr{F}\{v(t)\} = \int_0^\infty v(t)e^{-j\omega t}\,dt \tag{6.1}$$

The spectrum of the response function of the network is given by the product of $V(\omega)$ and the transfer function $H(\omega)$ of the network:

$$I(\omega) = H(\omega)V(\omega) \tag{6.2}$$

The response function is then obtained by employing inverse Fourier transform

$$i(t) = \mathscr{F}^{-1}\{I(\omega)\} = \frac{1}{2\pi}\int_{-\infty}^{\infty} I(\omega)e^{j\omega t}\, d\omega \tag{6.3}$$

This equation specifies the current for the initially relaxed system for $t \geq 0$. It is possible, of course, that the circuit is not initially relaxed. That is, there can be initial currents and initial charges existing in the circuit before $v(t)$ begins to act. When initial currents and initial charges exist, (6.3) is not the complete solution for the current, and it follows that the frequency spectrums of the voltage and current are not related by the simple relation given by (6.2). Of course, if there are currents and voltages before zero time, they must be due to some previous excitation and might possibly be incorporated into $v(t)$ to obtain a solution. Usually, there is no knowledge of the form of the excitations acting prior to $t = 0$, only a knowledge of the initial conditions. Since practical problems are specified in terms of initial currents and charges and suddenly applied excitations, we desire a solution procedure that takes initial conditions into account.

†6.2 Bilateral Laplace Transform

The development of the Laplace transform proceeds by consideration of the Fourier transform pair given in (4.1). These equations are rewritten here for convenience:

$$F(\omega) = \int_{-\infty}^{\infty} f(t)e^{-j\omega t}\, dt \tag{6.4a}$$

and

$$f(t) = \frac{1}{2\pi}\int_{-\infty}^{\infty} F(\omega)e^{j\omega t}\, d\omega \tag{6.4b}$$

Now, consider a function $\phi(t)$ defined as

$$\phi(t) = f(t)e^{-\sigma t} \tag{6.5}$$

where σ is a real constant. The Fourier transform of this function is

$$\mathscr{F}\{\phi(t)\} = \int_{-\infty}^{\infty} f(t)e^{-\sigma t}e^{-j\omega t}\, dt = \int_{-\infty}^{\infty} f(t)e^{-(\sigma + j\omega)t}\, dt = F(\sigma + j\omega) \tag{6.6}$$

It follows, therefore, that

$$\phi(t) = \frac{1}{2\pi}\int_{-\infty}^{\infty} F(\sigma + j\omega)e^{j\omega t}\, d\omega$$

We have, on rearrangement,

$$f(t) = \frac{1}{2\pi}\int_{-\infty}^{\infty} F(\sigma + j\omega)e^{(\sigma + j\omega)t}\, d\omega \tag{6.7}$$

The quantity $(\sigma + j\omega)$ is the complex frequency s, and so $d\omega = (1/j)\,ds$. When we combine these factors with (6.7), the limits of integration change from $\omega = -\infty$ and $+\infty$ to $s = \sigma - j\infty$ and $\sigma + j\infty$, with the result that

$$f(t) = \frac{1}{2\pi j}\int_{\sigma - j\infty}^{\sigma + j\infty} F(s)e^{st}\,ds \tag{6.8a}$$

Also, from (6.6), we have that

$$F(s) = \int_{-\infty}^{\infty} f(t)e^{-st}\,dt \tag{6.8b}$$

The path of integration in (6.8a) is the line from $-j\infty$ to $+j\infty$ in the s-plane, but displaced to the right of the origin by an amount σ, which is often referred to as the **Bromwich path**. In the light of these equations, the Fourier transform can be considered as a special case of the Laplace transform and can be obtained from (6.8) by setting $\sigma = 0$ or writing $s = j\omega$. We note that (6.8) defines the bilateral, or two-sided, Laplace transform pair. Here, the discussion is limited to the one-sided Laplace transform.

Because our development of the Laplace transform pair proceeded from the Fourier transform pair, it is required that a function $f(t)$ must satisfy the Dirichlet conditions to be Laplace transformable (see Section 4.1). Furthermore, since s is a complex variable, Equation (6.8a) involves integration in the complex plane. We will find that we can usually avoid carrying out such integrations in most applications; we will use tables instead.

An advantage of the Laplace transform is that it overcomes the major difficulties encountered in the use of the Fourier transform. Now, owing to the presence of the convergence factor $e^{-\sigma t}$ in the integrand of $F(s)$, the Laplace integral may exist even though the Fourier integral may not. As an example, the Laplace integral of the unit step function is readily evaluated, whereas the Fourier integral requires very special considerations.

6.3 One-Sided Laplace Transform

In systems problems, it is usually possible to restrict considerations to positive-time functions. The reason is that the response of physical systems can be determined for all $t \geq 0$ from a knowledge of the input for $t \geq 0$ and the initial conditions. That is, the history of the system prior to the reference time $t = 0$ is not necessary. Thus, in practical problems, the two-sided Laplace transform of (6.8b) is replaced by the one-sided Laplace transform, written $\mathscr{L}\{\ \}$ for convenience:

$$F(s) = \int_0^\infty f(t)e^{-st}\,dt \triangleq \mathscr{L}\{f(t)\} \tag{6.9}$$

The expression for the inverse transform is the same for both the one-sided and the two-sided transforms.

In our studies, we will consider piecewise continuous functions and those functions for which

$$\lim_{t\to\infty} f(t)e^{-ct} = 0 \qquad c = \text{real constant} \tag{6.10}$$

Functions of this type are known as functions of **exponential order c**. Also, it can be shown that $\int_0^\infty f(t)e^{-st}\,dt$ converges if

$$\int_0^\infty |f(t)e^{-st}|\,dt = \int_0^\infty |f(t)e^{-\sigma t}e^{-j\omega t}|\,dt$$
$$= \int_0^\infty |f(t)|\,|e^{-\sigma t}|\,|e^{-j\omega t}|\,dt = \int_0^\infty |f(t)|\,e^{-\sigma t}\,dt$$

converges. If our function is of exponential order c, we write the integral

$$\int_0^\infty |f(t)|\,e^{-\sigma t}\,dt = \int_0^\infty |f(t)|\,e^{-ct}e^{-(\sigma-c)t}\,dt$$

This integral shows that for σ in the range $\sigma > c$ (c is the abscissa of convergence), the integral converges and the Laplace integral behaves as defined:

$$F(s) = \int_0^\infty |f(t)e^{-st}|\,dt < \infty \qquad \text{Re}\{s\} > c \tag{6.11}$$

The abscissa of convergence may be positive, negative, or zero depending on the function. The importance of this result is that a finite number of infinite discontinuities are permissible so long as they have finite areas under them. In addition, the convergence is also uniform, which permits us to alter the order of integration in multiple integrals without affecting the results. The restriction in this equation, namely, $\text{Re}\{s\} > c$, indicates that when we wish to find the inverse Laplace transform, we must choose an appropriate path of integration in the complex plane. By doing so, it is guaranteed that the time function so obtained is unique.

■ Example 6.1

Find the Laplace transform of the unit step function $f(t) = u(t)$ and establish the region of convergence.

Solution By (6.9),

$$\mathscr{L}\{u(t)\} = \int_0^\infty u(t)e^{-st}\,dt = \int_0^\infty e^{-st}\,dt = -\frac{e^{-st}}{s}\bigg|_0^\infty = \frac{1}{s} \tag{6.12}$$

The region of convergence is found from the expression $\int_0^\infty |e^{-st}|\,dt = \int_0^\infty e^{-\sigma t}\,dt < \infty$, from which it follows that the region of convergence is the entire right-half plane $\sigma > 0$. ■

Example 6.2
Find the Laplace transform of the unit impulse function and establish the region of convergence.

Solution The delta function $\delta(t)$ is nonzero only at the origin, and, also, the area under this function is unity. Thus, for any function $\psi(t)$,

$$\int_{-\infty}^{\infty} \psi(t)\delta(t)\,dt = \int_{0-}^{0+} \psi(t)\delta(t)\,dt = \psi(0)\int_{0-}^{0+} \delta(t)\,dt = \psi(0)$$

For the particular case when $\psi = e^{-st}$, a function that has the value unity for $t = 0$,

$$\int_{-\infty}^{\infty} \delta(t)e^{-st}\,dt = \int_{0-}^{0+} \delta(t)e^{-st}\,dt = e^{-s0} = 1 \tag{6.13}$$

Because $\int_{-\infty}^{\infty} |\delta(t)e^{-st}|\,dt = \int_{-\infty}^{\infty} \delta(t)e^{-\sigma t}\,dt = 1$ is independent of the value of σ, the entire s-plane is the region of convergence. ■

Example 6.3
Deduce the Laplace transform of the function

$$f(t) = u(t) + e^{-t}u(t)$$

Solution By (6.9),

$$\mathscr{L}\{f(t)\} = \int_0^\infty u(t)e^{-st}\,dt + \int_0^\infty e^{-t}u(t)e^{-st}\,dt = \mathscr{L}\{u(t)\} + \mathscr{L}\{e^{-t}u(t)\}$$

$$= \left.\frac{e^{-st}}{-s}\right|_0^\infty + \left.\frac{e^{-(s+1)t}}{-(s+1)}\right|_0^\infty = \frac{1}{s} + \frac{1}{s+1} = \frac{2s+1}{s(s+1)}$$

Observe that when a function is the sum of many functions, its Laplace transform is the sum of the Laplace transform of each function. This superposition property is anticipated since integration is a linear operation. ■

The application of (6.9) to important common functions of time leads to the results contained in Table 6.1.

6.4 Properties of the Laplace Transform

The functions encountered in system theory often have discontinuities at $t = 0$, reflecting closing switches on sources or some other switching operation. Because of the discontinuity, it is usually convenient to define the value of $f(t)$ at $t = 0$ as the

Table 6.1 Elementary Laplace Transform Pairs

Entry No.	$f(t) = \frac{1}{2\pi j}\int_{\sigma - j\infty}^{\sigma + j\infty} F(s)e^{st}\,ds$	$F(s) = \int_0^{\infty} f(t)\bar{e}^{-st}\,dt$
1	$\delta(t)$	1
2	$u(t)$	$\frac{1}{s}$
3	$t^n \quad \text{for} \quad n > 0$	$\frac{n!}{s^{n+1}}$
4	e^{-at}	$\frac{1}{s+a}$
5	te^{-at}	$\frac{1}{(s+a)^2}$
6	$\frac{t^{n-1}e^{-at}}{(n-1)!}$	$\frac{1}{(s+a)^n}$
7	$\frac{1}{b-a}(e^{-at} - e^{-bt})\ a \neq b$	$\frac{1}{(s+a)(s+b)}$
8	$-\frac{1}{b-a}(ae^{-at} - be^{-bt})\ a \neq b$	$\frac{s}{(s+a)(s+b)}$
9	$\sin \omega t$	$\frac{\omega}{s^2 + \omega^2}$
10	$\cos \omega t$	$\frac{s}{s^2 + \omega^2}$
11	$e^{-at} \sin \omega t$	$\frac{\omega}{(s+a)^2 + \omega^2}$
12	$e^{-at} \cos \omega t$	$\frac{s+a}{(s+a)^2 + \omega^2}$
13	$\sinh \omega t$	$\frac{\omega}{s^2 - \omega^2}$
14	$\cosh \omega t$	$\frac{s}{s^2 - \omega^2}$
15	$\frac{\sqrt{a^2 + \omega^2}}{\omega} \sin(\omega t + \phi),\ \phi = \tan^{-1} \frac{\omega}{a}$	$\frac{s+a}{s^2 + \omega^2}$
16	$\frac{\omega_n}{\sqrt{1 - \zeta^2}} e^{-\zeta\omega_n t} \sin(\omega_n\sqrt{1 - \zeta^2})t \quad \lvert\zeta\rvert < 1$	$\frac{\omega_n^2}{s^2 + 2\zeta\omega_n s + \omega_n^2}$
17	$\frac{1}{a^2 + \omega^2} + \frac{1}{\omega\sqrt{a^2 + \omega^2}} e^{-at} \sin(\omega t - \phi),$ $\phi = \tan^{-1}\left(\frac{\omega}{-a}\right)$	$\frac{1}{s[(s+a)^2 + \omega^2]}$
18	$1 - \frac{1}{\sqrt{1 - \zeta^2}} e^{-\zeta\omega_n t} \sin(\omega_n\sqrt{1 - \zeta^2}\, t + \phi),$ $\phi = \cos^{-1} \zeta,\ \lvert\zeta\rvert < 1$	$\frac{\omega_n^2}{s(s^2 + 2\zeta\omega_n s + \omega_n^2)}$

Note: All the functions are assumed to have values for $t \geq 0$.

limit of $f(t)$ as t approaches zero from the positive direction. This limit is written $f(0+)$ and is consistent with the choice of system response for $t > 0$, where $f(0+)$ denotes initial conditions or impulses. Correspondingly, $f^{(n)}(0+)$ and $f^{(-n)}(0+)$ denote the value of the nth derivative and integral at the discontinuity, taken at $t = 0+$. In the light of this discussion, the definition of the direct Laplace transform can be written

$$F(s) = \lim_{\substack{R \to \infty \\ a \to 0+}} \int_a^R f(t)e^{-st}\,dt \qquad R > 0,\ a > 0 \tag{6.14}$$

The most useful properties of the Laplace transform follow directly from this equation. These properties are contained in Table 6.2.

Example 6.4

Prove entry 1 in Table 6.2 assuming that the functions $f_1(t)$ and $f_2(t)$ are Laplace transformable and that K_1 and K_2 are constants.

Solution From (6.14), we write

$$\begin{aligned} \mathscr{L}\{K_1 f_1(t) + K_2 f_2(t)\} &= \int_0^\infty [K_1 f_1(t) + K_2 f_2(t)]e^{-st}\,dt \\ &= \int_0^\infty K_1 f_1(t)e^{-st}\,dt + \int_0^\infty K_2 f_2(t)e^{-st}\,dt \\ &= K_1 F_1(s) + K_2 F_2(s) \end{aligned} \tag{6.15}$$

The integral is a linear operator. ■

Example 6.5

Prove entry 2 in Table 6.2.

Solution Begin with the basic definition of the Laplace transform and write

$$\mathscr{L}\left\{\frac{df(t)}{dt}\right\} = \int_0^\infty \frac{df(t)}{dt} e^{-st}\,dt$$

Integrate by parts by writing

$$u = e^{-st} \qquad du = -se^{-st}\,dt$$

$$dv = \frac{df}{dt}\,dt \qquad v = f$$

Then

$$\mathscr{L}\left\{\frac{df(t)}{dt}\right\} = f(t)e^{-st}\Big|_0^\infty + s\int_0^\infty f(t)e^{-st}\,dt$$

Table 6.2 Properties of the Laplace Transform

Property
1. Linearity $\mathscr{L}\{K_1 f_1(t) + K_2 f_2(t)\} = \mathscr{L}\{K_1 f_1(t)\} + \mathscr{L}\{K_2 f_2(t)\} = K_1 F_1(s) + K_2 F_2(s)$
2. Time derivative $\mathscr{L}\left\{\frac{d}{dt} f(t)\right\} = sF(s) - f(0+)$
3. Higher time derivative $\mathscr{L}\left\{\frac{d^n}{dt^n} f(t)\right\} = s^n F(s) - s^{n-1} f(0+) - s^{n-2} f^{(1)}(0+) - \cdots - f^{(n-1)}(0+)$ where $f^{(i)}(0+)$, $i = 1, 2, \ldots,$ and $n-1$ is the ith derivative of $f(\cdot)$ at $t = 0+$.
4. Integral with zero initial condition $\mathscr{L}\left\{\int_0^t f(\xi)\, d\xi\right\} = \frac{F(s)}{s}$
5. Integral with initial conditions $\mathscr{L}\left\{\int_0^t f(\xi)\, d\xi\right\} = \frac{F(s)}{s} + \frac{f^{(-1)}(0+)}{s}$ where $f^{(-1)}(0+) = \lim_{t \to 0+} \int_{-\infty}^{0} f(\xi)\, d\xi$
6. Multiplication by exponential $\mathscr{L}\{e^{-at} f(t)\} = F(s+a)$
7. Multiplication by t $\mathscr{L}\{t f(t)\} = -\frac{d}{ds} F(s)$; $\mathscr{L}\{t^n f(t)\} = (-1)^n \frac{dF(s)}{ds}$
8. Frequency shifting $\mathscr{L}\{f(t-\lambda) u(t-\lambda)\} = e^{-s\lambda} F(s)$
9. Scaling $\mathscr{L}\left\{f\left(\frac{t}{a}\right)\right\} = aF(as) \qquad a > 0$
10. Time convolution $\mathscr{L}\left\{\int_0^t f_1(t-\tau) f_2(\tau)\, d\tau\right] = \mathscr{L}\left\{\int_0^t f_1(\tau) f_2(t-\tau)\, d\tau\right\} \triangleq \mathscr{L}\{f_1(t) * f_2(t)\} = F_1(s) F_2(s)$
11. Frequency convolution $\mathscr{L}\{f_1(t) f_2(t)\} = \frac{1}{2\pi j} \int_{x-j\infty}^{x+j\infty} F_1(z) F_2(s-z)\, dz = \frac{1}{2\pi j} [F_1(s) * F_2(s)]$ where $z = x + jy$ and where x must be greater than the abscissa of absolute convergence for $f_1(t)$ over the path of integration.
12. Initial value $\lim_{t \to 0+} f(t) = \lim_{s \to \infty} sF(s)$ provided that this limit exists.
13. Final value $\lim_{t \to \infty} f(t) = \lim_{s \to 0} sF(s)$ provided that $sF(s)$ is analytic on the $j\omega$ axis and in the right half of the s-plane.
14. Division by t $\mathscr{L}\left\{\frac{f(t)}{t}\right\} = \int_s^{\infty} F(s')\, ds'$

Note: All the functions are assumed to have values for $t \geq 0$.

However, $\lim_{t\to\infty} f(t)e^{-st} = 0$; otherwise, the transform would not exist. Thus,

$$\mathscr{L}\left\{\frac{df(t)}{dt}\right\} = s\mathscr{L}\{f(t)\} - f(0+)$$

so that

$$\mathscr{L}\left\{\frac{df(t)}{dt}\right\} = sF(s) - f(0+) \tag{6.16}$$

Attention is called to the very important fact that this expression contains the term $f(0+)$. Reference to entry 1 in Table 6.1 shows that $f(0+)$ represents an impulse of strength $f(0+)$. This conclusion is true because the inverse Laplace transform of $f(0+)$ is equal to $f(0+)\delta(t)$. This result is very important in network problems since it shows that initial conditions associated with derivative functions are automatically included as series impulse functions in the network description. For example, if $f(t)$ denotes the current through an inductor, then terms of the form $v = L\, di/dt$ are included in the network equations. In this case, when such a term is Laplace transformed, there will be terms of the form

$$L\frac{di(t)}{dt} = LsI(s) - Li(0+)$$

where $i(0+)$ denotes the initial current through the inductor. This result shows that an inductor with an initial current can be regarded in subsequent calculations as the superposition of an initially relaxed inductor, which leads to the term $sLI(s)$ plus an impulse voltage source $-Li(0+)$ at time $t = 0$. ■

■ Example 6.6

Prove entry 3 in Table 6.2.

Solution For this evaluation, we use the result in Example 6.5 by noting that

$$\frac{d^2f(t)}{dt^2} = \frac{d}{dt}\left[\frac{df(t)}{dt}\right]$$

Then

$$\mathscr{L}\left\{\frac{d^2f(t)}{dt^2}\right\} = \mathscr{L}\left\{\frac{d}{dt}\frac{df(t)}{dt}\right\} = s\mathscr{L}\left\{\frac{df(t)}{dt}\right\} - \frac{df(0+)}{dt}$$

Again, using (6.16),

$$\mathscr{L}\left\{\frac{d^2f(t)}{dt^2}\right\} = s^2F(s) - sf(0+) - f^{(1)}(0+) \tag{6.17}$$

where the bracketed exponent number indicates the degree of the derivative.

The Laplace transform of the nth time derivative follows as a direct extension of the foregoing development. The result is entry 3 in Table 6.2. If all initial values are zero, this expression reduces to

$$\mathscr{L}\left\{\frac{d^n f(t)}{dt^n}\right\} = s^n F(s) \tag{6.18}$$

This relationship shows that the differential operator d^n/dt^n becomes s^n in the Laplace transforming process.

To see this relationship explicitly, consider a relaxed series RL circuit that is described by the Kirchhoff voltage law:

$$L\frac{di}{dt} + Ri = v(t) \qquad \text{or} \qquad L\frac{d^2q}{dt^2} + R\frac{dq}{dt} = v(t)$$

The Laplace transform of these equations becomes

$$LsI(s) + RI(s) = V(s) \qquad I(s) = \frac{V(s)}{Ls + R}$$

and

$$Ls^2Q(s) + RsQ(s) = V(s) \qquad Q(s) = \frac{V(s)}{s(Ls + R)}$$

We observe that a differential equation, when Laplace transformed, has been transformed to an algebraic equation. To find the unknowns $i(t)$ or $q(t)$, we merely require the inverse Laplace transform. This process is considered in detail in a later section. ■

■ **Example 6.7**

Prove entry 4 in Table 6.2.

Solution If the function $f(t)$ is Laplace transformable, then its integral is written

$$\mathscr{L}\left\{\int_0^t f(\xi)\, d\xi\right\} = \int_0^\infty \left[\int_0^t f(\xi)\, d\xi\right] e^{-st}\, dt$$

Integrate this integral by parts by writing

$$\begin{aligned}\mathscr{L}\left\{\int_0^t f(\xi)\, d\xi\right\} &= \int_0^\infty \left[\int_{-\infty}^t f(\xi)\, d\xi\right] \frac{d}{dt}\left[-\frac{e^{-st}}{s}\right] \\ &= \left[-\frac{e^{-st}}{s}\int_{-\infty}^t f(\xi)\, d\xi\right]\Bigg|_0^\infty + \int_0^\infty \frac{e^{-st}}{s}\frac{d}{dt}\left[\int_{-\infty}^t f(\xi)\, d\xi\right] dt \\ &= -\frac{e^{-s\infty}}{s}\int_{-\infty}^\infty f(\xi)\, d\xi + \frac{e^{-s0}}{s}\int_{-\infty}^0 f(\xi)\, d\xi + \frac{1}{s}\int_0^\infty f(t)e^{-st}\, dt\end{aligned}$$

The first integral is finite for bounded functions; hence, the exponent $e^{-s\infty}$ makes the term zero. Finally, therefore,

$$\mathscr{L}\left\{\int_{-\infty}^{t} f(\xi)\, d\xi\right\} = \frac{F(s)}{s} + \frac{1}{s} f^{(-1)}(0+)$$

The term $(1/s)f^{(-1)}(0+)$ is the initial value of the integral of $f(t)$ at $t = 0+$, and the (-1) in the exponent indicates integration.

Note by entry 2 in Table 6.1 that the term $(1/s)f^{(-1)}(0+)$ denotes a step function of amplitude $f^{(-1)}(0+)$. This factor is a very important result in network problems since it shows that initial conditions associated with integral functions are automatically included as step functions in the Laplace transform development. For example, if $f(t)$ denotes a current $i(t)$ through a capacitor, then the voltage across the capacitor is expressed by the relation

$$v(t) = \frac{q(t)}{C} = \frac{1}{C}\int_{-\infty}^{t} i(\xi)\, d\xi$$

The Laplace transform of such a term is

$$\mathscr{L}\left\{\frac{q(t)}{C}\right\} = \mathscr{L}\left\{\frac{1}{C}\int_{-\infty}^{t} i(\xi)\, d\xi\right\} = \frac{I(s)}{Cs} + \frac{i^{(-1)}(0+)}{Cs} = \frac{I(s)}{Cs} + \frac{q(0+)}{Cs} \qquad \textbf{(6.19)}$$

where $q(0+)$ denotes the charge on the capacitor at initial time $t = 0+$ and $q(0+)/C$ is the initial voltage across the capacitor, $v_c(0+)$. This result means that an initially charged capacitor can be regarded, insofar as the subsequent action in a circuit is concerned, as the superposition of an initially relaxed capacitor plus a series step function voltage source, or, equivalently (because of source transformations), as a shunting impulse current source. ■

■ **Example 6.8**

Prove entry 8 in Table 6.2.

Solution This entry relates to the transform of a function that has been translated along the time axis. The situation is illustrated in Figure 6.1, which shows the translation of a function $f(t)$ to the right by λ units of time, where λ is a positive constant. Upon introducing the translated function into (6.14), we

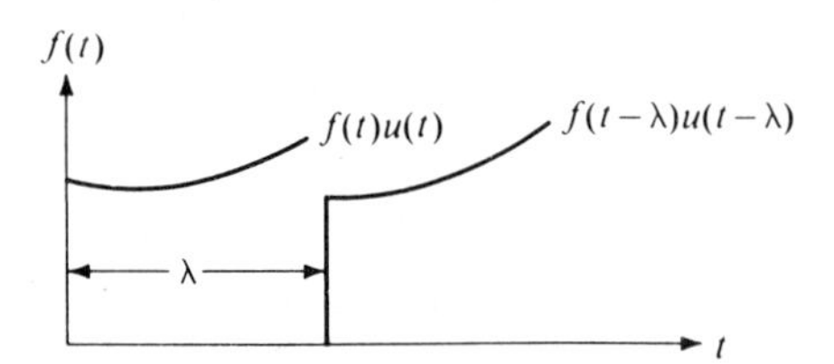

Figure 6.1 Function $f(t)u(t)$ and the Same Function Delayed by Time $t = \lambda$

obtain

$$\mathscr{L}\{f(t-\lambda)u(t-\lambda)\} = \int_0^{\infty} f(t-\lambda)u(t-\lambda)e^{-st}\,dt$$

Now, introduce a new variable $\tau = t - \lambda$, which converts this equation to

$$\begin{aligned}\mathscr{L}\{f(\tau)u(\tau)\} &= e^{-s\lambda}\int_{-\lambda}^{\infty} f(\tau)u(\tau)e^{-s\tau}\,d\tau \\ &= e^{-s\lambda}\int_0^{\infty} f(\tau)e^{-s\tau}\,d\tau = e^{-s\lambda}F(s)\end{aligned} \tag{6.20}$$

since $u(\tau) = 0$ for $-\lambda \le \tau \le 0$.

Similarly, we find that

$$\mathscr{L}\{f(t+\lambda)u(t+\lambda)\} = e^{s\lambda}F(s) \tag{6.21}$$

■

■ **Example 6.9**

Figure 6.2a shows a recurrent square wave. Deduce the Laplace transform of the first pulse and the total recurring waveform.

Solution Initially consider only the first pulse. This pulse can be decomposed into two step functions, as shown in Figure 6.2b. Its Laplace transform is given by

$$\mathscr{L}\{2[u(t) - u(t-1.5)]\} = 2\left(\frac{1}{s} - \frac{1}{s}e^{-1.5s}\right) = \frac{2}{s}(1 - e^{-1.5s})$$

where the shift property has been used.

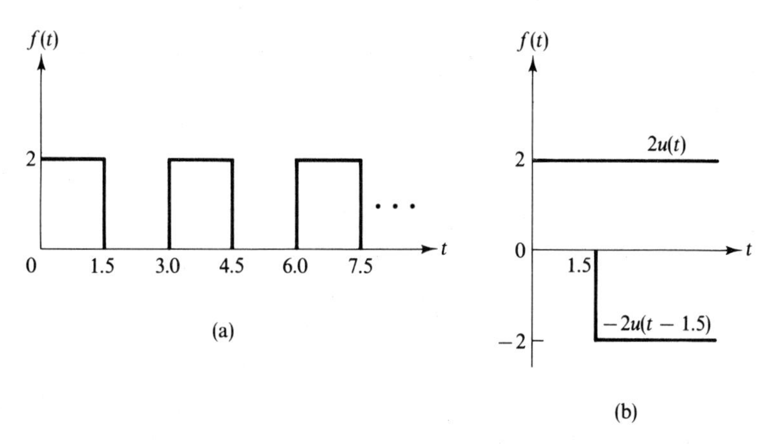

Figure 6.2 Illustrating the Decomposition Procedure of Signals. (a) Recurrent square wave. (b) Decomposition of the first pulse.

We can proceed by adding appropriately delayed step functions—for example, one at time 3 and terminating at 4.5, the next at 6 and terminating at 7.5, and so on. The same result can be obtained by noting that the second pulse can be obtained from the first pulse by effecting a translation in time by an amount 3. That is,

$$f_2(t) = f_1(t-3) \qquad t \geq 3$$

Thus, the Laplace transform function for the two-pulse group is

$$F(s) = F_1(s) + F_2(s) = F_1(s)(1 + e^{-3s}) = \frac{2}{s}(1 - e^{-1.5s})(1 + e^{-3s})$$

We continue this procedure and write

$$F(s) = F_1(s) + F_1(s)e^{-3s} + F_1(s)e^{-6s} + \cdots$$

which is

$$F(s) = F_1(s)(1 + e^{-3s} + e^{-6s} + \cdots)$$

This expression can be written

$$F(s) = \frac{F_1(s)}{1 - e^{-3s}}$$

Combine this result with the expression for $F_1(s)$ to find

$$F(s) = \frac{2}{s}\left(\frac{1 - e^{-1.5s}}{1 - e^{-3s}}\right)$$

or, finally,

$$F(s) = \frac{2}{s}\left(\frac{1}{1 + e^{-1.5s}}\right)$$

■

■ **Example 6.10**

Prove entry 10 in Table 6.2.

Solution This entry specifies the Laplace transform of the convolution of functions $f_1(t)$ and $f_2(t)$:

$$\begin{aligned}\mathscr{L}\{f_1(t) * f_2(t)\} &= \mathscr{L}\left\{\int_0^\infty f_1(t-\tau)f_2(\tau)\,d\tau\right\} \\ &= \int_0^\infty \left[\int_0^\infty f_1(t-\tau)f_2(\tau)\,d\tau\right]e^{-st}\,dt \\ &= \int_0^\infty f_2(\tau)\,d\tau \int_0^\infty f_1(t-\tau)e^{-st}\,dt\end{aligned}$$

By a change of variable, writing $t - \tau = \eta$ and so $dt = d\eta$, then

$$= \int_0^\infty f_2(\tau)\, d\tau \int_{-\tau}^\infty f_1(\eta) e^{-s(\eta+\tau)}\, d\eta$$

However, for positive time functions, $f_1(\eta) = 0$ for $\eta < 0$, which permits changing the lower limit of the second integral, and

$$= \int_0^\infty f_2(\tau) e^{-s\tau}\, d\tau \int_0^\infty f_1(\eta) e^{-s\eta}\, d\eta$$

which is

$$\mathscr{L}\{f_1(t) * f_2(t)\} = F_1(s)F_2(s) \tag{6.22}$$

■

■ **Example 6.11**

Find the Laplace transform of $\int_0^t (t - \tau) \cos \tau \, d\tau$.

Solution This expression is precisely in the form of entry 10, so that

$$\mathscr{L}\left\{\int_0^t (t - \tau) \cos \tau \, d\tau\right\} = \mathscr{L}\{t\}\mathscr{L}\{\cos t\}$$

However, we have that

$$\mathscr{L}\{t\} = \frac{1}{s^2} \qquad \mathscr{L}\{\cos t\} = \frac{s}{s^2 + 1}$$

Hence, it follows that

$$\mathscr{L}\left\{\int_0^t (t - \tau) \cos \tau \, d\tau\right\} = \frac{1}{s(s^2 + 1)}$$

■

■ **Example 6.12**

Determine the Laplace transform of the output of a system $f_o(t)$ whose impulse response is $h(t) = e^{-3t}u(t)$ and whose input is $f(t) = u(t)$.

Solution The output is the convolution of the input and the impulse response function. We thus write

$$f_o(t) = \int_0^\infty e^{-3\tau} u(\tau) u(t - \tau)\, d\tau = \int_0^t e^{-3\tau}\, d\tau$$

because $u(t - \tau) = 0$ for $\tau > t$. Observe that t is a parameter and τ is the independent variable. Thus,

$$\mathscr{L}\{f_o(t)\} \triangleq F_o(s) = \mathscr{L}\{e^{-3t}u(t)\} \times \mathscr{L}\{u(t)\} = \frac{1}{s + 3} \times \frac{1}{s} = \frac{1}{s(s + 3)}$$

We could also proceed by finding the Laplace transform of the last integral instead of using the convolution property:

$$\int_0^\infty \left[\int_0^t e^{-3\tau}\, d\tau\right] e^{-st}\, dt = \int_0^\infty \frac{1-e^{-3t}}{3} e^{-st}\, dt = \frac{1}{3s} - \frac{1}{3(s+3)} = \frac{1}{s(s+3)}$$ ■

■ Example 6.13

Prove entry 11 in Table 6.2.

Solution Before considering the details of the proof, it is well to point out the meaning of this result, which is known as the **initial value theorem**. Recall that for a Laplace-transformable function $f(t)$, we can deduce the corresponding $F(s)$. Further, for a specified $F(s)$, we can, by inversion, find the corresponding $f(t)$, and from this value of $f(t)$, the initial value $f(0)$ can be calculated. Entry 11 permits $f(0)$ to be calculated directly from $F(s)$ without the need for inversion.

To establish the result, consider (6.16) as $s \to \infty$. That is, examine the expression

$$\lim_{s\to\infty} \int_0^\infty \frac{df}{dt} e^{-st}\, dt = \lim_{s\to\infty} [sF(s) - f(0+)]$$

It is here assumed, of course, that $f(t)$ and its first derivative are Laplace transformable and that the limit of $sF(s)$ exists as s approaches infinity. However, the integral vanishes for $s \to \infty$, and, further, $f(0+)$ is independent of s, so that

$$\lim_{s\to\infty} [sF(s) - f(0+)] = 0$$

Furthermore, $f(0+) = \lim_{t\to 0+} f(t)$, so that

$$\lim_{s\to\infty} sF(s) = \lim_{t\to 0+} f(t) \tag{6.23}$$

If $f(t)$ has a discontinuity at the origin, this expression specifies the value of the impulse $f(0+)$. If $f(t)$ contains an impulse term, then the left-hand side does not exist and the initial value property does not hold. ■

■ Example 6.14

Apply the initial value theorem to the following two functions:

a. $F_1(s) = \dfrac{s}{s^2+3}$

b. $F_2(s) = \dfrac{s^2+s+3}{s^2+3}$

Solution By an application of the initial value theorem to (a),

$$\lim_{s\to\infty} sF(s) = \lim \frac{s^2}{s^2+3} = 1$$

When applied to function (b), the initial value of $f(t)$ cannot be found. The reason is readily discovered by writing $F_2(s)$ in the form

$$F_2(s) = 1 + \frac{s}{s^2 + 3}$$

which shows the presence of an impulse in the function. ■

■ Example 6.15

Apply the final value theorem to the following two functions:

a. $F_1(s) = \dfrac{s + a}{(s + a)^2 + b^2}$

b. $F_2(s) = \dfrac{s}{s^2 + b}$

Solution For the first function,

$$\lim_{s \to 0} sF(s) = \lim_{s \to 0} \frac{s(s + a)}{(s + a)^2 + b^2} = 0$$

For the second function, the theorem is not applicable because the function has singularities on the imaginary axis at $s = \pm jb$. ■

6.5 Systems Analysis: Transfer Functions of LTI Systems

The **transfer function**, or **system function**, $H(s)$ of an LTI system, an almost essential entity in systems analysis, is defined as the ratio of the Laplace transform of the output to the Laplace transform of the input. Thus, if the input is $f(t)$ and the output is $g(t)$, then

$$H(s) = \frac{\mathscr{L}\{\text{output}\}}{\mathscr{L}\{\text{input}\}} = \frac{G(s)}{F(s)} = \text{transfer function or system function} \qquad \textbf{(6.24)}$$

The output may be a voltage or a current anywhere in the system, and $H(s)$ is then appropriate to the selected output for a specified input. That is, $H(s)$ may be an impedance, an admittance, or a transfer entity in any given problem. The transfer function $H(s)$ describes the properties of the system alone. That is, the system is assumed to be in its quiescent state (zero state); hence, the initial conditions are assumed to be zero.

Recall that for a given system, the output–input relationship is given by a differential equation that describes the system. Thus, $H(s)$ can be written by inspection of the system's differential equation, but the differential operator p is replaced by the Laplace variable s.

The output time function is given by

$$g(t) = \mathscr{L}^{-1}\{H(s)F(s)\} \tag{6.25}$$

It is noted that when the input is a delta function, $f(t) = \delta(t)$, and since $\mathscr{L}\{\delta(t)\} = 1$, then

$$h(t) = \mathscr{L}^{-1}\{H(s)\} \tag{6.26}$$

This expression shows that the system function $H(s)$ is the transform of the impulse response of the system.

An important feature of the Laplace transform method is that it is not necessary to isolate and identify the system function since $H(s)$ appears automatically through the transform of the differential equation and is included in the mathematical operations. The situation changes considerably in those cases when the system consists of a number of subsystems that are interconnected to form the completed system. Now, one must take due account of whether the subsystems are interconnected in cascade, parallel, or feedback configurations.

The following examples illustrate how we can find the transfer function of a system from its time domain representation. Often, it is convenient to draw a block diagram of the system and then use Figure 2.25 to help in the reduction process.

■ Example 6.16

Determine the transfer function of the system shown in Figure 6.3a.

Solution The differential equation describing the system is

$$L\frac{di(t)}{dt} + Ri(t) = v_i(t)$$

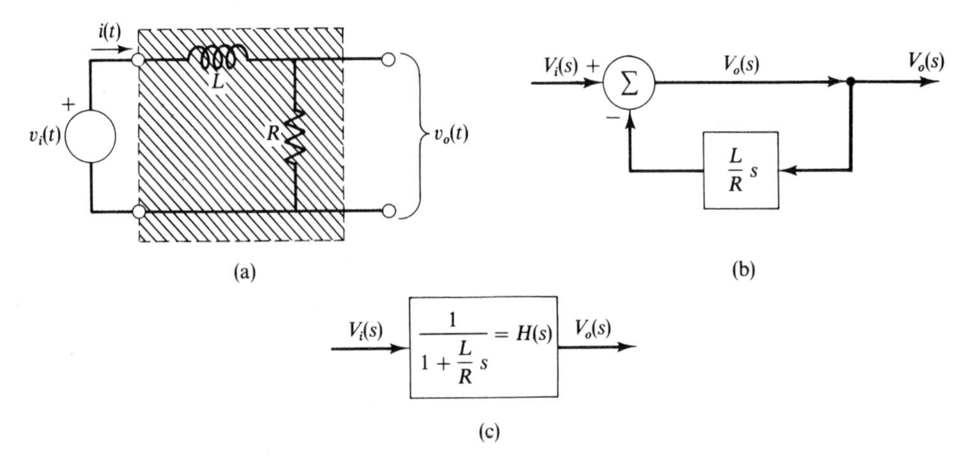

Figure 6.3 Electrical System and Its Block Diagram Representations. (a) Circuit diagram. (b) Block diagram. (c) Block diagram showing input–output function.

which we write

$$\frac{L}{R}\frac{dv_o(t)}{dt} + v_o(t) = v_i(t)$$

where

$$v_o(t) = Ri(t)$$

The Laplace transform of both sides of the differential equation, invoking the linearity and differentiation properties of the Laplace transform plus zero initial conditions, is

$$\frac{L}{R} sV_o(s) + V_o(s) = V_i(s) \tag{6.27}$$

From this equation,

$$H(s) = \frac{V_o(s)}{V_i(s)} = \frac{R/L}{s + R/L} \tag{6.28}$$

To obtain the block diagram representation of the system, (6.27) is written in the form

$$V_o(s) = V_i(s) - \frac{L}{R} sV_o(s)$$

This equation is shown in Figure 6.3b. This equation is solved for $V_o(s)$:

$$V_o(s) = \frac{V_i(s)}{1 + \frac{L}{R} s} \tag{6.29}$$

This result, which also follows from Figure 6.3b (see Figure 2.25), is shown in block diagram form in Figure 6.3c. ■

■ Example 6.17

Determine the transfer function $H(s) = V_1(s)/F(s)$ of the system shown in Figure 6.4a.

Solution We first develop the network equivalent diagram: It is shown in Figure 6.4b, where the velocities v_1 and v_2 are specified relative to ground as a fixed frame of reference. Observe that the force moves with velocity v_1; hence, this source is connected between ground and level v_1, as shown in Figure 6.4c. Observe also that the mass M_1 moves with velocity v_1 and is connected, therefore, between level v_1 and v_g. The damper D_1 moves with a relative velocity specified by v_1 and v_2; hence, it is connected between v_1 and v_2. Lastly, since both M_2 and D_2 move with velocity v_2, they are connected in parallel between v_2 and v_g. A rearrangement of the resulting geometry yields Figure 6.4d, a familiar circuit configuration for the mechanical system.

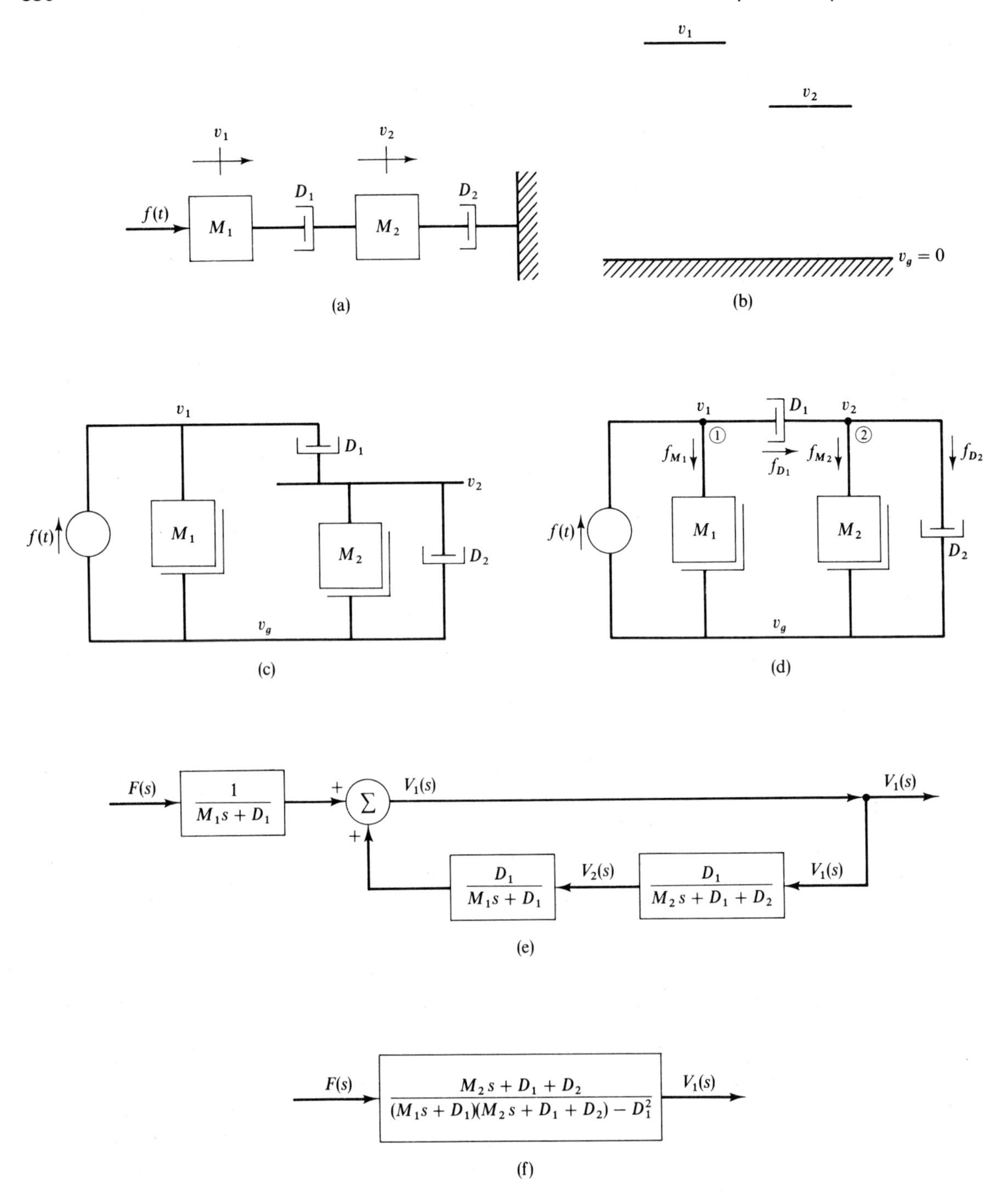

Figure 6.4 Mechanical System. (a) Physical model. (b), (c), and (d) Steps in developing the network diagram. (e) Block diagram. (f) Block diagram giving input–output relation.

Since the sum of the forces at each node must be zero, we obtain

$$M_1 \frac{dv_1}{dt} + D_1(v_1 - v_2) - f(t) = 0 \tag{6.30a}$$

$$M_2 \frac{dv_2}{dt} + D_1(v_2 - v_1) + D_2 v_2 = 0 \tag{6.30b}$$

In writing these equations, we assumed that nonsource terms were pointing away from the nodes and were assumed positive. This selection is arbitrary and must be kept consistent for all nodes. The Laplace transforms of these equations are

$$(M_1 s + D_1)V_1(s) - D_1 V_2(s) = F(s) \tag{6.31a}$$

$$-D_1 V_1(s) + (M_2 s + D_1 + D_2)V_2(s) = 0 \tag{6.31b}$$

To draw a block diagram of the system, we rearrange these equations to

$$V_1(s) = \frac{D_1}{M_1 s + D_1} V_2(s) + \frac{1}{M_1 s + D_1} F(s)$$

and

$$V_2(s) = \frac{D_1}{M_2 s + D_1 + D_2} V_1(s)$$

These relations are readily seen in Figure 6.4e.

We now write

$$\frac{V_1(s)}{F(s)\left(\dfrac{1}{M_1 s + D_1}\right)} = \frac{1}{1 - \dfrac{D_1^2}{(M_1 s + D_1)(M_2 s + D_1 + D_2)}}$$

from which

$$\frac{V_1(s)}{F(s)} = \frac{1/(M_1 s + D_1)}{1 - \dfrac{D_1^2}{(M_1 s + D_1)(M_2 s + D_1 + D_2)}}$$

$$= \frac{M_1 s + D_1 + D_2}{(M_1 s + D_1)(M_2 s + D_1 + D_2) - D_1^2}$$

The final configuration is shown in Figure 6.4f. ■

■ **Example 6.18** ***Electromechanical System***

Find the transfer function $H(s) = \Omega(s)/E(s)$ of the rotational electromechanical transducer shown in Figure 6.5a. Mechanical and air friction damping are taken into consideration by the damping constant D. The movement of the cylinder–pointer combination is restrained by a spring with spring constant K_s. The moment of inertia of the coil assembly is J. There are N turns on the coil. (In this example e's define voltages and v's define velocities.)

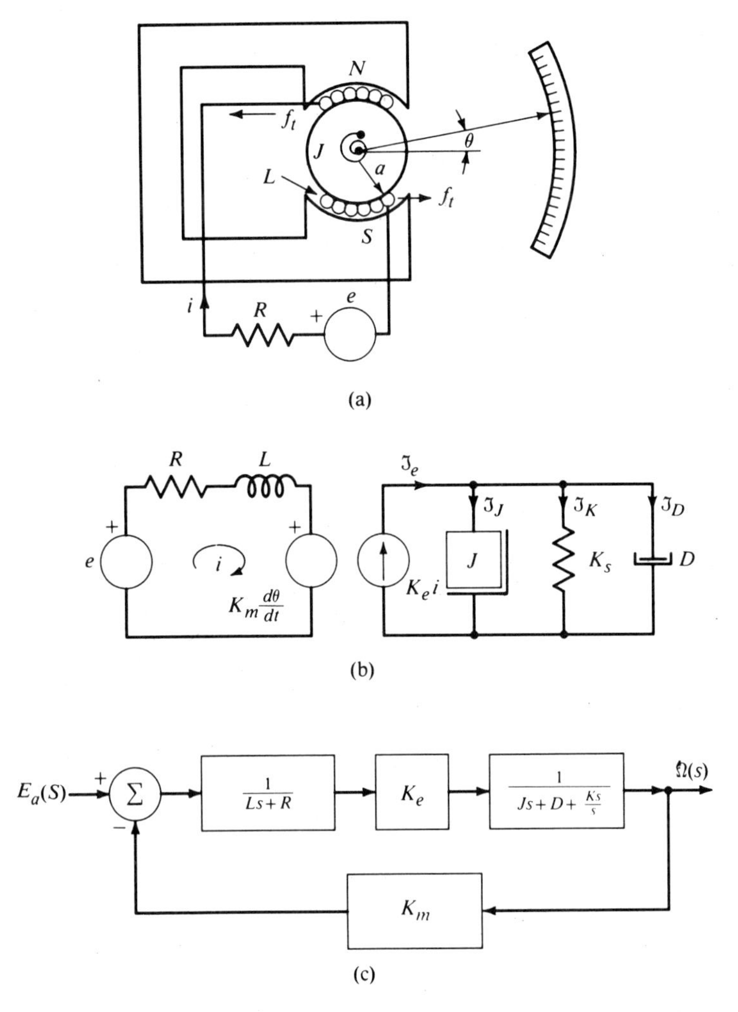

Figure 6.5 Rotational Electromechanical Transducer. (a) Physical model. (b) Circuit model. (c) Block diagram representation.

Solution Because there are N turns on the coil, there are $2N$ conductors of length l perpendicular to the magnetic field at a distance a from the center of rotation. Therefore, the electrical torque is

$$\mathscr{T}_e = f_t a = (2NBli)a = (2NBla)i = K_e i \tag{6.32}$$

where K_e is a constant depending on the physical and geometrical properties of the apparatus. The spring develops an equal and opposite torque, which is written

$$\mathscr{T}_s = K_s \theta \qquad K_s = \text{(newton-meter)/degree} \tag{6.33}$$

Owing to the movement of the coil in the magnetic field, a voltage is generated in the coil. This voltage is given by

$$e_m = 2NBlv = (2NBla)\frac{d\theta}{dt} = K_m \frac{d\theta}{dt} = K_m \omega \tag{6.34}$$

where K_m is equal to K_e. From the equivalent circuit representation of the system shown in Figure 6.5b, we obtain the equations

$$L\frac{di}{dt} + Ri + K_m \omega = e \qquad \text{Kirchhoff voltage law} \tag{6.35a}$$

$$J\frac{d\omega}{dt} + D\omega + K_s \int \omega\, dt = K_e i \qquad \text{D'Alembert's principle} \tag{6.35b}$$

The Laplace transform of these equations yields

$$(Ls + R)I(s) + K_m \Omega(s) = E(s) \tag{6.36a}$$

$$\left(Js + D + \frac{K_s}{s}\right)\Omega(s) - K_e I(s) = 0 \tag{6.36b}$$

Substitute the value of $I(s)$ from the second of these equations into the first and solve for the ratio $\Omega(s)/E(s)$. We obtain

$$H(s) \triangleq \frac{\Omega(s)}{E(s)} = \frac{K_e}{(Ls + R)\left(Js + D + \dfrac{K_s}{s}\right) + K_e K_m} \tag{6.37}$$

A block diagram representation of this system is shown in Figure 6.5c. ■

■ **Example 6.19** ***Bioengineering***

Determine the transfer function $H(s) \triangleq \Theta(s)/\mathscr{T}(s)$ for the mechanical system (pendulum) shown in Figure 6.6a. Aspects of this problem were discussed in Example 2.19. Draw a block diagram of the system and use block diagram reductions to deduce the transfer function.

Solution Carrying out the analysis of the system using D'Alembert's principle for rotational systems and making the approximation for small rotational angles, as was done in Example 2.19, the controlling differential equation is [see (2.95)]

$$J\frac{d^2\theta}{dt^2} + D\frac{d\theta}{dt} + Mgl\theta = \mathscr{T}(t) \tag{6.38}$$

Laplace-transform this equation to get

$$Js^2\Theta(s) + Ds\Theta(s) + Mgl\Theta(s) = \mathscr{T}(s) \tag{6.39}$$

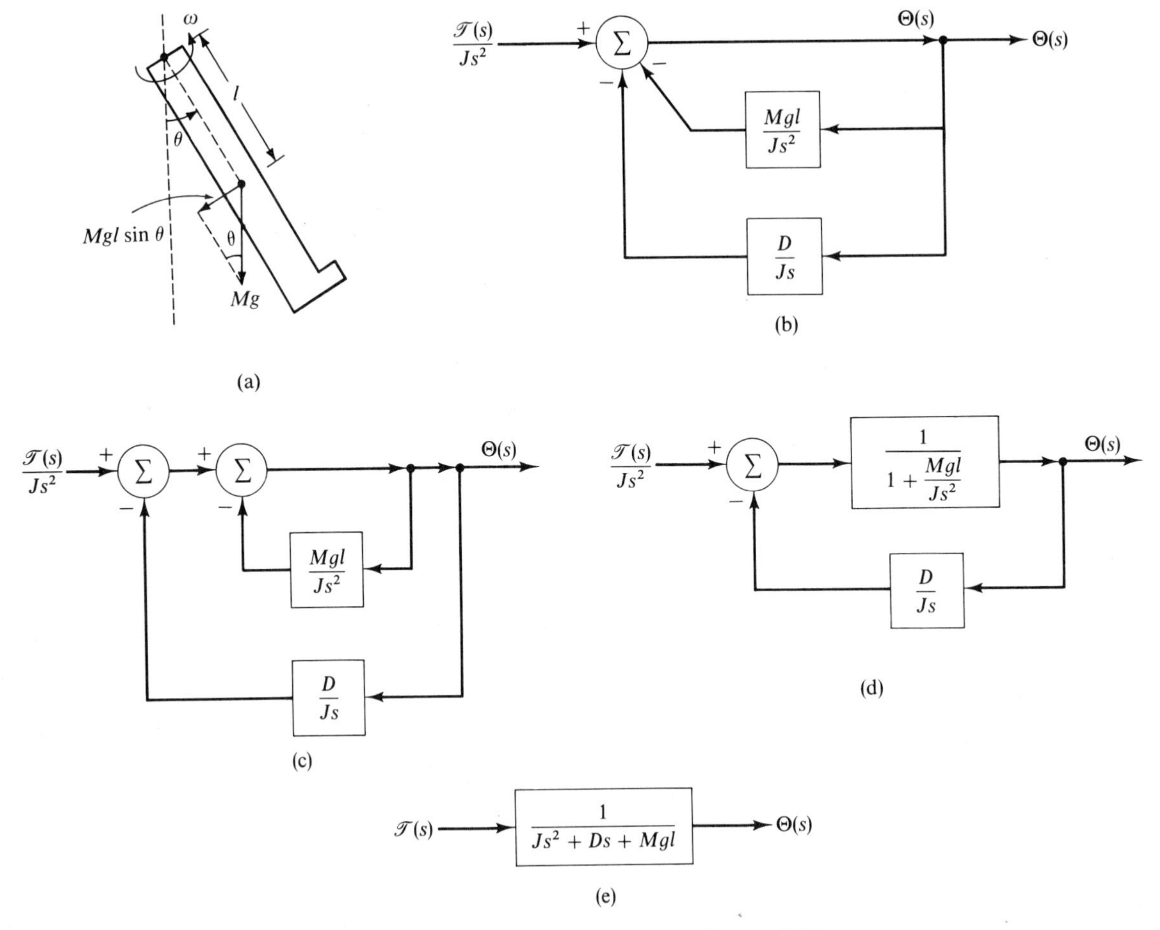

Figure 6.6 Mechanical System with Steps in Deducing the Input–Output $H(s)$

This equation can be solved directly for $H(s) = \Theta(s)/\mathcal{T}(s)$. The result is

$$\frac{\Theta(s)}{\mathcal{T}(s)} = \frac{1}{Js^2 + Ds + Mgl} \tag{6.40}$$

Suppose that we proceed from the block diagram of the system. Now, we write (6.39) in the form

$$\Theta(s) = -\frac{D}{Js}\Theta(s) - \frac{Mgl}{Js^2}\Theta(s) + \frac{1}{Js^2}\mathcal{T}(s)$$

This result is shown in Figure 6.6b. Now, we reduce the block diagram according to the rules given in Figure 2.25. Rearrange the block diagram as in Figure 6.6c and then reduce the innermost feedback loop. This inner loop has the value $1/(1 + Mgl/Js^2)$. The block diagram simplifies to that shown in Figure 6.6d.

Now, reduce this feedback loop to obtain finally

$$\frac{\Theta(s)}{\dfrac{\mathcal{T}(s)}{Js^2}} = \frac{1/(1 + Mgl/Js^2)}{1 + \dfrac{D}{Js}\dfrac{1}{(1 + Mgl/Js^2)}}$$

which becomes

$$\frac{\Theta(s)}{\mathcal{T}(s)} = \frac{1}{Js^2 + Ds + Mgl}$$

This expression is shown in Figure 6.6e. ■

■ **Example 6.20**

Determine the transfer function $H(s) \triangleq V_o(s)/V_i(s)$ of the system shown in Figure 6.7a.

Solution We have seen that in the Laplace transform operation, the operator d/dt in a differential equation is replaced by s and the operator $\int dt$ is replaced by $1/s$ in problems with zero initial conditions (see previous examples). Therefore, we can write the Kirchhoff voltage law in Laplace form by direct reference to Figure 6.7b. The equations are

$$(R_1 + L_1 s)I_1(s) - L_1 s I_2(s) = V_i(s) \tag{6.41a}$$

$$-L_1 s I_1(s) + (R_2 + L_1 s + L_2 s)I_2(s) = 0 \tag{6.41b}$$

$$L_2 s I_2(s) = V_o(s) \tag{6.41c}$$

These equations are shown in Figures 6.7c, 6.7d, and 6.7e, respectively. When the parts are combined, the resulting block diagram is that shown in Figure 6.7f. Using entries in Figure 2.25, the transfer function is easily determined and is given in Figure 6.7g. ■

6.6 Inverse Laplace Transform

As already discussed, the inverse Laplace transform is the integral that converts $F(s)$ into the equivalent $f(t)$. To perform the inverse transformation requires that the integration be performed in the complex plane along a path that insures that $f(t)$ is unique. There is, therefore, a one-to-one correspondence between the direct and the inverse transforms, as expressed by the pair

$$F(s) = \mathcal{L}\{f(t)\} \qquad f(t) = \mathcal{L}^{-1}\{F(s)\} \tag{6.42}$$

As examples, we have already found the following correspondences:

$$F(s) = \mathcal{L}\{e^{-t}u(t)\} = \frac{1}{s+1} \qquad \mathcal{L}^{-1}\left\{\frac{1}{s+1}\right\} = e^{-t} \tag{6.43}$$

$$F(s) = \mathcal{L}\{u(t - t_0)\} = \frac{e^{-t_0 s}}{s} \qquad \mathcal{L}^{-1}\left\{\frac{e^{-t_0 s}}{s}\right\} = u(t - t_0) \tag{6.44}$$

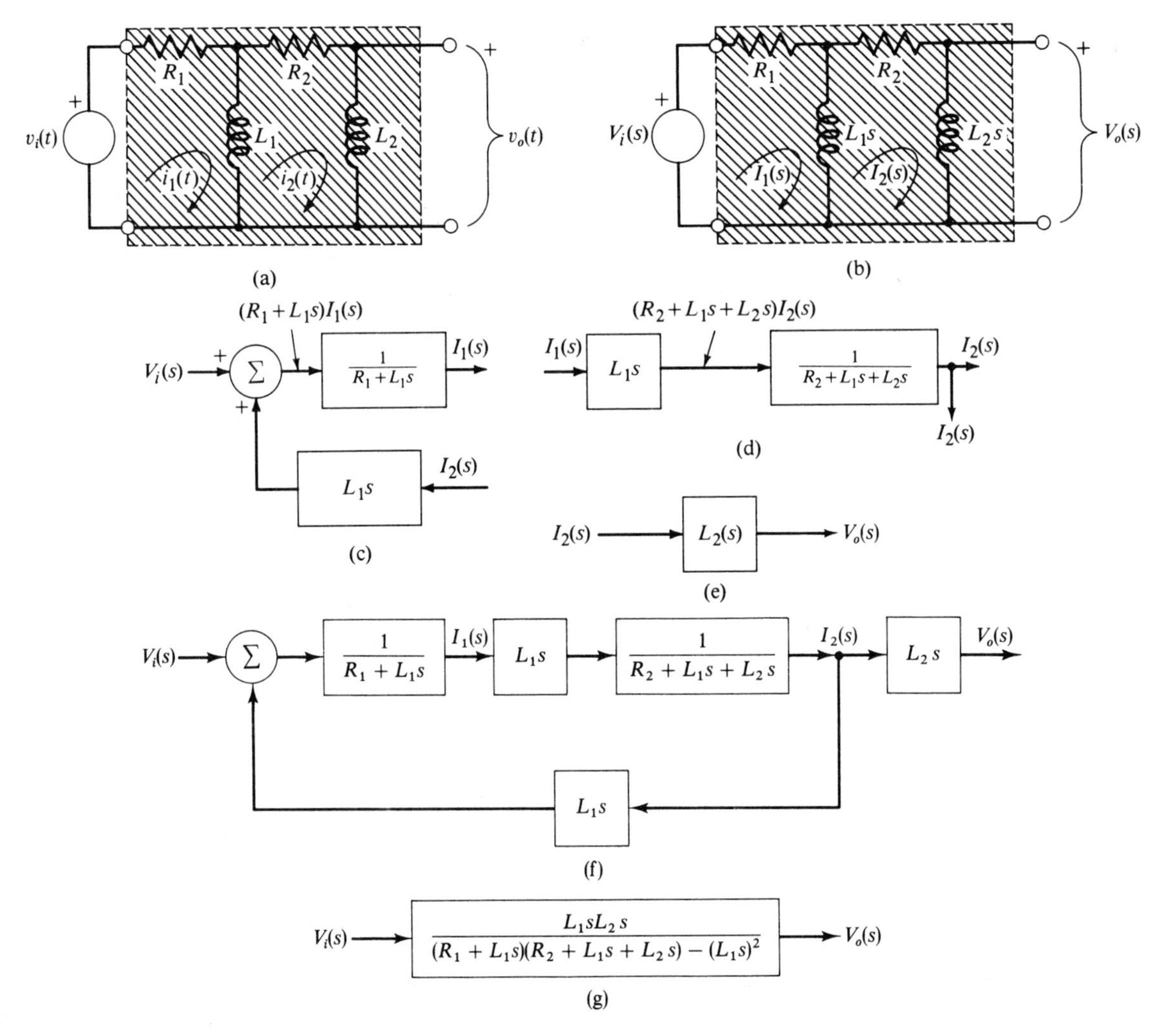

Figure 6.7 Illustrating Example 6.20

Consequently, we need merely refer to Table 6.1 to write the $f(t)$ appropriate to a given $\mathscr{L}^{-1}\{F(s)\}$. In the event that the available tables do not include a given $F(s)$ and if $F(s)$ cannot be reduced to available forms, recourse to the inversion integral will be necessary. The following examples illustrate some of the usual methods used in finding inverse Laplace transformations.

■ **Example 6.21**

Find the inverse Laplace transform of the function

$$F(s) = \frac{s-3}{s^2+5s+6} \tag{6.45}$$

Solution It is observed that the denominator can be factored into the form $(s+2)(s+3)$. Thus, $F(s)$ is written in partial fraction form:

$$F(s) = \frac{s-3}{(s+2)(s+3)} = \frac{A}{s+2} + \frac{B}{s+3} \tag{6.46}$$

where A and B are constants that must be determined.

To evaluate A, multiply both sides of (6.46) by $s+2$ and then set $s=-2$. The result is

$$A = F(s)(s+2)\Big|_{s=-2} = \frac{s-3}{s+3}\Big|_{s=-2} = -5$$

where the term $B(s+2)/(s+3)|_{s=-2}$ is identically zero. We proceed in the same manner to deduce the constant B. Multiply both sides by $s+3$ and set $s=-3$:

$$B = F(s)(s+3)\Big|_{s=-3} = \frac{s-3}{s+2}\Big|_{s=-3} = 6$$

The inverse transform is given by

$$\begin{aligned}\mathscr{L}^{-1}\{F(s)\} &= -5\mathscr{L}^{-1}\left\{\frac{1}{s+2}\right\} + 6\mathscr{L}^{-1}\left\{\frac{1}{s+3}\right\} \\ &= -5e^{-2t} + 6e^{-3t} \qquad t \geq 0\end{aligned}$$

where Table 6.1, entry 4, was used. ■

■ **Example 6.22**

Find the inverse Laplace transform of the function

$$F(s) = \frac{s+1}{[(s+2)^2+1](s+3)}$$

Solution This function is written in the form

$$F(s) = \frac{A}{s+3} + \frac{Bs+C}{[(s+2)^2+1]} = \frac{s+1}{[(s+2)^2+1](s+3)}$$

The value of A is evaluated by multiplying both sides of this equation by $s+3$ and then setting $s=-3$. The result is

$$A = (s+3)F(s)\Big|_{s=-3} = \frac{-3+1}{(-3+2)^2+1} = -1$$

To evaluate B and C, combine the two fractions:

$$\frac{-1[(s+2)^2+1] + (s+3)(Bs+C)}{[(s+2)^2+1](s+3)} = \frac{s+1}{[(s+2)^2+1](s+3)}$$

from which it follows that

$$-(s^2 + 4s + 5) + Bs^2 + (C + 3B)s + 3C = s + 1$$

Combine like-powered terms to write

$$(-1 + B)s^2 + (-4 + C + 3B)s + (-5 + 3C) = s + 1$$

Equating the coefficients of like powers of s, we then have

$$-1 + B = 0 \qquad -4 + C + 3B = 1 \qquad -5 + 3C = 1$$

From these equations, we obtain

$$B = 1 \qquad C = 2$$

The function $F(s)$ is written in the equivalent form

$$F(s) = \frac{-1}{s+3} + \frac{s+2}{(s+2)^2 + 1}$$

Now, using Table 6.1, the result is

$$f(t) = -e^{-3t} + e^{-2t} \cos t \qquad t \geq 0$$

■

In many cases $F(s)$ is the quotient of two polynomials with real coefficients. If the numerator polynomial is of the same or higher degree than the denominator polynomial, we must first divide the numerator polynomial by the denominator polynomial, the division being carried forward until the numerator polynomial of the remainder is of degree one less than the denominator polynomial. This procedure results in a polynomial in s plus a **proper fraction**. The proper fraction can be expanded into a partial fraction expansion. The result of such an expansion is an expression of the form

$$F'(s) = B_0 + B_1 s + \cdots + \frac{A_1}{s - s_2} + \frac{A_2}{s - s_2} + \cdots + \frac{A_{p1}}{s - s_p} + \frac{A_{p2}}{(s - s_p)^2} + \cdots + \frac{A_{pr}}{(s - s_p)^r} \qquad \textbf{(6.47)}$$

This expression has been written in a form to show three types of terms:

1. Polynomial.
2. Simple partial fraction including all terms with distinct roots.
3. Partial fraction appropriate to multiple roots.

To find the constants $A_1, A_2, \ldots$, the polynomial terms are removed, leaving the proper fraction

$$F'(s) - (B_0 + B_1 s + \cdots) = F(s) \qquad \textbf{(6.48)}$$

where

$$F(s) = \frac{A_1}{s - s_1} + \frac{A_2}{s - s_2} + \cdots + \frac{A_k}{s - s_k} + \frac{A_{p1}}{s - s_p} + \frac{A_{p2}}{(s - s_p)^2} + \cdots + \frac{A_{pr}}{(s - s_p)^r}$$

To find the constants A_k, which in complex variable terminology are the residues of the function $F(s)$ at the simple poles s_k, it is only necessary to note that as $s \to s_k$, the term $A_k/(s - s_k)$ will become large compared with all other terms. In the limit,

$$A_k = \lim_{s \to s_k} [(s - s_k)F(s)] \tag{6.49}$$

For each simple pole, upon taking the inverse transform, the result will be a simple exponential of the form

$$\mathscr{L}^{-1}\left\{\frac{A_k}{s - s_k}\right\} = A_k e^{s_k t} \tag{6.50}$$

Note also that since $F(s)$ contains only real coefficients, if s_k is a complex pole with residue A_k, there will also be a conjugate pole s_k^* with residue A_k^*. For such complex poles,

$$\mathscr{L}^{-1}\left\{\frac{A_k}{s - s_k} + \frac{A_k^*}{s - s_k^*}\right\} = A_k e^{s_k t} + A_k^* e^{s_k^* t}$$

These terms can be combined in the following way:

$$\begin{aligned} \text{response} &= (a_k + jb_k)e^{(\sigma_k + j\omega_k)t} + (a_k - jb_k)e^{(\sigma_k - j\omega_k)t} \\ &= e^{\sigma_k t}(a_k + jb_k)(\cos \omega_k t + j \sin \omega_k t) \\ &\quad + (a_k - jb_k)(\cos \omega_k t - j \sin \omega_k t) \\ &= 2e^{\sigma_k t}(a_k \cos \omega_k t - b_k \sin \omega_k t) \\ &= 2A_k e^{\sigma_k t} \cos (\omega_k t + \theta_k) \end{aligned} \tag{6.51}$$

where $\theta_k = \tan^{-1}(b_k/a_k)$ and $A_k = a_k/\cos \theta_k$.

When the proper fraction contains a multiple pole of order r, the coefficients in the partial fraction expansion $A_{p1}, A_{p2}, \ldots, A_{pr}$, which are involved in the terms

$$\frac{A_{p1}}{(s - s_p)} + \frac{A_{p2}}{(s - s_p)^2} + \cdots + \frac{A_{pr}}{(s - s_p)^r}$$

must be evaluated. A simple application of (6.49) is not adequate. Now, the procedure is to multiply both sides of (6.48) by $(s - s_p)^r$, which gives

$$\begin{aligned} (s - s_p)^r F(s) &= (s - s_p)^r \left(\frac{A_1}{s - s_1} + \frac{A_2}{s - s_2} + \cdots + \frac{A_k}{s - s_k}\right) \\ &\quad + A_{p1}(s - s_p)^{r-1} + \cdots + A_{p(r-1)}(s - s_p) + A_{pr} \end{aligned} \tag{6.52}$$

In the limit as $s = s_p$, all terms on the right vanish with the exception of A_{pr}. Suppose now that this equation is differentiated once with respect to s. The constant A_{pr} will vanish in the differentiation, but $A_{p(r-1)}$ will be determined by setting $s = s_p$. This procedure is continued to find each of the coefficients A_{pk}. Specifically, this procedure is specified by

$$A_{pk} = \frac{1}{(r-k)!} \frac{d^{r-k}}{ds^{r-k}} [F(s)(s-s_p)^r] \Big|_{s=s_p} \tag{6.53}$$

Example 6.23

Find the inverse transform of the following function:

$$F'(s) = \frac{s^3 + 2s^2 + 3s + 1}{s^2(s+1)}$$

Solution This fraction is not a proper fraction. The numerator polynomial is divided by the denominator polynomial by simple long division. The result is

$$F'(s) = 1 + \frac{s^2 + 3s + 1}{s^2(s+1)}$$

The proper fraction is expanded into partial fraction form:

$$F(s) = \frac{s^2 + 3s + 1}{s^2(s+1)} = \frac{A_{11}}{s} + \frac{A_{12}}{s^2} + \frac{A_2}{s+1}$$

The value of A_2 is deduced by using (6.49):

$$A_2 = [(s+1)F(s)]_{s=-1} = \frac{s^2 + 3s + 1}{s^2}\Big|_{s=-1} = -1$$

To find A_{11} and A_{12}, we proceed as specified by (6.53):

$$A_{12} = [s^2 F(s)]\Big|_{s=0} = \frac{s^2 + 3s + 1}{s+1}\Big|_{s=0} = 1$$

$$A_{11} = \frac{1}{1!}\left\{\frac{d}{ds}[s^2 F(s)]\right\}_{s=0} = \frac{d}{ds}\left[\frac{s^2 + 3s + 1}{s+1}\right]$$

$$= -\frac{s^2 + 3s + 1}{(s+1)^2} + \frac{2s+3}{s+1}\Big|_{s=0} = 2$$

Therefore,

$$F'(s) = 1 - \frac{1}{s} + \frac{1}{s^2} + \frac{2}{s+1}$$

From Table 6.1, the inverse transform is

$$f(t) = -1 + t + 2e^{-t} \qquad \text{for } t > 0$$

The $\delta(t)$ function does not appear in $f(t)$ because we consider $f(t)$ for $t > 0$. ■

■ Example 6.24

Two identical amplifiers are connected in cascade, as shown in Figure 6.8. It is assumed that isolation exists between them so that neither circuit loads the other, but the signals do transfer from the output of the first to the input of the second amplifier. The impulse response of each amplifier is $h(t) = te^{-t}$ for $t \geq 0$. Determine the unit step response of the combined circuit.

Solution Since, by definition, $H(s)$ is the Laplace transform of the impulse response of a system, then each amplifier is defined by

$$\mathscr{L}\{te^{-t}\} = H_1(s) = \frac{1}{(s+1)^2}$$

and the total system function is (see Figure 2.25)

$$H(s) = \frac{1}{(s+1)^4}$$

The unit step response is, since $V(s) = 1/s$,

$$y(t) = \mathscr{L}^{-1}\left\{\frac{1}{s(s+1)^4}\right\}$$

$$= \mathscr{L}^{-1}\left\{\frac{A_{11}}{(s+1)} + \frac{A_{12}}{(s+1)^2} + \frac{A_{13}}{(s+1)^3} + \frac{A_{14}}{(s+1)^4} + \frac{A}{s}\right\}$$

By (6.53),

$$A_{14} = \frac{1}{0!}\frac{d^0}{ds^0}\left[(s+1)^4 H(s)\right]_{s=-1} = 1\left[\frac{1}{s}\right]_{s=-1} = -1$$

$$A_{13} = \frac{1}{1!}\frac{d}{ds}\left[\frac{1}{s}\right]_{s=-1} = -1 \times \frac{1}{s^2}\bigg|_{s=-1} = -1$$

$$A_{12} = \frac{1}{2!}\frac{d^2}{ds^2}\left[\frac{1}{s}\right]_{s=-1} = \frac{1}{2}\left(\frac{2}{s^3}\right) = \frac{1}{s^3}\bigg|_{s=-1} = -1$$

$$A_{11} = \frac{1}{3!}\frac{d^3}{ds^3}\left[\frac{1}{s}\right]_{s=-1} = \frac{1}{6}\left(\frac{-3}{s^4}\right) = -\frac{1}{2}\left(\frac{1}{s^4}\right)_{s=-1} = -\frac{1}{2}$$

$$A = \left[s\frac{1}{s(s+1)^4}\right]_{s=0} = \frac{1}{(s+1)^4}\bigg|_{s=0} = 1$$

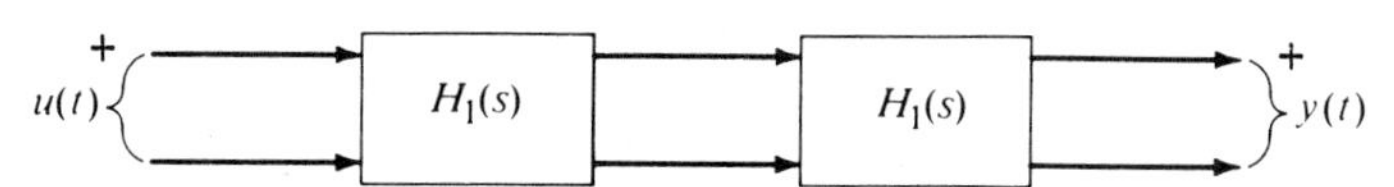

Figure 6.8 Two Amplifiers in Cascade

Then

$$y(t) = \mathscr{L}^{-1}\left[\frac{1}{s} - \frac{1}{2}\frac{1}{s+1} - \frac{1}{(s+1)^2} - \frac{1}{(s+1)^3} - \frac{1}{(s+1)^4}\right]$$

$$= u(t) - \frac{1}{2}e^{-t} - \frac{te^{-t}}{1!} - \frac{t^2e^{-t}}{2!} - \frac{t^3e^{-t}}{3!}$$ ■

6.7 Problem Solving by Laplace Transforms

Let us consider several examples that show the use of the Laplace transform in the solution of network problems.

■ **Example 6.25**
Assume that an initial current $i(0-)$ exists in the inductor (due to a circuit not shown) when a dc source is switched into the simple RL circuit shown in Figure 6.9. Determine the system current.

Solution The controlling differential equation for the circuit shown after closing the switch S at $t = 0$ is, by an application of the Kirchhoff voltage law,

$$L\frac{di}{dt} + Ri = v(t) = Vu(t)$$

By Laplace-transforming each term in this differential equation, we get

$$L[sI(s) - i(0+)] + RI(s) = \frac{V}{s}$$

This is rearranged to

$$(Ls + R)I(s) = \frac{V}{s} + Li(0+)$$

Solve for $I(s)$:

$$I(s) = \frac{V}{L}\frac{1}{s(s + R/L)} + \frac{i(0+)}{s + R/L}$$

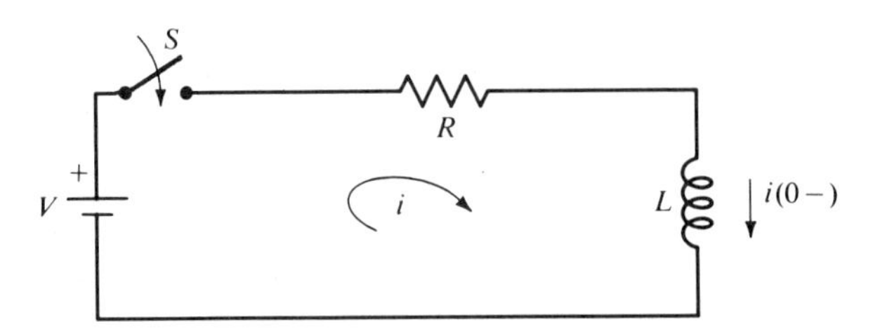

Figure 6.9 Series *RL* Circuit

This is written

$$I(s) = \frac{V}{R}\left(\frac{1}{s} - \frac{1}{s + R/L}\right) + \frac{1}{s + R/L}\, i(0+)$$

To determine $i(0+)$, invoke (2.53): Since the system L does not change, then $i(0+) = i(0-)$. Using the appropriate entries in Table 6.1, the inverse transform of this equation is

$$i(t) = \underbrace{\frac{V}{R}(1 - e^{-Rt/L})}_{\substack{\text{zero-state}\\ \text{response}}} + \underbrace{i(0+)e^{-Rt/L}}_{\substack{\text{zero-input}\\ \text{response}}} = \underbrace{\left[i(0+) - \frac{V}{R}\right]e^{-Rt/L}}_{\substack{\text{transient}\\ \text{response}}} + \underbrace{\frac{V}{R}}_{\substack{\text{steady}\\ \text{state}}} \qquad t \geq 0$$

Clearly, the first term on the right is the response of the initially relaxed system; the second term is the response of the system to the initial condition. The complete solution is the superposition of these two responses. The reader should also consult Section 2.3. ■

■ **Example 6.26**

Find the current in the initially relaxed circuit shown in Figure 6.10a. The input is the pulse shown in Figure 6.10b.

Solution The differential equation describing the system is

$$L\frac{di}{dt} + Ri = v(t)$$

The input signal is decomposed into two step functions, as shown in Figure 6.10c:

$$v(t) = u(t) - u(t - 1)$$

Now, apply the principle of superposition in the solution. First, we find the solution $i_1(t)$ for the input $u(t)$; next, we find the solution $i_2(t)$ when the input is $u(t - 1)$. The total solution is $i(t) = i_1(t) + i_2(t)$. This approach is valid because the system is linear.

The solution to the differential equation

$$L\frac{di_1}{dt} + Ri_1 = u(t)$$

is deduced by Laplace-transforming each term in the differential equation to

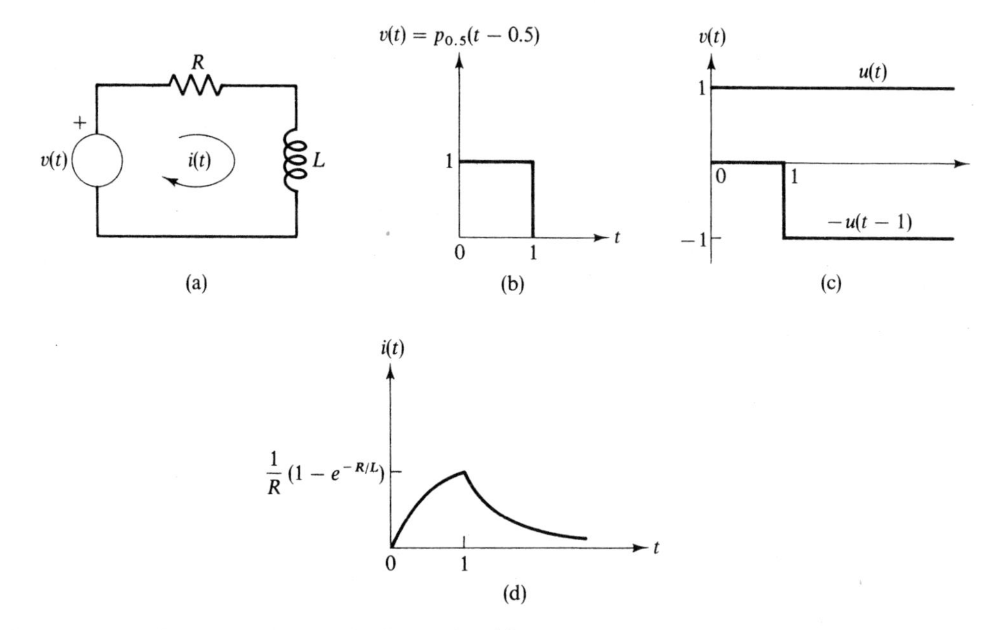

Figure 6.10 Illustrating Example 6.26 and the Principle of Superposition

find

$$(Ls + R)I_1(s) = \frac{1}{s}$$

Thus,

$$I_1(s) = \frac{1}{s(Ls + R)} = \frac{1}{R}\left(\frac{1}{s} - \frac{1}{s + R/L}\right)$$

with the time solution

$$i_1(t) = \frac{1}{R}(u(t) - e^{-Rt/L}) \qquad t \geq 0$$

Similarly, we obtain for $i_2(t)$,

$$L\frac{di_2}{dt} + Ri_2 = -u(t - 1)$$

Because the system is linear and time invariant, we can determine the response due to $-u(t)$ and then shift the response by one unit to the right. Thus, we have

$$i_2(t) = -\frac{1}{R}[u(t - 1) - e^{-R(t-1)/L}] \qquad t \geq 1$$

The total current is given by

$$i(t) = \begin{cases} i_1(t) & 0 \le t \le 1 \\ i_1(t) + i_2(t) & t > 1 \end{cases} = \begin{cases} \dfrac{1}{R}(1 - e^{-Rt/L}) & 0 \le t \le 1 \\ \dfrac{1}{R}(e^{-R/L} - 1)e^{-Rt/L} & t > 1 \end{cases}$$

The current $i(t)$ is shown in Figure 6.10d.

As an exercise, the reader should check the solution by first finding the impulse response of the system ($h(t) = (1/L)e^{-Rt/L}$) and then deducing the response $i(t) = p_{0.5}(t - 0.5) * h(t)$. ■

■ **Example 6.27**

A force $f(t)$ is applied to the mechanical system of negligible mass, as shown in Figure 6.11a. Find the velocity of the system.

Solution From Figure 6.11b, we write

$$Dv + K \int v\, dt = au(t)$$

Now, define a new variable $y(t) = \int_0^t v\, dt$; this equation takes the form

$$D \frac{dy}{dt} + Ky = au(t)$$

Clearly, $\int_{0-}^{0+} v\, dt = 0$ implies that $y(0+) = 0$. This equation, when Laplace transformed and rearranged, yields

$$Y(s) = \frac{a}{D} \frac{1}{(s + K/D)s}$$

The inverse transform of this expression is (see Example 6.25)

$$y(t) = \frac{a}{K}(1 - e^{-Kt/D}) \qquad \text{for } t \ge 0$$

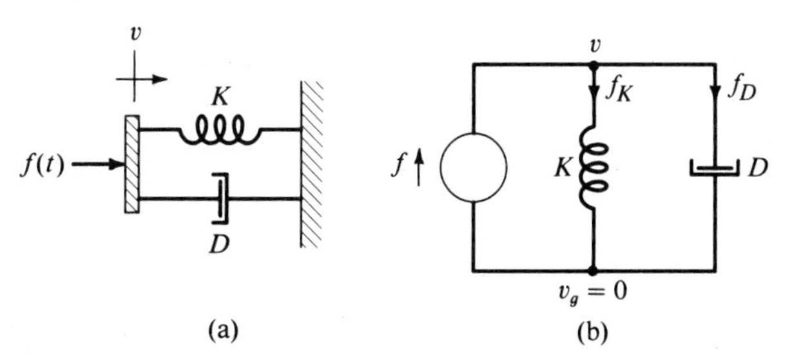

Figure 6.11 Simple Mechanical System (For Example, Car Shock Absorber). (a) Physical model. (b) Circuit equivalent form.

and, therefore,

$$v(t) \triangleq \frac{dy}{dt} = \frac{a}{D} e^{-Kt/D} \qquad \text{for } t > 0$$

We approach this problem from a different point of view, namely, the use of convolution. This approach requires that we find the impulse response of the system, which is specified by the equation

$$Dh(t) + K \int h(t)\, dt = \delta(t)$$

The Laplace transform of this equation is

$$DH(s) + \frac{K}{s} H(s) = 1$$

from which

$$H(s) = \frac{1}{D} \frac{s}{s + K/D} = \frac{1}{D} - \frac{K}{D^2} \frac{1}{s + K/D}$$

The inverse Laplace transform gives the relation

$$h(t) = \frac{1}{D} \delta(t) - \frac{K}{D^2} e^{-Kt/D} \qquad t \geq 0$$

For a step function input $v_i = au(t)$, the output is

$$\begin{aligned} v(t) = v_i(t) * h(t) &= \frac{a}{D} \int_{-\infty}^{\infty} \delta(\tau) u(t - \tau)\, d\tau \\ &\quad - \frac{Ka}{D^2} \int_{-\infty}^{\infty} e^{-K\tau/D} u(\tau) u(t - \tau)\, d\tau \\ &= \frac{a}{D} u(t) - \frac{Ka}{D^2} \int_0^t e^{-K\tau/D}\, d\tau = \frac{a}{D} u(t) + \frac{a}{D} (e^{-Kt/D} - 1) u(t) \\ &= \frac{a}{D} e^{-Kt/D} u(t) \end{aligned}$$

This result is precisely what we found before using a different approach.

We could also have taken the Laplace transform of the defining equation, which yields

$$DV(s) + \frac{KV(s)}{s} = a \frac{1}{s}$$

from which

$$V(s) = \frac{a}{D(s + K/D)}$$

The inverse of this function is

$$v(t) = \frac{a}{D} e^{-Kt/D} \qquad t \geq 0$$

as before. ■

■ **Example 6.28**

Refer to Figure 6.12a, which shows the switching of an inductor into a circuit with an initial current. Prior to switching, the circuit inductance is L_1; after switching, the total circuit inductance is $L_1 + L_2$. The switching occurs at $t = 0$. Determine the current in the circuit for $t \geq 0$.

Solution The current at $t = 0-$ is

$$i(0-) = \frac{V}{R}$$

To find the current after switching at $t = 0+$, we employ the law of conservation of flux linkages [see (2.54)]. We can write, over the switching period,

$$L_1 i(0-) = (L_1 + L_2)i(0+)$$

from which

$$i(0+) = \frac{L_1}{L_1 + L_2} i(0-) = \frac{L_1}{L_1 + L_2} \frac{V}{R}$$

The differential equation that governs the circuit response after the switch S is closed is

$$(L_1 + L_2)\frac{di}{dt} + Ri = Vu(t)$$

The Laplace transform of this equation yields

$$I(s) = \frac{V}{R}\left[\frac{1}{s} - \frac{1}{s + R/(L_1 + L_2)}\right] + \frac{1}{s + R/(L_1 + L_2)} i(0+)$$

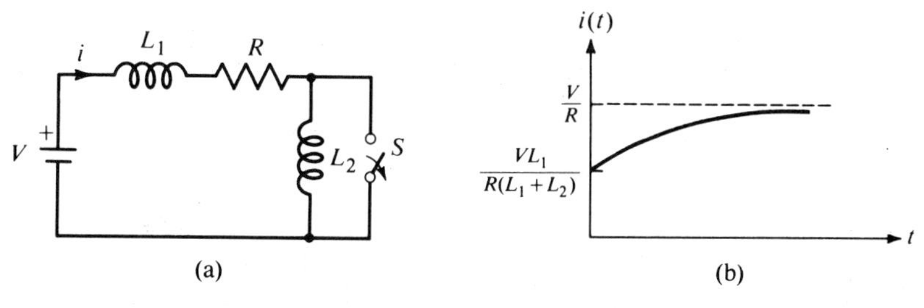

Figure 6.12 Switching L in a Circuit with Initial Current. (a) Circuit configuration. (b) Response of the RL circuit after L is switched.

Include the value of $i(0+)$ in this expression and then take the inverse Laplace transform. The result is

$$i(t) = \frac{V}{R}\left(1 - \frac{L_2}{L_1 + L_2} e^{-Rt/(L_1+L_2)}\right) \qquad \text{for } t \geq 0$$

The form of the variation of current is shown in Figure 6.12b. ■

■ Example 6.29

Find an expression for the response $v_2(t)$ for $t > 0$ in the circuit of Figure 6.13. The source $v_1(t)$, the current $i_L(0-)$ through $L = 2H$, and the voltage $v_c(0-)$ across the capacitor $C = 1$ F at the switching instant are all assumed to be known.

Solution After the switch is closed, the circuit is described by the loop equations:

$$\left(3i_1 + \frac{2di^1}{dt}\right) - \left(1i_2 + \frac{2di^2}{dt}\right) = v_1(t)$$

$$-\left(1i_1 + \frac{2di^1}{dt}\right) + \left(3i_2 + \frac{2di^2}{dt} + \int i_2\,dt\right) = 0$$

$$v_2(t) = 2i_2(t)$$

All terms in these equations are Laplace transformed. The result is the set of transformed equations

$$(3 + 2s)I_1(s) - (1 + 2s)I_2(s) = V_1(s) + 2[i_1(0+) - i_2(0+)]$$

$$-(1 + 2s)I_1(s) + \left(3 + 2s + \frac{1}{s}\right)I_2(s) = 2[-i_1(0+) + i_2(0+)] - \frac{q_2(0+)}{s}$$

$$V_2(s) = 2I_2(s)$$

The current through the inductor is

$$i_L(t) = i_1(t) - i_2(t)$$

We choose $t = 0+$ and write

$$i_L(0+) = i_1(0+) - i_2(0+)$$

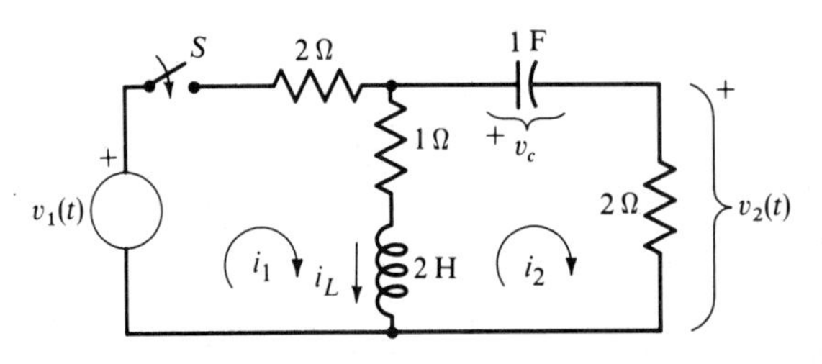

Figure 6.13 Circuit for Example 6.29

Also, since

$$\frac{1}{C}q_2(t) = \frac{1}{C}\int_{-\infty}^{t} i_2(t)\,dt = \frac{1}{C}\lim_{t=0+}\int_0^t i_2(t)\,dt + \frac{1}{C}\int_{-\infty}^{0} i_2(t)\,dt = 0 + v_c(0-)$$

then

$$\frac{q_2(0+)}{C} \triangleq v_c(0+) = v_c(0-) = i_2^{(-1)}(0) = \frac{q_2(0+)}{1}$$

The equation set is solved for $I_2(s)$, which is written by Cramer's rule,

$$I_2(s) = \frac{\begin{vmatrix} 3+2s & V_1(s) + 2i_L(0+) \\ -(1+2s) & -2i_L(0+) - \dfrac{v_c(0+)}{s} \end{vmatrix}}{\begin{vmatrix} 3+2s & -(1+2s) \\ -(1+2s) & 3+2s+\dfrac{1}{s} \end{vmatrix}}$$

$$= \frac{(3+2s)\left[-2i_L(0+) - \dfrac{v_c(0+)}{s}\right] + (1+2s)[V_1(s) + 2i_L(0+)]}{(3+2s)\left(\dfrac{2s^2+3s+1}{s}\right) - (1+2s)^2}$$

$$= \frac{-(2s^2+3s)v_c(0+) - 4si_L(0+) + (2s^2+s)V_1(s)}{8s^2+10s+3}$$

Further,

$$V_2(s) = 2I_2(s)$$

Then, upon taking the inverse transform,

$$v_2(t) = 2\mathcal{L}^{-1}\{I_2(s)\}$$

If the circuit contains no stored energy at $t = 0$, then $i_L(0+) = v_c(0+) = 0$ and now

$$v_2(t) = 2\mathcal{L}^{-1}\left\{\frac{(2s^2+s)V_1(s)}{8s^2+10s+3}\right\}$$

For the particular case when $v_i(t) = u(t)$ so that $V_1(s) = 1/s$,

$$v_2(t) = 2\mathcal{L}^{-1}\left\{\frac{2s+1}{8s^2+10s+3}\right\} = 2\mathcal{L}^{-1}\left\{\frac{2s+1}{8(s+1/2)(s+3/4)}\right\}$$

$$= \frac{1}{2}\mathcal{L}^{-1}\left\{\frac{1}{s+3/4}\right\} = \frac{1}{2}e^{-3t/4} \qquad t \geq 0$$

The validity of this result is readily confirmed since at the instant $t = 0+$, the inductor behaves as an open circuit and the capacitor behaves as a short circuit.

Thus, at this instant, the circuit appears as two equal resistors in a simple series circuit, and the voltage is shared equally. ■

Example 6.30

Find the velocity of the system shown in Figure 6.14a when the applied force is $f(t) = e^{-t}u(t)$. Use the Laplace transform method and assume zero initial conditions. Solve the same problem by means of the convolution technique. The input is the force and the output is the velocity.

Solution From Figure 6.14b, we write the controlling equation

$$\frac{dv}{dt} + 5v + 4\int_0^t v\,dt = e^{-t}u(t)$$

Laplace-transform this equation and then solve for $V(s)$. We obtain

$$V(s) = \frac{s}{(s+1)(s^2+5s+4)} = \frac{s}{(s+1)^2(s+4)}$$

Write this expression in the form

$$V(s) = \frac{A}{s+4} + \frac{B}{s+1} + \frac{C}{(s+1)^2}$$

where

$$A = \left.\frac{s}{(s+1)^2}\right|_{s=-4} = -\frac{4}{9}$$

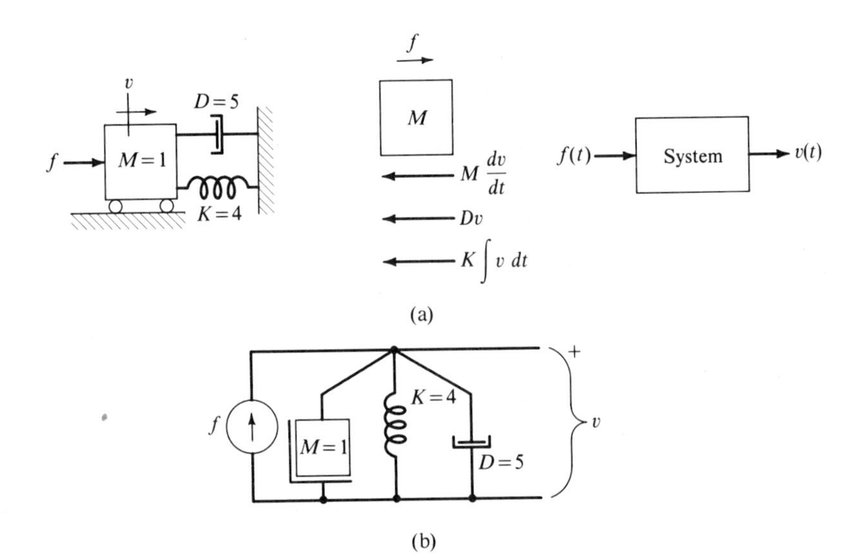

Figure 6.14 Illustrating Example 6.30. (a) Mechanical system. (b) Network representation.

$$B = \frac{1}{1!}\frac{d}{ds}\left(\frac{s}{s+4}\right)\bigg|_{s=-1} = \frac{4}{9}$$

$$C = \frac{s}{s+4}\bigg|_{s=-1} = -\frac{1}{3}$$

The inverse transform of $V(s)$ is given by

$$v(t) = -\frac{4}{9}e^{-4t} + \frac{4}{9}e^{-t} - \frac{1}{3}te^{-t} \qquad t \geq 0$$

To find $v(t)$ by the use of the convolution integral, we first find $h(t)$, the impulse response of the system. The quantity $h(t)$ is specified by

$$\frac{dh}{dt} + 5h + 4\int_0^t h\,dt = \delta(t)$$

where the system is assumed to be initially relaxed. The Laplace transform of this equation yields

$$H(s) = \frac{s}{s^2 + 5s + 4} = \frac{s}{(s+4)(s+1)} = \frac{4}{3}\frac{1}{s+4} - \frac{1}{3}\frac{1}{s+1}$$

The inverse transform of this expression is easily found to be

$$h(t) = \frac{4}{3}e^{-4t} - \frac{1}{3}e^{-t} \qquad t \geq 0$$

The output of the system to the input $e^{-t}u(t)$ is written

$$v(t) = \int_{-\infty}^{\infty} h(\tau)f(t-\tau)\,d\tau = \int_0^t e^{-(t-\tau)}\left[\frac{4}{3}e^{-4\tau} - \frac{1}{3}e^{-\tau}\right]d\tau$$

$$= e^{-t}\left[\frac{4}{3}\int_0^t e^{-3\tau}\,d\tau - \frac{1}{3}\int_0^t d\tau\right] = e^{-t}\left[\frac{4}{3}\left(\frac{1}{-3}\right)e^{-3\tau}\bigg|_0^t - \frac{1}{3}t\right]$$

$$= -\frac{4}{9}e^{-4t} + \frac{4}{9}e^{-t} - \frac{1}{3}te^{-t} \qquad t \geq 0$$

This result is identical with that found using the Laplace transform technique. ■

■ Example 6.31 *Medicine*

Refer to Example 5.11. Find the mass m_2 in the bloodstream for the case described given $K_1 = K_2 = 1$, $m_1(0) = 1$, $m_2(0) = 0$, and $w(t) = u(t)$.

Solution The controlling equations, given by (5.56) and (5.57), are

$$\frac{dm_1}{dt} = -m_1 + w$$

$$\frac{dm_2}{dt} = m_1 - m_2$$

The Laplace transforms of these equations are

$$sM_1(s) - 1 = -M_1(s) + \frac{1}{s}$$

$$sM_2(s) = M_1(s) - M_2(s)$$

Solve for $M_2(s)$ to obtain

$$M_2(s) = \frac{1}{s(s+1)} = \frac{1}{s} - \frac{1}{s+1}$$

The inverse transform yields

$$m_2(t) = 1 - e^{-t}$$

The complete solution to this system in state space form [see (5.64)] is found to be

$$\begin{bmatrix} m_1(t) \\ m_2(t) \end{bmatrix} = \begin{bmatrix} \displaystyle\sum_{n=0}^{\infty} \frac{(-1)^n}{n!} t^n \\ \displaystyle\sum_{n=1}^{\infty} \frac{(-1)^{n+1}}{n!} nt^n \end{bmatrix} + \begin{bmatrix} \displaystyle\sum_{n=0}^{\infty} \frac{(-1)^n}{n!} \int_0^t (t-\tau)^n \, d\tau \\ \displaystyle\sum_{n=1}^{\infty} \frac{(-1)^{n+1}}{n!} n \int_0^t (t-\tau)^n \, d\tau \end{bmatrix}$$

However, the integral

$$\int_0^t (t-\tau)^n \, d\tau = \frac{t^{n+1}}{n+1}$$

The resulting expression for $m_2(t)$ from the second of the set is

$$m_2(t) = \sum_{n=1}^{\infty} \frac{(-1)^{n+1}}{n!} nt^n + \sum_{n=1}^{\infty} \frac{(-1)^{n+1}}{n!} \frac{n}{n+1} t^{n+1}$$

$$= \sum_{n=1}^{\infty} \frac{(-1)^{n+1}}{(n-1)!} \left(1 + \frac{t}{n+1}\right) t^n$$

The numerical values of these two different-looking solutions for $m_2(t)$ are the same, as they should be. ■

6.8 Frequency Response of LTI Systems

In this section, we assume that all initial conditions are zero; hence, we address only the zero-input response. If nonzero initial conditions exist, we can always separate the zero-input response from the zero-state response.

We know that the output of an analog system is given by the convolution of the input and the impulse response of the system:

$$g(t) = \text{output} = f(t) * h(t) \tag{6.54}$$

where $f(t)$ is the input and $h(t)$ is the impulse response of the system. The Laplace

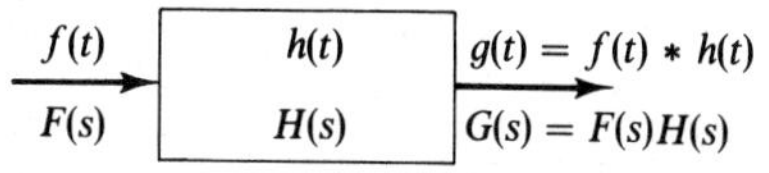

$f(t)$ $F(s)$ → $h(t)$ $H(s)$ → $g(t) = f(t) * h(t)$ $G(s) = F(s)H(s)$

Figure 6.15 Diagrammatic Representation of an Analog System

transform of both sides of (6.54) gives [see (6.22)]

$$G(s) = F(s)H(s) \tag{6.55}$$

The time and the transformed representations of a system are shown diagrammatically in Figure 6.15. Because $h(t)$ is the inverse Laplace transform of $H(s)$, then

$$h(t) = \mathscr{L}^{-1}\{H(s)\} = \mathscr{L}^{-1}\left\{\frac{G(s)}{F(s)}\right\} \tag{6.56}$$

When two systems are connected in cascade, as shown in Figure 6.16, we obtain the following relations:

$$g_1(t) = f(t) * h_1(t) \qquad G_1(s) = F(s)H_1(s)$$

and

$$g(t) = g_1(t) * h_2(t) \qquad G(s) = G_1(s)H_2(s)$$

By eliminating $G_1(s)$ from these two equations, we obtain

$$G(s) = H_1(s)H_2(s)F(s) = H(s)F(s)$$

which shows that the combined transfer function is given by

$$\boxed{H(s) = H_1(s)H_2(s)} \tag{6.57}$$

If n systems are connected in cascade, their total transfer function is

$$H(s) = H_1(s)H_2(s) \cdots H_n(s) \tag{6.58}$$

If two systems are connected in parallel, as shown in Figure 6.17, we have

$$g(t) = g_1(t) + g_2(t) = f(t) * h_1(t) + f(t) * h_2(t)$$

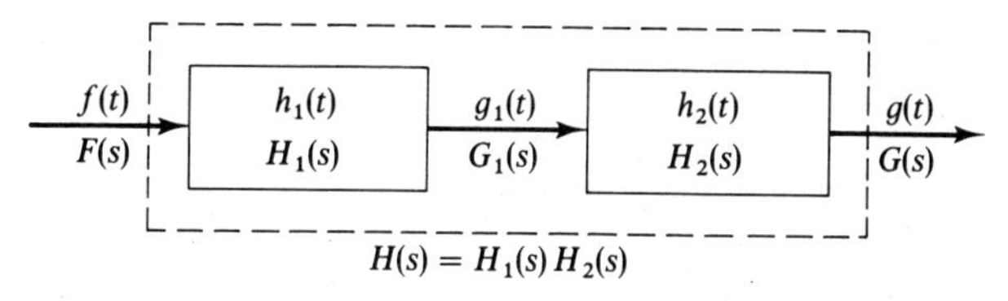

Figure 6.16 Representation of Two Systems in Cascade

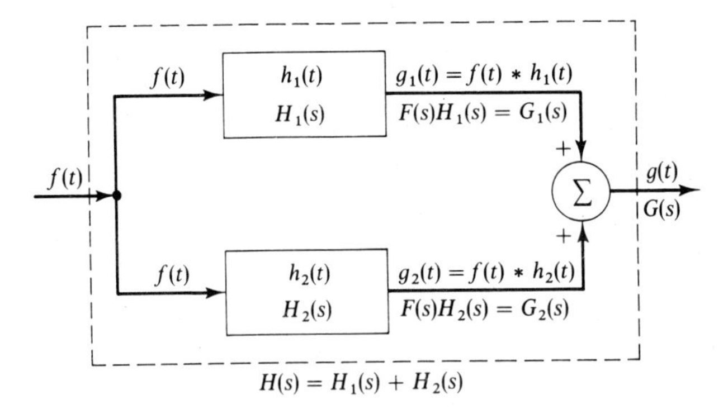

Figure 6.17 Representation of Two Systems in Parallel

from which

$$G(s) = F(s)H_1(s) + F(s)H_2(s) = F(s)[H_1(s) + H_2(s)] \tag{6.59}$$

This equation shows that the transfer function for two systems connected in parallel is given by

$$\boxed{H(s) = H_1(s) + H_2(s)} \tag{6.60}$$

For system connections with feedback, as shown in Figure 6.18, we write

$$g_1(t) = \pm g(t) * h_2(t) + f(t)$$

We also have the following relationship:

$$g(t) = g_1(t) * h_1(t) = \pm g(t) * h_2(t) * h_1(t) + f(t) * h_1(t)$$

This equation, when Laplace transformed, gives

$$G(s) = \pm G(s)H_2(s)H_1(s) + F(s)H_1(s)$$

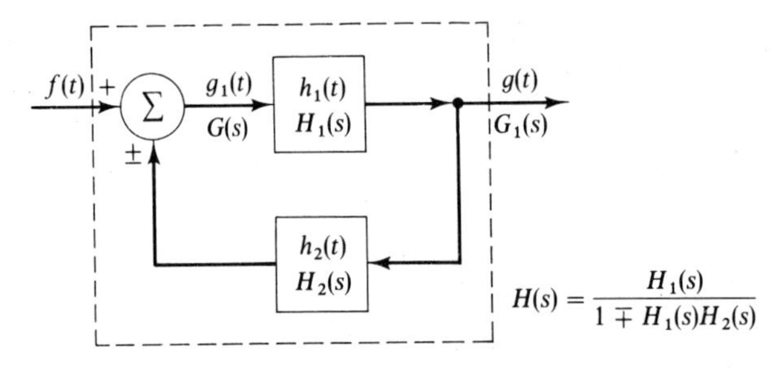

Figure 6.18 Representation of Systems in Feedback Form

from which

$$G(s) = F(s)\,\frac{H_1(s)}{1 \mp H_1(s)H_2(s)} \tag{6.61a}$$

and

$$H(s) = \frac{H_1(s)}{1 \mp H_1(s)H_2(s)} \tag{6.61b}$$

These results are consistent with those discussed for block diagram configurations (see Figure 2.25).

■ **Example 6.32**

Determine the transfer function for the system shown in Figure 6.19a. Also, find the amplitude and the phase response functions.

Solution The differential equations describing the system are

$$Ri_1 - Ri_2 = v \qquad L\frac{di_2}{dt} + Ri_2 - Ri_1 = 0$$

from which

$$I_1(s) = \frac{1}{R}\,V(s) + I_2(s) \qquad I_2(s) = I_1(s)\,\frac{R}{Ls + R}$$

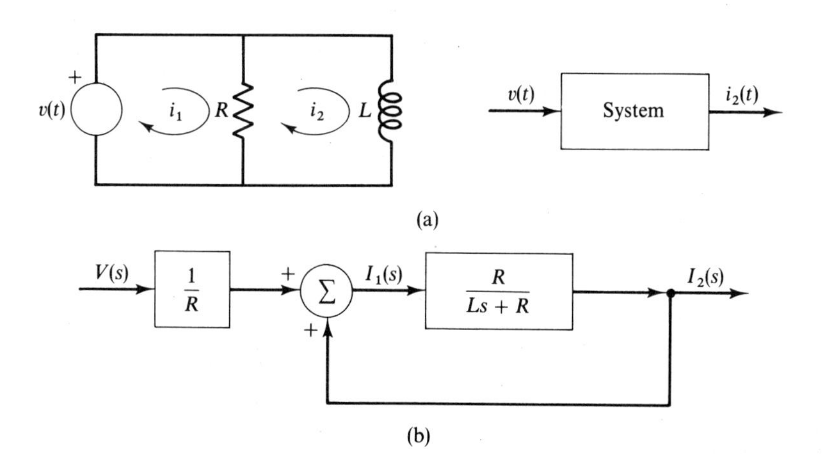

Figure 6.19 Illustrating Example 6.32

These two equations are shown in block diagram representation in Figure 6.19b. By block diagram simplification or by eliminating $I_1(s)$ from these equations, we obtain

$$H(s) = \frac{I_2(s)}{V(s)} = \frac{1}{Ls}$$

Therefore, writing $s = j\omega$,

$$H(j\omega) = \frac{1}{j\omega L}$$

As a consequence,

$$|H(j\omega)| = \frac{1}{\omega L}$$

$$\phi(\omega) = -\frac{\pi}{2} = \text{constant}$$ ■

■ **Example 6.33**

Deduce an expression for the current in the circuit shown in Figure 6.20 if a cosine function is applied with $\omega = 5$.

Solution An application of the Kirchhoff voltage law to the circuit yields

$$\frac{di(t)}{dt} + 2i(t) = v(t)$$

The transfer function is deduced by using a delta function as input:

$$\frac{dh(t)}{dt} + 2h(t) = \delta(t) \qquad (s + 2)H(s) = 1$$

Thus,

$$H(s) = \frac{1}{s + 2}$$

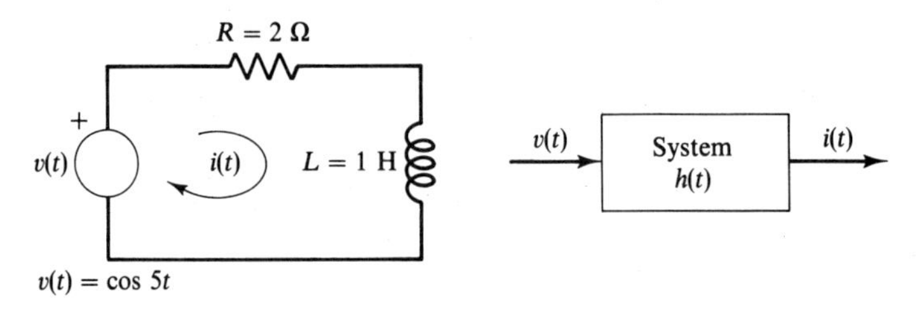

Figure 6.20 Illustrating Example 6.33

and

$$H(j5) = \frac{1}{j5+2} = \frac{1}{\sqrt{5^2+2^2}} e^{-\tan^{-1}(5/2)}$$

Now, proceeding as per Example 3.6, we obtain

$$i(t) = \text{Re}\left\{\frac{1}{j5+2} e^{j5t}\right\} = \frac{1}{\sqrt{29}} \cos(5t - \tan^{-1} 2.5)$$ ■

When there is a sum of exponential function inputs

$$f(t) = a_1 e^{j\omega_1 t} + a_2 e^{j\omega_2 t} + \cdots + a_n e^{j\omega_n t} \tag{6.62}$$

the output function becomes

$$g(t) = a_1 H(j\omega_1) e^{j\omega_1 t} + a_2 H(j\omega_2) e^{j\omega_2 t} + \cdots + a_n H(j\omega_n) e^{j\omega_n t} \tag{6.63}$$

■ **Example 6.34**

Repeat Example 6.33 for an input voltage $v(t) = 2 + 5\cos 3t + 6\sin 6t$.

Solution For the given circuit (see also Section 3.4),

$$H(s) = \frac{1}{s+2} \qquad H(j\omega) = \frac{1}{j\omega + 2}$$

Thus, we can write

$$\begin{aligned} i(t) &= \text{Re}\{2H(0)\}e^{j0t} + \text{Re}\left\{5\frac{1}{j3+2}\right\}e^{j3t} + \text{Im}\left\{6\frac{1}{j6+2}\right\}e^{j6t} \\ &= 1 + \frac{5}{\sqrt{13}}\cos\left(3t - \tan^{-1}\frac{3}{2}\right) + \frac{6}{\sqrt{40}}\sin\left(6t - \tan^{-1}\frac{6}{2}\right) \end{aligned}$$ ■

A basic and very important property of any system is its **filtering properties** that define how different frequencies are attenuated and phase shifted as they progress from the input to the output of the system. Further, the energy of a signal is associated with the amplitude of each harmonic. Thus, the filtering properties of a system will dictate the amount of energy that is to be transferred by the system and the percentage for each particular frequency component. Therefore, we generally prefer to plot amplitude $|H(j\omega)|$ and phase $\phi(\omega) = \tan^{-1}[H_i(\omega)/H_r(\omega)]$ versus frequency ω, where $H_i(\omega)$ and $H_r(\omega)$ are the imaginary and real components of $H(j\omega)$. Since both $|H(j\omega)|$ and $\phi(\omega)$ are frequency dependent, the specific attenuation and phase shift characteristics of a system will alter certain input signals more than others.

■ **Example 6.35**

Deduce and plot the frequency (filtering) characteristics of the circuit shown in Figure 6.21a.

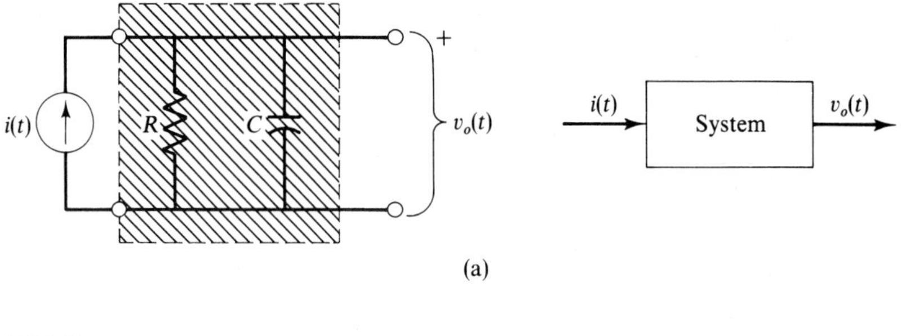

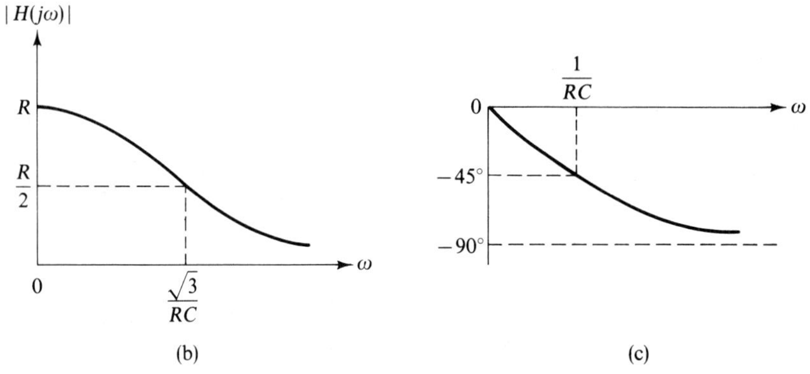

Figure 6.21 Illustrating Example 6.35

Solution An application of the Kirchhoff current law yields the equation

$$C\,\frac{dv_o(t)}{dt} + \frac{v_o(t)}{R} = i(t)$$

The transfer function is readily found to be

$$H(s) = \frac{V_o(s)}{I(s)} = \frac{1}{Cs + 1/R} = \frac{1}{C}\,\frac{1}{s + 1/RC}$$

The amplitude and phase spectrums are obtained by setting $s = j\omega$. These are

$$|H(j\omega)| = \frac{1}{C}\,\frac{1}{\sqrt{\omega^2 + (1/RC)^2}} \qquad \phi(\omega) = -\tan^{-1}(\omega RC)$$

These two characteristics are graphed in Figures 6.21b and 6.21c. ■

■ **Example 6.36**

Deduce and plot the frequency characteristics of the system shown in Figure 6.22.

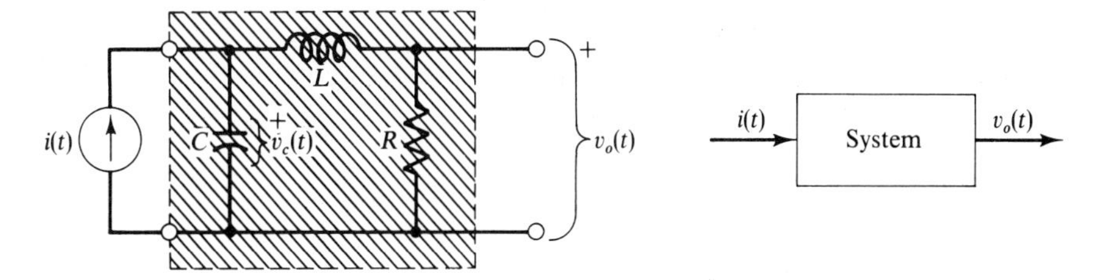

Figure 6.22 Illustrating Example 6.36

Solution From an inspection of the circuit, we write the two Kirchhoff current equations:

$$C\frac{dv_c(t)}{dt} + \frac{1}{L}\int [v_c(t) - v_o(t)]\,dt = i(t)$$

$$\frac{1}{L}\int [v_o(t) - v_c(t)]\,dt + \frac{v_o(t)}{R} = 0$$

The Laplace transforms of these equations are

$$CsV_c(s) + \frac{1}{Ls}[V_c(s) - V_o(s)] = I(s)$$

$$\frac{1}{Ls}[V_o(s) - V_c(s)] + \frac{V_o(s)}{R} = 0$$

Eliminate $V_c(s)$ from these last two equations and solve for $H(s) \triangleq V_o(s)/I(s)$. We obtain

$$H(s) \triangleq \frac{V_o(s)}{I(s)} = \frac{R}{LCs^2 + RCs + 1} = \frac{R/LC}{s^2 + (R/L)s + 1/LC}$$

Therefore,

$$|H(j\omega)| = \frac{R/LC}{\left[(-\omega^2 + 1/LC)^2 + \left(\frac{R}{L}\right)^2\omega^2\right]^{1/2}}$$

$$\phi(\omega) = -\tan^{-1}\left[\frac{(R/L)\omega}{1/LC - \omega^2}\right]$$

■

■ **Example 6.37**

A signal $2 + 3\sin 5t$ is the input to the system of Example 6.36. Find the output $v_o(t)$.

Solution The output is given by

$$\begin{aligned} v_o(t) &= \mathrm{Re}\{2H(j0)e^{j0t}\} + \mathrm{Im}\{3H(j5)e^{j5t}\} \\ &= \mathrm{Re}\{2|H(j0)|e^{j0t}e^{j\phi(0)}\} + \mathrm{Im}\{3|H(j5)|e^{j5t}e^{j\phi(5)}\} \\ &= 2\frac{R/LC}{[(1/LC)^2 + (R/L)^2 \times 0]^{1/2}} + 3\frac{R/LC}{[(-25 + 1/LC)^2 + (R/L)^2 \times 25]^{1/2}} \\ &\quad \times \sin\left(5t - \tan^{-1}\left[\frac{5R/L}{1/LC - 25}\right]\right) \end{aligned}$$

■

6.9 Laplace Transforms and the State Equations

It is of considerable interest to employ Laplace transforms in the solution of state equations, as closed-form solutions are often possible using these techniques. The general state equations have been found to be

$$\begin{aligned} \dot{\mathbf{x}} &= \mathbf{Ax} + \mathbf{Bw} \\ \mathbf{y} &= \mathbf{Cx} + \mathbf{Dw} \end{aligned} \tag{6.64}$$

However, we begin by considering the source-free case $\mathbf{w} = 0$. Thus, we write

$$\dot{\mathbf{x}} = \mathbf{Ax} \tag{6.65}$$

Laplace-transform this equation to get

$$s\mathbf{X}(s) - \mathbf{x}(0+) = \mathbf{AX}(s)$$

Rearrange this equation to the form

$$[s\mathbf{I} - \mathbf{A}]\mathbf{X}(s) = \mathbf{x}(0+)$$

from which we have

$$\mathbf{X}(s) = [s\mathbf{I} - \mathbf{A}]^{-1}\mathbf{x}(0+) \tag{6.66a}$$

which is written

$$\mathbf{X}(s) = \mathbf{\Phi}(s)\mathbf{x}(0+) \tag{6.66b}$$

where

$$\mathbf{\Phi}(s) \triangleq [s\mathbf{I} - \mathbf{A}]^{-1} = \frac{\text{transpose of cofactors of } [s\mathbf{I} - \mathbf{A}]}{\det[s\mathbf{I} - \mathbf{A}]} \tag{6.66c}$$

$\mathbf{\Phi}(s)$ is called the **characteristic matrix** of the system. See Appendix A also.

To find $\mathbf{x}(t)$ from (6.66b), the inverse Laplace transform is taken, which yields

$$\mathbf{x}(t) = \mathscr{L}^{-1}[\mathbf{\Phi}(s)\mathbf{x}(0+)] = \mathbf{\Phi}(t)\mathbf{x}(0+)$$

where

$$\mathscr{L}^{-1}[\mathbf{\Phi}(s)] = \mathbf{\Phi}(t) = e^{\mathbf{A}t} \tag{6.67}$$

[see (5.45)].

■ Example 6.38

Consider the system of Example 5.2, which is given in state form by (5.7), namely,

$$\begin{bmatrix} \dot{\mathbf{x}}_1 \\ \dot{\mathbf{x}}_2 \end{bmatrix} = \begin{bmatrix} 0 & 1 \\ -\dfrac{K}{M} & -\dfrac{D}{M} \end{bmatrix} \cdot \begin{bmatrix} x_1 \\ x_2 \end{bmatrix} + \begin{bmatrix} 0 \\ \dfrac{1}{M} \end{bmatrix} \mathbf{w} \qquad [y] = [1 \quad 0] \begin{bmatrix} x_1 \\ x_2 \end{bmatrix} \tag{6.68}$$

Assume that the source term is zero; $w = 0$. Further, assume that $K/M = 2$ and $D/M = 3$. Deduce the state transition matrix $\mathbf{\Phi}(t)$ of this system.

Solution The state equations become

$$\begin{aligned} \dot{x}_1 &= 0x_1 + x_2 \\ \dot{x}_2 &= -2x_1 - 3x_2 \end{aligned} \tag{6.69}$$

In Laplace-transformed form, these equations become

$$\begin{aligned} sX_1(s) - x_1(0+) &= 0X_1(s) + X_2(s) \\ sX_2(s) - x_2(0+) &= -2X_1(s) - 3X_2(s) \end{aligned}$$

Solve this system of equations for $X_1(s)$ and $X_2(s)$ to find

$$\begin{aligned} X_1(s) &= x_1(0+)\frac{s+3}{(s+1)(s+2)} + x_2(0+)\frac{1}{(s+1)(s+2)} \\ X_2(s) &= -x_1(0+)\frac{2}{(s+1)(s+2)} + x_2(0+)\frac{s}{(s+1)(s+2)} \end{aligned} \tag{6.70a}$$

In matrix form,

$$\begin{bmatrix} X_1(s) \\ X_2(s) \end{bmatrix} = \begin{bmatrix} \dfrac{s+3}{(s+1)(s+2)} & \dfrac{1}{(s+1)(s+2)} \\ \dfrac{-2}{(s+1)(s+2)} & \dfrac{s}{(s+1)(s+2)} \end{bmatrix} \begin{bmatrix} x_1(0+) \\ x_2(0+) \end{bmatrix} \tag{6.70b}$$

If we were to proceed according to (6.66a), we have

$$\mathbf{X}(s) = \left\{ s\begin{bmatrix} 1 & 0 \\ 0 & 1 \end{bmatrix} - \begin{bmatrix} 0 & 1 \\ -2 & -3 \end{bmatrix} \right\}^{-1} \mathbf{x}(0+)$$

where $\mathbf{A}$ is obtained from (6.68). The expansion of $[s\mathbf{I} - \mathbf{A}]^{-1}$ is given by

$$\begin{bmatrix} s & -1 \\ -2 & s+3 \end{bmatrix}^{-1} = \frac{\begin{bmatrix} s+3 & 1 \\ -2 & s \end{bmatrix}}{(s+1)(s+2)} = \begin{bmatrix} \dfrac{s+3}{(s+1)(s+2)} & \dfrac{1}{(s+1)(s+2)} \\ \dfrac{-2}{(s+1)(s+2)} & \dfrac{s}{(s+1)(s+2)} \end{bmatrix} \tag{6.71}$$

which agrees with (6.70b).

We can proceed from (6.70b) to obtain expressions for $x_1(t)$ and $x_2(t)$. This procedure involves taking the inverse transform of these equations. By so doing, we obtain

$$\begin{aligned} x_1(t) &= (2e^{-t} - e^{-2t})x_1(0+) + (e^{-t} - e^{-2t})x_2(0+) \\ x_2(t) &= (-2e^{-t} + 2e^{-2t})x_1(0+) + (-e^{-t} + 2e^{-2t})x_2(0+) \end{aligned} \tag{6.72}$$

where the coefficients multiplying $x_1(0+)$ and $x_2(0+)$ in these expressions are the inverse Laplace transform of the elements in the matrix $\mathbf{\Phi}(s)$. Specifically,

$$\begin{aligned} \mathscr{L}^{-1}\{\mathbf{\Phi}(s)\} &= \begin{bmatrix} \mathscr{L}^{-1}\left\{\dfrac{s+3}{(s+1)(s+2)}\right\} & \mathscr{L}^{-1}\left\{\dfrac{1}{(s+1)(s+2)}\right\} \\ \mathscr{L}^{-1}\left\{\dfrac{2}{(s+1)(s+2)}\right\} & \mathscr{L}^{-1}\left\{\dfrac{s}{(s+1)(s+2)}\right\} \end{bmatrix} \\ &= \begin{bmatrix} 2e^{-t} - e^{-2t} & e^{-t} - e^{-2t} \\ -2e^{-t} + 2e^{-2t} & -e^{-t} + 2e^{-2t} \end{bmatrix} \triangleq \mathbf{\Phi}(t) \end{aligned} \tag{6.73}$$

We could also have proceeded by using (5.45) that gives $\mathbf{\Phi}(t) = e^{\mathbf{A}t}$ in series form, as was done for this example in Example 5.10. To do this involves finding the various powers of $\mathbf{A}$ and substituting these values in (5.45). The result is given by (5.55), which is rewritten here:

$$\mathbf{\Phi}(t) = \begin{bmatrix} 1 - \dfrac{2t^2}{2!} + \dfrac{6t^3}{3!} - \dfrac{14t^4}{4!} + \cdots & t - \dfrac{3t^2}{2!} + \dfrac{7t^3}{3!} - \dfrac{15t^4}{4!} + \cdots \\ -2t + \dfrac{6t^2}{2!} - \dfrac{14t^3}{3!} + \dfrac{30t^4}{4!} + \cdots & 1 - 3t + \dfrac{7t^2}{2!} - \dfrac{15t^3}{3!} + \dfrac{31t^4}{4!} + \cdots \end{bmatrix} \tag{6.74}$$

By expanding the terms in (6.73), it will be found that they are identical with the series expansions given. ■

■ Example 6.39

The characteristic matrix $\mathbf{\Phi}(s)$ for a force-free system is defined by the system matrix

$$\mathbf{A} = \begin{bmatrix} 0 & 1 \\ -\frac{1}{2} & -1 \end{bmatrix}$$

Determine $\mathbf{\Phi}(t)$ for this system.

Solution We must evaluate

$$[s\mathbf{I} - \mathbf{A}]^{-1} = \mathbf{\Phi}(s) = \begin{bmatrix} s & -1 \\ \frac{1}{2} & s+1 \end{bmatrix}^{-1}$$

This becomes, by (6.66c),

$$[s\mathbf{I} - \mathbf{A}]^{-1} = \frac{\begin{bmatrix} s+1 & 1 \\ -\frac{1}{2} & s \end{bmatrix}}{s(s+1)+\frac{1}{2}} = \begin{bmatrix} \dfrac{s+1}{s^2+s+\frac{1}{2}} & \dfrac{1}{s^2+s+\frac{1}{2}} \\ \dfrac{-\frac{1}{2}}{s^2+s+\frac{1}{2}} & \dfrac{s}{s^2+s+\frac{1}{2}} \end{bmatrix}$$

The various elements of $\mathbf{\Phi}(t)$ are obtained by finding the inverse Laplace transform of each term in the matrix for $\mathbf{\Phi}(s)$. These elements are

$$\mathscr{L}^{-1}\left\{\frac{s+1}{s^2+s+\frac{1}{2}}\right\} = \mathscr{L}^{-1}\left\{\frac{s+1}{(s+\frac{1}{2})^2+\frac{1}{2}^2}\right\} = \mathscr{L}^{-1}\left\{\frac{(s+\frac{1}{2})+\frac{1}{2}}{(s+\frac{1}{2})^2+\frac{1}{2}^2}\right\}$$

$$= e^{-t/2}\cos\frac{t}{2} + e^{-t/2}\sin\frac{t}{2}$$

$$\mathscr{L}^{-1}\left\{\frac{1}{s^2+s+\frac{1}{2}}\right\} = 2e^{-t/2}\sin\frac{t}{2}$$

$$\mathscr{L}^{-1}\left\{\frac{-\frac{1}{2}}{s^2+s+\frac{1}{2}}\right\} = -e^{-t/2}\sin\frac{t}{2}$$

$$\mathscr{L}^{-1}\left\{\frac{s}{s^2+s+\frac{1}{2}}\right\} = \frac{(s+\frac{1}{2})-\frac{1}{2}}{s^2+s+\frac{1}{2}} = e^{-t/2}\cos\frac{t}{2} - e^{-t/2}\sin\frac{t}{2}$$ ■

To deduce the general expression for the state equations given in (6.64), we first focus attention on (6.64a). The Laplace transform of this equation is

$$s\mathbf{X}(s) - \mathbf{x}(0+) = \mathbf{A}\mathbf{X}(s) + \mathbf{B}\mathbf{W}(s) \tag{6.75}$$

This equation is rearranged to the form

$$[s\mathbf{I} - \mathbf{A}]\mathbf{X}(s) = \mathbf{x}(0+) + \mathbf{B}\mathbf{W}(s)$$

From this equation, we find

$$\mathbf{X}(s) = [s\mathbf{I} - \mathbf{A}]^{-1}\mathbf{x}(0+) + [s\mathbf{I} - \mathbf{A}]^{-1}\mathbf{B}\mathbf{W}(s) \tag{6.76a}$$

or, by (6.66c),

$$\mathbf{X}(s) = \mathbf{\Phi}(s)\mathbf{x}(0+) + \mathbf{\Phi}(s)\mathbf{B}\mathbf{W}(s) \tag{6.76b}$$

To find $x(t)$, we take the inverse Laplace transform of this equation, which is

$$\mathbf{x}(t) = \mathscr{L}^{-1}[\mathbf{\Phi}(s)\mathbf{x}(0+)] + \mathscr{L}^{-1}[\mathbf{\Phi}(s)\mathbf{B}\mathbf{W}(s)] \tag{6.77a}$$

which is

$$\mathbf{x}(t) = \mathbf{\Phi}(t)\mathbf{x}(0+) + \int_0^t \mathbf{\Phi}(t-\tau)\mathbf{B}\mathbf{w}(\tau)\,d\tau \tag{6.77b}$$

The second term in this expression is a generalization of the convolution integral in matrix form (see entry 10, Table 6.2).

Now, consider the output vector, which is obtained by Laplace-transforming the second of (6.64):

$$\mathbf{Y}(s) = \mathbf{C}\mathbf{X}(s) + \mathbf{D}\mathbf{W}(s) \tag{6.78}$$

Combine this equation with (6.76b) to write

$$\mathbf{Y}(s) = \mathbf{C}\mathbf{\Phi}(s)\mathbf{x}(0+) + [\mathbf{C}\mathbf{\Phi}(s)\mathbf{B} + \mathbf{D}]\mathbf{W}(s) \tag{6.79}$$

This expression shows that the output is the sum of the responses due to the initial state vector and that due to the drivers. By taking the inverse transform of this expression, we have

$$\mathbf{y}(t) = \mathbf{C}\mathbf{\Phi}(t)\mathbf{x}(0+) + \int_0^t [\mathbf{C}\mathbf{\Phi}(t-\tau)\mathbf{B} + \mathbf{D}\delta(t-\tau)]\mathbf{w}(\tau)\,d\tau \tag{6.80}$$

With zero initial conditions, (6.78) becomes

$$\mathbf{Y}(s) = [\mathbf{C}\mathbf{\Phi}(s)\mathbf{B} + \mathbf{D}]\mathbf{W}(s) = \mathbf{H}(s)\mathbf{W}(s) \tag{6.81}$$

where $\mathbf{H}(s)$ is the transfer matrix

$$\boxed{\mathbf{H}(s) = \mathbf{C}\mathbf{\Phi}(s)\mathbf{B} + \mathbf{D} = \mathbf{C}[s\mathbf{I} - \mathbf{A}]^{-1}\mathbf{B} + \mathbf{D}} \tag{6.82}$$

Note that since $Y_i(s)$, the ith term in (6.81), is given by

$$Y_i(s) = H_{i1}(s)W_1(s) + H_{i2}(s)W_2(s) + \cdots + H_{in}(s)W_n(s) \tag{6.83}$$

It is evident that the element $H_{ij}(s)$ of the matrix $\mathbf{H}(s)$ is the transfer function between $y_i(t)$ and $w_j(t)$. From this, we can write

$$H_{ij}(s) = \mathscr{L}\{h_{ij}(t)\} \tag{6.84}$$

which shows that $h_{ij}(t)$ is the response of the ith output to the jth input terminal.

Example 6.40

The state description of the network given in Example 5.10 is given by the equations

$$\begin{bmatrix} \dot{x}_1(t) \\ \dot{x}_2(t) \end{bmatrix} = \begin{bmatrix} 0 & 1 \\ -2 & -3 \end{bmatrix}\begin{bmatrix} x_1(t) \\ x_2(t) \end{bmatrix} + \begin{bmatrix} 0 & 0 \\ -1.5 & -1.5 \end{bmatrix} w(t)$$

$$\begin{bmatrix} y_1(t) \\ y_2(t) \end{bmatrix} = \begin{bmatrix} 1 & 0 \\ 0 & -1.5 \end{bmatrix}\begin{bmatrix} x_1(t) \\ x_2(t) \end{bmatrix} + \begin{bmatrix} 0 & 0 \\ -1.5 & 1.5 \end{bmatrix}\begin{bmatrix} w_1(t) \\ w_2(t) \end{bmatrix}$$

Deduce the response $x_2(t)$ for an input $w_2(t) = \delta(t)$.

Solution The characteristic matrix is

$$\mathbf{\Phi}(s) = [s\mathbf{I} - \mathbf{A}]^{-1} = \begin{bmatrix} s & -1 \\ 2 & s+3 \end{bmatrix}^{-1} = \frac{\begin{bmatrix} s+3 & 1 \\ -2 & s \end{bmatrix}}{(s+1)(s+2)}$$

$$= \begin{bmatrix} \dfrac{s+3}{(s+1)(s+2)} & \dfrac{1}{(s+1)(s+2)} \\ -\dfrac{2}{(s+1)(s+2)} & \dfrac{s}{(s+1)(s+2)} \end{bmatrix}$$

The transfer matrix, given by (6.82), is

$$\mathbf{H}(s) = \begin{bmatrix} 1 & 0 \\ 0 & -1.5 \end{bmatrix} \begin{bmatrix} \dfrac{s+3}{(s+1)(s+2)} & \dfrac{1}{(s+1)(s+2)} \\ \dfrac{-2}{(s+1)(s+2)} & \dfrac{s}{(s+1)(s+2)} \end{bmatrix} \begin{bmatrix} 0 & 1 \\ 3 & -3 \end{bmatrix} + \begin{bmatrix} 0 & 0 \\ -1.5 & -1.5 \end{bmatrix}$$

$$= \begin{bmatrix} \dfrac{3}{(s+1)(s+2)} & \dfrac{(s+3)-3}{(s+1)(s+2)} \\ -4.5\dfrac{s}{(s+1)(s+2)} - 1.5 & \dfrac{3+4.5s}{(s+1)(s+2)} + 1.5 \end{bmatrix}$$

For this problem, we are interested in the element $H_{22}(s)$. The inverse transform under consideration is

$$y_2(t) = \mathscr{L}^{-1}\{H_{22}(s) \times 1\} = \mathscr{L}^{-1}\left\{\frac{3+4.5s}{(s+1)(s+2)} + 1.5\right\}$$
$$= -1.5e^{-t} + 6e^{-2t} + 1.5\delta(t)$$

■

■ **Example 6.41** ***Arms Race***

Richardson's model* of an arms race between two nations A and B makes the following two assumptions: Only the two nations A and B are involved and only one kind of weapon or missile is available. Let $M_A(t)$ and $M_B(t)$ denote the number of missiles available to A and B, respectively. The Richardson model is given by

$$\dot{M}_A = -a_1 M_A + b_1 M_B + c_1$$
$$\dot{M}_B = a_2 M_A - b_2 M_B + c_2$$

where $\dot{M}_A$ and $\dot{M}_B$ give the rate of change of number of missiles in the two countries. The coefficients a_1, b_1, a_2, and b_2 are nonnegative constants. The

* From L.F. Richardson, "Generalized Foreign Politics," *British J. Psychol.*, Monograph Suppl. 23 (1939). See also N. Finizio and G. Ladas, *An Introduction to Differential Equations* (Belmont, CA: Wadsworth Publishing Co., 1982), p. 155.

constants b_1 and a_2 are "defense coefficients" of the respective nations; the constants a_1 and b_2 are "fatigue" and "expense" coefficients, respectively; and constants c_1 and c_2 are the "grievance coefficients" and indicate the effects of all other factors on the acquisition of missiles. Choose the following values: $a_1 = 2$, $b_1 = 1$, $a_2 = 2$, $b_2 = 1$, $c_1 = 1$, and $c_2 = 0$. Determine the solution to the Richardson equations if both nations start with the same number of missiles: $M_A(0) = M_B(0) = 1$.

Solution The Richardson equations in state space form with $M_A = x_1$ and $M_B = x_2$ become

$$\begin{bmatrix} \dot{x}_1 \\ \dot{x}_2 \end{bmatrix} = \begin{bmatrix} -2 & 1 \\ 2 & -1 \end{bmatrix} \begin{bmatrix} x_1 \\ x_2 \end{bmatrix} + \begin{bmatrix} 1 \\ 0 \end{bmatrix}$$

From this, we obtain

$$\mathbf{\Phi}(s) \triangleq [s\mathbf{I} - \mathbf{A}]^{-1} = \begin{bmatrix} s+2 & -1 \\ -2 & s+1 \end{bmatrix}^{-1} = \begin{bmatrix} \dfrac{s+1}{s(s+3)} & \dfrac{1}{s(s+3)} \\ \dfrac{2}{s(s+3)} & \dfrac{s+2}{s(s+3)} \end{bmatrix}$$

We can then write, by (6.76),

$$\begin{bmatrix} X_1(s) \\ X_2(s) \end{bmatrix} = \begin{bmatrix} \dfrac{s+1}{s(s+3)} & \dfrac{1}{s(s+3)} \\ \dfrac{2}{s(s+3)} & \dfrac{s+2}{s(s+3)} \end{bmatrix} \begin{bmatrix} 2 \\ 1 \end{bmatrix}$$

$$= \begin{bmatrix} 2\dfrac{s+1}{s(s+3)} + \dfrac{1}{s(s+3)} \\ 4\dfrac{1}{s(s+3)} + \dfrac{s+2}{s(s+3)} \end{bmatrix} = \begin{bmatrix} \dfrac{2s+3}{s(s+3)} \\ \dfrac{s+6}{s(s+3)} \end{bmatrix}$$

From this, we write

$$M_A(t) = x(t) = \mathscr{L}^{-1}\left\{\frac{2s+3}{s(s+3)}\right\} = \mathscr{L}^{-1}\left\{\frac{1}{s} + \frac{1}{s+3}\right\} = 1 + e^{-3t}$$

$$M_B(t) = x_2(t) = \mathscr{L}^{-1}\left\{\frac{s+6}{s(s+3)}\right\} = \mathscr{L}^{-1}\left\{\frac{2}{s} - \frac{1}{s+3}\right\} = 2 - e^{-3t}$$

Note that in assigning values to the coefficients, we had certain characteristics of nation A and nation B in mind. We set $a_2 = 2$ and $b_1 = 1$ because we assumed that nation A has better defenses. Also, because of a free economic system in nation A, a_1 was set equal to 2 and b_1 equal to 1. Further, we assumed that nation A has a high technology and production capability that is higher than nation B; hence, we set $c_1 = 2$ and $c_2 = 1$. The results are shown in Figure 6.23. Observe that after 0.15 units of time, the missile inventory will be reversed. ■

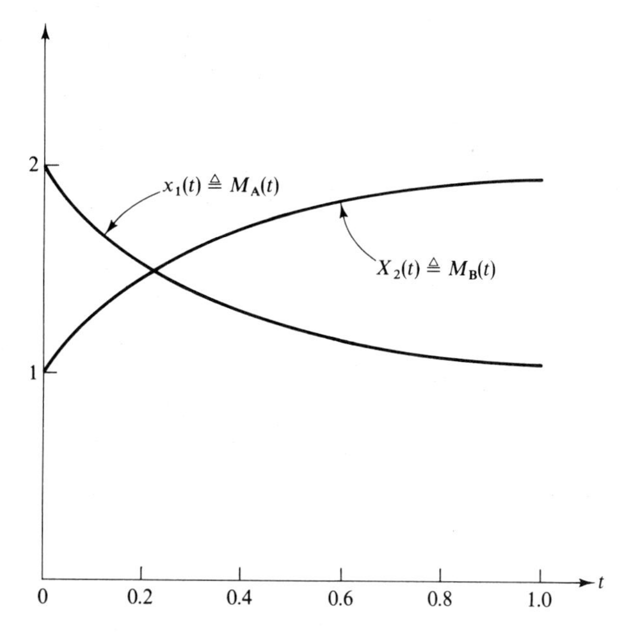

Figure 6.23 Illustrating Example 6.41

6.10 Stability of LTI Systems

The physical idea of stability is closely related to a bounded system response to a sudden disturbance or input. If the system is displaced slightly from its equilibrium state, several different behaviors are possible. If the system remains near the equilibrium state, the system is said to be **stable**. If the system tends to return to the equilibrium state or tends to a bounded or limited state, it is said to be **asymptotically stable**. Here, it should be noted that stability can be examined by studying a system either through its impulse response $h(t)$ or through its Laplace-transformed system function $H(s)$. We examine these approaches to a study of system stability.

Let us assume that we can expand the transfer function in terms of its roots as follows:

$$H(s) = \frac{A_1}{s - s_1} + \frac{A_2}{s - s_2} + \cdots + \frac{A_k}{s - s_k} + \cdots + \frac{A_n}{s - s_n} \tag{6.85}$$

The time response for an applied impulse due to the kth pole will be of the form $A_k e^{s_k t}$. Thus, the nature of the response will depend on the location of the root s_k in the s-plane. Because the controlling differential equation that describes the system has real coefficients, the roots are either real or, if complex, will occur in complex conjugate pairs. Three general cases exist that depend intimately on the order and location of the poles s_k in the s-plane. They are as follows:

1. The point representing s_k lies to the left of the imaginary axis in the s-plane.
2. The point representing s_k lies on the $j\omega$-axis.
3. The point representing s_k lies to the right of the imaginary axis in the s-plane.

We examine each of these alternatives for both simple-order and higher-order poles.

Simple-Order Poles

Case 1: The root is a real number $s_k = \sigma_k$, and it is located on the negative real σ-axis. The response due to this root will be of the form

$$\text{response} = A_k e^{\sigma_k t} \qquad \sigma_k < 0 \tag{6.86}$$

This expression indicates that after a lapse of time, the response will become vanishingly small.

For the case when a pair of complex conjugate roots exist, the response is given by

$$\text{response} = A_k e^{s_k t} + A_k^* e^{s_k^* t} \tag{6.87}$$

where A_k and A_k^* specify the appropriate amplitude factors. The response terms can be combined, noting that $A_k = a + jb$ and $s_k = \sigma_k + j\omega_k$:

$$\text{response} = (a + jb)e^{(\sigma_k + j\omega_k)t} + (a - jb)e^{(\sigma_k - j\omega_k)t}$$

or

$$\text{response} = 2\sqrt{a^2 + b^2}\, e^{\sigma_k t} \cos(\omega_k t + \beta_k) \qquad \sigma_k < 0 \tag{6.88a}$$

where

$$\beta_k = \tan^{-1}\left(\frac{b}{a}\right) \tag{6.88b}$$

This response is a damped sinusoid, and it ultimately decays to zero. The general conclusion is: Systems with only simple poles in the left-half plane are stable.

Case 2: The point representing s_k lies on the imaginary axis. This condition is a special case under Case 1, but now $\sigma_k = 0$. The response for complex conjugate poles is, from (6.88),

$$\text{response} = 2\sqrt{a^2 + b^2} \cos(\omega_k t + \beta_k) \tag{6.89}$$

Observe that there is no damping, and the response is thus a sustained oscillatory function. Such a system has a bounded response to a bounded input, and the system is defined to be **stable** even though it is oscillatory.

Case 3: The point representing s_k lies in the right-half plane. The response function will be of the form

$$\text{response} = A_k e^{s_k t} \tag{6.90}$$

for real roots and will be of the form

$$\text{response} = 2\sqrt{a^2 + b^2}\, e^{\sigma_k t} \cos(\omega_k t + \beta_k) \qquad \sigma_k > 0 \tag{6.91}$$

for conjugate complex roots. Because both functions increase with time without limit even for bounded inputs, the system for which these functions are roots is said to be **unstable**.

The conclusions that follow from these three cases are:

1. A system with simple poles is unstable if one or more of the poles of its transfer function appear in the right-half plane.
2. A system whose transfer function has simple poles is stable when all of the poles are in the left-half plane or on its boundary.

In fact, the distance of the poles from the imaginary axis gives a measure of the decay rate of the response with time. The impulse response of a system and the location of its simple poles are shown in Figure 6.24.

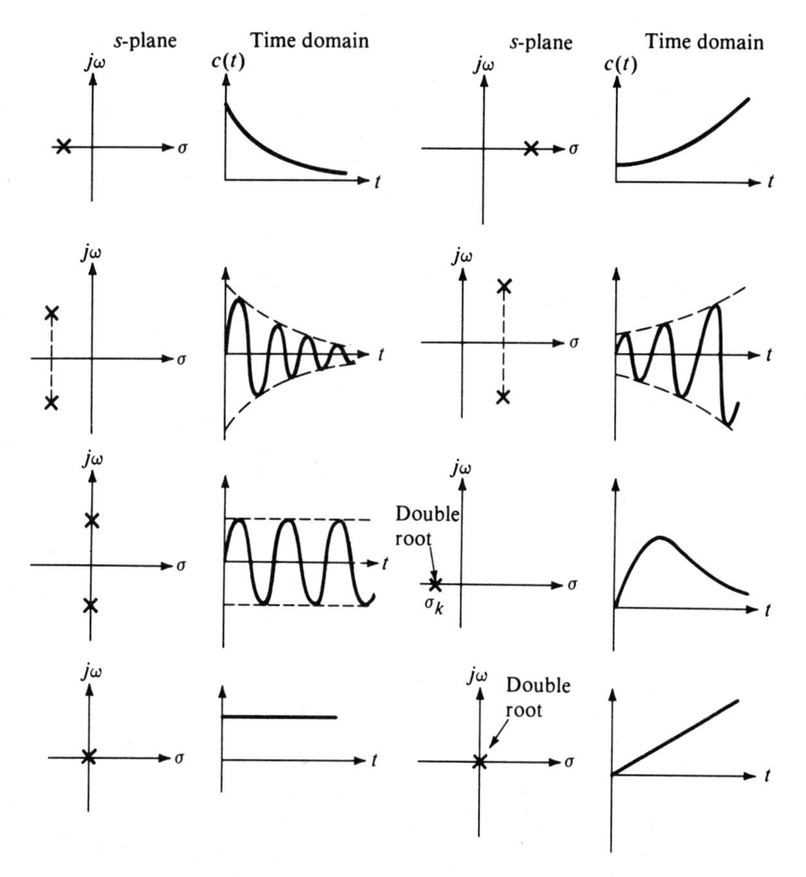

Figure 6.24 Location of Poles and Corresponding Impulse Response of the System

Multiple-Order Poles

We now examine the situation when multiple-order poles exist. We must again consider the three cases.

Case 1: Multiple real poles exist in the left-half plane. As previously discussed (see Table 6.1), a second-order real pole (two repeated roots) gives rise to the response function

$$\text{response} = (A_{k1} + A_{k2}\, t)e^{\sigma_k t} \tag{6.92}$$

For negative values of σ_k, the exponential time function decreases faster than the linearly increasing time factor. The response ultimately dies out, the rapidity of decay depending on the value of σ_k. The system with such poles is stable.

Case 2: Multiple poles exist on the imaginary axis. The response function is made up of the responses due to each pair of poles and is

$$\text{response} = (A_{k1} + A_{k2}\, t)e^{j\omega_k t} + (A_{k1}^* + A_{k2}^*\, t)e^{-j\omega_k t} \tag{6.93}$$

Following the procedure discussed above for the simple complex poles, this result can be written

$$\text{response} = 2\sqrt{a^2 + b^2}\cos(\omega_k t + \beta_k) + 2\sqrt{c^2 + d^2}\, t\cos(\omega_k t + \gamma_k) \tag{6.94}$$

The first term on the right is a sustained oscillatory function. The second term is a time-modulated oscillatory function that increases with time. Clearly, the system in this case is unstable.

Case 3: Multiple roots exist in the right-half plane. For real roots, the solution in this case will be

$$\text{response} = (A_{k1} + A_{k2}\, t)e^{\sigma_k t} \tag{6.95}$$

For complex roots, the solution will be

$$\text{response} = e^{\sigma_k t}[2\sqrt{a^2 + b^2}\cos(\omega_k t + \beta_k) + 2\sqrt{c^2 + d^2}\, t\cos(\omega_k t + \gamma_k)] \tag{6.96}$$

In both cases, owing to the factor $e^{\sigma_k t}$, the response increases with time and the system is unstable.

The foregoing considerations can be summarized as follows:

1. A system with multiple poles is unstable if one or more of its poles appear on the $j\omega$-axis or in the right-half plane.
2. When all of the poles of the system are confined to the left-half plane, the system is stable.

Problems

Section 6.3

1. Deduce the Laplace transforms of the following:
   a. Entries 5, 6, 9, and 12 in Table 6.1.
   b. $t^2 + 2t + 1$, $(1 + \cos 4t)/2$, $t \sin \omega t$, and $\sin \omega t/\omega t$ for $t \geq 0$
2. Find the Laplace transform and the region of convergence of the following functions for $t \geq 0$: $2 + 3t$, $4e^{-0.1t}$, $\sinh 2t$, $1 + \sin t$, and e^{2t}.
3. Find the Laplace transform of the following functions for $t \geq 0$: $2 - 8t^3$, $t \cos 2t$, $e^{-t} \cosh t$, $e^t \cos t$ and $\cos t - \sin t$.
4. Find the Laplace transform of the following functions for $t \geq 0$: $1 + e^{-2t}$, $p_1(t - 1)$, and $\cos 2t - e^t \sin 3t$.

Section 6.4

5. Prove entries 6, 7, 9, 13, and 14 in Table 6.2.
6. Find the Laplace transform of the functions illustrated in Figure 6.25.

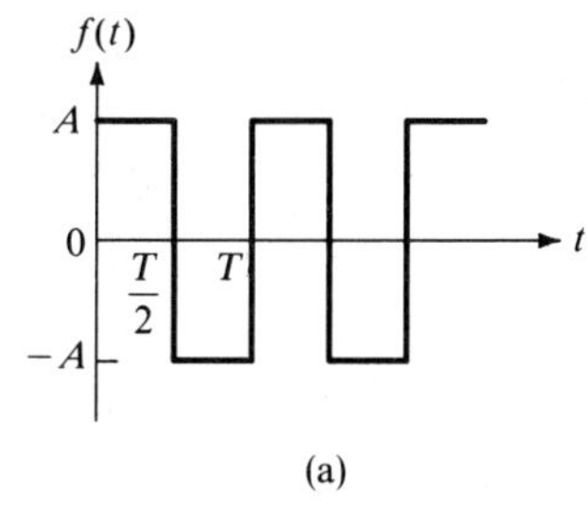

(a)

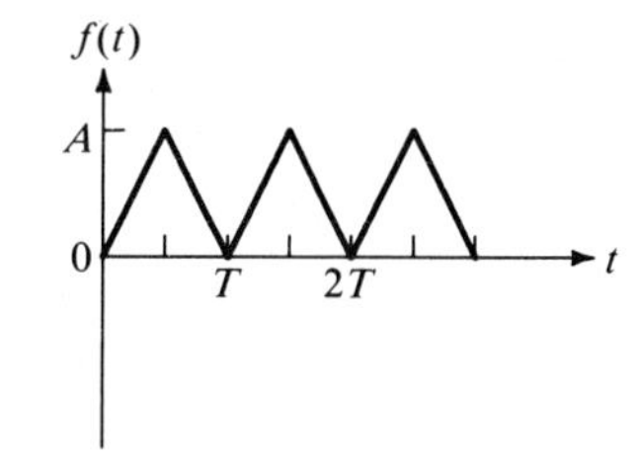

(b)

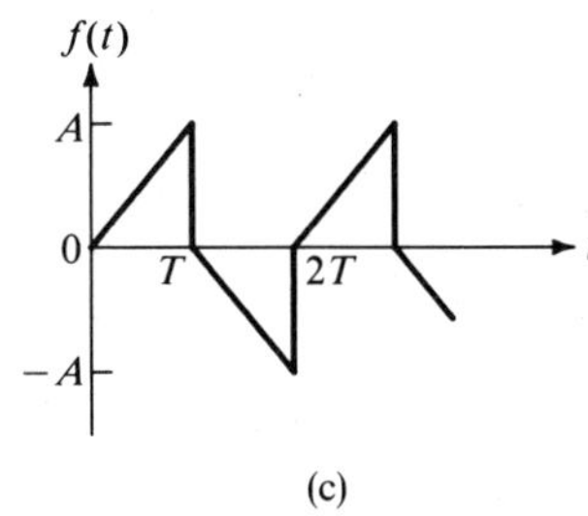

(c)

Figure 6.25

7. Apply the initial value and final value theorems to the following functions:

$$\frac{s}{s^2 + 3} \qquad \frac{s^2 + s + 3}{s^2 + 3} \qquad \frac{s}{s^2 - b^2} \qquad \frac{s + a}{(s + a)^2 + b^2}$$

8. Find the Laplace transforms of the following functions:

$$e^{-t}u(t - 2) + \frac{dg(t)}{dt} \qquad g(t) + \int_0^t e^{-|\xi|}\, d\xi$$

9. If $f(t)$ is an even function, find the relationship between $F(s)$ and $F(-s)$. Repeat for the case when $f(t)$ is an odd function.
10. Determine the Laplace transforms of the functions shown in Figure 6.26.

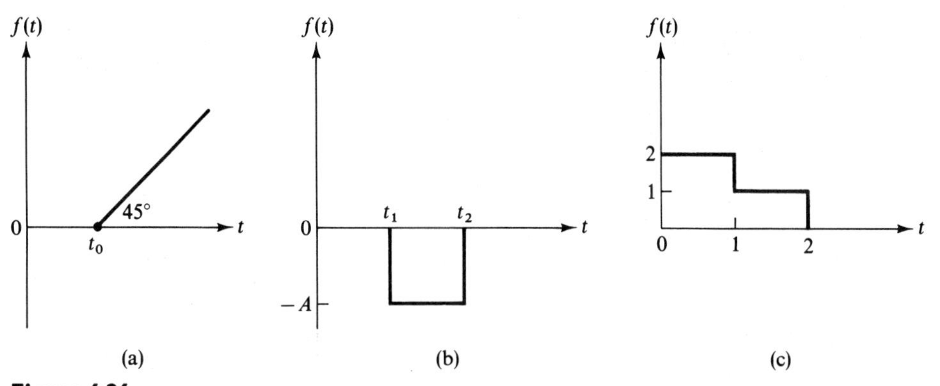

Figure 6.26

11. Find the Laplace transforms of the functions $f(t)$ shown in Figure 6.27 and then deduce the Laplace transform of the related $f_1(t)$ using the appropriate Laplace property for each case. *Note:* Functions are multiplied.

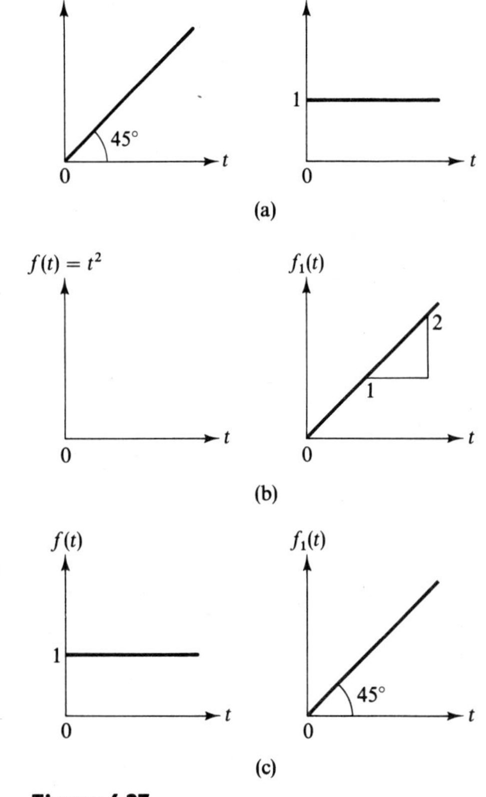

Figure 6.27

12. Find the Laplace transforms of the following functions: $e^{-at} \cos bt\, u(t)$, $te^{-at}u(t)$, and $\cos bt\, u(t)$.

Section 6.5

13. Draw the equivalent block diagram representation of the systems shown in Figure 6.28 and find the transfer function, as indicated, for each.

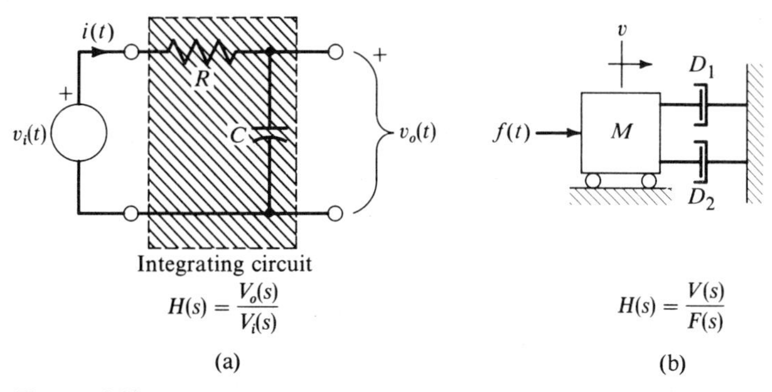

Figure 6.28

14. Draw the equivalent block diagram representation of the system (a microphone) shown in Figure 6.29 and find the transfer function $H(s) = E_o(s)/F_a(s)$. In this example, the voltage is designated e and the velocity v.

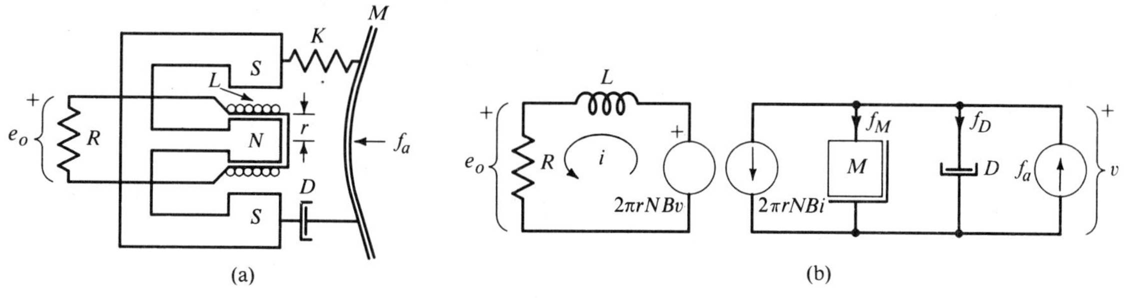

Figure 6.29

15. Find the equivalent block diagram representation of the systems shown in Figure 6.30 and determine the transfer function, as indicated, in each case.

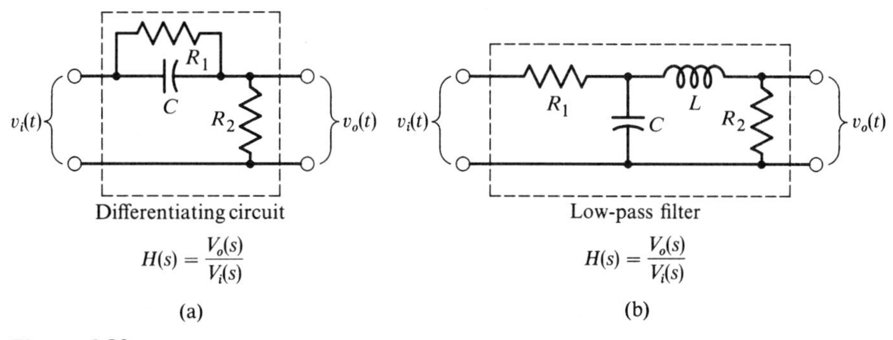

Figure 6.30

16. Determine the transfer functions $H(s) = C(s)/R(s)$ for the systems shown in Figure 6.31.

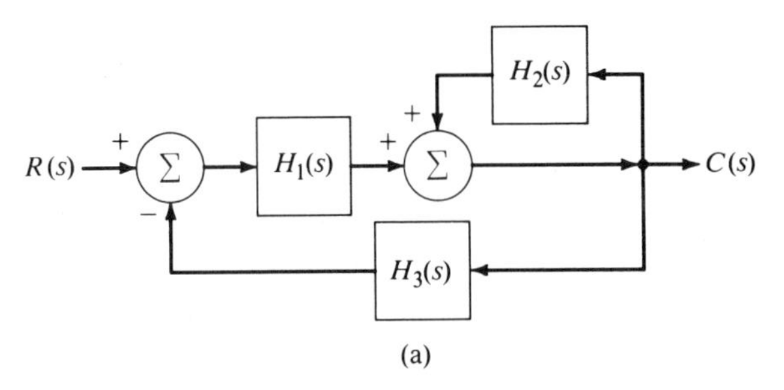

(a)

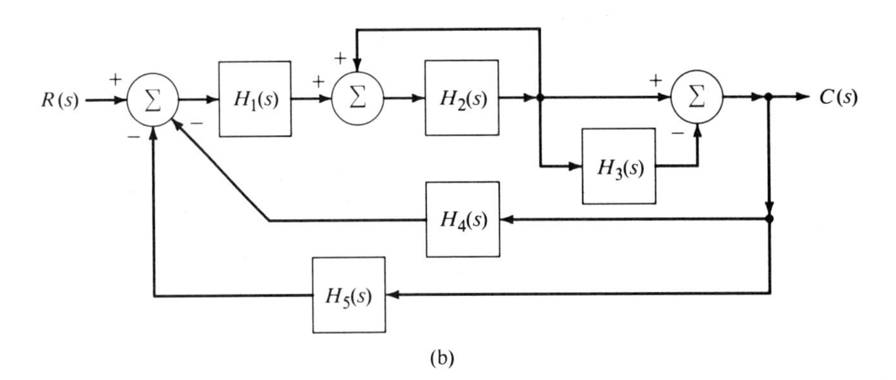

(b)

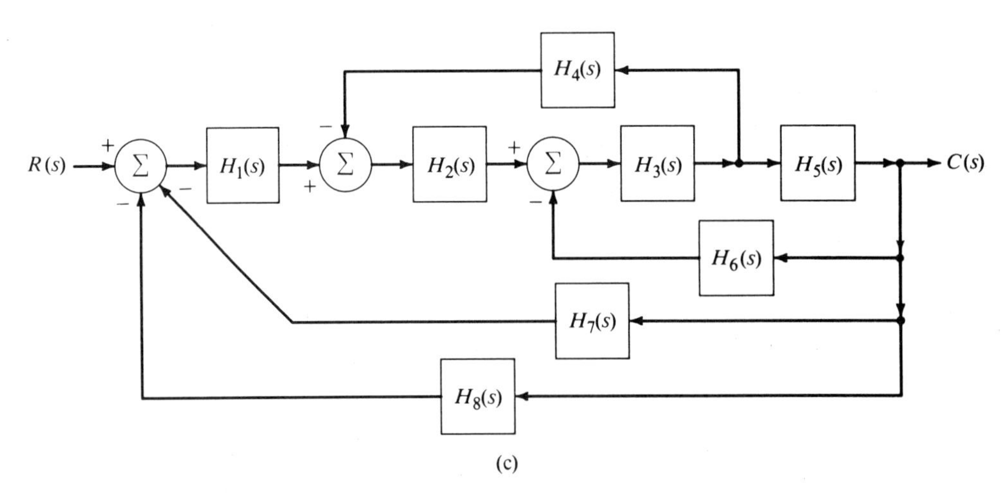

(c)

Figure 6.31

17. Determine the block diagram representation of the system shown in Figure 6.32 in the time domain and also find the transfer function $I(s)/V(s)$.

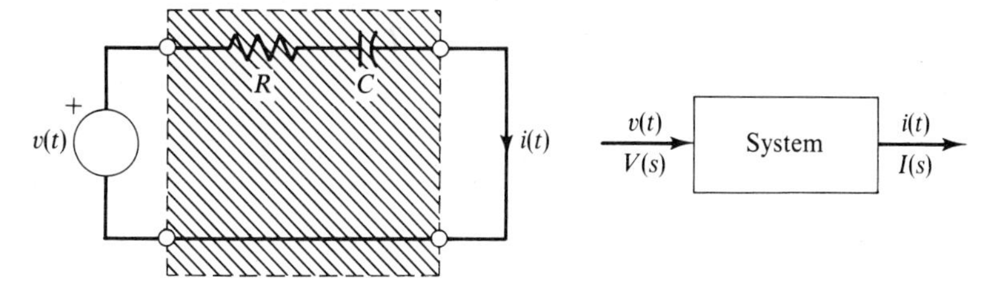

Figure 6.32

18. Determine the block diagram representation of the systems shown in Figure 6.33 in the time domain and find their transfer functions.

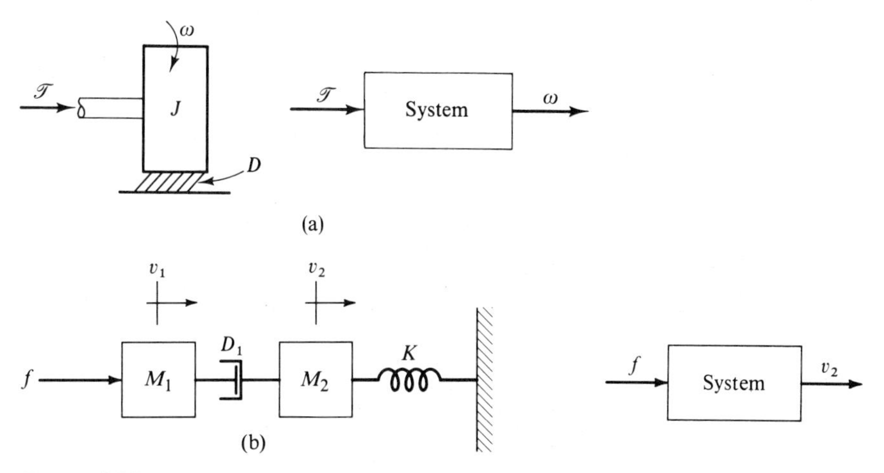

Figure 6.33

19. Find the transfer function for the systems shown in Figure 6.34.

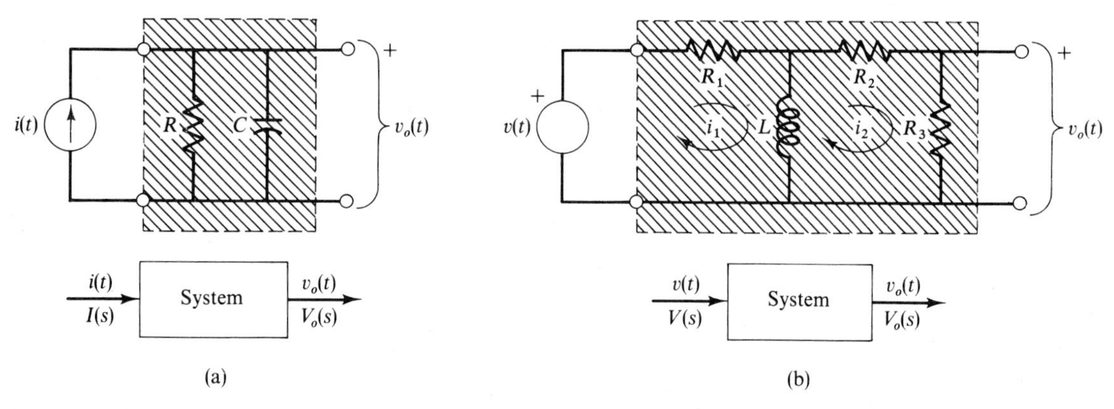

Figure 6.34

20. Find the transfer function for the system shown in Figure 6.35.

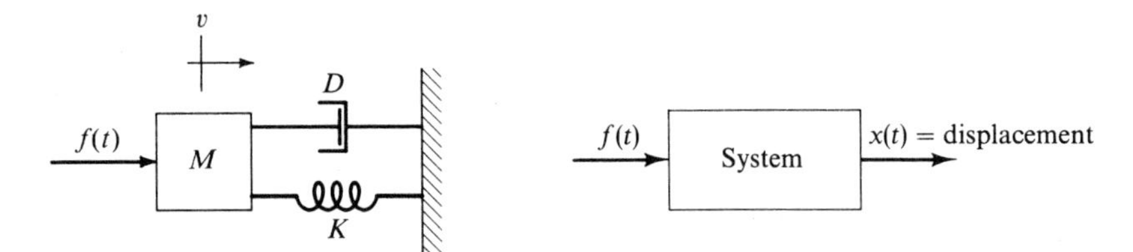

Figure 6.35

Section 6.6

21. Find the inverse Laplace transform of the following functions by means of partial fraction expansions:

a. $\frac{1}{s}-\frac{1}{s}e^{-2s}$ b. $\frac{2s+1}{s^2+4s+7}$ c. $\frac{1}{(s+2)^4}$ d. $\frac{s+1}{(s+2)(s+3)^2}$

e. $\frac{s^2+2s+1}{s^2(s+1)}$ f. $\frac{s^2+2s+1}{s^2+3s+5}$ g. $\frac{e^{-2s}}{(s+1)^2(s^2+3)}$

22. Find the inverse Laplace transform of the following functions:

a. $\frac{a}{s^2+b^2}$ b. $\frac{2}{s^2-5s+4}$ c. $\frac{2}{(s^2+1)^2}$ d. $\frac{2s-3}{(s+1)^2+25}$

e. $\frac{4}{(s-1)(s^2+1)}$ f. $\frac{s}{s^2-a^2}$

23. Find the inverse Laplace transform of the following:

a. $\frac{6}{s(s+3)}$ b. $\frac{s^2+2s+5}{(s+3)(s+5)^2}$ c. $\frac{5s+13}{s(s^2+4s+13)}$ d. $\frac{s}{(s^2+9)(s+2)}$

Section 6.7

24. Solve the following differential equations by Laplace transform methods:

a. $\frac{d^2y}{dt^2}+\frac{3dy}{dt}+2y=0 \qquad y(0+)=5, \frac{dy(0+)}{dt}=0$

b. $\frac{d^2y}{dt^2}+3\frac{dy}{dt}+2y=\delta(t)$ initially relaxed

c. $\frac{d^2y}{dt^2}+5y=\sin 2t+e^{-3t}$ initially relaxed

d. $\frac{d^2y}{dt^2}+3\frac{dy}{dt}+2y=t^2+3t \qquad y(0+)=2, \frac{dy(0+)}{dt}=-8$

25. Determine the driving point current in the circuits of Figure 6.36. Assume that these circuits are initially relaxed.

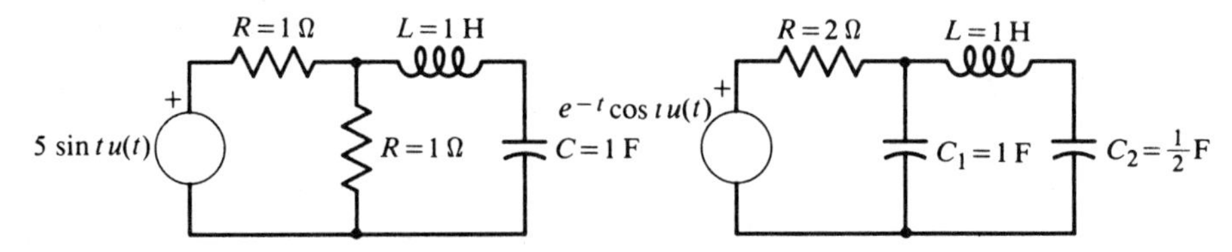

Figure 6.36

26. Determine the currents $i_1(t)$ and $i_2(t)$ in the network shown in Figure 6.37 subject to the following switching sequence: S_1 closed at $t = 0$; S_2 then closed at $t = 3$ s.

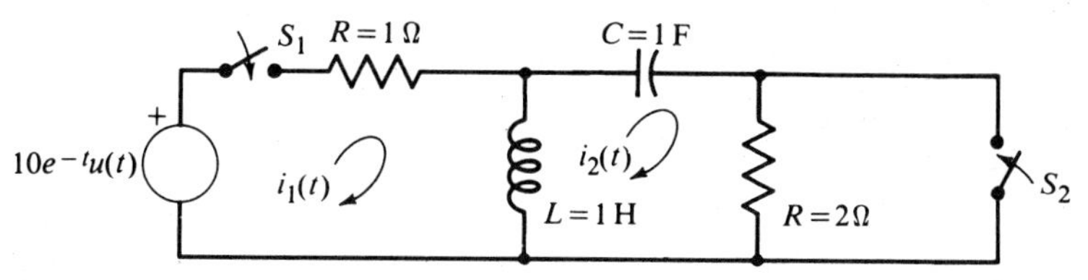

Figure 6.37

27. Find the velocity v for the system shown in Figure 6.38 if $f(0) = V_o$ and $f(t) = \sin(\omega t + \phi)u(t)$.

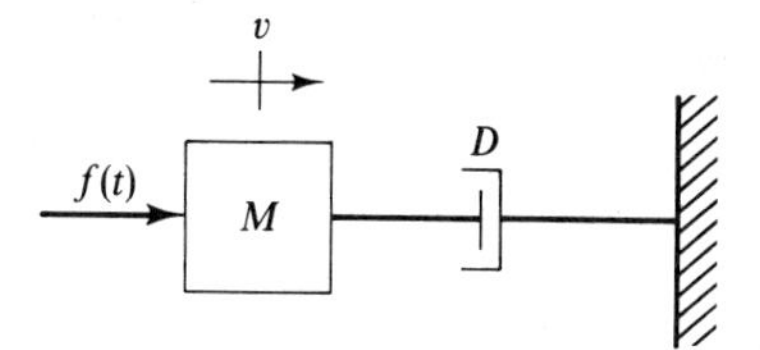

Figure 6.38

28. Determine the Laplace transform of the output $v_o(t)$ of the system shown in Figure 6.39 when the input is $v(t) = te^{-2t}u(t)$. Use the convolution property.

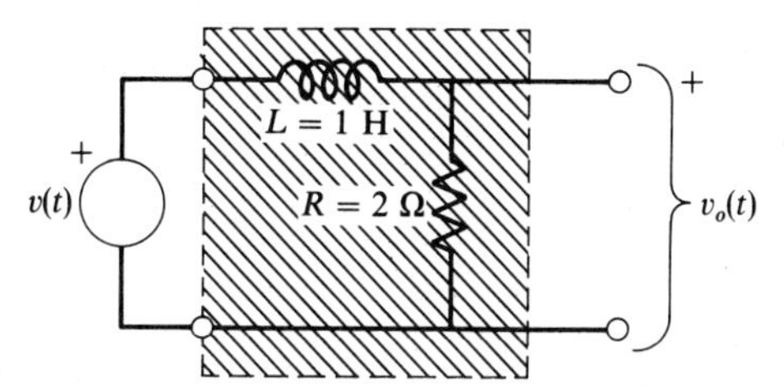

Figure 6.39

29. Refer to Figure 6.40a. Prove that the portion external to the rectangle can be replaced by the circuit of Figure 6.40b for initially relaxed conditions.
Hint: Consider the similarity of this result with the Thevenin theorem for the steady state.

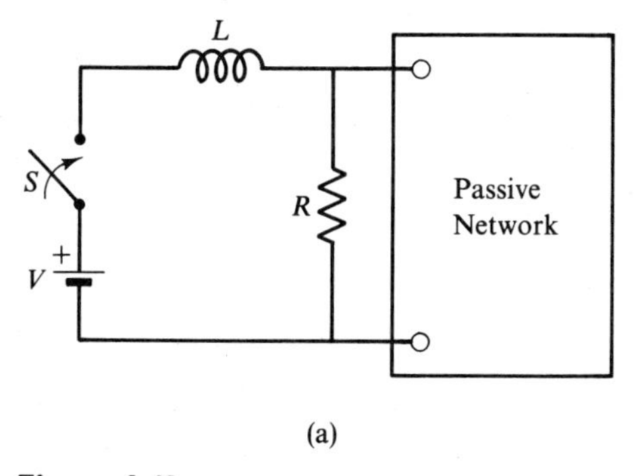

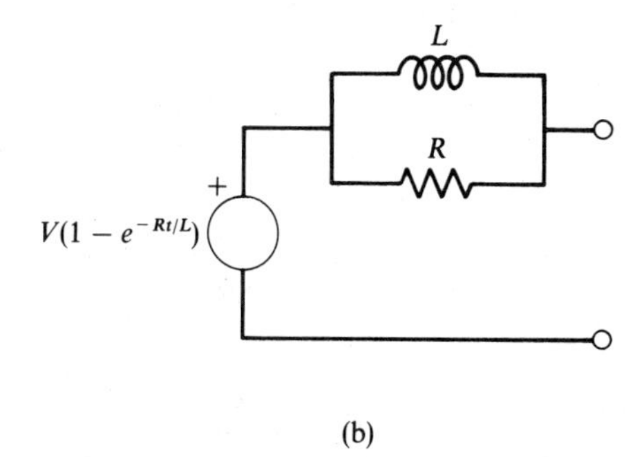

Figure 6.40

30. Determine the impulse response of a series RLC circuit for the following circuit constants:
    a. $R = 4$, $C = 1$, and $L = 1$ b. $R = 1$, $C = 4$, and $L = 1$ c. $R = 2$, $C = 0.1$, and $L = 1$
31. Determine the impulse response of the systems shown in Figure 6.41.

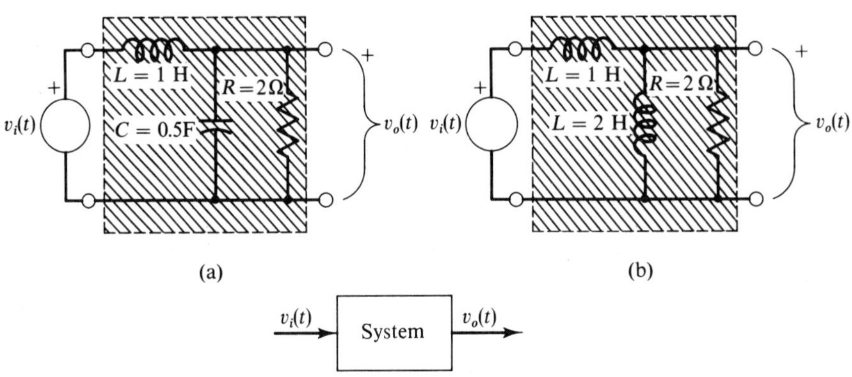

Figure 6.41

32. Determine the impulse response of the system shown in Figure 6.42. The input is $f(t)$ and the output is $v_2(t)$.

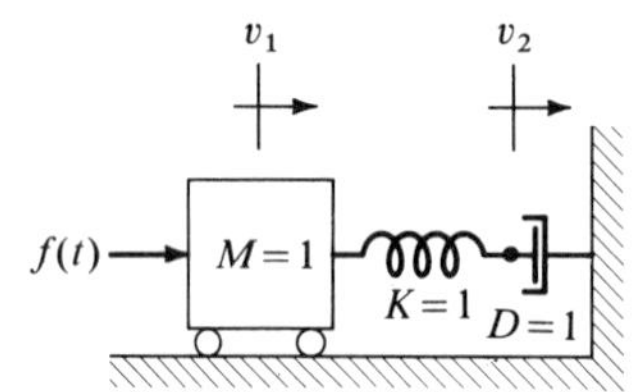

Figure 6.42

33. Use Laplace transform techniques to find the output voltage of the relaxed circuit shown in Figure 6.43 for an input voltage $v_i(t) = e^{-t}u(t)$. Verify your results using the convolution integral method.

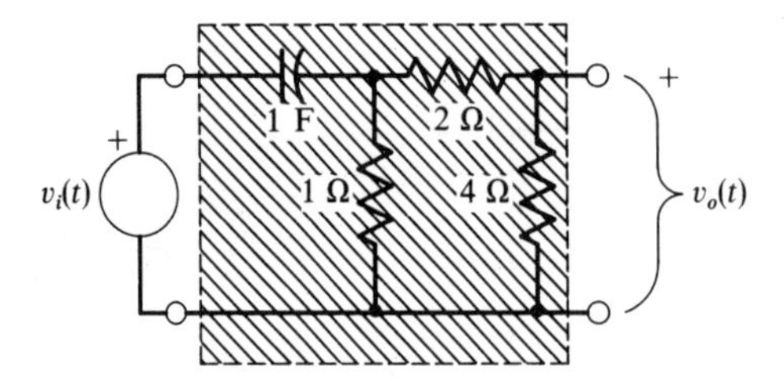

Figure 6.43

Section 6.8

34. Find the transfer function for the systems shown in Figure 6.44.

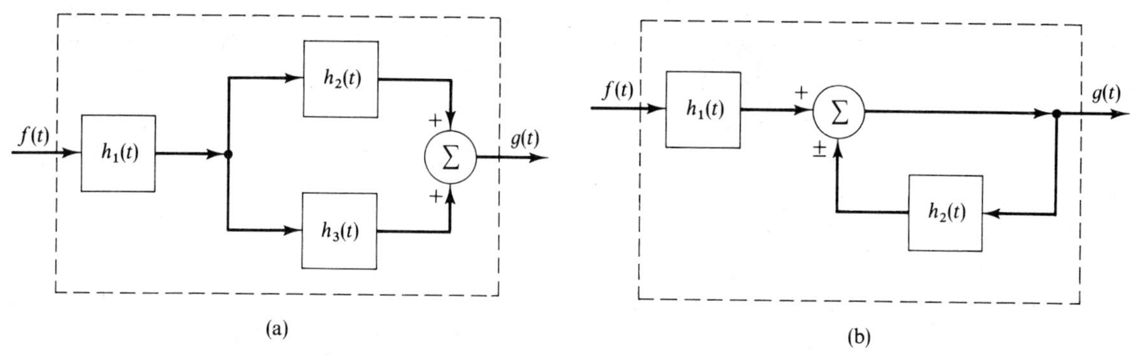

Figure 6.44

35. Deduce the transfer function for the system shown in Figure 6.45.

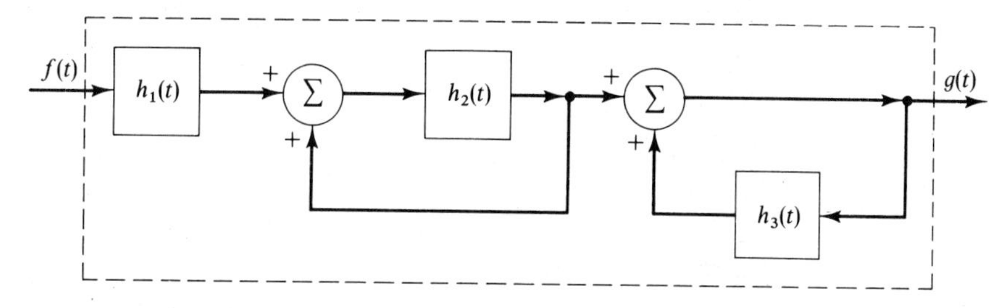

Figure 6.45

36. Determine the transfer functions of the systems shown in Figure 6.46.

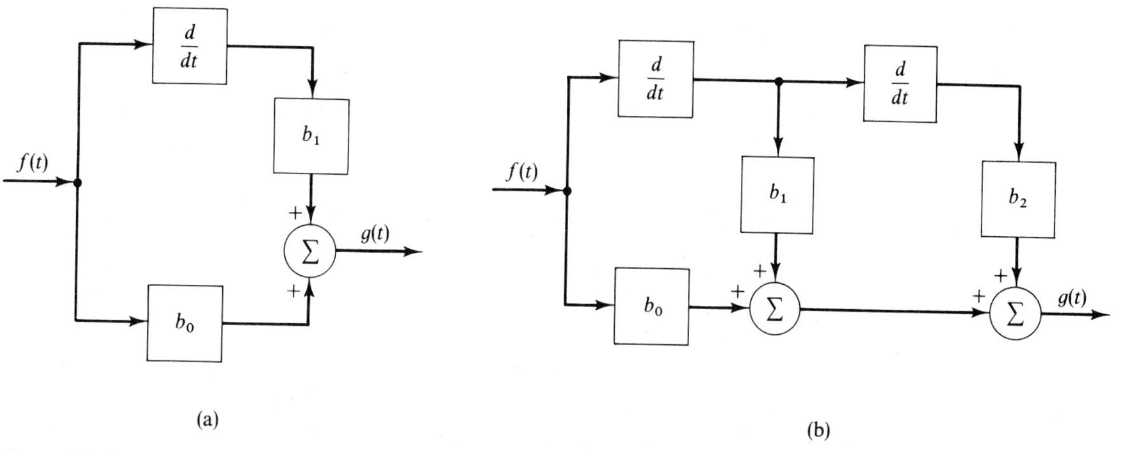

Figure 6.46

37. Determine the output of the circuits shown in Figure 6.47.

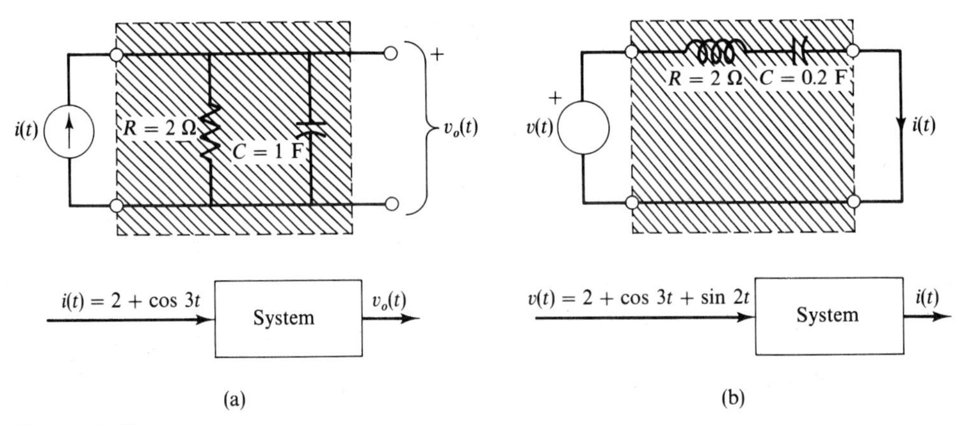

Figure 6.47

38. Determine and plot the amplitude filtering characteristics of the system shown in Figure 6.48.

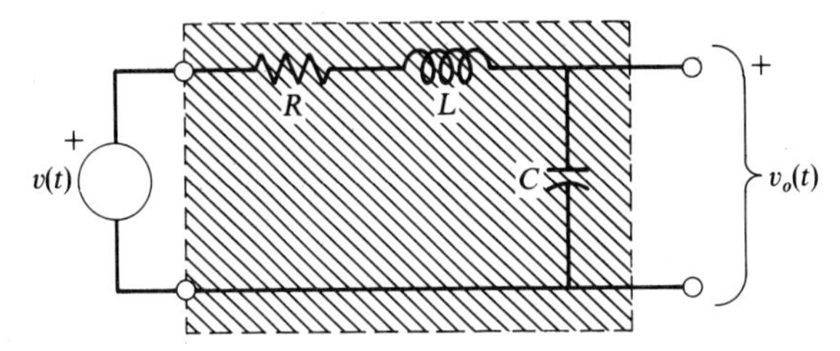

Figure 6.48

39. Determine and plot the transfer function $|H(j\omega)|^2$ versus ω on a linear-linear scale for the system shown in Figure 6.49. Start with $\omega = 1$. Now, plot these data on a $10 \log |H(j\omega)|^2$ versus ω on a linear-$\log_{10}$ scale. This second plot is known as the *Bode* plot, with the quantity $20 \log_{10} |H(j\omega)|$ in units of decibels (dB). Ten dB = 1 Bell.

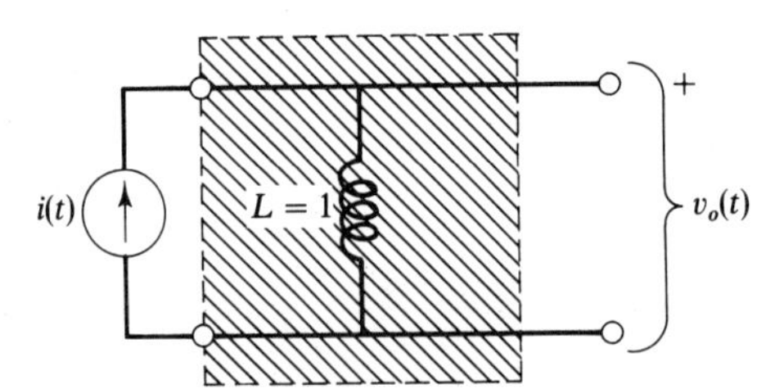

Figure 6.49

Section 6.9

40. Find the closed-form expression for $e^{\mathbf{A}t}$ for each of the following using Laplace transform methods:

a. $\mathbf{A} = \begin{bmatrix} 2 & 1 \\ 4 & 2 \end{bmatrix}$ **b.** $\mathbf{A} = \begin{bmatrix} 3 & 0 \\ 2 & 2 \end{bmatrix}$ **c.** $\mathbf{A} = \begin{bmatrix} -1 & 1 \\ 0 & -1 \end{bmatrix}$ **d.** $\mathbf{A} = \begin{bmatrix} 0 & 1 \\ -2 & -3 \end{bmatrix}$

41. Determine the inverse of the matrix $[s\mathbf{I} - \mathbf{A}]$, where

$$\mathbf{A} = \begin{bmatrix} 3 & 2 & 7 \\ 1 & 5 & 6 \\ -4 & -1 & -3 \end{bmatrix}$$

42. Refer to the circuit of Figure 6.50.

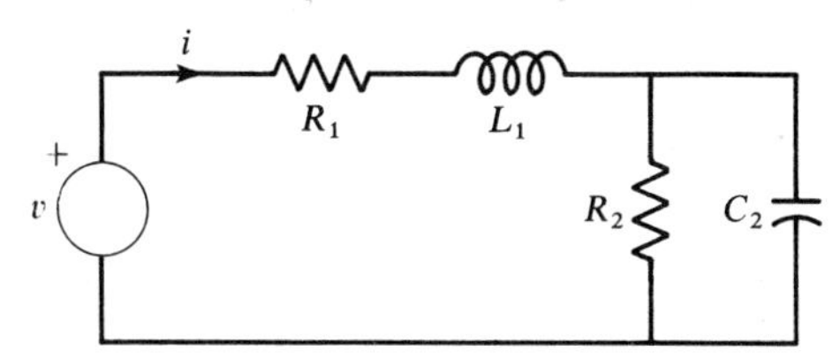

Figure 6.50

a. Write the differential equation that relates i to v.

b. Deduce a phase variable state model from the differential equation and draw the block diagram of the system from this.

c. Deduce a state model from the block diagram.

43. Use Laplace transform methods to find the solution to the following sets of equations:

a. $\begin{bmatrix} \dot{x}_1 \\ \dot{x}_2 \end{bmatrix} = \begin{bmatrix} -3 & 4 \\ -2 & 3 \end{bmatrix} \begin{bmatrix} x_1 \\ x_2 \end{bmatrix} \quad \begin{bmatrix} x_1(0) \\ x_2(0) \end{bmatrix} = \begin{bmatrix} -1 \\ 3 \end{bmatrix}$

b. $\begin{bmatrix} x_1 \\ x_2 \end{bmatrix} = \begin{bmatrix} 3 & -2 \\ 1 & 0 \end{bmatrix} \begin{bmatrix} x_1 \\ x_2 \end{bmatrix} \quad \begin{bmatrix} x_1(0) \\ x_2(0) \end{bmatrix} = \begin{bmatrix} -1 \\ 0 \end{bmatrix}$

44. Deduce the solution to the following set of equations using Laplace methods:

$$\begin{bmatrix} \dot{x}_1 \\ \dot{x}_2 \end{bmatrix} = \begin{bmatrix} 3 & -2 \\ 1 & 0 \end{bmatrix} \begin{bmatrix} x_1 \\ x_2 \end{bmatrix} + \begin{bmatrix} 1 \\ t \end{bmatrix} \quad \begin{bmatrix} x_1(0) \\ x_2(0) \end{bmatrix} = \begin{bmatrix} -\frac{1}{2} \\ -\frac{1}{4} \end{bmatrix}$$

Section 6.10

45. Systems are described by the following differential equations, $p = \dfrac{d}{dt}$:

$(p^2 + 3p + 7)y(t) = (2p + 1)v(t)$

$(p^3 + 2p^2 + 5p + 2)y(t) = (p^3 + 3p + 2)v(t)$

a. Determine the respective system functions.

b. From these system functions, determine the impulse response $h(t)$.

46. Determine the values of the constant k that causes the system shown in Figure 6.51 to be unstable and stable.

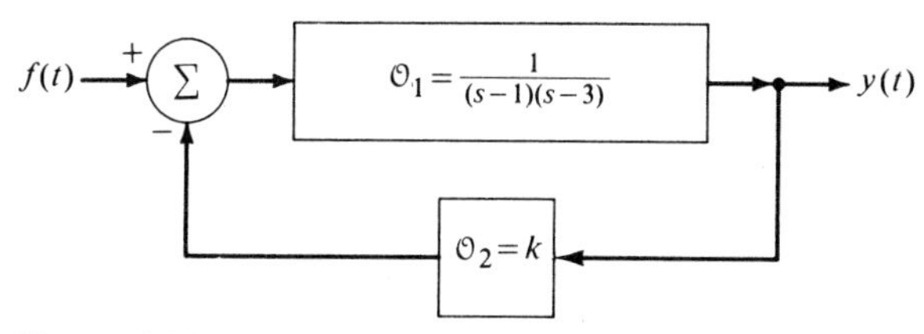

Figure 6.51

47. The output of a system is given by the relation $V_o(s) = H(s)V_i(s)$. If $v_i(t) = \sin \omega t$, show that the steady state output is given by $|H(j\omega)| \sin[\omega t + \phi(\omega)]$ provided that $H(s)$ has singularities only on the left-hand plane. What conclusion can you draw about the steady state response of an LTI system?

48. Sketch the surface $|H(s)|$ over the s-plane for the transfer function given below and draw conclusions by observing the intersection between the surface $|H(s)|$ and the plane $\sigma = 0$.

a. $H(s) = 1/(s - 0.5)$ **b.** $H(s) = 1/(s - 4)$

7

Z-Transform

The classical techniques for the solution of difference equations discussed in Chapter 5 do not lend themselves well to a systematic study of linear discrete time systems of an order higher than two. Additional details of higher-order difference equations are discussed below. The Z-transform method provides a powerful tool for solving difference equations of higher order and, hence, plays a very important role in digital systems analysis. This chapter includes a study of the Z-transform, its properties, and its applications.

The Z-transform method provides a technique for transforming a difference equation into an algebraic equation. Specifically, the Z-transform converts a sequence of numbers $\{y(k)\}$ into a function of a complex variable $Y(z)$, thereby allowing algebraic processes and well-defined mathematical procedures to be applied in the solution process. In this sense, the Z-transform plays the same general role in the solution of difference equations that the Laplace transform plays in the solution of differential equations, and in a roughly parallel way. Inversion procedures that parallel one another also exist. The parallelism with the development of the Laplace transform in Chapter 6 will be evident.

7.1 Z-Transform

To understand the essential features of the Z-transform, consider a **one-sided sequence** of numbers $\{y(k)\}$ taken at uniform time intervals. This sequence might be the values of a continuous function that has been sampled at uniform time intervals; it could, of course, be a number sequence. This number sequence is written

$$y(k) = \{y(0), y(1), y(2), \dots y(k), \dots\} \tag{7.1}$$

We now create the series

$$Y(z) = \frac{y(0)}{z^0} + \frac{y(1)}{z^1} + \frac{y(2)}{z^2} + \frac{y(3)}{z^3} + \cdots$$
$$= y(0) + y(1)z^{-1} + y(2)z^{-2} + \cdots \tag{7.2}$$

In this expression, z denotes the general complex variable and $Y(z)$ denotes the Z-transform of the sequence $\{y(k)\}$. In its more general form, the one-sided Z-transform of a sequence $\{y(k)\}$ is written

$$\boxed{Y(z) \triangleq \mathscr{Z}\{y(k)\} = \sum_{k=0}^{\infty} y(k)z^{-k}} \tag{7.3}$$

This expression can be taken as the definition of the Z-transform.

An interesting observation of (7.3) is that the position of each element in the series $Y(z)$ is dictated by the order of z^{-k} associated with each element $y(k)$. For example, the element $y(2)$ associated with z^{-2} is the second element in the sequence $\{y(k)\}$ and so is delayed by two time units from the start of the number sequence. We can thus consider z^{-1} as the unit delay operator that was introduced in Chapter 2 to relate delayed or shifted variables in difference equations. This interpretation is not explicit in the mathematical formalism of (7.3), but it is implied when the shifting properties of functions are considered. Often, this feature is helpful in understanding the details of a given expression. Moreover, this same concept will occur when we apply the Z-transform to the solution of difference equations. Initially, however, we study the mathematics of the Z-transform.

When the sequence of numbers is obtained by sampling a function $y(t)$ every T seconds—for example, by using an A/D converter—the numbers represent the sample values $y(kT)$ for $k = 0, 1, 2, \ldots$. This suggests that there is a relationship between the Laplace transform of a continuous function and the Z-transform of a sequence of samples of the function at the time instants $\ldots, -T, 0, T, 2T, \ldots$. To show that there is such a relationship, let $y(t)$ be a continuous function that is being sampled at the time instants $\ldots, -T, 0, T, 2T, \ldots$. The sampled function is [see (1.21)]

$$y_s(t) = y(t)comb_T(t) = \sum_{k=-\infty}^{\infty} y(kT)\delta(t - kT) \tag{7.4}$$

The Laplace transform of this expression is

$$Y_s(s) \triangleq \mathscr{L}\{y_s(t)\} = \mathscr{L}\left\{\sum_{k=-\infty}^{\infty} y(kT)\delta(t - kT)\right\} = \sum_{k=-\infty}^{\infty} y(kT)\mathscr{L}\{\delta(t - kT)\}$$
$$= \sum_{k=-\infty}^{\infty} y(kT)e^{-ksT} \tag{7.5}$$

noting that the Laplace operator operates on time t. If we make the substitution $z = e^{sT}$, then

$$Y_s(s)\Big|_{z=e^{sT}} = \sum_{k=-\infty}^{\infty} y(kT)z^{-k} = Y(z) \tag{7.6}$$

Here, $Y(z)$ is the Z-transform of the sequence of samples of $y(t)$, namely, $y(kT)$, with $k = 0, 1, 2, \ldots$. From this discussion, we observe that the Z-transform may be viewed as the Laplace transform of the sampled time function $y_s(t)$, with an appropriate change of variable. This interpretation is in addition to that given by (7.3), which, as already noted, specifies that $Y(z)$ is the Z-transform of the number sequence $\{y(k)\}$ for $k = \ldots, -2, -1, 0, 1, 2, \ldots$.

■ Example 7.1

Deduce the Z-transform of the discrete function

$$y(k) = \begin{cases} 0 & k \le 0 \\ 1 & k = 1 \\ 2 & k = 2 \\ 0 & k \ge 3 \end{cases}$$

Solution From the defining equation (7.3), we write

$$Y(z) = \mathscr{Z}\{y(k)\} = \frac{1}{z} + \frac{2}{z^2} = \frac{z+2}{z^2}$$

Observe that this function possesses a second-order pole at the origin and a zero at -2. Observe that $y(k)$ could be written $y(k) = \delta(k-1) + 2\delta(k-2)$. ■

■ Example 7.2

Deduce the Z-transform of the function

$$f(t) = Ae^{-at} \qquad t \ge 0 \tag{7.7}$$

which is sampled every T seconds—that is, $t = kT$.

Solution The sampled values are

$$\{f(kT)\} = A,\ Ae^{-aT},\ Ae^{-2aT}, \ldots$$

The Z-transform of this sequence is written

$$F(z) = A\left[1 + \frac{e^{-aT}}{z} + \left(\frac{e^{-aT}}{z}\right)^2 + \cdots\right]$$

This series can be written in closed form, recalling that

$$\frac{1}{1-x} = 1 + x + x^2 + x^3 + \cdots \qquad |x| < 1$$

Thus, we have that

$$F(z) = \frac{A}{[1 - (e^{-aT}/z)]} = \frac{Az}{z - e^{-aT}} \tag{7.8}$$

■

■ **Example 7.3**

Deduce the Z-transform of the function

$$f(t) = e^{-t} + 2e^{-2t} \qquad t \geq 0$$

which is sampled at time intervals $T = 0.1$ s.

Solution We use the results of Example 7.2 to write

$$F(z) = \frac{z}{z - e^{-0.1}} + \frac{2z}{z - e^{-0.2}}$$

This expression is

$$F(z) = \frac{z}{z - 0.905} + \frac{2z}{z - 0.819}$$

When written in this form, this equation is the partial fraction expansion of the function

$$F(z) = \frac{z(z - 0.819) + 2z(z - 0.905)}{(z - 0.905)(z - 0.819)} = \frac{3z^2 - 2.629z}{z^2 - 1.724z + 0.741}$$ ■

■ **Example 7.4**

Find the Z-transform of the given functions when sampled every T seconds:

a. $f(t) = u(t)$
b. $f(t) = tu(t)$
c. $f(t) = e^{-\beta t}u(t)$
d. $f(t) = \sin \omega t\ u(t)$

Solution

a. $\mathscr{Z}\{f(kT)\} = \mathscr{Z}\{u(kT)\} = \sum_{k=0}^{\infty} u(kT)z^{-k} = (1 + z^{-1} + z^{-2} + \cdots)$

$$= \frac{1}{1 - z^{-1}} = \frac{z}{z - 1} \qquad |z| > 1 \tag{7.9}$$

b. $$\mathscr{Z}\{f(kT)\} = \mathscr{Z}\{kTu(kT)\} = \sum_{k=0}^{\infty} kTu(kT)z^{-k}$$

$$= Tz^{-1} + 2Tz^{-2} + 3Tz^{-3} + \cdots$$

$$= -Tz\frac{d}{dz}(z^{-1} + z^{-2} + z^{-3} + \cdots)$$

$$= -Tz\frac{d}{dz}[z^{-1}(1 + z^{-1} + z^{-2} + \cdots)]$$

$$= -Tz\frac{d}{dz}\left[z^{-1}\frac{z}{z-1}\right] = \frac{Tz}{(z-1)^2} \qquad |z| > 1 \tag{7.10}$$

c. $$\mathscr{Z}\{f(kT)\} = \mathscr{Z}\{u(kT)e^{-\beta kT}\} = \mathscr{Z}\{u(kT)c^{-k}\}; \text{ where } e^{+\beta T} = c \text{ for convenience}$$

$$= \sum_{k=0}^{\infty} u(kT)c^{-k}z^{-k} = 1 + c^{-1}z^{-1} + c^{-2}z^{-2} + \cdots = \frac{1}{1 - \dfrac{1}{cz}}$$

$$= \frac{cz}{cz-1} = \frac{ze^{\beta T}}{ze^{\beta T} - 1} = \frac{z}{z - e^{-\beta T}} \qquad |z| > e^{-\beta T} \tag{7.11}$$

d. $$\mathscr{Z}\{f(kT)\} = \mathscr{Z}\{u(kT)\sin \omega kT\} = \mathscr{Z}\left\{u(kT)\frac{e^{j\omega kT} - e^{-j\omega kT}}{2j}\right\}$$

$$= \sum_{k=0}^{\infty} \frac{u(kT)}{2j} c_1^{-k}z^{-k} - \sum_{k=0}^{\infty} \frac{u(kT)}{2j} c_2^{-k}z^{-k}; \; c_1 = e^{-j\omega T},\; c_2 = e^{j\omega T}$$

$$= \frac{1}{2j}\left[\frac{c_1 z}{c_1 z - 1} - \frac{c_2 z}{c_2 z - 1}\right]$$

$$= \frac{z}{2j}\left[\frac{e^{-j\omega T}}{e^{-j\omega T}z - 1} - \frac{e^{j\omega T}}{e^{j\omega T}z - 1}\right] = \frac{z \sin \omega T}{z^2 - 2z\cos \omega T + 1} \qquad |z| > 1 \tag{7.12}$$

■

7.2 Convergence of the Z-Transform

The function $F(z)$ for a specified value of z may be either finite or infinite. The **region of convergence** is the set of z in the complex z-plane for which the magnitude of $F(z)$ is finite; whereas the set of z for which the magnitude of $F(z)$ is infinite is the **region of divergence.** The region of convergence is determined by considering the defining expression (7.3) and examining the complex values of z for which $\sum_{k=0}^{\infty} f(k)z^{-k}$ has finite values. If we write z in polar form $z = re^{j\theta}$, then

$$\sum_{k=0}^{\infty} |f(k)z^{-k}| = \sum_{k=0}^{\infty} |f(k)(re^{j\theta})^{-k}| = \sum_{k=0}^{\infty} |f(k)r^{-k}e^{-jk\theta}|$$

$$= \sum_{k=0}^{\infty} |f(k)r^{-k}||e^{-jk\theta}| = \sum_{k=0}^{\infty} |f(k)r^{-k}| \tag{7.13}$$

since $|e^{-jk\theta}| = [\cos^2 k\theta + \sin^2 k\theta]^{1/2} = 1$. For this sum to be finite, we find numbers M and R such that $|f(k)| \le MR^k$ for $k \ge 0$. Thus,

$$\sum_{k=0}^{\infty} |f(k)z^{-k}| \le M \sum_{k=0}^{\infty} R^k r^{-k} = M \sum_{k=0}^{\infty} \left(\frac{R}{r}\right)^k \tag{7.14}$$

For this sum to be finite, it is required that $R/r < 1$. That is, $F(z)$ is absolutely convergent for all z in the region outside of the circle of radius R. Conversely, the region $r = |z| < R$ is the region of divergence. A separate test is required to establish whether the boundary belongs to the region of convergence or the region of divergence. This test is shown by an example.

■ Example 7.5

Find the Z-transform of the signal specified and discuss its properties.

$$f(k) = \begin{cases} c^k & k = 0, 1, 2, \ldots \\ 0 & k = -1, -2, \ldots \end{cases} \tag{7.15}$$

The constant c takes the values:

a. $0 < c < 1$

b. $c > 1$

Solution The time sequences for the two cases are shown in Figures 7.1a and 7.1b. The Z-transform is given by

$$F(z) = \sum_{k=0}^{\infty} c^k z^{-k} = \sum_{k=0}^{\infty} (c^{-1}z)^{-k}$$
$$= 1 + cz^{-1} + c^2z^{-2} + \cdots + c^n z^{-n} + \cdots \tag{7.16}$$

Initially, we consider the sum of the first $n + 1$ terms of this geometric series which is given by (see Appendix B.4, Finite Summation Formulas)

$$F_n(z) = \frac{1 - (cz^{-1})^n}{1 - cz^{-1}} \tag{7.17}$$

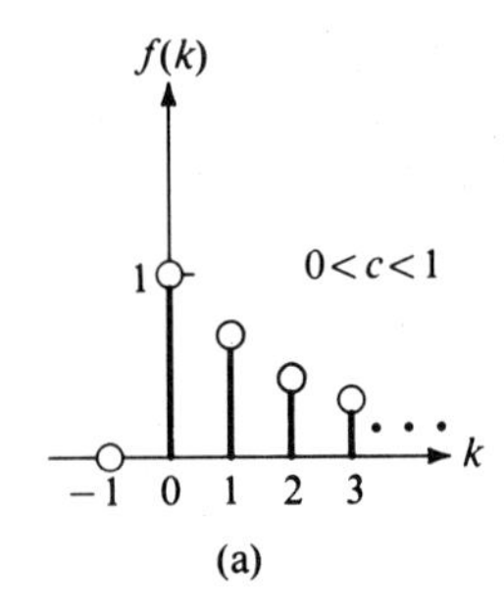

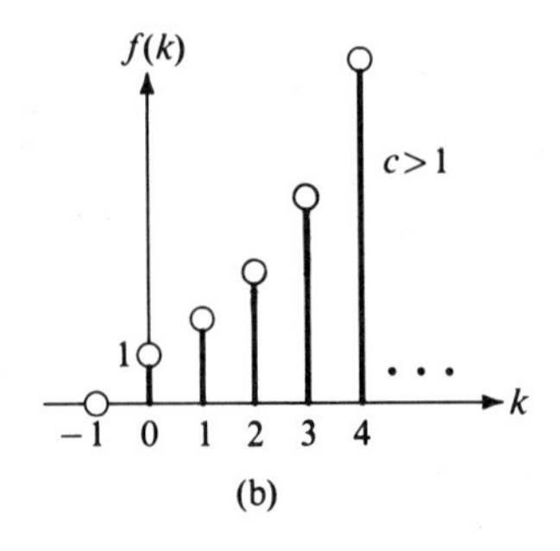

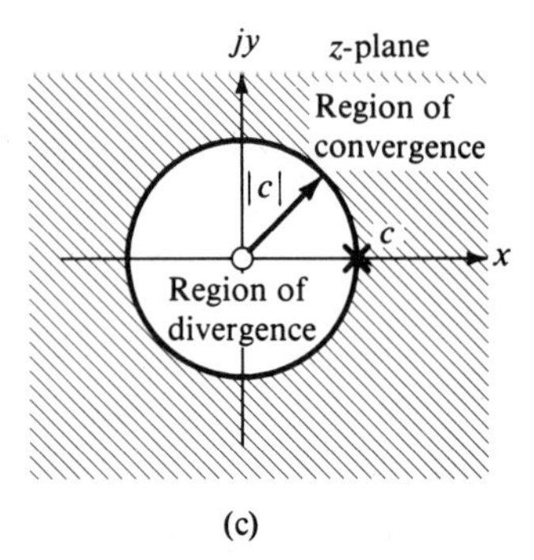

Figure 7.1 Discrete Signal c^k

Now, set

$$cz^{-1} = |cz^{-1}|e^{j\theta}$$

where θ is the argument of the complex number cz^{-1}. Hence, we write

$$(cz^{-1})^n = |cz^{-1}|^n e^{jn\theta}$$

Case 1: For values of z for which $|cz^{-1}| < 1$, the magnitude of the complex number $(cz^{-1})^n$ approaches zero as $n \to \infty$. As a consequence,

$$F(z) = \lim_{n\to\infty} F_n(z) = \frac{1}{1 - cz^{-1}} = \frac{z}{z - c} \qquad |cz^{-1}| < 1 \tag{7.18}$$

Case 2: For the general case where c is a complex number, the inequality $|cz^{-1}| < 1$ leads to $|c| < |z|$, which implies that the series converges when $|z| > |c|$ and diverges for $|z| < |c|$. Thus, we see that the regions of convergence and divergence in the complex plane for $F(z)$ are those shown in Figure 7.1c.

To establish whether the boundary of the circle in Figure 7.1c belongs to the region of convergence or the region of divergence, we apply L'Hospital's rule to (7.17). Thus,

$$\lim_{z\to c} F_n(z) = \lim_{z\to c} \frac{[d/d(cz^{-1})][1 - (cz^{-1})^n]}{[d/d(cz^{-1})][1 - (cz^{-1})]} = \lim_{z\to c} \frac{-n(cz^{-1})^{n-1}}{-1} = n$$

and, therefore,

$$\lim_{n\to\infty} F_n(z) \to \infty$$

Clearly, the boundary belongs to the region of divergence. ■

■ Example 7.6

Deduce the Z-transform and discuss the properties of the impulse functions

$$y(k) = \delta(k) = \begin{cases} 1 & k = 0 \\ 0 & k \neq 0 \end{cases} \tag{7.19a}$$

$$y(k) = \delta(k - N) = \begin{cases} 1 & k = N \\ 0 & k \neq N \end{cases} \tag{7.19b}$$

These functions are shown in Figure 7.2.

Solution From the basic definition, we can write that

$$Y(z) = y(0)z^{-0} = 1$$

Since $Y(z)$ is independent of z, the entire z-plane is the region of convergence. By

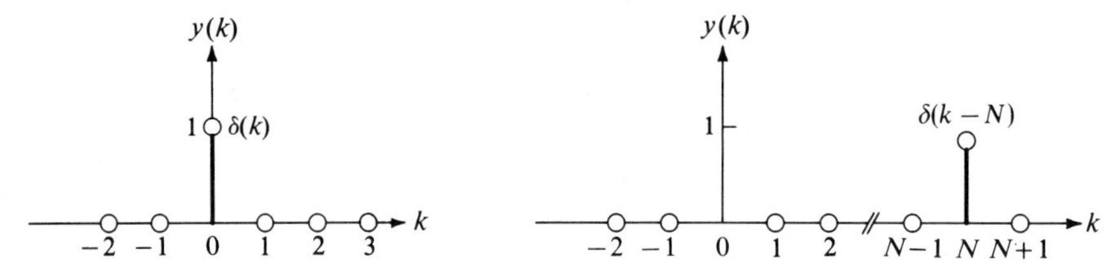

Figure 7.2 Discrete Delta Function

an application of the basic definition, we have

$$\begin{aligned}\mathscr{Z}\{\delta(k-N)\} \triangleq Y(z) &= \sum_{k=0}^{\infty} \delta(k-N)z^{-k} = 0 \times z^{-0} + 0 \times z^{-1} + \cdots \\ &\quad + 1 \times z^{-N} + 0 \times z^{-(N+1)} + \cdots \\ &= z^{-N}\end{aligned}$$

Since $Y(z) \to \infty$ only for $z = 0$, the entire z-plane is the region of convergence except for an infinitesimal region around the origin. ■

■ **Example 7.7**

Deduce the Z-transform of the function

$$y(k) = \begin{cases} a^k \sin(k\omega) & k \geq 0, \quad a > 0 \\ 0 & k < 0 \end{cases} \tag{7.20}$$

Indicate the region of divergence, the region of convergence, and the poles and zeros in the z-plane.

Solution The given function is shown in Figures 7.3a and 7.3b for two different values of a. Clearly, for $a = 1$, the function is a sinusoidal discrete signal. The Z-transform is given by

$$\begin{aligned}Y(z) &= \sum_{k=0}^{\infty} a^k \sin(k\omega) z^{-k} = \sum_{k=0}^{\infty} a^k \frac{(e^{jk\omega} - e^{-jk\omega})}{2j} z^{-k} \\ &= \frac{1}{2j} \sum_{k=0}^{\infty} (ae^{j\omega}z^{-1})^k - \frac{1}{2j} \sum_{k=0}^{\infty} (ae^{-j\omega}z^{-1})^k\end{aligned} \tag{7.21}$$

Sum the geometric series of (7.21) in the manner of (7.8) to write

$$\begin{aligned}Y(z) &= \frac{1}{2j}\left[\frac{1}{1 - ae^{j\omega}z^{-1}} - \frac{1}{1 - ae^{-j\omega}z^{-1}}\right] \\ &= \frac{z^{-1} a \sin\omega}{1 - 2az^{-1}\cos\omega + a^2 z^{-2}} \qquad |z| > a\end{aligned} \tag{7.22}$$

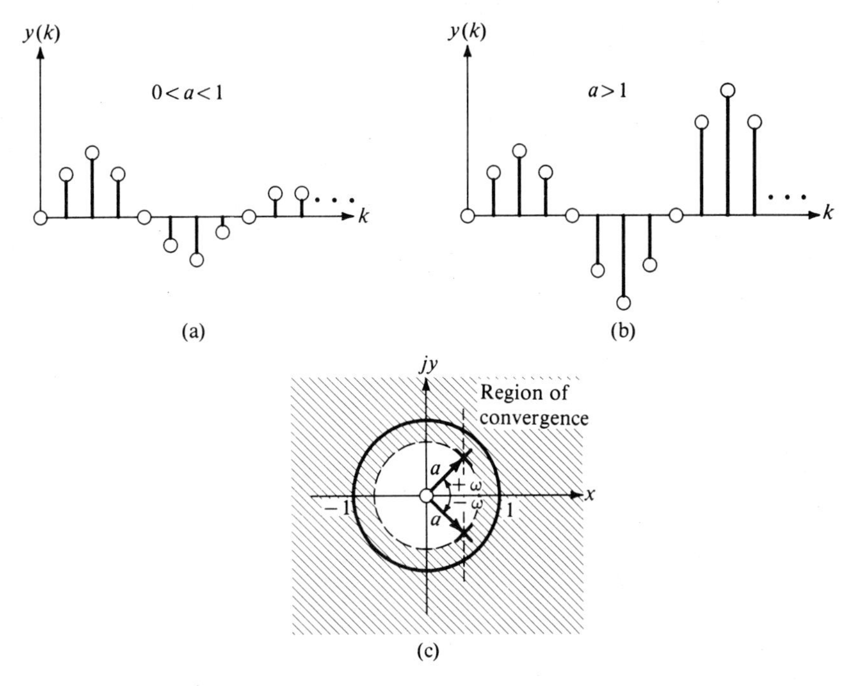

Figure 7.3 Discrete Signal $a^k \sin(k\omega)$, Its Poles and Zeros and Regions of Convergence

Multiply the numerator and denominator of this expression by z^2 to find

$$\begin{aligned}Y(z) &= \frac{za \sin \omega}{z^2 - 2a(\cos \omega)z + a^2} \\ &= \frac{za \sin \omega}{[z - a(\cos \omega + j \sin \omega)][z - a(\cos \omega - j \sin \omega)]} \\ &= \frac{za \sin \omega}{(z - ae^{j\omega})(z - ae^{-j\omega})}\end{aligned} \tag{7.23}$$

The zeros and poles are shown in Figure 7.3c for the case $a < 1$.

To examine the region of convergence, consider (7.21). It is seen that each of the series converges if $|ae^{j\omega}z^{-1}| = |az^{-1}||e^{j\omega}| = |az^{-1}| < 1$ or $|z| > a$. This region is shown in Figure 7.3c. ■

When the sequence $\{y(k)\}$ has values for both positive and negative k, the region of convergence of $Y(z)$ becomes an annular ring around the origin. Specifically, consider the sequence

$$y(k) = \begin{cases} 3^k & \text{for } k \geq 0 \\ 4^k & \text{for } k < 0 \end{cases}$$

This is a bilateral function, and the definition for the bilateral Z-transform equivalent to (7.3) is used:

$$\mathscr{Z}\{y(k)\} = \sum_{k=-\infty}^{\infty} y(k)z^{-k} \tag{7.24}$$

For our specific function,

$$Y(z) = \sum_{k=0}^{\infty} 3^k z^{-k} + \sum_{k=-\infty}^{-1} 4^k z^{-k} = \sum_{k=0}^{\infty} 3^k z^{-k} + \sum_{k=1}^{\infty} 4^{-k} z^k$$

The first summation converges as $k \to \infty$ provided that $|3z^{-1}| < 1$ or $|z| > 3$. If we set $R^+ = 3$ for positive k's, we see that the region of convergence for positive k's is $|z| > R^+$. Similarly, the second summation converges if $|4^{-1}z| < 1$ or $|z| < 4$, and the region of convergence for the negative k's is $|z| < R^-$ with $R^- = 4$. The sequence $y(k)$ and the region of convergence depicted as the double-lined region are shown in Figure 7.4.

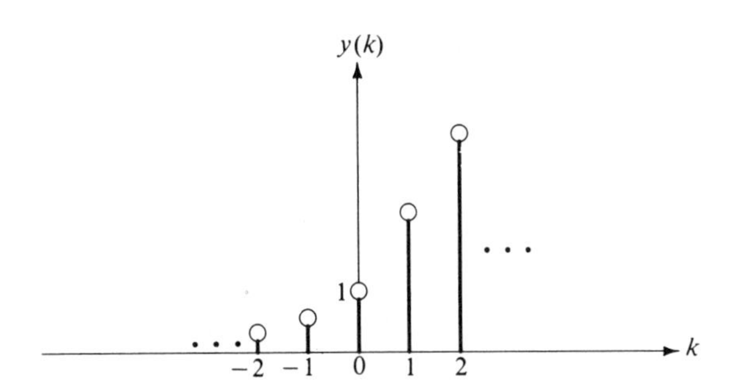

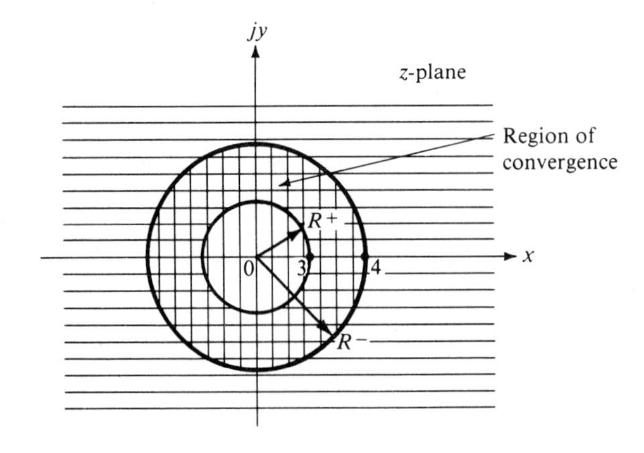

Figure 7.4 Region of Convergence for a Two-Sided Sequence

The reader can easily show, following parallel steps to the above, that the sequence

$$y(k) = \begin{cases} 4^k & \text{for} \quad k \geq 0 \\ 3^k & \text{for} \quad k < 0 \end{cases}$$

has no region of convergence.

From the foregoing discussion, we conclude that:

1. The region of convergence of a two-sided sequence is a ring in the z-plane centered at the origin.
2. The region of convergence of a sequence of finite duration is the entire z-plane, except possibly the points $z = 0$ and/or $z = \infty$.
3. If the sequence is right-handed—that is, $k \geq 0$—then the region of convergence is beyond a circle of finite radius.
4. If the sequence is left-handed—that is, $k < 0$—then the region of convergence is within a circle of finite radius.

The following example shows why it is important to specify the region of convergence.

■ Example 7.8

Specify the region of convergence for the two sequences

$$y_1(k) = a^k u(k) \tag{7.25a}$$

$$y_2(k) = -a^k u(-k-1) \tag{7.25b}$$

Solution The Z-transform of the first sequence is

$$Y_1(z) = \sum_{k=0}^{\infty} (az^{-1})^k = \frac{z}{z-a} = \frac{1}{1-az^{-1}} \tag{7.26}$$

For convergence, we must have $|az^{-1}| < 1$, which implies that the region of convergence is $|z| > |a|$.

The Z-transform of the second sequence is

$$Y_2(z) = -\sum_{k=-\infty}^{-1} a^k z^{-k} = -\sum_{k=1}^{\infty} a^{-k} z^k = 1 - \sum_{k=0}^{\infty} (a^{-1}z)^k = 1 + \frac{a}{z-a}$$

$$= \frac{z}{z-a} = \frac{1}{1-az^{-1}} \tag{7.27}$$

The region of convergence is found from the relation $|a^{-1}z| < 1$ or $|z| < |a|$. The sequences for $a > 1.3$ with their pole-zero configuration and their regions of convergence are shown in Figure 7.5.

We observe from (7.26) and (7.27) and Figure 7.5 that two completely different sequences can have the same analytical form in the z-domain and the same pole-zero configuration. Clearly, if we are given the Z-transform of a sequence, we must also know the region of convergence so that we can obtain a unique sequence in the time domain. ■

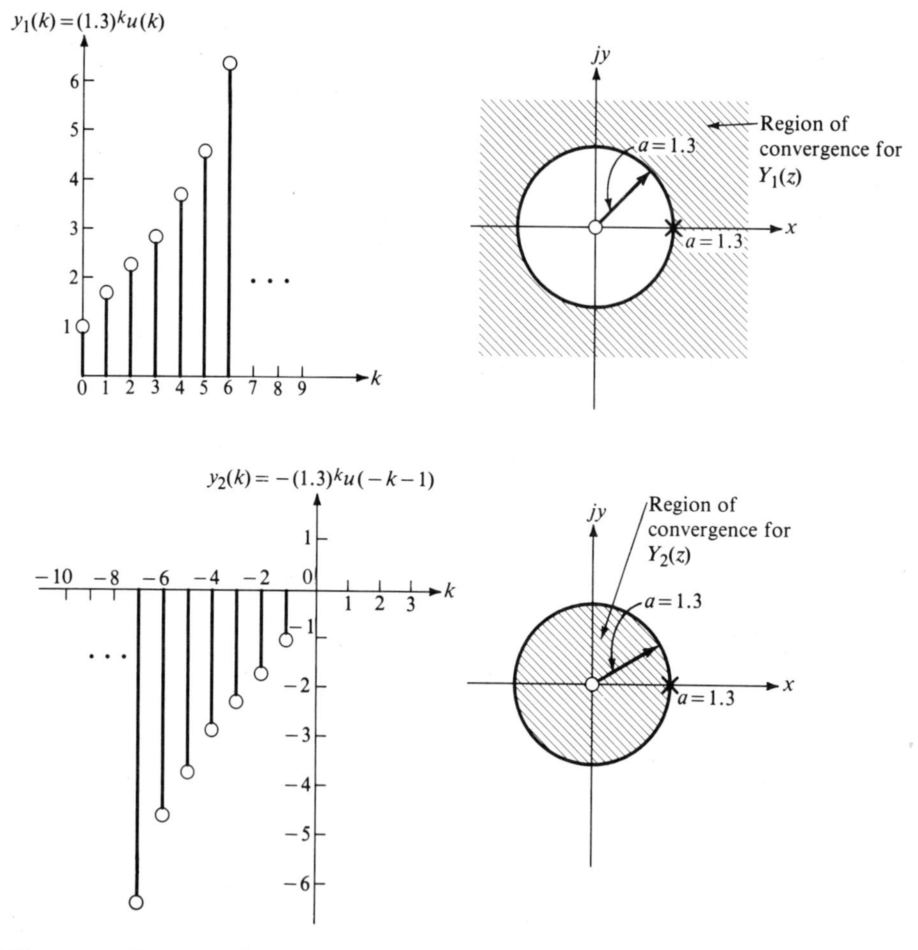

Figure 7.5 Illustrating Example 7.8

7.3 Properties of the Z-Transform

The most important basic properties of the Z-transform for one-sided sequences are developed next. The one-sided sequence is of great importance because all detected signals are of finite extent and their starting point can always be referenced at $t = 0$ ($k = 0$). A discussion of these properties follows.

Linearity. Consider the sequence $\{f(k)\} = \{ay_1(k) + by_2(k)\}$. The Z-transform is

$$\mathscr{Z}\{ay_1(k) + by_2(k)\} = a\mathscr{Z}\{y_1(k)\} + b\mathscr{Z}\{y_2(k)\} \tag{7.28}$$

where a and b are any constants. The region of convergence is $|z| > \max(R_1, R_2)$, where $|z| > R_1$ and $|z| > R_2$ are the regions of convergence of $y_1(k)$ and $y_2(k)$, respectively. The expression $\max(R_1, R_2)$ means the selection of the largest of the two numbers R_1 and R_2.

Right-Shifting Property. Consider the Z-transform of the sequence $\{f(k-n)\}$:

$$\mathscr{Z}\{y(k-n)\} = z^{-n}\mathscr{Z}\{y(k)\} = z^{-n}Y(z) \tag{7.29a}$$

$$= z^{-n}Y(z) + \sum_{i=0}^{n-1} y(i-n)z^{-i} \tag{7.29b}$$

Proof Begin with the definition of the Z-transform:

$$Y(z) = \sum_{k=0}^{\infty} y(k)z^{-k}$$

Multiply through by z^{-n} and then substitute $-m$ for $-n-k$. The result is

$$z^{-n}Y(z) = \sum_{m=n}^{\infty} y(m-n)z^{-m} = \sum_{m=0}^{\infty} y(m-n)z^{-m} = \sum_{k=0}^{\infty} y(k-n)z^{-k}$$

where, since m is a dummy index, it has been changed to the letter k. The third term in this expression is obtained by invoking the one-sided character of $y(k)$ with y (negative argument) $= 0$. For the case when we find that $y(-k)$ (initial condition) has values other than zero, we must add the quantity $y(-n) + y(1-n)z^{-1} + \cdots + y(-1)z^{-(n-1)}$ to the right-hand member of (7.29a); thus, m runs from 0 to $n-1$. The resulting equation is (7.29b). The multiplication by $z^{-n}(n > 0)$ creates a pole at $z = 0$ and deletes a pole at infinity. Therefore, the region of convergence is the same as the region of convergence of $y(k)$, with the possible exclusion of the origin.

■ **Example 7.9**

Find the Z-transform of the function shown in Figure 7.6a using the right-shifting property.

Solution First, consider the Z-transform of the unit step function $u(k)$ shown in Figure 7.6b, which is given by

$$U(z) = \sum_{k=0}^{\infty} u(k)z^{-k} = 1 + z^{-1} + z^{-2} + \cdots = \frac{1}{1+z^{-1}} = \frac{z}{z-1}$$

The discrete time function in Figure 7.6a is

$$y(k) = 2u(k-2) - 2u(k-5)$$

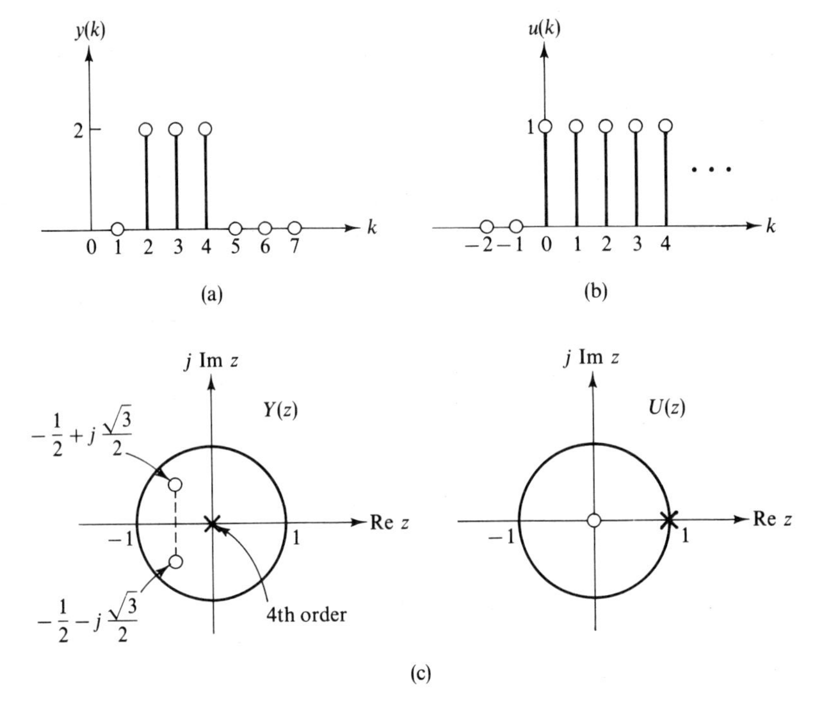

Figure 7.6 Illustration of a Shifted Discrete Signal

The Z-transform of this equation is, using (7.29a),

$$\mathscr{Z}\{y(k)\} = 2\mathscr{Z}\{u(k-2)\} - 2\mathscr{Z}\{u(k-5)\} = 2z^{-2}\mathscr{Z}\{u(k)\} - 2z^{-5}\mathscr{Z}\{u(k)\}$$

$$= \frac{2z}{z-1}\left[\frac{1}{z^2} - \frac{1}{z^5}\right] = \frac{2(z^2+z+1)}{z^4}$$

$$= \frac{2\left(z + \frac{1}{2} - j\frac{\sqrt{3}}{2}\right)\left(z + \frac{1}{2} + j\frac{\sqrt{3}}{2}\right)}{z^4}$$

The pole-zero configurations for $U(z)$ and $Y(z)$ are shown in Figure 7.6c. We observe from this figure that $U(z)$ does not have poles at zero, whereas the combination of its shifted version $y(k)$ does possess poles (multiple) at the origin. ■

Left-Shifting Property. The Z-transform of the sequence $\{y(k+n)\}$ is

$$\mathscr{Z}\{y(k+n)\} = z^n Y(z) - \sum_{k=0}^{n-1} y(k) z^{n-k} \tag{7.30}$$

Proof From the basic definition,

$$\mathscr{Z}\{y(k+1)\} = \sum_{k=0}^{\infty} y(k+1)z^{-k}$$

Now, set $k + 1 = m$ to find

$$\mathscr{Z}\{y(m)\} = \sum_{m=1}^{\infty} y(m)z^{-m+1} = z\sum_{m=1}^{\infty} y(m)z^{-m} = z\sum_{m=0}^{\infty} y(m)z^{-m} - zy(0)$$
$$= zY(z) - zy(0)$$

By a similar procedure, we can show that

$$\mathscr{Z}\{y(k+n)\} = z^n Y(z) - z^n y(0) - z^{n-1}y(1) - \cdots - zy(n-1)$$
$$= z^n Y(z) - \sum_{k=0}^{n-1} y(k)z^{n-k}$$

Because of the factor z^n, zeros are introduced at $z = 0$ and at infinity. Observe that if the function is defined by

$$y(k+n) = \begin{cases} f(k+n) & \text{for} \quad k = 0, 1, 2, \ldots \\ 0 & \text{for} \quad k = -n, -n-1, -n-2, \ldots \end{cases}$$

then the shifting property gives

$$\mathscr{Z}\{y(k+n)\} = z^n Y(z)$$

This result indicates that if n is a positive integer and $f(k) = 0$ for $k < n$, then the Z-transform contains no initial value terms.

Time Scaling. Consider the Z-transform of the sequence $\{a^k y(k)\}$:

$$\boxed{\mathscr{Z}\{a^k y(k)\} = Y(a^{-1}z) = \sum_{k=0}^{\infty} (a^{-1}z)^{-k} y(k)} \qquad \textbf{(7.31)}$$

Proof From the definition of the Z-transform,

$$\mathscr{Z}\{a^k y(k)\} = \sum_{k=0}^{\infty} a^k y(k)z^{-k} = \sum_{k=0}^{\infty} y(k)(a^{-1}z)^{-k}$$

Refer to Example 7.7. Earlier we found that the Z-transform of $y(k) = \sin k\omega$ $k = 0, 1, 2, \ldots$ is equal to $z \sin \omega/(z^2 - 2z \cos \omega + 1)$ (see Example 7.4 with $T = 1$). By an application of (7.31), we can write the Z-transform of the function $a^k y(k) = a^k \sin k\omega$ by inserting the value $a^{-1}z$ for z. This substitution leads to the result

$$\mathscr{Z}\{a^k \sin k\} = \frac{a^{-1}z \sin \omega}{a^{-2}z^2 - 2a^{-1}z \cos \omega + 1}$$

This result is the same as (7.22), which was deduced by a different approach.

Periodic Sequences. For a periodic sequence $\{y(k)\}$,

$$\mathscr{Z}\{y(k)\} = \frac{z^N}{z^N - 1}\mathscr{Z}\{y_{(1)}(k)\} \tag{7.32}$$

where N indicates the number of time units in a period, $y_{(1)}(k)$ is the first period of the periodic sequence, and $y(k) = y(k + N)$.

Proof The Z-transform of the first period is

$$\mathscr{Z}\{y_{(1)}(k)\} = \sum_{k=0}^{N-1} y_{(1)}(k)z^{-k} = Y_{(1)}(z)$$

Because the period is repeated every N discrete time units, we can use the right-shifting property to write

$$\begin{aligned}\mathscr{Z}\{y(k)\} &= \mathscr{Z}\{y_{(1)}(k)\} + \mathscr{Z}\{y_{(1)}(k - N)\} + \mathscr{Z}\{y_{(1)}(k - 2N)\} + \cdots \\ &= Y_1(z) + z^{-N}Y_1(z) + z^{-2N}Y_1(z) + \cdots \\ &= Y_1(z)(1 + z^{-N} + z^{-2N} + \cdots) = \frac{z^N}{z^N - 1}Y_1(z)\end{aligned}$$

■ **Example 7.10**

Find the Z-transform of the output of the system shown in Figure 7.7.

Solution From the diagram, the difference equation that describes the system is

$$y(k + 1) + 3y(k) = \delta(k + 1)$$

Take the Z-transform of both sides of this expression, recalling the linearity property, with the result

$$\mathscr{Z}\{y(k + 1)\} + 3\mathscr{Z}\{y(k)\} = \mathscr{Z}\{\delta(k + 1)\}$$

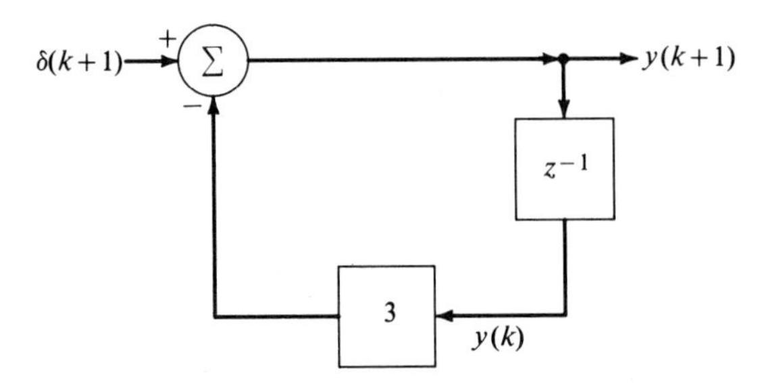

Figure 7.7 First-Order Discrete System

which, by applying the left-shifting property, yields

$$zY(z) - zy(0) + 3Y(z) = z$$

Solve for $Y(z)$:

$$Y(z) = \frac{z[1 + y(0)]}{z + 3}$$

We note that by setting $k = 0$ in the difference equation, we obtain $y(1) + 3y(0) = \delta(1)$, which indicates that $y(0) = 0$ because the input is applied one time unit later than $k = 0$. Therefore, $Y(z)$ becomes

$$Y(z) = \frac{z}{z + 3}$$

Suppose that we shift the time axis to the right by one time unit. The difference equation now assumes the form

$$y(k) + 3y(k - 1) = \delta(k)$$

The Z-transform of all terms in this equation and invoking the right-shifting property yield

$$Y(z) + 3z^{-1}Y(z) = 1$$

or

$$Y(z) = \frac{z}{z + 3}$$

a result which is identical with the previous result. ■

■ **Example 7.11**

Find the Z-transform of the signal shown in Figure 7.8.

Solution Use (7.32) with $N = 4$ to find

$$Y(z) = \frac{z^4}{z^4 - 1}\mathscr{Z}\{y_{(1)}(k)\} = \frac{z^4}{z^4 - 1}(1 + z^{-1} + z^{-2})$$

$$= \frac{z^2(z^2 + z + 1)}{z^4 - 1}$$ ■

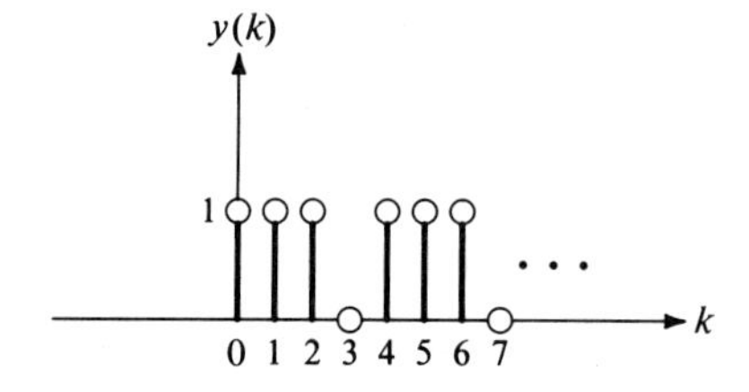

Figure 7.8 Periodic Discrete Function

Multiplication by k. Consider the sequence $\{ky(k)\}$:

$$\mathscr{Z}\{ky(k)\} = -z\frac{d}{dz}Y(z) \tag{7.33}$$

Proof From the basic definition,

$$\mathscr{Z}\{ky(k)\} = \sum_{k=0}^{\infty} ky(k)z^{-k} = z\sum_{k=0}^{\infty} y(k)(kz^{-k-1})$$
$$= z\sum_{k=0}^{\infty} y(k)\left[-\frac{d}{dz}z^{-k}\right] = -z\frac{d}{dz}\sum_{k=0}^{\infty} y(k)z^{-k} = -z\frac{d}{dz}Y(z)$$

■ **Example 7.12**

Deduce the Z-transforms of the functions $ku(k)$, $k^2u(k)$, $k(k+1)u(k)$, and $k(k-1)u(k)$.

Solution Since $\mathscr{Z}\{u(k)\} = z/(z-1)$, then, by (7.33), we have

$$\mathscr{Z}\{ku(k)\} = -z\frac{d}{dz}\left(\frac{z}{z-1}\right) = \frac{z}{(z-1)^2}$$

We can continue this procedure to find

$$\mathscr{Z}\{k^2u(k)\} = \mathscr{Z}\{k[ku(k)]\} = -z\frac{d}{dz}\left(\frac{z}{(z-1)^2}\right) = \frac{z(z+1)}{(z-1)^3}$$

However, $k(k+1) = k^2 + k$, and we thus have that

$$\mathscr{Z}\{k(k+1)u(k)\} = \frac{z(z+1)}{(z-1)^3} + \frac{z}{(z-1)^2} = \frac{2z^2}{(z-1)^3}$$

Similarly, we have that

$$\mathscr{Z}\{k(k-1)u(k)\} = \frac{z(z+1)}{(z-1)^3} - \frac{z}{(z-1)^2} = \frac{2z}{(z-1)^3}$$ ■

Division by k + a. The Z-transform of the sequence $\{y(k)/(k+a)\}$ for any real number a is

$$\mathscr{Z}\left\{\frac{y(k)}{k+a}\right\} = -z^a\int_0^z \frac{Y(v)}{v^{a+1}}\,dv \tag{7.34}$$

Proof Write $z^{-k}/(k+a)$ in the form of an integral in the basic Z-transform

$$\mathscr{Z}\left\{\frac{y(k)}{k+a}\right\} = \sum_{k=0}^{\infty}\frac{y(k)}{k+a}z^{-k} = \sum_{0}^{\infty} y(k)z^a\left(-\int_0^z v^{-k-a-1}\,dv\right)$$

Write this equation

$$= -z^a \int_0^z \frac{1}{v^{a+1}} \sum_0^\infty y(k)v^{-k}\, dv = -z^a \int_0^z \frac{Y(v)}{v^{a+1}}\, dv$$

Initial Value. Given a sequence that is zero for $k < k_0$, the value of the point $y(k_0)$ is

$$y(k_0) = z^{k_0} Y(z)\Big|_{z\to\infty} \tag{7.35}$$

Proof Consider the series

$$Y(z) = \sum_{k=k_0}^{\infty} y(k)z^{-k} = y(k_0)z^{-k_0} + y(k_0+1)z^{-(k_0+1)} + \cdots$$

Multiply both sides by z^{k_0} to obtain

$$y(k_0) + y(k_0+1)z^{-1} + y(k_0+2)z^{-2} + \cdots = z^{k_0}Y(z)$$

Ensure that all terms except the first approach zero as $z \to \infty$.

For example, consider the function given by (7.22). For this function, we have

$$y(0) = z^0 Y(z)\Big|_{z\to\infty} = \frac{z^{-1}a \sin \omega}{1 - 2az^{-1}\cos\omega + a^2z^{-2}}\Bigg|_{z\to\infty} = 0$$

which agrees with the value deduced from (7.20).

Final Value. Consider the limiting condition

$$\lim_{k\to\infty} y(k) = \lim_{z\to 1}(1 - z^{-1})Y(z) \qquad \text{if } y(\infty) \text{ exists} \tag{7.36}$$

Proof Begin with $y(k) - y(k-1)$ and consider

$$\mathscr{Z}\{y(k) - y(k-1)\} = Y(z) - z^{-1}Y(z) = \sum_{k=0}^{\infty} [y(k) - y(k-1)]z^{-k}$$

by the right-shifting property. This is written

$$(1 - z^{-1})Y(z) = \lim_{N\to\infty} \sum_{k=0}^{N} [y(k) - y(k-1)]z^{-k}$$

Take the limit as $z \to 1$, or

$$\lim_{z\to 1}(1 - z^{-1})Y(z) = \lim_{z\to 1}\lim_{N\to\infty} \sum_{k=0}^{N} [y(k) - y(k-1)]z^{-k}$$

Interchange the summations on the right:

$$= \lim_{N\to\infty} \lim_{z\to 1} \sum_{k=0}^{N} [y(k) - y(k-1)]z^{-k} = \lim_{N\to\infty} \sum_{k=0}^{N} [y(k) - y(k-1)]$$
$$= \lim_{N\to\infty} [y(0) - y(-1) + y(1) - y(0) + y(2) - y(1) + \cdots]$$
$$= \lim_{N\to\infty} y(N)$$

since $y(-1) = 0$. The limit $z \to 1$ will give meaningful results only when the point $z = 1$ is located within the region of convergence of $Y(z)$.

Convolution. For the sequence $\{y(k)\} = \{h(k) * x(k)\}$,

$$\mathscr{Z}\{y(k)\} = \mathscr{Z}\{h(k) * x(k)\} = \mathscr{Z}\left\{\sum_{n=0}^{\infty} h(k-n)x(n)\right\} = H(z)X(z) \tag{7.37}$$

where $h(k-n) = 0$ for $n > k$.

Proof The Z-transform of the convolution summation is

$$\mathscr{Z}\{y(k)\} \triangleq Y(z) = \sum_{k=0}^{\infty} z^{-k} \sum_{n=0}^{k} h(k-n)x(n)$$

Since h (negative argument) is zero, we can replace k by ∞ in the summation in n so that

$$\mathscr{Z}\{y(k)\} = \sum_{k=0}^{\infty} z^{-k} \sum_{n=0}^{\infty} h(k-n)x(n)$$

Write $k - n = m$ and invert the order of summation:

$$Y(z) = \sum_{n=0}^{\infty} x(n) \sum_{k=0}^{\infty} h(k-n)z^{-k} = \sum_{n=0}^{\infty} x(n)z^{-n} \sum_{m=-n}^{\infty} h(m)z^{-m}$$
$$= \sum_{n=0}^{\infty} x(n)z^{-n} \sum_{m=0}^{\infty} h(m)z^{-m} = X(z)H(z)$$

since $h(m) = 0$ for $m < 0$.

■ **Example 7.13**

The input signal sequence $x(m)$ and the impulse response $v(m)$ of a system are shown in Figures 7.9a and 7.9b. Deduce the output of the system $w(k)$.

Solution Figure 7.9c shows the folded signal $x(-m)$, and Figures 7.9d through 7.9h show steps in carrying out the convolution process. It is noted that when the shift $v(4-m)$ is introduced, the two functions do not coincide and their product is zero. The output signal $w(k)$ of this system is shown in Figure 7.9h. ■

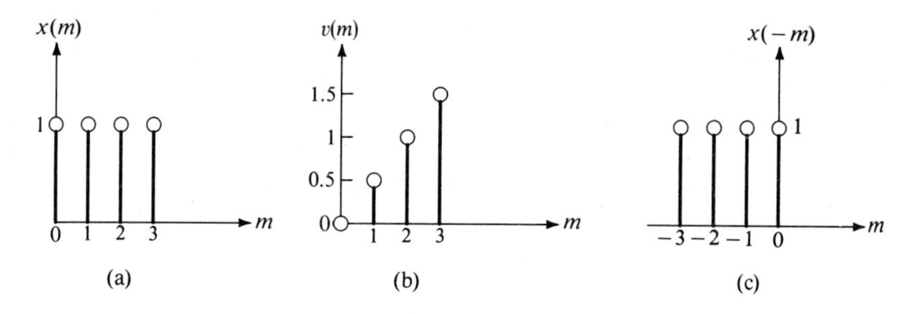

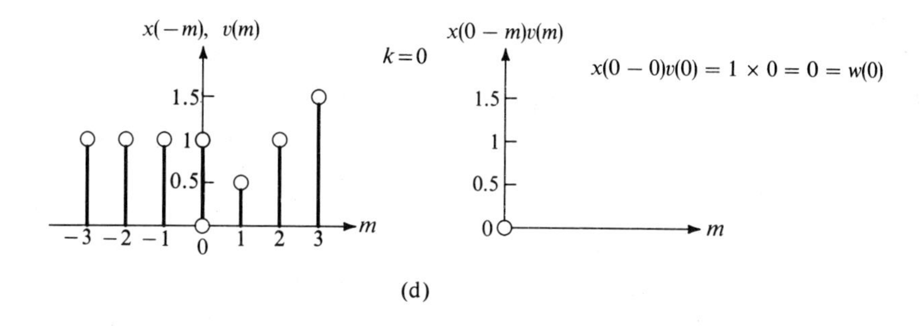

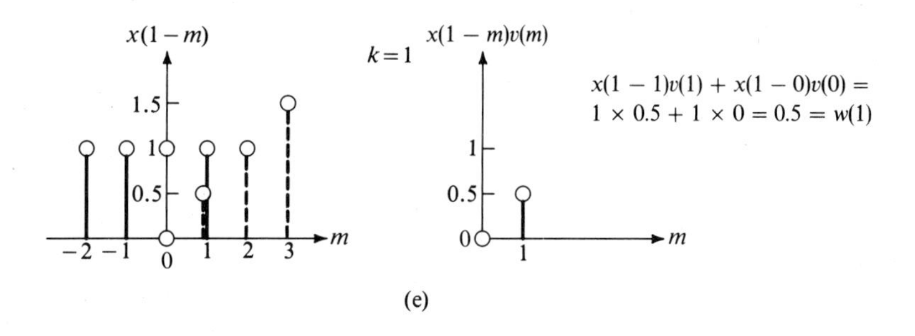

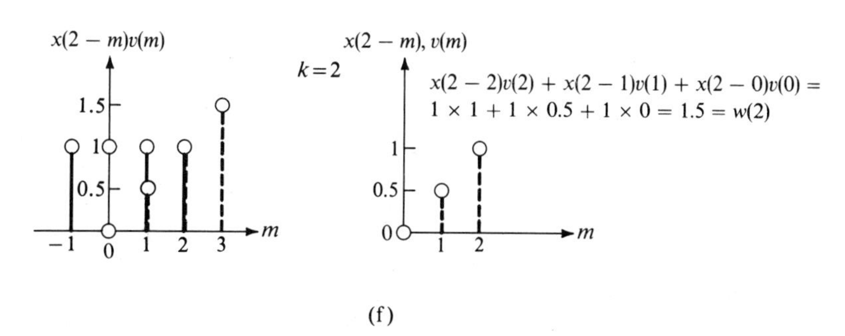

Figure 7.9 Convolution of Two Discrete Functions

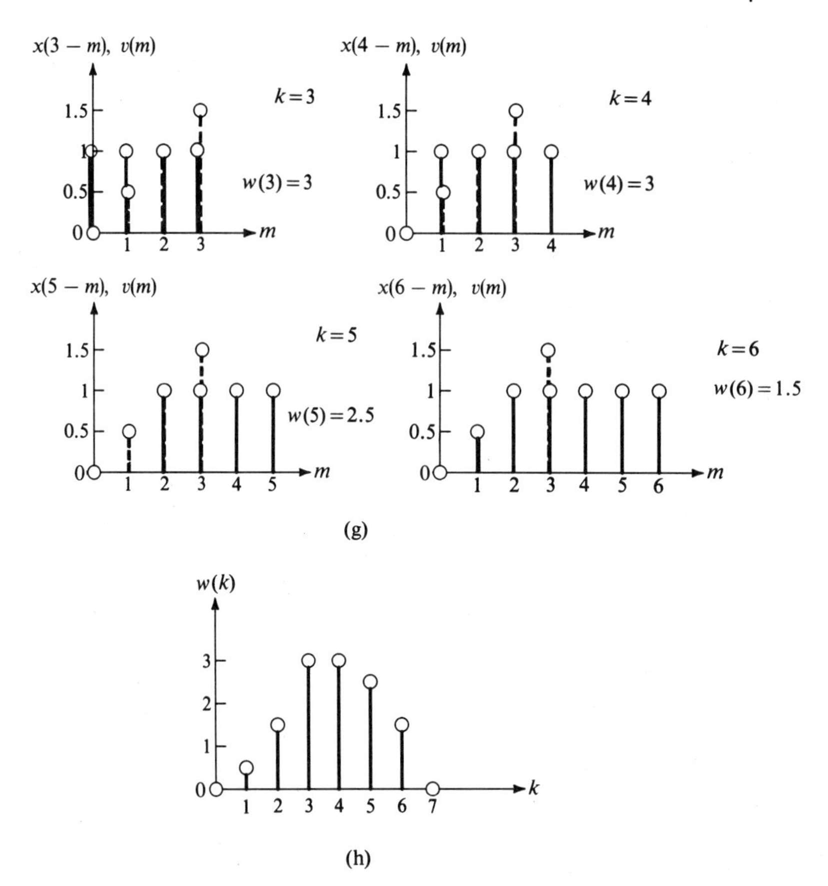

Figure 7.9 *(continued)*

■ Example 7.14

Find the Z-transform of the convolution of the following three functions:

$$y_1(k) = a_0\,\delta(k) + a_1\delta(k-1)$$
$$y_2(k) = b_0\,\delta(k) + b_1\delta(k-1)$$
$$y_3(k) = c_0\,\delta(k) + c_1\delta(k-1)$$

Solution The Z-transforms of these three functions are:

$$Y_1(z) = a_0 + a_1 z^{-1} \qquad Y_2(z) = b_0 + b_1 z^{-1} \qquad Y_3(z) = c_0 + c_1 z^{-1}$$

We observe that

$$[Y_1(z)Y_2(z)]Y_3(z) = Y_1(z)[Y_2(z)Y_3(z)]$$

from which it follows that

$$[y_1(k) * y_2(k)] * y_3(k) = y_1(k) * [y_2(k) * y_3(k)]$$

This result shows that convolution is **associative**. It is also **commutative** (see Problem 19). Thus, we can write

$$\begin{aligned}\mathscr{Z}\{y_1(k) * y_2(k) * y_3(k)\} &= Y_1(z)Y_2(z)Y_3(z)\\ &= [a_0 b_0 + (a_1 b_0 + a_0 b_1)z^{-1}\\ &\quad + a_1 b_1 z^{-2}](c_0 + c_1 z^{-1})\\ &= a_0 b_0 c_0 + (a_1 b_0 c_0 + a_0 b_1 c_0 + a_0 b_0 c_1)z^{-1}\\ &\quad +(a_1 b_0 c_1 + a_0 b_1 c_1 + a_1 b_1 c_0)z^{-2} + a_1 b_1 c_1 z^{-3}\end{aligned}$$

Now, apply the definition of the Z-transform to see that this result implies

$$\begin{aligned}y_1(k) * y_2(k) * y_3(k) &= a_0 b_0 c_0\, \delta(k) + (a_1 b_0 c_0 + a_0 b_1 c_0 + a_0 b_0 c_1)\delta(k-1)\\ &\quad +(a_1 b_0 c_1 + a_0 b_1 c_1 + a_1 b_1 c_0)\delta(k-2)\\ &\quad + a_1 b_1 c\delta(k-3)\end{aligned}$$

■

■ Example 7.15

Find the output of the system shown in Figure 7.10a if the input is that shown in Figure 7.10b. Express the system in its discrete form.

Solution A direct application of the Kirchhoff voltage law yields the equation

$$\frac{di(t)}{dt} + i(t) = v(t) \qquad \text{or} \qquad \frac{dv_o(t)}{dt} + v_o(t) = v(t)$$

The second equation follows from the first since $v_o(t) = i(t)R$ with $R = 1\ \Omega$.

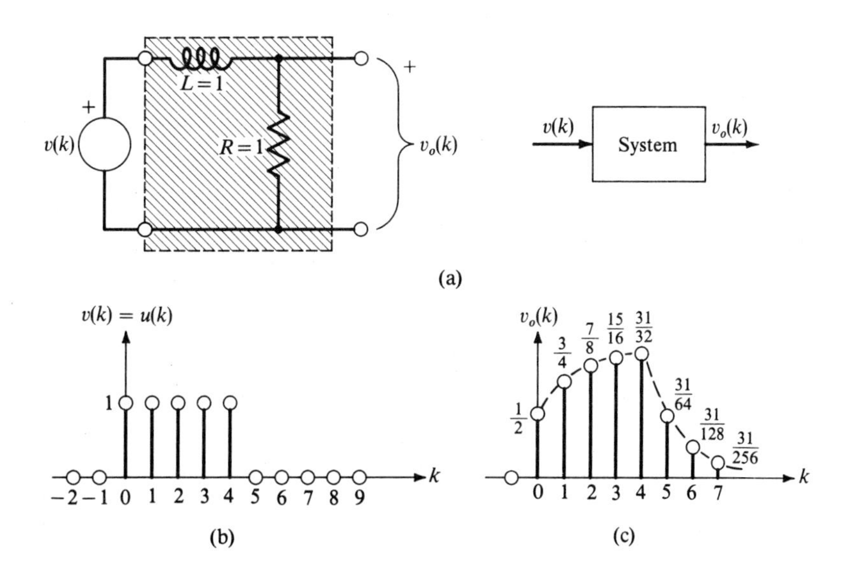

Figure 7.10 Impulse Response of an *RL* Circuit in Discrete Form

A direct conversion to approximate discrete form using (2.77a), $dv/dt \doteq v(k) - v(k-1)$ for $T = 1$, leads to

$$v_o(k) = \frac{1}{2}\, v(k) + \frac{1}{2}\, v_o(k-1)$$

Now, we proceed to determine the impulse response of the system. We use the fact that the Z-transform of the output of the system is equal to the system function $H(z)$ for a delta function input $v(k) = \delta(k)$. Also, the inverse transform of $H(z)$ is the impulse response $h(k)$. These two features are discussed in detail in Section 7.6. $H(z)$ is given by

$$H(z) = \frac{1}{2}\,\frac{1}{1 - \dfrac{1}{2}z^{-1}}$$

$$= \frac{1}{2}\left[1 + \left(\frac{1}{2}\right)z^{-1} + \left(\frac{1}{2}\right)^2 z^{-2} + \cdots\right]$$

It follows by (7.3) that

$$h(k) = \frac{1}{2}\left(\frac{1}{2}\right)^k \qquad k \geq 0$$

Since the output of a system is equal to the convolution of its input and its impulse response, this result can be used in the expression

$$v_o(k) = \sum_{n=0}^{k} h(k-n)v(n)$$

The outputs at successive time steps are

$$v_o(0) = h(0)v(0) = \frac{1}{2} \times 1 = \frac{1}{2}$$

$$v_o(1) = h(1)v(0) + h(0)v(1) = \frac{1}{4} \times 1 + \frac{1}{2} \times 1 = \frac{3}{4}$$

$$v_o(2) = h(2)v(0) + h(1)v(1) + h(0)v(2) = \frac{1}{8} \times 1 + \frac{1}{4} \times 1 + \frac{1}{2} \times 1 = \frac{7}{8}$$

$$\vdots$$

The output is shown in Figure 7.10c. Observe that the resulting shape is the same as that for the corresponding continuous system (see Example 6.26). ■

Bilateral Convolution. When the index k can assume positive and negative values, the bilateral convolution is specified by

$$y(k) = \sum_{n=-\infty}^{\infty} h(k-n)x(n) = \sum_{n=-\infty}^{\infty} h(n)x(k-n) \tag{7.38}$$

Table 7.1 Properties of the Z-Transform ($k \geq 0$)

1.	$\mathscr{Z}\{ay_1(k) + by_2(k)\}$	$aY_1(z) + bY_2(z)$
2.	$\mathscr{Z}\{y(k-n)\}$	$z^{-n}Y(z) + \sum_{m=1}^{n} y(-m)z^{-(n-m)}$
3.	$\mathscr{Z}\{y(k+n)\}$	$z^{n}Y(z) - \sum_{k=0}^{n-1} y(k)z^{n-k}$
4.	$\mathscr{Z}\{a^k y(k)\}$	$Y\left(\frac{z}{a}\right)$
5.	$\mathscr{Z}\{y_{(1)}(k)\}$	$\frac{z^N}{z^N - 1} Y_1(z)$ where $y_{(1)}(k)$ is the first period of a periodic sequence $y(k) = y(k+N)$
6.	$\mathscr{Z}\{h(k) * x(k)\}$	$H(z)X(z)$
7.	$\mathscr{Z}\{ky(k)\}$	$-z \frac{d}{dz} Y(z)$
8.	$\mathscr{Z}\{k^n y(k)\}$	$\left(-z \frac{d}{dz}\right)^n Y(z)$
9.	$\mathscr{Z}\left\{\frac{y(k)}{k+a}\right\}$	$-z^a \int_0^z \frac{Y(\tilde{z})}{\tilde{z}^{a+1}} d\tilde{z}$
10.	$y(k_0)$	$z^{k_0}Y(z)\Big\vert_{z\to\infty}$ where k_0 is the initial value of the sequence and $Y(z) = \sum_{k=0}^{\infty} y(k_0 + k)z^{-k}$
11.	$\lim_{k\to\infty} y(k)$	$\lim_{z\to 1}(1 - z^{-1})Y(z)$

Table 7.2 Properties of the Z-Transform of Sampled Functions ($k \geq 0$)

1.	$\mathscr{Z}\{ay_1(kT) + by_2(kT)\}$	$aY_1(z) + bY_2(z)$
2.	$\mathscr{Z}\{y(kT - mT)\}$	$z^{-m} \sum_{k=0}^{\infty} y(kT)z^{-k} = z^{-m}Y(z)$
3.	$\mathscr{Z}\{y(kT + mT)\}$	$z^m\left[Y(z) - \sum_{k=0}^{m-1} y(kT)z^{-k}\right]$
4.	$\mathscr{Z}\{a^{kT}y(kT)\}$	$Y(a^{-T}z)$
5.	$\mathscr{Z}\{kTy(kT)\}$	$-Tz \frac{dY(z)}{dz}$
6.	$y(k_0 T)$	$z^{k_0}Y(z)\Big\vert_{z\to\infty}$ $Y(z) = \sum_{k=0}^{\infty} y[(k_0 + k)T]z^{-k}$
7.	$\lim_{k\to\infty} y(kT)$	$\lim_{z\to 1}(1 - z^{-1})Y(z)$
8.	$\mathscr{Z}\{h(kT) * x(kT)\}$	$H(z)X(z)$

The Z transform is given by the product

$$\mathscr{Z}\{y(k)\} = H(z)X(z) \tag{7.39}$$

Table 7.1 (page 427) is a convenient tabulation of the Z-transform properties discussed above.

Table 7.2 (page 427) presents the properties of the Z-transform for sampled continuous signals at time intervals T. The verification of this table has been left as exercises in solving selected problems.

7.4 Z-Transform Pairs

It is implicit in the foregoing discussion that we can proceed in two directions: Given a sequence $\{f(k)\}$, the Z-transform $F(z)$ can be deduced according to Section 7.1. Also, given the Z-transform $F(z)$, the reverse process leads to $\{f(k)\}$ uniquely if the region of convergence is known. These processes are written functionally as

$$\mathscr{Z}\{f(k)\} \triangleq F(z) = \sum_{k=0}^{\infty} f(k)z^{-k} \tag{7.40a}$$

$$\mathscr{Z}^{-1}\{F(z)\} \triangleq \{f(k)\} = \frac{1}{2\pi j} \oint_C F(z)z^{k-1}\, dz \tag{7.40b}$$

where $\mathscr{Z}^{-1}$ denotes the inverse Z-transformation. As is evident from (7.40b), determining the inverse transform involves contour integration in the complex plane, where C is a circle of radius r that encloses all of the singularities of $F(z)z^{k-1}$. A proof of (7.40b) follows directly from the Cauchy integral theorem in complex variable theory, but is not given here.

For the case when a time function $f(t)$ is sampled at time units T, (7.40) takes the form

$$\mathscr{Z}\{f(kT)\} \triangleq F(z) = \sum_{k=0}^{\infty} f(kT)z^{-k} \tag{7.41a}$$

$$\mathscr{Z}^{-1}\{F(z)\} \triangleq \{f(kT)\} = \frac{1}{2\pi j} \oint F(z)z^{k-1}\, dz \tag{7.41b}$$

It is usually not necessary to carry out the mathematical details for Z-transform inversion using the inversion integral since, by its very nature, the transform pair, obtained according to (7.40), are valid either for a specified $\mathscr{Z}\{f(k)\}$ resulting in $F(z)$ or for the inverse transform of $F(z)$, $\mathscr{Z}^{-1}\{F(z)\}$, which results in the original $\{f(k)\}$.

Table 7.3 Common Z-Transform Pairs

Entry Number	$f(k)$ or $f(kT)$ for $k \geq 0$	$F(z) = \sum_{k=0}^{\infty} f(k)z^{-k}$	Radius of Convergence $\|z\| > R$
1.	$\delta(k)$	1	0
2.	$\delta(k-m)$	z^{-m}	0
3.	1	$\dfrac{z}{z-1}$	1
4.	k	$\dfrac{z}{(z-1)^2}$	1
5.	k^2	$\dfrac{z(z+1)}{(z-1)^3}$	1
6.	k^3	$\dfrac{z(z^2+4z+1)}{(z-1)^4}$	1
7.	a^k	$\dfrac{z}{z-a}$	$\|a\|$
8.	ka^k	$\dfrac{az}{(z-a)^2}$	$\|a\|$
9.	k^2a^k	$\dfrac{az(z+a)}{(z-a)^3}$	$\|a\|$
10.	$\dfrac{a^k}{k!}$	$e^{a/z}$	0
11.	$(k+1)a^k$	$\dfrac{z^2}{(z-a)^2}$	$\|a\|$
12.	$\dfrac{(k+1)(k+2)a^k}{2!}$	$\dfrac{z^3}{(z-a)^3}$	$\|a\|$
13.	$\dfrac{(k+1)(k+2)\cdots(k+m)a^k}{m!}$	$\dfrac{z^{m+1}}{(z-a)^{m+1}}$	$\|a\|$
14.	$\sin k\omega T$	$\dfrac{z \sin \omega T}{z^2 - 2z\cos \omega T + 1}$	1
15.	$\cos k\omega T$	$\dfrac{z(z - \cos \omega T)}{z^2 - 2z\cos \omega T + 1}$	1
16.	$a^k \sin k\omega T$	$\dfrac{az \sin \omega T}{z^2 - 2az\cos \omega T + a^2}$	$\|a\|^{-1}$
17.	$a^{kT} \sin k\omega T$	$\dfrac{a^T z \sin \omega T}{z^2 - 2a^T z\cos \omega T + a^{2T}}$	$\|a\|^{-T}$
18.	$a^k \cos k\omega T$	$\dfrac{z(z - a\cos \omega T)}{z^2 - 2az\cos \omega T + a^2}$	$\|a\|^{-1}$
19.	$e^{-akT} \sin k\omega T$	$\dfrac{ze^{-aT} \sin \omega T}{z^2 - 2e^{-aT}z\cos \omega T + e^{-2aT}}$	$\|z\| > \|e^{-\alpha T}\|$
20.	$e^{-akT} \cos k\omega T$	$\dfrac{z(z - e^{-\alpha T}\cos \omega T)}{z^2 - 2e^{-\alpha T}z\cos \omega T + e^{-2\alpha T}}$	$\|z\| > \|e^{-\alpha T}\|$
21.	$\dfrac{k(k-1)}{2!}$	$\dfrac{z}{(z-1)^3}$	1

Table 7.3 *(continued)*

Entry Number	$f(k)$ or $f(kT)$ for $k \geq 0$	$F(z) = \sum_{k=0}^{\infty} f(k)z^{-k}$	Radius of Convergence $\lvert z \rvert > R$
22.	$\frac{k(k-1)(k-2)}{3!}$	$\frac{z}{(z-1)^4}$	1
23.	$\frac{k(k-1)(k-2)\cdots(k-m+1)}{m!} a^{k-m}$	$\frac{z}{(z-a)^{m+1}}$	1
24.	e^{-akT}	$\frac{z}{z-e^{-\alpha T}}$	$\lvert e^{-\alpha T} \rvert$
25.	ke^{-akT}	$\frac{ze^{-\alpha T}}{(z-e^{-\alpha T})^2}$	$\lvert e^{-\alpha T} \rvert$

The situation parallels that which exists for the Laplace transform pair.

A table of common Z-transform pairs is given in Table 7.3. The table contains transform pairs that are useful for most purposes.

A number of the entries in this table follow directly from the results in Section 7.1. For example, by the proper selection of the exponent a in Example 7.2, we deduce the following: For $a = 0$, we have entry 3; for $a = \pm j\omega T$, entries 14 and 15 follow. The other entries can be found by direct application of (7.40).

7.5 Inverse Z-Transform

As already discussed in our studies, we assume that an $F(z)$ corresponds to a sequence $\{f(k)\}$ that is bounded as $k \to +\infty$. To find the inverse Z-transform, we cast the transformed function into a form that is amenable to simple tabular lookup using Table 7.3. The approach parallels that followed in performing similar operations using Laplace transforms. The functions with which we will be concerned are rational functions of z—that is, they are the ratio of two polynomials. Ordinarily, these are **proper functions** since the degree of the numerator polynomial is less than the degree of the denominator polynomial. If these functions are not proper fractions, then, as discussed in Section 6.6, the numerator polynomial is divided by the denominator polynomial, the long division process being continued until the numerator polynomial of the remainder is of one degree less than the denominator polynomial. This results in power terms plus a proper fraction. The following examples illustrate the most commonly used procedures. Where existing tables are inadequate, recourse can be made to the inversion integral, with the solution carried out using details of complex function theory.

■ Example 7.16

Determine the inverse Z-transform of the function

$$F(z) = \frac{1}{1 - 0.1z^{-1}} \tag{7.42}$$

Solution The function possesses a simple pole at $z = 0.1$, with the function converging outside the unit circle in the complex plane. Proceed by dividing the numerator by the denominator, which results in an infinite series in powers of z^{-1}:

$$\begin{array}{r|l} & 1 + 0.1z^{-1} + (0.1)^2z^{-2} + \cdots \\ 1 - 0.1z^{-1} & 1 \\ & \underline{1 - 0.1z^{-1}} \\ & 0.1z^{-1} \\ & \underline{0.1z^{-1} - (0.1z^{-1})^2} \\ & (0.1z^{-1})^2 \quad \cdots \end{array}$$

Thus, we have that

$$F(z) = 1 + 0.1z^{-1} + (0.1)^2z^{-2} + (0.1)^3z^{-3} + \cdots$$

It follows from (7.3) that the corresponding sequence is

$$\{f(k)\} = \begin{cases} 1,\ 0.1,\ (0.1)^2,\ (0.1)^3, \ldots & k \geq 0 \\ 0 & k < 0 \end{cases} \tag{7.43a}$$

which is the sequence

$$\{f(k)\} = 0.1^k \qquad k \geq 0 \tag{7.43b}$$

■

■ **Example 7.17**

Find the inverse Z-transform of the function

$$F(z) = \frac{1}{(1 - 0.2z^{-1})(1 + 0.2z^{-1})} = \frac{1}{1 - 0.04z^{-2}} \tag{7.44}$$

Solution One approach is to proceed as in the foregoing example. By long division, the following polynomial results

$$F(z) = 1 + 0.04z^{-2} + (0.04)^2z^{-4} + \cdots = (0.2)^{2k}(z^{-1})^{2k}$$

with region of convergence $|z| > 0.2$. This series corresponds to the sequence

$$f(k') = \begin{cases} (0.2)^{k'} & k' = 2k \quad k \geq 0 \\ 0 & k' = 2k + 1 \quad k > 0 \\ 0 & \quad k < 0 \end{cases} \tag{7.45}$$

A different approach calls for separating the function $F(z)$ into partial fraction form. Now, two factors must be considered: (1) The resulting function must be a proper fraction, and (2) many entries in Table 7.3 involve z in the numerator of the resulting expression for $F(z)$. This need is achieved by considering

$F(z)/z$. Thus, we modify $F(z)$ to $F(z)/z$:

$$F(z) = \frac{1}{1 - 0.04z^{-2}} = \frac{z^2}{z - 0.04} \qquad \frac{F(z)}{z} = \frac{z}{(z - 0.2)(z + 0.2)}$$

$$= \frac{A}{z - 0.2} + \frac{B}{z + 0.2}$$

where

$$A = \left.\frac{z}{z + 0.2}\right|_{z=0.2} = \frac{0.2}{0.4} = 0.5 \qquad B = \left.\frac{z}{z - 0.2}\right|_{z=-0.2} = \frac{-0.2}{-0.4} = 0.5$$

$$F(z) = \frac{1}{2}\left[\frac{z}{z - 0.2} + \frac{z}{z + 0.2}\right]$$

From appropriate entries in Table 7.3, the inverse transform is

$$f(k) = \begin{cases} \frac{1}{2}[(0.2)^k + (-0.2)^k] & k \geq 0 \\ 0 & k < 0 \end{cases} \tag{7.46}$$

The reader can easily verify that (7.45) and (7.46) yield identical results. ■

■ **Example 7.18**

Find the inverse Z-transform of the function

$$F(z) = \frac{1}{(1 - 0.2z^{-1})z^{-2}} \tag{7.47}$$

Solution This function is written as

$$F(z) = \frac{z^3}{z - 0.2}$$

By long division, we obtain

$$F(z) = z^2 + 0.2z + (0.2)^2 \frac{z}{z - 0.2}$$

From Table 7.3, the inverse transform is

$$f(k) = \delta(k + 2) + 0.2\delta(k + 1) + (0.2)^2(0.2)^k$$

where the last term is applicable for $k \geq 0$. Therefore, this equation is equivalent to

$$f(k) = \begin{cases} 0.2^{k+2} & k \geq -2 \\ 0 & k < -2 \end{cases} \tag{7.48}$$

It is recalled that (7.47) could be expanded into the form

$$F(z) = z^2 + 0.2z + (0.2)^2z^0 + (0.2)^3z^{-1} + (0.2)^4z^{-2} + \cdots$$

$$= z^2\left[1 + \frac{0.2}{z} + \frac{(0.2)^2}{z^2} + \cdots\right]$$

The inverse transform of the bracketed term is 0.2^k, and the factor z^2 indicates a shift to the left of two sample periods. Thus, Equation (7.48) is realized.

From the above, we note that to find the inverse Z-transform, we must:

a. Initially ignore any factor of the form z^k, for k an integer.
b. Expand the remaining part into partial fraction form.
c. Use Z-transform tables or properties to obtain the inverse Z-transform of each term in the expansion.
d. Combine the results and perform the necessary shifting required by z^k omitted in step a.

■

■ **Example 7.19**

Find the inverse Z-transform of the function

$$F(z) = \frac{z^2 - 3z + 8}{(z-2)(z+2)(z+3)}$$

Solution Expand $F(z)/z$ in partial fraction form for reasons already discussed:

$$\frac{F(z)}{z} = \frac{z^2 - 3z + 8}{z(z-2)(z+2)(z+3)} = \frac{A}{z} + \frac{B}{z-2} + \frac{C}{z+2} + \frac{D}{z+3}$$

where

$$A = z\,\frac{F(z)}{z}\bigg|_{z=0} = -\frac{2}{3}$$

$$B = (z-2)\,\frac{F(z)}{z}\bigg|_{z=2} = \frac{z^2 - 3z + 8}{z(z+2)(z+3)}\bigg|_{z=2} = \frac{3}{20}$$

$$C = (z+2)\,\frac{F(z)}{z}\bigg|_{z=-2} = \frac{z^2 - 3z + 8}{z(z-2)(z+3)}\bigg|_{z=-2} = \frac{9}{4}$$

$$D = (z+3)\,\frac{F(z)}{z}\bigg|_{z=-3} = \frac{z^2 - 3z + 8}{z(z-2)(z+2)}\bigg|_{z=-3} = -\frac{26}{15}$$

Therefore,

$$F(z) = -\frac{2}{3} + \frac{3}{20}\,\frac{z}{z-2} + \frac{9}{4}\,\frac{z}{z+2} - \frac{26}{15}\,\frac{z}{z+3}$$

This leads to the following value for $\{f(k)\}$ using Table 7.3:

$$f(k) = -\frac{2}{3}\,\delta(k) + \frac{3}{20}\,2^k + \frac{9}{4}\,(-2)^k - \frac{26}{15}\,(-3)^k$$

■

■ **Example 7.20**

Find the inverse Z-transform of the function

$$F(z) = \frac{z^2 - 9}{(z-1)(z-2)^3} \tag{7.49}$$

Observe that this function has a single- and a third-order pole.

Solution The function $F(z)/z$ is expanded in partial fraction form as follows:

$$\frac{F(z)}{z} = \frac{z^2 - 9}{z(z-1)(z-2)^3} = \frac{A}{z} + \frac{B}{z-1} + \frac{C_{11}}{z-2} + \frac{C_{12}}{(z-2)^2} + \frac{C_{13}}{(z-2)^3} \tag{7.50}$$

We can find three of the unknown constants using the relations

$$A = \left.\frac{z^2-9}{(z-1)(z-2)^3}\right|_{z=0} = \frac{-9}{(-1)(-8)} = -\frac{9}{8}$$

$$B = \left.\frac{z^2-9}{z(z-2)^3}\right|_{z=1} = \frac{1-9}{1 \times (-1)} = \frac{-8}{-1} = 8$$

$$C_{13} = \left.\frac{z^2-9}{z(z-1)}\right|_{z=2} = \frac{4-9}{2(1)} = -\frac{5}{2}$$

These constants are combined with (7.50), leaving a relation involving the two remaining constants C_{11} and C_{12}. One procedure for finding these constants is to select any two appropriate values for z, thereby creating a set of two equations with two unknowns C_{11} and C_{12}. In particular, if we choose $z = 3$ and $z = 4$, we obtain the following expressions:

$$C_{11} + C_{12} = -\frac{9}{8}$$

$$2C_{11} + C_{12} = -8$$

from which we find that

$$C_{11} = -\frac{55}{8} \qquad C_{12} = \frac{46}{8}$$

The solution is obtained using Table 7.3. The result is

$$\begin{aligned} f(k) &= -\frac{9}{8}\,\delta(k) + 8u(k) - \frac{55}{8} \times 2^k + \frac{46}{8}(k+1)2^k - \frac{5}{2}\,\frac{(k+1)(k+2)}{2!}\,2^k \\ &= -\frac{9}{8}\,\delta(k) + 8u(k) + \left[-\frac{55}{8} + \frac{46}{8}(k+1) - \frac{5(k+1)(k+2)}{4}\right]2^k \end{aligned}$$

■

A more formal method for the evaluation of the constants in the partial fraction expansion of a function with multiple roots is essentially that discussed for Laplace transform expansions given in (6.53). This method considers the expansion for one of these multiple-order roots to be of the form

$$F(z) = \frac{F_1(z)}{(z-p)^n} = \frac{A_1}{z-p} + \frac{A_2}{(z-p)^2} + \frac{A_3}{(z-p)^3} + \cdots + \frac{A_n}{(z-p)^n} \tag{7.51}$$

Table 7.4 Z-Transforms for the Expansion (7.51)

Entry Number	$F(z)$	$f(k-1)$		Radius of Convergence
1.	$\frac{1}{z-a}$	a^{k-1}	$k \geq 1$	$\lvert z \rvert > a$
2.	$\frac{1}{(z-a)^2}$	$(k-1)a^{k-2}$	$k \geq 1$	$\lvert z \rvert > a$
3.	$\frac{1}{(z-a)^3}$	$\frac{1}{2!}(k-1)(k-2)a^{k-3}$	$k \geq 1$	$\lvert z \rvert > a$
	$\vdots$			
4.	$\frac{1}{z-a}$	$-a^{k-1}$	$k \leq 0$	$\lvert z \rvert < a$
5.	$\frac{1}{(z-a)^2}$	$-(k-1)a^{k-2}$	$k \leq 0$	$\lvert z \rvert < a$
6.	$\frac{1}{(z-a)^3}$	$-\frac{1}{2!}(k-1)(k-2)a^{k-3}$	$k \leq 0$	$\lvert z \rvert < a$

The constants A_i are found using the relations

$$
\begin{aligned}
A_n &= (z-p)^n F(z)\Big|_{z=p} \\
A_{n-1} &= \frac{d}{dz}[(z-p)^n F(z)]\Big|_{z=p} \\
&\vdots \\
A_{n-k} &= \frac{1}{k!}\frac{d^k}{dz^k}[(z-p)^n F(z)]\Big|_{z=p} \\
&\vdots \\
A_1 &= \frac{1}{(n-1)!}\frac{d^{n-1}}{dz^{n-1}}[(z-p)^n F(z)]\Big|_{z=p}
\end{aligned}
\tag{7.52}
$$

Table 7.4 is particularly useful in carrying out the details of (7.52).

7.6 Transfer Function

The Z-transform provides a very important technique in the solution of difference equations. As part of this process, the transfer function plays an important role.

■ **Example 7.21**

Deduce an expression for the impulse response of the circuit shown in Figure 7.11a using Z-transform techniques.

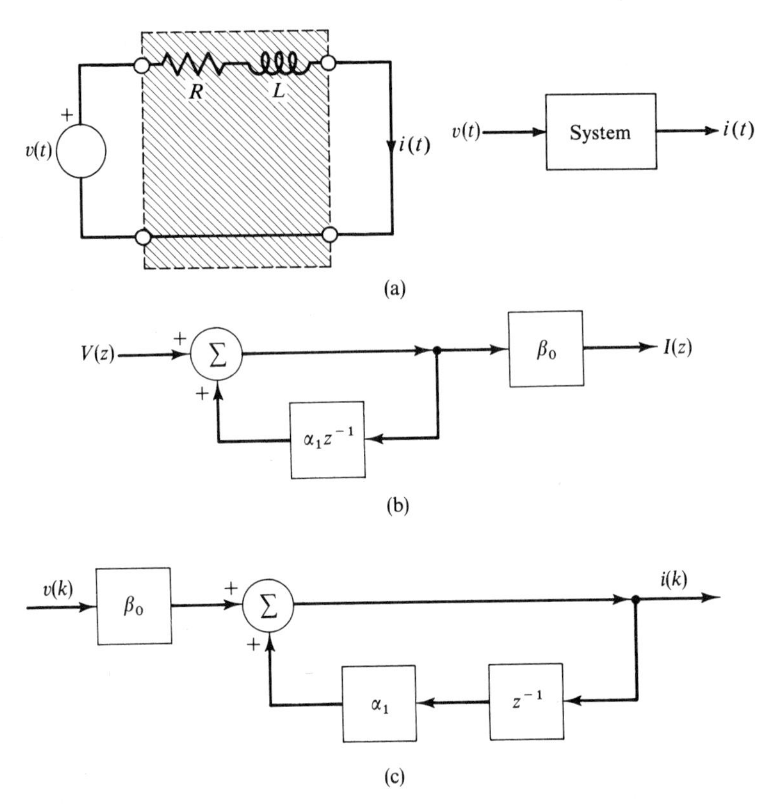

Figure 7.11 Series *RL* Circuit

Solution The controlling equation of the circuit is

$$L\frac{di(t)}{dt} + Ri(t) = v(t)$$

The approximate discrete form of this equation is, for $T = 1$ [see (2.77a)],

$$L[i(k) - i(k-1)] + Ri(k) = v(k)$$

from which

$$i(k) = \frac{1}{L+R}v(k) + \frac{L}{L+R}i(k-1) \triangleq \beta_0 v(k) + \alpha_1 i(k-1)$$

Using the appropriate entries in Table 7.1, the Z-transform of this equation becomes

$$I(z) = \beta_0 V(z) + \alpha_1 z^{-1} I(z) \qquad \textbf{(7.53a)}$$

$$I(z) = \frac{\beta_0}{1 - \alpha_1 z^{-1}} V(z) = H(z)V(z) \qquad \textbf{(7.53b)}$$

This equation relates the input–output relation explicitly in the transformed domain of a discrete system. The quantity $H(z) = I(z)/V(z)$ is the **system or transfer function** for the discrete system. Further, the inverse transform of $H(z)$ is the impulse response $h(k)$ of the system. Thus, for our circuit with a delta function excitation,

$$I(z) = \frac{\beta_0}{1 - \alpha_1 z^{-1}} \triangleq H(z) \tag{7.54}$$

The inverse transform is

$$h(k) = (\alpha_1)^k \beta_0 \qquad k \geq 0 \tag{7.55}$$

Figures 7.11b and 7.11c show the feedback configuration of the discrete system in the transformed and the time domains. ■

■ Example 7.22

Determine the response of the first-order system specified by (7.53) to a unit step sequence by Z-transform and convolution methods.

Solution The unit step sequence, which is written

$$u(k) = \begin{cases} 1 & k = 0, 1, 2, \ldots \\ 0 & k < 0 \end{cases}$$

has the Z-transformed value

$$U(z) = \frac{z}{z - 1} = \frac{1}{1 - z^{-1}}$$

The response, by writing y for i, is given by [see (7.53b)]

$$Y(z) = \frac{\beta_0}{1 - \alpha_1 z^{-1}} \frac{1}{1 - z^{-1}} = \beta_0 \left[\frac{A}{1 - \alpha_1 z^{-1}} + \frac{B}{1 - z^{-1}} \right]$$

where

$$A = \left. \frac{1}{1 - z^{-1}} \right|_{z^{-1} = 1/\alpha_1} = \frac{\alpha_1}{\alpha_1 - 1}$$

$$B = \left. \frac{1}{1 - \alpha_1 z^{-1}} \right|_{z^{-1} = 1} = \frac{1}{1 - \alpha_1}$$

Thus,

$$Y(z) = \frac{\beta_0}{1 - \alpha_1} \left(\frac{-\alpha_1}{1 - \alpha_1 z^{-1}} + \frac{1}{1 - z^{-1}} \right)$$

The inverse transform is

$$y(k) = \frac{\beta_0}{1 - \alpha_1} [-\alpha_1 (\alpha_1)^k + (1)^k] = \frac{\beta_0}{1 - \alpha_1} (1 - \alpha_1^{k+1}) \qquad k \geq 0$$

It is recalled that the derivative of the step function response of a system is its impulse response. To show that this result is consistent with the result of Example 7.21, we consider the derivative of $y(k)$ in its discrete form representation. Ignoring the constant factor $\beta_0/(1 - \alpha_1)$ for the moment, we obtain

$$\frac{y(k) - y(k-1)}{1} = 1 - \alpha_1^{k+1} - 1 + \alpha_1^k = (1 - \alpha_1)\alpha_1^k$$

Therefore, the impulse response is given by

$$\frac{y(k) - y(k-1)}{1} = h(k) = \frac{\beta_0}{1 - \alpha_1}\alpha_1^k(1 - \alpha_1) = \beta_0 \alpha_1^k \qquad k \geq 0$$

which is (7.55), as it should be.

We can proceed to find the output in the foregoing example by using the convolution equation. Here we write, using the result of Example 7.21,

$$y(k) = \sum_{n=0}^{k} h(k-n)u(n) = \sum_{n=0}^{k} \beta_0 \alpha_1^{k-n} u(n)$$

The output at successive time steps is

$$\begin{aligned} y(0) &= \beta_0(\alpha_1)^0 = \beta_0 \\ y(1) &= \beta_0(\alpha_1 + 1) \\ y(2) &= \beta_0(\alpha_1^2 + \alpha_1 + 1) \\ &\vdots \\ y(k) &= \beta_0(\alpha_1^k + \alpha_1^{k-1} + \cdots + 1) = \beta_0\left(\frac{1 - \alpha_1^{k+1}}{1 - \alpha_1}\right) \end{aligned}$$

This result is identical with that above using the Z-transform method. ■

When discrete systems are interconnected, the rules that apply to continuous systems (see Section 6.8) are also applicable for discrete systems. For example, if two systems with impulse response functions $h_1(k)$ and $h_2(k)$, respectively, are connected in cascade, the combined impulse response of the total system is

$$h(k) = h_1(k) * h_2(k) \tag{7.56a}$$

and in the Z-domain, this specifies that

$$\boxed{H(z) = H_1(z)H_2(z) = \mathscr{Z}\{h_1(k) * h_2(k)\}} \tag{7.56b}$$

■ **Example 7.23**

Deduce the transfer function for the system shown in Figure 7.12a.

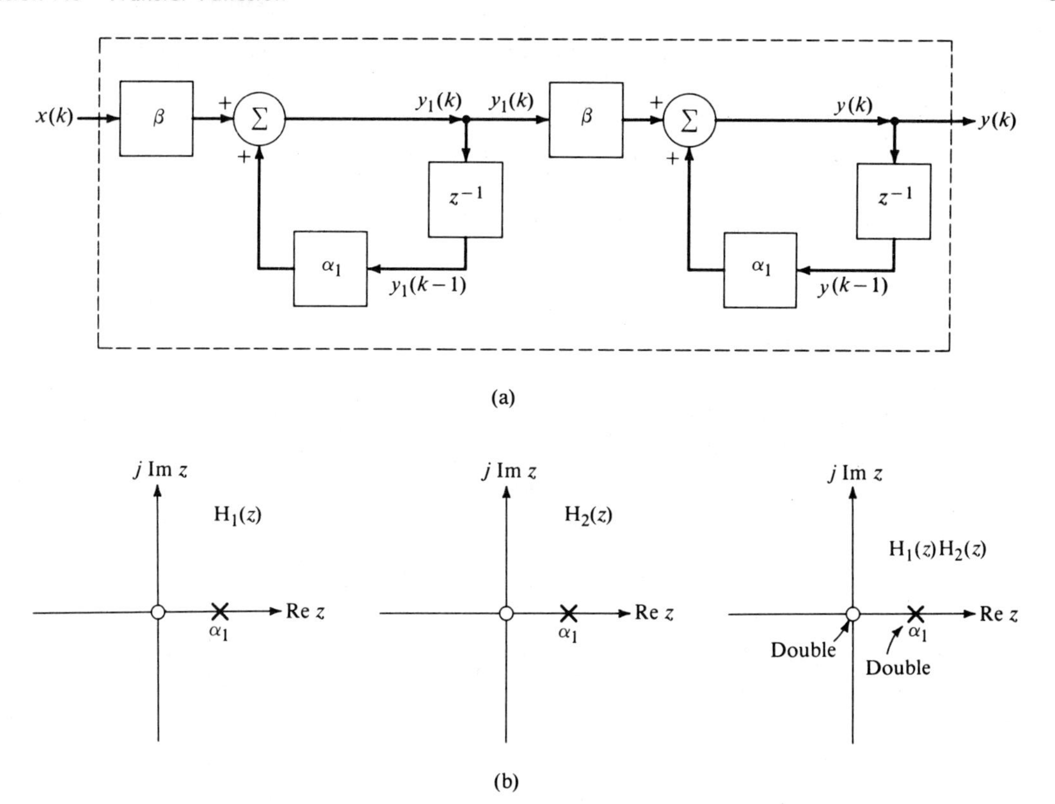

Figure 7.12 Two First-Order Discrete Systems in Cascade

Solution Consider initially the portion of the system between $x(k)$ and $y_1(k)$ described by the difference equation

$$y_1(k) = \beta x(k) + \alpha_1 y_1(k-1)$$

The Z-transform of this expression is

$$Y_1(z) = \beta X(z) + \alpha_1 z^{-1} Y_1(z)$$

from which

$$Y_1(z) = \frac{\beta}{1 - \alpha_1 z^{-1}} X(z) = H_1(z)X(z)$$

The portion of the system between $y_1(k)$ and $y(k)$ is described by a similar equation whose Z-transform is

$$Y(z) = \frac{\beta}{1 - \alpha_1 z^{-1}} Y_1(z) = H_2(z)Y_1(z)$$

Substitute the known expression for $Y_1(z)$ into this final expression to obtain

$$Y(z) = \left(\frac{\beta}{1-\alpha_1 z^{-1}}\right)\left(\frac{\beta}{1-\alpha_1 z^{-1}}\right)X(z) = H_1(z)H_2(z)X(z) = H(z)X(z)$$

where

$$H(z) = H_1(z)H_2(z) = \left(\frac{\beta}{1-\alpha_1 z^{-1}}\right)^2$$

The pole-zero configurations for each system and for the combined system are shown in Figure 7.12b. ■

■ Example 7.24

Find the transfer function for the second-order system shown in Figure 7.13a and sketch the pole-zero configuration.

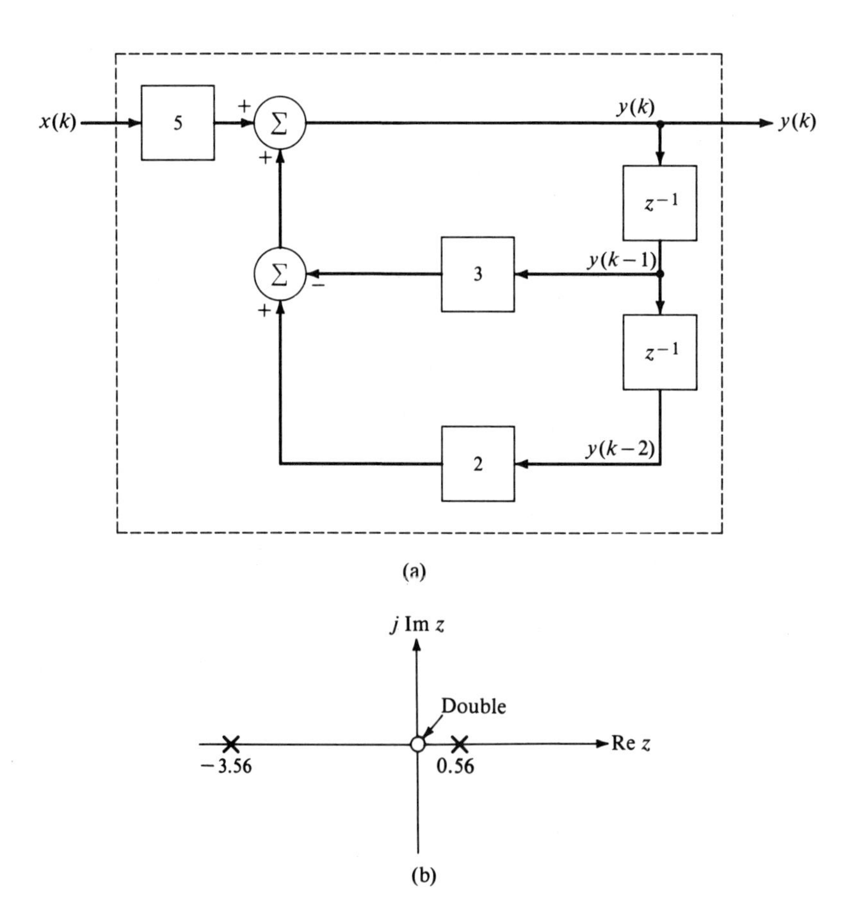

Figure 7.13 Second-Order Discrete System

Solution The difference equation describing the system is

$$y(k) + 3y(k-1) - 2y(k-2) = 5x(k)$$

The Z-transform of this equation is

$$Y(z) + 3z^{-1}Y(z) - 2z^{-2}Y(z) = 5X(z)$$

Solving for $H(z)$, we obtain

$$H(z) \triangleq \frac{Y(z)}{X(z)} = \frac{5}{1 + 3z^{-1} - 2z^{-2}} = \frac{5z^2}{z^2 + 3z - 2}$$

The pole-zero configuration is shown in Figure 7.13b. ■

In the general case of an nth-order discrete system for which the difference equation is of the form

$$y(k) + a_1 y(k-1) + \cdots + a_n y(k-n) = b_0 x(k) + b_1 x(k-1) + \cdots + b_m x(k-m) \quad \textbf{(7.57)}$$

we obtain, by taking the Z-transform of all terms in this equation and solving for the ratio $Y(z)/X(z)$,

$$H(z) \triangleq \frac{Y(z)}{X(z)} = \frac{b_0 + b_1 z^{-1} + \cdots + b_m z^{-m}}{1 + a_1 z^{-1} + \cdots + a_n z^{-n}} = \frac{\sum_{k=0}^{m} b_k z^{-k}}{1 + \sum_{k=1}^{n} a_k z^{-k}} \quad \textbf{(7.58)}$$

This relation shows that if we know $H(z)$ of a system, then the output function $Y(z)$ to any input $X(z)$ [or, equivalently, $x(k)$] can be determined.

If we set $a_1, a_2, \ldots a_n$ equal to zero, Equation (7.57) becomes

$$y(k) = b_0 x(k) + b_1 x(k-1) + \cdots + b_m x(k-m) \quad \textbf{(7.59)}$$

This expression defines an mth-order **FIR filter**, and such filters are examined in some detail in Chapter 8. The block diagram of an FIR filter is shown in Figure 7.14a.

For the case when $b_0 = 1$ and $b_1, b_2, \ldots b_m$ all equal zero, the difference equation becomes

$$y(k) + a_1 y(k-1) + \cdots + a_n y(k-n) = x(k) \quad \textbf{(7.60)}$$

This equation defines an nth order **IIR filter**. A block diagram representation of this equation is shown in Figure 7.14b.

Finally, if none of the constants is zero in (7.58), the block diagram representation is that shown in Figure 7.14c.

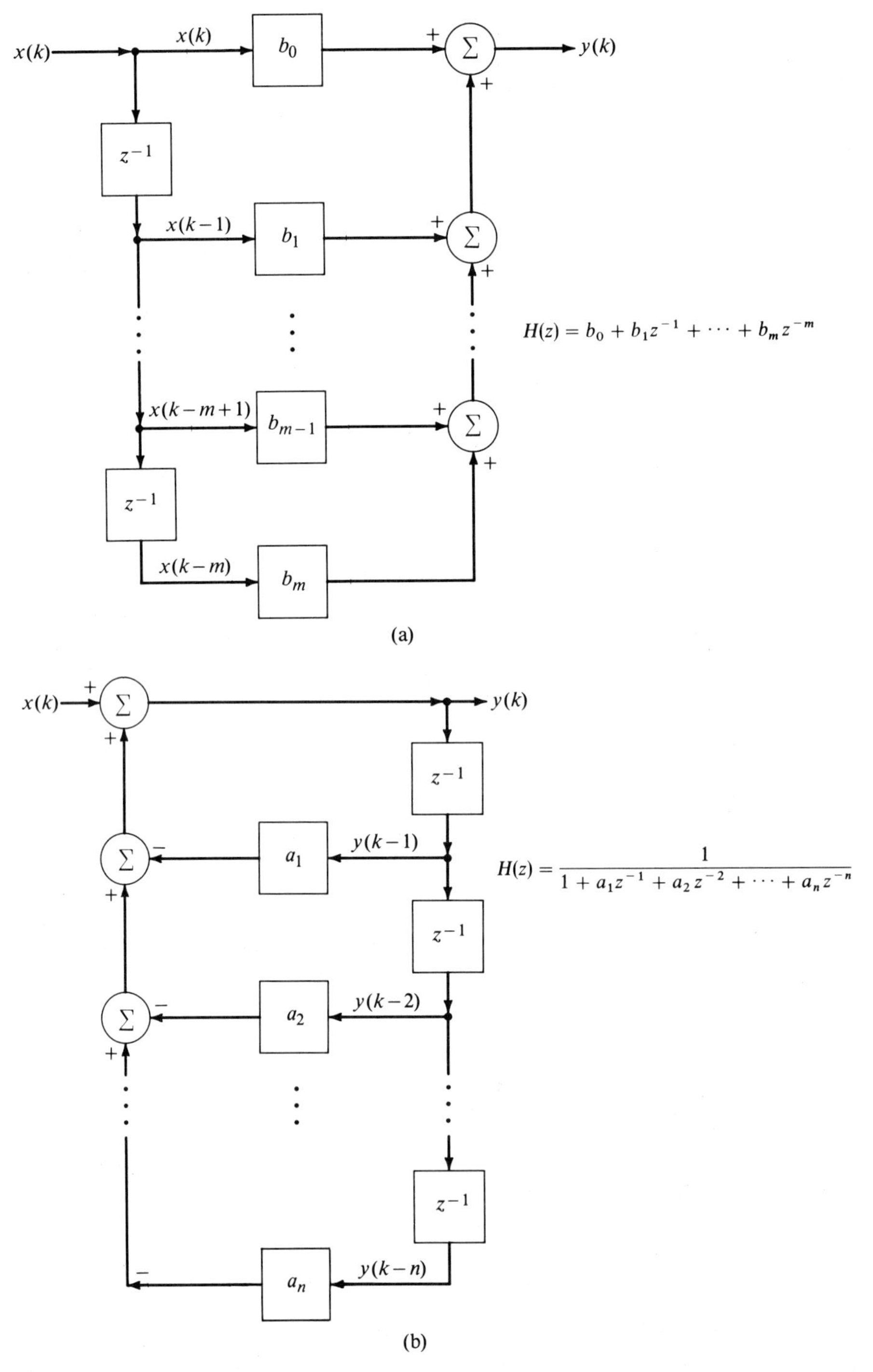

Figure 7.14 One Possible Way of Representing Three Types of Filters

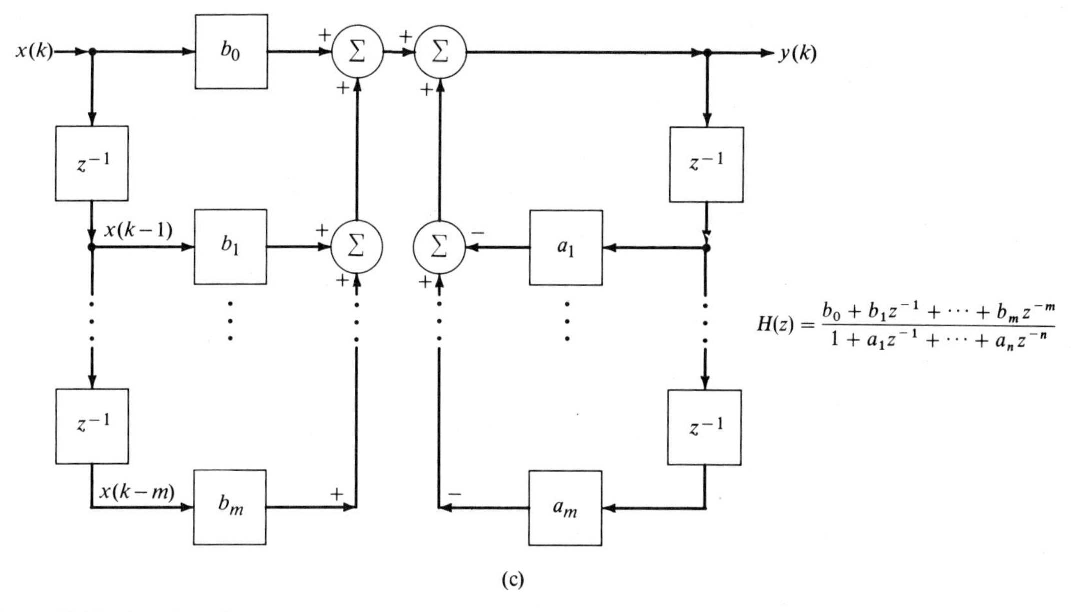

(c)

Figure 7.14 *(continued)*

7.7 Frequency Response of Discrete Systems

Suppose that the input to the system is the function z^k. Then, using the convolution property of system response, the output is given by

$$y(k) = z^k * h(k) = \sum_{n=0}^{\infty} h(n) z^{k-n} = z^k \sum_{n=0}^{\infty} h(n) z^{-n} = z^k H(z) \tag{7.61}$$

If we set $z = e^{j\omega}$ in this expression, we have

$$y(k) = e^{j\omega k} H(e^{j\omega}) \tag{7.62}$$

With this chosen form for z, (7.58) becomes

$$\boxed{H(e^{j\omega}) = \frac{b_0 + b_1 e^{-j\omega} + b_2 e^{-j2\omega} + \cdots + b_m e^{-jm\omega}}{1 + a_1 e^{-j\omega} + a_2 e^{-j2\omega} + \cdots + a_n e^{-jn\omega}} = H(z)\Big|_{z = e^{j\omega}}} \tag{7.63}$$

This function is the **frequency response function.**

For simplicity, we consider the simple transfer function

$$\begin{aligned} H(e^{j\omega}) &= \frac{b_0}{1 + a_1 e^{-j\omega}} \\ &= \frac{b_0}{[(1 + a_1 \cos\omega)^2 + (a_1 \sin\omega)^2]^{1/2}} e^{-j\tan^{-1}[a_1 \sin\omega/(1 + a_1 \cos\omega)]} \end{aligned}$$

From this, we can see for $\omega = -\omega$ that $|H(e^{j\omega})|$ is an even function and that $\phi(\omega) = \arg H(e^{j\omega})$ is an odd function of ω. We may write, therefore,

$$|H(e^{j\omega})|^2 = H(e^{j\omega})H(e^{j\omega})^* = H(e^{j\omega})H(e^{-j\omega}) = H(z)H(z^{-1})\Big|_{z=e^{j\omega}} \tag{7.64}$$

The second equality is valid because the coefficients of $H(e^{j\omega})$ are real. Of course, $H(z^{-1})$ possesses the property that its poles and zeros are the reciprocals of those of $H(z)$. It follows, therefore, that the poles and zeros of $H(z)H(z^{-1})$ will occur in pairs that are arranged in an inverse manner with respect to the unit circle. Consider, for example, the transfer function

$$H(z) = \frac{b_0 + b_1 z^{-1} + b_2 z^{-2}}{a_0 + a_1 z^{-1} + a_2 z^{-2}} \tag{7.65}$$

The amplitude squared is given by

$$|H(z)|^2\Big|_{z=e^{j\omega}} = H(z)H(z^{-1})\Big|_{z=e^{j\omega}} = \frac{d_2 z^2 + d_1 z + d_0 + d_1 z^{-1} + d_2 z^{-2}}{c_2 z^2 + c_1 z + c_0 + c_1 z^{-1} + c_2 z^{-2}}\Bigg|_{z=e^{j\omega}}$$

$$= \frac{d_0 + \sum_{k=1}^{2} 2d_k \cos k\omega}{c_0 + \sum_{k=1}^{2} 2c_k \cos k\omega} \tag{7.66}$$

where

$$c_k = \sum_{n=0}^{n-k} a_n a_{k+n} \qquad d_k = \sum_{m=0}^{m-k} b_m b_{k+m} \tag{7.67}$$

For example,

$$c_0 = \sum_{n=0}^{2-0} a_n a_{0+n} = a_0 a_0 + a_1 a_1 + a_2 a_2$$

$$c_1 = \sum_{n=0}^{2-1} a_n a_{1+n} = a_0 a_1 + a_1 a_2$$

$$c_2 = \sum_{n=0}^{2-2} a_n a_{2+n} = a_0 a_2$$

■ Example 7.25

Find the frequency response of the systems shown in Figures 7.15a, 7.15b, and 7.15c. Note that a single basic unit is used in different configurations.

Solution The difference equation that describes the system shown in Figure 7.15a is

$$y(k) = 2x(k) + x(k-1)$$

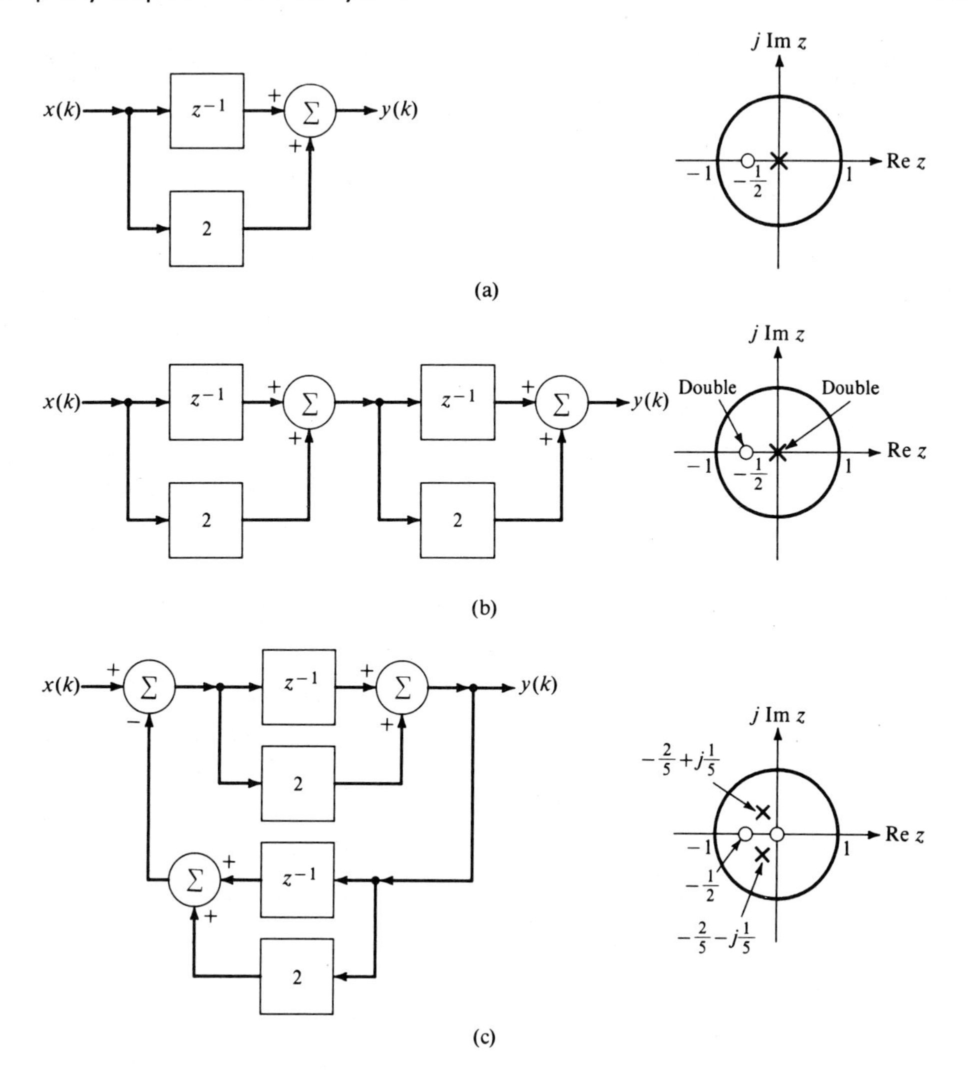

Figure 7.15 Three Types of Interconnected Systems

The system function for this system follows from the Z-transform of this equation:

$$H(z) \triangleq \frac{Y(z)}{X(z)} = 2 + z^{-1}$$

The frequency response is obtained from (7.66) and is

$$\left[H(z)H(z^{-1}) \Big|_{z=e^{j\omega}} \right]^{1/2} = (5 + 4 \cos \omega)^{1/2}$$

This expression is plotted in Figure 7.16a as curve A as a function of ω.

Figure 7.15b shows two system units connected in cascade. In this configuration, the magnitude of the frequency response is given by

$$\left[\left|H^2(z)H^2(z^{-1})\right|_{z=e^{j\omega}}\right]^{1/2} = (33 + 40\cos\omega + 8\cos 2\omega)^{1/2}$$

This function is plotted in Figure 7.16b.

Figure 7.15c shows two basic units connected in a feedback configuration (refer to Section 2.5). The frequency response magnitude is given by

$$\left[\left|\frac{H(z)}{1 + H^2(z)}\,\frac{H(z^{-1})}{1 + H^2(z^{-1})}\right|_{z=e^{j\omega}}\right]^{1/2} = \left(\frac{5 + 4\cos\omega}{42 + 48\cos\omega + 10\cos 2\omega}\right)^{1/2}$$

A plot of this expression is given in Figure 7.16c. Observe that in all cases considered, the amplitude functions are periodic, with period 2π. ■

Note that if we set $z = e^{j\omega T}$ in (7.61), we obtain the expression

$$y(k) = e^{jk\omega T}H(e^{j\omega T}) \tag{7.68}$$

and (7.63) has the form

$$H(e^{j\omega T}) = \frac{b_0 + b_1 e^{-j\omega T} + \cdots + b_m e^{-jm\omega T}}{1 + a_1 e^{-j\omega T} + \cdots + a_n e^{-jn\omega T}} \triangleq H(z)\Big|_{z=e^{j\omega T}} \tag{7.69}$$

When the sampling time T is different from unity, the frequency response function is a function of T and the folding frequency is equal to $\omega_s/2 = \pi/T$ [refer to (4.50)].

■ **Example 7.26**

First, find the frequency response function of the system shown in Figure 7.15a if the input is sampled every T seconds. Second, find the output of the system, if the input is $x(kT) = \cos k\omega T$.

Solution From the figure, taking into consideration the sampling interval T, we obtain the difference equation

$$y(kT) = 2x(kT) + x[(k-1)T]$$

The system function for this system is

$$H(z) \triangleq \frac{Y(z)}{X(z)} = 2 + z^{-1}$$

and the frequency response function is then given by

$$\left[H(z)H(z^{-1})\Big|_{z=e^{j\omega T}}\right]^{1/2} = (5 + 4\cos\omega T)^{1/2}$$

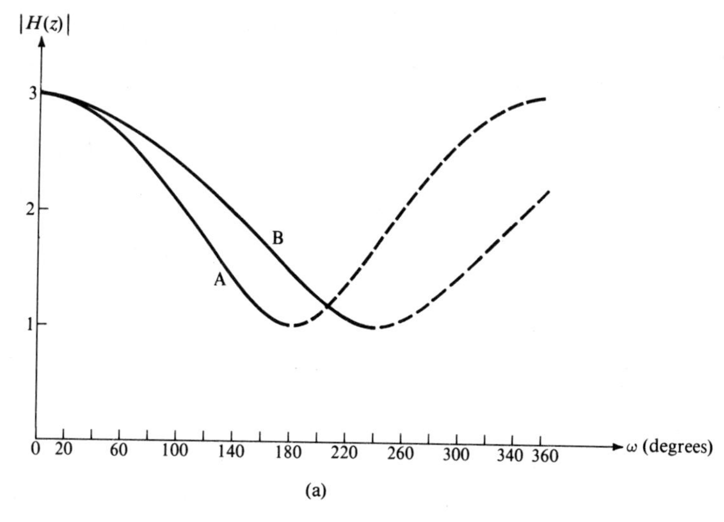

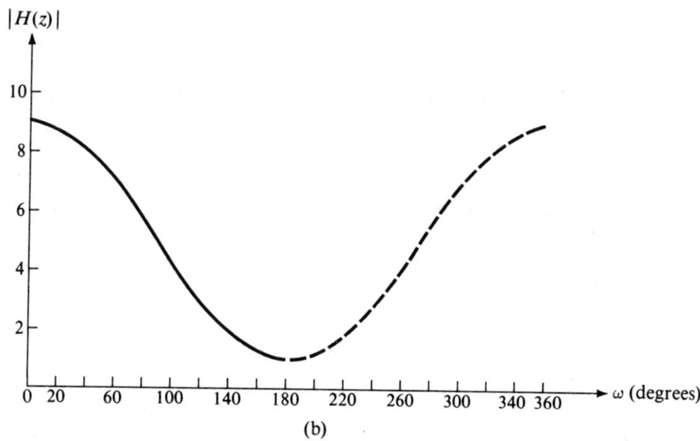

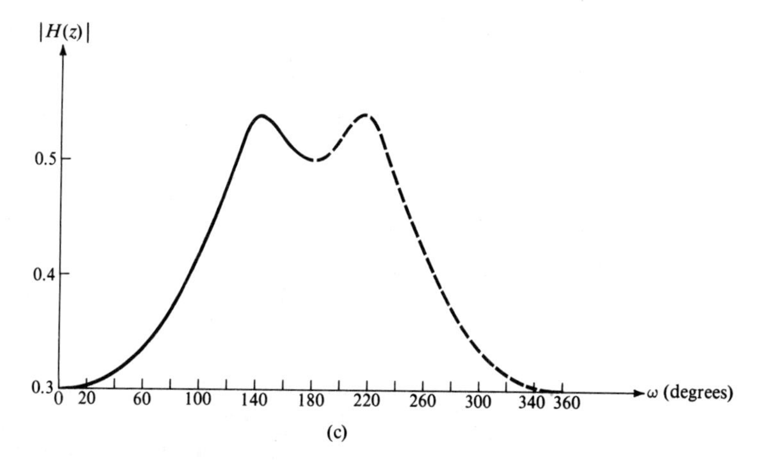

Figure 7.16 Amplitude–Frequency Responses of the Systems Shown in Figure 7.15

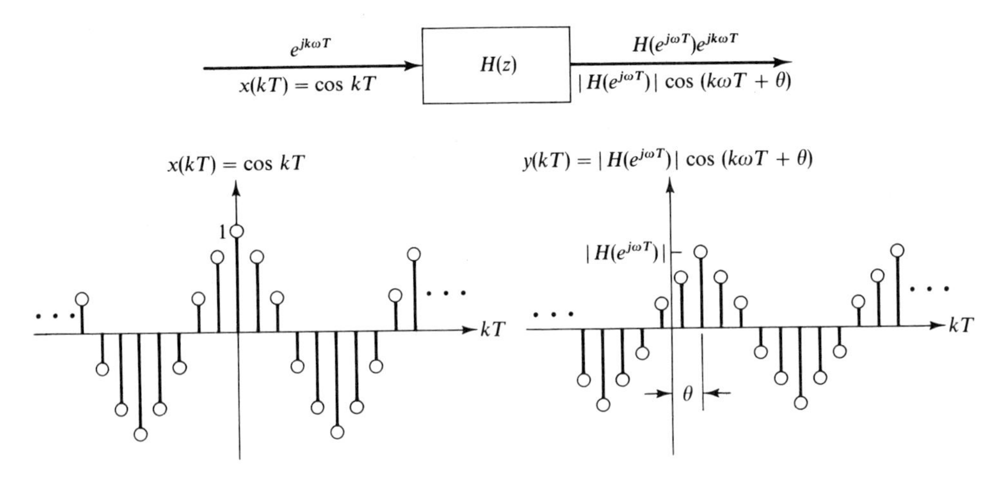

Figure 7.17 Illustrating the Effect of a Discrete System on a Sampled Cosine Function

This function with $T = 0.75$ is shown in Figure 7.16a, curve B. Also, we find that

$$\theta = \arg H(z) = \arg\left[\frac{2z + 1}{z}\right]_{z = e^{j\omega T}} = \arg\left[\frac{2 \cos \omega T + 1 + j2 \sin \omega T}{e^{j\omega T}}\right]$$

$$= \tan^{-1}\left(\frac{2 \sin \omega T}{1 + 2 \cos \omega T}\right) - \omega T$$

Since $\pi/0.75$ corresponds to 240°, we observe that the minimum has been shifted to that angle. Therefore, the new function becomes periodic with period $2 \times 240° = 480°$. The output is the function

$$y(kT) = |H(e^{j\omega T})| \cos(k\omega T + \theta)$$

This expression shows that if the input is a sampled cosine function, the output is also a sampled cosine function, but with an altered amplitude and a phase shift. A diagrammatic representation of the discussion is shown in Figure 7.17. ■

A point to be noted regarding sampled systems is that the period of the amplitude and phase functions is $2\pi/T = 2\omega_N$, where

$$\omega_N = \frac{\pi}{T} \tag{7.70}$$

where ω_N is the **Nyquist frequency.** (These results are in accord with the discussion in Section 4.5.) This discussion indicates that two signals $\cos \omega t$ and $\cos(\omega + 2\omega_N)t$, when sampled at this frequency, have the same number of sampled points. This assertion is shown graphically in Figure 7.18. This discussion suggests that when we

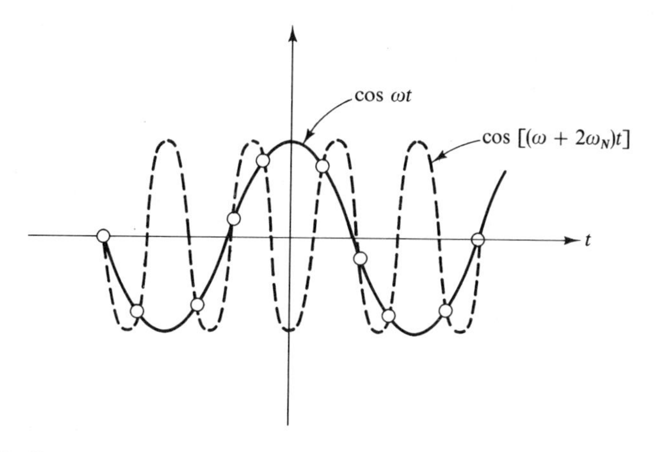

Figure 7.18 Illustrating Nyquist Frequency Sampling

use digital systems to simulate analog systems, T must be selected so that ω_N is larger than the highest frequency contained in the analog signal. Hence, it suffices to consider the discrete system in the frequency range $-\omega_N$ to ω_N.

7.8 Z-Transform Solution to Difference Equations

We now study the use of Z-transform methods in the solution of linear difference equations with constant coefficients. Some problems have already been completed in foregoing sections, but this matter should be reviewed in a somewhat more systematic manner by means of a number of examples.

■ **Example 7.27**

Solve the discrete time problem defined by the equation

$$y(k) + 2y(k-1) = 3.5u(k) \tag{7.71}$$

with $y(-1) = 0$ and

$$u(k) = \begin{cases} 1 & k = 0, 1, \ldots \\ 0 & k = -1, -2, \ldots \end{cases}$$

Solution Begin by taking the Z-transform of both sides of (7.71). This is

$$\mathscr{Z}\{y(k)\} + 2\mathscr{Z}\{y(k-1)\} = 3.5\mathscr{Z}\{u(k)\}$$

By Tables 7.1 and 7.3, we write

$$Y(z) + 2z^{-1}Y(z) = 3.5\,\frac{z}{z-1}$$

Solve for $Y(z)$ to obtain

$$Y(z) = 3.5\frac{z}{z-1}\frac{z}{z+2} = \frac{7}{6}\frac{z}{z-1} + \frac{7}{3}\frac{z}{z-(-2)}$$

The inverse Z-transform of this equation is

$$y(k) = 1.167u(k) + 2.33(-2)^k u(k)$$

■

Example 7.28

Repeat Example 7.27, but now with initial condition $y(-1) = 4$.

Solution We again begin by taking the Z-transform of both sides of (7.71):

$$\mathscr{Z}\{y(k)\} + 2\mathscr{Z}\{y(k-1)\} = 3.5\mathscr{Z}\{u(k)\}$$

which is [see (7.29)]

$$Y(z) + 2z^{-1}Y(z) + 2y(-1) = 3.5U(z)$$

Upon solving for $Y(z)$, we obtain

$$Y(z) = \underbrace{\frac{3.5}{1+2z^{-1}}U(z)}_{\substack{\text{zero-state}\\ \text{response}}} - \underbrace{\frac{2y(-1)}{1+2z^{-1}}}_{\substack{\text{zero-input}\\ \text{response}}}$$

The inverse transform of the zero-input response is the solution of the homogeneous difference equation

$$y(k) + 2y(k-1) = 0$$

a result that can be readily verified by setting consecutively $k = 0, 1, 2, \ldots$ in the equation. Specifically, the results are

$$\text{zero-input response} = \mathscr{Z}^{-1}\left\{-\frac{2y(-1)}{1+2z^{-1}}\right\}$$

$$\begin{aligned}\text{zero-state response} &= \mathscr{Z}^{-1}\left\{\frac{3.5}{1+2z^{-1}}\cdot\frac{1}{1-z^{-1}}\right\}\\ &= \mathscr{Z}^{-1}\left\{\frac{3.5z^2}{(z+2)(z-1)}\right\}\\ &= \mathscr{Z}^{-1}\left\{3.5z\left(\frac{A}{z+2} + \frac{B}{z-1}\right)\right\}\\ &= \mathscr{Z}^{-1}\left\{3.5\left(\frac{2}{3}\frac{z}{z+2} + \frac{1}{3}\frac{z}{z-1}\right)\right\}\end{aligned}$$

The inverse transform of the zero-state response is the solution of (7.71) with zero initial conditions. The complete solution is the sum of these two responses.

We can write the complete solution in two forms:

$$y(k) = \underbrace{1.167u(k) + 2.33(-2)^k u(k)}_{\text{zero-state}} - \underbrace{8(-2)^k u(k)}_{\text{zero-input}}$$

and

$$y(k) = \underbrace{1.167u(k)}_{\text{steady state}} - \underbrace{5.67(-2)^k u(k)}_{\text{transient}}$$

A similar situation was described in Section 2.3 for linear time-invariant analog systems. ■

■ **Example 7.29**

Determine the output of the discrete approximation of the system shown in Figure 7.19a for a sampling time T. The output for $T = 0.2$ and $T = 1$ are to be plotted, and the results compared with the output of the continuous system. The input is a unit step current source $i(t) = u(t)$, and an initial condition $v_o(0) = 2v$.

Solution The differential equation describing the system is

$$\frac{dv_o(t)}{dt} + 2v_o(t) = i(t)$$

The analogous discrete form of this equation is [see (2.77)]

$$\frac{v_o(kT) - v_o(kT - T)}{T} + 2v_o(kT) = i(kT)$$

From this,

$$v_o(kT) = \frac{T}{1 + 2T} i(kT) + \frac{1}{1 + 2T} v_o(kT - T)$$

The Z-transform of this equation gives, after simplifying,

$$V_o(z) = \underbrace{\frac{T}{1 + 2T - z^{-1}} I(z)}_{\substack{\text{zero-state} \\ \text{response}}} + \underbrace{\frac{1}{1 + 2T - z^{-1}} v_o(-T)}_{\substack{\text{zero-input} \\ \text{response}}}$$

Thus, we obtain

$$\text{zero-input response} = \mathscr{Z}^{-1}\left\{\frac{2}{1 + 2T - z^{-1}}\right\} = 2\left(\frac{1}{1 + 2T} \frac{1}{1 - \dfrac{z^{-1}}{1 + 2T}}\right)$$

$$= 2\left(\frac{1}{1 + 2T}\right)^{k+1} u(k)$$

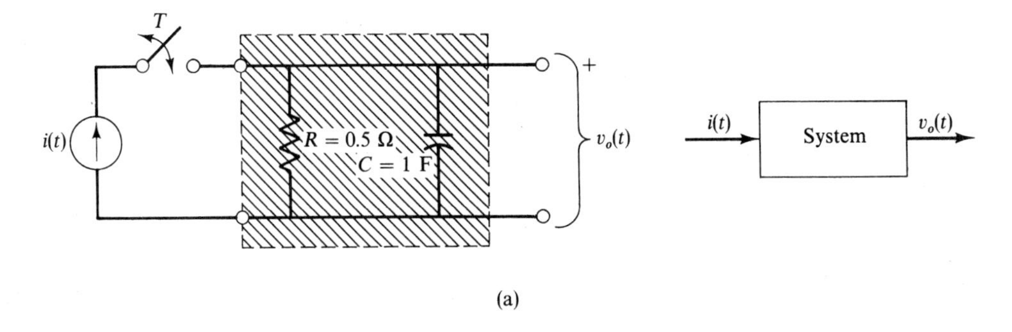

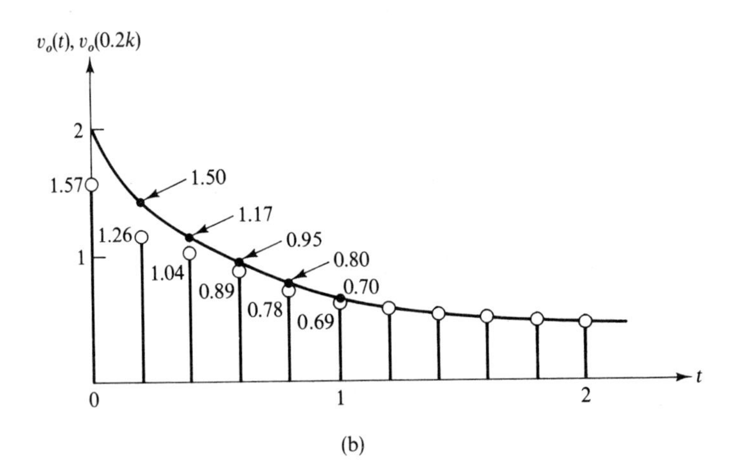

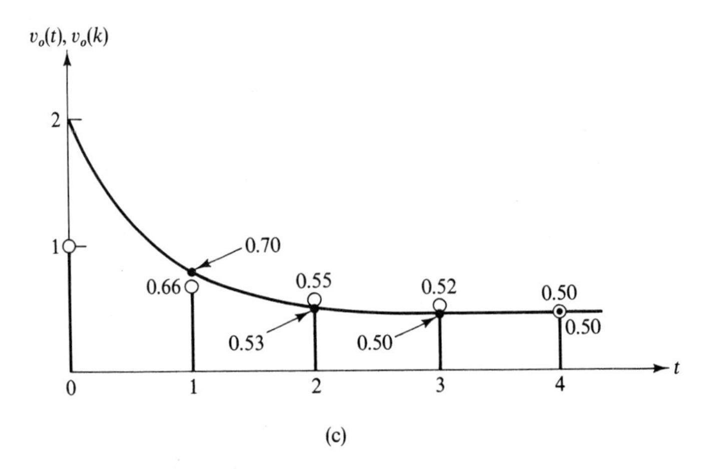

Figure 7.19 Illustrating Example 7.29

$$\text{zero-state response} = \mathcal{Z}^{-1}\left\{\frac{T}{1+2T}\frac{1}{1-\frac{1}{1+2T}z^{-1}}\frac{1}{1-z^{-1}}\right\}$$

$$= \frac{T}{1+2T}\mathcal{Z}^{-1}\left\{\frac{-a}{1-a}\frac{1}{1-az^{-1}} + \frac{1}{1-a}\frac{1}{1-z^{-1}}\right\}$$

$$= -\frac{T}{1+2T}\frac{a}{1-a}a^k u(k) + \frac{T}{1+2T}\frac{1}{1-a}u(k)$$

where $a = 1/(1+2T)$ and $v_o(-T) = 2$.

For the case $T = 0.2$, the solution is given by

$$v_o(0.2k) = \frac{1.5}{(1.4)^{k+1}} + 0.5u(k) \qquad k = 0, 1, 2, \ldots$$

This result is shown in Figure 7.19b, together with the solution for the continuous case, which is easily found to be (see Example 2.10)

$$v_o(t) = 0.5 + 1.5e^{-2t}$$

For the case $T = 1$, the solution is given by

$$v_o(k) = \frac{1.5}{3^{k+1}} + 0.5u(k) \qquad k = 0, 1, 2, \ldots$$

A plot of this equation is given in Figure 7.19c. ■

■ Example 7.30

Solve the difference equation

$$ay(k-2) - by(k-1) + y(k) = u(k-1) \tag{7.72}$$

The constants a and b are to be selected so that the second-order system is:

a. Critically damped.
b. Underdamped.
c. Overdamped.

The starting conditions are zero: $y(-2) = y(-1) = 0$.

Solution The Z-transform of both sides of (7.72) and solving for $Y(z)$ yield

$$Y(z) = \frac{z}{z^2 - bz + a}\frac{z}{z-1} \tag{7.73}$$

The denominator of the first factor has two roots that are specified by

$$z_{1,2} = \frac{b \pm \sqrt{b^2 - 4a}}{2} \tag{7.74}$$

Critically Damped Case (two equal real roots): We set $b^2 = 4a$ and select $b = 0.8$ in (7.73). We thus obtain

$$Y(z) = \frac{z}{(z - 0.4)^2} \frac{z}{(z - 1)}$$

This is expanded into the form

$$Y(z) = \frac{Az}{z - 1} + \frac{Bz}{z - 0.4} + \frac{Cz^2}{(z - 0.4)^2} \tag{7.75}$$

By straightforward methods, the constants in this expansion are found to be $A = 1(0.6)^2$, $B = -(0.4)/(0.6)^2$, and $C = -1/0.6$. The inverse transform of this equation is the expression

$$y(k) = \frac{1}{(0.6)^2} [u(k) - (1 + 0.6k)0.4^k] \tag{7.76}$$

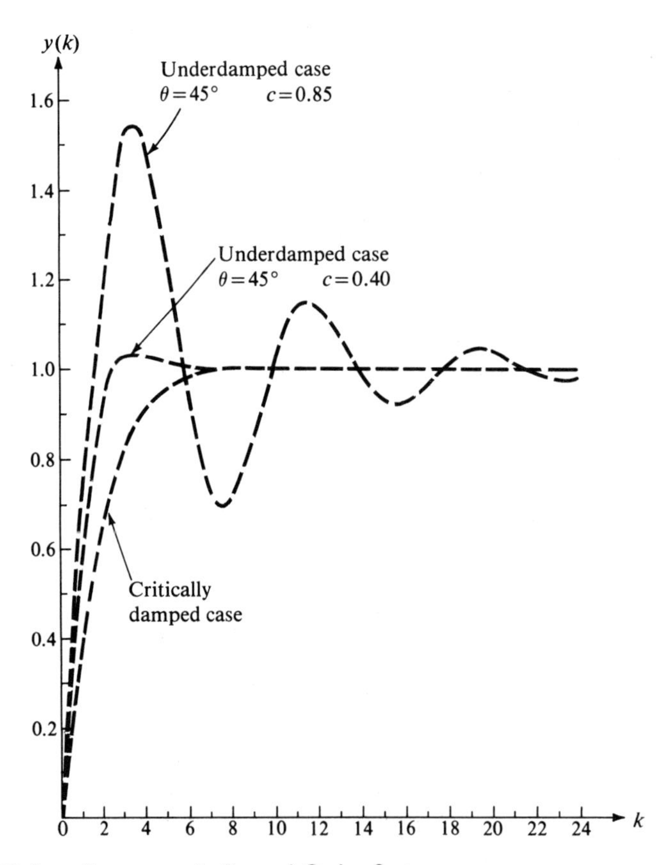

Figure 7.20 Step Response of a Second-Order System

The quantity in the bracket, which is the normalized value of $y(k)$, is shown in Figure 7.20. Had we selected the value of b to be larger than 0.8, the curve would have taken longer to reach the value unity, the steady state response of the system.

Underdamped Case: For $b^2 < 4a$, two complex conjugate roots of (7.74) exist, and these roots are poles of $Y(z)$. To proceed, we write the denominator of $Y(z)$ in the form

$$z^2 - bz + a = (z - ce^{j\theta})(z - ce^{-j\theta}) \tag{7.77}$$

By expanding the right-hand side and equating like powers of z, we find that

$$a = c^2 \qquad \text{and} \qquad b = 2c\cos\theta$$

Thus, if a and b are known, then c and θ are readily obtained. By combining (7.77) with (7.73), we write

$$Y(z) = \frac{z}{(z - ce^{j\theta})(z - ce^{-j\theta})}\,\frac{z}{z-1}$$

This fraction is now expanded into fractional form, which is

$$Y(z) = \frac{1}{1 - 2c\cos\theta + c^2}\,\frac{z}{z-1} - \frac{e^{j\theta}}{2j\sin\theta(1 - ce^{j\theta})}\,\frac{z}{z - ce^{j\theta}} + \frac{e^{-j\theta}}{2j\sin\theta(1 - ce^{-j\theta})}\,\frac{z}{z - ce^{-j\theta}}$$

The inverse Z-transform of this equation is

$$y(k) = \frac{1}{1 - 2c\cos\theta + c^2}\,u(k) - \frac{e^{j\theta}}{2j\sin\theta(1 - ce^{j\theta})}\,c^k e^{jk\theta} + \frac{e^{-j\theta}}{2j\sin\theta(1 - ce^{-j\theta})}\,c^k e^{-jk\theta}$$

This expression can be written in more convenient form by writing $1 - ce^{j\theta} = re^{-j\phi}$; then, $1 - ce^{-j\theta} = re^{j\phi}$, and the equation for $y(k)$ takes the form

$$y(k) = \frac{1}{r^2}\left[u(k) - \frac{rc^k}{\sin\theta}\sin[(k+1)\theta + \phi]\right] \tag{7.78}$$

If we choose $c = 0.85$ and $\theta = 45°$, we find that $r = 0.721$ and $\phi = 56.426°$. The normalized value of $y(k)$ under these conditions is plotted in Figure 7.20. If we had chosen $c = 0.4$ and $\theta = 45°$, then $r = 0.771$ and $\phi = 21.524°$. The curve resulting from this choice of r, θ is also contained in Figure 7.20. From these two curves, we can conclude that as c decreases, the speed with which $y(k)$ approaches its steady state value increases.

Overdamped Case: The requirement in this case is that $b^2 > 4a$, so that the two roots given by (7.74) are real and different. The response of the system is easily found by proceeding in the manner discussed above. ■

Example 7.31 ***Transmission Line***
Determine the voltage $v(k)$ for the resistor ladder circuit shown in Figure 7.21. This configuration can represent, in lumped parameter form, a continuous transmission line that is dominantly resistive.

Solution Write the Kirchhoff voltage law for the $k + 1$ loop, namely,

$$R_2\, i(k+2) - (R_1 + 2R_2)i(k+1) + R_2\, i(k) = 0 \tag{7.79}$$

This equation applies for any loop except the input and output loops. The input and output loops serve in determining the two unknown constants that arise in the solution of the second-order difference equation.

The Z-transform of this equation results in the expression (see Table 7.1)

$$I(z) = \frac{R_2\, i(0)z^2 + R_2\, i(1)z - (R_1 + 2R_2)i(0)z}{R_2\, z^2 - (R_1 + 2R_2)z + R_2} \tag{7.80}$$

For simplicity, let $R_1 = 1$ and $R_2 = 2$. The equation for $I(z)$ becomes

$$I(z) = \frac{z[i(0)z + i(1) - 2.5i(0)]}{z^2 - 2.5z + 1} \tag{7.81}$$

The voltage law in the input, or first loop, gives us the relationship (for $R_1 = 1$ and $R_2 = 2$)

$$i(1) = 1.5i(0) - 0.5v \tag{7.82}$$

Combine this equation with (7.81), and we find

$$I(z) = i(0)\,\frac{z(z - 3/2) + z[1/2 - 0.5v/i(0)]}{z^2 - 2.5z + 1}$$

which can be written

$$I(z) = i(0)\left[\frac{z(z - 3/2)}{(z-2)(z-0.5)} + \frac{z[0.5 - 0.5v/i(0)]}{(z-2)(z-0.5)}\right] \tag{7.83}$$

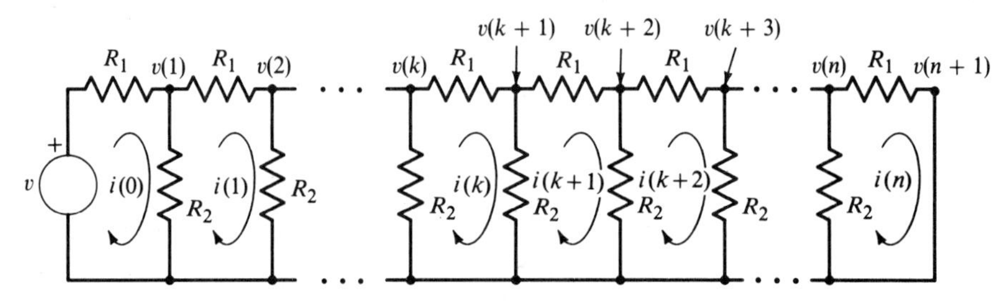

Figure 7.21 Resistor Ladder Network

This expression can be expanded into fractional form, from which the inverse that expresses $i(k)$ in explicit form is readily obtained. The unknown $i(0)$ that appears in the final expression can be found from the last, or output, loop by noting that the solution must be satisfied there also. ■

7.9 Z-Transform Solution to Discrete Time State Equations

Just as the Laplace transform provides a vehicle for solving the continuous time (analog) state equations, the Z-transform provides a vehicle for solving discrete time (digital) state equations. We begin with the state equations

$$\mathbf{x}(k+1) = \mathbf{A}\mathbf{x}(k) + \mathbf{B}\mathbf{w}(k) \tag{7.84a}$$

$$\mathbf{y}(k) = \mathbf{C}\mathbf{x}(k) + \mathbf{D}\mathbf{w}(k) \tag{7.84b}$$

where $\mathbf{A}$, $\mathbf{B}$, $\mathbf{C}$, and $\mathbf{D}$ are constant matrixes. The Z-transform of these equations yields

$$z\mathbf{X}(z) = \mathbf{A}\mathbf{X}(z) + \mathbf{B}\mathbf{W}(z) + z\mathbf{x}(0) \tag{7.85a}$$

$$\mathbf{Y}(z) = \mathbf{C}\mathbf{X}(z) + \mathbf{D}\mathbf{W}(z) \tag{7.85b}$$

These relations are valid because the Z-transform of a matrix (or vector) is the Z-transform of each element of the matrix. That is, for a 2×2 matrix,

$$\mathscr{Z}\begin{bmatrix} a_{11}(k) & a_{12}(k) \\ a_{21}(k) & a_{22}(k) \end{bmatrix} = \begin{bmatrix} \mathscr{Z}\{a_{11}(k)\} & \mathscr{Z}\{a_{12}(k)\} \\ \mathscr{Z}\{a_{21}(k)\} & \mathscr{Z}\{a_{22}(k)\} \end{bmatrix} = \mathbf{A}(z)$$

Therefore, the Z-transform of $\mathbf{x}(k+1)$ is (see also Appendix A)

$$\mathscr{Z}\begin{bmatrix} x_1(k+1) \\ x_2(k+1) \end{bmatrix} = \begin{bmatrix} zX_1(z) - zx_1(0) \\ zX_2(z) - zx_2(0) \end{bmatrix} = \begin{bmatrix} zX_1(z) \\ zX_2(z) \end{bmatrix} - \begin{bmatrix} zx_1(0) \\ zx_2(0) \end{bmatrix}$$

$$= z\begin{bmatrix} X_1(z) \\ X_2(z) \end{bmatrix} - z\begin{bmatrix} x_1(0) \\ x_2(0) \end{bmatrix} = z\mathbf{X}(z) - z\mathbf{x}(0)$$

From (7.85), we write (see Problem 55)

$$\mathbf{X}(z) = [z\mathbf{I} - \mathbf{A}]^{-1}\mathbf{B}\mathbf{W}(z) + [z\mathbf{I} - \mathbf{A}]^{-1}z\mathbf{x}(0) \tag{7.86a}$$

$$\mathbf{Y}(z) = (\mathbf{C}[z\mathbf{I} - \mathbf{A}]^{-1}\mathbf{B} + \mathbf{D})\mathbf{W}(z) + \mathbf{C}[z\mathbf{I} - \mathbf{A}]^{-1}z\mathbf{x}(0) \tag{7.86b}$$

The fundamental matrix $\mathbf{\Phi}(z)$ for the discrete system is defined by

$$\mathbf{\Phi}(z) = \mathscr{Z}\{\mathbf{\Phi}(k)\} = z[z\mathbf{I} - \mathbf{A}]^{-1} \tag{7.87}$$

It was shown in (5.132) that the state transition matrix $\mathbf{\Phi}(k)$ was

$$\mathbf{\Phi}(k) = \mathbf{A}^k \tag{7.88}$$

It follows, therefore, that

$$\mathbf{\Phi}(z) = \mathscr{Z}\{\mathbf{\Phi}(k)\} = \mathscr{Z}\{\mathbf{A}^k\} = z[z\mathbf{I} - \mathbf{A}]^{-1} = [\mathbf{I} - z^{-1}\mathbf{A}]^{-1} \tag{7.89}$$

Equation (7.86) can thus be written

$$\mathbf{X}(z) = \mathbf{\Phi}(z)z^{-1}\mathbf{B}\mathbf{W}(z) + \mathbf{\Phi}(z)\mathbf{x}(0) \tag{7.90a}$$

$$\mathbf{Y}(z) = [\mathbf{C}\mathbf{\Phi}(z)z^{-1}\mathbf{B} + \mathbf{D}]\mathbf{W}(z) + \mathbf{C}\mathbf{\Phi}(z)\mathbf{x}(0) \tag{7.90b}$$

The relation between the excitation and the response function in the absence of initial conditions is, from (7.90b),

$$\mathbf{Y}(z) = [\mathbf{C}\mathbf{\Phi}(z)z^{-1}\mathbf{B} + \mathbf{D}]\mathbf{W}(z)$$

and the Z-domain transfer matrix is

$$\mathbf{H}(z) = \mathbf{C}\mathbf{\Phi}(z)z^{-1}\mathbf{B} + \mathbf{D} \tag{7.91}$$

We note that even though there is not an exact analogy between the Z-domain and the s-domain forms for the corresponding fundamental matrixes, nevertheless, the extra z in the definition for $\mathbf{\Phi}(z)$ disappears in the expression for $\mathbf{H}(z)$.

Example 7.32

Suppose that the state space equations for a given discrete time-invariant system have the form

$$\begin{bmatrix} x_1(k+1) \\ x_2(k+1) \end{bmatrix} = \begin{bmatrix} 0 & 1 \\ -2 & -3 \end{bmatrix}\begin{bmatrix} x_1(k) \\ x_2(k) \end{bmatrix} + \begin{bmatrix} 0 \\ 1 \end{bmatrix} w(k)$$

$$y(k) = [1 \quad 0]\begin{bmatrix} x_1(k) \\ x_2(k) \end{bmatrix}$$

with $y(0) = y(1) = 1$. Find $y(k)$ for $w(k) = u(k)$.

Solution We need the following quantities:

a. $$[z\mathbf{I} - \mathbf{A}]^{-1} = \left(\begin{bmatrix} z & 0 \\ 0 & z \end{bmatrix} - \begin{bmatrix} 0 & 1 \\ -2 & -3 \end{bmatrix}\right)^{-1} = \frac{\begin{bmatrix} z+3 & 1 \\ -2 & z \end{bmatrix}}{z(z+3)+2}$$

b. $$w(z) = \mathscr{Z}\{u(k)\} = \frac{z}{z-1}$$

c. Initial conditions $\mathbf{x}(0)$. From the state equations, we have

$$x_1(1) = x_2(0)$$
$$y(0) = x_1(0) = 1$$
$$y(1) = x_1(1) = x_2(0) = 1$$

so that $\mathbf{x}(0) = [x_1(0)x_2(0)]^T = [1 \quad 1]^T$.

Introduce these quantities into (7.86), and we obtain

$$Y(z) = \left([1 \quad 0] \frac{\begin{bmatrix} z+3 & 1 \\ -2 & z \end{bmatrix}}{z^2+3z+2} \begin{bmatrix} 0 \\ 1 \end{bmatrix} \right) \frac{z}{z-1} + [1 \quad 0] \frac{\begin{bmatrix} z+3 & 1 \\ -2 & z \end{bmatrix}}{z^2+3z+2} \begin{bmatrix} z \\ z \end{bmatrix}$$

which can be rewritten

$$\frac{Y(z)}{z} = \frac{1}{(z-1)(z+1)(z+2)} + \frac{z+4}{(z+1)(z+2)}$$

By employing known techniques for inverting the Z-transform, we obtain

$$y(k) = \frac{5}{2}(-1)^k + \frac{1}{6}(1)^k - \frac{5}{3}(-2)^k$$

■

■ **Example 7.33** ***Epidemiology***

We assume that the probability that a person will change from good health (state 1) to infected state (state 2) during an epidemic is 0.75. We further assume that the probability of remaining sick for the next three days is 0. Further, the probability of returning to good health after the sickness is 1.0, and the probability of remaining healthy is 0.25. A graphical representation of this two-state system is shown in Figure 7.22. Determine the state at the kth time unit (1 time unit = 3 days) for an initial state at $k = 0$ denoted as $\mathbf{x}_0 = [1 \quad 0]$, which specifies that the person is initially in good health.

Solution We write

$$\mathbf{x}(k) = \begin{bmatrix} x_1(k) \\ x_2(k) \end{bmatrix} \tag{7.92}$$

where $x_1(k)$ is the probability that the system is in state 1 (healthy) k unit times after $k = 0$, and $x_2(k)$ is the probability that the system is in state 2 (sick) k units after $k = 0$. Also, the state transition probabilities $\mathbf{M}$ are expressed in matrix form:

$$\mathbf{M} = [p_{ij}] = \begin{bmatrix} 0.25 & 0.75 \\ 1.0 & 0 \end{bmatrix} \tag{7.93}$$

It follows from the statement of the problem that we must have

$$\mathbf{x}(k+1) = \mathbf{M}^T\mathbf{x}(k) \tag{7.94}$$

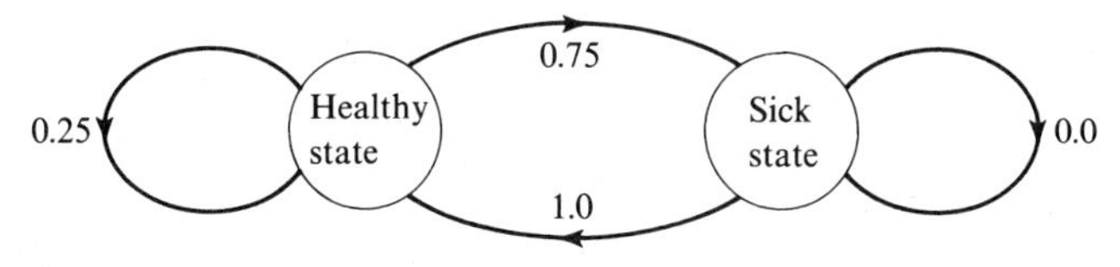

Figure 7.22 Illustrating Example 7.33

To verify this conclusion, we note that after 1 time unit for the given initial state, we would have

$$\begin{bmatrix} x_1(1) \\ x_2(1) \end{bmatrix} = \begin{bmatrix} 0.25 & 1.0 \\ 0.75 & 0 \end{bmatrix} \begin{bmatrix} 1 \\ 0 \end{bmatrix} = \begin{bmatrix} 0.25 \\ 0.75 \end{bmatrix}$$

which agrees with indicated conditions.

We obtain, by continued substitutions in (7.94),

$$\begin{aligned} \mathbf{x}(1) &= \mathbf{M}^T\mathbf{x}(0) \\ \mathbf{x}(2) &= \mathbf{M}^T\mathbf{x}(1) = \mathbf{M}^T\mathbf{M}^T\mathbf{x}(0) = (\mathbf{M}^T)^2\mathbf{x}(0) \\ \mathbf{x}(3) &= \mathbf{M}^T\mathbf{x}(2) = \mathbf{M}^T(\mathbf{M}^T)^2\mathbf{x}(0) = (\mathbf{M}^T)^3\mathbf{x}(0) \\ &\vdots \end{aligned}$$

It follows, therefore, that

$$\mathbf{x}(k) = (\mathbf{M}^T)^k\mathbf{x}(0) \tag{7.95}$$

The Z-transform of (7.94) is (see Table 7.1, entry 3)

$$z\mathbf{X}(z) - z\mathbf{x}(0) = \mathbf{M}^T\mathbf{X}(z)$$

from which

$$\mathbf{X}(z) = [z\mathbf{I} - \mathbf{M}^T]^{-1}z\mathbf{x}(0) \tag{7.96}$$

By comparing this expression with (7.95), we see that the inverse Z-transform of $[z\mathbf{I} - \mathbf{M}^T]^{-1}z$ is equal to $(\mathbf{M}^T)^k$. For our case,

$$\begin{aligned} \mathbf{X}(z) &= \left(\begin{bmatrix} z & 0 \\ 0 & z \end{bmatrix} - \begin{bmatrix} 0.25 & 1.0 \\ 0.75 & 0 \end{bmatrix} \right)^{-1} z \begin{bmatrix} 1 \\ 0 \end{bmatrix} \\ &= \frac{z}{(z-1)\left(z+\frac{3}{4}\right)} \begin{bmatrix} z & 1 \\ \frac{3}{4} & z-\frac{1}{4} \end{bmatrix} \begin{bmatrix} 1 \\ 0 \end{bmatrix} = \frac{z}{(z-1)\left(z+\frac{3}{4}\right)} \begin{bmatrix} z \\ \frac{3}{4} \end{bmatrix} \\ &= \begin{bmatrix} \dfrac{z^2}{(z-1)\left(z+\frac{3}{4}\right)} \\ \dfrac{3}{4}\dfrac{z}{(z-1)\left(z+\frac{3}{4}\right)} \end{bmatrix} \end{aligned} \tag{7.97}$$

From this result, we find

$$\begin{aligned} x_1(k) &= \mathscr{Z}^{-1}\left\{ \frac{z^2}{(z-1)\left(z+\frac{3}{4}\right)} \right\} = \mathscr{Z}^{-1}\left\{ \frac{4}{7}\frac{z}{z-1} + \frac{3}{7}\frac{z}{z+\frac{3}{4}} \right\} \\ &= \frac{4}{7}u(k) + \frac{3}{7}\left(-\frac{3}{4}\right)^k \end{aligned} \tag{7.98}$$

$$x_2(k) = \mathscr{Z}^{-1}\left\{\frac{3}{4}\frac{z}{(z-1)\left(z+\frac{3}{4}\right)}\right\} = \mathscr{Z}^{-1}\left\{\frac{3}{7}\frac{z}{z-1} - \frac{3}{7}\frac{z}{z+\frac{3}{4}}\right\}$$

$$= \frac{3}{7}u(k) - \frac{3}{7}\left(-\frac{3}{4}\right)^k \qquad \textbf{(7.99)}$$

It follows from these results that after a long time, the probability that a healthy person is in state 1 (healthy) is 4/7 and in state 2 (sick) is 3/7. ■

7.10 More on Higher-Order Difference Equations

We have already addressed the solution of difference equations of higher order by state variable techniques. We have not systematically studied the solution of difference equations using classical techniques and do so now.

Direct Method of Solution

The class of linear discrete systems now under survey is described by the difference equation

$$a_n y(k+n) + a_{n-1}y(k+n-1) + \cdots + a_1 y(k+1) + a_0 y(k) = r(k) \qquad \textbf{(7.100)}$$

where n is a positive integer, the coefficients a_i are constants, and $r(k)$ is a function of k with $k = 0, 1, 2, \ldots$. We know that such an equation can arise when a differential equation is transformed into an equivalent difference equation using the approximate conversions given by (2.91), namely,

$$\frac{dy}{dt} \doteq \frac{y[(k+1)T] - y(kT)}{T} \qquad \textbf{(7.101a)}$$

$$\frac{d^2y}{dt^2} \doteq \frac{y[(k+2)T] - 2y[(k+1)T] + y(kT)}{T^2} \qquad \textbf{(7.101b)}$$

$$\frac{d^3y}{dt^3} \doteq \frac{y[(k+3)T] - 3y[(k+2)T] + 3y[(k+1)T] - y(kT)}{T^3} \qquad \textbf{(7.101c)}$$

and so on. If we substitute $k-1, k-2, k-3, \ldots$ in (7.101), the corresponding set is

$$\frac{dy}{dt} \doteq \frac{y(kT) - y[(k-1)T]}{T} \qquad \textbf{(7.102a)}$$

$$\frac{d^2y}{dt^2} \doteq \frac{y(kT) - 2y[(k-1)T] + y[(k-2)T]}{T^2} \qquad \textbf{(7.102b)}$$

$$\frac{d^3y}{dt^3} \doteq \frac{y(kT) - 3y[(k-1)T] + 3y[(k-2)T] - y[(k-3)T]}{T^3} \qquad \textbf{(7.102c)}$$

When the coefficients a_i in (7.100) are independent of k, the equation describes a **time-invariant system**; otherwise, the system is **time varying.** We assume in the following that the coefficients a_n and a_0 are nonzero for all $k = 0, 1, 2, \ldots$, so that (7.100) is of *order n*. For $T = 1$, the second-order difference equation can always be written in the form

$$\boxed{y(k+2) + \alpha_1 y(k+1) + \alpha_0\, y(k) = x(k)} \tag{7.103a}$$

where

$$\alpha_1 = \frac{a_1}{a_2} \qquad \alpha_0 = \frac{a_0}{a_2} \qquad x(k) = \frac{r(k)}{a_2} \tag{7.103b}$$

The homogeneous equivalent of this equation is

$$\boxed{y(k+2) + \alpha_1 y(k+1) + \alpha_0\, y(k) = 0} \tag{7.104}$$

We assert that a complete and unique solution to (7.103a) can be found if the initial conditions are known, say,

$$y(0) = A \qquad y(1) = B \tag{7.105}$$

where A and B are constants. In this connection, we state certain theorems without proof (see Finizio and Ladas*):

Definition 7.1

If $\{a(k)\}$ and $\{b(k)\}$ denote two sequences, the determinant

$$C[a(k), b(k)] = \begin{vmatrix} a(k) & b(k) \\ a(k+1) & b(k+1) \end{vmatrix} \tag{7.106}$$

is known as their **Casoratian** or their **Wronskian** determinant.

Theorem 7.1

Two solutions $y_1(k)$ and $y_2(k)$ of the linear homogeneous difference equation (7.104) are linearly independent if and only if their Casoratian

$$C[y_1(k), y_2(k)] = \begin{vmatrix} y_1(k) & y_2(k) \\ y_1(k+1) & y_2(k+1) \end{vmatrix} \tag{7.107}$$

is different from zero for all values of $k = 0, 1, 2, \ldots$.

---

* N. Finizio, and G. Ladas, *An Introduction to Differential Equations* (Belmont, CA: Wadsworth Publishing Co., 1982).

■ Theorem 7.2

If $y_1(k)$ and $y_2(k)$ are two linear independent solutions of (7.104) and if $y_p(k)$ is the particular solution to the nonhomogeneous equation (7.103a), then the general solution to (7.103a) is

$$y(k) = y_h(k) + y_p(k) = C_1 y_1(k) + C_2 y_2(k) + y_p(k) \tag{7.108}$$

where C_1 and C_2 are arbitrary constants that can be determined from appropriate initial conditions.

■ Theorem 7.3

The difference equation

$$a_2 y(k+2) + a_1 y(k+1) + a_0 y(k) = 0 \tag{7.109}$$

with constant and real coefficients, with a_2, $a_0 \neq 0$, and with the roots of the characteristic equation

$$a_2 \lambda^2 + a_1 \lambda + a_0 = 0 \tag{7.110}$$

denoted λ_1 and λ_2, has the possible solutions shown in Table 7.5.

Proof Assume that $y(k) = c\lambda^k$ is a solution of (7.100). Then

$$a_2 \lambda^{k+2} + a_1 \lambda^{k+1} + a_0 \lambda^k = 0$$

or

$$a_2 \lambda^2 + a_1 \lambda + a_0 = 0$$

which is (7.110).

■ Example 7.34

Solve the homogeneous equation

$$y(k+2) + 2y(k+1) - 3y(k) = 0 \tag{7.111}$$

subject to the initial conditions $y(0) = 1$ and $y(1) = 0$.

Solution The characteristic equation is

$$\lambda^2 + 2\lambda - 3 = 0$$

with roots $\lambda = 1$ and $\lambda = -3$. Therefore, the solution to the homogeneous equation is

$$y_h(k) = C_1(-3)^k + C_2(1)^k \tag{7.112}$$

Now, apply the initial conditions that lead to

$$y_h(0) = 1 = C_1 + C_2$$
$$y_h(1) = 0 = C_1(-3)^1 + C_2 1^1$$

Table 7.5 Solutions to Homogeneous Difference Equations

Difference Equation $a_2 y(k+2) + a_1 y(k+1) + a_0 y(k) = 0$	Characteristic Equation $a_2 \lambda^2 + a_1 \lambda + a_0 = 0$
Characteristic roots	Solutions
$\lambda_1 \neq \lambda_2$	$y(k) = c_1 \lambda_1^k + c_2 \lambda_2^k$
$\lambda_1 = \lambda_2 = \lambda$	$y(k) = c_1 \lambda^k + c_2 k \lambda^k$
$\lambda_1 = a + jb$	$y(k) = c_1 r^k \cos k\theta + c_2 r^k \sin k\theta$
$\lambda_2 = a - jb$	$r = [a^2 + b^2]^{1/2}$ $\cos\theta = \frac{a}{r}$ $\sin\theta = \frac{b}{r}$ $-\pi < \theta \leq \pi$
$a_n y(k+n) + a_{n-1} y(k+n-1)$ $\cdots + a_0 y(k) = 0$	$a_n \lambda^n + a_{n-1} \lambda^{n-1} + \cdots + a_0 = 0$
$\lambda_1 \neq \lambda_2 \neq \cdots \neq \lambda_n$	$y(k) = \sum_{i=1}^{n} c_i \lambda_i^k$
$\lambda_j \equiv$ root of multiplicity m	$y(k) = \sum_{i=1}^{n-m} c_i \lambda_i^k + c_j \lambda_j^k + c_{j+1} k \lambda_j^k + \cdots + c_{j+m} k^{m-1} \lambda_j^k$
pair of roots $a \pm jb$ of multiplicity m	$y(k) = \sum_{i=1}^{n-2m} c_i \lambda_i^k + d_1 r^k \cos k\theta + d_2 k r^k \cos k\theta + \cdots + d_m k^{m-1} r^k \cos k\theta + d_{m+1} r^k \sin k\theta + d_{m+2} k r^k \sin k\theta + \cdots + d_{2m} k^{m-1} r^k \sin k\theta$

Solving these two equations simultaneously yields $C_1 = 1/4$ and $C_2 = 3/4$. The final solution is

$$y_h(k) - \frac{1}{4}(-3)^k + \frac{3}{4}(1)^k \tag{7.113}$$

Now, suppose that we shift the axis by 2 units. Equation (7.111) becomes

$$y(k) + 2y(k-1) - 3y(k-2) = 0 \tag{7.114}$$

The characteristic equation is unchanged, and the homogeneous solution is given by (7.112), namely,

$$y_h(k) = C_1(-3)^k + C_2(1)^k \tag{7.115}$$

as before. However, considering the shifted axis with respect to the original axis, the initial conditions change, with $y(0) \to y(-2)$ and $y(1) \to y(-1)$. Thus, the initial conditions become $y(-2) = 1$ and $y(-1) = 0$. Applying these initial conditions to (7.115) and solving for C_1 and C_2 result in the expression

$$y_h(k) = \frac{9}{4}(-3)^k + \frac{3}{4}(1)^k \tag{7.116}$$

By taking the time shift of two units into consideration, the reader can easily verify that the two solutions are identical. ■

■ **Example 7.35**

Solve (7.111) and (7.114) employing Z-transform methods.

Solution The Z-transform of (7.111) is, from Table 7.1, entry 3,

$$z^2Y(z) - y(0)z^{2-0} - y(1)z^{2-1} + 2zY(z) - 2y(0)z^{1-0} - 3Y(z) = 0$$

from which

$$Y(z) = \frac{z(z+2)}{(z-1)(z+3)} = \frac{3}{4}\frac{z}{z-1} + \frac{1}{4}\frac{z}{z+3}$$

The inverse transform gives the result

$$y(k) = \frac{3}{4}(1)^k + \frac{1}{4}(-3)^k \qquad k \geq 0$$

The Z-transform of (7.114) is, from Table 7.1, entry 2,

$$Y(z) + 2z^{-1}Y(z) + 2y(-1)z^{-(1-1)} - 3z^{-2}Y(z) - 3y(-1)z^{-(2-1)} - 3y(-2)z^{-(2-2)} = 0$$

from which

$$Y(z) = \frac{3z^2}{(z-1)(z+3)} = \frac{3}{4}\frac{z}{z-1} + \frac{9}{4}\frac{z}{z+3}$$

The inverse Z-transform is

$$y(k) = \frac{3}{4}(1)^k + \frac{9}{4}(-3)^k \qquad k \geq 0$$

Both results agree with those obtained in Example 7.34, as they should. ■

■ **Example 7.36 *Optical System***

Determine the ray trajectories of a system of thin lenses $L_0, L_1, \ldots L_n$ with identical focal lengths, as shown in Figure 7.23a.

Solution Refer initially to the two lenses shown in Figure 7.23b. In the figure, $r(k)$ denotes the height of the ray entering the thin lens L_k, and $\dot{r}(k)$ denotes the slope of this ray. Further, the slope of the ray between the two

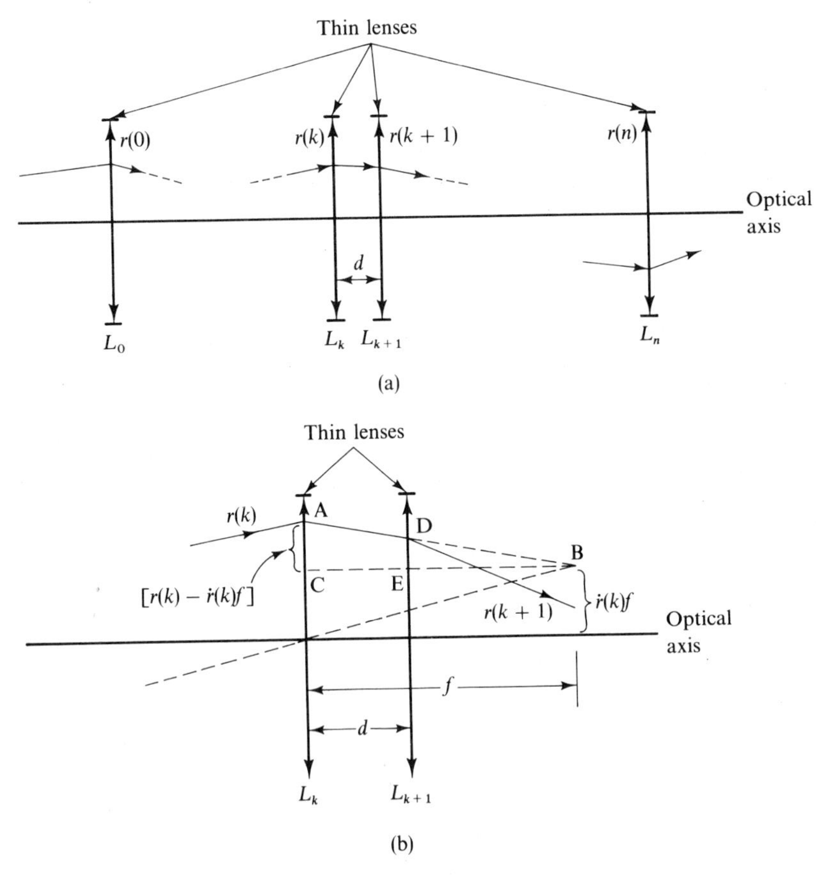

Figure 7.23 System of Thin Lenses

lenses is

$$\dot{r}(k+1) = \frac{\dot{r}(k)f - r(k)}{f} = -\frac{1}{f}r(k) + \dot{r}(k) \tag{7.117}$$

where f is the focal length of the lens. By examination of the similar triangles ABC and BDE, we find the height:

$$r(k+1) = r(k) - \frac{d}{f}r(k) + \dot{r}(k)d \tag{7.118}$$

Now, increase the index of this equation by writing $k + 1$ for k and combine the resulting equation with (7.117) and (7.118) to eliminate $\dot{r}(k)$. From these equations, we obtain

$$r(k+2) - \left(2 - \frac{d}{f}\right)r(k+1) + r(k) = 0 \tag{7.119}$$

The characteristic equation of this difference equation is

$$\lambda^2 - \left(2 - \frac{d}{f}\right)\lambda + 1 = 0 \tag{7.120}$$

with roots

$$\lambda_1 = \frac{2 - \frac{d}{f} + \sqrt{\frac{d^2}{f^2} - 4\frac{d}{f}}}{2} \qquad \lambda_2 = \frac{2 - \frac{d}{f} - \sqrt{\frac{d^2}{f^2} - 4\frac{d}{f}}}{2} \tag{7.121}$$

We consider the solutions for three important cases.

Case 1: $d = 4f$. In this case, the roots become $\lambda_1 = \lambda_2 = -1$, and the general solution is

$$r(k) = [C_1 + C_2 k](-1)^k \tag{7.122}$$

The value of $r(k)$ becomes unbounded with increasing k; this condition denotes an unstable system. Physically, this instability means that the rays will diverge from the guiding system.

Case 2: $d > 4f$. Now, λ_1 and λ_2 are real and different. For the particular case for $d = 8f$, the general solution is readily found to be

$$r(k) = C_1\left(\frac{-6 + \sqrt{32}}{2}\right)^k + C_2\left(\frac{-6 - \sqrt{32}}{2}\right)^k \tag{7.123}$$

Case 3: $d < 4f$. In this case, λ_1 and λ_2 are conjugate complex roots $\lambda_1 = a + jb$ and $\lambda_2 = a - jb$. The general solution is of the form

$$\begin{aligned} r(k) &= Ce^{j\phi}(a + jb)^k + Ce^{-j\phi}(a - jb)^k \\ &= Ce^{j\phi}R^k e^{jk\theta} + Ce^{-j\phi}R^k e^{-jk\theta} \\ &= 2CR^k \cos(k\theta + \phi) \end{aligned} \tag{7.124}$$

where C and ϕ are arbitrary constants, $R = \sqrt{a^2 + b^2}$, and $\theta = \tan^{-1}(a/b)$. This form of solution shows that $r(k)$ is a real quantity. If R is less than unity but very close to it, $r(k)$ oscillates indicating that the ray will be guided by the structure. The same result can be found by direct reference to Table 7.5. ■

■ Theorem 7.4

The particular solution to the nonhomogeneous difference equation

$$y(k + 2) + \alpha_1 y(k + 1) + \alpha_0 y(k) = x(k) \tag{7.125}$$

where α_1 and α_0 are constants, $x(k)$ is a given sequence, $\alpha_0 \neq 0$, and $y_1(k)$ and $y_2(k)$ are two linearly independent solutions of the corresponding homogeneous

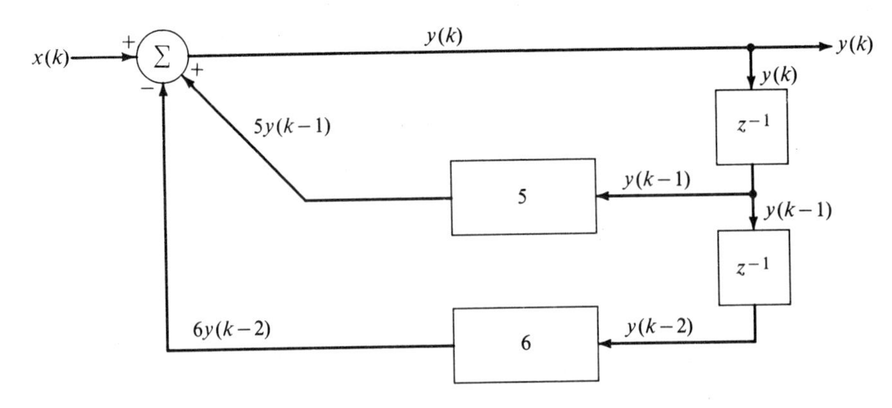

Figure 7.24 Discrete Time System

equation, is

$$y_p(k) = \sum_{n=0}^{k-1} x(n) \frac{y_1(n+1)y_2(k) - y_2(n+1)y_1(k)}{y_1(n+1)y_2(n+2) - y_2(n+1)y_1(n+2)} \tag{7.126}$$

■ **Example 7.37**

Consider the discrete time system shown in Figure 7.24. Find the general solution if the input sequence is $x(k) = 3^k$ and initial conditions are $y(0) = 1$ and $y(1) = 0$.

Solution From Figure 7.24, the controlling difference equation of the system is

$$y(k) - 5y(k-1) + 6y(k-2) = 3^k \tag{7.127}$$

The characteristic equation obtained from the corresponding homogeneous equation is

$$\lambda^2 - 5\lambda + 6 = 0$$

with roots $\lambda_1 = 2$ and $\lambda_2 = 3$. The solutions are

$$y_1(k) = 2^k \qquad y_2(k) = 3^k \tag{7.128}$$

We employ these solutions in (7.126) to determine the particular solution.

We now shift (7.125) 2 time units and (7.127) 2 time units. The shifted difference equation is

$$y(k+2) - 5y(k+1) + 6y(k) = 3^{k+2} = 9 \cdot 3^k \tag{7.129}$$

The particular solution is

$$y_p(k) = 9\sum_{n=0}^{k-1} 3^n \frac{2^{n+1}3^k - 3^{n+1}2^k}{2^{n+1}3^{n+2} - 3^{n+1}2^{n+2}} = 9\sum_{n=0}^{k-1} 3^n \frac{2^{n+1}3^k - 3^{n+1}2^k}{2^n 3^n(2 \times 3^2 - 3 \times 2^2)}$$

$$= \frac{9}{6}\left[\sum_{n=0}^{k-1} 2 \times 3^k - \sum_{n=0}^{k-1} \frac{3^{n+1}}{2^n} 2^k\right] = 9k \times 3^{k-1} - 9 \times 2^{k-1} \sum_{n=0}^{k-1} \left(\frac{3}{2}\right)^n$$

$$= 2k \times 3^k - 9 \times 2^{k-1}\left[\frac{1 - \left(\frac{3}{2}\right)^k}{1 - \left(\frac{3}{2}\right)}\right] = 3k(3)^k - 9(3^k - 2^k) \tag{7.130}$$

We note, however, that the second term of the particular solution is a linear combination of the homogeneous solutions and can thus be eliminated. The general solution is then

$$y(k) = C_1 2^k + C_2 3^k + 3k(3^k) \tag{7.131}$$

Subjecting this solution to the given initial conditions yields

$$C_1 + C_2 = 1$$
$$2C_1 + 3C_2 = 9$$

From these, we find that $C_1 = 12$ and $C_2 = -11$. The complete solution is

$$y(k) = 12(2)^k - 11(3)^k + 3k(3^k) \tag{7.132}$$

We now solve this problem by Z-transform methods. The Z-transform of (7.129) is

$$z^2 Y(z) - y(0)z^2 - y(1)z - 5zY(z) + 5y(0)z + 6Y(z) = 9\frac{z}{z-3}$$

which can be written

$$Y(z) = 9\frac{z}{(z-3)^2(z-2)} + \frac{z^2}{(z-3)(z-2)} - 5\frac{z}{(z-3)(z-2)}$$

The terms on the right are expanded as follows:

$$9\frac{z}{(z-3)^2(z-2)} = 9\frac{z}{z-2} - 12\frac{z}{z-3} + 3\frac{z^2}{(z-3)^2}$$

$$\frac{z^2}{(z-3)(z-2)} = 3\frac{z}{z-3} - 2\frac{z}{z-2}$$

$$-\frac{5z}{(z-3)(z-2)} = -5\frac{z}{z-3} + 5\frac{z}{z-2}$$

By Table 7.1, these yield

$$\mathscr{Z}^{-1}\{Y(z)\} = y(k) = 9 \times 2^k - 12 \times 3^k + 3(k+1)3^k$$
$$+3 \times 3^k - 2 \times 2^k - 5 \times 3^k + 5 \times 2^k$$
$$= 12 \times 2^k - 11 \times 3^k + 3k \times 3^k$$

which is (7.132) as anticipated. ■

Method of Undetermined Coefficients

Another method for finding the particular solution of a nonhomogeneous equation is the method of **undetermined coefficients**. This method is particularly efficient for input functions that are linear combinations of the following:

1. k^n, where n is a positive integer or zero.
2. β^k, where β is a nonzero constant.
3. $\cos \gamma k$, where γ is a nonzero constant.
4. $\sin \gamma k$, where γ is a nonzero constant.
5. A product of two or more sequences of these four types.

This method works because any derivative of the input function $x(k)$ is also possible as a linear combination of functions of the five types listed. For example, the function $2k^2$ or any derivative of $2k^2$ is a linear combination of the sequences k^2, k, and 1, all of which are of type 1. Hence, what is required in any case is the appropriate sequences for which any derivative of the input function $x(k)$ can be constructed by a linear combination of these sequences. Clearly, if $x(k) = \cos 3k$, the appropriate sequences are $\cos 3k$ and $\sin 3k$. The following examples clarify these ideas.

■ **Example 7.38**

Deduce the particular solution to Example 7.37.

Solution Since 3^k is a solution of the homogeneous equation, we assume a solution of the form $y_p(k) = Ak \times 3^k$. Substitute this assumed solution into (7.127), which yields

$$Ak \times 3^k - 5A(k-1)3^{k-1} + 6A(k-2)3^{k-2} = 3^k$$

from which

$$\frac{3}{9} A3^k = 3^k$$

Hence, $A = 3$, and the particular solution is $y_p(k) = 3k \times 3^k$, as already found. ■

■ **Example 7.39**

Find the particular solution for the system shown in Figure 7.25.

Solution Note that this system is the system of Figure 7.24 with a driving function $2.5 \times 5^k + 2^k$. The defining difference equation is

$$y(k) - 5y(k-1) + 6y(k-2) = 2.5 \times 5^k + 2^k \quad \textbf{(7.133)}$$

As found in Example 7.37, the roots of the characteristic equation are $\lambda_1 = 2$ and $\lambda_2 = 3$; hence, the general solution to the homogeneous equation is

$$y_p(k) = C_1 2^k + C_2 3^k \quad \textbf{(7.134)}$$

Observe that $x(k)$ is a linear combination of two sequences of type 2,

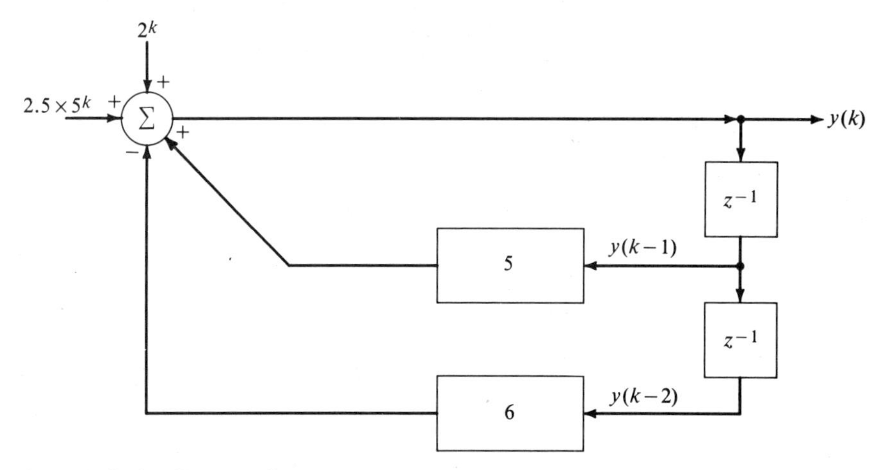

Figure 7.25 Second-Order Discrete System

namely, 2^k and 5^k. However, 2^k is already a solution to the homogeneous equation, which suggests that we choose $k2^k$ as one sequence. Thus, we try, as a particular solution,

$$y_p(k) = A5^k + Bk2^k \tag{7.135}$$

where the constants A and B are undetermined coefficients. These constants can be found by substituting (7.135) into (7.133). When this is done, we obtain

$$A5^k + Bk2^k - 5[A5^{k-1} + B(k-1)2^{k-1}] + 6[A5^{k-2} + B(k-2)2^{k-2}] = 2.5 \times 5^k + 2^k$$

Rearranging terms, we have

$$\left(A - 5A \times \frac{1}{5} + 6A \times \frac{1}{25}\right)5^k + \left(Bk + \frac{5B - 5Bk}{2} + \frac{6Bk - 12B}{4}\right)2^k = 2.5 \times 5^k + 2^k$$

By equating coefficients of similar terms, we find that

$$A = \frac{62.5}{6} \qquad B = -2$$

The particular solution is, therefore,

$$y_p(k) = \frac{62.5}{6} \times 5^k - 2k2^k \tag{7.136}$$

■

■ **Example 7.40**

Find the particular solution of the nonhomogeneous equation

$$y(k) - y(k-2) = 5k^2 \tag{7.137}$$

Table 7.6 Method of Undetermined Coefficients

$x(k)$	$y_p(k)$
k^n	$A_1 k^n + A_2 k^{n-1} + \cdots + A_n k + A_{n+1}$
β^k	$A\beta^k$
$\cos \gamma k$ or $\sin \gamma k$	$A_1 \sin \gamma k + A_2 \cos \gamma k$
$k^n \beta^k$	$\beta^k(A_1 k^n + A_2 k^{n-1} + \cdots + A_n k + A_{n+1})$
$\beta^k \sin \gamma k$ or $\beta^k \cos \gamma k$	$\beta^k(A_1 \sin \gamma k + A_2 \cos \gamma k)$

Solution The roots of the characteristic equation are readily found to be $\lambda_1 = 1$ and $\lambda_2 = -1$. Thus, the solution to the homogeneous equation is

$$y_h(k) = C_1(1)^k + C_2(-1)^k$$

We observe that the function $5k^2$ and its derivatives can be found by the linear combination of sequences k^2, k, and 1. However, 1 is a solution of the homogeneous equation; so, we choose as a trial solution k times the sequences k^2, k, and 1:

$$y_p(k) = Ak^3 + Bk^2 + Ck \tag{7.138}$$

Substitute this trial solution into (7.137) and equate coefficients of like-power terms. The coefficients are found to be $A = 5/6$, $B = 5/2$, and $C = 5/3$. ■

Table 7.6 gives the suggested forms for the particular solutions for a specified $x(k)$.

■ **Example 7.41** ***Solid State***

A set of atoms in a one-dimensional lattice is spaced a distance d apart. Refer to Figure 7.26a to develop the difference equation for the system and solve the equation if the displacements of the first $k = 0$ and the last $k = K + 1$ atoms are zero. A constant force is applied to all the atoms.

Solution From the figure, it is evident that the kth atom will experience a force towards the axis

$$f(k) = -\frac{T}{d}\{[y(k) - y(k-1)] + [y(k) - y(k+1)]\}$$

or

$$y(k+1) - 2y(k) + y(k-1) = \frac{d}{T} f(k) \tag{7.139}$$

where T is the tension due to atomic forces holding the atoms to their equilibrium points. In the continuous case, the force is equal to $m(d^2y/dt^2)$ (Newton's law).

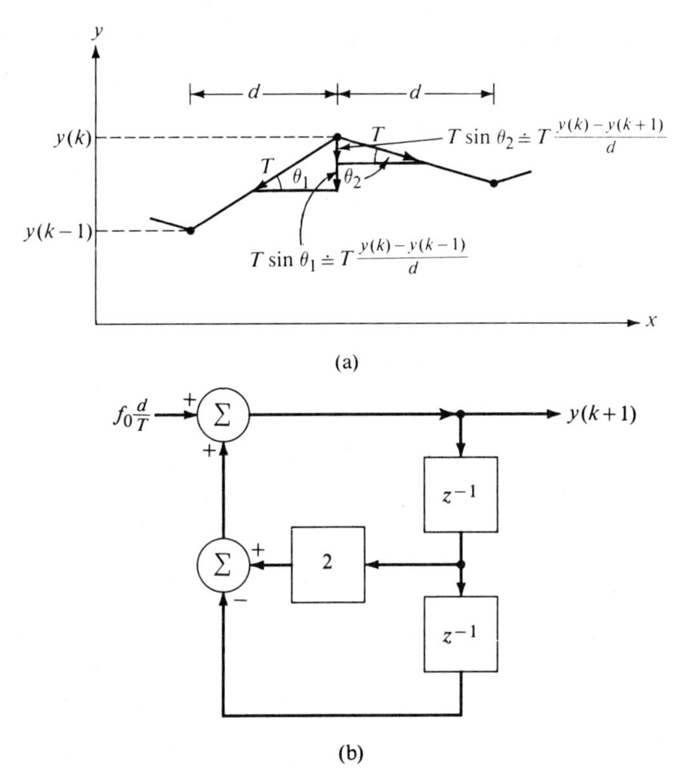

Figure 7.26 Three Adjacent Atoms in a Lattice

For a constant force $f(k) = f_0$ applied to each atom, (7.139) becomes

$$y(k+1) - 2y(k) + y(k-1) = \frac{f_0 d}{T} \quad \textbf{(7.140)}$$

A block diagram representation of this equation is given in Figure 7.26b. The homogeneous second-order equation is found to have a double root: $\lambda_1 = \lambda_2 = 1$. The solution to the homogeneous equation is

$$y_h(k) = C_1 + C_2 k \quad \textbf{(7.141)}$$

Since 1 and k are solutions of the homogeneous equation, we try, as a particular solution,

$$y_p(k) = Ak^2 \quad \textbf{(7.142)}$$

Substitute this trial solution into (7.140), which verifies it to be the appropriate form with

$$A = \frac{f_0 d}{2T} \quad \textbf{(7.143)}$$

Therefore, the general solution of (7.140) is

$$y(k) = C_1 + C_2 k + \frac{f_0 d}{2T} k^2 \tag{7.144}$$

An application of the boundary conditions leads to $C_1 = 0$ and $C_2 = -(f_0 d/2T)(K + 1)$. The final general solution is

$$y(k) = \frac{f_0 d}{2T} k^2 - \frac{f_0 d}{2T}(K + 1)k = -\frac{f_0 d}{2T}(K + 1 - k)k \qquad 0 \le k \le K + 1 \tag{7.145}$$

where K is the total number of atoms. ■

Problems

Section 7.1

1. Write $X(z)$ for the sequences $\{x(k)\}$ shown in Figure 7.27.

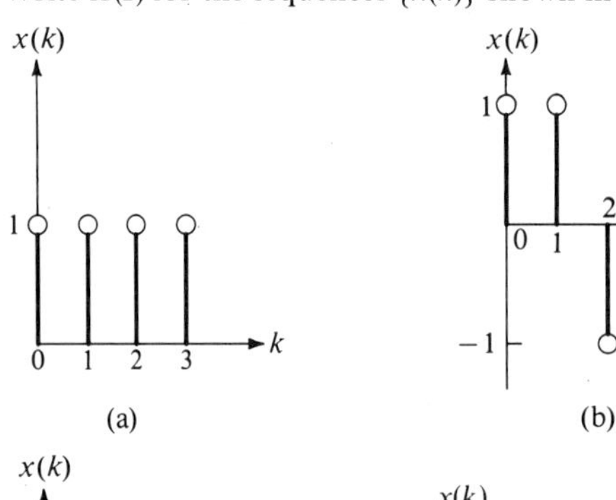

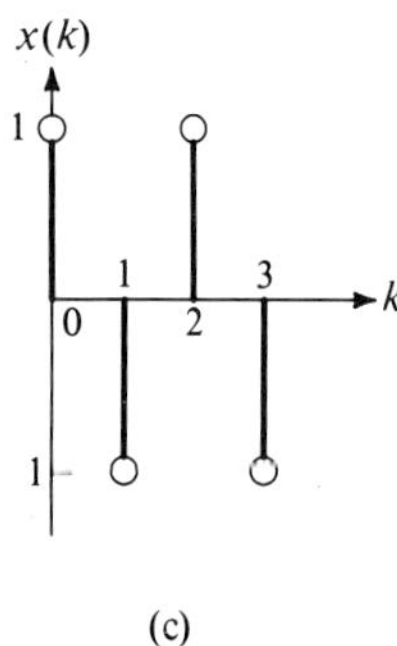

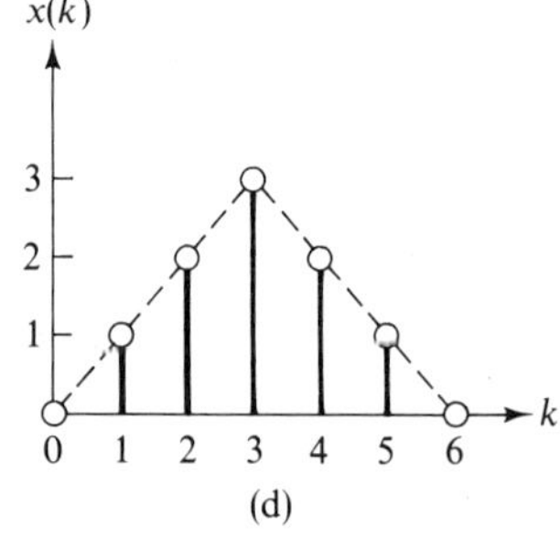

Figure 7.27

2. Determine the Z-transforms of the following sequences:

a. $f(k) = \begin{cases} (\frac{1}{2})^k & k = 0, 1, 2, \ldots \\ 0 & k \text{ negative} \end{cases}$

b. $f(k) = \begin{cases} 0 & k \le 0 \\ -1 & k = 1 \\ a^k & k = 2, 3, \ldots \end{cases}$

c. $f(t) = \begin{cases} 0 & t < 0 \\ t^2 & t \geq 0, \text{ sampled every } T \text{ seconds} \end{cases}$

3. Find the time sequences $\{f(k)\}$ corresponding to the following z-domain functions:

   a. $\dfrac{z^2}{(z-1)(z-2)}$ b. $\dfrac{z+4}{(z-2)^2}$ c. $\dfrac{3z^4 - 3z^3 + 6z^2 + 4z + 7}{z(z^2 - 6z + 9)}$

4. Find the Z-transform of the following functions:

   a. $\delta(k)$ b. $\delta(k - k_0)$, where k_0 is a positive integer

5. Determine the Z-transform of the following functions:

   a. $f(k) = 2\delta(k) + 3\delta(k-1) + 2\delta(k-2)$

   b. $f(k) = 2\delta(k-2) + 4\delta(k-4)$

   c. $f(k) = \{1, -a, a^2, -a^3, a^4, -a^5, \ldots\} = \{(-a)^k\}$

Section 7.2

6. Find the Z-transforms and their region of convergence and plot the pole-zero configurations of the sequences given for $k \geq 0$.

   a. $\{y(k)\} = 1 + k$ b. $\{y(k)\} = k^2$ c. $\{y(k)\} = a^k + a^{-k}$ $a > 1$ d. $\{y(k)\} = e^{jk\theta}$

7. Determine the Z-transform of the function

$$y(k) = \begin{cases} a^k \cos kb & k \geq 0, a > 0 \\ 0 & k < 0 \end{cases}$$

   Indicate the regions of convergence and divergence and show the zeros and poles on the z-plane.

8. Determine the Z-transforms and their regions of convergence and plot the pole configurations of the following sequences:

   a. $y(k) = \begin{cases} 2 & k = 0, 1, 2, 3, 4 \\ 3^k & k = 5, 6, \ldots \end{cases}$

   b. $y(k) = \left(\dfrac{1}{3}\right)^k + \left(\dfrac{1}{4}\right)^k \quad k = 0, 1, 2, \ldots$

9. Determine the Z-transform and the region of convergence and plot the pole-zero configuration of the following sequence:

$$y(k) = \begin{cases} 2^k & 0 \leq k \leq 5 \\ 0 & \text{otherwise} \end{cases}$$

10. Show that the region of convergence of the sequence $y(k) = a(b)^k$ for $k = 0, 1, 2, \ldots$ depends only on b.

11. Determine the Z-transform and the region of convergence of the sequence $y(k) = e^{j\omega k}$ for $k = 0, 1, 2, \ldots$.

12. Determine the Z-transforms of the following functions when sampled every T seconds:

    a. $\cos \omega t\, u(t)$ b. $a^t \sin \omega t\, u(t)$ c. $a^t \cos \omega t\, u(t)$

    d. $e^{-at} \sin \omega t\, u(t)$ e. $e^{-at} \cos \omega t\, u(t)$ f. $a^t u(t)$

13. Determine the Z-transforms and the region of convergence of the following functions that are sampled every T seconds:

    a. $e^{-at}u(t)$ a is a real number. b. $[u(t) - u(t - 4T)]$

Section 7.3

14. Generalize (7.33) and show that $\mathscr{Z}\{k^n y(k)\} = [-z(d/dz)]^n Y(z)$.

15. Two sequences are given. Determine their Z-transforms, their regions of convergence, and their pole-zero configuration. Compare the two results and state your observations. **a.** $y(k) = 2e^{-k}$, $k = 0, 1, 2, \ldots$ **b.** $y(k) = 2e^{-(k-2)}u(k-2)$, $k = 0, 1, 2, \ldots$

16. Determine the Z-transforms and the regions of convergence of the following sequences: **a.** $y(k) = e^{\pm j\omega_0 k}x(k)$ **b.** $y(k) = z_0^k x(k)$.

17. Deduce the Z-transform of the sequence shown in Figure 7.28 and compare the pole-zero configurations between $u(k)$ and $y_{(1)}(k)$.

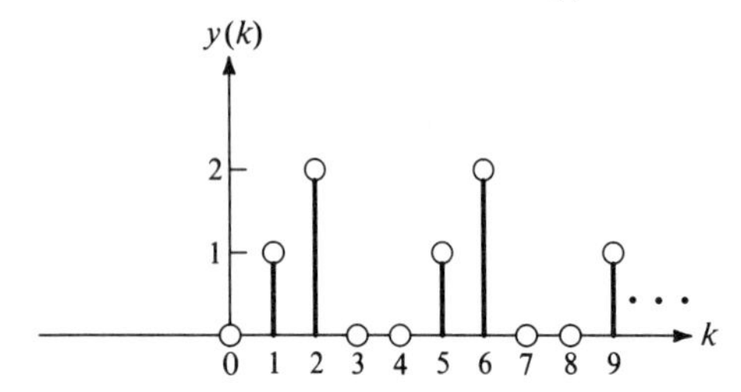

Figure 7.28

18. Given the relationship $\mathscr{Z}\{u(k)\} = 1/(1 - z^{-1})$, use (7.33) to obtain the inverse transform of $Y(z) = z^{-1}/(1 - z^{-1})^2$.

19. Prove that the operation of convolution is commutative; hence, we have the following: $y(k) = \sum_{n=0}^{k} h(k-n)x(n) = \sum_{n=0}^{k} h(n)z(k-n)$.

20. Deduce the Z-transform of the output $y(k)$ of the system shown in Figure 7.29 if the input is a unit step function $u(k)$ and $h_3(k) = 0.5^k u(k)$.

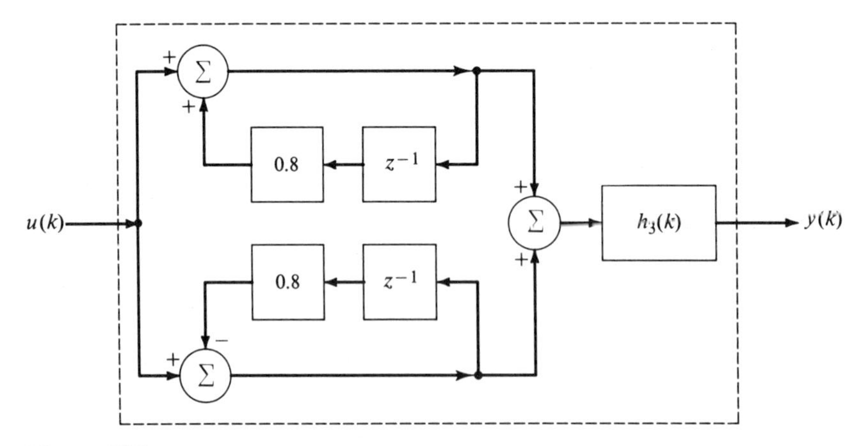

Figure 7.29

21. Use the convolution theorem to find the voltage output of the system shown in Figure 7.30 for an input current $i(k) = e^{-0.2k}$ for $k = 0, 1, 2, \ldots$. Compare these results with the results for the corresponding continuous time case.

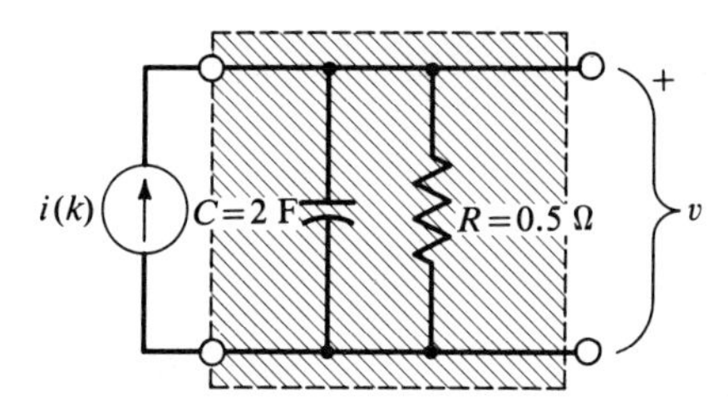

Figure 7.30

22. Show that the Z-transform of the function $y(t)u(t)$ sampled every T seconds and shifted to the right by mT seconds is $\mathscr{Z}\{y(kT - mT)u(kT - mT)\} = z^{-m}\sum_{k=0}^{\infty} y(kT)e^{-k} = z^{-m}Y(z)$.
23. Deduce the Z-transform of the shifted function $(kT - 2T)[u(kT - 2T) - u(kT - 5T)]$.
24. Show that the Z-transform of the function $y(t)u(t)$ sampled every T seconds and shifted to the left by mT seconds is $\mathscr{Z}\{y(kT + mT)u(kT + mT)\} = z^{m}[Y(z) - \sum_{k=0}^{m-1} y(kT)z^{-k}]$.
25. Determine the Z-transform of the output of the system shown in Figure 7.31.

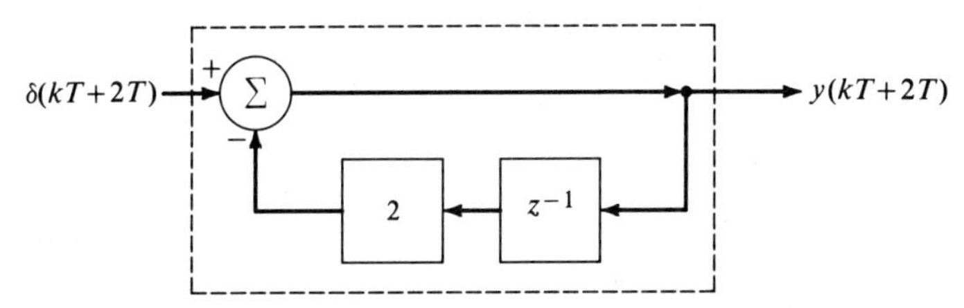

Figure 7.31

26. Deduce the Z-transform of the following functions using the time-scaling property:
    a. $a^k e - \alpha_k u(k)$ **b.** $a^k \cos k\omega\, u(k)$ **c.** $ka^k u(k)$
    d. $a^k e - \alpha_k \sin k\omega u(k)$
27. Show that the Z-transform of the function $y(t) = a^t y(t)u(t)$ sampled every T seconds (time-scaling property of sampled signals) is $\mathscr{Z}\{a^{kT} y(kT)u(kT)\} = Y(a^{-T}z)$.
28. Determine the Z-transform of the sequences shown in Figure 7.32.

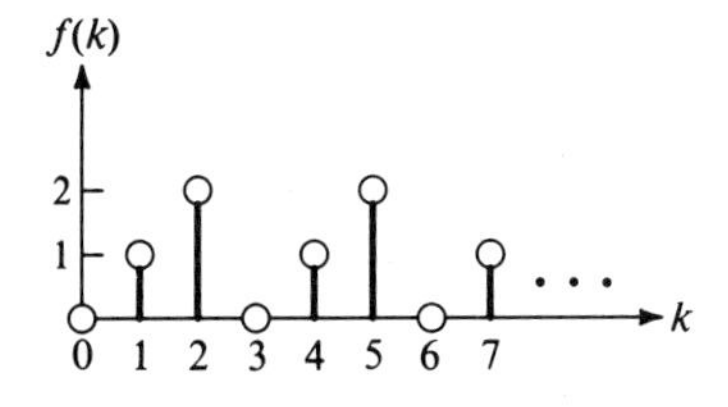

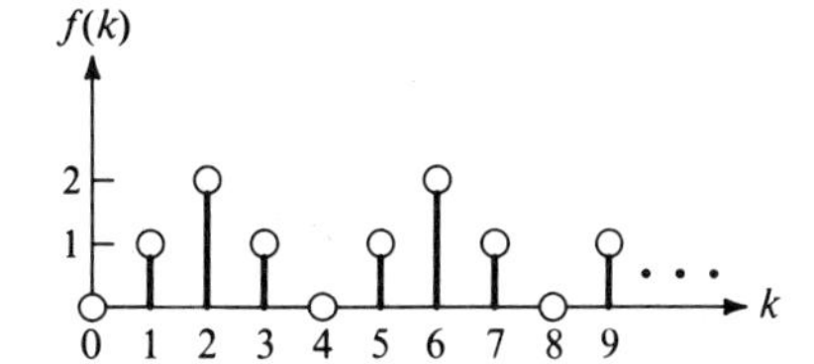

Figure 7.32

29. Show that the Z-transform of the function $u(t) = ty(t)u(t)$ sampled every T seconds is $\mathscr{Z}\{(kT)y(kT)u(kT)\} = -Tz[dY(z)/dz]$; $Y(z) = \sum_{k=0}^{\infty} y(kT)z^{-k}$.
30. Use the results of Problem 29 to deduce the Z-transforms of the following functions:
    a. $kTu(kT)$ **b.** $(kT)^2 u(kT)$ **c.** $kT(kT + 1)u(kT)$
    d. $kT(kT - 1)u(kT)$

31. Show that the initial and final values of a sampled function $y(t)$ are given by

a. $y(k_0 T) = z^{k_0} Y(z)\Big|_{z \to \infty} \qquad Y(z) = \sum_{k=0}^{\infty} y[(k_0 + k)T]z^{-k}$

b. $\lim_{k \to \infty} y(kT) = \lim_{z \to 1}(z - 1)Y(z) \qquad Y(z) = \sum_{k=0}^{\infty} y(kT)z^{-k}$

32. Show that the Z-transform of the convolution of two sampled functions is given by $\mathscr{Z}\{y(kT)\} \triangleq \mathscr{Z}\{h(kT) * x(kT)\} = H(z)X(z)$.

33. Determine the response of the system shown in Figure 7.33 in discrete form. Assume $T = 0.5$. Comment on the similarities and differences between the results of this problem and those of Example 7.15. Use the convolution theorem of the input–output relationship of LTI systems.

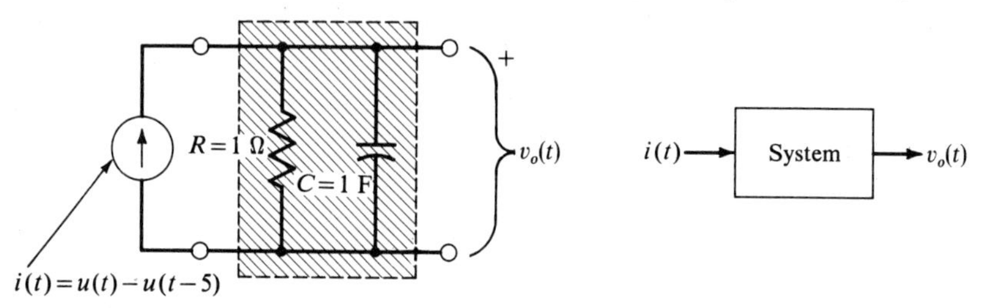

Figure 7.33

34. Using the right-shifting property, determine the discrete time function $y(k)$ if its Z-transform is $Y(z) = 1/(c - z)$.

Section 7.4

35. Deduce the functions $f(k)$ specified by the following one-sided Z-transforms. Employ fraction expansions.

a. $1/[(1 - z^{-1})(1 - 2z^{-1})]$ **b.** $z^{-1}/[(2 - z^{-1})^2]$ **c.** $[z^2(z + 2)]/(z^2 + 4z + 3)$

Section 7.5

36. Determine the inverse functions for the following Z-transforms:

a. $z/[(z - 1)(z - 2)] \quad 1 < |z| < 2$ **b.** $z^2/[(z - 1)^2(z - 2)] \quad 1 < |z| < 2$

c. $z^3/[(z - 1)(z - 2)^2] \quad 1 < |z| < 2$ **d.** Repeat part (c) for the entire region $|z| > 1$.

37. Find the inverse Z-transform of the function $F(z) = (z^2 - 3z + 8)/[(z - 2)(z + 2)(z + 3)]$ for $3 < |z| < 2$ and for $2 < |z| < 3$.

38. Determine the inverse Z-transform of the function $F(z) = (z \sin \alpha)/[z^2 - (2 \cos \alpha)z + 1]$ for $|z| > 1$.

39. Deduce the inverse transforms of the following functions:

a. $(z + 2)/[z^2(z - 1)]$ **b.** $(z^3 + 2z^2 + z + 1)/(z^3 + z^2 - 5z + 3)$

40. Derive the Z-transforms of the sequences shown in Figure 7.34 and then deduce the inverse transforms.

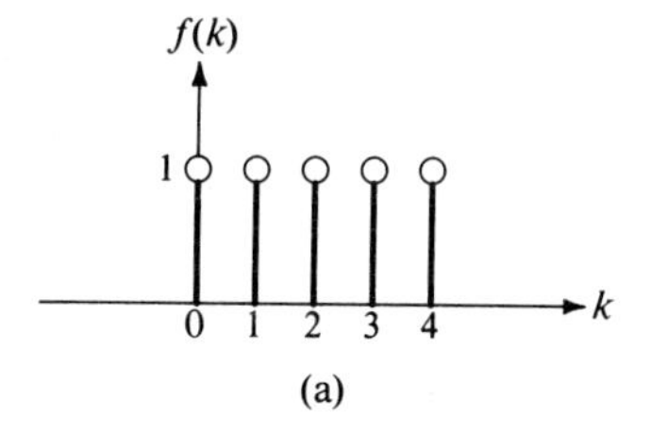

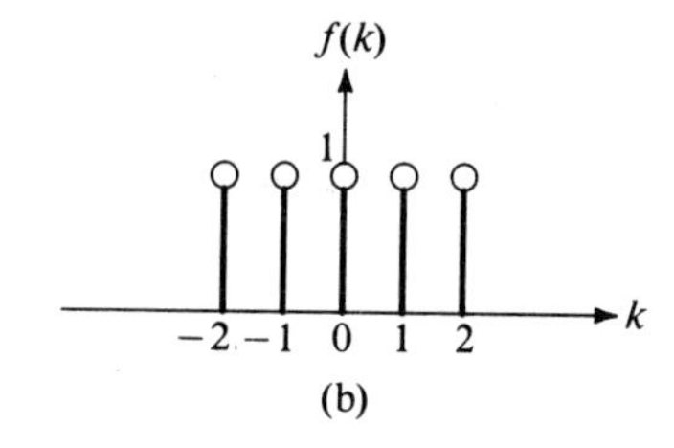

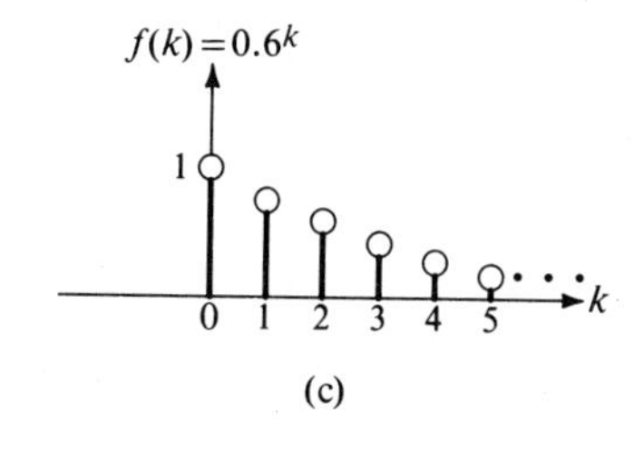

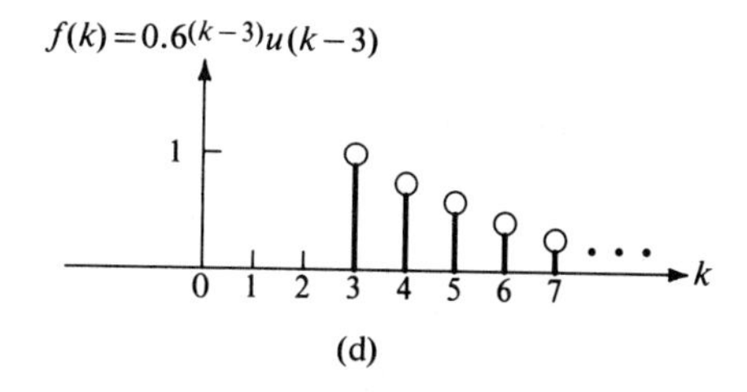

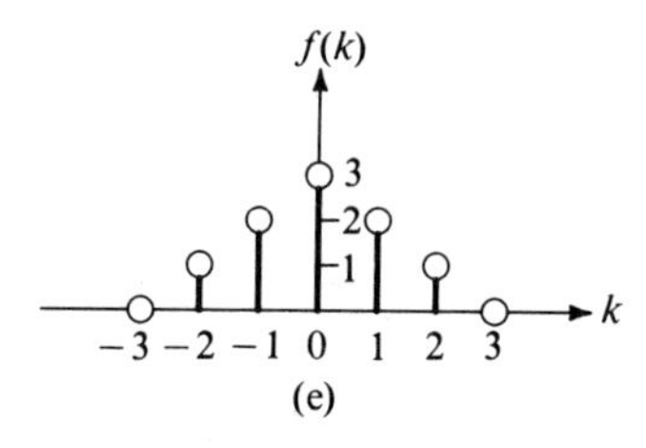

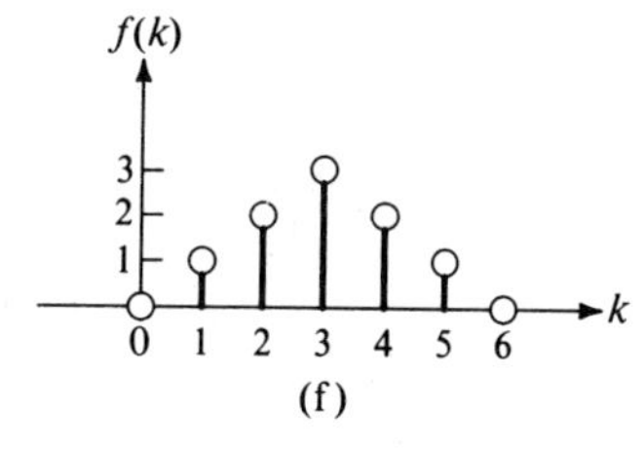

Figure 7.34

41. Deduce the inverse Z-transform of the following functions:
a. $(18z^2 - 12z)/[(z-3)(z-1)]$ **b.** $z^2/[(z-2)(z-1)^2]$

Section 7.6

42. A discrete time system function is

$$H(z) = \frac{2(3 - z^{-1})}{1 - 2z^{-1} + z^{-2}}$$

The input is the signal specified by $x(0) = 0$, $x(1) = 1$, $x(2) = 2$, and $x(3) = 0$. Determine $y(k)$.

43. A discrete time system function is

$$H(z) = \frac{2 + z^{-1}}{1 + 3z^{-1} + z^{-2}}$$

The input is the unit step sequence $u(k)$. Determine the system response.

44. A system is described by its system function

$$H(z) = \frac{\alpha_1 z}{z - \beta_1} + \frac{\alpha_2 z}{z - \beta_2}$$

β_1 and β_2 are real and have magnitudes less than unity. Show three block diagram configurations that have this $H(z)$.

45. Find the transfer functions of the systems shown in Figure 7.35.

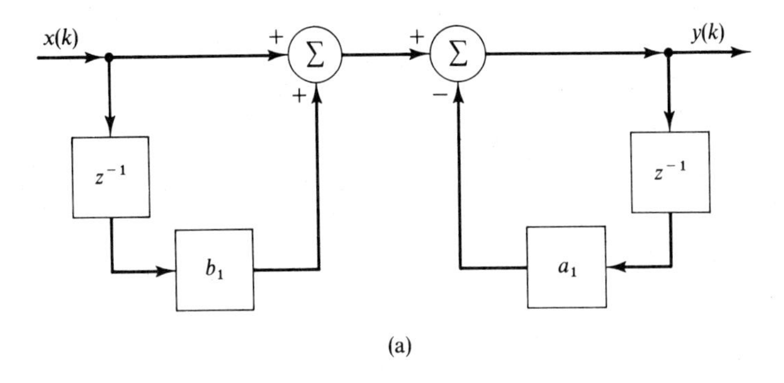

(a)

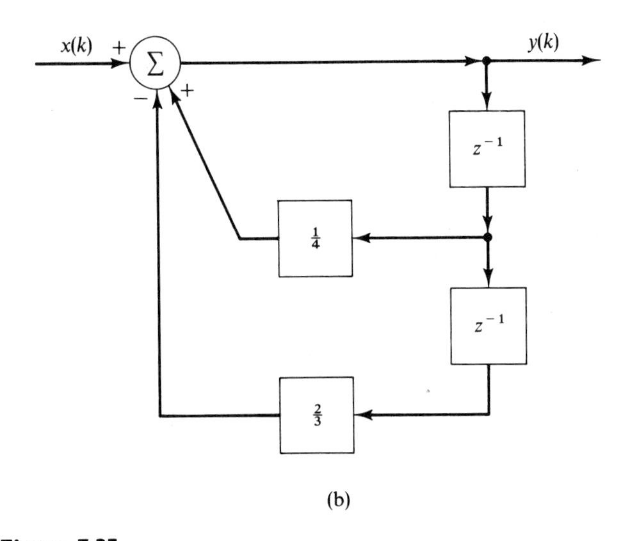

(b)

Figure 7.35

Section 7.7

46. Sketch the general shape of $H(e^{j\omega})$ as a function of ω given

$$H(z) = \frac{(z^2 + 1)(z^2 - 1)}{z^4 + 0.8}$$

47. Find the frequency response of the systems shown in Figure 7.36.

48. A system is defined by the difference equation $y(k) = \alpha_y(k - 1) + (1 - \alpha)x(k)$. Determine the response of the system to the input signal

$$x(k) = \begin{cases} \sin k\omega T & k = 0, 1, 2, \ldots \\ 0 & k < 0 \end{cases}$$

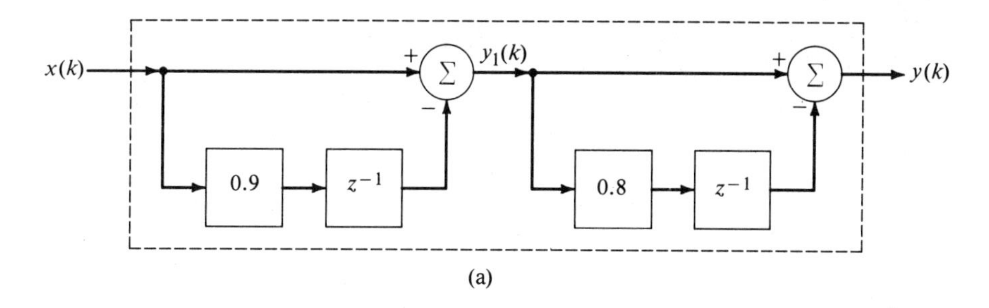

(a)

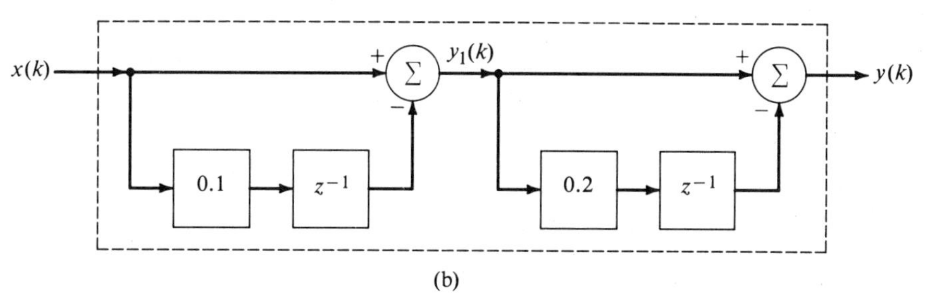

(b)

Figure 7.36

Section 7.8

49. A system is described by the difference equation $y(k) + 3y(k-1) + 5y(k-2) = x(k-2) - 2x(k-1)$.

a. The input sequence is $\{x(k)\} = 3^k$. Write the Z-transform of the system.

b. Deduce the system function.

c. If the initial conditions are zero, determine the output response.

50. A system is described by the difference equation $y(k+3) - 5y(k+2) + 2y(k+1) + 7y(k) = x(k+2)$. With $x(k) = 0$ for $k > 0$, $y(0) = 0$, $y(1) = 1$, and $y(2) = 5$, determine the output for $k \geq 1$.

51. **a.** Deduce the voltage equation for the ladder network shown in Figure 7.37.

b. Assume that all the resistors have resistances equal to 1 Ω. Deduce the voltage $v(k)$ for $k = 0, 1, 2, \ldots$.

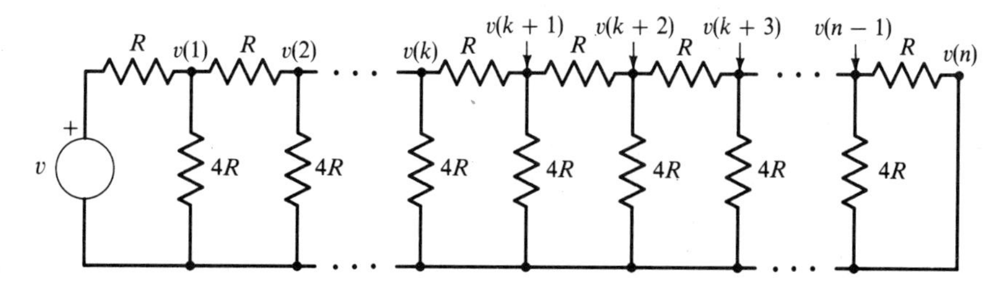

Figure 7.37

52. Use Z-transform techniques to determine the solution to the following difference equations and state your observations:

a. $3y(k) + 2y(k-1) = 5u(k-1) \qquad y(-1) = 0$

b. $3y(k+1) + 2y(k) = 5u(k) \qquad y(0) = 0$

53. Use Z-transform techniques to find the solution to the following difference equations ($k > 0$) and zero initial conditions:

a. $v(k+1) + v(k) = -2$

b. $y(k+1) + y(k) = 2\sin(k\pi/4)$

c. $y(k+2) - y(k) = 9$

d. $y(k+2) - 7y(k+1) + 10y(k) = 2^k$

54. Refer to the system shown in Figure 7.38. Deduce the zero-state response and the zero-input response. Also, find its transfer function. Use appropriate substitutions to create an analogous discrete system. With a sampling time $T = 0.2$, an input function $f(t) = e^{-t}u(t)$, and initial condition $v(0) = 1$, determine the output $v(0.2k)$. Determine the impulse response function $h(k)$.

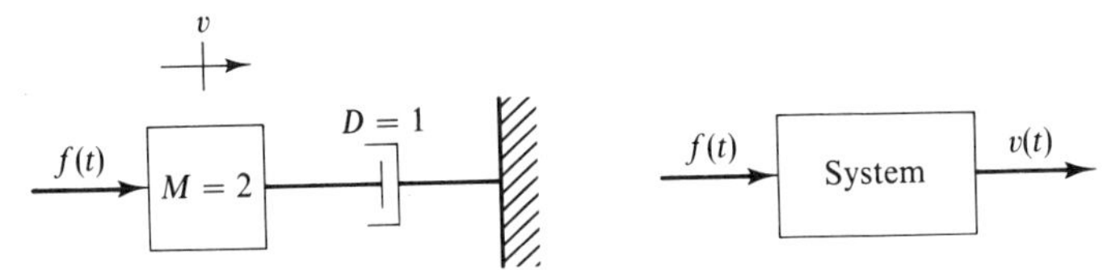

Figure 7.38

Section 7.9

55. Verify (7.86).

56. Determine the matrix $(\mathbf{M}^T)^k$ of Example 7.33 and interpret your results.

57. ***Telephone Communications.*** A local switch on a telephone has two states: on and off. The on state is state 1; the off position is state 2. Further, we note that if the system is occupied for 1 time unit (3 minutes), it will remain occupied for the next time unit with probability 1/4 and unoccupied with probability 3/4. However, if the unit is unoccupied (state 2), it will remain in state 2 with probability 1/8 and return to state 1 with probability 7/8. If the initial state is $\mathbf{x}_0 = [1 \quad 0]^T$, determine its state at time unit k.

58. Use Z-transform methods to deduce the output of the system specified by

$$\begin{bmatrix} x_1(k+1) \\ x_2(k+1) \end{bmatrix} = \begin{bmatrix} 0 & 1 \\ 0 & 3 \end{bmatrix} \begin{bmatrix} x_1(k) \\ x_2(k) \end{bmatrix} + \begin{bmatrix} 0 \\ 1 \end{bmatrix} u(k)$$

$$y(k) = [1 \quad 0] \begin{bmatrix} x_1(k) \\ x_2(k) \end{bmatrix}$$

Assume zero initial conditions.

Section 7.10

59. Solve the homogeneous equations.

a. $y(k+2) - 3y(k+1) + 2y(k) = 0 \qquad y(0) = 2,\ y(1) = 4$

b. $y(k+2) - 8y(k+1) + 15y(k) = 0 \qquad y(0) = 0,\ y(1) = 1$

60. Solve the homogeneous equations.

a. $y(k) - 3y(k-1) + 2y(k-2) = 0 \qquad y(-2) = 2,\ y(-1) = 4$

b. $y(k) - 8y(k-1) + 15y(k-2) = 0 \qquad y(-2) = 0,\ y(-1) = 1$

61. Solve the homogeneous equations.
a. $y(k) - 7y(k-1) + 10y(k-2) = 0 \qquad y(-2) = 0,\ y(-1) = 1$
b. $y(k) + 6y(k-1) + 18y(k-2) = 0 \qquad y(-2) = 0,\ y(-1) = 1$

62. Solve the equations given in Problem 60 using Z-transform methods.

63. ***Fibonacci Numbers.*** The sequence 1, 1, 2, 3, 5, 8, 13, ... is called the **Fibonacci sequence.** Observe that after the second element, each term is the sum of the two preceding terms. Therefore, if $y(k)$ denotes the kth term in the sequence, we know the Fibonacci sequence is the unique solution of the initial value problem $y(k+2) = y(k+1) + y(k)$, where $k = 1, 2, 3, \ldots$, $y(0) = 0$, and $y(1) = 1$. Show that the solution is

$$y(k) = \frac{1}{\sqrt{5}}\left[\left(\frac{1+\sqrt{5}}{2}\right)^k - \left(\frac{1-\sqrt{5}}{2}\right)^k\right]$$

64. Determine the distance traveled by the system shown in Figure 7.39 if $x(0) = 0$ and $x(1) = 1$ with the sampling time $T = 1$. Use Z-transform methods.

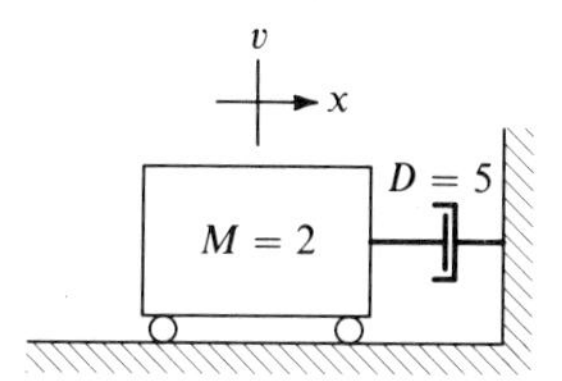

Figure 7.39

65. ***Population Model.*** A pair of adult rabbits (2 months old or older) is assumed to produce a pair of rabbits every month. Every new pair of rabbits is assumed to follow the same sequence. How many pairs will there be after k months if we begin (initial condition) with a pair of newborn rabbits? (This is the Fibonacci rabbit problem.)

66. Use Z-transform methods to solve the following difference equations:
a. $y(k+1) - y(k) = 2^k \quad y(0) = 1$ **b.** $y(k+1) - 3y(k) = 2 \quad y(0) = 0$
c. $y(k+1) + 3y(k) = -2 \quad y(0) = 1$ **d.** $y(k+1) - y(k) = 2k \quad y(0) = 0$

67. Use Z-transform techniques to solve the following difference equations:
a. $y(k+2) - 8y(k+1) + 15y(k) = 5 \times 2^k \quad y(0) = y(1) = 0$
b. $y(k+2) - y(k) = 3 \quad y(0) = y(1) = 0$

68. ***National Income.**** A national income model is given by the equation $n(k) = c(k) + i(k) + g(k)$, where $c(k)$ = consumer expenditures, $i(k)$ = induced private investment, and $g(k)$ = government expenditure. A well-known economist specifies that $c(k) = an(k-1)$ and $i(k) = b[c(k) - c(k-1)] = ab[n(k-1) - n(k-2)]$, where a and b are constants (a is referred to as the *marginal propensity to consume*). Thus, at any accounting period—for example, say every four months—the national income is given by $n(k) = a(1+b)n(k-1) - abn(k-2) + g(k)$. Determine the national income if $a = 1$, $b = 1$, $g(k) = u(k)$, and $n(-1) = n(-2) = 0$. Use Z-transform methods.

* From J. A. Cadzow, *Discrete Time Systems* (Englewood Cliffs, NJ: Prentice-Hall, 1973), p. 66. See also A. P. Samuelson, "Interactions Between the Multiplier Analysis and the Principle of Acceleration," *Rev. of Economic Statistics*, **21**, 1939, p. 75.

Elements of Digital Filter Design

The term *filter*, as used in this text, is a frequency-selective network designed to operate on an input signal to produce a desired output signal. That is, a filter passes signals of certain frequencies and blocks signals of other frequencies. The signals may be continuous time entities that may be stated in time or frequency terms. The signals may also be discrete time entities, and these signals, too, may be stated in time or frequency terms.

Filters are usually categorized according to their behavior in the frequency domain and are specified in terms of their magnitude and phase characteristics. Based on their magnitude or transfer response, filters are classified as low-pass, high-pass, bandpass, and bandstop. Based on phase characteristics, filters are often linear phase devices. However, ideal characteristics are not physically realizable, and a number of different approaches to filter design have been developed over the years in an effort to achieve acceptable approximations to ideal responses.

Early developments in filter design include constant-K, m-derived filters, and variants of these. These filter design techniques, known as **classical**, resulted in quite acceptable filters. Modern filter design techniques, which date from the 1930s, employ a two-step procedure. The first step is to find an analytic approximation to the specified filter characteristic as a transfer function. The second step is a physical realization of this transfer function by passive or active networks.

The digital filter design procedures presented in this chapter draw heavily on the methods of continuous frequency filter design. Therefore, the chapter begins with a review of continuous filter design and then proceeds to digital filter design.*

* This chapter follows closely Chapter 11 in A. D. Poularikas and S. Seely, *Signals and Systems* (Boston: PWS-KENT Publishing Co., 1985).

8.1 General Aspects of Filters

The four categories of filters—low-pass, high-pass, bandpass, and bandstop—are illustrated in Figure 8.1 in terms of their ideal response performances. Well-developed procedures exist for approximating these response characteristics and involve such functions as Butterworth, Chebyshev, elliptic, and others. The use of these functions has the advantage that the formulas for them are well established and design tables are available.

The filter design process can vary considerably depending on the service for which the filter is intended. Filters in the simplest class are often called "brute force" filters and include the simple shunt C, series L, RC or LC-type filters. These filters are used for filtering the ac ripple components produced when a power supply rectifier is employed to convert ac into dc. Here, the filter requirement is to permit the dc to pass unimpeded while attenuating the ac ripple components produced in the rectification process. These filters are essentially low-pass devices with cutoff at 0 Hz. They are not very frequency selective, but multiple sections in cascade can be used if improved ac attenuation is desired. In addition to such passive filters, an electronic regulator can be used, a unit that serves not only to maintain the output voltage at a constant level with load, but also serves to greatly reduce the ripple. From this point of view, the electronic regulator can be considered to be an active filter.

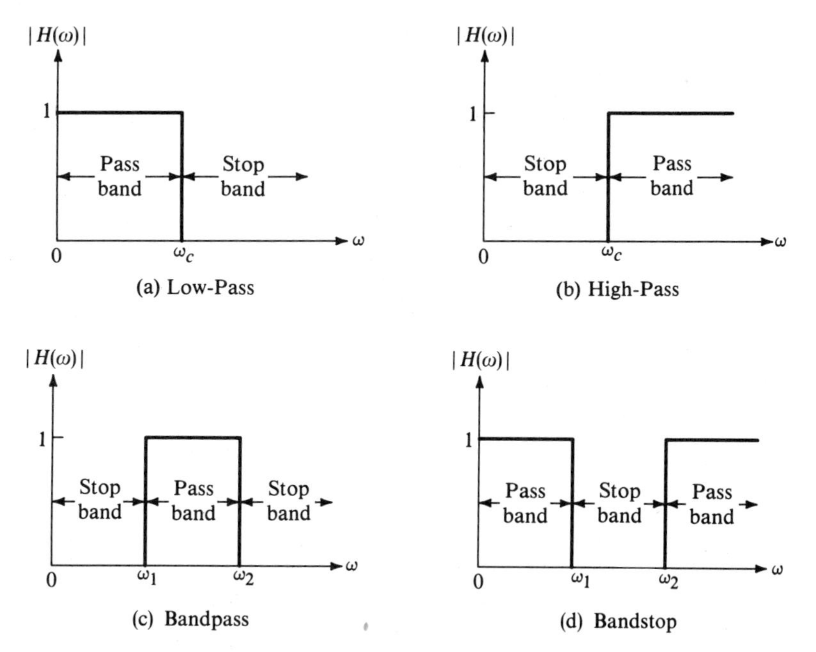

Figure 8.1 Ideal Frequency Response Characteristics of Analog Filters. (a) Low-Pass. (b) High-pass. (c) Bandpass. (d) Bandstop.

As a step in meeting our interests in digital filter design, we first study the approximation problem in the analog domain and then the means for converting from the s-plane in which the $H(s)$ approximation exists to the z-plane and the corresponding $H(z)$. The developed system function $H(z)$ can then be realized by discrete systems, either by transformation to difference equation form, which can be adapted to computer calculations, or by direct hardware implementation. The resulting difference equation can be considered to denote a digital filter approximation to the analog filter.

Converting from the analog to the digital domain involves time sampling. In these transformations, a constant sampling rate will be assumed. This requirement is not necessary, and multirate filters have been developed. In multirate filters, different sampling rates are used in various stages of the filtering operation, resulting in a multistage filter. In a multistage implementation, each step is a combined filter and sample rate change operation. Such multistage filters include decimators, interpolars, and narrow-band, low-pass filters. Often, optimization techniques provide improved flexibility in meeting certain filter specifications. Within the scope of this text, only straightforward, classical, analog-to-digital filter design procedures are considered.

From a practical point of view, the implementation of the filter on a general-purpose digital computer places accuracy constraints on the realization of the transfer function. This problem arises because the registers can contain only a finite number of binary bits at any one instant. Therefore, the filter coefficients that can be defined with infinite precision over the real number field can only be represented by a finite number of binary digits in a hardware register. As a result, filter coefficients, as well as the arithmetic performed with a digital filter, are subject to approximation errors and uncertainty. These limitations can cause the frequency response of the filter to differ measurably from the design model. The reason is that the specified filter is very sensitive to the polynomial coefficients of $H(s)$ and to the coefficients of $H(z)$ in the case of digital filters. The sensitivity of response to coefficient quantization can be large, particularly if the poles of $H(z)$ are close to the unit circle, and sensitivity considerations require attention in practical implementation practices. Narrow-band filters are particularly sensitive to coefficient word length and generally require large word length in order to meet frequency response requirements. These sources of error within a digital filter are referred to as **roundoff noise**, and methods have been developed to reduce their effect.

It is important to understand that when we talk about filters, we actually mean systems. Filters (systems) can be of diverse nature. For example, a painting is a two-dimensional optical signal (input) to our eyes. The filter (system) that processes and interprets the optical signal is our eye–brain combination, and the output is the painting that we actually see. To show that our eye–brain combination is a filter, we can perform the following simple experiment. Look at a newspaper picture at close range: Observe that it consists of black dots of different intensity plus sharp characteristics from black to white areas. Now, move the picture away at arm's length: Observe that the "sharpness" has disappeared, and the picture looks "smoother." Because the high frequencies in the optical signal do not pass through our eye–brain

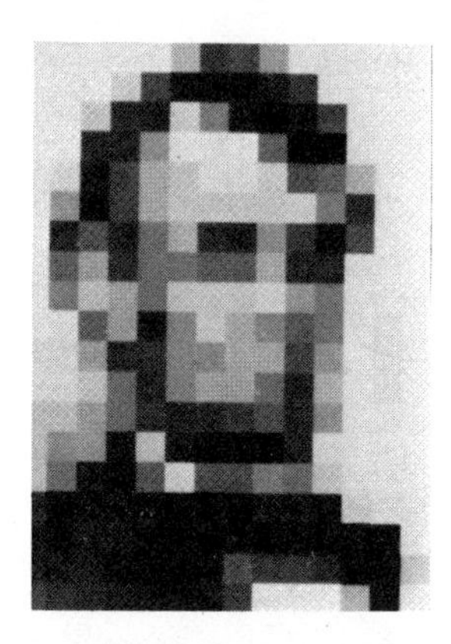

Figure 8.2 Observe the Effect of Filtering of Your Visual System by Studying the Figures When Held Several Feet Away. (Figure 1 from "Masking in Visual Recognition: Effects of Two-Dimensional Filtered Noise," Harmon, L., et al. *Science*, Vol. 180, 15 June 1973, p. 1194. Copyright 1973 by the AAAS.

filter (actually a bandpass filter), smoothing of the picture occurs. This same phenomenon was discussed in Chapter 3 when we tried to reproduce a discontinuous periodic wave by retaining only the lower-frequency components. The digitized figure in Figure 8.2 can be used as an illustration of the foregoing discussion.

Other examples of nonelectrical systems that possess filtering characteristics include the economy of the country (input = goods and services, output = gross national product); the structure of a building (input = earthquake vibrations, output = building oscillations); the heartbeat (input = message for girl or boy, output = number of heartbeats per minute); and the airplane (input = direction and speed of wind, output = direction of the flaps). From this brief discussion, it can be seen that the study of filters—electrical, mechanical, biological, chemical and so on—can be far-ranging and is most important.

8.2 Butterworth Filter

We now examine the use of the Butterworth function to approximate the low-pass filter shown in Figure 8.1a. The features of this function are illustrated graphically in Figure 8.3. In this case, our attention is limited to the **amplitude function**.

The **amplitude response** of the nth-order normalized Butterworth filter is given by

$$|H_n(j\omega)| = \frac{1}{\sqrt{1+\omega^{2n}}} \qquad n = 1, 2, 3, \ldots \tag{8.1a}$$

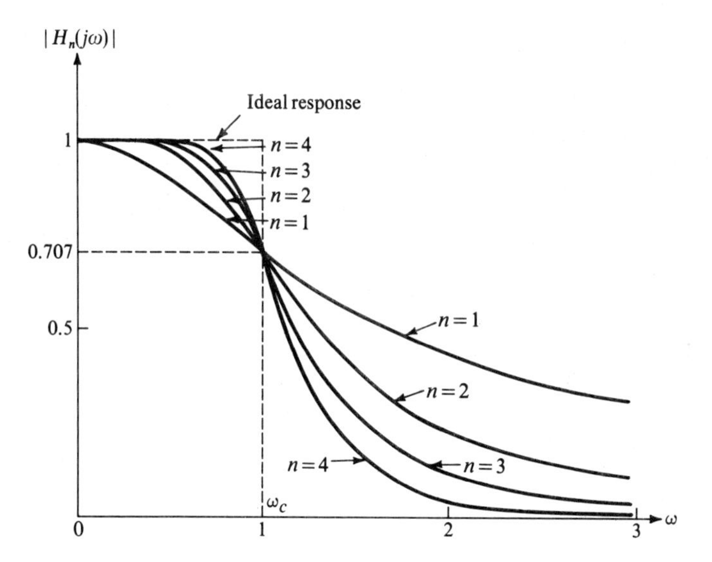

Figure 8.3 Butterworth Amplitude Response

in which it is assumed that the cutoff frequency ω_c is normalized to unity. We must always keep in mind that for a specified frequency ω, the corresponding equation is of the form

$$|H_n(j\omega)| = \frac{1}{\sqrt{1 + (\omega/\omega_c)^{2n}}} \tag{8.1b}$$

It is this form that must be used when we are asked to find the Butterworth filter in non-normalized form.

As shown in Figure 8.3, the response is monotonically decreasing with its maximum value $|H_n(j\omega)|_{\max} = 1$ at $\omega = 0$. Further, the so-called cutoff point at the normalized $\omega_c = 1$ is

$$H_n(j1) = \frac{1}{\sqrt{2}} H_n(j\omega)\bigg|_{\max} = 0.707 H_n(j\omega)\bigg|_{\max}$$

for all orders. Because the functions of all orders approach the value $H_n(j0) = 1$ smoothly without overshoots, this function is called **maximally flat**. It is observed that the approximation to the ideal square wave improves as n increases.

To obtain the transfer function form of the Butterworth filter, we make use of the fact that $H_n(j\omega) = H_n(s)|_{s=j\omega}$ and rewrite (8.1) in squared form:

$$H_n(s)H_n(-s) = \frac{1}{1 + [(j\omega)^2/j^2]^n} = \frac{1}{1 + (-s^2)^n} \tag{8.2}$$

We write the denominator polynomial in the form

$$D(s)D(-s) = 1 + (-s^2)^n \tag{8.3}$$

The roots of this function are deduced from

$$1 + (-s^2)^n = 0$$

from which it follows that

$$(-1)^n s^{2n} = -1 = e^{j(2k-1)\pi} \qquad k = 1, 2, 3, \dots 2n \tag{8.4}$$

so that

$$s^{2n} = e^{j(2k-1)\pi} e^{jn\pi}$$

The kth root is

$$s_k = \sigma_k + j\omega_k = e^{j(2k+n-1)\pi/2n} = je^{j(2k-1)\pi/2n} \tag{8.5}$$

In expanded form, this expression is

$$\boxed{s_k = -\sin\left[(2k-1)\frac{\pi}{2n}\right] + j\cos\left[(2k-1)\frac{\pi}{2n}\right]} \qquad 1 \le k \le 2n \tag{8.6}$$

It can be seen from (8.5) that the roots of s_k are on a unit circle and are spaced $\pi/2n$ radians apart. Moreover, no s_k can occur on the $j\omega$-axis since $2k - 1$ cannot be an even integer. We thus see that there are n left-half plane roots and n right-half plane roots. The left-half plane roots are associated with $H(s)$ since σ_k is negative for these roots, and the right-half plane roots are associated with $H(-s)$. These results are shown in Figure 8.4 for the case $n = 4$:

$$s_1 = e^{j5\pi/8} \qquad s_2 = e^{j7\pi/8} \qquad s_3 = e^{j9\pi/8} \qquad s_4 = e^{j11\pi/8}$$

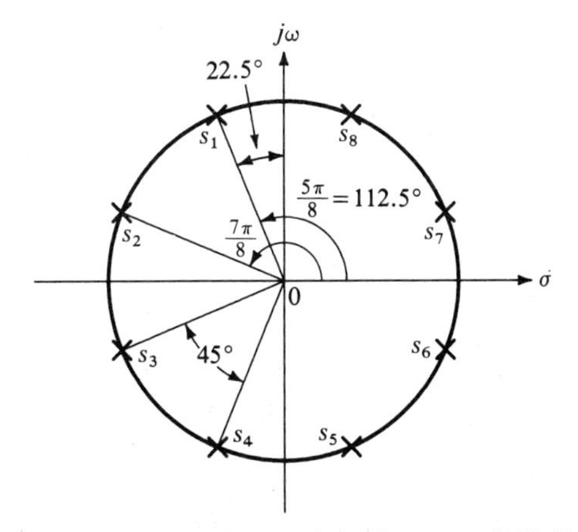

Figure 8.4 Location of the Zeros of the Function (8.3) Shown for $n = 4$

so that

$$D(s) = (s - s_1)(s - s_2)(s - s_3)(s - s_4)$$
$$= 1 + 2.6131s + 3.4142s^2 + 2.6131s^3 + s^4$$

We emphasize that this expression for $D(s)$ is for the normalized condition $\omega_c = 1$. For $\omega_c \neq 1$, we must substitute s/ω_c for s in the expression.

The normalized $D(s)$ of the Butterworth function of order n is the polynomial

$$D(s) = 1 + a_1 s + a_2 s^2 + \cdots + a_{n-1} s^{n-1} + s^n \tag{8.7}$$

with the coefficients being computed in the manner shown above. Note that a_0 and a_n are always unity because the poles are all on the unit circle. Table 8.1 gives the values of the coefficients for these functions for $n = 2$ to $n = 8$, and Table 8.2 gives the Butterworth polynomials (8.7) in factored form.

The steps to find the transfer function of a Butterworth filter are summarized as follows:

1. Use the normalized form of (8.1), $\omega_c = 1$, to obtain the value of n or $-10 \log_{10} |H_n(j\omega)|^2 = 10 \log_{10}(1 + \omega^{2n}) \geq$ dB attenuation for frequencies above $\omega = k\omega_c = k \times 1$, where k is some given positive number.

Table 8.1 Coefficients of Butterworth Polynomials

n	a_1	a_2	a_3	a_4	a_5	a_6	a_7
2	1.4142						
3	2.0000	2.0000					
4	2.6131	3.4142	2.6131				
5	3.2361	5.2361	5.2361	3.2361			
6	3.8637	7.4641	9.1416	7.4641	3.8637		
7	4.4940	10.0978	14.5918	14.5918	10.0978	4.4940	
8	5.1528	13.1371	21.8462	25.6884	21.8462	13.1371	5.1258

Table 8.2 Factors of Butterworth Polynomials

n	Factored Polynomial
1	$s + 1$
2	$s^2 + 1.4142s + 1$
3	$(s + 1)(s^2 + s + 1)$
4	$(s^2 + 0.7654s + 1)(s^2 + 1.8478s + 1)$
5	$(s + 1)(s^2 + 0.6180s + 1)(s^2 + 1.6180s + 1)$
6	$(s^2 + 0.5176s + 1)(s^2 + 1.4142s + 1)(s^2 + 1.9319s + 1)$
7	$(s + 1)(s^2 + 0.4450s + 1)(s^2 + 1.2470s + 1)(s^2 + 1.8019s + 1)$
8	$(s^2 + 0.3902s + 1)(s^2 + 1.1111s + 1)(s^2 + 1.6639s + 1)(s^2 + 1.9616s + 1)$
9	$(s + 1)(s^2 + 0.3473s + 1)(s^2 + s + 1)(s^2 + 1.5321s + 1)(s^2 + 1.8794s + 1)$

2. If the deduced value of n is nonintegral, select the next higher integer as the order of the filter. For example, if in a specific case $n = 3.3$, we would select a fourth-order filter.
3. Use Table 8.2 to obtain the normalized transfer function:

$$H(s) = \frac{1}{D(s)}$$

4. Substitute s/ω_c for ω in step 3 for the non-normalized form.
5. In case we wish to normalize $|H(s/\omega_c)|$ with amplitude starting with unity, multiply $|H(s/\omega_c)|$ by the value of the constant of the polynomial $D(s/\omega_c)$.

■ Example 8.1

Deduce the transfer function of a Butterworth filter that has an attenuation of at least 10 dB at twice the cutoff frequency, where $\omega_c = 2.5 \times 10^3$ rad/s.

Solution We initially find the normalized Butterworth filter. At $\omega = 2\omega_c = 2 \times 1$ ($\omega_c = 1$, normalized),

$$|H_n(j2)|^2 = \frac{1}{1 + 2^{2n}} \tag{8.8}$$

The dB attenuation is given by

$$-10 \log_{10}|H_n(j2)|^2 = 10 \log_{10}(1 + 2^{2n}) \geq 10$$

from which $\text{antilog}_{10} 1 = 1 + 2^{2n}$. We find that

$$1 + 2^{2n} \geq 10 \qquad \text{or} \qquad 2^{2n} \geq 9$$

The order of the filter must then be $n = (\ln_2 9)/2 = 1.584$; hence, a second-order Butterworth filter satisfies this requirement. The corresponding transfer function of the normalized filter is (see Table 8.2)

$$H_2(s) = \frac{1}{s^2 + 1.4142s + 1} \tag{8.9}$$

The magnitude and phase of this filter are shown in Figure 8.5. For a cutoff frequency $\omega_c = 2.5 \times 10^3$, the transfer function is

$$H(s) = H_2(s/\omega_c) = \frac{1}{1.6 \times 10^{-7}s^2 + 5.6569 \times 10^{-4}s + 1} \tag{8.10}$$

where $\omega_c = 2.5 \times 10^3$ rad s^{-1}, which was specified initially.

The denominator polynomial has conjugate complex roots with negative real parts. We split the function $D(s)$ of (8.10) into two polynomials, separating the even and odd powers of s:

$$D(s) = e(s) + o(s) = (1.6 \times 10^{-7}s^2 + 1) + (5.6569 \times 10^{-4}s) \tag{8.11}$$

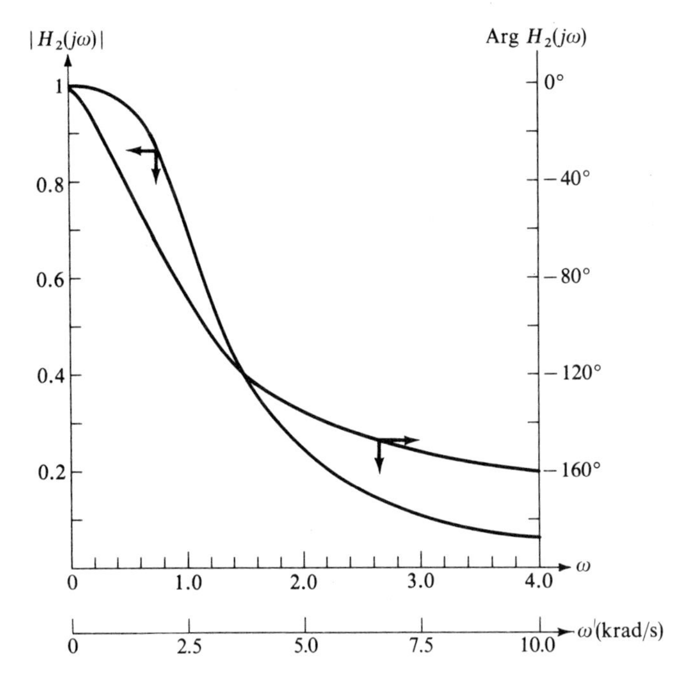

Figure 8.5 Phase and Amplitude Characteristics of the Second-Order Butterworth Filter

The roots of each component are purely imaginary (zero included), and, additionally, the roots alternate; thus, $-2.5 \times 10^3 < s < 2.5 \times 10^3$. Polynomials that possess these properties are known as **Hurwitz polynomials**.

Observe also that (8.10) is of the general form

$$H(s) = \frac{1}{a_n s^n + a_{n-1}s^{n-1} + \cdots + a_0} = \frac{k}{D(s)} \tag{8.12}$$

It can be shown that a transfer function of this form can be realized with passive elements if and only if $D(s)$ is a Hurwitz polynomial.

Suppose that we wish to find a two-port network of the terminated form shown in Figure 8.6a appropriate to (8.10). Since $D(s)$ is of second order, the lossless two-port network shown in Figure 8.6b appears to be an appropriate form. The transfer function of this circuit is

$$\frac{V_o(s)}{V_i(s)} = H(s) = \frac{1}{CLs^2 + (C + L)s + 2} \tag{8.13}$$

This form differs from (8.10) by the factor 2 in the denominator. If we multiply the numerator and denominator of (8.10) by 2, we obtain an equivalent transfer

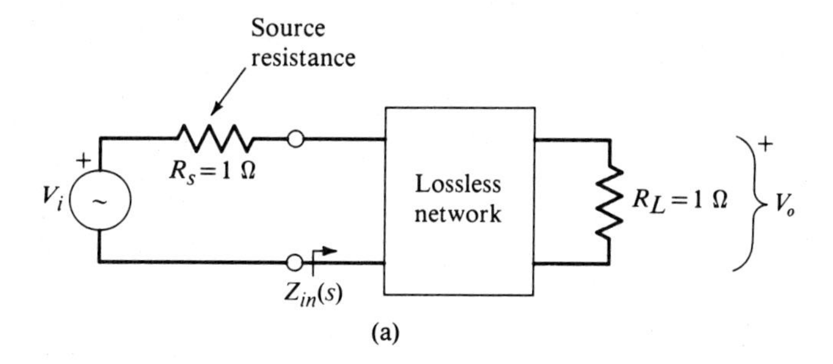

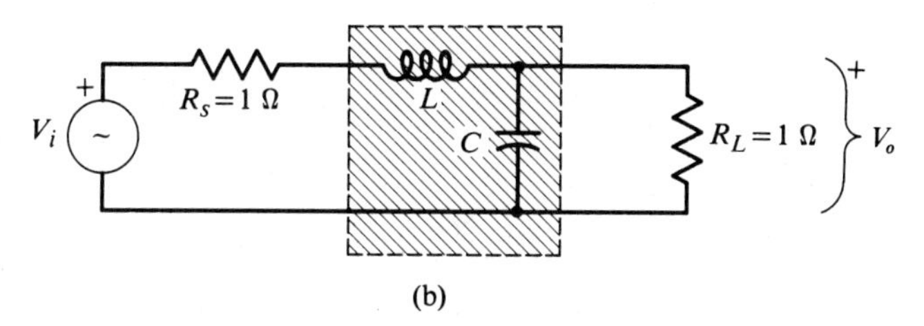

Figure 8.6 Second-Order Butterworth Filter

function

$$\frac{H(s)}{2} = \frac{1}{3.2 \times 10^{-7}s^2 + 1.1314 \times 10^{-3}s + 2} \tag{8.14}$$

By comparing these two equations, we obtain

$$CL = 3.2 \times 10^{-7} \qquad C + L = 1.1314 \times 10^{-3}$$

These expressions can be solved to yield $C = 5.7 \times 10^{-4}$ F and $L = 5.6 \times 10^{-4}$ H. ■

■ **Example 8.2**

A Butterworth filter must have an attenuation of at least 20 dB at 6 kHz, twice the cutoff frequency. Deduce the transfer function of the appropriate low-pass filter.

Solution The normalized Butterworth filter is first determined. Thus, at $\omega = 2\omega_c = 2 \times 1$,

$$|H_n(j2)|^2 = \frac{1}{1 + 2^{2n}}$$

from which we have

$$-10 \log_{10}|H_n(j2)|^2 = 10 \log_{10}(1 + 2^{2n}) \geq 20$$

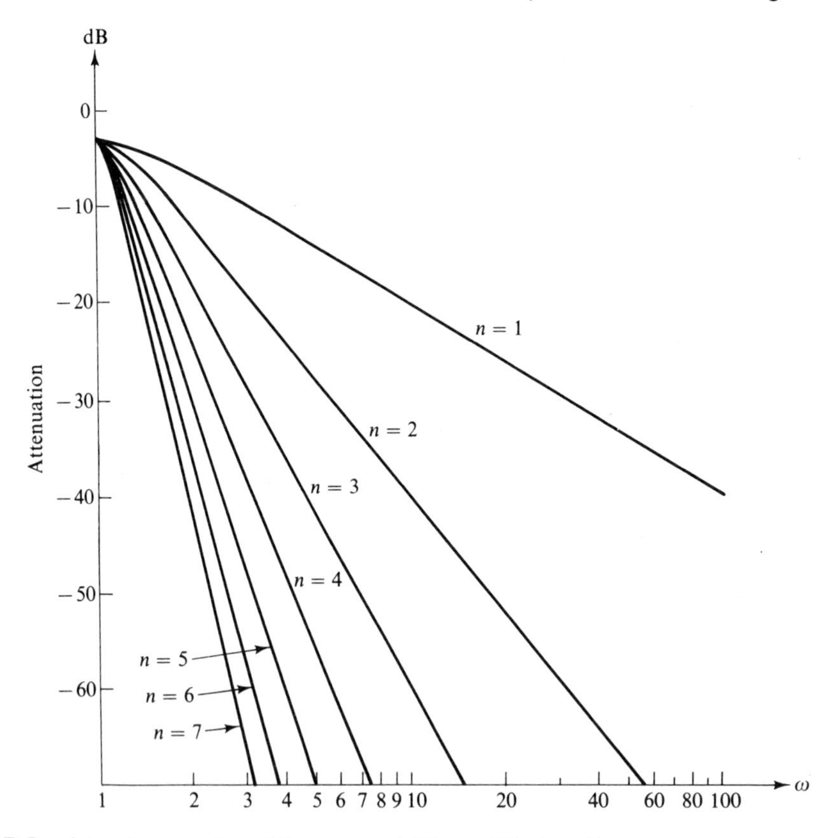

Figure 8.7 Bandstop Attenuation of Butterworth Filter of Various Degrees

Then, $\text{antilog}_{10}\, 2 \leq 1 + 2^{2n}$, which yields

$$1 + 2^{2n} \geq 10^2 = 100$$

From this expression, we find that $n - 3.3$. Hence, a fourth-order Butterworth filter satisfies the specifications. The transfer functions of the normalized filter is

$$H_4(s) = \frac{1}{1 + 2.6131s + 3.4142s^2 + 2.6131s^3 + s^4} \tag{8.15}$$

A ready check of the order of the filter is possible by reference to Figure 8.7. Observe that when $\omega/\omega_c = 2$ and $n = 3$, the filter provides an attenuation of 18.5 dB, while that for $n = 4$ provides an attenuation of 24 dB. Clearly, a filter with $n = 4$ is required.

The amplitude and phase characteristics of this filter are shown in Figure 8.8. With a cutoff frequency of 3 kHz, the denormalizing factor is

$$s/\omega_c = s/2\pi \times 3{,}000 = s/18{,}849.54$$

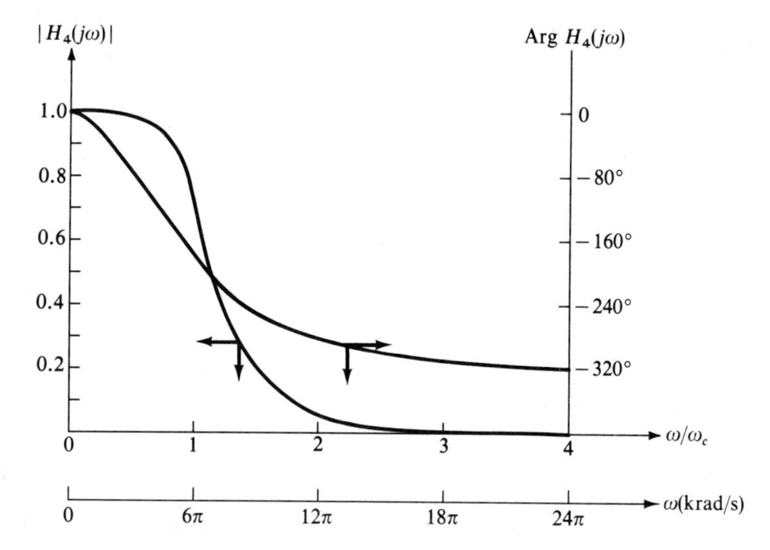

Figure 8.8 Amplitude and Phase Characteristics of the Fourth-Order Butterworth Filter

The filter transfer function is

$$H(s) = H_4(s/\omega_c) = \frac{1}{1 + 1.3863 \times 10^{-4}s + 9.609 \times 10^{-9}s^2 + 3.9017 \times 10^{-13}s^3 + 7.9213 \times 10^{-18}s^4}$$

■

8.3 Chebyshev Low-Pass Filter

An examination of Figure 8.3 shows that the Butterworth low-pass amplitude response approaches the ideal in the region of small ω and also in the region of large ω, but is not a very good approximation in the neighborhood of the cutoff frequency ($\omega = 1$). The Chebyshev low-pass filter possesses sharper cutoff response than the Butterworth filter, but it does possess amplitude variations within the pass band. The features of the Chebyshev response are shown in Figures 8.9a and 8.9b for n even ($= 4$) and n odd ($= 5$), respectively. A number of general properties are contained in these figures:

1. The oscillations in the pass band have equal amplitudes for a given value of ε.
2. The curves for n even always start from the trough of the ripple, whereas the curves for n odd always start from the peak.
3. At the normalized cutoff frequency of 1, all curves pass through the same point, which is shown in the figure as $1/(1 + \varepsilon^2)$.

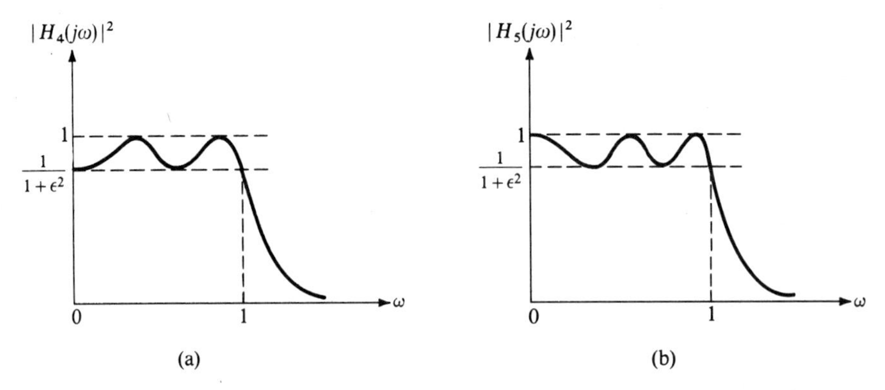

Figure 8.9 General Shape of Chebyshev Approximations. (a) n even (=4). (b) n odd (=5).

The amplitude response of the Chebyshev low-pass filter is specified by

$$|H_n(j\omega)| = \frac{1}{\sqrt{1+\varepsilon^2 C_n^2(\omega)}} = \frac{1}{\sqrt{1+\varepsilon^2 C_n^2(s/j)}} \qquad n = 1, 2, 3, \ldots \tag{8.16}$$

where ε is a constant and where $C_n(\omega)$ is the Chebyshev polynomial given by the equations

$$C_n(\omega) = \cos(n \cos^{-1} \omega) \qquad \text{for } |\omega| \le 1 \tag{8.17a}$$

$$= \cosh(n \cosh^{-1} \omega) \qquad \text{for } |\omega| > 1 \tag{8.17b}$$

The analytic form of the Chebyshev polynomials for orders 0 to 10 are tabulated in Table 8.3. Figure 8.10 shows the Chebyshev polynomials $C_n(\omega)$ of (8.17) for $\omega \ge 0$.

Table 8.3 Chebyshev Polynomials

n	$C_n(\omega)$
0	1
1	ω
2	$2\omega^2 - 1$
3	$4\omega^3 - 3\omega$
4	$8\omega^4 - 8\omega^2 + 1$
5	$16\omega^5 - 20\omega^3 + 5\omega$
6	$32\omega^6 - 48\omega^4 + 18\omega^2 - 1$
7	$64\omega^7 - 112\omega^5 + 56\omega^3 - 7\omega$
8	$128\omega^8 - 256\omega^6 + 160\omega^4 - 32\omega^2 + 1$
9	$256\omega^9 - 576\omega^7 + 432\omega^5 - 120\omega^3 + 9\omega$
10	$512\omega^{10} - 1280\omega^8 + 1120\omega^6 - 400\omega^4 + 50\omega^2 - 1$

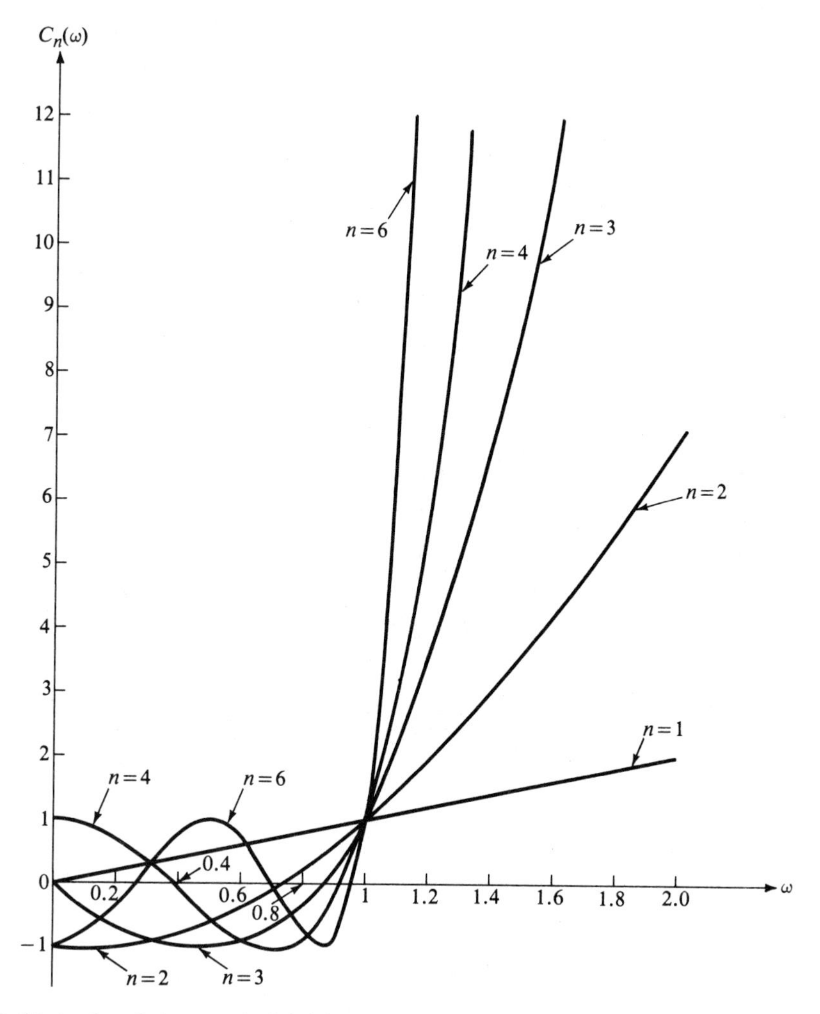

Figure 8.10 Chebyshev Polynomials $C_n(\omega)$ for $\omega \geq 0$

By (8.17) and the recurrence relationship

$$C_{n+1}(\omega) = 2\omega C_n(\omega) - C_{n-1}(\omega) \qquad n = 1, 2, \ldots \tag{8.18a}$$

$$C_1(\omega) = \omega C_0(\omega) \tag{8.18b}$$

the nth-order Chebyshev polynomial possesses the following properties:

1. For any n, $\quad 0 \leq |C_n(\omega)| \leq 1 \quad$ for $0 \leq |\omega| \leq 1$
   $\qquad |C_n(\omega)| > 1 \quad$ for $|\omega| > 1$
2. $C_n(\omega)$ is monotonically increasing for $\omega > 1$ for all n.
3. $C_n(\omega)$ is an odd polynomial if n is odd.
   $C_n(\omega)$ is an even polynomial if n is even.

4. $C_n(0) = 0$ for n odd.
$|C_n(0)| = 1$ for n even.

The curves in Figure 8.10, together with (8.16), show that $|H_n(j\omega)|$ attains its maximum value of 1 at the zeros of $C_n(\omega)$ and its minimum value of $1/\sqrt{1+\varepsilon^2}$ at the points where $C_n(\omega)$ attains its maximum value of 1. Thus, the ripples in the pass band $0 \le \omega \le 1$ have a peak-peak amplitude

$$r = 1 - \frac{1}{\sqrt{1+\varepsilon^2}} \tag{8.19}$$

The ripple in decibels is given by

$$r_{\text{dB}} = -20\log_{10}\frac{1}{\sqrt{1+\varepsilon^2}} = 10\log_{10}(1+\varepsilon^2) \tag{8.20}$$

Outside of the pass band $\omega > 1$, $|H_n(j\omega)|$ decreases monotonically.

In the unnormalized case when $\omega_c \neq 1$, the Chebyshev low-pass filter is defined by

$$|H_n(j\omega)| = \frac{1}{\sqrt{1+\varepsilon^2 C_n^2(\omega/\omega_c)}} = \frac{1}{\sqrt{1+\varepsilon^2 C_n^2(s/j\omega_c)}} \qquad n = 1, 2, 3, \ldots \tag{8.21}$$

To find the pole locations of $H_n(s)$, where $s = j\omega$, we study the denominator of the normalized function ($\omega_c = 1$)

$$H_n(s)H_n(-s) = \frac{1}{1+\varepsilon^2 C_n^2(s/j)} \tag{8.22}$$

More specifically, the poles of the function occur when $C_n(s/j) = \pm\sqrt{-1/\varepsilon^2}$ or when [see (8.17)]

$$\cos[n\cos^{-1}(s/j)] = \pm j/\varepsilon \tag{8.23}$$

To proceed, we define

$$\cos^{-1}(s/j) = \alpha - j\beta \tag{8.24}$$

Combine this with (8.23), from which

$$\cos n\alpha \cosh n\beta + j(\sin n\alpha \sinh n\beta) = \pm\frac{j}{\varepsilon} \tag{8.25}$$

because $\cos jx = \cosh x$ and $\sin jx = j\sinh x$. Equate real and imaginary terms on each side of this equation:

$$\cos n\alpha \cosh n\beta = 0 \tag{8.26a}$$

$$\sin n\alpha \sinh n\beta = \pm\frac{1}{\varepsilon} \tag{8.26b}$$

It follows from (8.26a) since $\cosh n\beta \neq 0$, that

$$\alpha = (2k-1)\frac{\pi}{2n} \qquad k = 1, 2, 3, \ldots 2n \tag{8.27}$$

Because $\sin n\alpha = \pm 1$, (8.26b), together with (8.27), yields for β:

$$\beta = \pm\frac{1}{n}\sinh^{-1}\left(\frac{1}{\varepsilon}\right) \tag{8.28}$$

Equation (8.24) can be used to specify the poles:

$$s_k = j\cos(\alpha - j\beta) = -\sin\left[(2k-1)\frac{\pi}{2n}\right]\sinh\left[\frac{1}{n}\sinh^{-1}\left(\frac{1}{\varepsilon}\right)\right] + j\cos\left[(2k-1)\frac{\pi}{2n}\right]\cosh\left[\frac{1}{n}\sinh^{-1}\left(\frac{1}{\varepsilon}\right)\right] \tag{8.29}$$

These points are located on an ellipse in the s-plane, as shown in Figure 8.11 for $n = 4$. To prove that the locus is an ellipse, let

$$s_k = \sigma_k + j\omega_k \tag{8.30a}$$

$$\sigma_k = -\sin\left[(2k-1)\frac{\pi}{2n}\right]\sinh\left[\frac{1}{n}\sinh^{-1}\left(\frac{1}{\varepsilon}\right)\right] \tag{8.30b}$$

$$\omega_k = \cos\left[(2k-1)\frac{\pi}{2n}\right]\cosh\left[\frac{1}{n}\sinh^{-1}\left(\frac{1}{\varepsilon}\right)\right] \tag{8.30c}$$

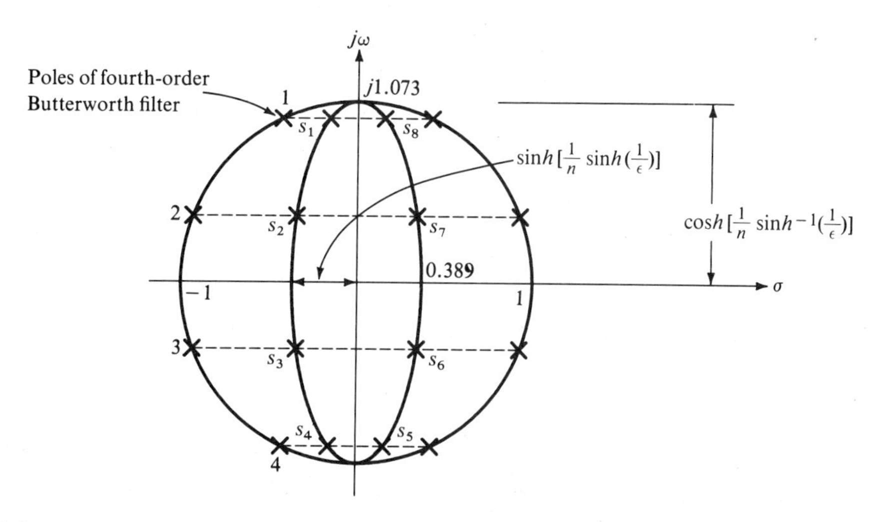

Figure 8.11 Location of Zeros of Function (8.21) on the s-Plane Shown for $n = 4$ and $\varepsilon = 0.458$

It follows from (8.30b) and (8.30c) that

$$\frac{\sigma_k^2}{\left\{\sinh\left[\frac{1}{n}\sinh^{-1}\left(\frac{1}{\varepsilon}\right)\right]\right\}^2}+\frac{\omega_k^2}{\left\{\cosh\left[\frac{1}{n}\sinh^{-1}\left(\frac{1}{\varepsilon}\right)\right]\right\}^2}=1 \tag{8.31}$$

This equation is the equation of the ellipse shown in Figure 8.11. Equation (8.30c) shows that the imaginary parts are the same as if the zeros had been uniformly spaced on a circle of radius $\cosh[(1/n)\sinh^{-1}(1/\varepsilon)]$ since this quantity is constant for a particular n and ε. Therefore, the graphical construction indicated can be used to locate the roots.

We can use the same reasoning as was done in Section 8.2 to show that the desired response can be obtained by limiting considerations to the zeros on the left-half plane. The transfer function is of the form

$$H(s)=\frac{K}{a_0+a_1 s+a_2 s^2+\cdots+a_{n-1}s^{n-1}+s^n} \tag{8.32}$$

The steps to find a Chebyshev filter are summarized as follows:

1. For a specified dB ripple, ε is deduced from (8.20).
2. The attenuation in dB at a specified frequency that is a multiple of the critical frequency must satisfy the equation [see (8.21)]

$$-10\log_{10}|H_n(j\omega)|^2=10\log_{10}\left[1+\varepsilon^2 C_n^2\left(\frac{\omega}{\omega_c}\right)\right]\geq \text{dB}$$

3. From step 2, n is determined. Next, use (8.29) to obtain the roots.
4. The constant K of (8.32) is selected to meet the dc gain level dictated by the problem at hand.
5. The normalized transfer function is then given by

$$\frac{H(s)}{K}=\frac{1}{(-1)^n\prod_{k=1}^{n}\left(\frac{s}{s_k}-1\right)} \tag{8.33}$$

6. For the case when $\omega_c\neq 1$, the transfer function is

$$\frac{H(s)}{K}=\frac{1}{(-1)^n\prod_{k=1}^{n}\left[\frac{(s/\omega_c)}{s_k}-1\right]} \tag{8.34}$$

Table 8.4 gives the coefficients in the denominator of (8.32), and Table 8.5 gives the factors in the polynomial of (8.32) for two different values of ripple amplitude r.

■ Example 8.3

Design a Chebyshev filter with 1 dB ripple in the pass band and an attenuation of at least 20 dB at twice the cutoff frequency, specified as 3 kHz.

Table 8.4 Coefficients of the Polynomial in (8.32)

n	a_0	a_1	a_2	a_3	a_4	a_5	a_6	a_7
				$r = 0.5$ dB	$\varepsilon = 0.3493$			
1	2.8628							
2	1.5162	1.2456						
3	0.7157	1.5349	1.2529					
4	0.3791	1.0255	1.7169	1.1974				
5	0.1789	0.7525	1.3096	1.9374	1.1725			
6	0.0948	0.4324	1.1719	1.5898	2.1718	1.1592		
7	0.0447	0.2821	0.7557	1.6479	1.8694	2.4127	1.1512	
8	0.0237	0.1525	0.5736	1.1486	2.1840	2.1492	2.6567	1.1461
				$r = 1.0$ dB	$\varepsilon = 0.5088$			
1	1.9652							
2	1.1025	1.0977						
3	0.4913	1.2384	0.9883					
4	0.2756	0.7426	1.4539	0.9528				
5	0.1228	0.5805	0.9744	1.6888	0.9368			
6	0.0689	0.3071	0.9393	1.2021	1.9308	0.9283		
7	0.0307	0.2137	0.5486	1.3575	1.4288	2.1761	0.9231	
8	0.0172	0.1073	0.4478	0.8468	1.8369	1.6552	2.4230	0.9198

Table 8.5 Factors of the Polynomial in (8.32)

n	Factored Polynomial
	$r = 0.5$ dB $\quad \varepsilon = 0.3493$
1	$s + 2.8628$
2	$s^2 + 1.4256s + 1.5162$
3	$(s^2 + 0.6265)(s^2 + 0.6265s + 1.1424)$
4	$(s^2 + 0.3507s + 1.0635)(s^2 + 0.8467s + 0.3564)$
5	$(s + 0.3623)(s^2 + 0.2239s + 1.0358)(s^2 + 0.5862s + 0.4768)$
6	$(s^2 + 0.1553s + 1.0230)(s^2 + 0.4243s + 0.5900)(s^2 + 0.5796s + 0.1570)$
	$r = 1.0$ dB $\quad \varepsilon = 0.5088$
1	$s + 1.9652$
2	$s^2 + 1.0978s + 1.1025$
3	$(s + 0.4942)(s^2 + 0.4941s + 0.9942)$
4	$(s^2 + 0.2791s + 0.9865)(s^2 + 0.6737s + 0.2794)$
5	$(s + 0.2895)(s^2 + 0.1789s + 0.9883)(s^2 + 0.4684s + 0.4293)$
6	$(s^2 + 0.1244s + 0.9907)(s^2 + 0.3398s + 0.5577)(s^2 + 0.4641s + 0.1247)$

Solution Follow the steps outlined above to obtain:

a. $1 = 10\log_{10}(1+\varepsilon^2)$, from which $10^{0.1} = 1+\varepsilon^2$. Thus, $\varepsilon = \sqrt{1.2589 - 1} = 0.5088$.

b. $10\log_{10}[1 + 0.5088^2 C_n^2(2)] \geq 20$, from which $1 + 0.5088^2 C_n^2(2) \geq 10^2$. Thus, $C_n^2(2) \geq 99/0.5088^2 = 382.42$. From Table 8.3, we obtain $C_1^2(2) = 2^2 = 4$ and $C_2^2(2) = (2\times 2^2 - 1)^2 = 49$. $C_3^2(2) = (4\times 2^2 - 3\times 2)^2 = 676$. Because $C_3^2(2) > 382.42$, we choose $n = 3$.

c. From (8.30), we obtain

$$a_1 = \sigma_1 + j\omega_1 = -\sin\left(\frac{\pi}{6}\right)\sinh\left[\frac{1}{3}\sinh^{-1}\left(\frac{1}{0.5088}\right)\right] + j\cos\left(\frac{\pi}{6}\right) \times \cosh\left[\frac{1}{3}\sinh^{-1}\left(\frac{1}{0.5088}\right)\right]$$
$$= -0.2471 + j0.9660$$

In a similar manner, we find

$$s_2 = \sigma_2 + j\omega_2 = -0.4942 \qquad s_3 = \sigma_3 + j\omega_3 = -0.2471 - j0.9660$$

d. Assume $K = 1$.

e. The normalized transfer function is

$$H_3(s) = \frac{s_1 s_2 s_3}{(-1)^3(s-s_1)(s-s_2)(s-s_3)}$$
$$= \frac{-0.4913}{(-1)^3[s^3 - (s_1+s_2+s_3)s^2 + (s_1s_2 + s_1s_3 + s_2s_3)s - s_1s_2s_3]}$$
$$H_3(s) = \frac{0.4913}{s^3 + 0.9883s^2 + 1.2384s + 0.4913} \tag{8.35}$$

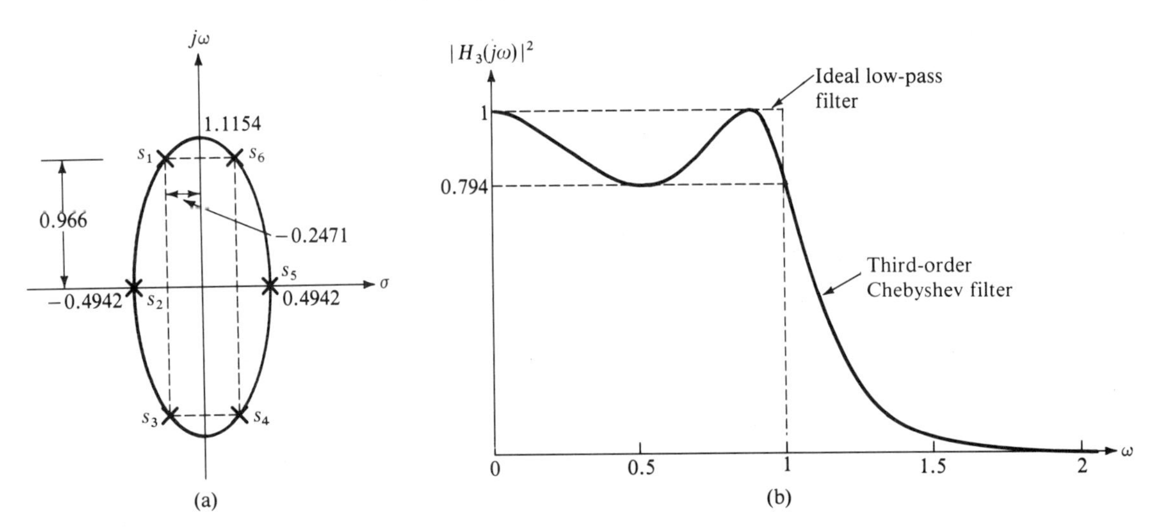

Figure 8.12 Illustrating Example 8.3

f. In this example, $\omega_c = 2\pi \times 3 \times 10^3 = 6\pi \times 10^3$, and the final function is

$$H_3\left(\frac{s}{6\pi \times 10^3}\right) = \frac{0.4913}{(s/6\pi \times 10^3)^3 + 0.9883(s/6\pi \times 10^3)^2 + 1.2384(s/6\pi \times 10^3) + 0.4913} \tag{8.36}$$

Figure 8.12a shows graphically the location of the three poles, and Figure 8.12b gives a plot of the normalized third-order Chebyshev filter of (8.35):

$$|H_3(j\omega)|^2 = \frac{1}{1 + 0.2589(4\omega^3 - 3\omega)^2} \tag{8.37}$$

■

8.4 Elliptic Filters

We have found that the Butterworth filter approximation possesses a monotonic characteristic in both the pass band and in the stop band, while the Chebyshev approximation has a magnitude response that varies between equal maximum and equal minimum values in the pass band and that decreases monotonically in the stop band. Moreover, the willingness to accept a ripple in the pass band of the Chebyshev filter results in a sharper cutoff characteristic in the stop band.

Another approximation exists that is characterized by a magnitude response that is equiripple in both the pass band and in the stop band, as shown in Figure 8.13. This approximation is given by the amplitude function

$$H(j\omega) = \frac{1}{\sqrt{1 + \varepsilon^2 R_n^2(\omega)}} \tag{8.38}$$

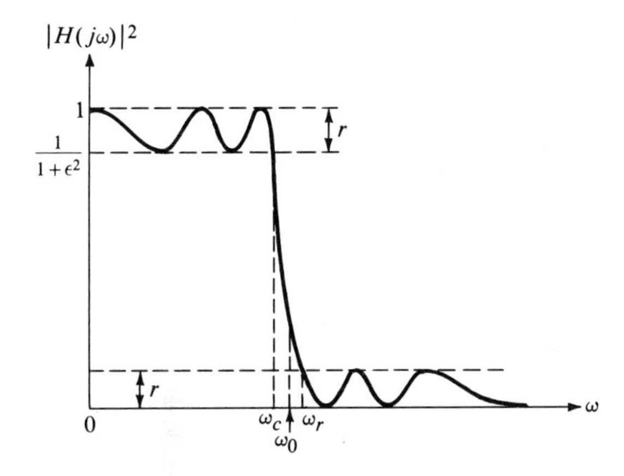

Figure 8.13 Magnitude-Squared Response of an Elliptic Filter

where $R_n(\omega)$ is a Chebyshev rational function. The roots of the rational function are related to the Jacobi elliptic sine functions, and the resulting filter is called an **elliptic filter**. The elliptic function filter is not discussed here, but note that the response curve for the elliptic filter is sharper in the cutoff region than the response curves for Chebyshev and Butterworth filters for a given value of n.

8.5 Phase Characteristics

The prior discussion focused on the amplitude response of low-pass filters. These results show that in most respects, the Chebyshev filter is superior to the Butterworth, and, in some cases, the elliptic filter is superior to both. However, phase characteristics have been ignored in these discussions, and these characteristics generally become progressively worse (less linear) as the amplitude response is improved. The phase characteristic is often an important factor since a linear phase response with frequency is necessary if we wish to transmit a pulse through a network without distortion, even though a time delay may ensue. As we will see, a digital FIR filter does have a linear phase characteristic.

It is possible to obtain a realizable approximation to an ideal constant delay function e^{-s} rather than emphasizing the amplitude function. One method for obtaining such a realizable approximation leads to an $H(s)$ that is specified in terms of Bessel polynomials. This study is not undertaken here.

8.6 Frequency Transformations

Our initial studies have been confined to low-pass filters. By appropriate frequency transformations, $H_n(s)$ for a normalized low-pass filter can be used to obtain $H_n(s)$ for other normalized filters, including: another low-pass filter and high-pass, bandpass, and bandstop types. We consider these transformations next.

Low-Pass to Low-Pass Transformation

To achieve a low-pass to low-pass transformation, we must introduce a function of ω such that

$$\omega = 0 \text{ transforms to } w = 0$$

$$\omega = \pm\infty \text{ transforms to } w = \pm\infty$$

$$\omega = 1 \text{ transforms to } w = w_c$$

A function that accomplishes this desired transformation is given by

$$s = \frac{S}{w_c} \quad \text{or} \quad \omega = \frac{w}{w_c} \tag{8.39}$$

Low-Pass to Bandpass Transformation

The required function must effect the following correspondence:

$\omega = 0$ transforms to $w = \pm w_0$, the center frequency
$\omega > 0$ transforms to $w > w_0$ and $w < -w_0$
$\omega < 0$ transforms to $w_0 > w > -w_0$

Figure 8.14 shows these relationships in graphical form.

The transformation that accomplishes the required correspondence between the low-pass and the bandpass case is given by

$$s = \frac{s_n^2 + w_0^2}{s_n(w_c - w_{-c})} = \frac{s_n^2 + w_c w_{-c}}{s_n W} \tag{8.40}$$

where $w_0^2 = w_c w_{-c}$, and $W = w_c - w_{-c}$ = bandwidth. From the factor $w_c w_{-c}$, it is evident that only a geometric symmetry exists. Hence, to obtain the bandpass $H(s)$ from the low-pass $H(s)$, substitute $(s_n^2 + w_0^2)/s_n W$ for the variable s.

■ **Example 8.4**

Design a bandpass filter that meets the following specifications:

a. The 3 dB attenuation occurs at 8,000 rad/s and at 12,000 rad/s.
b. The attenuation must be at least 20 dB for frequencies lower than 4,000 rad/s and higher than 20,000 rad/s.

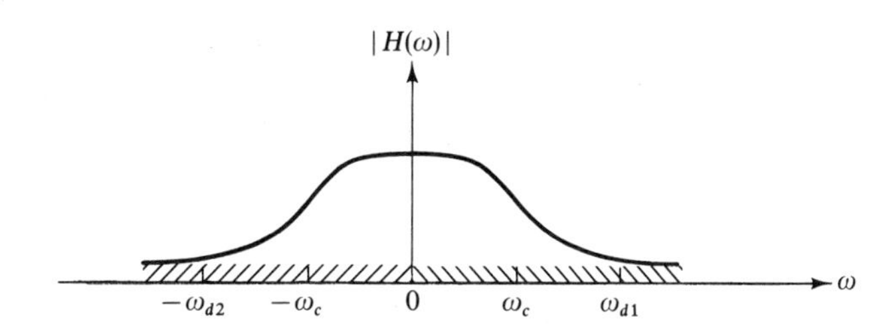

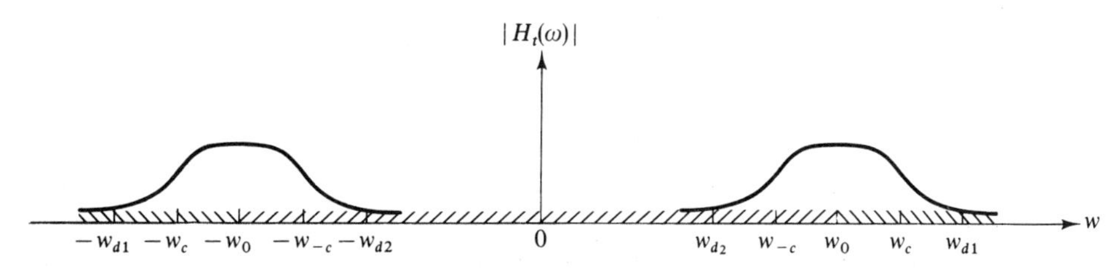

Figure 8.14 Transformation from a Low-Pass to a Bandpass Filter

Solution The requisite transformation is given by ($w_c = 12 \times 10^3$ rad/s; $w_{-c} = 8 \times 10^3$ rad/s)

$$s = \frac{s_n^2 + 9.6 \times 10^7}{s_n \times 4 \times 10^3} \quad \text{or} \quad j\omega = \frac{-w^2 + 8 \times 10^3 \times 12 \times 10^3}{jw \times 4 \times 10^3} \quad \text{or}$$

$$\omega = \frac{w^2 - 9.6 \times 10^7}{w \times 4 \times 10^3} \tag{8.41}$$

Now, substitute $w_{d2} = 4 \times 10^3$ rad/s in this equation, from which

$$\omega_{d2} = -\frac{1.6 \times 10^7 - 9.6 \times 10^7}{4 \times 10^3 \times 4 \times 10^3} = 5$$

Substitute $w_{d1} = 2 \times 10^4$ in the equation to find

$$\omega_{d1} = \frac{4 \times 10^8 - 9.6 \times 10^7}{2 \times 10^4 \times 4 \times 10^3} = 3.8$$

Since 3.8 is smaller than 5, we must design a normalized filter with $\omega_c = 1$ and $\omega_{d1} = 3.8$. However, from Figure 8.7, we find that a Butterworth filter at $\omega = 3.8$ meets line $n = 2$ just below 20 dB, which satisfies the specifications, with its normalized function (see Table 8.2)

$$H_2(s) = \frac{1}{s^2 + 1.414s + 1} \tag{8.42}$$

Combine (8.41) with (8.42) to find the desired bandpass filter transfer function:

$$H_n(s) = \frac{1}{\left(\dfrac{s_n^2 + 9.6 \times 10^7}{s_n \times 4 \times 10^3}\right)^2 + 1.414\left(\dfrac{s_n^2 + 9.6 \times 10^7}{s_n \times 4 \times 10^3}\right) + 1} \tag{8.43}$$

Introduce $s_n = jw$ into this equation to obtain

$$H(jw) = \frac{-1.6w^2}{(w^4/10^{-7}w^4 - 20.8w^2 + 9.216 \times 10^8) - j(5.656 \times 10^{-4}w^3 - 54297.6w)} \tag{8.44}$$

A plot of $20 \log_{10}|H(jw)|$ versus w rad/s is shown in Figure 8.15. Observe that the -3 dB points are at 8×10^3 rad/s and 12×10^3 rad/s as originally specified. In addition, the attenuation at 4×10^3 rad/s and 20×10^3 rad/s exceeds -20 dB, also as required. ■

Low-Pass to High-Pass Transformation

To effect this transformation, we write for $s \to w_c/s_n$. Specifically, if we wish to design a second-order Butterworth high-pass filter with cutoff frequency w_c, we

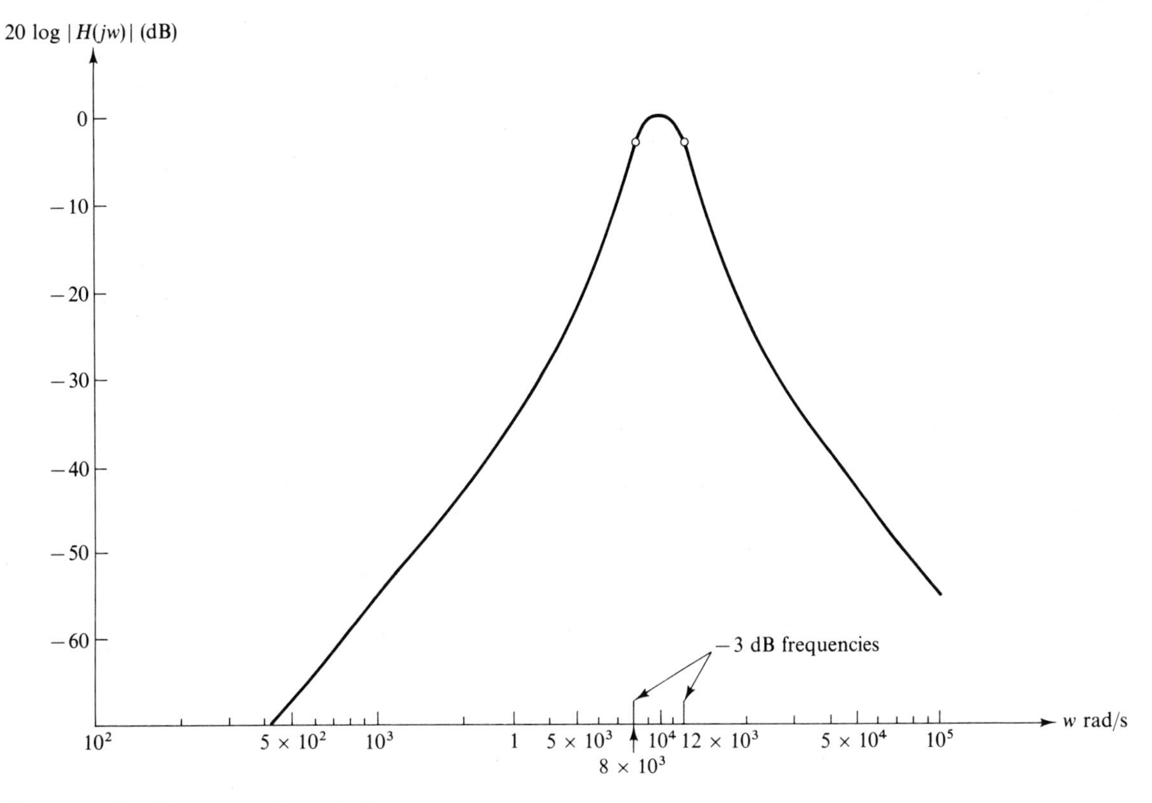

Figure 8.15 Illustrating Example 8.4

start, for example, with the normalized second-order Butterworth low-pass filter

$$H_2(s) = \frac{1}{s^2 + 1.414s + 1}$$

and substitute w_c/s_n for s. The high-pass filter is then described by

$$H_n(s) = \frac{1}{\left(\frac{w_c}{s_n}\right)^2 + 1.414\,\frac{w_c}{s_n} + 1} = \frac{s_n^2}{s_n^2 + 1.414w_c\,s_n + w_c^2} \tag{8.45}$$

■ **Example 8.5**

Design a second-order Butterworth high-pass filter with a cutoff frequency of $w_c = 800 \times 2\pi$ rad/s.

Solution We use (8.45) to obtain ($s_n = jw$):

$$H(jw) = \frac{-w^2}{-w^2 + w_c^2 + j1.414w_c\,w} \tag{8.46}$$

A plot of 20 log$|H(jw)|$ versus w rad/s is shown in Figure 8.16. ■

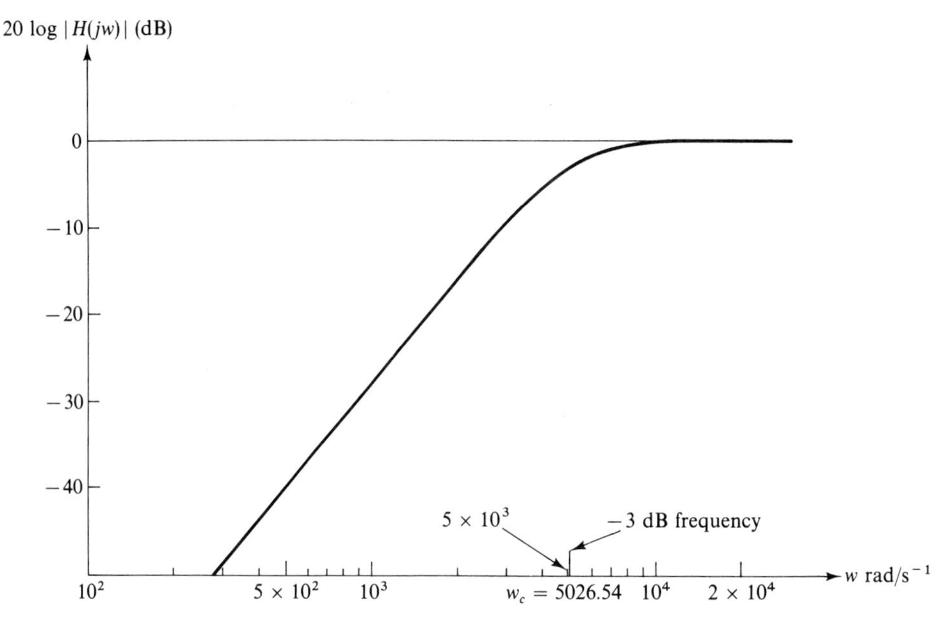

Figure 8.16 Illustrating Example 8.5

Low-Pass to Bandstop Transformation

This transformation is roughly the inverse of that for the low-pass to bandpass filter. It is (see Figure 8.14)

$$s = \frac{s_n(w_{d1} - w_{d2})\omega_{d1}}{s_n^2 + w_{d1}w_{d2}} = \frac{jw(w_{d1} - w_{d2})\omega_{d1}}{-w^2 + w_{d1}w_{d2}} \tag{8.47}$$

The procedure for the use of this transformation parallels that for the low-pass to bandpass transformation.

■ **Example 8.6**

Design a bandstop filter to meet the following specifications:

a. The attenuation between 1500 rad/s and 2200 rad/s must be at least 20 dB.
b. The attenuation for ω less than 500 rad/s and larger than 2800 rad/s must be less than -3 dB.

Solution For the data given, Equation (8.47) yields

$$f(s_n) = s = \frac{s_n(2200 - 1500)\omega_{d1}}{s_n^2 + 2200 \times 1500} \quad \text{or} \quad f(\omega) = \omega = \frac{w700\omega_{d1}}{-w^2 + 3.3 \times 10^6} \tag{8.48}$$

The values of $f(w)$ for $f(2800)$ and $f(500)$ are

$$f(2800) = \frac{2800 \times 700\omega_{d1}}{-(2800)^2 + 3.3 \times 10^6} = -0.4317\omega_{d1}$$

$$f(500) = \frac{500 \times 700\omega_{d1}}{-(500)^2 + 3.3 \times 10^6} = 0.1147\omega_{d1}$$

Since we require that the attenuation be less than -3 dB for $\omega \geq -0.4317\omega_{d1}$ and $\omega \leq 0.1147\omega_{d1}$, the pass band cutoff frequency of the original low-pass filter is chosen to be $\omega_c = 0.4317\omega_{d1}$. Begin with the normalized $\omega_c = 1$; then, $\omega_{d1} = 1/0.4317 = 2.32$ rad/s. Thus, the low-pass filter that we must first design has a 3 dB pass band cutoff frequency at 1 rad/s and an attenuation of at least 20 dB at frequencies larger than -2.32 rad/s. From Figure 8.7, we see that we require a third-order Butterworth filter to meet these requirements. The transfer function is

$$H(s) = \frac{1}{(s + 1)(s^2 + s + 1)} \tag{8.49}$$

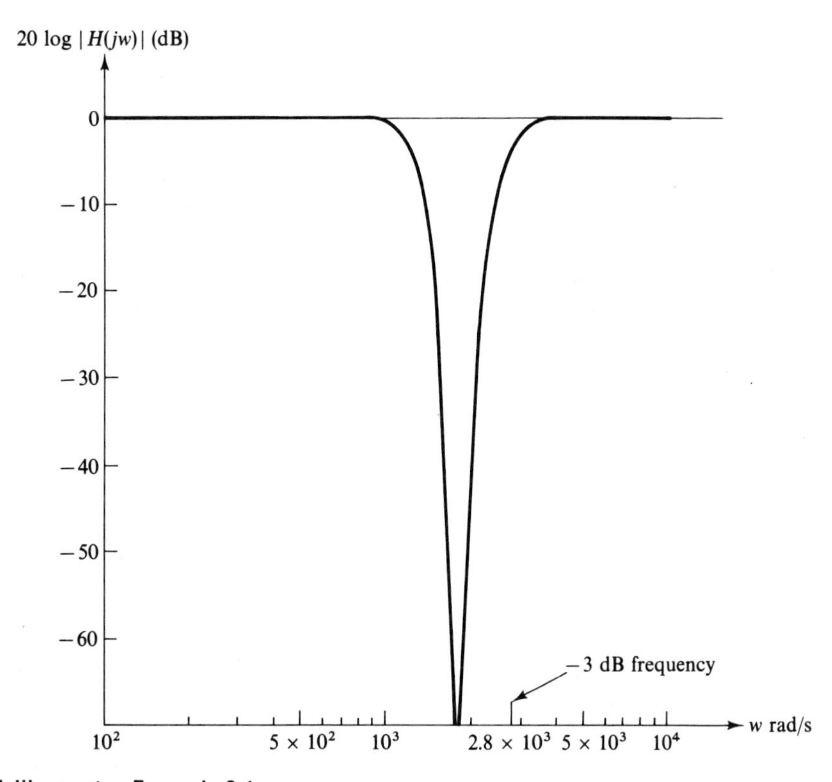

Figure 8.17 Illustrating Example 8.6

By combining (8.47) with (8.49) for $\omega_{d1} = 2.32$, we determine the bandstop characteristic

$$H_n(s) = \frac{1}{\left(\dfrac{s_n 700 \times 2.32}{s_n^2 + 3.3 \times 10^6} + 1\right)\left[\left(\dfrac{s_n \times 700 \times 2.32}{s_n^2 + 3.3 \times 10^6}\right)^2 + \dfrac{s_n \times 700 \times 2.32}{s_n^2 + 3.3 \times 10^6} + 1\right]} \tag{8.50}$$

This transfer function is plotted in Figure 8.17 (page 509) by setting $s_n = jw$. ■

8.7 Digital Filters

It has already been noted that any device or process that transforms an input sequence of numbers into an output sequence of numbers might be called a digital filter. The digital filter is considered to be a computational algorithm for carrying out this transformation process according to some prescribed rule. This rule is either a difference equation or the convolution summation. Digital filter design is concerned with the selection of the coefficients of the difference equation or with the unit delta function response $h(k)$ used in the convolution summation.

As discussed, digital filter design often stems from analog filters of the low-pass or high-pass class by the use of transformations that yield an equivalent z-plane expression for a given analog description in the s-plane or in the time domain. In essence, in this procedure, we establish a roughly equivalent sampled form for a given analog function. A number of different methods exist for these transformations, and these methods depend on the initial description of the filter type and its technical requirements. Different approaches are employed depending on whether the difference equation description of the discrete time system is a **finite duration impulse response** (FIR) or an **infinite duration impulse response** (IIR) system. Recall that for an FIR system, the difference equation relates the output to the present and past values of the input only. For an IIR system, the present output value depends on the immediate past values of the output and the present and past values of the input. That is, an IIR system involves a recursive process that involves the present and past values to update the output. More precisely, FIR and IIR describe digital filters relative to the length of their sampled response sequences since it is possible to implement an FIR digital filter in a recursive fashion and an IIR digital filter in a nonrecursive manner.

8.8 Finite Impulse Response (FIR) Filters

FIR filters (nonrecursive) are filters whose present output is determined from the present and past inputs, but is independent of its previous outputs. Because no feedback is present, FIR filters are stable. Furthermore, such filters are associated with zero phase or linear phase characteristics, and so no phase distortion occurs in the output.

Linear phase FIR digital filters have many advantages, such as guaranteed stability, freedom from phase distortion, and low coefficient sensitivity. Such filters are used where frequency dispersion is harmful. The design of such filters is well established. However, the design problem has the shortcoming of complexity, particularly in sharp filters. Several methods have been proposed in the literature for reducing the complexity of sharp filters.

The design of FIR filters is approached from two points of view: (1) by employing the discrete Fourier series, and (2) by employing the discrete Fourier transform. In both cases, $H(z)$ is used to obtain the appropriate $h(k)$ that is used in the design process. These procedures suffer from the fact that a large number of samples are required to approximate $h(k)$. Further, because Fourier approximations are involved, ripples exist in the stopband. The inclusion of window functions does much to eliminate these ripples. Details of these procedures follow.

Discrete Fourier Series Method

In this procedure, the assumed analog filter response function $H(j\omega)$ is replaced by a periodic function to allow the function to be expressed by a Fourier series, but with the restriction that the series representation is constrained to the range of the original function. Then, as discussed in Section 3.5, we approximate the continuous time function by a sampled function that adequately represents the original function in sampled form. This procedure involves replacing the infinite integral by a finite summation, the number of terms in the expansion being limited to a value N that is sufficiently large to limit the aliasing errors in the respective coefficients.

For the desired periodic digital filter $H(e^{j\omega T})$, we write

$$H(e^{j\omega T}) = \sum_{k=-\infty}^{\infty} h(kT)e^{-jk\omega T} \tag{8.51}$$

where the time function $h(t)$ is taken at $t = kT$, so that

$$h(kT) = \frac{1}{\omega_s}\int_{-\omega_2/2}^{\omega_2/2} H(e^{j\omega T})e^{jk\omega T}\, d\omega \qquad \omega_s = \frac{2\pi}{T} \qquad \omega_d = \omega T \tag{8.52}$$

Note that the notation has changed from that in Section 3.5; we now write $H(e^{j\omega T})$ in place of $H(j\omega)$ [or $F(j\omega)$], where $h(kT)$ is written in place of $\tilde{\alpha}_n$. If we set $z = e^{j\omega T}$, then (8.51) becomes

$$H(z) = \sum_{k=-\infty}^{\infty} h(kT)z^{-k} \tag{8.53}$$

In practice, the form of the function under survey is described by a discrete Fourier series with a finite number of sample values. A typical filter description is illustrated

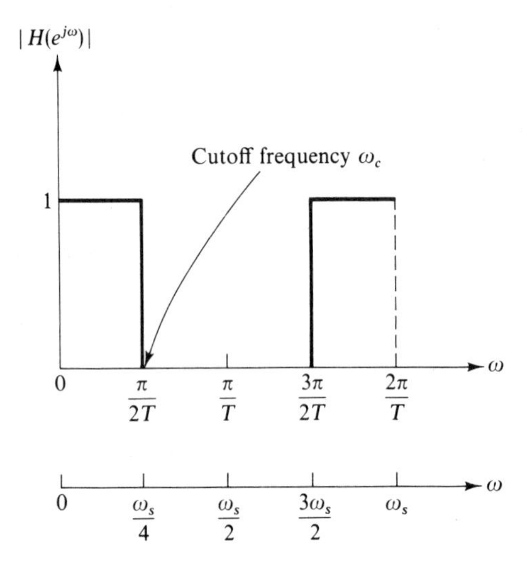

Figure 8.18 Ideal Low-Pass Filter Characteristics

in Figure 8.18. This description requires that

$$h(kT) = 0 \qquad \text{for } k > \frac{N-1}{2} \qquad \text{and} \qquad k < -\frac{N-1}{2} \tag{8.54}$$

and (8.53) becomes

$$H'(z) = h(0) + \sum_{k=1}^{(N-1)/2} [h(-kT)z^k + h(kT)z^{-k}] \tag{8.55}$$

This sequence is noncausal because of the terms involving z^k. To obtain a causal filter, we multiply $H'(z)$ by $z^{-(N-1)/2}$ to obtain the expression

$$H(z) = z^{-(N-1)/2}H'(z) \tag{8.56}$$

The factor $z^{-(N-1)/2}$ introduces a delay, or phase, factor proportional to frequency ω. Consequently, a filter with an initially zero phase characteristic for all frequencies is converted into one that has a linear phase with frequency and so introduces no distortion in the output. Observe also that if $h(kT)$ is real, then $H'(z)$ is real.

The following steps are required in the design of an FIR filter using the Fourier series approach:

1. From the given amplitude–frequency characteristic $H(j\omega) = H(e^{j\omega_d})$, obtain the sequence $\{h(kT)\}$ using (8.52).
2. Truncate the sequence $\{h(kT)\}$ by choosing $-(N-1)/2 < k < (N-1)/2$.
3. Use (8.55) to find $H'(z)$, and then use (8.56) to determine the desired filter $H(z)$.
4. Plot $|H(e^{j\omega_d})|$ versus ω_d.

Example 8.7

Determine the FIR filter that approximates the ideal filter shown in Figure 8.19a using the Fourier series method. Sketch the resulting $|H_d(e^{j\omega_d})|$. Choose $N = 5$, $N = 9$, and $N = 15$.

Solution By (8.52), we have

$$h(kT) = \frac{T}{2\pi}\int_{-\pi/4T}^{\pi/4T} e^{jk\omega T}\, d\omega = \frac{1}{\pi k}\sin\frac{k\pi}{4}$$

The sampling frequency $\omega_s = \pi/T$. The sampled values $\{h(k)\}$ are

$k =$	0	1	2	3	4	5	6	7	8
$\{h(k)\}$		$\frac{1}{\pi}\times 0.707$	$\frac{1}{2\pi}\times 1$	$\frac{1}{3\pi}\times 0.707$	0	$-\frac{1}{5\pi}\times 0.707$	$-\frac{1}{6\pi}\times 1$	$-\frac{1}{7\pi}\times 0.707$	0
	0.250	0.225	0.159	0.075	0	-0.045	-0.053	-0.032	0

Observe that the sequence is symmetric about the midpoint; hence, the transfer function for $N = 5$ can be written, as per (8.55),

$$\begin{aligned} H'(z) &= h(0) + \sum_{k=1}^{(5-1)/2} [h(-k)z^k + h(k)z^{-k}] \\ &= 0.25 + 0.225z + 0.225z^{-1} + 0.159z^2 + 0.159z^{-2} \end{aligned}$$

We thus obtain

$$\begin{aligned} H(z) = z^{-2}H'(z) &= 0.25z^{-2} + 0.225z^{-1} + 0.225z^{-3} + 0.159 + 0.159z^{-4} \\ &= 0.159 + 0.225z^{-1} + 0.25z^{-2} + 0.225z^{-3} + 0.159z^{-4} \end{aligned}$$

If we set $z = e^{j\omega_d}$ in this equation, we obtain

$$\begin{aligned} H(e^{j\omega_d}) = (&0.159 + 0.225\cos\omega_d + 0.25\cos 2\omega_d \\ &+ 0.225\cos 3\omega_d + 0.159\cos 4\omega_d) \\ &-j(0.225\sin\omega_d + 0.25\sin 2\omega_d + 0.225\sin 3\omega_d + 0.159\sin 4\omega_d) \end{aligned}$$

$|H(e^{j\omega_d})|$ is plotted in Figure 8.19b.

By following the same procedure for $N = 9$ and $N = 15$, we obtain the following transfer functions, respectively:

$$\begin{aligned} H(z) &= 0.075 + 0.159z^{-1} + 0.225z^{-2} + 0.25z^{-3} + 0.225z^{-4} \\ &\quad + 0.159z^{-5} + 0.075z^{-6} - 0.045z^{-7} - 0.053z^{-8} \\ H(z) &= -0.032 - 0.053z^{-1} - 0.045z^{-2} + 0.075z^{-4} + 0.159z^{-5} \\ &\quad + 0.225z^{-6} + 0.25z^{-7} + 0.225z^{-8} + 0.159z^{-9} + 0.075z^{-10} \\ &\quad - 0.045z^{-12} - 0.053z^{-13} - 0.032z^{-14} \end{aligned}$$

The expression $|H(e^{j\omega_d})|$ for $N = 15$ is also plotted in Figure 8.19b. The same curves for $N = 5$ and $N = 15$ are plotted on a logarithmic scale in Figure 8.19c. These place the variations in sharp focus since the magnitude function becomes $-\infty$ at points where the magnitude function becomes 0 on the linear scale. The

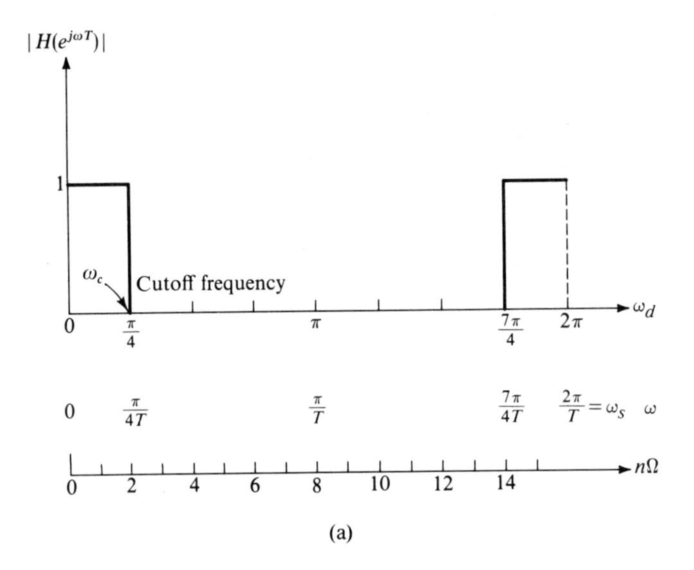

(a)

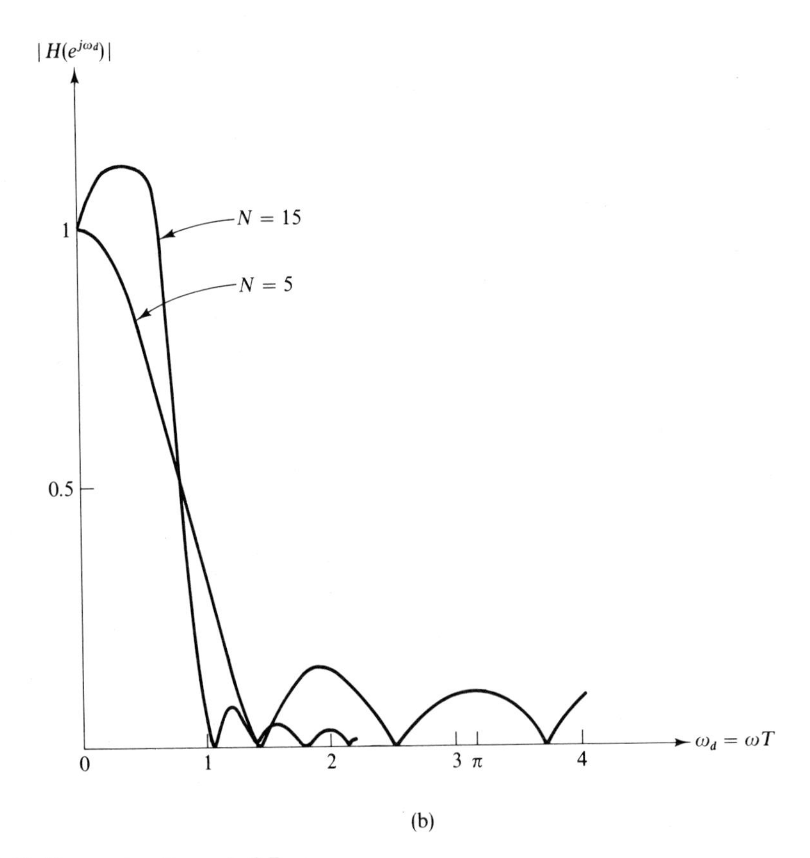

(b)

Figure 8.19 Illustrating Example 8.7

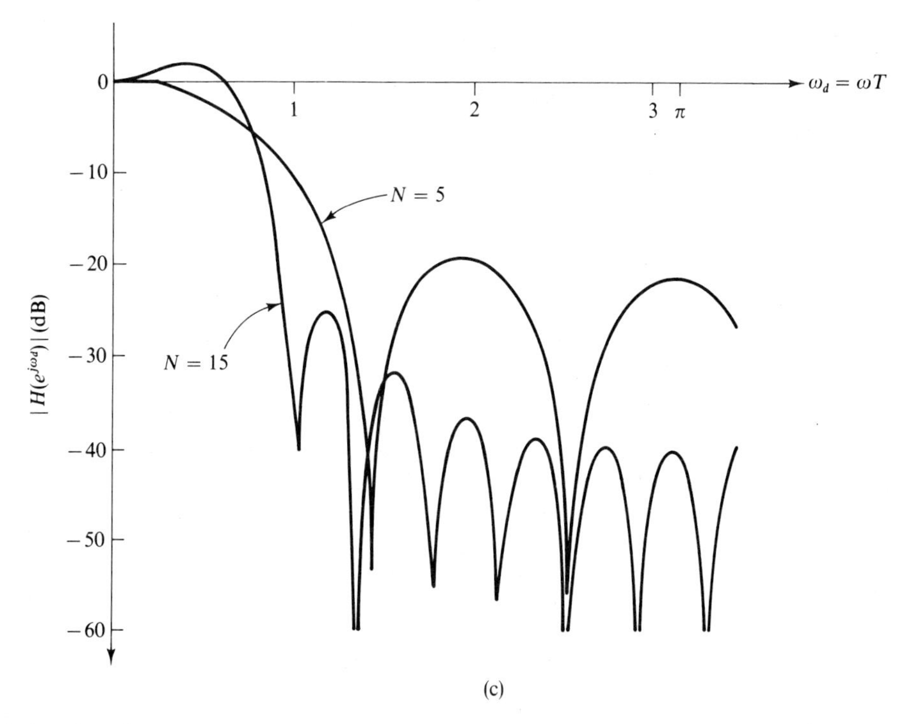

Figure 8.19 *(continued)*

reader should remember that these graphs are symmetric about $\omega_d = \pi$ and are periodic with period 2π.

Observe that the truncation of the series representation of the ideal magnitude function causes the appearance of ripples in the amplitude characteristics; the smaller the value of N, the wider is the spread of the ripples. If we view the series termination of the magnitude function as a multiplication of the original sequence by a rectangular window, the oscillations in the frequency domain arise because of leakage. The leakage can be reduced by multiplying the sequence by a more appropriate window or weighting sequence. ■

As noted, the leakage problem can be reduced appreciably by the use of an appropriately chosen window to modify the truncated magnitude function. If we denote the window function as $w(kT)$, the modified truncated sequence of the Fourier coefficients is specified by

$$h(kT) = \begin{cases} h(kT)w(kT) & 0 \leq k \leq N-1 \\ 0 & \text{otherwise} \end{cases} \tag{8.57}$$

where

$$w(kT) = \begin{cases} w(kT) & 0 \leq k \leq N-1 \\ 0 & \text{otherwise} \end{cases} \tag{8.58}$$

Three commonly used window functions are ($T = 1$)

1. Hamming window:

$$w(k) = 0.54 + 0.46 \cos(k\pi/K) \qquad |k| \le K = \frac{N-1}{2} \tag{8.59}$$

2. Blackman window:

$$w(k) = 0.42 + 0.5 \cos(k\pi/K) + 0.08 \cos(2\pi k/K) \qquad |k| \le K = \frac{N-1}{2} \tag{8.60}$$

3. Hann, or Hanning, window:

$$w(k) = 0.5 + 0.5 \cos(k\pi/K) \qquad |k| \le K = \frac{N-1}{2} \tag{8.61}$$

The following example illustrates the use of window functions.

■ **Example 8.8**

Consider again the ideal filter characteristics shown in Figure 8.19. Examine the effects of a Hamming window on the FIR approximation. Choose $N = 15$. Plot $|H(e^{j\omega_d})|$ versus ω_d.

Solution The specification of $N = 15$ implies that $K = 7$. Now, the truncated impulse response is

$$h(k) = \frac{1}{\pi k} \sin \frac{k\pi}{4} \left[0.54 + 0.46 \cos\left(\frac{k\pi}{7}\right) \right] \qquad k = 0, \pm 1, \pm 2, \ldots \pm 7$$

The specific values for $h(k)$ are

$$\begin{aligned} h(0) &= 0.25 \times 1 = 0.25 \\ h(\pm 1) &= 0.225 \times [0.54 + 0.46 \cos(\pi/7)] = 0.215 \\ h(\pm 2) &= 0.159 \times [0.54 + 0.46 \cos(2\pi/7)] = 0.131 \\ h(\pm 3) &= 0.048 \qquad h(\pm 4) = 0 \qquad h(\pm 5) = -0.011 \\ h(\pm 6) &= -0.007 \qquad h(\pm 7) = -0.003 \end{aligned}$$

The resulting noncausal FIR filter is

$$H'(z) = \sum_{k=-7}^{7} h(k) z^{-k}$$

The corresponding causal filter is

$$\begin{aligned} H(z) = z^{-7} H'(z) = &-0.003 - 0.007z^{-1} - 0.011z^{-2} + 0.048z^{-4} \\ &+ 0.131z^{-5} + 0.215z^{-6} + 0.25z^{-7} + 0.215z^{-8} + 0.131z^{-9} \\ &+ 0.043z^{-10} - 0.011z^{-12} - 0.007z^{-13} - 0.003z^{-14} \end{aligned}$$

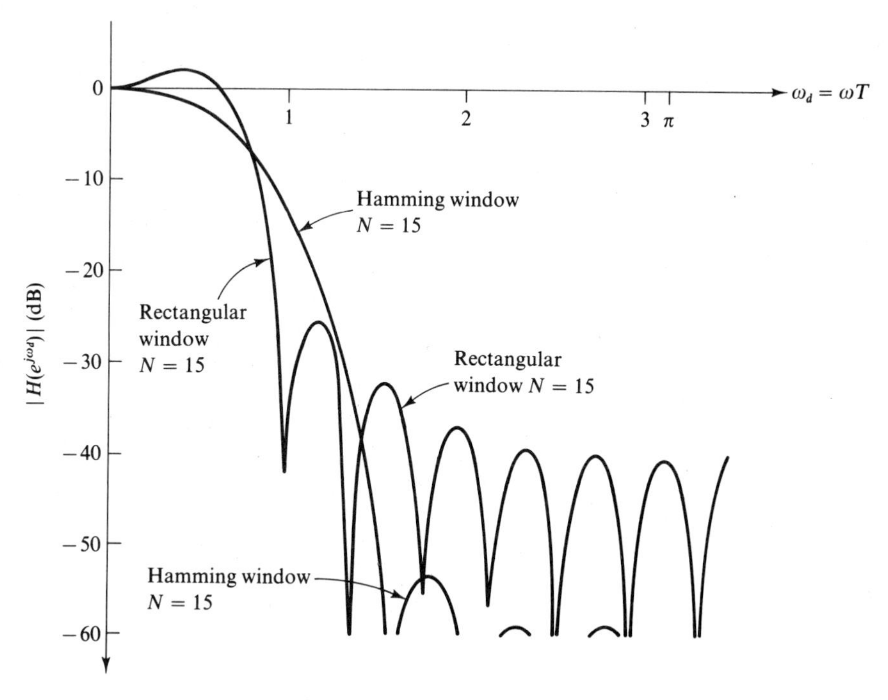

Figure 8.20 Illustrating the Effect of Windowing

Figure 8.20 shows the digital filter truncated by a rectangular window (simple sequence truncation) and by a Hamming window. It is evident from these plots that the Hamming window effectively removes the ripples that existed in the stopband, and it also enlarges the transition band. ■

In the event that an analytic form for $|H(e^{j\omega T})|$ is not readily available, it is possible to proceed by sampling the given function and then working with the truncated equations for $H(e^{j\omega T})$ in the form

$$H(n\Omega) = \sum_{k=0}^{N-1} h(kT)e^{-j2\pi kn/N} = \sum_{k=0}^{N-1} h(kT)e^{-jn\Omega kT} \tag{8.62}$$

where

$$k = 0, 1, \ldots N-1 \qquad \Omega = \frac{\omega_s}{N} = \frac{2\pi}{NT} \qquad \omega_s = \frac{2\pi}{T}$$

The appropriate form for $h(kT)$ is

$$h(kT) = \frac{1}{N}\sum_{n=0}^{N-1} H(n\Omega)e^{jn\Omega kT} \qquad n = 0, 1, \ldots N-1 \tag{8.63}$$

The procedure then continues as in Example 8.7.

Example 8.9

Repeat Example 8.7 to find the values of $h(kT)$ by employing direct sampling of the given $|H(e^{j\omega T})|$ with $N = 15$.

Solution The sampled values of $|H(e^{j\omega T})|$ for $N = 15$ are

$$\{H(e^{j\omega T})\} = \{1, 1, 0.5, 0, 0, 0, 0, 0, 0, 0, 0, 0, 0, 0.5, 1\}$$

Observe that we have used the average value of the function at the points of discontinuity. By (8.58), we write

$$h(0T) = \frac{1}{15}(1 + 1e^{j(2\pi/15)\times 0} + 0.5e^{j2(2\pi/15)\times 0} + 0e^{j3(2\pi/15)\times 0} + \cdots$$
$$+ 0.5e^{j13(2\pi/15)\times 0} + 1e^{j14(2\pi/15)\times 0}) = 0.267$$
$$h(1T) = \frac{1}{15}(1 + 1e^{j(2\pi/15)\times 1} + 0.5e^{j2(2\pi/15)\times 1} + 0e^{j3(2\pi/15)\times 1} + \cdots$$
$$+ 0.5e^{j13(2\pi/15)\times 1} + 1e^{j14(2\pi/15)\times 1}) = 0.233$$

Continuing with this procedure, the several values for $h(kT)$ are

$$h(2T) = 0.149 \qquad h(3T) = -0.054 \qquad h(4T) = -0.013$$
$$h(5T) = -0.033 \qquad h(6T) = -0.021 \qquad h(7T) = -0.003$$

The limited agreement of these values with those in Example 8.7 indicates the need for a greater number of samples. ■

Discrete Fourier Transform Method

An interesting question that arises is how the procedure employed using the discrete Fourier series method compares with that using the discrete Fourier transform since both are periodic sequences, both sample the given characteristic, and both deduce $H(n\Omega)$ in the same way. In fact, we have already noted that the DFT is simply the sampled DFS. To illustrate the use of the DFT, refer again to Example 8.8. For the sampled $h(k)$ and the window function $w(k)$, we write, as before,

$$h_w(k) = h(k)w(k)$$

The DFT of this expression is

$$H_d(e^{j\omega}) = \sum_{k=-\infty}^{\infty} h(w)\, w(k)\, e^{-jk\omega}$$
$$= \sum_{k=-\infty}^{\infty} \left[\frac{1}{2\pi}\int_{-\pi}^{\pi} H_d(e^{j\psi})e^{jk\psi}\, d\psi\right] w(k)\, e^{-jk\omega}$$

Change the variable to ψ to avoid confusion and interchange the summation and integration operations:

$$H(e^{j\omega}) = \frac{1}{2}\int_{-\pi}^{\pi} H_d(e^{j\psi})\left[\sum_{k=-\infty}^{\infty} w(k)e^{-j(\omega-\psi)k}\right] d\psi$$

$$= \frac{1}{2\pi}\int_{-\pi}^{\pi} H_d(e^{j\psi})W(e^{j(\omega-\psi)})\, d\psi$$

This expresses $H(e^{j\omega})$ as the convolution of $H_d(e^{j\psi})$ with $W(e^{j\psi})$, the transform of the window sequence $w(k)$. Here, since $H_d(e^{j\psi})$ and $W(e^{j\psi})$ are periodic, this is a circular convolution. The result is the frequency convolution

$$H(e^{j\omega}) = H_d(e^{j\psi}) * W(e^{-j\psi})$$

This procedure yields the same result as that obtained in Example 8.8.

A common feature of the methods discussed above is that the resulting filters generally require a large number of terms in the expansion and, hence, a large number of multiplications in the design procedure. A number of methods for the design of optimum linear phase FIR filters that employ iterative approximation techniques are known, and these methods yield improved designs.

8.9 Impulse-Invariant Response Method in IIR Filters

In the impulse-invariant design method, the impulse response $h(kT)$ of a discrete filter is chosen to equal a sampled version of the impulse response $h(t)$ of a desired continuous time filter. Suppose that the system function of an analog filter that has certain desired characteristics is specified by

$$H(s) = \sum_{i=1}^{m} \frac{A_i}{(s + s_i)} \tag{8.64a}$$

Assume that all poles are distinct; hence, the impulse response function is

$$h(t) = \mathscr{L}^{-1}\{H(s)\} = \sum_{i=1}^{m} A_i e^{-s_i t} \tag{8.64b}$$

If $h(kT)$ is the corresponding sampled version of $h(t)$, then we can write

$$H(z) = \sum_{k=0}^{\infty} h(kT)z^{-k}$$

so that

$$H(z) = \sum_{k=0}^{\infty} z^{-k} \sum_{i=1}^{m} A_i e^{-s_i kT} = \sum_{i=1}^{m} A_i \sum_{k=0}^{\infty} z^{-k} e^{-s_i kT}$$

which is, using the well-known formula of geometric series,

$$\boxed{H(z) = \sum_{i=1}^{m} \frac{A_i}{1 - e^{-s_i T} z^{-1}}} \tag{8.65}$$

A comparison of (8.64) and (8.65) shows that a continuous time filter specified by the system function $H(s)$ transforms into a digital filter specified by $H(z)$ via **impulse-invariant techniques** by setting

$$s + s_i = 1 - e^{-s_i T} z^{-1} \tag{8.66}$$

Observe, therefore, that $H(z)$ can be obtained from $H(s)$ without evaluating $h(t)$ or $h(kT)$. As already noted, some degree of approximation exists in this transformation because the digital filter is necessarily band limited and periodic, whereas $H(s)$, being a rational function of s, is not band limited. Because the frequency response of the digital filter comprises fewer frequency components than the analog filter, an *added*, or *folded*, difference due to the different number of terms of the series exists. This phenomenon is equivalent to that discussed in connection with the sampling theorem in Chapter 4. No error due to sampling occurs if $|H(j\omega)| = 0$ for $|\omega| > \omega_s/2$.

The design of an IIR digital filter employs the following steps:

1. Begin with a given filter specification.
2. Create an analog transfer function $H(s)$ that meets the specifications of step 1.
3. Determine the impulse response of the analog filter by means of the Laplace inversion technique, $h(t) = \mathscr{L}^{-1}\{H(s)\}$.
4. Sample $h(t)$ at T-second intervals, thereby creating a sequence $\{h(kT)\}$.
5. Deduce $H(z)$ of the resulting digital filter by taking the Z-transform of the discrete function $h(kT)$, $H(z) = \sum_{k=0}^{\infty} h(kT)z^{-k}$.

As an alternative procedure, proceed with steps 1 and 2 and then apply transformation (8.66).

Example 8.10

Determine the digital equivalent of the first-order Butterworth filter. The cutoff frequency is $20/2\pi$ Hz.

Solution The normalized analog transfer function is found in Table 8.2 for the designated filter:

$$H(s) = \frac{1}{s+1}$$

The system transfer function is given by

$$H\left(\frac{s}{\omega_c}\right) = H\left(\frac{s}{2\pi \times 20/2\pi}\right) = \frac{1}{(s/20)+1} = \frac{20}{s+20}$$

The impulse response of this filter is given by

$$h(t) = \mathscr{L}^{-1}\left\{H\left(\frac{s}{20}\right)\right\} = \mathscr{L}^{-1}\left\{\frac{20}{s+20}\right\} = 20e^{-20t} \qquad t \geq 0$$

The Z-transform of the discrete function $h(kT)$ is [see (8.65)]

$$H(z) = 20 \sum_{k=0}^{\infty} e^{-20kT} z^{-k} = 20 \sum_{k=0}^{\infty} (e^{-20T} z^{-1})^k = \frac{20}{1 - e^{-20T} z^{-1}}$$

Note that we could have found $H(z)$ simply by setting $s + 20 = 1 - e^{-20T} z^{-1}$ in $H(s/\omega_c)$, as shown in (8.65).

To proceed for the specified sampling time $T = 0.005$ s, we deduce the absolute value of the analog transfer function:

$$\left| H\left(\frac{j\omega}{20}\right) \right| = \frac{1}{|(j\omega/20) + 1|} = \frac{1}{\sqrt{1 + (j\omega/20)^2}}$$

It is convenient to plot this function versus ω_d, where $\omega = \omega_d/T$. This equality is found from the relation $z = e^{j\omega T}$ or $j\omega = 1/T \ln z = (1/T)j\omega_d$. The equivalent expression becomes

$$|H(j\omega_d)| = \frac{1}{\sqrt{1 + [j\omega_d/(20 \times 0.005)]^2}} = \frac{1}{\sqrt{1 + (10\omega_d)^2}}$$

This equation is plotted as the lower curve in Figure 8.21.

The equivalent expression for the discrete function is

$$|H(e^{j\omega_d})| = \frac{20}{|1 - e^{-20 \times 0.005} e^{-j\omega_d}|} = \frac{20}{|1 - 0.9048 e^{-j\omega_d}|}$$

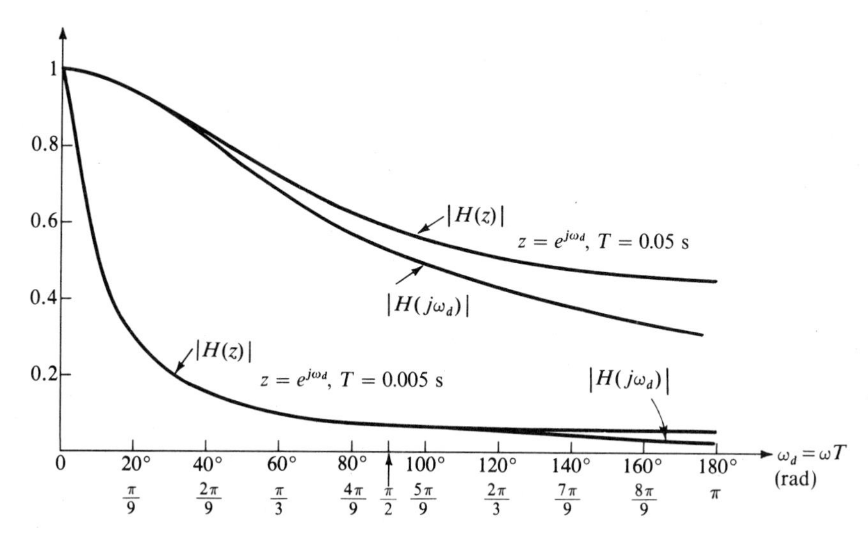

Figure 8.21 Comparison Between the Analog Filter and Its Corresponding Digital Filter for Two Sampling Times

Note, however, that $H(e^{j0}) = 210.084$ is the value of $H(e^{j\omega_d})$ for $\omega_d = 0$ (or $z = 1$). We thus consider the normalized function

$$\frac{|H(e^{j\omega_d})|}{210.084} = \frac{20}{210.084} \frac{1}{[(1 - 0.9048 \cos \omega_d)^2 + (0.9048 \sin \omega_d)^2]^{1/2}}$$

which is also plotted in Figure 8.21 (lower curve).

For the case when $T = 0.05$ s,

$$H(e^{j\omega_d}) = \frac{20}{|1 - e^{-20 \times 0.05} e^{-j\omega_d}|} = \frac{20}{|1 - 0.3679 e^{-j\omega_d}|}$$

The value of $H(e^{j0}) = 31.641$ at $\omega_d = 0$, and the normalized relation becomes

$$\frac{|H(e^{j\omega_d})|}{31.641} = \frac{20}{31.641} \frac{1}{[(1 - 0.3679 \cos \omega_d)^2 + (0.3679 \sin \omega_d)^2]^{1/2}}$$

This relation is plotted in Figure 8.21 (upper curve) together with $|H(j\omega_d)| = 1/\sqrt{1 + \omega_d^2}$ since $\omega = \omega_d/0.05$.

Figure 8.21 clearly shows the effect of sampling times T. The upper curves for $T = 0.05$ start to separate at about $\omega_d = 30°$, which is equal to $30°/57.2958° = 0.5236$ radians; hence, the error begins to be pronounced at the frequency roughly equal to $f = \omega_d/2\pi T = 0.5236/2\pi \times 0.05 = 1.666$ Hz. The error for the lower curves with $T = 0.005$ begins at about $90°$, or 1.571 radians; hence, the error starts at the frequency $f = 1.571/2\pi \times 0.005 = 50.0$ Hz, which is above the cutoff frequency. Thus, an aliasing error is present in one case, but not in the other. This calculation indicates that good accuracy is achieved with this digital filter if we choose the sampling time $T \ll 0.05$ s.

Had we continued the plots of the above curves from $\omega_d = 180° = \pi$ to $\omega_d = 2\pi$, the curves of $|H(z)|$ would have repeated themselves, being symmetric about $\omega_d = \pi$. However, the curves for $|H(j\omega)|$ would have continued to decrease, as expected from the form of $H(j\omega)$. ■

■ Example 8.11

Determine the digital equivalent of a Butterworth third-order low-pass filter and find T if the sampling frequency is 15 times the cutoff frequency.

Solution The normalized system function of this filter is deduced from Table 8.1 or Table 8.2. It is

$$H_n(s) = \frac{1}{1 + 2s + 2s^2 + s^3} = \frac{1}{(s + 1)(s^2 + s + 1)} = \frac{A_1}{s + s_1} + \frac{A_2}{s + s_2} + \frac{A_3}{s + s_3}$$

where

$$s_1 = 1 \qquad s_2 = \frac{1}{2}(-1 + j\sqrt{3}) \qquad s_3 = \frac{1}{2}(-1 - j\sqrt{3})$$

Evaluating the constants A in this expression, we find that

$$A_1 = 1 \qquad A_2 = \frac{2}{-3 - j\sqrt{3}} \qquad A_3 = A_2^* = \frac{2}{-3 + j\sqrt{3}}$$

The impulse response of this system is given by

$$h(t) = A_1 e^{-t} + A_2 e^{-s_2 t} + A_3 e^{-s_3 t}$$

Further, $\omega_s = 2\pi/T = 15\omega_c = 15$, from which the sampling time is $T = 0.419$. The sampled impulse response function is

$$h(0.419k) = A_1 e^{-0.419k} + A_2 e^{-0.419 s_2 k} + A_3 e^{-0.419 s_3 k}$$

The Z-transform of this function is

$$\begin{aligned} H(z) &= \frac{z}{z - e^{-0.419}} + A_2 \frac{z}{z - e^{-0.419 s_2}} + A_3 \frac{z}{z - e^{-0.419 s_3}} \\ &= \frac{z}{z - 0.658} + \frac{z(-z + 1.406)}{z^2 - 2.306z + 1.5204} \\ &= \frac{-0.242z^{-1} + 0.595z^{-2}}{1 - 2.964z^{-1} + 3.037z^{-2} - 1.000z^{-3}} \end{aligned}$$

■

In general, a digital filter designed using the impulse-invariant method results in a transfer function in the form of the ratio of two polynomials. The difference equation written from this system function is a recursive expression, and the filter so realized is an infinite impulse response (IIR) filter. Clearly, the impulse-invariant response method is equivalent to analog filtering of an impulse-sampled input signal. The fact has already been discussed that for a sampled signal to approximate the continuous signal, the sampling rate (Nyquist rate) must be at least twice the highest frequency component contained in the signal. However, a practical analog filter $H(s)$ is never strictly band limited. Therefore, an aliasing error occurs when this design method is used. As a practical matter, if the sampling frequency is five or more times the cutoff frequency of the low-pass analog filter, the aliasing effect on the frequency response is extremely small.

■ Example 8.12

Determine the digital filter equivalent of the RC network shown in Figure 8.22. It is desired that the 3 dB cutoff frequency be 1/5 of the sampling frequency.

Solution By simple analysis, the transfer function is

$$H(s) = \frac{1/RC}{s + 1/RC} = \frac{\omega_c}{s + \omega_c}$$

where

$$\omega_c = \frac{1}{RC} = \frac{1}{5}\frac{2\pi}{T}$$

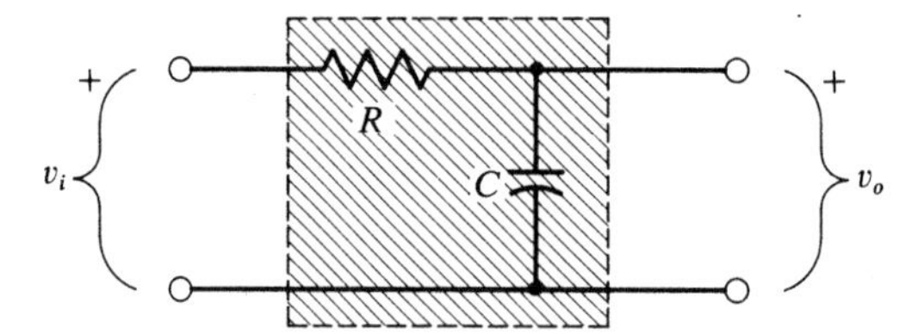

Figure 8.22 *RC* Network under Survey

We then write $H(s)$ in the form

$$H(s) = \frac{0.4\pi/T}{s + 0.4\pi/T}$$

By the impulse-invariant method, the digital equivalent $H(z)$ is (for numerical convenience, it was multiplied by T)

$$H(z) = \frac{T \times 0.4\pi/T}{1 - e^{-0.4\pi}z^{-1}} = \frac{1.2566}{1 - 0.285z^{-1}}$$

The equivalent difference equation is then found from

$$(1 - 0.285z^{-1})Y(z) = 1.2566X(z)$$

from which we can write

$$y(k) = 1.2566x(k) + 0.285y(k - 1)$$

■

■ **Example 8.13**

The normalized transfer function of the third-order Chebyshev filter of Example 8.3 is

$$H_3(s) = \frac{0.4913}{0.4913 + 1.2384s + 0.9883s^2 + s^3} \tag{8.67}$$

Determine the following:

a. The corresponding impulse-invariant digital filter.
b. The amplitude characteristics of the digital filter.
c. The impulse response $h(t)$ of $H_3(s)$.
d. The sampled response $h(kT)$ of the digital filter for $T = 1$.

Solution

a. Begin with the Chebyshev function in factored form:

$$H_3(s) = \frac{0.4913}{(s + 0.2471 - j0.9660)(s + 0.2471 + j0.9660)(s + 0.4942)}$$

This expression is written in partial fraction form:

$$H_3(s) = \frac{A_1}{s + 0.2471 - j0.9660} + \frac{A_2}{s + 0.2471 + j0.9660} + \frac{A_3}{s + 0.4942} \tag{8.68}$$

where

$$A_1 = \frac{0.4913}{2j \times 0.9660(0.2471 + j0.9660)}$$

$$A_2 = \frac{0.4913}{-2j \times 0.9660(0.2471 - j0.9660)}$$

$$A_3 = \frac{0.4913}{(0.2471 + j0.9660)(0.2471 - j0.9660)} = 0.4942$$

Now, set each quantity $s + s_i = 1 - e^{-s_i T} z^{-1}$ in (8.68) [see (8.66)], which specifies the impulse-invariant digital filter representation

$$H_3(z) = \frac{A_1}{1 - e^{-0.2471T + j0.9660T} z^{-1}} + \frac{A_2}{1 - e^{-0.2471T - j0.9660T} z^{-1}} + \frac{A_3}{1 - e^{-0.4942T} z^{-1}} \quad \textbf{(8.69)}$$

b. The corresponding frequency response is obtained by substituting $z = e^{j\omega_d} = e^{j\omega T}$ in (8.69). The resulting expression is

$$H_3(e^{j\omega T}) = \frac{A_1}{1 - e^{-0.2471T + j0.9660T} e^{-j\omega T}} + \frac{A_2}{1 - e^{-0.2471T - j0.9660T} e^{-j\omega T}} + \frac{A_3}{1 - e^{-0.4942T} e^{-j\omega T}} \quad \textbf{(8.70)}$$

This expression is plotted in Figure 8.23 for $T = 1$.

c. Apply the inverse Laplace transform to (8.68) to find the impulse response $h(t)$, which is given by

$$\begin{aligned} h(t) &= A_1 e^{-0.2471t} e^{j0.9660t} + A_2 e^{-0.2471t} e^{-j0.9660t} + A_3 e^{-0.4942t} \\ &= e^{-0.2471t}[A_1 e^{j0.9660t} + A_1^*(e^{j0.9660t})^*] + 0.4942 e^{-0.4942t} \\ &= e^{-0.2471t} \times 0.51 \cos(0.966t + 165.65^\circ) + 0.4942 e^{-0.4942t} \end{aligned} \quad \textbf{(8.71)}$$

Figure 8.24 shows the impulse response corresponding to (8.71).

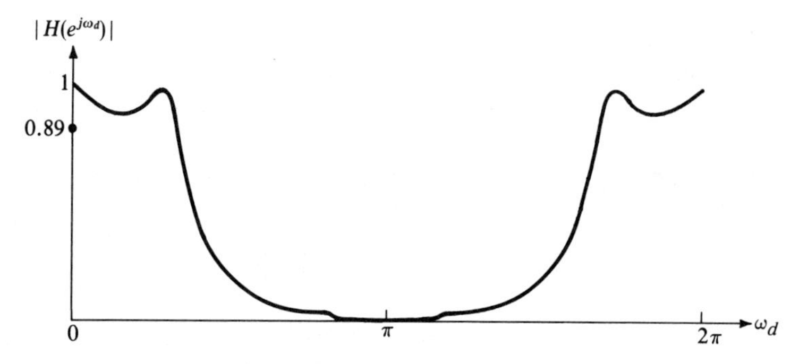

Figure 8.23 Frequency Response of the Chebyshev Filter under Review

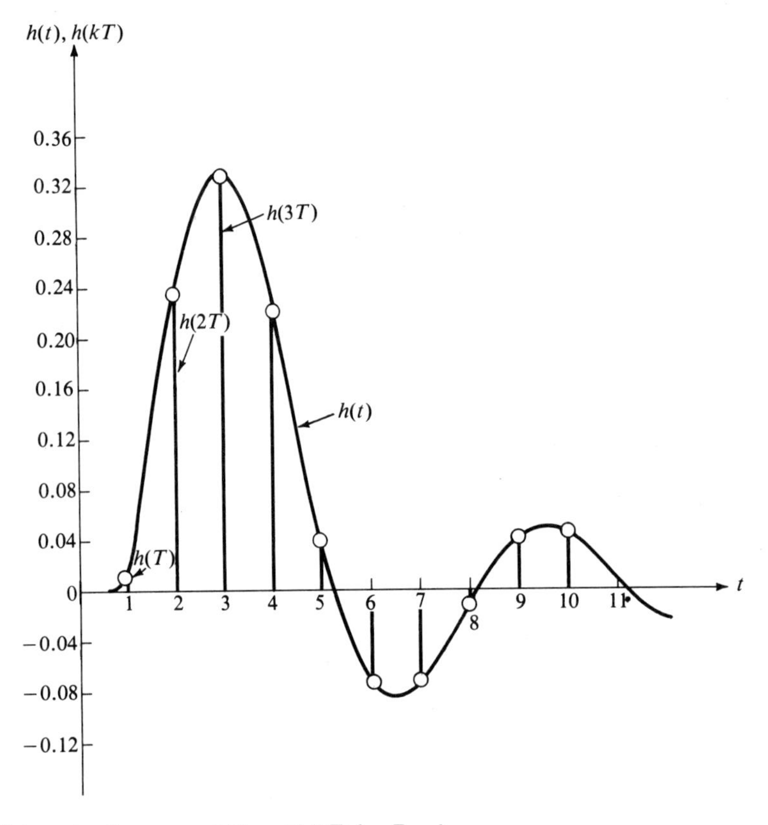

Figure 8.24 Impulse Responses $h(t)$ and $h(kT)$ for $T = 1$

d. The discrete impulse response $h(kT)$ for $T = 1$ is obtained from $h(t)$ for $t = kT$:

$$h(k) = 0.51e^{-0.2471k}\cos(0.966k + 165.65^\circ) + 0.4942e^{-0.4942k}$$

■

■ Example 8.14

Determine the impulse-invariant digital filter corresponding to the second-order Butterworth filter.

Solution The second-order Butterworth filter is given by

$$H(s) = \frac{1}{s^2 + 1.414s + 1} = \frac{1}{(s + 0.707)^2 + (0.707)^2}$$

$$= \frac{1}{0.707} \frac{0.707}{(s + 0.707)^2 + (0.707)^2}$$

From the Laplace transform, Table 6.1, the impulse response of the system is

$$h(t) = 1.414e^{-0.707t} \sin 0.707t = 1.414e^{-0.707t}\left(\frac{e^{j0.707t} - e^{-j0.707t}}{2j}\right)$$

$$= \frac{1.414}{2j}\left[e^{(j0.707-0.707)t} - e^{-(j0.707+0.707)t}\right]$$

The Z-transform of this function is

$$H(z) = \mathscr{Z}\{h(kT)\} = \frac{1.414}{2j}\left[\sum_{k=0}^{\infty} e^{(j0.707-0.707)kT}z^{-k}\right.$$

$$\left. - \sum_{k=0}^{\infty} e^{-(j0.707+0.707)kT}z^{-k}\right]$$

$$= \frac{1.414}{2j}\left[\frac{1}{1 - e^{(j0.707-0.707)T}z^{-1}}\right.$$

$$\left. - \frac{1}{1 - e^{-(j0.707+0.707)T}z^{-1}}\right]$$

$$= 1.414\frac{ze^{-0.707T}\sin 0.707T}{z^2 - 2e^{-0.707T}(\cos 0.707T)z + e^{-1.414T}}$$ ■

8.10 Bilinear Transformation

It is possible to avoid the folding problem of the impulse-invariant response transformation discussed in the foregoing section by using the bilinear transformation. We write the relationships

$$s = \frac{2}{T}\frac{z-1}{z+1} \tag{8.72a}$$

and

$$z = \frac{1 + Ts/2}{1 - Ts/2} \tag{8.72b}$$

In terms of the z-plane, this algebraic transformation uniquely maps the left-half of the s-plane, as shown in Figure 8.25a, into the interior of the unit circle in the z-plane, as shown in Figure 8.25b. Because no folding occurs, no folding errors will arise. However, a shortcoming of this transformation is that the frequency response is nonlinear—that is, warped—in the digital domain.

If we insert $z = e^{j\omega_d}$ into (8.72a), we obtain a relationship between the frequency ω of the analog filter and frequency ω_d of the digital filter. We find that

$$s = \sigma + j\omega = \frac{2(e^{j\omega_d} - 1)}{T(e^{j\omega_d} + 1)} = \frac{2e^{j\omega_d/2}(e^{j\omega_d/2} - e^{-j\omega_d/2})}{Te^{j\omega_d/2}(e^{j\omega_d/2} + e^{-j\omega_d/2})} = j\frac{2}{T}\tan\frac{\omega_d}{2} \tag{8.73}$$

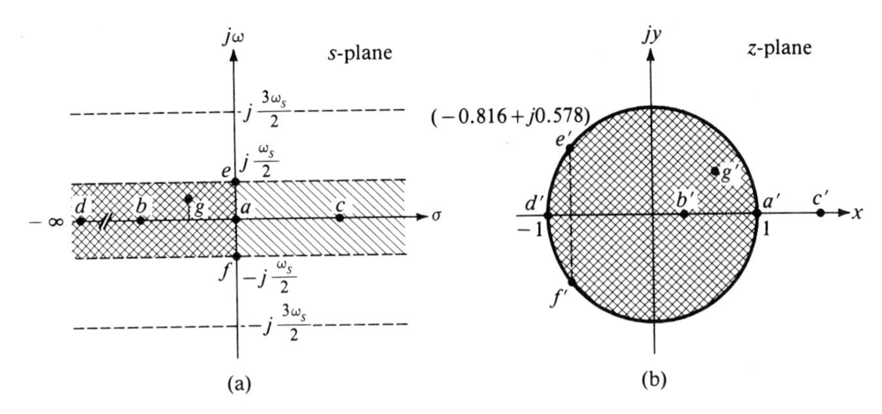

Figure 8.25 s-Plane to z-Plane Mapping. (a) A step in finding the inverse Z-transform. (b) Mapping of the s-plane onto the z-plane.

From this equation, by equating real and imaginary parts separately, we obtain

$$\sigma = 0 \tag{8.74a}$$

$$\omega = \frac{2}{T}\tan\frac{\omega_d}{2} \tag{8.74b}$$

Observe that the relationship between the two frequencies ω and ω_d is a nonlinear one. This effect is the **warping** effect. Figure 8.26a shows the warping relationship graphically. It is evident from the plot that the sampling time T changes the ωT axis by stretching or compressing it. Figure 8.26b clearly shows the warping effect. Note that the shapes of $H(j\omega)$ and $H(e^{j\omega_d})$ are similar, but the higher-frequency bands are reduced disproportionately.

Compensation can be made for the effect of warping by prewarping the continuous filter design in such a way that upon applying the bilinear transformation, the critical frequencies will be shifted back to the original values. The details of this procedure are rather complicated and are not carried out.*

■ Example 8.15

Use the bilinear transformation to determine the characteristic of a digital filter if the corresponding analog filter has the transfer function

$$H(s) = \frac{H_0}{s - s_1} \tag{8.75}$$

* For details, see A. D. Poularikas and S. Seely, *Signals and Systems* (Boston: PWS-KENT Publishing Co., 1985).

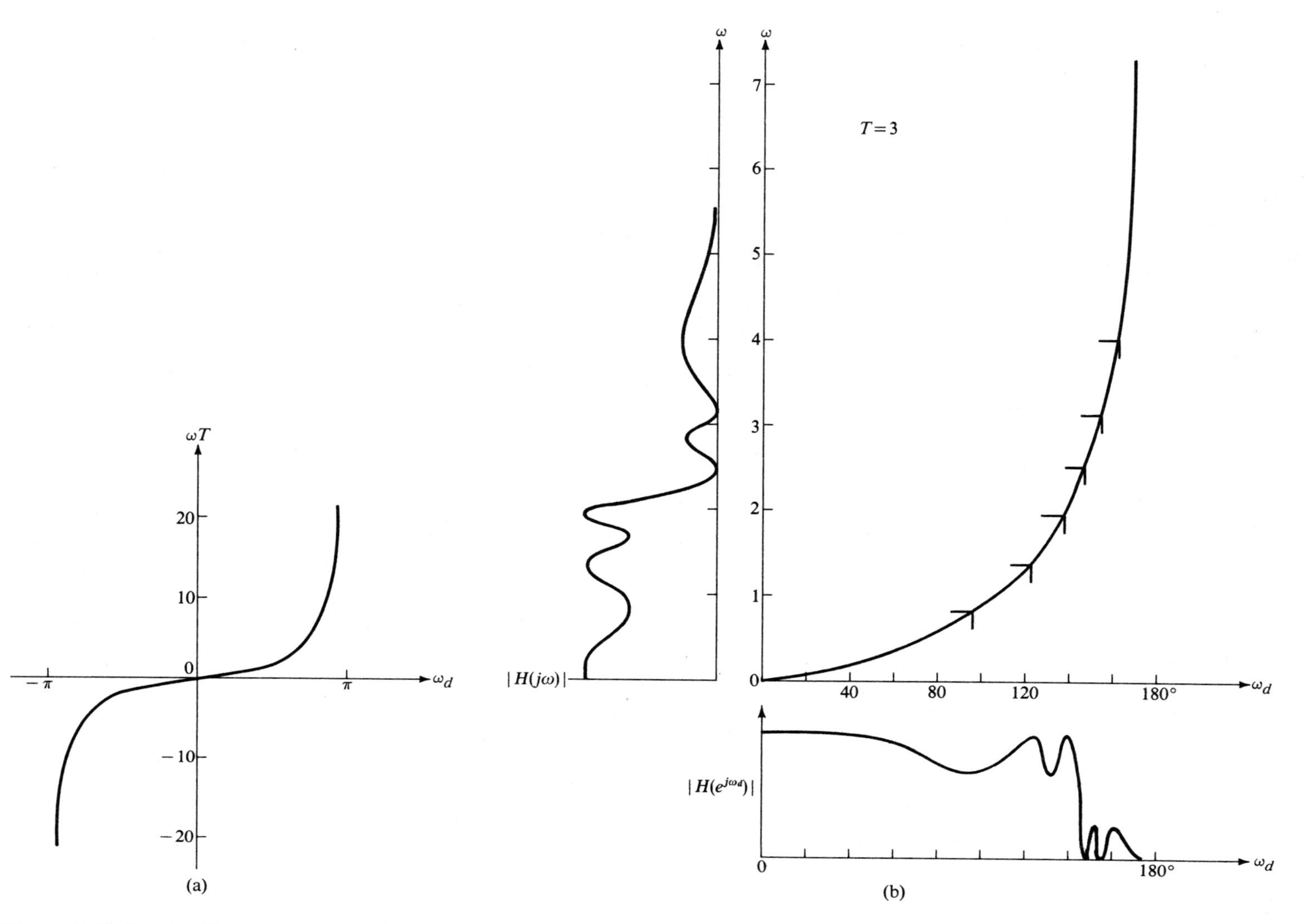

Figure 8.26 Graphic Illustration of ω and ω_d in Bilinear Transformation

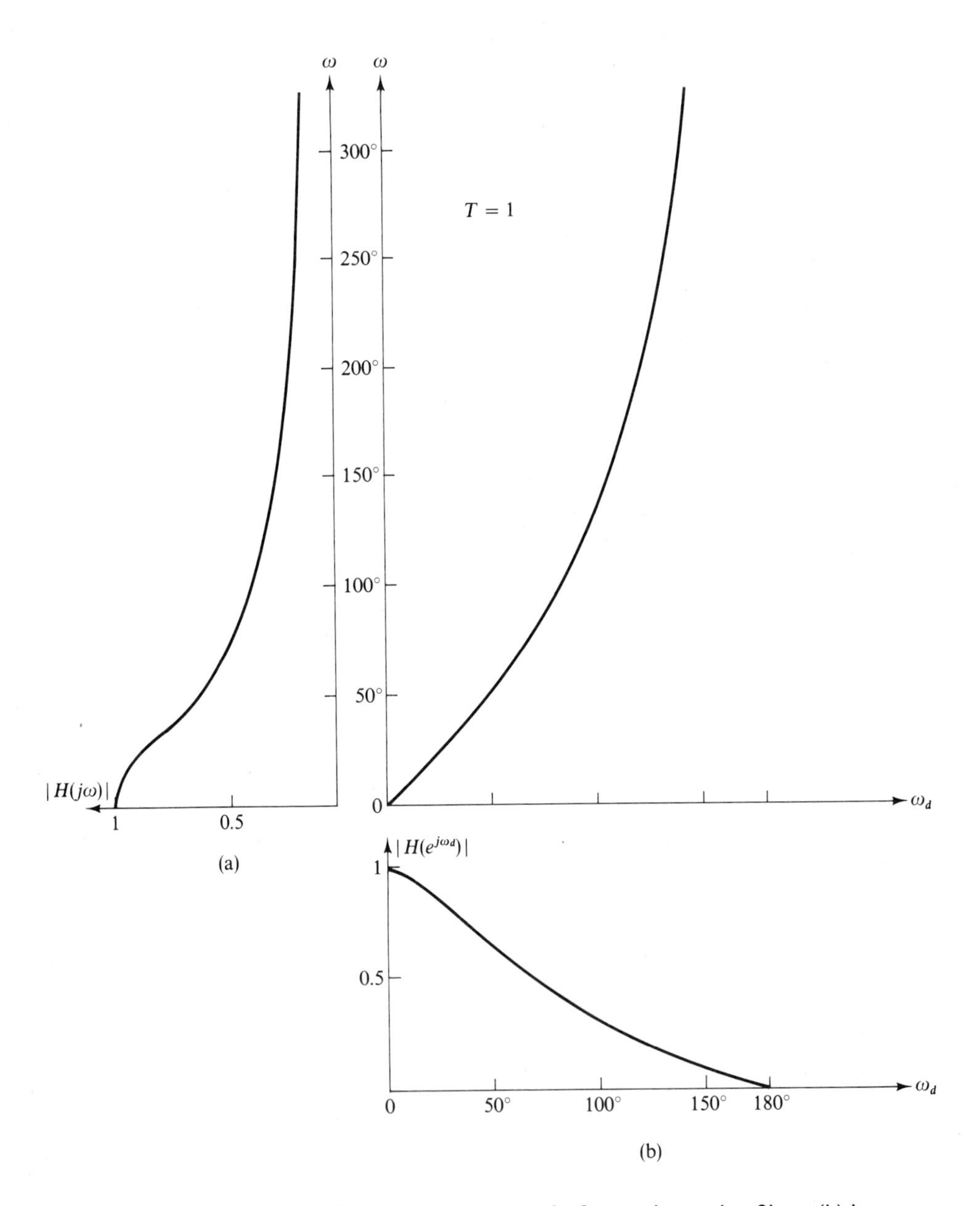

Figure 8.27 Illustrating Example 8.15. (a) Frequency response of a first-order analog filter. (b) Its corresponding digital filter.

Solution By the use of (8.72), we obtain

$$H(z) = H(s)\Big|_{s=2(z-1)/T(z+1)} = \frac{H_0}{\dfrac{2z-1}{Tz+1} - s_1} = H_0 T \frac{z+1}{(2-s_1T)z - (2+s_1T)} \tag{8.76}$$

To illustrate the variation graphically, we choose $H_0 = 0.8$, $s_1 = 0.8$, and $T = 1$. Figures 8.27a and 8.27b give the frequency response of the analog filter and the digital filter, respectively. The two transfer functions are given by

$$|H(s)| = \frac{0.8}{\sqrt{\omega^2 + (0.8)^2}} \tag{8.77a}$$

$$|H(z)| = 0.8 \frac{\sqrt{(\cos\omega_d + 1)^2 + \sin^2\omega_d}}{\sqrt{(1.2\cos\omega_d - 2.8)^2 + (1.2\sin\omega_d)^2}} \tag{8.77b}$$

The figures show the corresponding frequencies of the two filters, including the cutoff value of the digital filter. The nonlinear relation between the two curves is clearly evident. ■

■ **Example 8.16**

We wish to design a digital Butterworth filter that meets the following conditions:

a. The 3 dB cutoff point ω_d is to occur at 0.4π rad/s.
b. $T = 50\ \mu s$
c. At $2\omega_d$, the attenuation is to be 15 dB.

Solution First, we find the analog-equivalent criteria for the requisite digital filter. Using (8.74), we have

$$\omega_c = \frac{2}{T}\tan\frac{\omega_d}{2} = \frac{2}{50\times10^{-6}}\tan\frac{0.4\pi}{2} = 29.1\times10^3\ \text{rad/s}$$

$$\omega\Big|_{15\ \text{dB}} = \frac{2}{T}\tan\frac{2\omega_d}{2} = \frac{2}{50\times10^{-6}}\tan 2\times\frac{0.4\pi}{2} = 123.1\times10^3\ \text{rad/s}$$

By (8.1) with $\omega = \omega/\omega_c$, we obtain

$$-10\log|H(j123.1\times10^3)|^2$$

$$= -10\log\left|\frac{1}{1+[(123.1\times10^3)/(29.1\times10^3)]^{2n}}\right| \geq 15$$

from which

$$1 + \left(\frac{123.1\times10^3}{29.1\times10^3}\right)^{2n} \geq 31.62$$

From this expression, we find that

$$n \geq 1.18$$

Hence, the minimal order of the Butterworth filter to meet the specifications is $n = 2$. The form of the filter is, from Table 8.2,

$$H_2(s) = \frac{1}{s^2 + 1.4142s + 1}$$

The analog filter satisfying the specifications is

$$H(s) = H_2\left(\frac{s}{\omega_c}\right) = H_2\left(\frac{s}{29.1 \times 10^3}\right) = \frac{1}{\left(\dfrac{s}{29.1 \times 10^3}\right)^2 + \left(\dfrac{1.4142}{29.1 \times 10^3}\right)s + 1}$$

$$H(s) = \frac{(29.1 \times 10^3)^2}{s^2 + 41.1532 \times 10^3 s + (29.1 \times 10^3)^2}$$

Introduce (8.72) into this equation to write

$$H(z) = \frac{29.1^2 \times 10^6}{\left(\dfrac{2}{T}\right)^2 \dfrac{(z-1)^2}{(z+1)^2} + 41.1532 \times 10^3 \left(\dfrac{2}{T}\right)\dfrac{(z-1)}{(z+1)} + 29.1^2 \times 10^6}$$

$$= \frac{2.117 + 4.234z^{-1} + 2.117z^{-2}}{10.232 - 3.766z^{-1} + 2.002z^{-2}}$$

This is the final digital Butterworth design. ■

8.11 Frequency Transformations for Digital Filters

Frequency transformations are available for digital filters in parallel with those discussed in Section 8.6 for analog filters. These transformations permit a low-pass filter design to be adapted to another low-pass filter, a high-pass filter, a bandpass filter, or a bandstop digital filter. We consider these transformations in the sections that follow.

Low-Pass to Low-Pass Transformation

This transformation is specified by

$$z^{-1} \rightarrow \frac{z^{-1} - \alpha}{1 - \alpha z^{-1}} \qquad \text{or} \qquad z \rightarrow \frac{z - \alpha}{1 - \alpha z} \tag{8.78}$$

where

$$\alpha = \frac{\sin[(\omega_{dc} - \omega'_{dc})/2]}{\sin[(\omega_{dc} + \omega'_{dc})/2]}$$

ω_{dc} = cutoff frequency of the given filter

ω'_{dc} = cutoff frequency of the desired filter

Example 8.17

Deduce a low-pass digital filter with $\omega'_{dc} = 30$ rad/s using the low-pass digital filter of Example 8.10 for the case $T = 0.05$ s.

Solution The given digital filter has the system function

$$H(z) = \frac{20}{1 - e^{-20 \times 0.05} z^{-1}} = \frac{20}{1 - 0.3679 z^{-1}} \tag{8.79}$$

We now apply the transformation specified by (8.78). The result is

$$H(z) = \frac{20}{1 - 0.3679[(z^{-1} - \alpha)/(1 - \alpha z^{-1})]}$$
$$= \frac{20 - 20\alpha z^{-1}}{(1 + 0.3679\alpha) - (\alpha + 0.3679) z^{-1}} \tag{8.80}$$

where the constant α is given by

$$\alpha = \frac{\sin[(1 - 1.5)/2]}{\sin[(1 + 1.5)/2]} = -0.2607$$

since $\omega'_{dc}/\omega_{dc} = 30/20 = 1.5$. Figure 8.28 shows the plots for the original and for the transformed filters. Observe that the value of the filters at $\omega_c = 1$ (20 rad/s) and $\omega_c = 1.5$ (30 rad/s) are the same, a result that was expected in light of the requirements imposed on the problem. ■

Low-Pass to High-Pass Transformation

The required transformation is given by

$$z^{-1} \to -\frac{z^{-1} + \alpha}{1 + \alpha z^{-1}} \qquad \text{or} \qquad z - \frac{z + \alpha}{1 + \alpha z} \tag{8.81}$$

where

$$\alpha = -\frac{\cos[(\omega_{dc} + \omega'_{dc})/2]}{\cos[(\omega_{dc} - \omega'_{dc})/2]}$$

Example 8.18

Using the digital filter of Example 8.10, determine a high-pass digital filter with $\omega'_{dc} = 30$ rad/s and $T = 0.05$ s.

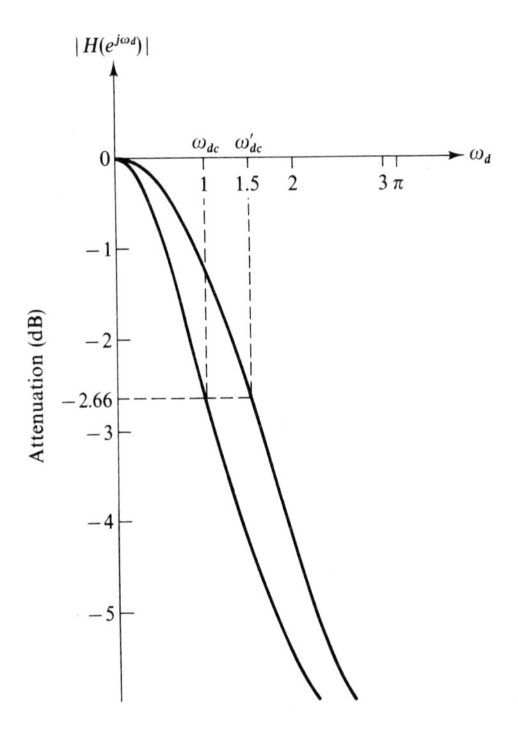

Figure 8.28 Low-to-Low Transformation of Digital Filters

Solution We begin with the given digital filter:

$$H(z) = \frac{20}{1 - 0.3679z^{-1}} \tag{8.82}$$

Now, apply the transformation specified by (8.81):

$$H(z) = \frac{20}{1 - 0.3679[-(z^{-1} + \alpha)/(1 + \alpha z^{-1})]}$$

$$= \frac{20 + 20\alpha z^{-1}}{(1 + 0.3679\alpha) + (0.3679 + \alpha)z^{-1}}$$

where the constant α is given by

$$\alpha = -\frac{\cos[(1 + 1.5)/2]}{\cos[(1 - 1.5)/2]} = -0.9795$$

since $\omega'_{dc}/\omega_{dc} = 30/20 = 1.5$. Figure 8.29 shows the plot of the transformed filter. Observe that at the frequency $\omega'_{dc} = 30$ rad/s, which is equivalent to $\omega'_{dc}/\omega_{dc} = 30/20 = 1.5$ in normalized form, the attenuation is -2.66 dB, as expected from an inspection of Figure 8.28. ■

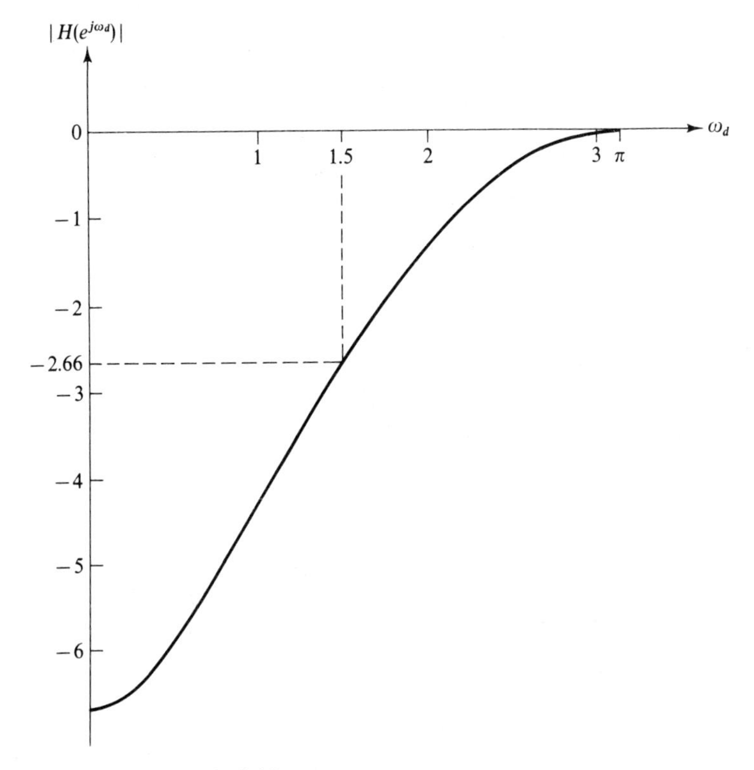

Figure 8.29 Illustrating Example 8.18

Low-Pass to Bandpass Transformation

This transformation is given by

$$z^{-1} \rightarrow \frac{z^{-2} + \dfrac{2\alpha\beta}{\beta+1} z^{-1} + \dfrac{\beta-1}{\beta+1}}{\dfrac{\beta-1}{\beta+1} z^{-2} + \dfrac{2\alpha\beta}{\beta+1} z^{-1} + 1} \tag{8.83}$$

where

$$\alpha = \frac{\cos[(\omega'_{du} + \omega'_{dl})/2]}{\cos[(\omega'_{du} - \omega'_{dl})/2]}$$

$$\beta = \cot\left[\frac{\omega'_{du} - \omega_{dl}}{2}\right]\tan\frac{\omega_{dc}}{2}$$

ω'_{du} = desired upper cutoff frequency

ω'_{dl} = desired lower cutoff frequency

ω'_0 = center frequency

Observe that two of the three parameters ω_0', ω_{du}', and ω_{dl}' are free, with the third being constrained by the other two.

■ Example 8.19

Determine a bandpass digital filter with upper cutoff frequency $\omega_{du}' = 80$ rad/s and lower cutoff frequency $\omega_{dl}' = 40$ rad/s. Use the first-order digital filter of Example 8.7 with $T = 0.05$ s.

Solution Use the results of (8.83) to obtain

$$\alpha = \frac{\cos[(80+40)/2]}{\cos[(80-40)/2]} = \frac{\cos 60}{\cos 20} = -2.3337$$

$$\beta = \cot\left(\frac{80-40}{2}\right)\tan\left(\frac{20}{2}\right) = 0.4470 \times 0.6483 = 0.2898$$

where $\omega_{dc} = 20$ rad/s, given in Example 8.10. Thus, we obtain

$$H(z) = \frac{20}{1 - 0.9048\left(\dfrac{z^{-2} + az^{-1} + b}{bz^{-2} + az^{-1} + 1}\right)}$$

$$= \frac{20b - 20az + 20z^2}{(b + 0.3679) - 1.3679az + (1 + 0.3179b)z^2}$$

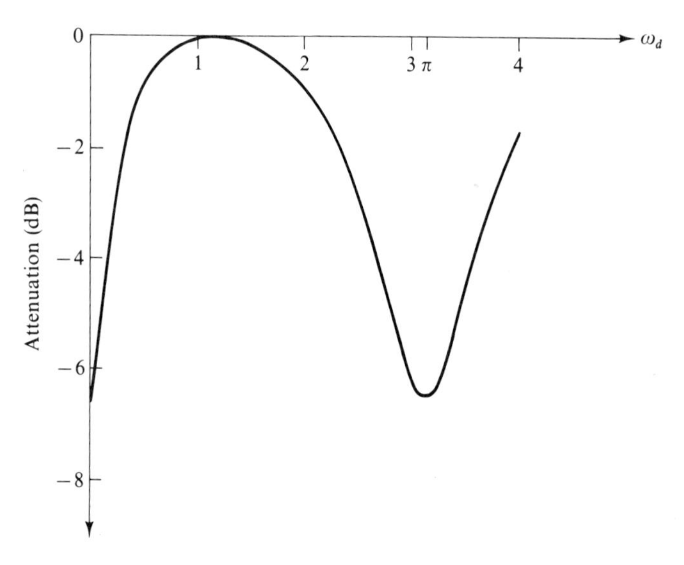

Figure 8.30 Illustrating Example 8.19

where

$$a = \frac{2\alpha\beta}{\beta + 1} = \frac{-2 \times 2.3337 \times 0.2898}{1.2898} = -1.04869$$

$$b = \frac{\beta - 1}{\beta + 1} = \frac{0.2898 - 1}{0.2898 + 1} = -0.55063$$

A normalized plot of $H(e^{j\omega_d})$ is shown in Figure 8.30. ■

Low-Pass to Bandstop Transformation

This transformation is given by

$$z^{-1} \rightarrow \frac{z^{-2} - \dfrac{2\alpha}{1+\beta} z^{-1} + \dfrac{1-\beta}{1+\beta}}{\dfrac{1-\beta}{1+\beta} z^{-2} - \dfrac{2\alpha}{1+\beta} z^{-1} + 1} \tag{8.84}$$

where

$$\alpha = \frac{\cos[(\omega'_{du} + \omega'_{dl})/2]}{\cos[(\omega'_{du} - \omega'_{dl})/2]}$$

$$\beta = \tan\left[\frac{\omega'_{du} - \omega'_{dl}}{2}\right] \tan \frac{\omega_{dc}}{2}$$

ω'_{du} = desired upper cutoff frequency

ω'_{dl} = desired lower cutoff frequency

8.12 Recursive versus Nonrecursive Designs

A comparison of the important features of different filter designs is helpful. In recursive IIR filters, the poles of the transfer function can be placed anywhere within the unit circle in the frequency plane. As a result, IIR filters can usually match physical systems well. Also, high selectivity can be achieved using low-order transfer functions. With nonrecursive FIR filters, on the other hand, the poles are fixed at the origin, and high selectivity can be achieved only by using a relatively high order transfer function with its resulting computations. For the same filter specifications, the order of the nonrecursive filter might be 5 to 10 times that of the recursive structure, with the consequent need for more electronic parts. Often, however, a recursive structure might not meet the specifications and, in such cases, the nonrecursive filter can be used. An advantage in the design of the nonrecursive filter is that FFT techniques can be used in the calculations.

Hardware implementation of filters requires that storage of input and output data and also arithmetic operations be implemented, which requires using finite word length registers—for example, 8, 12, or 16 bits. As a result, certain errors will occur. These errors are categorized as follows:

1. Quantization errors due to arithmetic operations, such as rounding off and truncation.
2. Quantization errors due to representing the input signal by a set of discrete values.
3. Quantization errors when the filter coefficients are represented by a finite number of bits.

It is left to the filter designer to decide on the various trade-offs between cost and precision in trying to reach a specified goal.

Problems

Section 8.2

1. Show that the square of (8.1) is identical with (8.2).
2. First, deduce $D(s)$ for the third-order Butterworth filter, and next, demonstrate that $D(s)D(-s) = 1 + (-s^2)^3 = 1 - (j\omega)^6 = 1 + \omega^6$.
3. Design a low-pass Butterworth filter that has an attenuation of at least 20 dB at three times the frequency $\omega_c = 2 \times 10^4$ rad/s.
4. Deduce the transfer function of a Butterworth filter that has an attenuation of at least 10 dB at twice the cutoff frequency $\omega_c = 10^5$ rad/s. Find the values of L and C for the filter shown in Figure 8.6.
5. Determine the impulse response functions of the first-order and third-order Butterworth filters.
6. Using (8.5), derive the transfer function for a third-order Butterworth low-pass filter, locate its poles, and compare your results with those given in Table 8.2.
7. Show that the high-frequency rolloff of an nth order Butterworth filter is $20n$ dB/decade. Also, show that the first $(2n - 1)$ derivatives of an nth order Butterworth filter are zero at $\omega = 0$.
8. Find the value of n for a Butterworth filter that satisfies the condition specified in Figure 8.31.

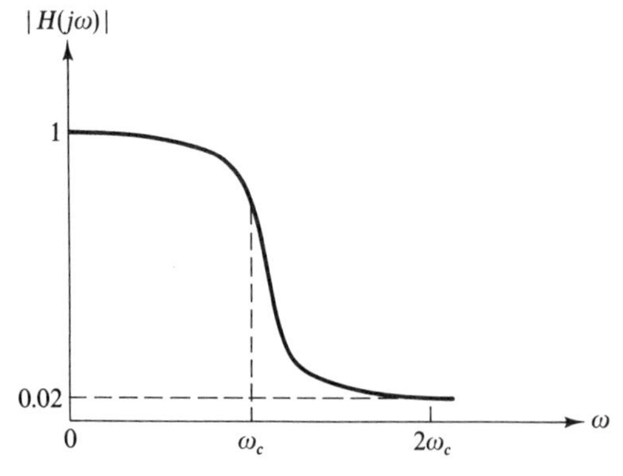

Figure 8.31

9. Design a Butterworth filter that meets the following specifications: pass band, 0 kHz to 5 kHz; attenuation, amplitude to be down 60 dB at 8 kHz.

Section 8.3

10. Use (8.17) to find $C_n(\omega)$ for $n = 0, 1, 2, 3$ for both $|\omega| \leq 1$ and $\omega > 1$.
11. The ripple of a Chebyshev filter in decibels is given by (a) $r_{dB} = 0.05$, (b) $r_{dB} = 0.1$, and (c) $r_{dB} = 1.5$. Find the corresponding ε's.
12. Write the Chebyshev functions $|H_2(j\omega)|$ and $|H_3(j\omega)|$ if $\omega_c = 4$ rad/s and $\varepsilon = 1$.
13. For $n = 3$ and $\varepsilon = 0.8$, determine the poles of a low-pass Chebyshev filter. Plot the poles on the complex plane. Find the major and minor axes of the ellipse that they define.
14. Design a low-pass Chebyshev filter with 1.2 dB ripple in the pass band and an attenuation of at least 30 dB at three times the cutoff frequency of 8 rad/s.
15. Determine the transfer function of a second-order Chebyshev low-pass filter with a cutoff frequency of $100/2\pi$ Hz, a 0.5 dB ripple in the pass band, and a unit magnitude at $\omega = 0$.
16. Design a Chebyshev low-pass filter to meet the following specifications: (a) bandwidth, 10^3 rad/s; (b) ripple, 0.1 dB; and (c) attenuation at least 30 dB for $\omega \geq 6 \times 10^3$ rad/s. Find the transfer function of this filter.

Section 8.6

17. The design of Problem 14 is to provide the basis for a high-pass filter with cutoff at 3 rad/s. Specify the transfer function.
18. Design a pass band filter to meet the following specifications: (a) The 3 dB attenuations are at $1500 \times 2\pi$ rad/s and at $2500 \times 2\pi$ rad/s, and (b) the attenuation should be at least 30 dB for frequencies lower than $700 \times 2\pi$ rad/s and higher than $5000 \times 2\pi$ rad/s.
19. Design a bandstop filter with attenuation at least 30 dB between 10^4 Hz and 1.3×10^4 Hz. The attenuation for ω less than 4×10^3 Hz and more than 16×10^3 Hz must be less than -3 dB.

Section 8.8

20. Repeat Example 8.7 for $T = 1$ and $N = 7$. Compare your results with those given in Example 8.7.
21. Deduce $H(z)$ for an FIR filter with $T = 1$ and $N = 11$ that approximates the transfer function shown in Figure 8.32. Plot the results for $H_d(e^{j\omega_d})$ and compare with the given $H(j\omega)$.

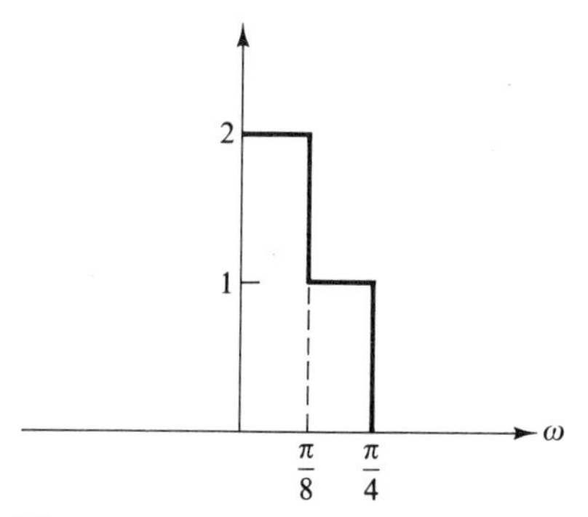

Figure 8.32

22. Determine the coefficients $h(kT)$ for $T = 1$ and $N = 11$ for an FIR filter that approximates the transfer function shown in Figure 8.33. Employ two methods: (1) using the continuous Fourier series, and (2) sampling $|H(j\omega)|$ and deducing $h(kT)$ therefrom.

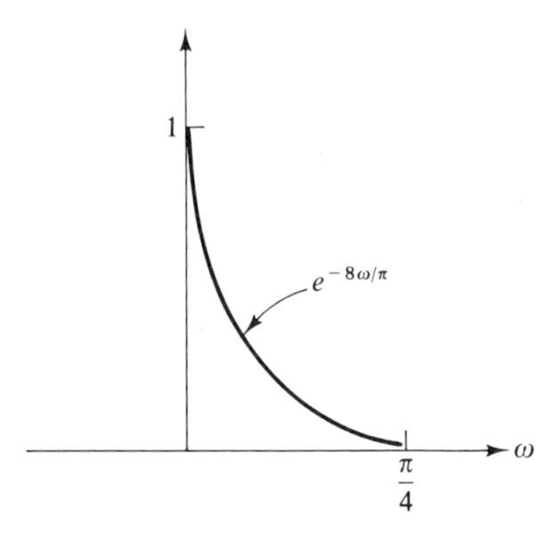

Figure 8.33

23. Evaluate the frequency response $W(e^{j\theta})$ for the triangular (Bartlett) window shown in Figure 8.34. How does this response compare with that of the rectangular window?

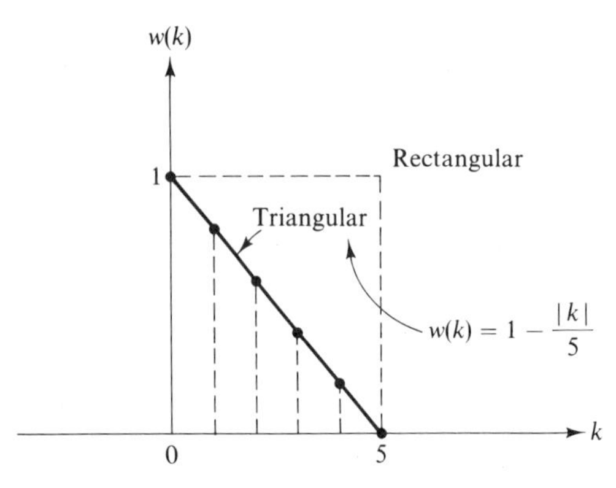

Figure 8.34

Section 8.9

24. **a.** Find $H(z)$ using the impulse-invariant method for a first-order normalized Chebyshev filter having a 0.5 dB ripple factor.

b. Deduce the amplitude characteristics of the digital filter.

c. Find the impulse response $h(t)$ of $H_n(s)$.

25. Determine the digital equivalent of a first-order Chebyshev filter with a 1 dB ripple in the pass band. The cutoff frequency is 100 rad/s. Use the value $T = 10^{-3}$.

26. Suppose that two RC sections, as discussed in Example 8.9, are cascaded. A buffer amplifier is used between sections to avoid loading. Find the digital filter equivalent of this combination. Can we infer from the results that the digital filter is made up of two identical digital sections in cascade?

27. Repeat Example 8.10 with $T = 0.1$ s and $T = 0.0025$ s.

28. Deduce the second-order Butterworth digital filter with cutoff frequency $f_c = 100$ Hz and a sampling rate of 1250 Hz.

29. Determine the following for the second-order Chebyshev filter with a pass band ripple of 0.5 dB:

a. The corresponding impulse-invariant digital filter.
b. The impulse response $h(t)$ of $H_n(s)$.
c. The unit sample response $h(kT)$ of the digital filter for $T = 1$.
d. The amplitude characteristics of the digital filter.

Section 8.10

30. Use bilinear methods to design a digital Chebyshev filter with a 1 dB ripple in the pass band that meets the following conditions (see Example 8.3): (a) The 3 dB cutoff point ω_d is to occur at 0.4π rad/s, (b) $T = 50\ \mu$s, and (c) the attenuation at $2\omega_d$ is to be at least 20 dB.

Appendix

Matrix Mathematics

A.1 Introduction

We find extensive use of matrixes in representing systems of equations with both continuous and discrete variables. They are particularly important in studies involving state variables.

To introduce a matrix, consider the following set of linear algebraic equations:

$$\begin{aligned} a_{11}x_1 + a_{12}x_2 + \cdots + a_{1n}x_n &= w_1 \\ a_{21}x_1 + a_{22}x_2 + \cdots + a_{2n}x_n &= w_2 \\ \vdots \qquad \vdots \qquad\qquad \vdots \quad &\quad \vdots \\ a_{n1}x_1 + a_{n2}x_2 + \cdots + a_{nn}x_n &= w_n \end{aligned}$$

Here, the x's may denote the state variables of a system and the w's may be the excitation (input) functions. The a's are linear coefficients that are defined by the system. In matrix form, this set of equations is written

$$\begin{bmatrix} a_{11} & a_{12} & \cdots & a_{1n} \\ a_{21} & a_{22} & \cdots & a_{2n} \\ \vdots & \vdots & & \vdots \\ a_{n1} & a_{n2} & \cdots & a_{nn} \end{bmatrix} \begin{bmatrix} x_1 \\ x_2 \\ \vdots \\ x_n \end{bmatrix} = \begin{bmatrix} w_1 \\ w_2 \\ \vdots \\ w_n \end{bmatrix}$$

It is usually written more simply as

$$\mathbf{Ax} = \mathbf{w} \qquad \text{or} \qquad \sum_{j=1}^{n} a_{ij}x_j = w_i \qquad i = 1, 2, \ldots n$$

where

$$\mathbf{A} = \begin{bmatrix} a_{11} & a_{12} & \cdots & a_{1n} \\ a_{21} & a_{22} & \cdots & a_{2n} \\ \vdots & \vdots & & \vdots \\ a_{n1} & a_{n2} & \cdots & a_{nn} \end{bmatrix} \qquad \mathbf{x} = \begin{bmatrix} x_1 \\ x_2 \\ \vdots \\ x_n \end{bmatrix} \qquad \mathbf{w} = \begin{bmatrix} w_1 \\ w_2 \\ \vdots \\ w_n \end{bmatrix}$$

Observe that the matrixes as defined here are arrays of coefficients; there is no numerical value associated with any of these arrays.

The matrix **A** comprises the coefficients a_{ij}, where i refers to the row and j refers to the column; hence, a_{ij} is the coefficient belonging to the ith row and jth column. Clearly, matrixes may be square, rectangular, columnar, or row. The relationship among the number of rows and columns in matrixes is important in certain operations. Let us examine some of these relations.

A.2 Definitions

A matrix is ordinarily defined by the character of the array, the elements of the array, or some special property of the array. The important definitions follow:

1. **Elements of a matrix A:** the coefficients a_{ij}.
2. **Order of a matrix:** A matrix of m rows and n columns is called an $m \times n$ matrix.
3. **Square matrix:** a matrix of order $m \times m$.
4. **Column matrix:** a matrix containing only one column; hence, of order $m \times 1$.
5. **Row matrix:** a matrix containing only one row; it is of order $1 \times m$.
6. **Real matrix:** All elements of the matrix are real.
7. **Complex matrix:** Some or all elements of the matrix are algebraically complex.
8. **Zero or null matrix:** All elements of the matrix are zero.
9. **Sparse matrix:** Many of the elements of the matrix are zero (no quantitative measure is given).
10. **Diagonal matrix:** a square matrix with nonzero elements only along the diagonal.
11. **Unit matrix:** a diagonal matrix whose elements are unity.
12. **Transposed matrix:** A transposed matrix $\mathbf{A}^T$ has rows and columns that are interchanged with rows and columns of the original matrix **A**. That is, if $\mathbf{A} = [a_{ij}]$, then $\mathbf{A}^T = [a_{ji}]$.
13. **Complex conjugate of a matrix:** $\mathbf{A}^*$ is the complex conjugate of matrix **A** if each element of $\mathbf{A}^*$ is the complex conjugate of the corresponding element of **A**. Clearly, for real matrixes, $\mathbf{A} = \mathbf{A}^*$.
14. **Determinant of a matrix:** the determinant that has the same elements as the matrix.
15. **Trace of a matrix:** the sum of the diagonal elements of the matrix.

16. **Rank of a matrix:** the number of dimensions spanned by the rows (or columns) considered as n (or m) vectors. The rank of an $n \times n$ nonsingular matrix is n. The rank of an $n \times n$ singular matrix is less than n. Equivalently, we say that an $n \times n$ matrix $\mathbf{A}$ is of rank $r < n$ if there exists a submatrix $r \times r$ of $\mathbf{A}$ that is nonsingular (has a nonzero determinant) and any other submatrix of order higher than r is singular (has a zero determinant).
17. **Cofactor of the element a_{ij}:** the signed minor of a_{ij}. That is, cofactor $a_{ij} = (-1)^{i+j}$ minor a_{ij}, where minor a_{ij} is the determinant of the matrix formed by omitting the ith row and jth column of the original matrix $\mathbf{A}$.
18. **Adjoint of matrix A:** the transposed cofactor of $\mathbf{A}$.
19. **Nonsingular matrix:** a square matrix whose rows or columns are linearly independent. In this case, $\det|\mathbf{A}| \neq 0$.

Additional definitions will be introduced as details of matrix operations are discussed.

A.3 Matrix Algebra

The following sections discuss some of the more important algebraic operations involving matrixes.

Equality of Matrixes. Two matrixes are equal if and only if each of their corresponding elements is equal. This condition prescribes the requirement that for two matrixes to be equal, they must contain the same number of rows and columns.

Addition and Subtraction. The sum or difference of two matrixes $\mathbf{A}$ and $\mathbf{B}$, both of the same order, is

$$\mathbf{A} + \mathbf{B} = [a_{ij} + b_{ij}] \qquad \begin{matrix} i = 1, 2, \ldots m \\ j = 1, 2, \ldots n \end{matrix} \tag{A.1}$$

For example, we have

$$\begin{bmatrix} 2 & 3 \\ 4 & -5 \end{bmatrix} + \begin{bmatrix} -1 & 3 \\ -2 & 2 \end{bmatrix} = \begin{bmatrix} 1 & 6 \\ 2 & -3 \end{bmatrix}$$

$$\begin{bmatrix} 2 & 3 \\ 4 & -5 \end{bmatrix} - \begin{bmatrix} -1 & 3 \\ -2 & 2 \end{bmatrix} = \begin{bmatrix} 3 & 0 \\ 6 & -7 \end{bmatrix}$$

Matrix Multiplication. The product of matrix $\mathbf{A}$ of m rows and n columns and matrix $\mathbf{B}$ of n rows and p columns is matrix $\mathbf{C}$ of m rows and p columns with the elements as follows:

$$\mathbf{C} = \mathbf{AB} \tag{A.2}$$

where

$$c_{ij} = \sum_{k=1}^{m} a_{ik} b_{kj} \qquad \begin{matrix} i = 1, 2, \dots m \\ j = 1, 2, \dots p \end{matrix} \tag{A.3}$$

For example,

$$\begin{bmatrix} a_{11} & a_{12} \\ a_{21} & a_{22} \end{bmatrix} \begin{bmatrix} b_{11} & b_{12} \\ b_{21} & b_{22} \end{bmatrix} = \begin{bmatrix} a_{11}b_{11} + a_{12}b_{21} & a_{11}b_{12} + a_{12}b_{22} \\ a_{21}b_{11} + a_{22}b_{21} & a_{21}b_{12} + a_{22}b_{22} \end{bmatrix}$$

$$[2 \times 2] \qquad [2 \times 2] \qquad\qquad [2 \times 2]$$

$$\begin{bmatrix} a_{11} & a_{12} \\ a_{21} & a_{22} \end{bmatrix} \begin{bmatrix} x_1 \\ x_2 \end{bmatrix} = \begin{bmatrix} a_{11}x_1 + a_{12}x_2 \\ a_{21}x_1 + a_{22}x_2 \end{bmatrix}$$

$$[2 \times 2] \qquad [2 \times 1] \qquad [2 \times 1]$$

Conformable Matrixes. Two matrixes that can be multiplied together are said to be conformable. Note that matrix product **AB** might exist, whereas matrix **BA** might not exist. That is, **AB** might satisfy the condition for matrix multiplication, whereas **BA** might not do so. In general, $\mathbf{AB} \neq \mathbf{BA}$.

Commutable Matrixes. Two matrixes **A** and **B** are commutative if $\mathbf{AB} = \mathbf{BA}$.

Matrix Division. Matrix division is not a defined operation. The equivalent operation involving the inverse of a matrix is explained below.

Zero Matrix. The zero matrix, denoted by **0**, is a matrix whose elements are all zero.

Diagonal Matrix. A diagonal matrix is a matrix whose off-diagonal elements are all zeros.

Unit Matrix. The unit matrix, denoted by **I**, is a diagonal matrix with all diagonal elements being unity. Note that $\mathbf{IA} = \mathbf{AI} = \mathbf{A}$.

Upper and Lower Triangular Matrixes. An upper triangular matrix is one whose elements below the diagonal are all zeros. A lower triangular matrix is one whose elements above the diagonal are all zeros. The diagonal elements need not be zero.

Note: An upper triangular matrix added to or multiplied by an upper triangular matrix results in an upper triangular matrix, with similar properties for lower triangular matrixes.

Transpose of a Matrix. A transposed matrix $\mathbf{A}^T$ is obtained from a given matrix **A** by an interchange of rows and columns. Hence, if $\mathbf{A} = [a_{ij}]$, then $\mathbf{A}^T = [a_{ji}]$; the transpose of matrix **A** indicates that the element in the ith row and jth column of **A**

becomes the element in the jth row and ith column of $\mathbf{A}^T$. For example, if

$$\mathbf{A} = \begin{bmatrix} 1 & -3 & 4 \\ 6 & 4 & -1 \\ -2 & -5 & 9 \end{bmatrix} \qquad \mathbf{A}^T = \begin{bmatrix} 1 & 6 & -2 \\ -3 & 4 & -5 \\ 4 & -1 & 9 \end{bmatrix}$$

Determinant of a Matrix. The determinant of a square $n \times n$ matrix $\mathbf{A}$ is the sum of the signed products of all combinations of n elements, where each element belongs to a different row and column. That is,

$$\Delta(\mathbf{A}) = \det \mathbf{A} = |\mathbf{A}| = \sum^{n!} (-1)^p a_{1p_1} a_{2p_2} \cdots a_{np_n} \tag{A.4}$$

The set $p_1, p_2, \ldots p_n$ is a permutation of $1, 2, \ldots n$, and the sum in (A.4) is taken over all permutations, which is $n!$. The exponent p of (-1) is the number of transpositions it takes to go from the permutation $p_1, p_2, \ldots p_n$ to the natural order $1, 2, \ldots n$. For example,

$$\Delta(\mathbf{A}) = \begin{vmatrix} a_{11} & a_{12} & a_{13} \\ a_{21} & a_{22} & a_{23} \\ a_{31} & a_{32} & a_{33} \end{vmatrix}$$

$$= a_{11} \begin{vmatrix} a_{22} & a_{23} \\ a_{32} & a_{33} \end{vmatrix} - a_{12} \begin{vmatrix} a_{21} & a_{23} \\ a_{31} & a_{33} \end{vmatrix} + a_{13} \begin{vmatrix} a_{21} & a_{22} \\ a_{31} & a_{32} \end{vmatrix}$$

$$= a_{11}a_{22}a_{33} - a_{11}a_{23}a_{32} - a_{12}a_{21}a_{33} + a_{12}a_{23}a_{31} + a_{13}a_{21}a_{32} - a_{13}a_{22}a_{31}$$

Note that the second factor $a_{11}a_{23}a_{32}$ requires only one transposition to create the natural order $a_{11}a_{23}a_{32}$, whereas for the factor $a_{13}a_{21}a_{32}$, two transpositions are required: $a_{13}a_{21}a_{32}$ and $a_{12}a_{21}a_{33}$.

Minor Determinant. The determinant $\Delta(\mathbf{M}_{ij})$ of the matrix $\mathbf{A}$ is formed by deleting the ith row and jth column of the determinant $\Delta(\mathbf{A})$. The cofactor is given by

$$c_{ij} = (-1)^{i+j}\Delta(\mathbf{M}_{ij}) \tag{A.5}$$

For example, the cofactor c_{23} of the matrix is

$$\mathbf{A} = \begin{bmatrix} 1 & -3 & 1 \\ 2 & 6 & -4 \\ 2 & 3 & 5 \end{bmatrix} \qquad c_{23} = (-1)^{2+3}\Delta(\mathbf{M}_{23}) = (-1)\begin{vmatrix} 1 & -3 \\ -2 & 3 \end{vmatrix}$$

$$= -(3-6) = 3$$

Adjoint Matrix. The adjoint of matrix $\mathbf{A}$ is the transpose of the matrix of cofactors of $\mathbf{A}$:

$$adj(\mathbf{A}) = [c_{ij}]^T \tag{A.6}$$

For example,

$$adj\begin{bmatrix} 2 & -4 \\ 6 & -3 \end{bmatrix} = \begin{bmatrix} -3 & -6 \\ 4 & 2 \end{bmatrix}^T = \begin{bmatrix} -3 & 4 \\ -6 & 2 \end{bmatrix}$$

Inverse of a Matrix. The inverse of matrix **A** is

$$\mathbf{A}^{-1} = \frac{adj(\mathbf{A})}{\Delta(\mathbf{A})} \tag{A.7}$$

For example, to deduce the inverse $\mathbf{A}^{-1}$ given

$$\mathbf{A} = \begin{bmatrix} 2 & 3 & 1 \\ 1 & 0 & 0 \\ 2 & 1 & 1 \end{bmatrix} \quad \text{requires} \quad [c_{ij}] = \begin{bmatrix} 0 & -1 & 1 \\ - & 2 & 04 \\ 0 & 1 & -3 \end{bmatrix}$$

$$adj(\mathbf{A}) \triangleq [c_{ij}]^T = \begin{bmatrix} 0 & -2 & 0 \\ -1 & 0 & 1 \\ 1 & 4 & -3 \end{bmatrix} \qquad \Delta(\mathbf{A}) = -2$$

$$\mathbf{A}^{-1} = \frac{adj(\mathbf{A})}{\Delta(\mathbf{A})} = \begin{bmatrix} 0 & 1 & 0 \\ \frac{1}{2} & 0 & -\frac{1}{2} \\ -\frac{1}{2} & -2 & \frac{3}{2} \end{bmatrix}$$

Inverse of Product of Matrixes. From the fact that

$$(\mathbf{AB})(\mathbf{AB})^{-1} = \mathbf{I} \qquad \text{and} \qquad \mathbf{ABB}^{-1}\mathbf{A}^{-1} = \mathbf{AIA}^{-1} = \mathbf{AA}^{-1} = \mathbf{I}$$

it then follows that

$$(\mathbf{AB})^{-1} = \mathbf{B}^{-1}\mathbf{A}^{-1} \tag{A.8}$$

That is, the inverse of the product of two nonsingular matrixes of the same order is the product of the inverse matrixes in reverse order.

Transpose of a Product. Consider two conformable matrixes **A** and **B**. A typical term of their product is

$$[\mathbf{AB}]^T = [ab]_{ij}^T = [ab]_{ji} = \sum_k a_{jk} b_{ki} = \sum_k b_{ik}^T a_{kj}^T = [b^T a^T]_{ij}$$

This development shows that

$$\mathbf{AB}^T = \mathbf{B}^T\mathbf{A}^T \tag{A.9}$$

Thus, the transpose of a matrix product is the product of the transpose of the component matrixes in reverse order.

A.4 Functions of a Matrix

We consider the following set of algebraic equations:

$$\mathbf{Ax} = \lambda\mathbf{x} \tag{A.10}$$

where

$\mathbf{A}$ = a known real square matrix of order $n \times n$

$\mathbf{x}$ = an unknown column vector

λ = a scalar parameter (often the complex number s)

Here, of course, the vectors $\mathbf{x}$ and $\lambda\mathbf{x}$ have the same direction. An important question is, Are there any directions that remain invariant by the transformation defined by $\mathbf{A}$? A nontrivial solution of (A.10) exists only for certain specific values of the scalar parameter λ. To find these values, write (A.10) in the form

$$(\mathbf{A} - \lambda\mathbf{I})\mathbf{x} = 0 \tag{A.11}$$

This expression has a nontrivial solution $\mathbf{x}$ if and only if

$$\det(\mathbf{A} - \lambda\mathbf{I}) = |\mathbf{A} - \lambda\mathbf{I}| = 0 \tag{A.12}$$

For a 2×2 matrix, $\Delta(\mathbf{A} - \lambda\mathbf{I}) = 0$ becomes

$$\lambda^2 - (a_{11} + a_{22})\lambda + (a_{11}a_{22} - a_{12}a_{21}) = 0$$

This equation is called the **characteristic equation** of matrix $\mathbf{A}$. The roots of this equation are called the **eigenvalues** of matrix $\mathbf{A}$.

An equation of degree n has n roots, some of which may be repeated and some or all of which may be real or complex. If the coefficients a are all real, the complex roots occur in conjugate pairs. If we write the eigenvalues of $\mathbf{A}$ as $\lambda_1, \lambda_2, \ldots \lambda_k$, the determinant can be written

$$g(\lambda) = |\mathbf{A} - \lambda\mathbf{I}| = (\lambda - \lambda_1)^{r_1}(\lambda - \lambda_2)^{r_2} \cdots (\lambda - \lambda_i)^{r_i} \cdots (\lambda - \lambda_k)^{r_k} \tag{A.13}$$

where the r_i specify the order of root λ_i. Note specifically that when $\mathbf{A}$ is symmetric, the eigenvalues are real.

Corresponding to each eigenvalue there exists a nonzero column vector $\mathbf{x}$ that satisfies (A.11). The **eigenvector** (column) corresponding to the eigenvalue λ_i is designated $\mathbf{x}_i$.

■ Example A.1

Find the eigenvalues and eigenvectors of the matrix

$$\mathbf{A} = \begin{bmatrix} 2 & 4 \\ 8 & 6 \end{bmatrix}$$

Solution By (A.12), we obtain

$$\begin{vmatrix} 2 - \lambda & 4 \\ 8 & 6 - \lambda \end{vmatrix} = \lambda^2 - 8\lambda - 20 = 0$$

From this polynomial, we find the two roots to be $\lambda_1 = 10$ and $\lambda_2 = -2$. Because (A.11) must be satisfied by each eigenvalue, we obtain

$$\begin{bmatrix} 2-10 & 4 \\ 8 & 6-10 \end{bmatrix}\begin{bmatrix} x_{11} \\ x_{12} \end{bmatrix} = \begin{bmatrix} 0 \\ 0 \end{bmatrix} \qquad \begin{bmatrix} 2+2 & 4 \\ 8 & 6+2 \end{bmatrix}\begin{bmatrix} x_{21} \\ x_{22} \end{bmatrix} = \begin{bmatrix} 0 \\ 0 \end{bmatrix}$$

The first of these yields the relations

$$-8x_{11} + 4x_{12} = 0 \qquad \text{and} \qquad 8x_{11} - 4x_{12} = 0$$

Therefore, appropriate to λ_1 are

$$x_{12} = 2x_{11} \qquad x_{12} = 2x_{11}$$

Therefore, if we select one component, say $x_{11} = 1$, the second is determined from the above relation. Hence, the unnormalized eigenvector is

$$\mathbf{x}_1 = \begin{bmatrix} 1 \\ 2 \end{bmatrix}$$

From the fact that $\mathbf{x}_1^T\mathbf{x}_1 = |x_1|^2$, we obtain

$$[1 \quad 2]\begin{bmatrix} 1 \\ 2 \end{bmatrix} = 1^2 + 2^2 = 5$$

Therefore, the normalized eigenvector is

$$\mathbf{x}_1 = \frac{1}{\sqrt{5}}\begin{bmatrix} 1 \\ 2 \end{bmatrix}$$

From the second relation, corresponding to λ_2, we have

$$4x_{21} + 4x_{22} = 0 \qquad \text{and} \qquad 8x_{21} + 8x_{22} = 0$$

Hence, if $x_{21} = 1$, then $x_{22} = -1$. By following the same procedure as above, the normalized eigenvector belonging to $\lambda_2 = -2$ is

$$\mathbf{x}_2 = \frac{1}{\sqrt{2}}\begin{bmatrix} 1 \\ -1 \end{bmatrix}$$

■

If we create a matrix $\mathbf{E}$ whose columns are the eigenvectors of matrix $\mathbf{A}$, then the following condition holds:

$$\mathbf{D} = \mathbf{E}^{-1}\mathbf{A}\mathbf{E} \qquad \textbf{(A.14)}$$

where $\mathbf{D}$ is a *diagonal* matrix. For example, for the matrix $\mathbf{A}$ in Example A.1,

$$\mathbf{E} = \begin{bmatrix} 1 & 1 \\ 2 & -1 \end{bmatrix} \qquad \mathbf{E}^{-1} = \frac{1}{-3}\begin{bmatrix} -1 & -1 \\ -2 & 1 \end{bmatrix}$$

$$\mathbf{D} = \frac{1}{-3}\begin{bmatrix} -1 & -1 \\ -2 & 1 \end{bmatrix}\begin{bmatrix} 2 & 4 \\ 8 & 6 \end{bmatrix}\begin{bmatrix} 1 & 1 \\ 2 & -1 \end{bmatrix} = -\frac{1}{3}\begin{bmatrix} -30 & 0 \\ 0 & 6 \end{bmatrix} = \begin{bmatrix} 10 & 0 \\ 0 & -2 \end{bmatrix}$$

Observe that the diagonal elements of **D** are the eigenvalues of **A**. If we premultiply (A.14) by **E** and postmultiply by $\mathbf{E}^{-1}$, we obtain the relation

$$\mathbf{A} = \mathbf{EDE}^{-1} \tag{A.15}$$

We can use this relation to show that the nth power of **A** is given by

$$\mathbf{A}^n = \mathbf{ED}^n\mathbf{E}^{-1} \tag{A.16}$$

To prove this assertion, consider $\mathbf{A}^3$, which we write

$$\mathbf{A}^3 = \mathbf{ED}\underbrace{\mathbf{E}^{-1}\mathbf{E}}_{\mathbf{I}}\mathbf{D}\underbrace{\mathbf{E}^{-1}\mathbf{E}}_{\mathbf{I}}\mathbf{DE}^{-1} = \mathbf{ED}^3\mathbf{E}^{-1} \tag{A.17}$$

Similarly, we have

$$\mathbf{A}^{1/2} = \mathbf{ED}^{1/2}\mathbf{E}^{-1} \tag{A.18}$$

This equation is valid since we have

$$\mathbf{A}^{1/2}\mathbf{A}^{1/2} = \mathbf{ED}^{1/2}\mathbf{E}^{-1}\mathbf{ED}^{1/2}\mathbf{E}^{-1} = \mathbf{EDE}^{-1} = \mathbf{A} \tag{A.19}$$

It is not always possible to diagonalize a matrix. However, if we can find n linearly independent eigenvectors corresponding to an $n \times n$ matrix, then diagonalization is possible, with the diagonal elements equal to the eigenvalues of the matrix. The transformation vector **E** is known as a **similarity** transformation.

A.5 Cayley-Hamilton Theorem

The Cayley-Hamilton theorem is important in matrix theory. The theorem states:

Theorem A.1

Every $n \times n$ matrix satisfies its own characteristic equation. Specifically, if we write (A.12) in the form

$$g(\lambda) = |\mathbf{A} - \lambda\mathbf{I}| = \lambda^n + a_{n-1}\lambda^{n-1} + \cdots + a_0 = 0 \tag{A.20}$$

then the Cayley-Hamilton theorem specifies that

$$\mathbf{g}(\mathbf{A}) = \mathbf{A}^n + a_{n-1}\mathbf{A}^{n-1} + \cdots + a_0\mathbf{I} = \mathbf{0} \tag{A.21}$$

Example A.2

Show that the matrix

$$\mathbf{A} = \begin{bmatrix} 2 & 8 \\ 4 & 6 \end{bmatrix}$$

satisfies the Cayley-Hamilton theorem.

Solution The characteristic equation is

$$\begin{vmatrix} 2-\lambda & 8 \\ 4 & 6-\lambda \end{vmatrix} = 0 \quad \text{or} \quad \lambda^2 - 8\lambda - 20 = 0$$

The eigenvalues are $\lambda_1 = 10$ and $\lambda_2 = -2$. Therefore, we obtain

$$\begin{bmatrix} 2 & 8 \\ 4 & 6 \end{bmatrix}^2 - 8\begin{bmatrix} 2 & 8 \\ 4 & 6 \end{bmatrix} - 20\begin{bmatrix} 1 & 0 \\ 0 & 1 \end{bmatrix}$$

$$= \begin{bmatrix} 36 & 64 \\ 32 & 68 \end{bmatrix} + \begin{bmatrix} -16 & -64 \\ -32 & -48 \end{bmatrix} + \begin{bmatrix} -20 & 0 \\ 0 & -20 \end{bmatrix} = \begin{bmatrix} 0 & 0 \\ 0 & 0 \end{bmatrix}$$

■

Note that we can write (A.21) in the polynomial form:

$$\mathbf{g(A)} = (\mathbf{A} - \lambda_1\mathbf{I})(\mathbf{A} - \lambda_2\mathbf{I}) \cdots (\mathbf{A} - \lambda_n\mathbf{I}) = \mathbf{0} \tag{A.22}$$

For example, the matrix

$$\mathbf{A} = \begin{bmatrix} 0 & 1 \\ -1 & -2 \end{bmatrix}$$

has eigenvalues -1 of multiplicity 2. Thus, from (A.22), we have

$$\left(\begin{bmatrix} 0 & 1 \\ -1 & -2 \end{bmatrix} + 1\begin{bmatrix} 1 & 0 \\ 0 & 1 \end{bmatrix}\right)^2 = \begin{bmatrix} 1 & 1 \\ -1 & -1 \end{bmatrix}^2 = \begin{bmatrix} 0 & 0 \\ 0 & 0 \end{bmatrix}$$

Properties of Cayley-Hamilton Theorem

There are a number of important properties of the Cayley-Hamilton theorem.

1. Any power of an $n \times n$ matrix $\mathbf{A}$ can be expressed in terms of a linear combination of $\mathbf{A}^m$ for $m = 0, 1, \ldots (n-1)$. For example, if we have $\mathbf{A}^2 - 8\mathbf{A} - 20\mathbf{I} = \mathbf{0}$, then $\mathbf{A}^2$ can be expressed in terms of $\mathbf{A}$ and $\mathbf{I}$, namely,

   $$\mathbf{A}^2 = 8\mathbf{A} - 20\mathbf{I}$$

   From this, we can write

   $$\mathbf{A}^3 = 8\mathbf{A}^2 - 20\mathbf{AI} = 8(8\mathbf{A} - 20\mathbf{I}) - 20\mathbf{A} = 44\mathbf{A} - 160\mathbf{I}$$

   $$\mathbf{A}^4 = 44\mathbf{A}^2 - 160\mathbf{A} = 44(8\mathbf{A} - 20\mathbf{I}) - 160\mathbf{A} = 192\mathbf{A} - 880\mathbf{I}$$

   $$\vdots$$

2. If $\mathbf{A}^{-1}$ exists, then its inverse can be found by (A.21). For example, if $\mathbf{A}^2 - 8\mathbf{A} - 20\mathbf{I} = \mathbf{0}$, then we have $\mathbf{I} = (1/20)\mathbf{A}^2 - (8/20)\mathbf{A}$. Multiply this result by $\mathbf{A}^{-1}$ to find that (*Note*: $\mathbf{A}^{-1}\mathbf{I} = \mathbf{A}^{-1}$)

   $$\mathbf{A}^{-1} = \frac{1}{20}\mathbf{A} - \frac{8}{20}\mathbf{I}$$

From property 1, we observe that for an $n \times n$ matrix $\mathbf{A}$, any power of $\mathbf{A}$ can be expressed in terms of the weighted sum of matrixes involving $\mathbf{A}^{n-1}, \mathbf{A}^{n-2}, \ldots \mathbf{A}$, and

I. As a result, functions of matrixes that can be expressed in power series form, say,

$$f(\mathbf{A}) = \zeta_0 \mathbf{I} + \zeta_1 \mathbf{A} + \cdots + \zeta_n \mathbf{A}^n + \cdots = \sum_{k=0}^{\infty} \zeta_k \mathbf{A}^k \tag{A.23}$$

can be expressed as

$$f(\mathbf{A}) = \gamma_0 \mathbf{I} + \gamma_1 \mathbf{A} + \cdots + \gamma_{n-1} \mathbf{A}^{n-1} = \sum_{k=0}^{n-1} \gamma_k \mathbf{A}^k \tag{A.24}$$

Observe that (A.23) has the same form as (5.45), the expansion of the fundamental matrix $\mathbf{\Phi}(t) = e^{\mathbf{A}t}$. The ζ factors are functions of the γ factors and n. Therefore, we can write the infinite sum of powers of $\mathbf{A}$, as in the expansion of $e^{\mathbf{A}t}$, as a polynomial in $\mathbf{A}$ in degree not exceeding $n - 1$:

$$e^{\mathbf{A}t} = \gamma_0 \mathbf{I} + \gamma_1 \mathbf{A} + \cdots + \gamma_{n-1} \mathbf{A}^{n-1} \tag{A.25}$$

where the γ's are functions of t. We view $e^{\mathbf{A}t}$ as a function of $\mathbf{A}$ with t as a parameter.

To find the γ's, we return to the characteristic equation of matrix $\mathbf{A}$:

$$g(\lambda) = |\mathbf{A} - \lambda \mathbf{I}| = \lambda^n + a_{n-1}\lambda^{n-1} + \cdots + a_0 = 0 \tag{A.26}$$

By following the same steps as before, we can express the eigenvalues λ^n, λ^{n+1}, ... in terms of λ, λ^2, ... λ^{n-1}. Thus,

$$\lambda^n = -a_{n-1}\lambda^{n-1} - a_{n-2}\lambda^{n-2} - \cdots - a_1\lambda - a_0 \tag{A.27}$$

$$\lambda^{n+1} = -a_{n-1}\lambda^{n} - a_{n-2}\lambda^{n-1} - \cdots - a_1\lambda^2 - a_0\lambda \tag{A.28}$$

By substituting (A.27) for λ^n into (A.28), we observe that λ^{n+1} can be represented as a polynomial of order $n - 1$. Therefore, a polynomial in λ, say,

$$f(\lambda) = \zeta_0 + \zeta_1\lambda + \zeta_2\lambda^2 + \cdots = \sum_{k=0}^{\infty} \zeta_k \lambda^k \tag{A.29}$$

can be written

$$f(\lambda) = \gamma_0 + \gamma_1\lambda + \gamma_2\lambda^2 + \cdots + \gamma_{n-1}\lambda^{n-1} = \sum_{k=0}^{n-1} \gamma_k \lambda^k \tag{A.30}$$

The n unknowns γ_0, γ_1, and γ_{n-1} must be found since the eigenvalues λ are known. Note that (A.30) is valid for any λ that is a solution of the characteristic equation (A.26)—that is, for any eigenvalue of the matrix $\mathbf{A}$.

Let us suppose that the eigenvalues are distinct with values λ_1, λ_2, ... λ_n. Substitute these values in (A.30), which yields n equations in n unknowns:

$$\begin{aligned} f(\lambda_1) &= \gamma_0 + \gamma_1\lambda_1 + \cdots + \gamma_{n-1}\lambda_1^{n-1} \\ f(\lambda_2) &= \gamma_0 + \gamma_1\lambda_2 + \cdots + \gamma_{n-1}\lambda_2^{n-1} \\ &\vdots \\ f(\lambda_n) &= \gamma_0 + \gamma_1\lambda_n + \cdots + \gamma_{n-1}\lambda_n^{n-1} \end{aligned} \tag{A.31}$$

This set of equations can be solved for the coefficients γ_i. By comparing (A.31) with (A.24), we see that these coefficients are exactly those in (A.24). Thus, the coefficients required for the matrix expression $f(\mathbf{A})$ are given as the solution to the linear scalar system of equations given by (A.31).

■ Example A.3

Obtain an expression for $f(\mathbf{A})$, where

$$\mathbf{f}(\mathbf{A}) = \mathbf{A}^{25} \quad \text{and} \quad \mathbf{A} = \begin{bmatrix} 0 & -3 \\ 1 & -4 \end{bmatrix}$$

Solution The characteristic equation is

$$g(\lambda) = |\mathbf{A} - \lambda\mathbf{I}| = \begin{bmatrix} 0-\lambda & -3 \\ 1 & -4-\lambda \end{bmatrix} = \lambda^2 + 4\lambda + 3 = 0$$

The eigenvalues are $\lambda_1 = -1$ and $\lambda_2 = -3$. From (A.30), we obtain

$$\lambda^{25} = \gamma_0 + \gamma_1\lambda \triangleq f(\lambda)$$

By (A.31),

$$(-1)^{25} = \gamma_0 + \gamma_1(-1)$$
$$(-3)^{25} = \gamma_0 + \gamma_1(-3)$$

Solving these equations, the unknowns γ_0 and γ_1 are found to be

$$\gamma_0 = -1\frac{1}{2} + \frac{1}{2}(3)^{25}$$

$$\gamma_1 = -\frac{1}{2} + \frac{1}{2}(3)^{25}$$

The solution for $\mathbf{A}^{25}$ is obtained using (A.24):

$$\mathbf{f}(\mathbf{A}) = \mathbf{A}^{25} = \gamma_0\mathbf{I} + \gamma_1\mathbf{A} = \left(-1\frac{1}{2} + \frac{1}{2}(3)^{25}\right)\begin{bmatrix} 1 & 0 \\ 0 & 1 \end{bmatrix}$$

$$+\left(-\frac{1}{2} + \frac{1}{2}(3)^{25}\right)\begin{bmatrix} 0 & -3 \\ 1 & -4 \end{bmatrix}$$

$$= \begin{bmatrix} -1\frac{1}{2} + \frac{1}{2}(3)^{25} & -3\left(-\frac{1}{2} + \frac{1}{2}(3)^{25}\right) \\ -\frac{1}{2} + \frac{1}{3}(3)^{25} & -4\left(-\frac{1}{2} + \frac{1}{2}(3)^{25}\right) \end{bmatrix}$$

■

■ Example A.4

Compute $e^{\mathbf{A}t}$ for the matrix $\mathbf{A}$ given by

$$\mathbf{A} = \begin{bmatrix} 2 & 0 \\ 1 & 1 \end{bmatrix}$$

Solution We must consider the equation

$$\mathbf{f(A)} = e^{\mathbf{A}t} = \gamma_0 \mathbf{I} + \gamma_1 \mathbf{A}$$

The characteristic equation is

$$g(\lambda) = |\mathbf{A} - \lambda\mathbf{I}| = \begin{bmatrix} 2-\lambda & 0 \\ 1 & 1-\lambda \end{bmatrix} = (2-\lambda)(1-\lambda) = 0$$

which gives the two roots $\lambda_1 = 1$ and $\lambda_2 = 2$. To determine the γ's, consider the system of equations specified by (A.31):

$$e^t = \gamma_0 + \gamma_1$$
$$e^{2t} = \gamma_0 + \gamma_1(2)$$

Observe that we have substituted the relation $f(A) = e^{-At}$ with its equivalent $f(\lambda)e$. The values of γ_0 and γ_2 are

$$\gamma_0 = 2e^t - e^{2t}$$
$$\gamma_1 = e^{2t} - e^t$$

Thus, we have

$$e^{\mathbf{A}t} = (2e^t - e^{2t})\begin{bmatrix} 1 & 0 \\ 0 & 1 \end{bmatrix} + (e^{2t} - e^t)\begin{bmatrix} 2 & 0 \\ 1 & 1 \end{bmatrix} = \begin{bmatrix} e^{2t} & 0 \\ e^{2t} - e^t & e^t \end{bmatrix}$$ ■

For the case when λ_i is a k-fold multiple root of the characteristic equation, the functions $f(\lambda)$ and $g(\lambda)$ satisfy the following equations:

$$\begin{aligned} f(\lambda)\Big|_{\lambda=\lambda_i} &= g(\lambda)\Big|_{\lambda=\lambda_i} \\ \frac{df(\lambda)}{d\lambda}\Big|_{\lambda=\lambda_i} &= \frac{dg(\lambda)}{d\lambda}\Big|_{\lambda=\lambda_i} \\ \frac{d^2f(\lambda)}{d\lambda^2}\Big|_{\lambda=\lambda_i} &= \frac{d^2g(\lambda)}{d\lambda^2}\Big|_{\lambda=\lambda_i} \\ &\vdots \\ \frac{d^{k-1}f(\lambda)}{d\lambda^{k-1}}\Big|_{\lambda=\lambda_i} &= \frac{d^{k-1}g(\lambda)}{d\lambda^{k-1}}\Big|_{\lambda=\lambda_i} \end{aligned} \tag{A.32}$$

■ **Example A.5**

Find the function $\mathbf{f(A)} = e^{-\mathbf{A}t}$ given

$$\mathbf{A} = \begin{bmatrix} 1 & 0 & 4 \\ 0 & 2 & 0 \\ 0 & 1 & 2 \end{bmatrix}$$

Solution The eigenvalues of **A** are found to be $\lambda_1 = 1$ with multiplicity 1 and $\lambda_2 = 2$ with multiplicity 2. From (A.31), we write

$$\mathbf{f}(\mathbf{A}) = e^{-\mathbf{A}t} \quad \text{or} \quad f(\lambda) = e^{-\lambda t}$$
$$\mathbf{g}(\mathbf{A}) = \gamma_2 \mathbf{A}^2 + \gamma_1 \mathbf{A} + \gamma_0 \mathbf{I} \quad \text{or} \quad g(\lambda) = \gamma_2 \lambda^2 + \gamma_1 \lambda + \gamma_0$$

The coefficients γ_2, γ_1 and γ_0 are found from the conditions

$$f(\lambda)\Big|_{\lambda=1} = g(\lambda)\Big|_{\lambda=1}$$
$$f(\lambda)\Big|_{\lambda=2} = g(\lambda)\Big|_{\lambda=2}$$
$$\frac{df(\lambda)}{d\lambda}\Big|_{\lambda=2} = \frac{dg(\lambda)}{d\lambda}\Big|_{\lambda=2}$$

These conditions yield, respectively, the relations

$$\begin{aligned} e^{-t} &= \gamma_2 + \gamma_1 + \gamma_0 \\ e^{-2t} &= 4\gamma_2 + 2\gamma_1 + \gamma_0 \\ -te^{-2t} &= 4\gamma_2 + \gamma_1 + 0\gamma_0 \end{aligned}$$

The solution of this system of equations yields

$$\gamma_2 = e^{-t} - (te^{-2t} + e^{-2t}) \qquad \gamma_1 = (4 + 3t)e^{-2t} - 4e^{-t}$$
$$\gamma_0 = 4e^{-t} - (2t + 3)e^{-2t}$$

The matrix $e^{-\mathbf{A}t}$ is given by

$$\begin{aligned} e^{-\mathbf{A}t} &= \gamma_2 \mathbf{A}^2 + \gamma_1 \mathbf{A} + \gamma_0 \mathbf{I} \\ &= \gamma_2 \begin{bmatrix} 1 & 4 & 12 \\ 0 & 4 & 0 \\ 0 & 4 & 4 \end{bmatrix} + \gamma_1 \begin{bmatrix} 1 & 0 & 4 \\ 0 & 2 & 0 \\ 0 & 1 & 2 \end{bmatrix} + \gamma_0 \begin{bmatrix} 1 & 0 & 0 \\ 0 & 1 & 0 \\ 0 & 0 & 1 \end{bmatrix} \\ &= \begin{bmatrix} (\gamma_2 + \gamma_1 + \gamma_0) & 4\gamma_2 & 12\gamma_2 + 4\gamma_1 \\ 0 & 4\gamma_2 + 2\gamma_1 + \gamma_0 & 0 \\ 0 & 4\gamma_2 + \gamma_1 & 4\gamma_2 + 2\gamma_1 + \gamma_0 \end{bmatrix} \end{aligned}$$

■

References for this section are as follows:

1. Franklin, J.N. *Matrix Theory*. Englewood Cliffs, NJ: Prentice Hall, 1968.
2. Perlis, S. *Theory of Matrices*. Reading, MA: Addison-Wesley, 1952.

Problems

Section A.3

1. Deduce the product of the following matrixes:

a. $\begin{bmatrix} -2 & 3 \\ 4 & -1 \end{bmatrix}\begin{bmatrix} 1 \\ 2 \end{bmatrix}$ b. $\begin{bmatrix} -2 & 3 \\ 4 & -1 \end{bmatrix}\begin{bmatrix} 1 & -3 \\ 2 & -1 \end{bmatrix}$

c. $\begin{bmatrix} 3 & 0 & 1 \\ 4 & -1 & 6 \\ 0 & 0 & 3 \end{bmatrix}\begin{bmatrix} 2 & 1 \\ 4 & 6 \\ 5 & -1 \end{bmatrix}$ d. $\begin{bmatrix} a_1 \\ a_2 \\ a_3 \end{bmatrix}[b_1 \quad b_2 \quad b_3]$ e. $[a_1 \quad a_2 \quad a_3]\begin{bmatrix} b_1 \\ b_2 \\ b_3 \end{bmatrix}$

2. Determine the transpose of the following matrixes:

a. $[3 \quad 4 \quad 1] = \mathbf{A}$ b. $\begin{bmatrix} 1 \\ 4 \\ -6 \end{bmatrix} = \mathbf{B}$ c. $\begin{bmatrix} 1 & -3 \\ 6 & 1 \\ 4 & 2 \end{bmatrix} = \mathbf{C}$

d. $\begin{bmatrix} 3 & 6 & 1 \\ 4 & -2 & -3 \end{bmatrix} = \mathbf{D}$ e. $\begin{bmatrix} 3 & 1 & -7 \\ 6 & -2 & 4 \\ 9 & 8 & 7 \end{bmatrix} = \mathbf{E}$

3. Determine the cofactors of the following matrixes:

a. $\begin{bmatrix} 2 & 4 \\ -6 & -1 \end{bmatrix}$ b. $\begin{bmatrix} 2 & 4 & 6 \\ -1 & 0 & 3 \\ 0 & -1 & 4 \end{bmatrix}$

4. Deduce the inverse of the following matrixes:

a. $\mathbf{A} = \begin{bmatrix} -1 & 3 \\ 4 & -5 \end{bmatrix}$ b. $\mathbf{B} = \begin{bmatrix} 2 & 3 & 4 \\ 1 & 0 & 3 \\ 0 & 0 & 1 \end{bmatrix}$

5. Determine the values of the determinant of a second-order matrix after completing each of the following operations: (a) Interchange two rows or columns, (b) multiply a row (or column) by a scalar, and (c) add a scalar times a row (or column) to another row (or column). Specifically, how do the indicated operations affect the values of the determinants?

Section A.4

6. Determine the eigenvalues and eigenvectors for the following matrixes:

a. $\mathbf{A} = \begin{bmatrix} 1 & 2 \\ 4 & 3 \end{bmatrix}$ b. $\mathbf{B} = \begin{bmatrix} 4 & 3 \\ 1 & 2 \end{bmatrix}$

7. Given the matrix

$$\mathbf{A} = \begin{bmatrix} 0 & 1 \\ -2 & -3 \end{bmatrix},$$

determine $\mathbf{A}^3$ using the diagonalization approach.

Section A.5

8. Verify the Cayley-Hamilton theorem for the following matrixes:

a. $\mathbf{A} = \begin{bmatrix} 1 & 2 \\ 4 & 3 \end{bmatrix}$ b. $\mathbf{B} = \begin{bmatrix} 0 & 1 \\ -1 & -2 \end{bmatrix}$ c. $\mathbf{C} = \begin{bmatrix} -11 & -10 & 5 \\ 5 & 4 & -5 \\ -20 & -20 & 4 \end{bmatrix}$

9. Find $\mathbf{A}^{20}$ and $\mathbf{A}^{-1}$ for the matrix

$$\mathbf{A} = \begin{bmatrix} 0 & -1 \\ 1 & -2 \end{bmatrix}.$$

10. Determine $\mathbf{f}(\mathbf{A}) = \mathbf{A}^{20}$ for the matrix

$$\mathbf{A} = \begin{bmatrix} -1 & 0 \\ 1 & -2 \end{bmatrix}$$

using the method of Example A.3.

11. Determine $\mathbf{f}(\mathbf{A}) = \mathbf{A}^k$ for

$$\mathbf{A} = \begin{bmatrix} 1/2 & 0 \\ 1/4 & 1/4 \end{bmatrix}.$$

12. Determine $e^{\mathbf{A}t}$ for

$$\mathbf{A} = \begin{bmatrix} 2 & -2 \\ 2 & 6 \end{bmatrix}.$$

Appendix

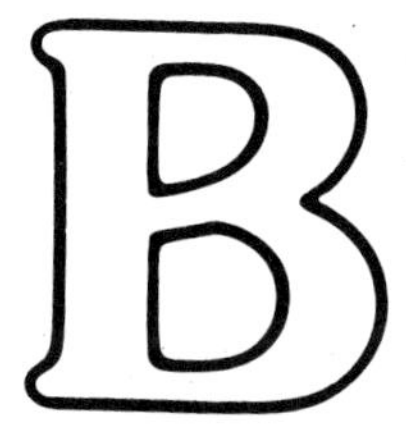

Mathematical Formulas

This appendix gives a listing of a number of mathematical forms that are of value in our studies.

B.1 Trigonometric Identities

$$\cos(-\alpha) = \cos \alpha$$

$$\sin(-\alpha) = -\sin \alpha$$

$$\cos\left(\alpha \pm \frac{\pi}{2}\right) = \mp \sin \alpha$$

$$\sin\left(\alpha \pm \frac{\pi}{2}\right) = \pm \cos \alpha$$

$$\cos(\alpha \pm \pi) = -\cos \alpha$$

$$\sin(\alpha \pm \pi) = -\sin \alpha$$

$$\cos^2 \alpha + \sin^2 \alpha = 1$$

$$\cos^2 \alpha - \sin^2 \alpha = \cos 2\alpha$$

$$\cos(\alpha \pm \beta) = \cos \alpha \cos \beta \mp \sin \alpha \sin \beta$$

$$\sin(\alpha \pm \beta) = \sin \alpha \cos \beta \pm \cos \alpha \sin \beta$$

$$\cos \alpha \cos \beta = \tfrac{1}{2}[\cos(\alpha - \beta) + \cos(\alpha + \beta)]$$

$$\sin\alpha\sin\beta = \tfrac{1}{2}[\cos(\alpha-\beta) - \cos(\alpha+\beta)]$$

$$\sin\alpha\cos\beta = \tfrac{1}{2}[\sin(\alpha-\beta) + \sin(\alpha+\beta)]$$

$$a\cos\alpha + b\sin\alpha = \sqrt{a^2 - b^2}\cos[\alpha - \tan^{-1}(b/a)]$$

$$\cos^2\alpha = \tfrac{1}{2}(1 + \cos 2\alpha)$$

$$\cos^3\alpha = \tfrac{1}{4}(3\cos\alpha + \cos 3\alpha)$$

$$\cos^4\alpha = \tfrac{1}{8}(3 + 4\cos 2\alpha + \cos 4\alpha)$$

$$\cos^5\alpha = \tfrac{1}{16}(10\cos\alpha + 5\cos 3\alpha + \cos 5\alpha)$$

$$\cos^k\alpha = \sum_{n-0}^{k} \frac{2^{-k}k!\cos[(2n-k)\alpha]}{n!(k-n)!}$$

$$\sin^2\alpha = \tfrac{1}{2}(1 - \cos 2\alpha)$$

$$\sin^3\alpha = \tfrac{1}{4}(3\sin\alpha - \sin 3\alpha)$$

$$\sin^4\alpha = \tfrac{1}{8}(3 - 4\cos 2\alpha + \cos 4\alpha)$$

$$\sin^5\alpha = \tfrac{1}{16}(10\sin\alpha - 5\sin 3\alpha + \sin 5\alpha)$$

$$\sin^k\alpha = \begin{cases} \displaystyle\sum_{n=0}^{k} \frac{2^{-k}k!(-1)^{k-n+1}\cos[(2n-k)\alpha]}{n!(k-n)!} & k = 2, 6, 10, \ldots \\ \displaystyle\sum_{n=0}^{k} \frac{2^{-k}k!(-1)^{k-n}\cos[(2n-k)\alpha]}{n!(k-n)!} & k = 4, 8, 12, \ldots \\ \displaystyle\sum_{n=0}^{k} \frac{2^{-k}k!(-1)^{k-n}\sin[(2n-k)\alpha]}{n!(k-n)!} & k = 1, 5, 9, \ldots \\ \displaystyle\sum_{n=0}^{k} \frac{2^{-k}k!(-1)^{k-n+1}\sin[(2n-k)\alpha]}{n!(k-n)!} & k = 3, 7, 11, \ldots \end{cases}$$

$$e^{j\alpha} = \cos\alpha + j\sin\alpha$$

$$\cosh\alpha = \cos j\alpha$$

$$\cos\alpha = \tfrac{1}{2}(e^{j\alpha} + e^{-j\alpha})$$

$$\sinh\alpha = -j\sin j\alpha$$

$$\sin\alpha = \frac{j}{2}(e^{-j\alpha} - e^{j\alpha})$$

$$\tanh\alpha = -j\tan j\alpha$$

B.2 Orthogonality

$$\sum_{n=0}^{N-1} \cos\frac{2\pi k}{N}n\cos\frac{2\pi l}{N}n = 0 \qquad \text{for } 1 \le k, l \le N-1, \text{ and } k \ne l$$

$$\sum_{n=0}^{N-1} \sin \frac{2\pi k}{N} n \sin \frac{2\pi l}{N} n = 0 \qquad \text{for } 1 \le k, l \le N-1, \text{ and } k \ne l$$

$$\sum_{n=0}^{N-1} \sin \frac{2\pi k}{N} n \cos \frac{2\pi l}{N} n = 0 \qquad \text{for } 1 \le k, l \le N-1, \text{ and } k \ne l$$

$$\sum_{n=0}^{N-1} \cos^2 \frac{2\pi k}{N} n = \begin{cases} N/2 & \text{for } 1 \le k \le N-1 \text{ and } k \ne N/2 \\ N & \text{for } k = 0, N/2 \end{cases}$$

$$\sum_{n=0}^{N-1} \sin^2 \frac{2\pi k}{N} n = \begin{cases} N/2 & \text{for } 1 \le k \le N-1 \text{ and } k \ne N/2 \\ 0 & \text{for } k = 0, N/2 \end{cases}$$

The above formulas are correct if all k, l, and n are replaced by k mod N and l mod N.

B.3 Summation of Trigonometric Forms

$$\sum_{n=0}^{N-1} \cos \frac{2\pi k}{N} n = \begin{cases} 0 & \text{for } 1 \le k \le N-1 \\ N & \text{for } k = 0, N \end{cases}$$

$$\sum_{n=0}^{N-1} \sin \frac{2\pi k}{N} n = \begin{cases} 0 & \text{for } 1 \le k \le N-1 \\ N & \text{for } k = 0, N \end{cases}$$

(k, l, and n are integers.)

B.4 Summation Formulas

Finite Summation Formulas

$$\sum_{k=0}^{n} a_k = \frac{1 - a^{n+1}}{1 - a}, \; a \ne 1$$

$$\sum_{k=0}^{n} ka^k = a[1 - (n+1)a^n + na^{n+1}]/(1-a)^2$$

$$\sum_{k=0}^{n} k^2 a^k = a[(1+a) - (n+1)^2 a^n + (2n^2 + 2n - 1)a^{n+1} - n^2 a^{n+2}]/(1-a)^3$$

$$\sum_{k=0}^{n} k = n(n+1)/2$$

$$\sum_{k=0}^{n} k^2 = n(n+1)(2n+1)/6$$

$$\sum_{k=0}^{n} k^3 = n^2(n+1)^2/4$$

$$\sum_{k=0}^{2n-1} (2k+1) = n^2$$

Infinite Summation Formulas

$$\sum_{k=0}^{\infty} a^k = \frac{1}{(1-a)}, \qquad |a| < 1$$

$$\sum_{k=0}^{\infty} k a^k = \frac{a}{(1-a)^2}, \qquad |a| < 1$$

$$\sum_{k=0}^{\infty} k^2 a^k = \frac{a^2 + a}{(1-a)^3}, \qquad |a| < 1$$

B.5 Series Expansions

$$e^{\alpha} = 1 + \alpha + \frac{\alpha^2}{2!} + \frac{\alpha^3}{3!} + \cdots$$

$$\ln(1+\alpha) = \alpha - \frac{\alpha^2}{2} + \frac{\alpha^3}{3} - \frac{\alpha^4}{4} + \cdots \qquad |\alpha| < 1$$

$$\sin \alpha = \alpha - \frac{\alpha^3}{3!} + \frac{\alpha^5}{5!} - \frac{\alpha^7}{7!} + \cdots$$

$$\cos \alpha = 1 - \frac{\alpha^2}{2!} + \frac{\alpha^4}{4!} - \frac{\alpha^6}{6!} + \cdots$$

$$\tan \alpha = \alpha + \frac{\alpha^3}{3} + \frac{2\alpha^5}{15} + \frac{17\alpha^7}{315} + \cdots \qquad |\alpha| < \frac{\pi}{2}$$

$$\sin^{-1} \alpha = \alpha + \frac{\alpha^3}{6} + \frac{3}{2 \cdot 4}\frac{\alpha^5}{5} + \frac{3 \cdot 5}{2 \cdot 4 \cdot 6}\frac{\alpha^7}{7} + \cdots \qquad |\alpha| < 1$$

$$\cos^{-1} \alpha = \frac{\pi}{2} - \sin^{-1} \alpha$$

$$\tan^{-1} \alpha = \alpha - \frac{\alpha^3}{3} + \frac{\alpha^5}{5} - \frac{\alpha^7}{7} + \cdots \qquad |\alpha| < 1$$

$$\sinh \alpha = \alpha + \frac{\alpha^3}{3!} + \frac{\alpha^5}{5!} + \frac{\alpha^7}{7!} + \cdots$$

$$\cosh \alpha = 1 + \frac{\alpha^2}{2!} + \frac{\alpha^4}{4!} + \frac{\alpha^6}{6!} + \cdots$$

$$\tanh \alpha = \alpha - \frac{\alpha^3}{3} + \frac{2\alpha^5}{15} - \frac{17\alpha^7}{315} + \cdots \qquad |\alpha| < \frac{\pi}{2}$$

$$\sinh^{-1} \alpha = \alpha - \frac{\alpha^3}{6} + \frac{3}{2 \cdot 4}\frac{\alpha^5}{5} - \frac{3 \cdot 5}{2 \cdot 4 \cdot 6}\frac{\alpha^7}{7} + \cdots \qquad |\alpha| < 1$$

$$\tanh^{-1} \alpha = \alpha + \frac{\alpha^3}{3} + \frac{\alpha^5}{5} + \frac{\alpha^7}{7} + \cdots \qquad |\alpha| < 1$$

$$(1 + \alpha)^n = 1 + n\alpha + \frac{n(n-1)}{2!}\alpha^2 + \frac{n(n-1)(n-2)}{3!}\alpha^3 + \cdots \quad |\alpha| < 1$$

B.6 Logarithms

$$\log_b N = \log_a N \log_b a = \frac{\log_a N}{\log_a b}$$

B.7 Some Definite Integrals

$$\int_0^\infty x^2 e^{-ax}\, dx = \frac{2}{a^3}$$

$$\int_0^\infty x^n e^{-ax}\, dx = \frac{n!}{a^{n+1}} \qquad a > 0$$

$$\int_0^\infty e^{-r^2 x^2}\, dx = \frac{\sqrt{\pi}}{2r} \qquad r > 0$$

$$\int_0^\infty x e^{-r^2 x^2}\, dx = \frac{1}{2r^2}$$

$$\int_0^\infty \frac{e^{-ax}}{x} \sin mx\, dx = \tan^{-1} \frac{m}{a} \qquad a > 0$$

$$\int_0^\infty \frac{\sin mx}{x}\, dx = \frac{\pi}{2}$$

Bibliography

Ahmed, N., and Natarajan, T. *Discrete-Time Signals and Systems.* Reston, VA: Reston, 1983.

Cadzow, J.A. *Discrete Time Systems.* Englewood Cliffs, NJ: Prentice-Hall, 1973.

Chen, C. *One-Dimensional Digital Signal Processing.* New York: Marcel Dekker, 1979.

Finizio, N., and Ladas, G. *An Introduction to Differential Equations.* Belmont, CA: Wadsworth Publishing Co., 1982.

Gabel, R.A., and Roberts, R.A. *Signals and Linear Systems, 2nd ed.* New York: Wiley & Sons, 1980.

Jong, M.T. *Methods of Discrete Signal and System Analysis.* New York: McGraw-Hill, 1982.

McClamroch, N.H. *State Models of Dynamic Systems.* New York: Springer-Verlag, 1980.

McGillem, C.D. *Continuous and Discrete Signals and System Analysis, 2nd ed.* New York: Holt, Rinehart and Winston, 1984.

Mayhan, R.J. *Discrete-Time and Continuous Time Linear Systems.* Reading, MA: Addison-Wesley, 1984.

Neff, H.P., Jr. *Continuous and Discrete Linear Systems.* New York: Harper & Row, 1984.

Oppenheim, A.V.; Willsky, A.S.; and Young, I.T. *Signals and Systems.* Englewood Cliffs, NJ: Prentice-Hall, 1983.

Papoulis, A. *Circuits and Systems.* New York: Holt, Rinehart and Winston, 1980.

Peled, A., and Liu, B. *Digital Signal Processing.* New York: Wiley & Sons, 1976.

Poularikas, A.D., and Seely, S. *Signals and Systems.* Boston: PWS-KENT Publishing Co., 1985.

Reid, J.G. *Linear System Fundamentals.* New York: McGraw-Hill, 1983.

Seely, S., and Poularikas, A.D. *Electromagnetics—Classical and Modern Theory and Applications.* New York: Marcel Dekker, 1979.

Seely, S., and Poularikas, A.D. *Electrical Engineering—Introduction and Concepts.* Beaverton, OR: Matrix, 1982.

Stanley, W.D.; Dougherty, G.R.; and Dougherty, R. *Digital Signal Processing, 2nd ed.* Reston, VA: Reston, 1984.

Terrell, T.J. *Introduction to Digital Filters.* London: The Macmillan Press Ltd., 1980.

Ziemer, R.E.; Tranter, W.H.; and Fannin, D.R. *Signals and Systems, Continuous and Discrete.* New York: Macmillan, 1983.

Answers to Selected Problems

Chapter 1

8. a.

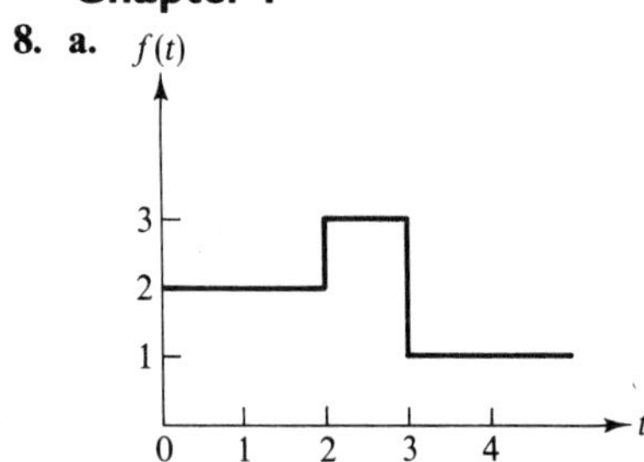

b.

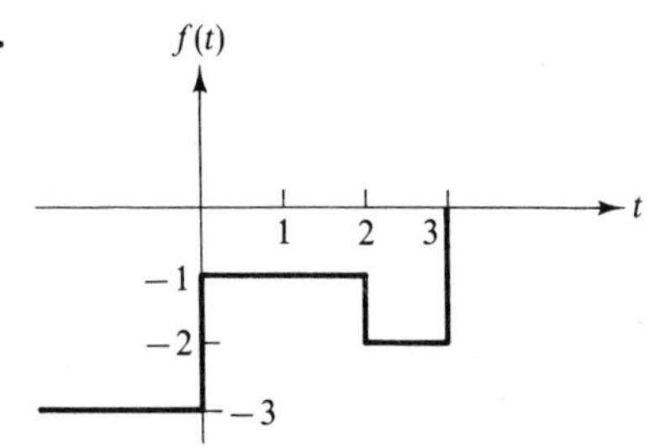

10. a. $\omega = 3.4 \times 10^{-6}$ rad/s **c.** $\omega = 4\pi \times 10^{-3}$ rad/s
d. $\omega = 3$ **e.** $2\pi/8$

12. b.

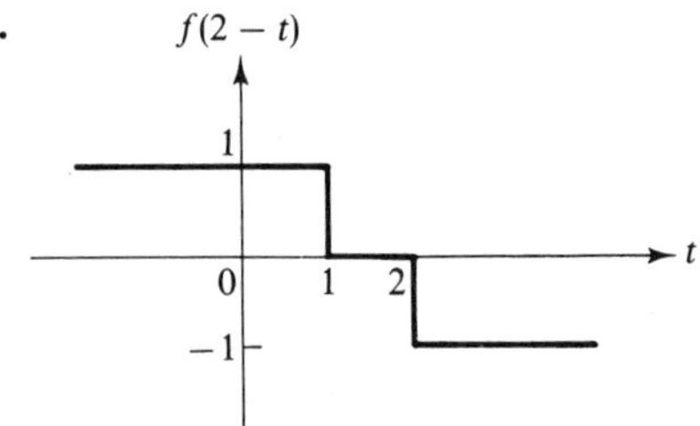

14. b.

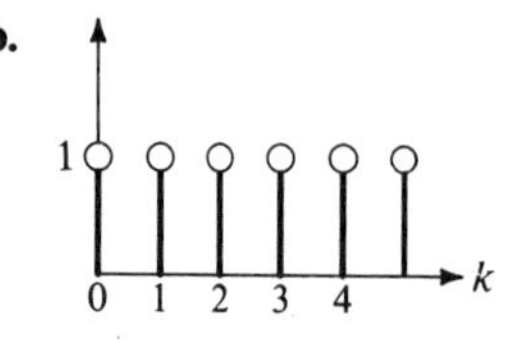

e.

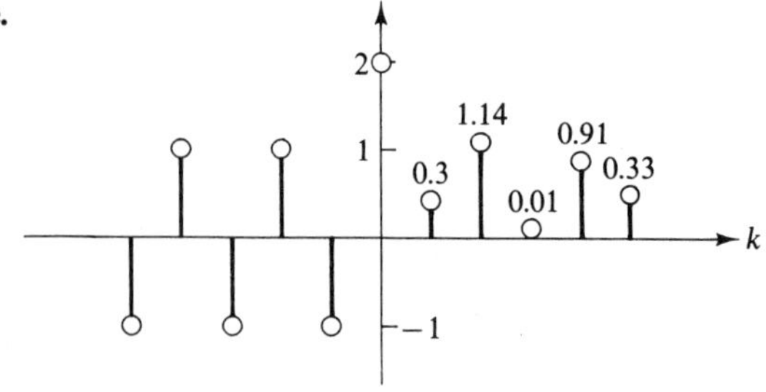

15. **c.**

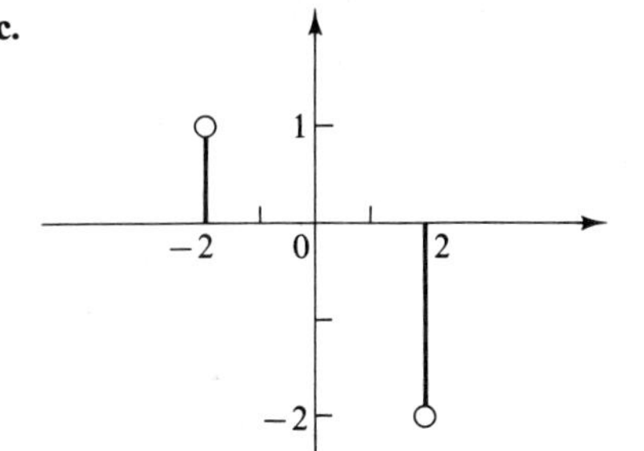

d.

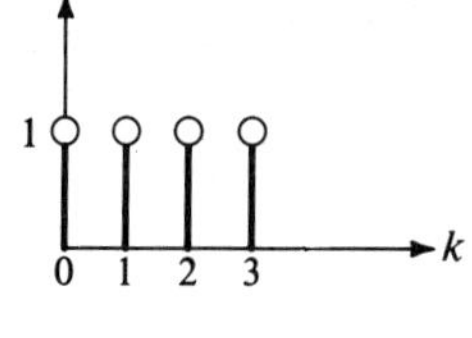

19. **c.** -1 **d.** -1 **e.** 1

21. **a.** 0 **b.** $2/e$

22. **b.** $e + 2/e$

24. $1.2 \times 10^6 - 10^3$, $1.2 \times 10^6 + 10^3$

29. **b.** and **c.**

Chapter 2

2. **a.**

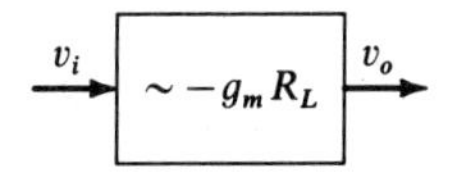

b.

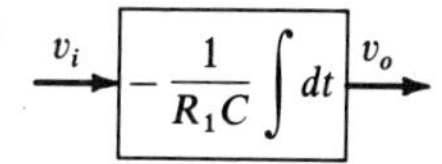

4. 15 joules

5. **b.** $\frac{1}{2}\delta(t - 1.5) + \pi/2 \cos \pi t$

7. 3.729 volts, 1.86 coulombs

9. **b.** $L/2[i^2(t_2) - i^2(t_1)]$ **c.** $(C/2)[u^2(t_2) - u^2(t_1)]$

10. $i(t) = 5 \times 10^{-3}$ A, $E_R + E_C = E_{\text{source}}$

11. **b.**

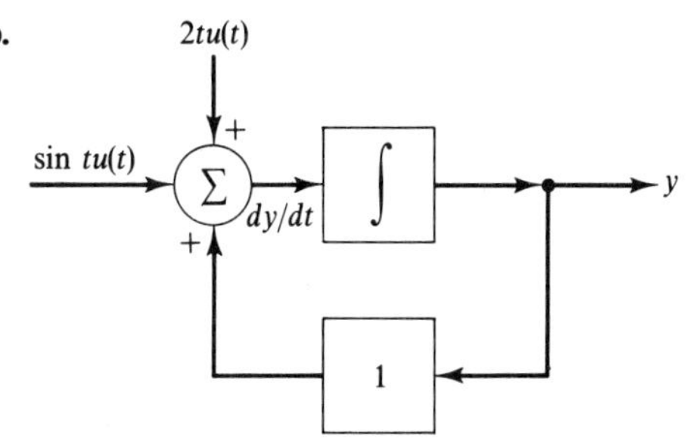

13. $v(t) = 6(1 - e^{-t}) - 4t + 2t^2$

17. $q_{zi}(t) = 2 \times 10^{-3}e^{-5t}$ $q_{zs}(t) = 2 \times 10^{-3} + 2.5 \times 10^{-3}e^{-t} - 4.5 \times 10^{-3}e^{-5t}$

18. $v(t) = 4u(t)$

20. $x(t) = 2(e^{-0.5t} - e^{-t})$

22. $t = 7.9$ hr

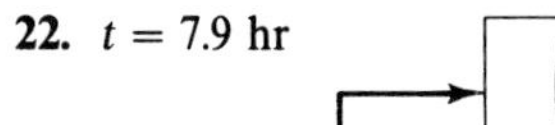

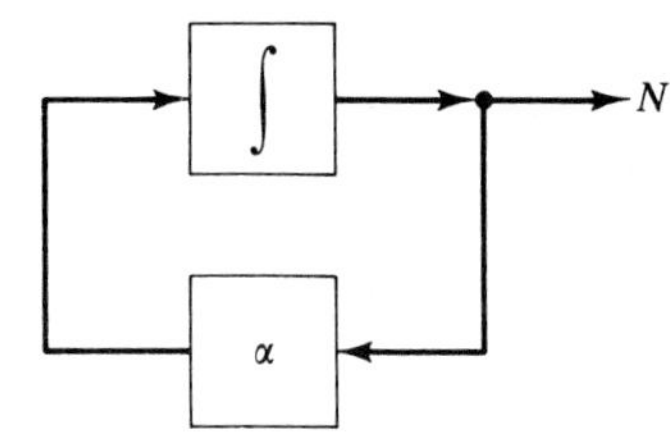

23. b. $\frac{L_1}{R_1} = \frac{L_2}{R_2}$

24.

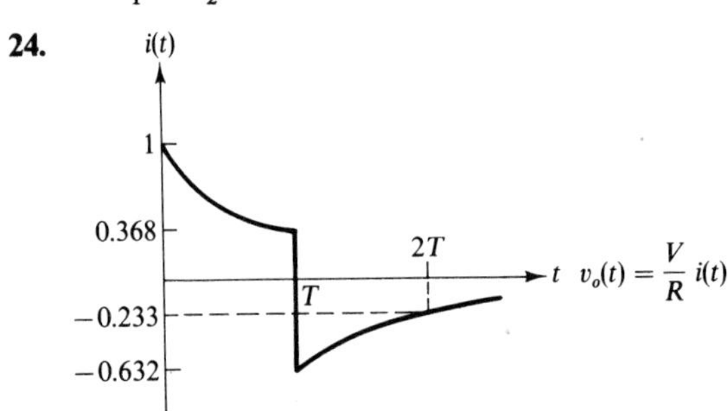

27. b.

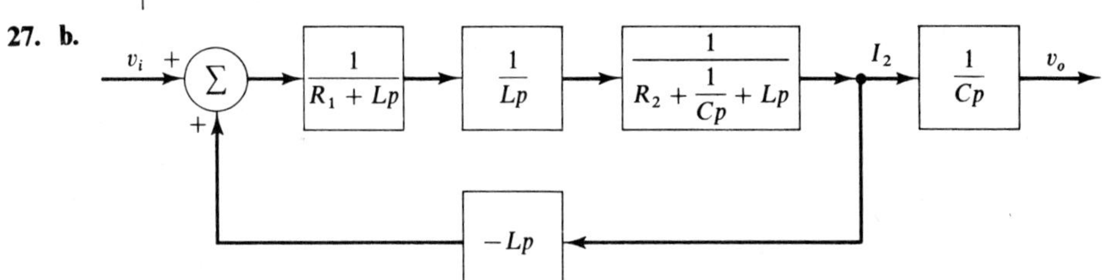

29. b. $\frac{1}{ap + p^2 + b}$

31.

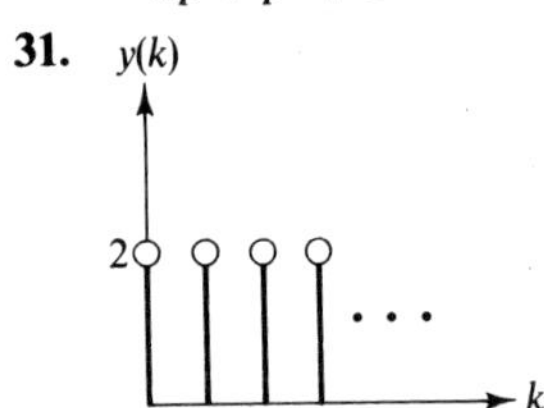

33. $g(k) = \{-1, 0, 1, 2, 1\}$

34. $g(k) = 0.5[v(k) + v(k-1)]$; output smoother than input

35. $g(k) = v(k) + v(k-1) - g(k-1) - g(k-2) - g(k-3)$

38. a. $v_o(t) = 2(e^{-t} - e^{-2t})$

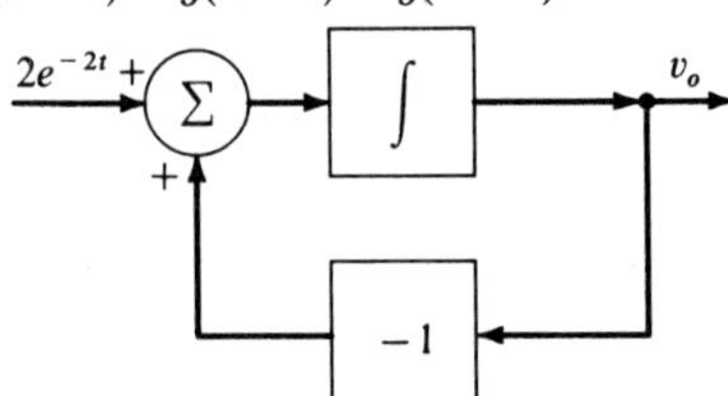

b. $v(kT) = \dfrac{1}{1-T} v[(k-1)T] + \dfrac{2T}{1-T} e^{-2kT}$

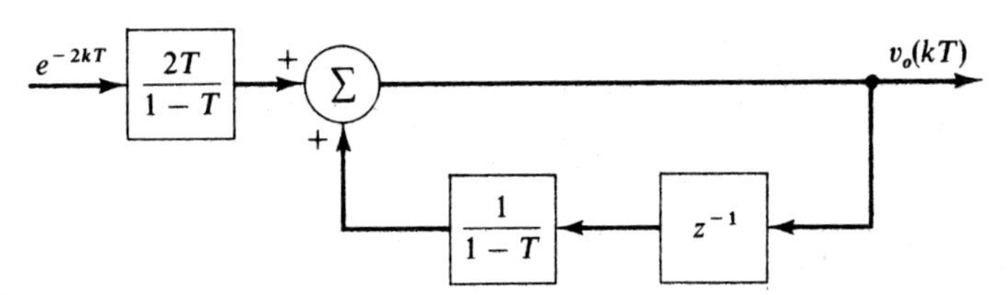

39. $g(k) = \sum_{n=0}^{k} 2^{n+2}$

40. $g(k) = 5 \times 2^k$

42. **a.** $y_p(t) = 2t$ **b.** $y_p(t) = \frac{1}{4}te^{2t}$ **c.** $y_p(t) = -\frac{1}{2}\sin t$

45. **a.**

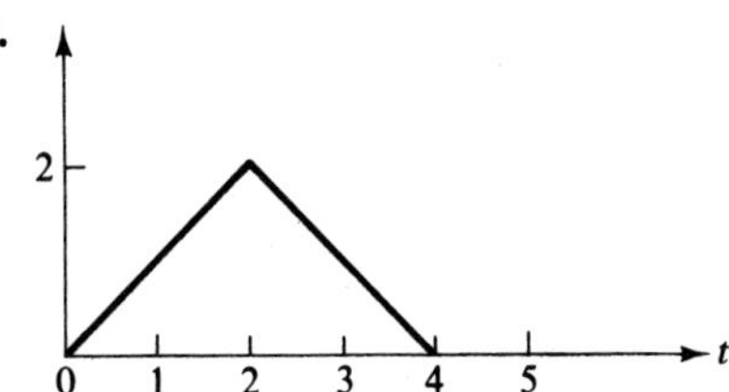

b.

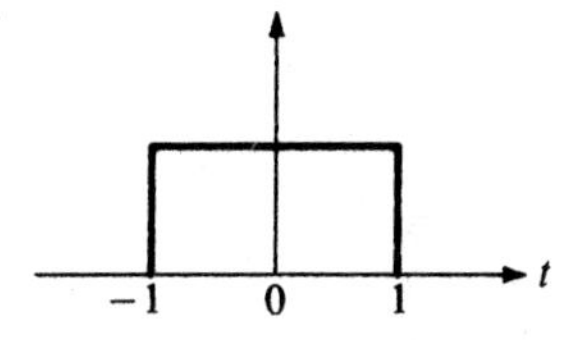

d.

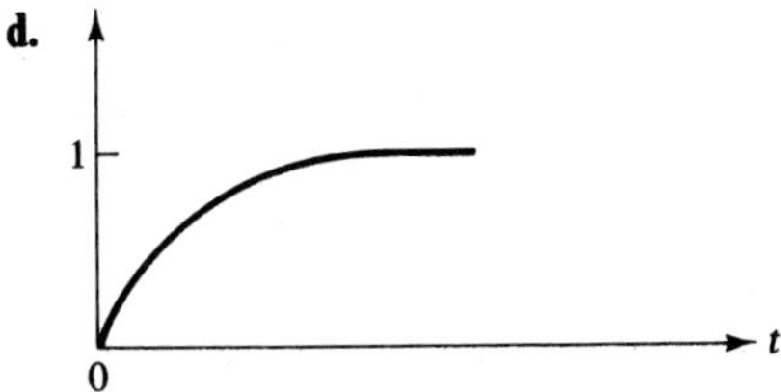

46. **b.** $g(t) = 2(1 - ee^{-t}) \quad 1 < t < 3;\ g(t) = 2e^{-t}(e^3 - e) \quad t > 3,\ g(t) = 0,\ t < 1$

48. **a.** $g(t) = \frac{1}{12}t^4$ **b.** $g(t) = \frac{1}{60}t^6$

51. $q(t) = -\frac{1}{4} + \frac{1}{2}t + \frac{5}{4}e^{-2t}$

52. **a.** $V_o(t) = \frac{5}{4}(e^{-t} - e^{-5t})$ **b.** $v_o(t) = \frac{1}{4}(-e^{-t} + 5e^{-5t})$

54. **a.** $h(t) = \frac{1}{2}e^{-2t}$

55. $v_o(t) = 1 - ee^{-t} \quad 1 < t < 3;\ v_o(t) = 1 - ee^{-t} + e^3e^{-t} \quad t > 3$

56. $v_o(t) = 2(1 - e^{3/2}e^{-t/2}) \quad 3 \le t \le 5;\ v_o(t) = [2e^{5/2} - 2e^{3/2}]e^{-t/2} \quad t \ge 5$

58. **a.** $v_o(t) = \frac{2}{3}(1 - e^{6(t-2)}) \quad t > 2$

59. $v_o(t) = \frac{1}{3}(e^{-t} - e^{-4t}) \quad t > 0$

61. **c.**

62. $v(k) = \{0.25, 0.375, 0.438, 0.469, \ldots\}$
63. **a.** $g(k) = 4^{k+1} - 3^{k+1}$ **c.** $g(k) = k + 1$
65. **b.** $g(k) = \{0.5, 1.5, 1.5, 0.5\}$
67. **a.** $g(t) = 1 - e^{-1}e^{t} \quad -1 < t < 1; g(t) = 0 \quad t > 1; g(t) = (e - e^{-1})e^{t}$

Chapter 3

2. Real $y = e^{-2t}(2 \cos 2t - \sin 2t)$, imaginary $y = e^{-2t}(2 \sin 2t + \cos 2t)$

4. 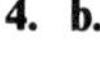 **b.**

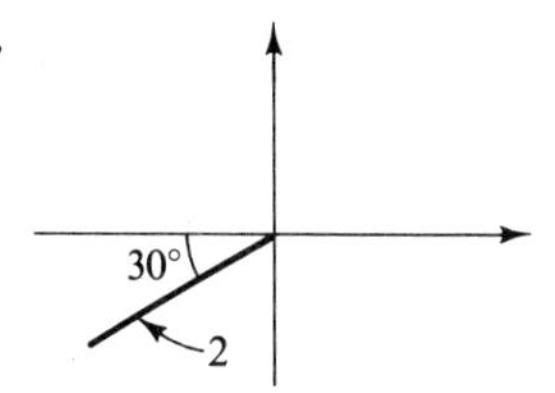

f.

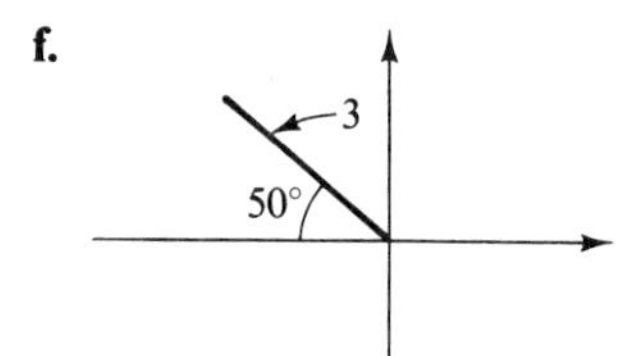

5. **a.** $r_1^2 = a_1^2 + b_1^2$ **b.** $\frac{1}{2} + j\dfrac{b_2}{2a_2}$ **c.** $2a_3$ **e.** a_1/a_2
6. **a.** $3.16e^{j18.43^\circ}$ **c.** $1.41e^{j15^\circ}$ **d.** $10.95e^{-j41.56^\circ}$ **f.** $5e^{j67.87^\circ}$
10. **a.** is not periodic, but the rest are.
11. T must be a rational number.
18. **a.** $f(t) = \pi^2/3 + 4 \sum_{n=1}^{\infty}[(-1)^n/n^2]\cos nt$ **b.** $f(t) = -(2/\pi) \sum_{n=1}^{\infty}[(-1)^n/n]\sin n\pi t$
19. **a.** $f(t) = (2t_0/\pi) \sum_{n=1}^{\infty}[(-1)^{n+1}/n]\sin(n\pi t/t_0)$
22. **b.** $A_0 = \frac{2}{3}$, $A_n = (2/\pi n)[\sin n\pi/9 + \sin(2n\pi/9)]$, $B_n = (2/\pi n)[-\cos(n\pi/9) + \cos(2n\pi/9)]$
23. **a.** For $T = 2$, $A_0 = 1$, $A_n = (2/n\pi)\sin 0.5n\pi$, $B_n = 0$
25. **a.** $f(t) = -(4A/\pi)(\sin \omega_0 t + \frac{1}{3} \sin 3\omega_0 t + \frac{1}{5} \sin 5\omega_0 t + \cdots)$
    c. $f(t) = (A/2) - (A/\pi) \sum_{n=1}^{\infty}(-1)^n \sin n\omega_0 t/n$
28. **a.** $v(t) = (1/2\omega_0)\sin(\omega_0 t - 90^\circ)$ **b.** $v(t) = 2 \sin(\omega_0 t)$
    d. $v(t) = [2\omega_0/(1 - 4\omega_0^2)]\sin(\omega_0 t + 90^\circ)$
    e. $v_o(t) = (3\omega_0/\sqrt{4 + 9\omega_0^2})\sin[\omega_0 t + 90^\circ - \tan^{-1}(3\omega_0/2)]$
29. **b.** $v = (2\omega_1\sqrt{1 + 4\omega_1^2})\cos(\omega_1 t - \tan^{-1} 2\omega_1) + (2\omega_2\sqrt{1 + 4\omega_2^2})\sin(\omega_2 t - \tan^{-1} 2\omega_2)$
31. $f_o(t) = 4/\pi - 8/\pi(\frac{1}{3} \cos \pi 10^3 t + \frac{1}{15} \cos 2\pi 10^3 t)$
32. **a.** $W^2 = (\sqrt{2}/2) - j(\sqrt{2}/2)$, $W^5 = -0.383 - j0.924$, $W^8 = -1 + j0$
33. $N = 4, f(m\tau) = 5 \cos[(2\pi/4)m]$, $\alpha_0 = 0$, $\alpha_1 = \frac{5}{2}$, $\alpha_2 = 0$, $\alpha_3 = \frac{5}{2}$
37. $\{0, 1, 2, 3, 3, 3, 3, 2, 1, 0, \ldots\}$

Chapter 4

1. **b.** $F(\omega) = (E/j\omega)[(1 - \cos \omega T) + j \sin \omega T]$
2. **a.** $F(\omega) = (2/\omega)\sin 2\omega - j[(1/\omega^2)\sin 2\omega - (2/\omega)\cos 2\omega]$
4. **a.** $|F(\omega)|_{\omega \to \infty} = 1$ **b.** $|F(\omega)|_{\omega \to \infty} = 1$
6. **a.** $|F(\omega)| = 2 \sin 3\omega/\omega \quad \text{Arg } F(\omega) = -2\omega$
   b. $|F(\omega)| = 4(\sin 2\omega/\omega \cos) 2\omega \quad \text{Arg } |F(\omega)| = 0$
   d. $|F(\omega)| = [2 \sin(\omega - 3)]/(\omega - 3) \quad \text{Arg } |F(\omega)| = 0$
   e. $|F(\omega)| = \frac{2}{3} \sin 2[(\omega - 2)/3]/[(\omega - 2)/3] \quad \text{Arg } F(\omega) = 0$
7. **a.** $F(\omega) = 2\pi e^{a\omega}$ **b.** $F(\omega) = \pi e^{-|\omega|}$ **c.** $F(\omega) = \pi p_a|\omega|$
   d. $F(\omega) = -2\pi[d^2\delta(\omega)/d\omega^2]$

10. $g(t) = \frac{1}{2}(e^{-t} - e^{-3t})$

11. **a.** $G(\omega) = [1/(1 + j\omega)][1/(2 + j\omega)]$, $H(\omega) = 1/(2 + j\omega)$
b. $G(\omega) = [1/(2 + j\omega)][1/(2 - \omega^2 + j2\omega)]$

13. Bandpass filter

15. **a.** $|F(\omega)| = 4(\sin \omega \sin 3\omega)/\omega^2$ Arg $F(\omega) = -3\omega$
b. $|F(\omega)| = 4(\sin 2\omega \sin \omega)/\omega^2$ Arg $F(\omega) = 0$

16. In the positive domain: $10^9 + 2\pi \times 10^6$ rad/s, $10^9 - 2\pi \times 10^6$ rad/s

17. **a.** $|\Omega(\omega)| = 1/\sqrt{D^2 + \omega^2 J^2}$ Arg $\Omega(\omega) = -\tan^{-1}(J\omega/D)$
b. $|V_o(\omega)| = \omega L R_2/[(R_1 R_2)^2 + [\omega L(R_1 + R_2)]^2]^{1/2}$
Arg $V_o(\omega) = -\tan^{-1}[\omega L(R_1 + R_2)/R_1 R_2] + \pi/2$

18. **b.** $|\mathscr{F}\{p(t)\}| = (2 \sin \omega)/\omega$ Arg $\mathscr{F}\{p(t)\} = 0$
$|\mathscr{F}\{p(2t - 2)\}| = [2 \sin(\omega/2)]/\omega$ Arg $\mathscr{F}\{p(2t - 2)\} = -\omega$

19. $|G(\omega)| = (2 \sin \omega)/\omega[4 + (\omega + \omega_0)^2]^{1/2}$ Arg $G(\omega) = -\tan^{-1}[(\omega + \omega_0)/2]$

20. $V(\omega) = [a_1(I_m/2)][\delta(\omega + \omega_0) + \delta(\omega - \omega_0)] + a_1 BM(\omega)$
$+\pi a_2 I_m^2 \delta(\omega) + \frac{1}{4} a_2 I_m^2[\delta(\omega + 2\omega_0) + \delta(\omega - 2\omega_0)]$
$+a_2 I_m B[M(\omega - \omega_0) + M(\omega + \omega_0)] + a_2 B^2 \mathscr{F}\{m^2(t)\}$;
$\mathscr{F}\{m^2(t)\} \le$ two times the bandwidth of $M(\omega)$

22. $F(\omega) = [\sin(\omega - 2\pi)]/(\omega - 2\pi) + [\sin(\omega + 2\pi)]/(\omega + 2\pi)$

23. **a.** $F(\omega) = \pi\delta(\omega + \omega_0)(e^{-j3\omega t_0} + je^{-j\omega t_0}) + \pi\delta(\omega - \omega_0)(e^{-j3\omega t_0} - je^{j\omega t_0})$
c. $F(\omega) = (\pi/2)[\delta(\omega - \omega_2 - \omega_1) + \delta(\omega - \omega_2 + \omega_1) + \delta(\omega + \omega_2 - \omega_1) + \delta(\omega + \omega_2 + \omega_1)]$

24. **a.** $F(\omega) = 6e^{j(\pi/2)} \sum_{n=-\infty}^{\infty} [(1 - \cos n\pi)/n\pi]\delta(\omega - n\pi)$

29. **a.** $F_1(\omega) = F_0(\omega) + F_0(-\omega)$ **b.** $F_2(\omega) = F_0(\omega) + e^{j2\omega}F_0(\omega)$
c. $F_3(\omega) = F_0(\omega) - F_0(-\omega)$ **d.** $F_4(\omega) = j\, dF_0(\omega)/d\omega$

31. **a.**

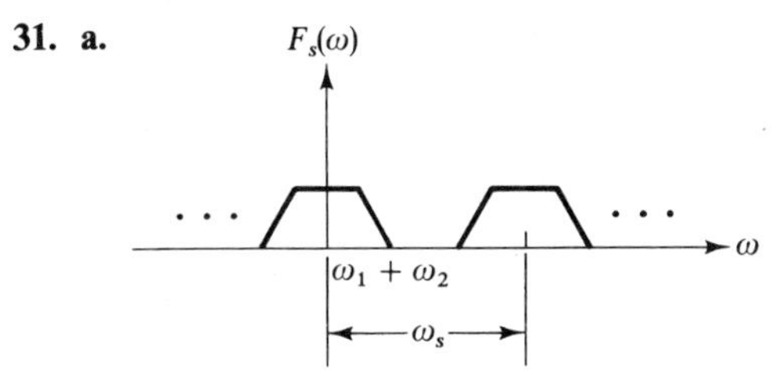

b.

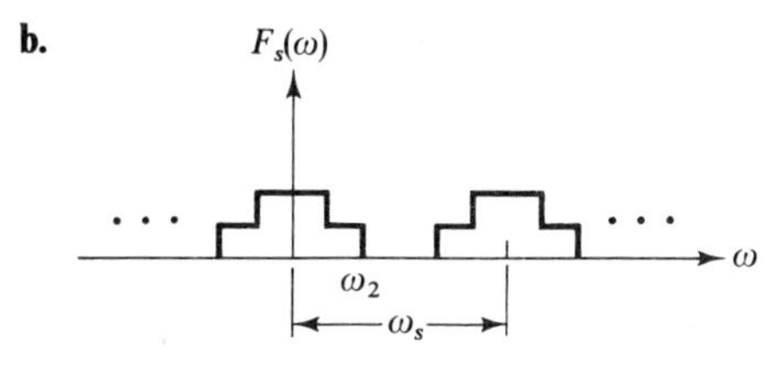

37. $\omega_N = 0.632a$

38. $T_s = \pi/\omega_2$

40. For $m \ne n$, the unit phasors cancel in pairs.

44. $|F(n\pi/3)| = \sin(2\pi n/3)/\sin(n\pi/6)$ Arg $F(n\pi/3) = -5\pi n/6$

50. $F(08\pi/5) = 5$, $F(i8\pi/5) = 0$ $i = 1, 2, 3, 4$

Chapter 5

1. **a.** $v_o = v_c = x$, $v_0 = y$, $a = -1/RC$, $b = 1/RC$, $v = w$,
$\dot{x} = ax + bw$, $y = x$

b. $i_1 = x_1$, $v_c = x_2$, $\dot{\mathbf{x}} = \begin{bmatrix} a_{11} & a_{12} \\ a_{21} & a_{22} \end{bmatrix}\mathbf{x} + \begin{bmatrix} 1/L \\ 0 \end{bmatrix} v$,
$y = [c_{11}\, c_{12}]\mathbf{x}$, $a_{11} = -(R_1 R_2 + R_2 R_3 + R_3 R_1)/L(R_2 + R_3)$,
$a_{12} = -R^2/L(R_2 + R_3)$, $a_{21} = R_3/C(R_2 + R_3)$, $a_{22} = -1/C(R_2 + R_3)$,
$c_{11} = R_2 R_3 C/(R_2 + R_3)$, $c_{12} = -R_2 C/(R_2 + R_3)$

2. $\dot{\mathbf{x}} = \begin{bmatrix} 0 & 1 \\ -K/J & 0 \end{bmatrix}\mathbf{x} + \begin{bmatrix} 0 \\ 1/J \end{bmatrix}\mathscr{T} \qquad y = [1 \quad 0]\mathbf{x}$

3. $\mathbf{x} = \begin{bmatrix} -(1/C_1R_1) + (1/C_1R_1) & 1/C_1R_2 \\ 1/C_2R_2 & -1/C_2R_2 \end{bmatrix}\mathbf{x} + \begin{bmatrix} 1/C_1R_1 \\ 0 \end{bmatrix}v$

$y = [-1 \quad 1]\mathbf{x} + v,\ v_{C_2} = x_2,\ v_{C_1} = x_1$

5. $\dfrac{dx}{dt} = -\dfrac{K}{mC_p}x + \dfrac{1}{mC_p}Q \qquad y = x + T_0$

6. $\dot{\mathbf{x}} = \begin{bmatrix} -R_f/L_f & 0 \\ GI_a/J & -D/J \end{bmatrix}\mathbf{x} + \begin{bmatrix} 1/L_f \\ 0 \end{bmatrix}v_f$

$y = [0 \quad 1]\mathbf{x},\ i_f = x_1,\ \omega = x_2$

7. **a.** $\dot{x}_1 = -ax_1 + w,\ y = x_1$

b. $\dot{x}_1 = -ax_1 + (b - a)w,\ y = x_1 + w$

d. $\dot{x}_1 = -x_3 + w,\ \dot{x}_2 = x_1 - x_3 + w,\ \dot{x}_3 = -x_2 - x_3,\ y = x_3$

8. **c.** $\dot{x}_1 = -\frac{3}{2}x_1 + x_2 + \frac{1}{2}w,\ \dot{x}_2 = -\frac{1}{2}x_1 + x_3 + w,\ \dot{x}_3 = -2x_1 + \frac{3}{2}w,\ y = x_1$

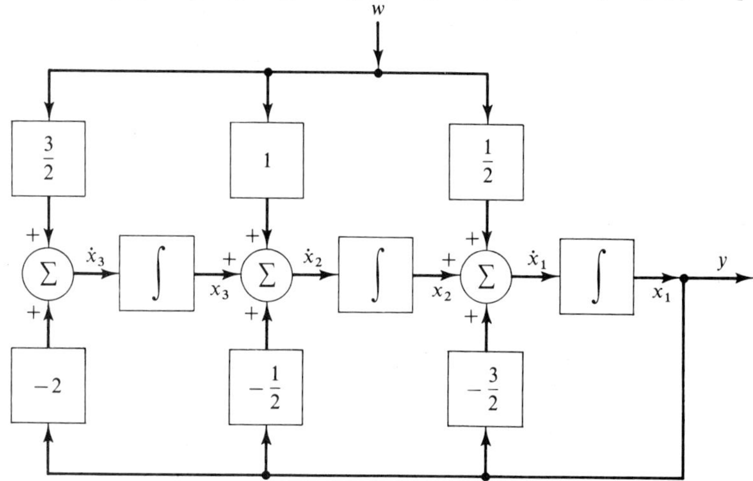

10. $\dot{x}_1 = x_2,\ \dot{x}_2 = a_0x_1 + b_0w,\ y = x_1$

11.

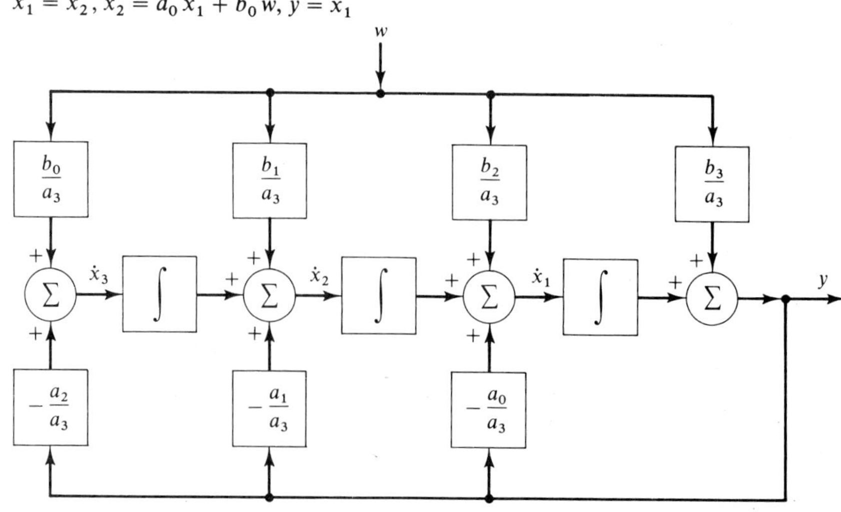

12. **c.** $\dot{x}_1 = x_2$, $\dot{x}_2 = -x_1 - 2x_2 + w$, $y = 5x_1 + 2x_2$
d. $\dot{x}_1 = x_2$, $\dot{x}_2 = x_3$, $\dot{x}_3 = -x_1 - x_2 - x_3 + w$, $y = x_1 + x_2$

13. **a.** $\dot{x}_1 = x_2$, $\dot{x}_2 = -\frac{1}{3}x_1 - \frac{2}{3}x_2 + \frac{1}{3}(w+2)$, $y = x_1$
b. $\dot{x}_1 = x_2$, $\dot{x}_2 = x_3$, $\dot{x}_3 = -x_1 - 3x_2 - 2x_3 + w$, $y = x_1 + x_2$

14. **a.** $\mathbf{A}^k = \begin{bmatrix} \alpha^k & 0 \\ 0 & \alpha^k \end{bmatrix}$ **b.** $\mathbf{A}^k = \begin{bmatrix} \beta^k & 0 \\ 0 & \beta^k \end{bmatrix}$ k = even, $\mathbf{A}^k = \begin{bmatrix} 0 & \beta^k \\ \beta^k & 0 \end{bmatrix}$ k = odd

c. $\mathbf{A}^k = \begin{bmatrix} \alpha^k & k\alpha^{k-1} \\ 0 & \alpha^k \end{bmatrix}$

17. **a.** $\dfrac{\partial \mathbf{\Phi}}{\partial t} = e^{-t/2}\begin{bmatrix} -\sin(t/2) & \cos(t/2) - \sin(t/2) \\ \frac{1}{2}[\sin(t/2) - \cos(t/2)] & -\cos(t/2) \end{bmatrix}$

b. $\mathbf{\Phi}(0) = \mathbf{I}$, $\dfrac{\partial \mathbf{\Phi}(0)}{\partial t} = \begin{bmatrix} 0 & 1 \\ -\frac{1}{2} & -1 \end{bmatrix}$

19. $\mathbf{h}(t) = \begin{bmatrix} 3e^{-t} - 3e^{-2t} & -e^{-t} + 2e^{-2t} \\ 45e^{-t} - 9e^{-2t} & 45e^{-t} + 6e^{-2t} \end{bmatrix}$ $t > 0$

20. $\mathbf{h}(t) = \begin{bmatrix} 3t - \dfrac{9t^2}{2!} + 21\dfrac{t^3}{3!} - 45\dfrac{t^4}{4!}\cdots & 1 - \dfrac{11t^2}{2!} + 27\dfrac{t^3}{3!} - 59\dfrac{t^4}{4!}\cdots \\ -3 + 9t - 21\dfrac{t^2}{2!} + 45\dfrac{t^3}{3!} - 93\dfrac{t^4}{4!}\cdots & 3 - 7t + 15\dfrac{t^2}{2!} - 31\dfrac{t^3}{3!} - 63\dfrac{t^4}{4!}\cdots \end{bmatrix}$ $t > 0$

21. $h(t) = \sum_{n=1}^{\infty} \dfrac{(-1)^{n+1}}{n!} t^n$

22. $x_1(t) = 1$, $x_2(t) = \frac{1}{2} + \frac{1}{2}e^{-2t}$, $h(t) = e^{-t}$

24. **a.** Canonical form: $\mathbf{x}(k+1) = \begin{bmatrix} 0 & -\frac{1}{2} \\ 1 & -\frac{5}{2} \end{bmatrix}\mathbf{x}(k) + \begin{bmatrix} -1 \\ 0 \end{bmatrix}w(k)$, $[y(k)] = [0 \quad -\frac{1}{2}]\mathbf{x}(k)$

First, solve for $y(k)$ and then define $x_1(k+1) = -2y(k+2) - 5y(k+1)$. Next, decrease $x_1(k+1)$ by one and define $x_2(k+1) = -2y(k+1)$. Read also Example 5.25. Phase variable form:

$\mathbf{x}(k+1) = \begin{bmatrix} 0 & 1 \\ -\frac{1}{2} & -\frac{5}{2} \end{bmatrix}\mathbf{x}(k) + \begin{bmatrix} 0 \\ \frac{1}{2} \end{bmatrix}w(k)$, $y(k) = [1 \quad 0]\mathbf{x}(k)$

b. Canonical form: $\mathbf{x}(k+1) = \begin{bmatrix} 0 & -\frac{5}{3} \\ 1 & -\frac{2}{3} \end{bmatrix}\mathbf{x}(k) + \begin{bmatrix} -\frac{3}{5} \\ -\frac{2}{5} \end{bmatrix}w(k)$, $y(k) = [0 \quad -\frac{5}{3}]\mathbf{x}(k)$

Phase variable form: $\mathbf{x}(k+1) = \begin{bmatrix} 0 & 1 \\ -\frac{5}{3} & -\frac{2}{3} \end{bmatrix}\mathbf{x}(k) + \begin{bmatrix} 0 \\ \frac{1}{3} \end{bmatrix}w(k)$, $y(k) = [3 \quad 2]\mathbf{x}(k)$

28. **b.** $\mathbf{x}(k) = \begin{bmatrix} -2k \\ 1 + k \end{bmatrix}$

29. $\mathbf{x}(k) = \begin{bmatrix} \sum_{k=0}^{k-1} b^k \\ \sum_{k=0}^{k} b^k \end{bmatrix}$

Chapter 6

1. **b.** $(s^2 + 2s + 2)/s^3$, $(s^2 + 8)/s(s^2 + 4^2)$, $2\omega s/(s^2 + \omega^2)^2$, $(1/\omega)\tan^{-1} \omega/s$

2. $(2s^2 + 3s)/s^3$ $\sigma > 0$, $4/(s + 0.1)$ $\sigma > -0.1$, $2/(s^2 - 4)$ $\sigma > -2$,
$1/s + 1/(s^2 + 1)$ $\sigma > 0$, $1/(s - 2)$ $\sigma > 2$

4. $2(s + 1)/s(s + 2)$, $(1 - e^{-2s})/s$, $(s^3 - 5s^2 + 10s - 12)/((s^2 + 4)[(s - 1)^2 + 9])$

6. **a.** $(A/s)\tanh(Ts/4)$ **b.** $2(A/Ts)^2 \tanh(Ts/4)$

8. $[1/(s + 1)]e^{-2(s+1)} + sG(s) - g(0+)$, $G(s) + (1/s) + [1/s(s + 1)]$

9. $F(s) = F(-s)$, $F(s) = -F(-s)$

10. **a.** $(1/s^2)e^{-st_0}$ **b.** $A/s[e^{-st_2} - e^{-st_1}]$

11. **a.** $F(s) = 1/s^2$ **b.** $F(s) = 2/s^2$ **c.** $F(s) = 1/s$

12. $(s + a)/[(s + a)^2 + b^2]$, $1/(s + a)^2$, $s/(s^2 + b^2)$

13. **a.**

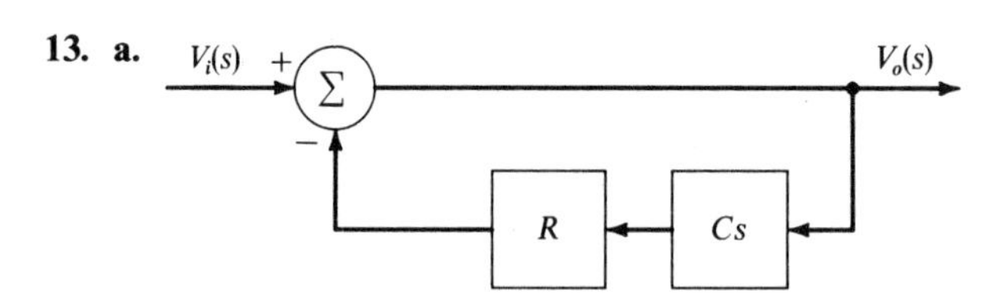

14.

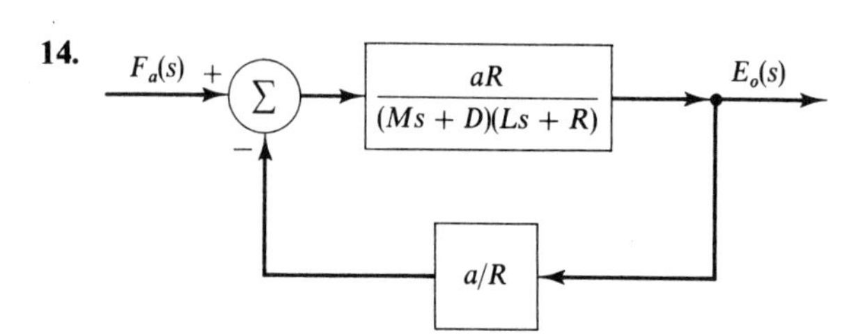

16. **a.** $H_1(s)/[1 + H_2(s) + H_1(s)H_3(s)]$
b. $H_1(s)H_2(s)(1 - H_3(s)/\{1 - H_2(s) + H_1(s)H_2(s)[1 - H_3(s)](H_4 + H_5)\}$

17. $I(s)/V(s) = Cs/(1 + RCs)$

20. $V(s)/F(s) = s/(Ms^2 + Ds + K)$

21. **a.** $u(t) - u(t-2)$ **b.** $2e^{-2t}\cos\sqrt{3}\,t - \sqrt{3}\,e^{-2t}\sin\sqrt{3}\,t$
d. $-e^{-2t} + e^{-3t} + 2te^{-3t}$ **e.** $u(t) + t$

22. **a.** $(a/b)\sin bt$ **b.** $-\frac{2}{3}e^{-t} + \frac{2}{3}e^{4t}$ **d.** $2e^{-t}\cos 5t - e^{-t}\sin 5t$
e. $2(e^t - \cos t - \sin t)$ **f.** $\cosh at$

23. **a.** $2u(t) - 2e^{-3t}$ **b.** $2e^{-3t} - e^{-5t} - 10te^{-5t}$

24. **a.** $y(t) = 10e^{-t} - 5e^{-2t}$ **b.** $y(t) = e^{-t} - e^{-2t}$
d. $y(t) = -\frac{1}{2} + (t^2/2) - 3e^{-t} + 5.5e^{-2t}$

28. t^2e^{-2t}

30. **a.** $h(t) = 1.08e^{-3.732t} - 0.078e^{-0.268t}$ **b.** $h(t) = e^{-(1/2)t} - \frac{1}{2}te^{-(1/2)t}$

31. **b.** $v_o(t) = 2e^{-3t}$

32. $v_2(t) = 1.155e^{-0.5t}\sin 0.866t$

34. **a.** $H(s) = H_1(s)H_2(s) + H_1(s)H_3(s)$
b. $H(s) = H_1(s)/[1 \mp H_2(s)]$

35. $H(s) = H_1(s)H_2(s)/[1 - H_2(s)][1 - H_3(s)]$

36. **b.** $H(s) = b_0 + b_1 s + b_2 s^2$

40. **b.** $\mathbf{\Phi}(t) = \begin{bmatrix} e^{3t} & 0 \\ 2^{3t} - 2e^{2t} & e^{2t} \end{bmatrix}$ **c.** $\mathbf{\Phi}(t) = \begin{bmatrix} e^{-t} & te^{-t} \\ 0 & e^{-t} \end{bmatrix}$

43. **a.** $\mathbf{x}(t) = \begin{bmatrix} 7e^t - 8e^{-t} \\ 7e^t - 4e^{-t} \end{bmatrix}$ **b.** $\mathbf{x}(t) = \begin{bmatrix} e^t - 2e^{2t} \\ e^t - e^{2t} \end{bmatrix}$

46. $k < -3$, stable; $k > -3$, unstable

Chapter 7

1. **a.** $X(z) = (z^3 + z^2 + z + 1)/z^3$ **b.** $X(z) = (z^3 + z^2 - z - 1)/z^3$
2. **a.** $F(z) = 2z/(2z - 1)$ **b.** $F(z) = [z/(z - a)] - [(z + a + 1)/z]$
3. **a.** $\{f(k)\} = \{1, 3, 7, 15, \ldots\}$ **b.** $\{f(k)\} = \{0, 1, 8, 28, \ldots\}$
5. **b.** $F(z) = (2z^2 + 4)/z^4$ **c.** $F(z) = z/(z + a)$
6. **a.** $Y(z) = z^2/(z - 1)^2$ $|z| > 1$, $z = 0$ double zero, $z = 1$ double pole
   c. $Y(z) = [z/(z - a)] + [az/(az - 1)]$ $|z| > a$, zeros at $z = 0$ and $z = (a^2 + 1)/2a$, poles at $z = a$ and $z = 1/a$
8. **b.** $Y(z) = [2z(z - \frac{7}{24})]/[(z - \frac{1}{3})(z - \frac{1}{4})]$ $|z| > \frac{1}{3}$, zeros at $z = 0$ and $z = -7/24$, poles at $z = \frac{1}{3}$ and $z = \frac{1}{4}$
11. $Y(z) = \dfrac{z}{z - e^{j\omega}}$ $|z| > 1$
13. **a.** $\dfrac{z}{z - e^{-aT}}$ $|z| > e^{-aT}$ **b.** $\dfrac{z^3 + z^2 + z + 1}{z^3}$ $|z| > 0$
15. Introduces an additional pole
17. $[z^2(z + 2)]/(z^4 - 1)$
20. $Y(z) = [1/(1 - z^{-1})][1/(1 - 0.5z^{-1})][2/(1 - 0.64z^{-2})]$
23. $Tz^{-3} + 2Tz^{-4} + 3T2^{-5}$
25. $Y(z) = z/(z + 2)$
26. **a.** $z/(z - ae^{-\alpha})$ **b.** $[z(z - a\cos\omega)]/(z^2 - 2az\cos\omega + a^2)$
   c. $az/(z - a)^2$
28. **a.** $F(z) = [z(z + 2)]/[(z^2 + z + 1)(z - 1)]$
30. **a.** $Tz/(z - 1)^2$ **b.** $[T^2z(z + 1)]/(z - 1)^3$
   c. $[z^2(T^2 + T) + z(T^2 - T)]/(z - 1)^3$
34. $y(k) = -c^{k-1}u(k - 1)$
35. **a.** $f(k) = -u(k) + 2^{k+1}u(k)$ **b.** $f(k) = k(\frac{1}{2})^{k+1}$
36. **a.** $y(k) = \begin{cases} -2^k & k \le 0 \\ -1^{k-1} & k > 1 \end{cases}$ **b.** $y(k) = \begin{cases} -2^{k+1} & k \le 0 \\ -1^{k-1} - \frac{1}{3}(k - 1)1^{k-2} & k \ge 1 \end{cases}$
39. **a.** $f(k) = -3\delta(k) - 3\delta(k - 1) - 2\delta(k - 2) + 3u(k)$
40. **c.** $F(z) = \dfrac{z}{z - 0.6}$ **d.** $F(z) = \dfrac{1}{z^2(z - 0.6)}$
41. **a.** $f(k) = 7 \times 3^{k+1} - 3$ $k \ge 0$ **b.** $f(k) = 2^{k+1} - 2 - k$ $k \ge 0$
42. $y(k) = -2u(k) + 12k + 2\delta(k) - 4\delta(k - 1)$
43. $y(k) = 0.6u(k) + 1.37(-2.617)^k + 0.029(-0.383)^k$
45. **a.** $H(z) = (1 + b_1z^{-1})/(1 + a_1z^{-1})$ **b.** $H(z) = 1/(1 - \frac{1}{4}z^{-1} + \frac{2}{3}z^{-2})$
49. **b.** $H(z) = (1 - 2z)/(z^2 + 3z + 5)$
50. $f(k) = \{1, 5, 23, 98, \ldots\}$
52. **a.** $y(k) = u(k) - (-\frac{2}{3})^k$
53. **a.** $y(k) = u(k) - (-1)^k$ **c.** $y(k) = -9\delta(k) + 4.5u(k) + 4.5(-1)^k$
   d. $y(k) = \frac{1}{9}5^k - \frac{1}{9}2^k - (k/6)2^k$
56. $(\mathbf{M}^T)^k = \begin{bmatrix} \frac{4}{7}u(k) + \frac{3}{7}(-\frac{3}{4})^k & \frac{4}{7}u(k) - \frac{4}{7}(-\frac{3}{4})^k \\ \frac{3}{7}u(k) - \frac{3}{7}(-\frac{3}{4})^k & \frac{3}{7}u(k) + \frac{4}{7}(-\frac{3}{4})^k \end{bmatrix}$

The (i, j)th element gives the probability that the system will be in state i at stage k given that the initial state is j at stage $k = 0$.

57. $x_1(k) = \frac{7}{8}u(k) + \frac{6}{13}(-\frac{5}{8})^k$, $x_2(k) = \frac{24}{52}u(k) + \frac{32}{52}(\frac{5}{8})^k$

58. $y(k) = \frac{1}{3}\delta(k) - \frac{1}{2}u(k) + \frac{1}{6}3^k$

59. **a.** $y_h(k) = 2^{k+1}$ **b.** $y_h(k) = \frac{1}{2}5^k - \frac{1}{2}3^k$

60. **a.** $y_h(k) = 2^{k+3}$ **b.** $y_h(k) = \frac{1}{2}5^{k+2} - \frac{1}{2}3^{k+2}$

62. $Y(z) = \dfrac{8z}{z-2}$ and $y(k) = 2^{k+3}$

63. $Y(z) = z/(z^2 - z - 1) = z/([z - (1 + \sqrt{5})/2][z - (1 - \sqrt{5})/2])$

64. $x(k) = \frac{2}{5}[1 - (-1.5)^k]$

65. $y(k) = y(k-1) + y(k-2)$ $y(0) = 1, y(k-2) = 1;$
$y(k) = 1/\sqrt{5}([(1 + \sqrt{5})/2]^{k+1} - [(1 - \sqrt{5})/2]^{k+1})$

66. **a.** $y(k) = 2^k$ **b.** $y(k) = -u(k) + 3^k$ **c.** $y(k) = -\frac{1}{2}u(k) + \frac{3}{2}(-3)^k$

67. **a.** $y(k) = \frac{5}{3}2^k - \frac{5}{2}3^k + \frac{5}{6}5^k$ **b.** $y(k) = \frac{3}{4}(-1)^k - \frac{3}{4}(1)^k + \frac{3}{2}k$

68. $n(k) = u(k) + \frac{3}{2}k + k^2/2$

Chapter 8

2. $s_1 = \exp(j4\pi/6)$, $s_2 = \exp(j6\pi/6)$, $s_3 = \exp(j8\pi/6)$, $s_4 = \exp(j10\pi/6)$,
$s_5 = \exp(j12\pi/6)$, $s_6 = \exp(j14\pi/6)$

3. $10 \log_{10}(1 + 3^{2n}) \geq 20$, then $n = \dfrac{\log_3(99)}{2} = 2.09$. Use $n = 3$.

4. $L = 1.414 \times 10^{-5}$ H, $C = 1.414 \times 10^{-5}$ F

5. $h(t) = e^{-t} + (2/\sqrt{3})e^{-(1/2)t}\cos[(\sqrt{3}/2)t - \tan^{-1}\sqrt{3} - \pi/2]$ $t > 0$

6. $s_1 = \exp(j2\pi/3)$, $s_2 = \exp(j\pi)$, $s_3 = \exp(j4\pi/3)$, $s_4 = \exp(j5\pi/3)$, $s_5 = \exp(j2\pi)$, $s_6 = \exp(j7\pi/3)$

8. $n = 5.64$; hence, $n = 6$.

9. $n = 14.7$; hence, $n = 15$.

10. See Table 8.3.

11. **a.** $\varepsilon = 0.1076$ **b.** $\varepsilon = 0.1526$ **c.** $\varepsilon = 0.6423$

12. $|H_2(j\omega)| = 8/[128 - 16\omega^2 + \omega^4]^{1/2}$

13. $s_1 = -0.1781 + j0.9193$, $s_2 = -0.3563$, $s_3 = -0.1781 - j0.9193$

14. See also Example 8.3. **a.** $\varepsilon = 0.564$ **b.** $C_3^2(3) = (4 \times 3^3 - 3 \times 3)^2 = 9801$; hence, third-order filter.
c. $s_1 = -0.2303 + j0.9634$, $s_2 = -0.2303$, $s_3 = -0.2303 - j0.9634$
d. Assume $K = 1$. **e.** Normalized $(\omega_c = 1) H_3(s) = s_1 \cdot s_2 \cdot s_3[(-1)^3(s - s_1)(s - s_2)(s - s_3)]$,
$H_3(s/8) = s_1 s_2 s_3/[(-1)^3(s/8 - s_1)(s/8 - s_2)(s/8 - s_3)]$

15. Use Table 8.5. $H_2(s/\omega_c) = 15162/(s^2 + 14.256s + 15162)$

18. $\omega_{d2} = 4.657$, $\omega_{d1} = -4.25$. Since $-4.25 < 4.657$, we must design a normalized filter with $\omega_c = 1$ and $\omega_{d1} = 4.25$. Hence, third-order Butterworth filter.

$$H(s_n) = 1\Bigg/\left(\frac{s_n^2 + 4\pi^2 3.75\ 10^6}{s_n\ 2\pi 10^3} + 1\right)\left(\left[\frac{s_n^2 + 4\pi^2 3.75\ 10^6}{s_n 2\pi 10^3}\right]^2 + \frac{s_n^2 + 4\pi 3.75\ 10^6}{s_n\ 2\pi 10^3} + 1\right)$$

20. $H(z) = 0.0375 + 0.0796z^{-1} + 0.1125z^{-2} + 0.25z^{-3} + 0.1125z^{-4}$
$+ 0.0796z^{-5} + 0.0375z^{-6}$

23. **a.** $w(k) = \text{Bartlett} = 1 - |k|/5$. $W(e^{j\theta}) = \frac{1}{5}\sum_{-5}^{5} w(k)e^{-jk\theta}$,
$\theta = 0$, $W(e^{j0}) = 1$, $\theta = \pi/8$, $W(e^{j\pi/8}) = 0.726$, $\theta = 2\pi/8$, $W(e^{j2\pi/8}) = 0.23$,
$\theta = 2.5\pi/8$, $W(e^{j2.5\pi/8}) = 0.0724$, $\theta = 3\pi/8$, $W(e^{j3\pi/8}) = 0.306$,
$\theta = 3.5\pi/8$, $W(e^{j3.5\pi/8}) = 0.0082$, $\theta = 4\pi/8$, $W(e^{j\pi/8}) = 0.04$

24. **c.** $h(t) = e^{-2.8628t}$ (see Table 8.5)

25. $H(s/\omega_c) = 100/(s + 1.965 \times 10^2)$, $h(t) = 100e^{-196.5t}$, $H(z) = 100/(1 - e^{-0.1965}z^{-1})$

27. Proceed exactly as Example 8.10.

28. $H_n(z) = 1.358z/(z^2 - 0.1329z + 0.413)$

30. $H(z) = [(1 + z^{-1})(1 + 2z^{-1} + z^{-2})]/[(1.8687 - 0.8804z^{-1})(2.1458 + 1.0437z + 0.7873z^{-2})]$

Appendix A

1. **e.** $(a_1b_1 + a_2b_2 + a_3b_3)$

2. **b.** $\mathbf{B}^T = [1 \quad 4 \quad -6]$

c. $\mathbf{C}^T = \begin{bmatrix} 1 & 6 & 4 \\ -3 & 1 & 2 \end{bmatrix}$ **e.** $\mathbf{E}^T = \begin{bmatrix} 3 & 6 & 9 \\ 1 & -2 & 8 \\ -9 & 4 & 7 \end{bmatrix}$

3. **a.** $c_{11} = (-1)^{1+1}(\Delta\mathbf{M}_{11}) = (-1)^2(-1) = -1$, $c_{12} = 6$, $c_{21} = -4$, $c_{22} = 2$
b. $c_{11} = 3$, $c_{12} = 4$, $c_{21} = -22$, etc

4. **a.** $\mathbf{A} = \begin{bmatrix} \frac{5}{7} & \frac{3}{7} \\ \frac{4}{7} & \frac{1}{7} \end{bmatrix}$ **b.** $\mathbf{B} = \begin{bmatrix} 0 & 1 & -3 \\ \frac{1}{3} & -\frac{2}{3} & \frac{2}{3} \\ 0 & 0 & 1 \end{bmatrix}$

5. **a.** Changes sign **b.** Multiplied by that constant
c. No change

6. **a.** $\mathbf{x}^{(1)} = (1/\sqrt{2})\begin{bmatrix} 1 \\ -1 \end{bmatrix}$, $\mathbf{x}^{(2)} = (1/\sqrt{5})\begin{bmatrix} 1 \\ 2 \end{bmatrix}$ **b.** $\mathbf{x}^{(1)} = (1/\sqrt{2})\begin{bmatrix} 1 \\ -1 \end{bmatrix}$,
$\mathbf{x}^{(2)} = (1/\sqrt{10})\begin{bmatrix} 1 \\ -3 \end{bmatrix}$

7. $\mathbf{A}^3 = \begin{bmatrix} 6 & 7 \\ 14 & -15 \end{bmatrix}$

9. $\mathbf{A}^{20} = -20\mathbf{A} - 19\mathbf{I}$

10. $\mathbf{f}(\mathbf{A}) = \begin{bmatrix} 1 & 0 \\ 1 - 2^{20} & 2^{20} \end{bmatrix}$

11. $\mathbf{A}^k = (\frac{1}{4})^k \begin{bmatrix} 2^k & 0 \\ 2^k - 1 & 1 \end{bmatrix}$

12. $e^{-\mathbf{A}t} = \begin{bmatrix} e^{4t} + 4te^{4t} + 2te^{4t} & -2te^{4t} \\ 2te^{4t} & e^{4t} + 2te^{4t} \end{bmatrix}$

Index

Aliasing, in sampling, 234
  elimination using bilinear transformation, 527
Amplitude modulation. *See* Modulation, amplitude.
Amplitude spectrum
  continuous time, 149, 184
  discrete, 242
  Fourier integral, 184
  Fourier series, 149
Analog system, digital simulation, 73
Analog to digital converter, 2, 21
Analytic function, 3
Approximation
  differential equation by difference equation, 75, 83
  signal
    using interpolation formulas, 27
    using orthogonal functions, 23
Autocorrelation, 113
Auxiliary equation, of difference equation, 46, 71, 462

Bandlimited signals, 230
  sampling theorem for, 230
Basis functions, 22
  Legendre polynomials, 25
  orthonormal, 23
Bilinear transformation, 527
Block diagram, 62
  properties of, 65
  reduction of, 67
  in system description, 63
Bromwich path, 334
Butterworth filter
  analog, 487
  digital, 520

Canonic form of state equations, 283, 315
Casoration, 462
Causal system, 36
Cayley-Hamilton theorem, 550
  properties of, 551
Characteristic matrix, 380. *See also* Fundamental matrix.
Characteristic roots, 463. *See also* Eigenvalues.
  of a matrix, 548
Chebyshev filter
  analog, 495
  digital, 524
Comb function, 17
  Fourier transform of, 221
Communication systems, 4
Complete solution
  difference equation. *See* Z-transform.
  differential equation. *See* Differential equations; Laplace transform.
  state equations. *See* State, solutions.
Complex Fourier series, 143
Conservation
  charge, 56
  flux linkages, 56
Continuous time systems
  impulse response of, from differential equations, 97
  stability of, 387
  state variable description, 277
  transfer function of. *See* System function.
  transform analysis of. *See* Fourier integral transform; Laplace transform.
Convergence
  of Fourier series, 143
  of Laplace integral, 335
  Z-transform, 407
Convergence regions, 335, 408. *See also* Region of convergence.
Convolution, 87
  circular or periodic, 156, 247
  in continuous Fourier series, 156
  in continuous time systems, 89, 94
  in discrete Fourier series, 172
  in discrete Fourier transform, 240
  Fourier transform of, 212, 214
  frequency, 214
  Laplace transform of, 345
  matrix, integral, 302
  Z-transform of, 422
Convolution summation, 109, 422
Correlation
  autocorrelation, 113
  cross-correlation, 113
Critical frequencies
  poles and zeros, 388

D'Alembert principle, 50, 51
Decomposition of signals. *See* Fourier series.
Deconvolution, 97
Delay operations, 68, 342
Delta function
  approximation, 14
  definition, 14
  in digital systems, 108
  relation to step function, 17
  transform of
    discrete Fourier transform, 252
    Fourier transform, 184, 218
    Laplace transform, 336
    Z-transform, 409
  use in impulse response, 97
Delta sampling, 235
Demodulation, 201
Difference equations, 69
  approximation of differential equations, 75, 83
  block diagram, 70, 74

Difference equations (*continued*)
characteristic equation of, 71
first order, 70
higher order, 71, 83, 461
homogeneous equation, 462
impulse response from, 111
nonhomogeneous equation, 467
normal form, 310
solution of
analytic, 461
convolution methods, 108
direct, 71
undetermined coefficients, 470
using state variables, 320
using Z-transforms, 449
state variable representation, 309, 457
Differential equations
homogeneous equations, 46
initial conditions, 55
normal form of, 290
particular solution, 48
solution of
standard methods of, 45
using convolution, 94
using Fourier transforms, 203
using Laplace transforms, 362
variation of parameters method, 46
Digital filters, 484, 510
FIR, 510
design by discrete Fourier transform, 518
design by Fourier series method, 511
phase characteristics, 511
use of window functions, 515
frequency response of, 513
frequency transformations for, 532
IIR, 519
bilinear transformation, 527
folding, 520
warping, 528
recursive vs. nonrecursive, 537
round-off noise, 486
Digital simulation, 73, 83
Digital system entities, 68
Discrete Fourier series, 163
convolution, 172
in FIR filter design, 511
Discrete Fourier transform, 183, 240
convolution, periodic, 247
frequency, 349
definition of, 241
evaluation of, 243
fast Fourier transform. *See* Fast Fourier transform.
in FIR filters, 518
inverse, 241
leakage, 260
Parseval's theorem, 251
properties of, 243
table of, 253
relation to, Fourier integral, 240
discrete Fourier series, 241
windows in, 261
Discrete time systems, 68
convolution in, 108
definition, 36
delay operator, 68
difference equation of, 70
equivalent for continuous time system, 73
frequency response, 443
fundamental matrix. *See* Fundamental matrix.
impulse response of, 111, 321
properties of, 109
solution to homogeneous difference equation, 71, 462
state variable representations, 309
solutions of, 320
system function, 435, 447
Z-transform analysis of, 449
Discrete transforms
discrete Fourier transform. *See* Discrete Fourier transform.
fast Fourier transform. *See* Fast Fourier transform.
Discretization, 2
Distortion, 4

Eigenfunction, 94, 548
Eigenvalue, 94, 548
definition, 94
Hermitian, 94
Elements, system
electrical, 37
mechanical, rotational, 43
mechanical, translational, 40
Encryption, 3
Equilibrium state, 387
Error function, 239
Euler formula, 11
Even function, 151
Exp($\mathbf{A}t$), 295. *See also* State, fundamental matrix.
Exponential function, 11, 134
Fast Fourier transform, 183, 262
base-2 algorithm, 263
data flow graph for, 264
decimation in frequency
Sande, 268
decimation in time
Cooley-Tukey, 266
matrix approach, 263
Filtering properties, 377
Filters, 485
approximation to prescribed function
Butterworth, 487
Chebyshev, 495
elliptic, 503
brute force, 485
classical types, 484
digital. *See* Digital filters.
finite impulse response (FIR), 510
frequency transformations for, 504
ideal, 485
infinite impulse response (IIR), 519
phase characteristic, 504
Filter transformation, 504, 532
Final value theorem
for Laplace transform, 347
for Z-transform, 421
FIR (finite impulse response) filter, 441, 510. *See also* Digital filters.
Flux linkage, conservation of, 56
Folding. *See* Convolution.
Fourier integral transform, 184
convolution
frequency, 214
time, 212
definition of, 184
delta function, 184, 218
interpretation of, 190
leakage, 260
modulation property, 198
Parseval's theorem, 208
power density, 209
properties of, 190, 217
relation to
discrete Fourier transform, 240
Laplace transform, 334
sampling
fundamentals of, 226
theorem, 230
spectrum function, 184
step function, 220
system function, 204
table of, 222
Fourier series, 133

Fourier series (*continued*)
choice of origin, 153
continuous functions, 139
convergence of, 143
convolution, 156
Dirichlet conditions, 139
discrete, 136, 163
energy relation, 150
exponential, 134
finite signals, 155
Gibbs phenomenon, 145
properties of
Parseval's theorem, 150
spectrum, amplitude, 149
symmetry, effects of, 151
system function, 160, 162
table of, 149
trigonometric, 146
Free body diagram, 106
Frequency, complex, 334
Frequency convolution, 214
Frequency response, 372
Function
analytic, 3
Butterworth, 487
Chebyshev, 496
comb, 17
delta, 14
error, 239
exponential order, 335
impulse. *See* Delta function.
interpolation in sampling, 231
Legendre polynomial, 25
maximally flat, 488
norm of, 23
sampled, 226
singularity, 13, 405
transfer. *See* System function.
weighting, 6
window. *See* Window function.
Fundamental matrix, 295
calculation of, 295
discrete time system, 320
Laplace transform of, 380
Z-transform of, 457

Generalized function, 184
Gibbs phenomenon, 145

Homogeneous solution, 46
continuous time systems, 46
discrete time systems, 71, 462
Hurwitz polynomial, 492

IIR (infinite impulse response) filters, 519. *See also* Digital filters.
Improper fraction, 358, 430
Impulse function. *See also* Delta function.
Fourier transform of, 96, 205
Laplace transform of, 348
replacement of initial conditions by, 340
resolution of signal into, 87
Z-transform of, 422, 437
Impulse invariant response method, 519
Impulse response, 87, 89, 97
calculation of
from difference equation, 108
from differential equation, 97
relation to step response, 98
by state variable method
continuous time, 309
discrete time, 321
by transform methods
Laplace, 348
Impulse train
Fourier transform of, 221
use in sampling theory, 231
Indicial response, 98
Infinite impulse response (IIR), 441. *See also* Digital filters.
Information theory, 5
bit, 5
capacity, fiber optics, 8
entropy in, 7
Initial conditions
evaluation of integration constants, 55
Laplace transform of, 340
Initial state, 308
relaxed, 55
Initial value theorem
in Laplace transforms, 346
in Z-transforms, 421
Input-output relation. *See* System function.
Interpolating function in sampling theory, 231
Inverse matrix. *See* Matrix, inverse.
Inverse transforms
discrete Fourier, 241
Fourier integral, 184
Laplace, 334, 354
Z-transform, 428

Laplace transform, 331
bilateral, 333
characteristic matrix, 380
convergence, abscissa of, 335
convolution theorem, 372
defining integral, 333
expansion theorem, 358
final value theorem, 347
of fundamental matrix, 380
impulse function, 348
initial conditions, 340
initial value theorem, 346
inversion integral, 334, 354
partial fraction expansion, 358
linear time invariant system, 372
one-sided, 334
problem solving using, 362
proper fraction, 358
properties of, 336
table of, 339
relation to Fourier integral, 333
s-plane, 334
stability, 387
multiple order poles, 390
simple poles, 388
state equations, 380
characteristic matrix, 380
solution of, 380, 383
system analysis, 347
system function, 347
table of, 337
two-sided, 334
Linear difference equations. *See* Difference equations.
Linear differential equations. *See* Differential equations.
Linear filters, response of. *See* Filters.
Linear system, definition of, 36
Linear time invariant system, 24, 36
Long division method of inverting Z-transforms, 430
Low-pass filter, continuous time, 485
digital, 484

Matrix, 542
algebra of, 544
Cayley-Hamilton theorem, 550
properties of, 551
characteristic equation of, 548
definitions, 543
discrete time transfer, 457
eigenvalues of, 548
eigenvectors of, 548
functions of, 548

Matrix (*continued*)
fundamental. *See* Fundamental matrix.
inverse, 547
nonsingular, 547
state transition. *See* Fundamental matrix.
transpose function, 380
Maximally flat function, 488
Memoryless system, 278
Models and modeling, 36
electrical elements, 37
mechanical elements, rotational, 43
translational, 40
Modulation
amplitude, 19, 198
modulation index, 198
theorem for Fourier transforms, 195
Multiplexing, frequency division, 210

Network behavior
calculation of fundamental matrix, 295
convolution integral, 89
impulse response, 87, 89, 97
principle of superposition, 89, 162
zero-input, zero-state, 45
Network function. *See* System function.
Newton's law, 40
Noncausal functions, 36
Nonlinear system, definition of, 36
Nonperiodic signals, 183
Nonrecursive process, 441
Normal form of differential equations, 290
procedure for determining, 290
Normalization, 24
Nyquist frequency, 448

Odd function, 151
One-sided Laplace transform, 334
One-sided sequence, 404
Z-transform of, 404
Operator, representation of systems, 62, 89
Orthogonal functions, 23. *See also* Basis functions.
Orthogonality
of basis function, 23
of exponentials, 24, 135
of sinusoids, 135
Orthogonal vectors, 22
Orthonormal functions, 23

Parseval's theorem
discrete Fourier transform, 251
Fourier integral, 218
Fourier series, 150
Partial fraction expansion
in Laplace transforms, 357
in *Z*-transforms, 433
Particular response, state variable formulation, 302
Periodic function, Fourier series, 133
Fourier transform of, 227
Laplace transform of, 337, 343
Periodic signals, 133
continuous time, 8
discrete time, 11
Phase of network function, 161
Physical systems, elements of. *See* Elements, system.
Pole
location and stability, 387
multiple order, 390
of network function, 387
Polynomials
approximation of signals, 27
Butterworth, 490
Legendre, 25
Chebyshev, 496
Hurwitz, 492
Positive time function, 55
Prewarping with bilinear transformation, 527
Proper fraction, 358, 430
Pulse function, 13
Pulse train, Fourier series of, 149, 171

Radius of convergence, 408
of *Z*-transform, 407
Rational function
inverse Laplace transform of, 356
inverse *Z*-transform of, 430
Rectangular pulse, spectrum of, 148
Recursive filter
design by bilinear method, 527
design by impulse invariant method, 519
Region of convergence, Laplace transform, 335
Z-transform, 407
Residue, 359
Resistor ladder network, 456
Response, forced, 48
impulse. *See* Impulse response.
indicial, 98
state, continuous time
forced, 302
force free, 295
initial state, 305
state, discrete time
forced, 302
force free, 320
initial state, 320
step, 47
zero input, 47, 303
zero state, 47, 303
Response function. *See* System function.
Roots of characteristic equation, 380

Sampled signals, 19
Fourier transform of, 227
reconstruction from, 233, 238
Sampling, aliasing, 234
by delta function, 19
frequency (rate), 226
fundamentals of, 226
interval, 226
Nyquist interval, 233
Sampling theorem, 230
s-domain and stability, 387
Sequence, weighting, 515
Z-transform of, 403
Series
Fourier. *See* Fourier series.
Maclaurin, 9
Taylor, 26
Shift operator, 68
Signal
conditioning of, 19
discrete time, 68. *See also* Sampled signals.
energy, 150
Fourier integral representation, 184
Fourier series representation, 133
nonperiodic, 13, 14
periodic, 9, 133
sinusoid, 11, 136
power, 150
representation by orthogonal functions, 23
sampled, 2
Signum function (*sgn*), 219
Fourier transform of, 219
Simulation, digital of differential equations, 74, 83
Sinc(*x*), definition of, 14

Solution
difference equations. *See* Difference equations.
differential equations. *See* Differential equations.
state equations. *See* State, solutions of.
Spectrum, amplitude. *See* Amplitude spectrum.
amplitude modulated signal, 19, 198
s-plane, 331, 334
Square wave, Fourier series representation, 143, 149
Laplace transform, 343
Stability, relation to pole location, 387
State
characteristic matrix, 295
definition, 277
equations, 277
block diagram, 279, 310
differential equations, 278
discrete time, 309
fundamental matrix, 295, 320, 380, 457. *See* also Fundamental matrix.
impulse response, 303
solutions
continuous time, complete, 302
continuous time, force free, 295
discrete time, impulse response, 320, 321
discrete time, using Cayley-Hamilton theorem, 552
impulse, 321
Laplace methods, 383
periodic inputs, 307
sampled inputs, 324
space, 277
transition matrix, 295
variables, selections of, 278
vector, 278
initial state, 308
State equations, 278
first canonical form, 283, 316
phase variable form, 290, 311
solutions of. *See* State, solutions.
Step function
continuous time, 13
Fourier transform, 220
Laplace transform, 335
discrete, 18
Step response, related to impulse response, 98
Superposition, 24
Superposition and convolution, 89
Symmetry property, Fourier transform, 191
System equations, normal form of, 290
System function, 96, 160
continuous time system, 94
discrete system, 309, 435, 447
filters. *See* Filters.
frequency response, 443, 447
fundamental matrix. *See* Fundamental matrix.
matrix, 384, 458
relation to impulse response, 96, 206
roots of, 387
state models, continuous time. *See* State equations.
discrete time. *See* State equations.
Systems, block diagram for, 62
causal, 36
classification, 36
continuous time. *See* Continuous time systems.
discrete time. *See* Discrete time systems.
distributed, 33
linear time invariant, 24, 36
lumped, 33
memory of, 277
nonlinear, 36
periodic inputs, 158
stability of. *See* Stability.
state representation. *See* State.

Taylor expansion, 26
Time convolution
Fourier series, 156
Fourier transform, 212
Time invariance, 36, 89
Time signals, sampling of, 2, 19, 226
Transfer function. *See* System function.
Transfer matrix. *See* Fundamental matrix.
Transform
discrete Fourier. *See* Discrete Fourier transform.
fast Fourier. *See* Fast Fourier transform.
Fourier. *See* Fourier integral transform.
Laplace. *See* Laplace transform.
Z-. *See* Z-transform.
Transform pairs, tables of
Fourier, 202
Laplace, 337
Z-, 429
Transition matrix. *See* Fundamental matrix.
Transmission function. *See* System function.
Trigonometric form of Fourier series, 146
conversion from exponential, 143
Truncated series. *See* Fourier series; Discrete time.
Two-sided Laplace transform, 333
convergence of, 334
inverse, 334, 356
Two-sided sequence, Z-transform, 412

Underdamped response, 455
Undetermined coefficients, method of, 470
Unit delay operator, 68
Unit impulse. *See* Delta function.
Unit step function, 13, 18
Laplace transform of, 335
Unit step response, indicial admittance, 98
Unit step sequence, 437
Z-transform of, 406
Unstable system. *See* Stability.

Vandermonde matrix, 27
Variables
across, 37
through, 37
Vectors, basis set, 23

Warping, with bilinear transformation, 527
Waveform. *See* Signal.
Window function, 261
Wronskian (Casoration), 462

Zero-input response, 45
Zero-state response, 47
Z-transform, 403
convergence, 407
of one-sided, 408
of two-sided, 412
convolution, 422
bilateral, 426
definition
one-sided, 404

Z-transform (*continued*)
two-sided, 412
expansion theorem, 434
frequency response, 443, 447
inversion, direct division, 430
inversion integral, 428
partial fraction expansion, 406, 430
problem solving using, 449
properties of, 414, 427
solution of difference equations, 449
state variable application, 457
system function, 435, 447, 458
table of, 429
two-sided, 412

Figure 4.26 *(continued from inside front cover)*

$f(t) = \dfrac{1}{2\pi}\displaystyle\int_{-\infty}^{\infty} F(\omega)e^{j\omega t}\,d\omega$	$F(\omega) = \displaystyle\int_{-\infty}^{\infty} f(t)e^{-j\omega t}\,dt$
$f(t) = \begin{cases} A & (T-a) < \lvert t\rvert < (T+a) \\ 0 & \text{otherwise} \end{cases}$	$F(\omega) = 4A\,\dfrac{\cos T\omega \sin a\omega}{\omega}$
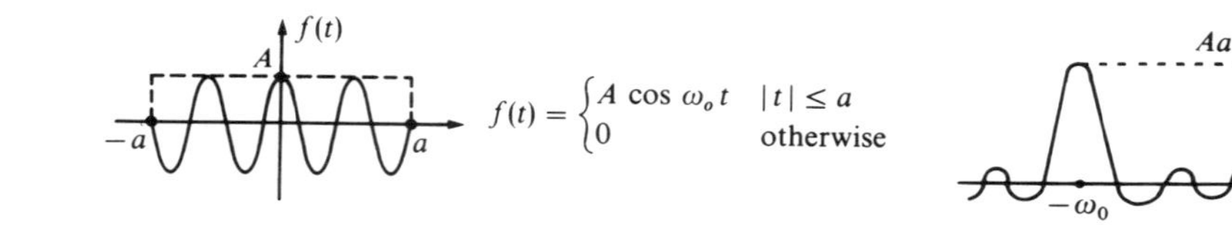 $f(t) = \begin{cases} A\cos\omega_o t & \lvert t\rvert \le a \\ 0 & \text{otherwise} \end{cases}$	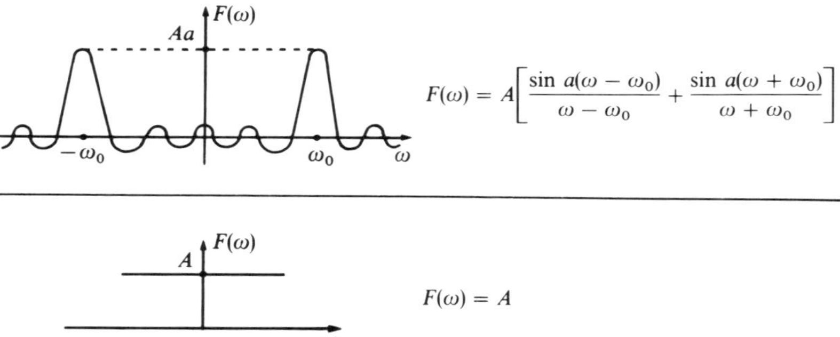 $F(\omega) = A\left[\dfrac{\sin a(\omega-\omega_0)}{\omega-\omega_0} + \dfrac{\sin a(\omega+\omega_0)}{\omega+\omega_0}\right]$
$f(t) = A\,\delta(t)$	$F(\omega) = A$
$f(t) = \begin{cases} A & t>0 \\ 0 & \text{otherwise} \end{cases}$	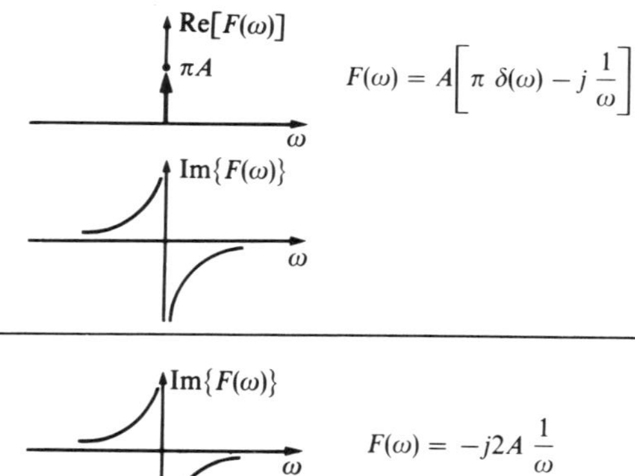 $F(\omega) = A\left[\pi\,\delta(\omega) - j\,\dfrac{1}{\omega}\right]$
$f(t) = \begin{cases} A & t>0 \\ 0 & t=0 \\ -A & t<0 \end{cases}$	$F(\omega) = -j2A\,\dfrac{1}{\omega}$

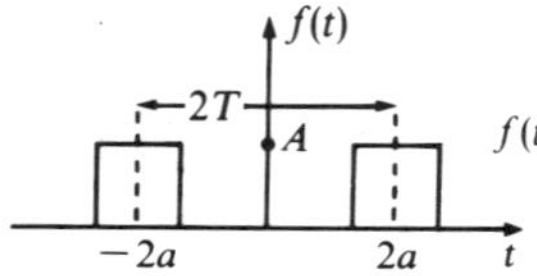

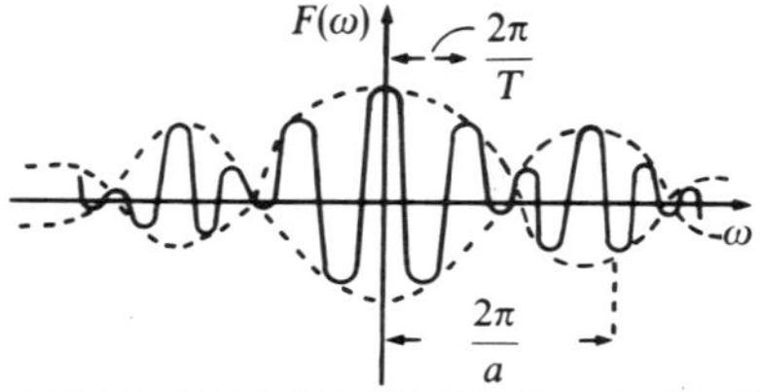

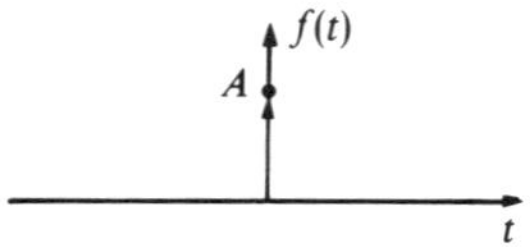

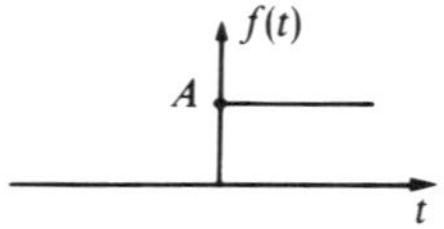

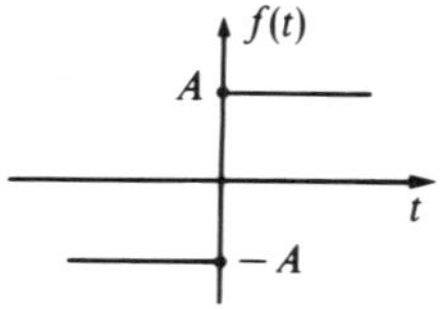